D1517367

THE WESTERN PACIFIC

ISLAND ARCS
MARGINAL SEAS
GEOCHEMISTRY

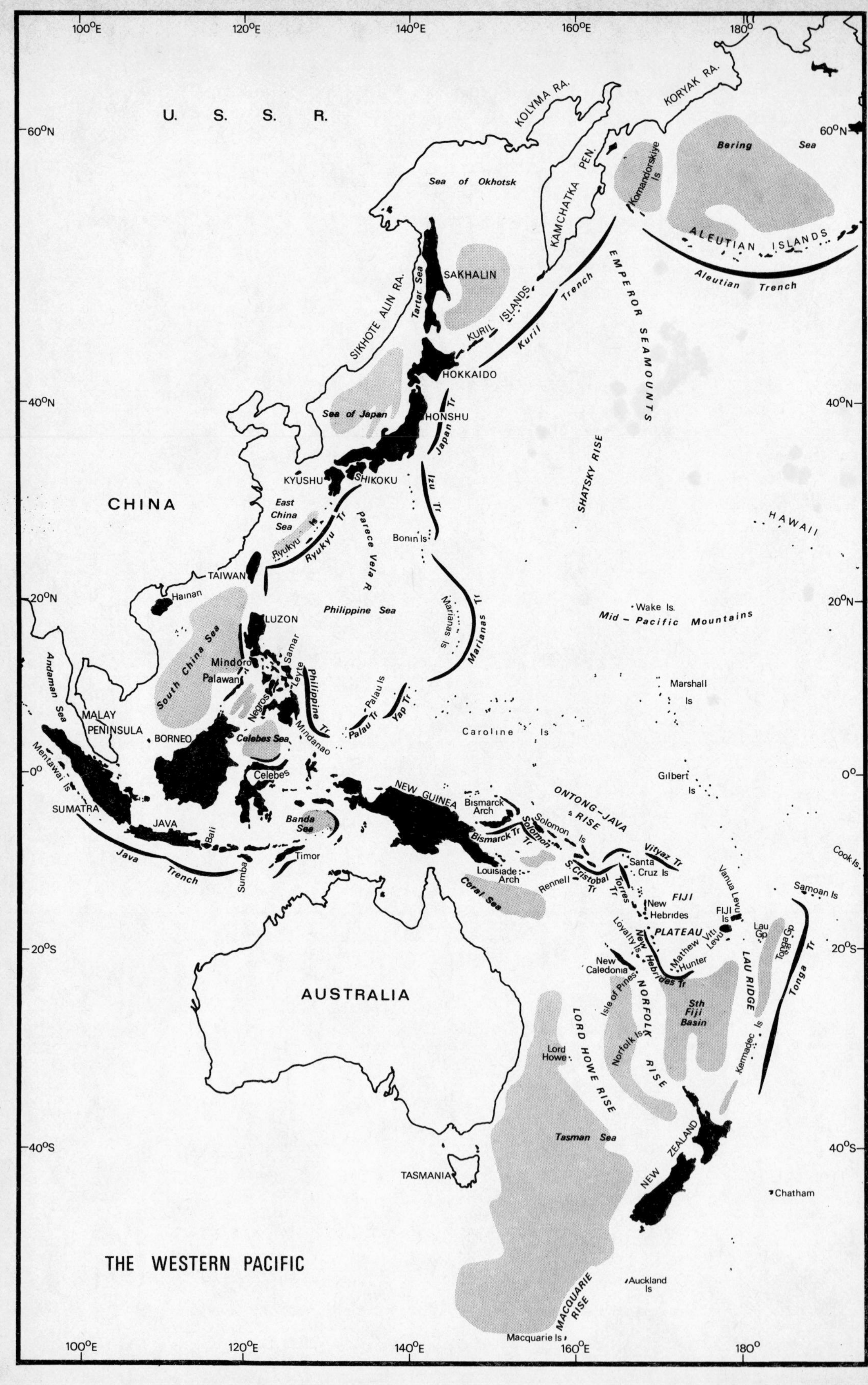

100°E
120°E
140°E
160°E
180°
U. S. S. R.
60°N
KOLYMA RA.
KORYAK RA.
Sea of Okhotsk
KAMCHATKA PEN.
Komandorskiye Is
Bering Sea
ALEUTIAN ISLANDS
Aleutian Trench
SAKHALIN
Tartar Sea
SIKHOTE ALIN RA.
KURIL ISLANDS
Kuril Trench
EMPEROR SEAMOUNTS
HOKKAIDO
40°N
Sea of Japan
HONSHU
Japan Tr
Izu Tr
SHATSKY RISE
KYUSHU
SHIKOKU
CHINA
East China Sea
Ryukyu Is
Ryukyu Tr
Parece Vela R.
Bonin Is
HAWAII
TAIWAN
Hainan
20°N
Philippine Sea
Marianas Is
Marianas Tr
Wake Is.
Mid - Pacific Mountains
LUZON
South China Sea
Samar
Mindoro
Palawan
Leyte
Andaman Sea
Negros
Philippine Tr
Palau Is
Palau Tr
Yap Tr
Marshall Is
MALAY PENINSULA
BORNEO
Celebes Sea
Mindanao
Caroline Is
Mentawai Is
0°
Celebes
NEW GUINEA
Gilbert Is
ONTONG-JAVA RISE
SUMATRA
Bismarck Arch
Solomon Is
JAVA
Bali
Banda Sea
Bismarck Tr
Solomon Tr
Vityaz Tr
Java Trench
Sumba
Timor
Louisiade Arch
Santa Cruz Is
Cook Is.
Coral Sea
Rennell
S. Cristobal Tr
Torres Tr
FIJI
Vanua Levu
Samoan Is
New Hebrides
FIJI Is
PLATEAU
Lau Gp
Tonga Gp
Loyalty Is
Mathew
Viti Levu
20°S
New Caledonia
New Hebrides Tr
Hunter
LAU RIDGE
Tonga Tr
AUSTRALIA
Isle of Pines
NORFOLK RISE
Sth Fiji Basin
LORD HOWE RISE
Lord Howe
Norfolk Is
Kermadec Is
Tasman Sea
NEW ZEALAND
40°S
TASMANIA
Chatham
THE WESTERN PACIFIC
MACQUARIE RISE
Auckland Is
Macquarie Is

THE WESTERN PACIFIC

ISLAND ARCS
MARGINAL SEAS
GEOCHEMISTRY

PATRICK J. COLEMAN

EDITOR

UNIVERSITY OF WESTERN AUSTRALIA PRESS

1973

First published in 1973 by University of Western Australia Press
Nedlands, Western Australia
with permission of the Australian Academy of Science

Eastern States of Australia, New Zealand, Papua and New Guinea, and Hawaii:
Melbourne University Press, P.O. Box 278, Carlton South, Vic. 3053
United Kingdom, Europe, Middle East, Africa and the Caribbean:
Angus & Robertson (U.K.) Ltd, 2 Fisher Street, London WC IR 4QA, United Kingdom
Singapore, Thailand, Malaysia, Indonesia, Hong Kong, Philippines:
Angus & Robertson (S.E. Asia) Pty Ltd, 159, Block 2, Ground Floor, Boon Keng Road, Singapore 12
United States, its territories and possessions, Canada, excepting Hawaii:
Crane, Russak & Company, Inc., 52 Vanderbilt Avenue, New York, N.Y. 10017, U.S.A.

Library of Congress Catalog Number 72-80968
ISBN 0-85564-060-X

Set in Times New Roman by Monofoto, Perth, Western Australia,
and by Modgraphic, Adelaide, South Australia
Printed and bound by the Griffin Press, Adelaide, South Australia

Registered in Australia for transmission by post as a book

List of Contributors*

* For full postal addresses see individual papers.

Foreword

The Twelfth Pacific Science Congress was held in Canberra, 18 to 29 August 1971, under the patronage and direction of The Australian Academy of Science, with Sir Otto Frankel as the Chairman of the Organizing Committee. Professor Martin F. Glaessner (University of Adelaide) was Chairman of Section D (Geological Structure and Mineral Resources in the Pacific); he was primarily responsible for framing the original section programme, which covered aspects of Pacific geology and geophysics that have grown enormously over the last ten years and continue to grow. The scheme is reflected in the titles of the component symposia.

Symposium D1 (Convener: C. C. von der Borch)—Structure and tectonic history of the Pacific Ocean Basin—dealt with the Basin as an entity. Symposium D2 (Convener: P. J. Coleman)—Island arcs and related structures of the Western Pacific Region—moved out of the Basin proper and passed into the complex of island festoons which form its western border. Symposium D3 (Convener: L. V. Hawkins)—Evolution of the Continental Shelves and marginal areas of the Western Pacific—was concerned with the crucial areas between the arcs and the continents. Symposium D4 (Convener: N. H. Fisher)—Mineral Resources of the Western Pacific—covered an array of economic deposits from a variety of standpoints, theoretical and pragmatic.

These were the original four parts of Section D. Geochemists of the Australian National University proposed a fifth, Symposium D5 (Convener: I. McDougall)—Petrology and Geochemistry of island arcs in relation to tectonic environment. This filled a gap and neatly complemented the other fields.

It became clear that the programmes proposed would add much to geological and geophysical knowledge of the Western Pacific and that the proceedings deserved publication. Unfortunately, the Australian Academy of Science was not able to subsidize publication and it was left to individual organizers to arrange this for their own sections or symposia if they felt strongly enough about it. I did. It seemed to me that the fields covered by the programme were developing at such a rapid and haphazard rate that new data, new ways of looking at old data, new ideas and hypotheses, were fast getting out of hand, and at least a fair sample of them needed to be put quickly into print within the one set of covers. The result would be, as it were, a declaration of the state of affairs as of August, 1971, even though out of date when produced. These and other arguments imposed on me the role of editor. Dr Fisher lightened the load by offering to produce D4 as a separate publication of the Bureau of Mineral Resources, Canberra.

This book is therefore an essential record of Section D proceedings: Symposia D1 (Pacific Basin), D2 (Island arcs), D3 (Marginal areas) and D5 (Geochemistry of arcs). Despite an extremely rigorous deadline most contributors produced manuscripts. Some are represented by original or revised abstracts. The titles of symposia

D1 and D3 have been altered so that they reflect more accurately the content of the relevant manuscripts submitted.

As might be expected, notions derived from the 'New Global Tectonics' dominated the actual proceedings of Section D. They do in this book but not as much, so reflecting a relatively lower manuscript response by contributors from the U.S.A. If the book has gained in balance then that is the only good thing I can say about this lack.

Contributors were invited to incorporate in their manuscripts second thoughts or corrections, occasioned by discussion and by listening to other speakers, either as formal postscripts or as revised versions of their original text (this explains the change in title of some papers). Not all contributors responded to this invitation, probably because of my request to assist in reducing publication costs by limiting the length of manuscripts.

All contributions to the section had to be delivered in English and so also the manuscripts submitted. This placed an additional load on those authors whose native tongue is not English, a fair number. Although they measured up remarkably well, their manuscripts required a good deal of additional 'translation'. I adopted the stance that the rendering into more acceptable, conventional English should go as far as making clear what the author was driving at but not much further. I hope this has been done even if some papers, as a result, have a certain quaintness of style, to me not at all objectionable. The alternative, a full and complete re-writing, would have taken far too much time. Inasmuch as the articles are records of proceedings I have not adopted a severe editorial stance in matters of substance or of opinion.

The papers are arranged in order of their respective symposia, although some obviously bridge two or more in their content. A full-scale editorial review of all papers is not possible, but a random set of observations, general in scope and without invidious intent, is in order.

Two main attitudes—sometimes amounting to prejudices—can be found in the array of articles. The less popular of the two might be termed 'fixist' or *in situ*. This argues, usually from a wide scattering of geological and geophysical evidence, that such prime features as trenches, arcs, marginal seas, and ocean basins are essentially developed *in situ* as a result of mantle processes and mantle-crust interaction. The nature of the processes (convective movements, abyssal fractures extending to the mantle, reduction in silica content by mass erosion of particular areas and so on) is not spelt out in detail. Gross translational movements of continents are not envisaged.

The dominant sibling derives, of course, from the notion of plate tectonics along with sea-floor spreading—the 'New Global Tectonics'. The ideas and data which come within this loose terminology are now sufficiently organized to warrant at least theory status, a most elegant theory if judged by the variety of scientific disciplines which contribute to it. The articles in this book show, however, that it is a vexed theory: although they include the mutually accepted axioms there are many private versions; certain severe obstacles, pin-pointed by Professor S. W. Carey, are not faced boldly; above all, the nature of the deep, subcrystal processes presumed responsible (the driving engine) is as little defined as that called for by the proponents of formation of continental crust and oceanic crust *in situ*.

Apart from the man himself, no contributor adopted a severely Careyan outlook in which the key idea is an expanding earth. Nevertheless, some contributors (including plate adherents) have used notions and ideas which owe their substance to Carey. The terms 'sphenochasm' and 'rhombochasm' (of a number publicized by him) are sufficiently known and demonstrable as objective entities to warrant open recognition. Perhaps tacit recognition is the finer compliment. This book is deficient insofar as it lacks a full expose by Professor Carey.

The reader will also notice how identical sets of data can be interpreted in almost diametrically opposite terms, apparently with full objectivity, by this or that author. This is particularly obvious in articles dealing with the North-west Pacific, an area with an embarrassment of data and interpreters thereof. The South-west Pacific picture suffers less on both counts.

The explanation of this phenomenon partly lies in the polarization of the author's views; roughly speaking whether he is pro- or anti-plate theory. But a large part also has to do with the acceptance and in what measure of older long-established concepts. Among these would be geosynclines, continental accretion, convection currents, 'continental' and 'oceanic' crust, even the Mohorovicic discontinuity as a definer of continental margins.

According to one's degree of acceptance or non-acceptance of these and other geological household gods one will give different, even opposing, answers to these questions. Do modern geosynclines exist and if so where are they? Are island arcs essentially novel tectonic features or have they always been part of the geological scene? Is the Pacific a unique ocean basin? Do the margins of continents have a genetic relation to the margins of plates? What is the minimum size of a plate or platelet? Are the deep-sea trenches sites of maximum sediment fill? One could go on.

The point of these questions is to stress the mutability of concepts generally. The geosyncline was a liberating and fruitful concept which promoted understanding of whole systems of rocks and fired new approaches and ideas in all branches of geology. There were many areas and sequences, however, which failed to fit the model and so the concept was expanded to fit the reality by way of a complex and soon unusable classification. What is the status of the geosyncline (in the older linear orthogeosyncline sense) today? Another, if lesser example, is the tectogene. This too was a fruitful idea, which assisted in the understanding of island arc formation, but having served its purpose, Hess himself assisted in its demise.

It is now a responsibility of the plate theorists, as proponents of the current mode, to look over their shoulders as it were and re-evaluate these old concepts. This should not be too difficult. One of the attractions, to me, of the plate tectonics/sea-floor spreading theory is that it gives substance to earlier shadowy concepts: from tectogene to zone of subduction is a short but enriching step.

The reader will also notice that few articles, of the many which could do so, attempt to place their data within wide contexts. There is a failure to appreciate the factor of scale, and hence a risk of failing to see the forest for the trees. This is a familiar stage in the development of embracive theories such as plate tectonics. But a risky one. It seems to me that a conclusion reached on an area which could be tucked away in a corner of a region is likely to be a particular kind of conclusion and not applicable as a generalization.

This book does not supply the answer as to why marginal seas and island arcs are essentially peculiar to the Western Pacific, nor dwell on the manifest asymmetry of its major features. It does little more than touch on the problem of relationships between spreading centres and continents, for example Antarctica and North America. No long-term history of a subduction zone is suggested. No article deals squarely with the phenomenon of marginal seas, those enigmatic barriers to the intimacy between island arcs and continents, which accretionists and classic geosynclinal theorists would demand. Karig's paper comes closest, although his projected thermal diapirs are going to intrigue geochemists for some little time yet, and students of mechanics also. Short of an acceptance of an expanding earth, the laterally-directed forces required are immense and cannot be accounted for in terms of a quasi-isostatic adjustment.

The geochemical contributions bulk large in this book. Reading these, one senses that geochemists find the mobilist stance a liberating one. They do not hesitate to stand in judgment on the more extravagant of geophysical enthusiasms. In contrast to some past records, the articles show a proper appreciation of sampling theory and the fact that specimens must be meaningfully linked in time and position, that is, within a total geological context, as well as being subject to rigorous analysis. The geochemical content in this book fulfils the premonition that geochemistry will play an increasingly significant role in the solution of newly-recognized tectonic problems.

Those papers which deal with a large span of geological time are intriguing. Reading these, one senses that the simplistic view of uniformitarianism—that geological history is made up of repeated orderly sequences of the same processes—may not be true even for the Phanerozoic. The effort to locate old subduction zones as fossil indicators of previous plate configurations at various times in the Phanerozoic (before the Mesozoic) is obviously not easy. The manifest difficulties involved in this search and the incidental evidence thrown up by it, leaves one with a sense of unease: is it a chimera that is being sought? Perhaps the Palaeozoic, Mesozoic and Cenozoic have even more to justify their definition as discrete acts in the Phanerozoic play than has for long been thought sufficient.

A critical point needs to be made: it seems to me that the gulf between the main protagonists, the 'fixists' and the 'mobilists' is more apparent than real. This gulf will be narrowed by the geodetic observations which will soon become available by the use of refined lunar and satellite instruments, and also by geochemical work in both field and laboratory. Following this, the mobilists will take seriously data which is at present beyond their consideration, because it is of fixist origin; the fixists will react similarly. Carey's proposition will soon be vindicated (or not), perhaps within the next five years.

Although some of what I have so far written points to unresolved problems and so hardly amounts to a 'hard-sell' approach, I do not find comfortable the role of the impartial editor. To be positive, and indulge myself, I state my belief that this book will serve as a comprehensive working reference for those interested in the geology of the Western Pacific and so justify its creation. It will direct attention to the geological, geochemical and geophysical riches which still await recognition in the South-west Pacific. To achieve this objective has been my emotional mainspring. A number of articles may tempt earth scientists to hold their judgment suspended on even elegant geological hypotheses. In these there is always much fashion, as evanescent as the kind which began with the wearing of animal skins.

The difficult part of this foreword is to acknowledge suitably the help I have had from many colleagues and instrumentalities. The Australian Academy of Science gave permission to proceed with the publication of the book. The most significant material assistance was given by West Australian Petroleum Pty Ltd (WAPET) and Burmah Oil Company of Australia. Maintaining a tradition of disinterested help for academic projects, these companies provided generous cash subsidies which made it possible to proceed with the book.

I want to thank Martin Glaessner (our Chairman), Norman Fisher, Chris von der Borch, Laric Hawkins and Ian McDougall (my fellow conveners) for the encouragement they have given me during the time of editing. Ian McDougall has been especially helpful. My colleagues in the Department of Geology, University of Western Australia, have borne patiently my demands on their patience and expertise. For typing of manuscripts, drafting of figures and photography, and clerical assistance I thank Mrs K. Shaw, Mrs L. Hockley and Mrs J. White; Mr T. Bellis, Mrs K. Nielsen and Mr J. Ferguson; Mr C. Hughes and Mr A. Gayski.

Finally, in an almost exclusive sense, I want both to praise and apologize to the contributors who can collectively claim this book as their own. They met the most rigorous deadlines and, indeed, a spectrum of demands from me which at times bordered on the impertinent. I hope I have served them well. They deserved more than I was able to give them.

University of Western Australia
August 1972

Patrick J. Coleman

Contents

Features of the Pacific Ocean basin

Island arcs and related structures of the Western Pacific region

Part I

Part II

Part III

Marginal areas of the Western Pacific

Petrology and geochemistry of island arcs in relation to tectonic environment

FEATURES OF THE PACIFIC OCEAN BASIN

Introduction

C. C. von der Borch

Discipline of Earth Sciences, Flinders University, Bedford Park, South Australia 5033, Australia

During the past decade, many new and revolutionary ideas have emerged from multination geophysical and geological exploration of the ocean basins. These observations appear to herald what earth scientists have long desired: a unified theory of global tectonics. This, in turn, has given impetus to the long contentious idea of continental drift, which now wears the new cloak of 'plate tectonics'.

Opportunities to test directly these new and far-reaching hypotheses emerged in the late 1960s. Perhaps the most notable of these was afforded by the now legendary 'Deep Sea Drilling Project' which has obtained and dated core samples from many areas of the world's ocean basins. Results of this project have been in remarkable accord with the plate tectonic theory.

Many geophysical observations made at sea suffer from a lack of resolution due to the great depth of water separating instruments and sea floor. With this in mind, deep-towed instrument packages have recently been developed that enable measurements to be made essentially at the bottom of the ocean. A remarkable increase in the resolution of, for example, magnetic data, has been observed with such equipment, and this promises to have far-reaching effects in the interpretation of sea-floor magnetic anomalies.

It is evident from the foregoing that several major inter-related facets of oceanographic research are currently to the forefront. These are:

(1) Fundamental geophysical observations in ocean basins, including seismicity, marine gravity and magnetism.

(2) Testing of theories, which are often based largely on geophysical observations, by the direct sampling of the oceanic sediment column.

(3) Refinement of the geophysical observations to increase their resolution.

It is gratifying to note that the above major fields of modern oceanic endeavour were well covered in Symposium D1 of the Twelfth Pacific Science Congress. It is also pleasing to note the international flavour of this Symposium, which included contributors from Japan, U.S.S.R., U.S.A., Australia, France and New Zealand.

Gravity Anomalies in the Pacific Ocean

YOSHIBUMI TOMODA
Ocean Research Institute
University of Tokyo, Nakano, Tokyo 164, Japan

ABSTRACT

Geophysical implications of free-air gravity anomalies in the Pacific Ocean are discussed based on a number of typical gravimetric results obtained over island arcs, trenches, marginal basins, active ridges, inactive ridges and seamounts.

A free-air gravity anomaly is a first approximation to an isostatic anomaly which indicates mass excess or mass deficiency beneath the surface. By the use of free-air anomalies it is speculated how present mass distributions are formed in the process of ocean-floor spreading.

It is proposed that the Western Pacific is a kind of marginal basin (or basins), in which island arcs have migrated oceanwards as a result of the mass transported beneath the incipient and then developing marginal basin between the continent and island arc.

RESULTS OF MEASUREMENT AND THEIR GEOPHYSICAL IMPLICATIONS

With the use of the Tokyo Surface Ship Gravity Meter (Tomoda & Kanamori 1962) on board R.V. *Hakuho Maru* of the Ocean Research Institute and R.V. *Umitaka Maru* of Tokyo University of Fisheries, gravity profiles amounting to about 200,000 km were measured, chiefly in the Pacific, during the past ten years (Tomoda & Segawa 1966, 1967; Tomoda 1967, 1968; Tomoda, Ozawa & Segawa 1968; Tomoda *et al.* 1968; Segawa 1970; Tomoda, Segawa & Tokuhiro 1970).

Based upon these results, the picture of gravity anomalies in the Pacific Ocean is summarized as follows:

1. Free-air gravity anomalies are positive over an island arc and negative over the accompanying trench, composing a mass dipole. Mass excess at the island arc seems to compensate mass deficiency at the trench.

2. For marginal basins bordered by an island arc and a continent, the free-air gravity anomalies are positive, without exception.

3. In some trench profiles, free-air gravity anomalies are highly negative but not as much as in other profiles. Variation in magnitude of this negative anomaly seems to suggest various stages of trench development.

4. The seamount, especially in the central Pacific, has a gravimetric trough around it. It suggests that the seamount is in isostatic equilibrium, despite its small horizontal dimension.

5. In profiles across fracture zones, a gravimetric fault, that is to say, a jump in

free-air gravity anomaly from negative to positive value, is sometimes found at the fracture zone (Dehlinger *et al.* 1967).

6. The features of the active ridge of the South-east Pacific do not seem to differ much from those of the Mid-Atlantic Ridge (Talwani *et al.* 1965). That is, the free-air gravity anomaly is slightly positive over the crest province and is negative or zero over its flanks.

7. For inactive ridges, isostatic equilibrium seems to be perfectly achieved.

Several examples which represent these typical characteristics will now be discussed.

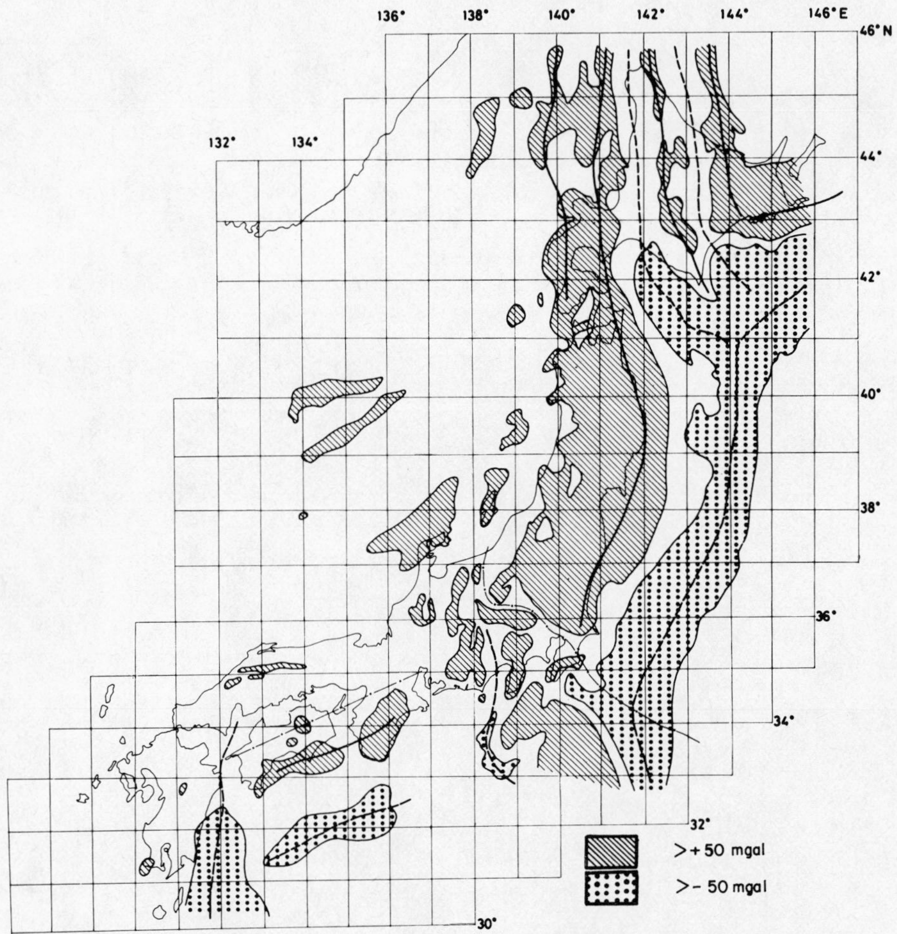

Fig. 1 Schematic view of free-air gravity anomalies in and around Japan

Island arc and trench

As shown in a gravity map of the areas near and around Japan (Tomoda, Segawa & Tokuhiro 1970), the total area of +50 mgal is nearly equal to that of the area of

—50 mgal (Fig. 1). As a free-air gravity anomaly may be considered to be the first approximation to an isostatic anomaly, it is concluded that mass excess of the Japanese island arc is nearly equal to mass deficiency at the trench. In other words, the mass forming the Japanese island arc could be interpreted as transported from the trench. When we consider the island arc and the trench as a couple, it can be said that isostatic equilibrium is achieved there in favour of conservation of mass. This isostasy is different from what is called 'Airy-Heiskanen isostasy', and statically unstable. Considering the mechanical strength of the crust, the trench cannot be permanently stable, and it becomes necessary to assume a downward motion of mantle convection or movement of a plate beneath the trench.

Marginal basins

The Sea of Japan and the Bismarck Sea can be considered to be typical marginal basins in the Pacific. Both are areas of positive anomaly. In the Sea of Japan, the free-air gravity anomaly is +50 mgal at the Yamato Bank, nearly zero at the central basin and +10-20 mgal as an average. In the Bismarck Sea, the maximum free-air anomaly is +80 mgal, the minimum value is +50 mgal and the average is greater than 60 mgal (Fig. 2).

It is well known that the same characteristics can be seen for the East China Sea and it is not impossible to interpret them as caused by excess mass composed of a thick

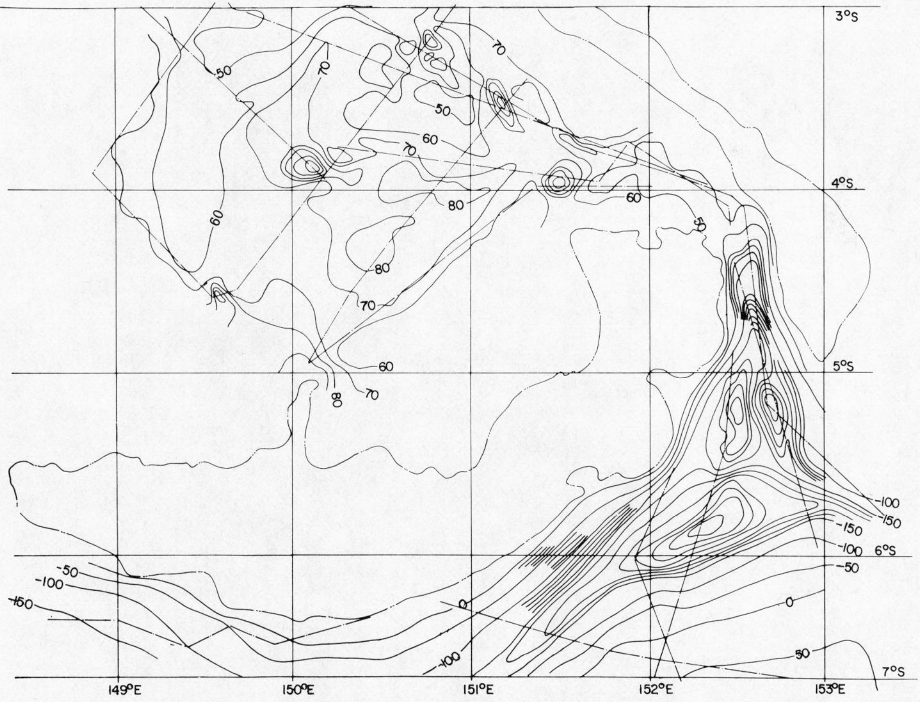

Fig. 2 Free-air gravity anomalies of the Bismarck Sea (unit: mgal)

sedimentary layer on the oceanic crust (Tsuboi *et al.* 1956). From the gravimetric point of view, it will be clear that isostatic equilibrium is not achieved in those basins, and it will be necessary to assume an upward force to support the excess mass, if the strength of the crust is insufficient. For its origin, it is not difficult to envisage a force caused by mass excess transported beneath the marginal basin by the aid of mantle convection or by a plate moving from the trench to beneath the island arc.

The Bismarck Sea, whose free-air gravity anomaly is two or three times larger than usual marginal basins, may be interpreted as a region below which two lithospheric plates meet together, one from the north and the other from the south, and overlap to form a mass excess.

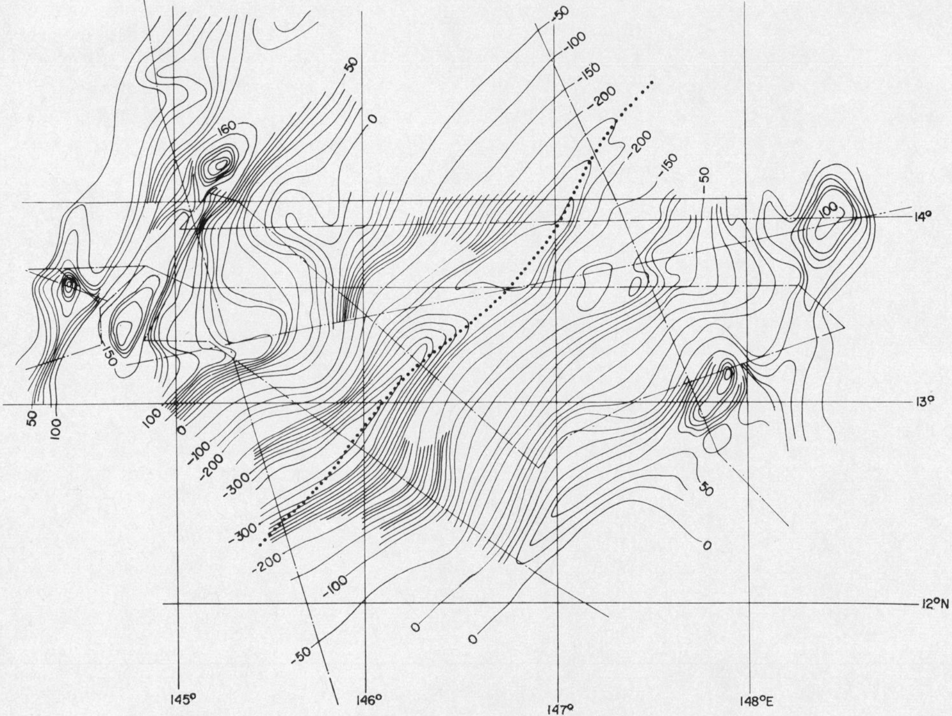

Fig. 3 Free-air gravity anomalies of the Mariana Trench (unit: mgal), ... axis of topographic trench

Boundary between continent and ocean
(continental margin with or without a trench)

It is a general fact with trenches that the axis of minimum free-air gravity anomaly does not coincide with the axis of maximum water depth. Generally speaking, the gravimetric axis lies on the continental side of the bathymetric axis. This fact is interpreted as an effect of continental crust beside the trench. That is, the thicker the continental crust becomes, the larger is the deviation of the gravimetric trench axis toward the continental side.

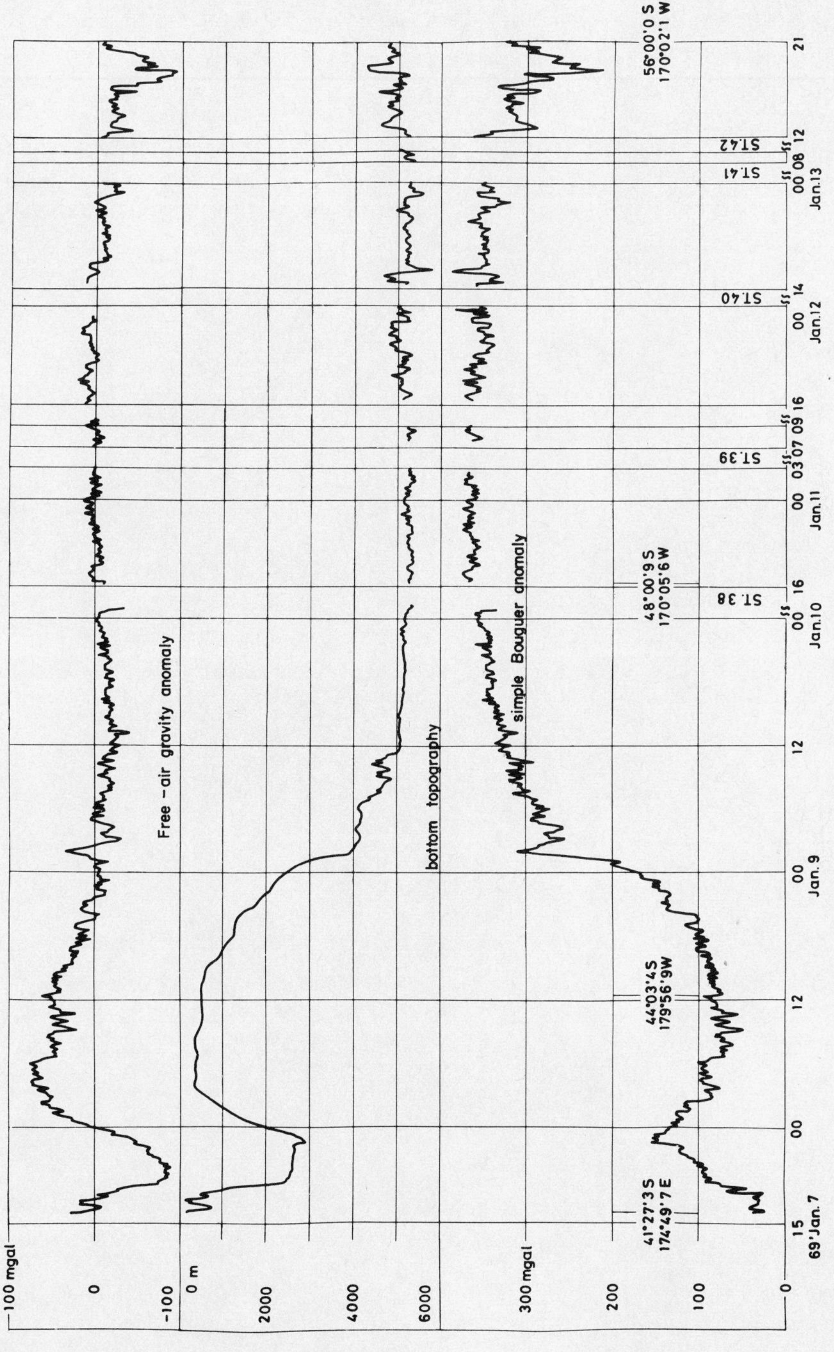

Fig. 4 Gravity anomalies over the continental shelf of New Zealand

Another remarkable result with trenches is that various magnitudes of negative anomaly are observed over the trench irrespective of its water depth. This may be due to variation in isostatic equilibrium there.

The Mariana Trench and its adjacent areas are considered to be a typical example of a trench not influenced by the continent and not isostatic. In the Mariana Trench, gravimetric and bathymetric trench axes coincide, Bouguer gravity anomalies are about +400 mgal outside the trench and +200 mgal near and around Guam Island, at which the structure is continental compared with the surrounding regions.

The boundary between the continental shelf of New Zealand and the South-west Pacific basin is in remarkable contrast to the Mariana type (Fig. 4). As clearly seen from the profile of free-air gravity anomalies, isostatic equilibrium is perfectly achieved at the margin of the continental shelf of New Zealand. Crustal structure changes suddenly from continental to oceanic. This boundary is also identified both by the sudden disappearance of local magnetic anomalies which characterizes the oceanic basin of this area and by a large isolated magnetic anomaly running alongside it.

It is a well-known hypothesis that the crust of oceanic basins is produced at the crest of the mid-oceanic ridge, moves as a conveyor belt towards the continent and sinks downwards beneath the continent, forming a trench (Dietz 1961, Hess 1962). The deep basin east of the continental shelf of New Zealand, according to the sea-floor spreading hypothesis, may be considered to have originated at the crest of the South Pacific-Antarctic Ridge (Cullen 1967). A serious problem we face then, is why we cannot find a trench east of the continental shelf. Why is isostatic equilibrium perfectly achieved at this boundary?

In order to consider these problems, several related gravimetric and bathymetric profiles are arranged according to varied stages of isostatic equilibrium (Fig. 5). Examples shown are the Mariana Trench, the Japan Trench, the Solomon Trench, the Philippine Trench, the South Sandwich Trench, and so on, but the geographical positions of these examples are not important in this report. What is important is that the boundary between continent and ocean floor can be divided into two groups, one having a trench, the other not.

From these examples, it will be suggested that for the continental margin without a trench, the oceanic crust produced at the crest of the active ridge does not have enough length to reach the continent. On the other hand, if the total length of the oceanic crust produced at the crest is long enough, it will sink down beneath the continent, forming a trench. Various stages of Fig. 5 will show the length or production-rate of oceanic crust at the related active ridge.

Seamounts

The great number of seamounts in the Pacific may be classified into three types: (1) seamounts belonging to the Emperor Range; (2) seamounts belonging to the so-called Darwin Rise (central Pacific); (3) seamounts belonging to the coral-reef regions such as the Caroline and Marshall Basins.

This classification was originally conceived by consideration of their magnetic characteristics (Tomoda 1969).

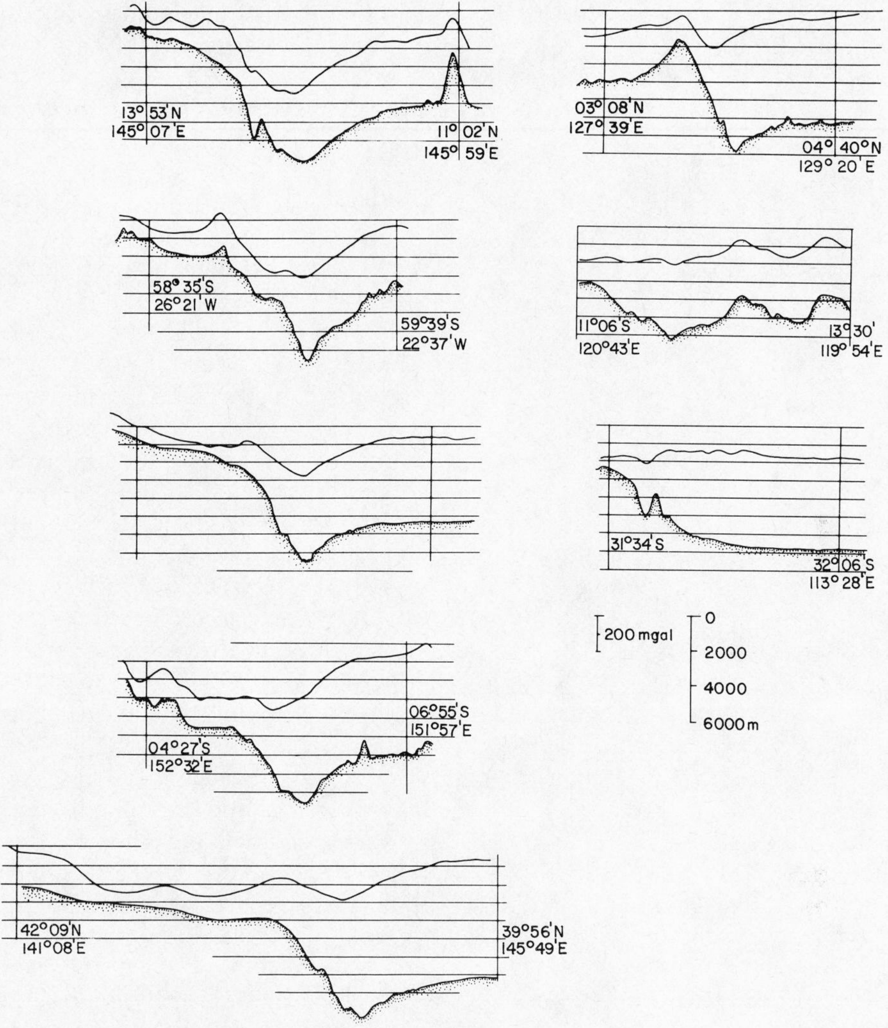

Fig. 5 Various profiles of the boundary between continent and ocean. Figures show successively, in order from the top left to the bottom left and then from the top right to the bottom right, regions with smaller rate of motion, or production rate of the lithosphere, and so gradual development of the continental margin from a non-isostatic trench to an isostatic continent-ocean boundary.

From the gravimetric point of view, the difference between these three types of seamount is not so clear. We have few data on the seamounts of the coral-reef region due to certain technical difficulties during the surveys. However, what is important is that all seamounts seem to be in isostatic equilibrium, though their horizontal dimension is only about 30 miles. From the topographic point of view, these seamounts seem to be isolated, small masses placed on a flat ocean floor. From the gravimetric

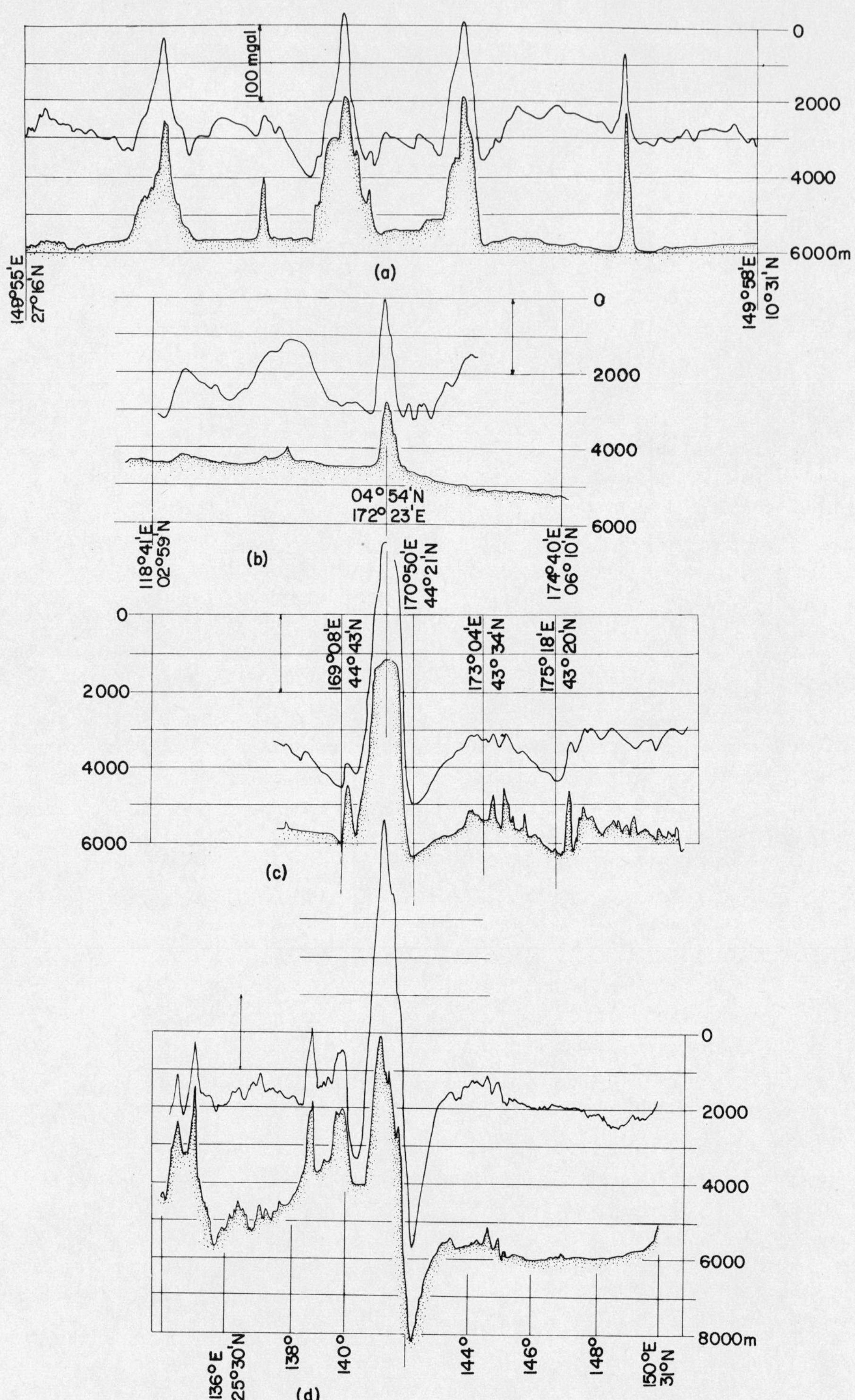
100 mgal
0
2000
4000
6000m
(a)
149°55'E
27°16'N
149°58'E
10°31'N
0
2000
4000
6000
04° 54'N
172° 23'E
118°41'E
02°59'N
(b)
174°40'E
06°10'N
170°50'E
44°21'N
169°08'E
44°43'N
173°04'E
43°34'N
175°18'E
43°20'N
(c)
0
2000
4000
6000
8000m
136°E
25°30'N
138°
140°
144°
146°
148°
150°E
31°N
(d)

point of view, however, all seamounts have gravimetric troughs surrounding them. The free-air gravity anomaly truly reflects the topographic seamount, but this anomaly (corresponding to the topography) lies within a gravimetric trough whose horizontal extent is two or three times larger than that of the actual seamount (Fig. 6*a*). This kind of gravity anomaly cannot be explained by a sedimentary layer skirting the foot of the seamount, and so it is necessary to consider its root at depth. Detailed gravimetric surveys of the Suiko Seamount belonging to the Emperor Seamount Range (Segawa 1970) showed that the root lies not immediately beneath the seamount but to its eastern side. Although detailed surveys are not yet completed, the roots of seamounts in the west-central Pacific seem to lie directly beneath the seamount.

Is it unreasonable to consider that the Airy-Heiskanen isostatic equilibrium is achieved with a seamount of diameter less than 30 miles? How can we explain the fact that the roots do not always lie directly beneath the seamounts, but that there may be an offset of seamount and its root?

It is clear that the seamount originates beneath the surface of the earth: beneath the crust. It is not difficult to consider that the root of a seamount is produced, at first, at the 'sink' of mantle convection or junction point of two different fractures. The seamount will then be produced, in part by buoyancy of the root and in part by the intrusion of material of the upper mantle which rises up through the crack in the crust. For the Suiko Seamount, it is necessary to assume a slender pillar of large density from the upper mantle to the top of the seamount.

Fracture zones and gravimetric faults

The North-east Pacific is characterized by fracture zones as represented by the famous Mendocino Fault. As shown from several gravity profiles across the Mendocino Fault (Dehlinger *et al.* 1967), the free-air gravity anomaly is positive north of the fault and is negative to the south. Gravity differences on both sides of the fault reflect differences in water depth; the negative region continues southward about 100 miles (Fig. 7). It is clear that isostatic equilibrium is not achieved in the region. Difference in crustal structure north and south of the fracture zone, investigated by seismic and gravimetric work, lies in the difference in depth of both basaltic layer and the Mohorovicic discontinuity. This crustal structure can possibly explain difference of amplitude of local magnetic anomalies in these regions. On the other hand, in order to keep the dynamic balance of the region, it may be necessary to consider the downward force acting at these regions of negative free-air anomaly.

Another example of a gravimetric fault is shown in the profile of the Tasman Sea from the east coast of Australia to New Caledonia (Fig. 8). Free- air gravity anomaly distribution in the Tasman Sea is divided into two regions by the Lord Howe Rise; the anomaly is about -10 mgal on an average in the western region of the rise and

---

Fig. 6 Gravimetric characteristics of seamounts and island arcs. (a) and (b) Mid-Pacific seamounts; (c) Emperor Seamount Range (Suiko Seamount); (d) Izu-Mariana Arc. Note that extent of the areas of negative gravity anomaly on each side of sea-seamounts is the same in (a) and (b), but that in (d) the island arc negative gravity anomaly is asymmetric. (c) has an intermediate character between (a), (b) and (d).

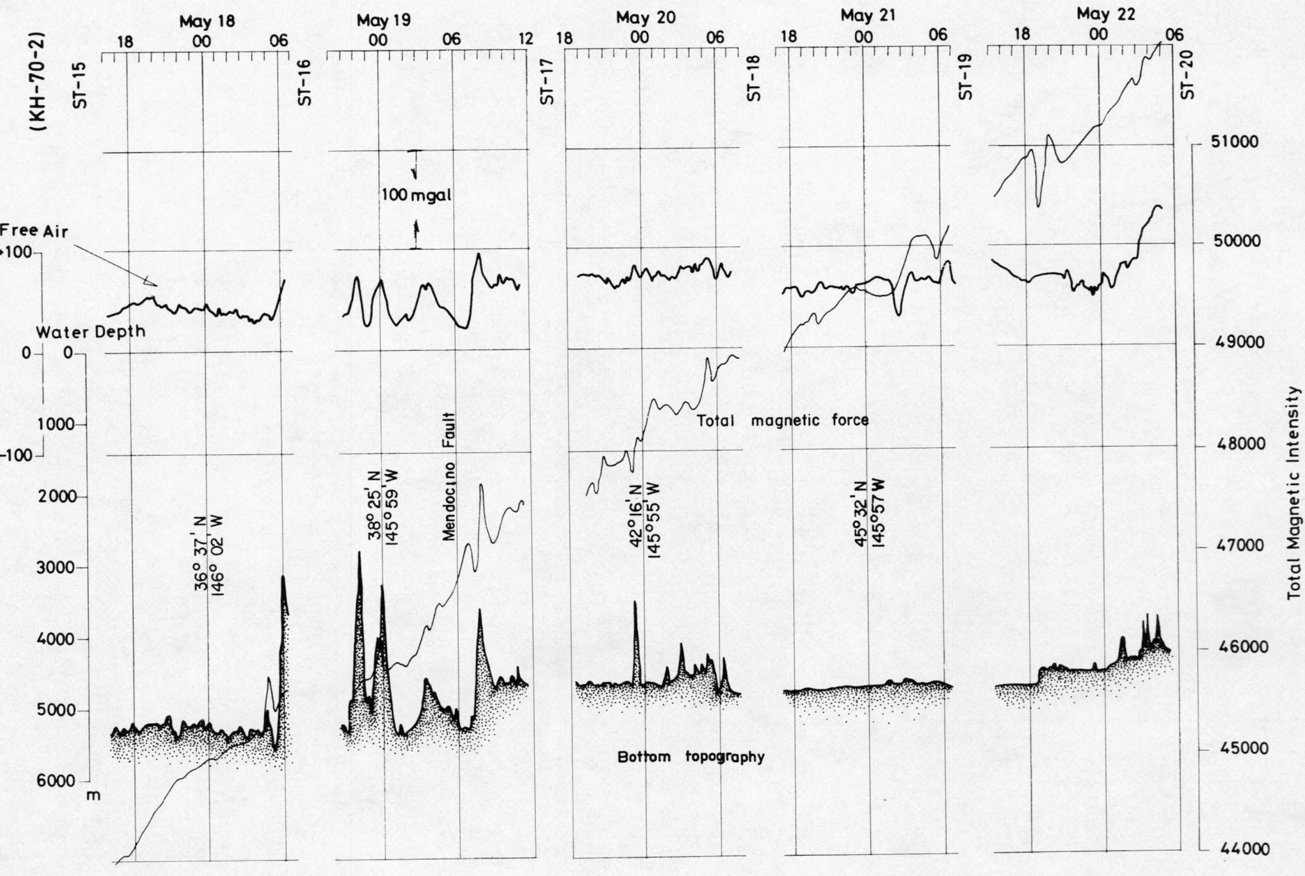

Fig. 7 Gravimetric fault at the Mendocino Fault, North-east Pacific

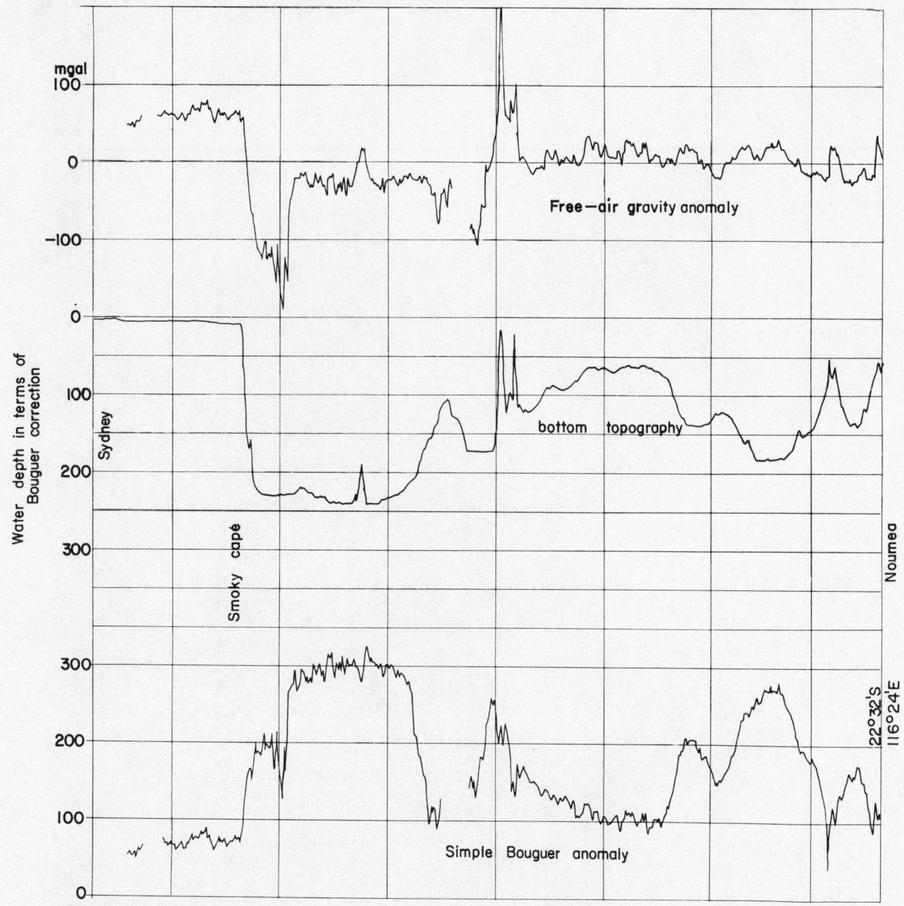

Fig. 8 Example of gravimetric fault in the Tasman Sea, South-west Pacific

nearly zero in the eastern part. The situation is similar to the profile of the Sea of Japan from the central part of the Sea of Japan and the Yamato Bank. This may suggest that the Tasman Sea is a marginal basin like the Sea of Japan, the gravimetric fault suggesting an abrupt change of the crust beneath it.

Ridge and basin

One of the typical active ridges in the Pacific is the South Pacific-Antarctic Ridge. Fig. 9 shows an example of a profile for the ridge. Topographically, it may be divided into three regions, the crest province, the flank province and the adjacent basin. Free-air gravity anomalies do not reflect the general topographic feature of the ridge. The general character of the anomalies show positive at the crest province and zero or negative over its north flank; the anomaly is divided into positive and negative zones, the two regions being separated by the boundary between the crest and flank.

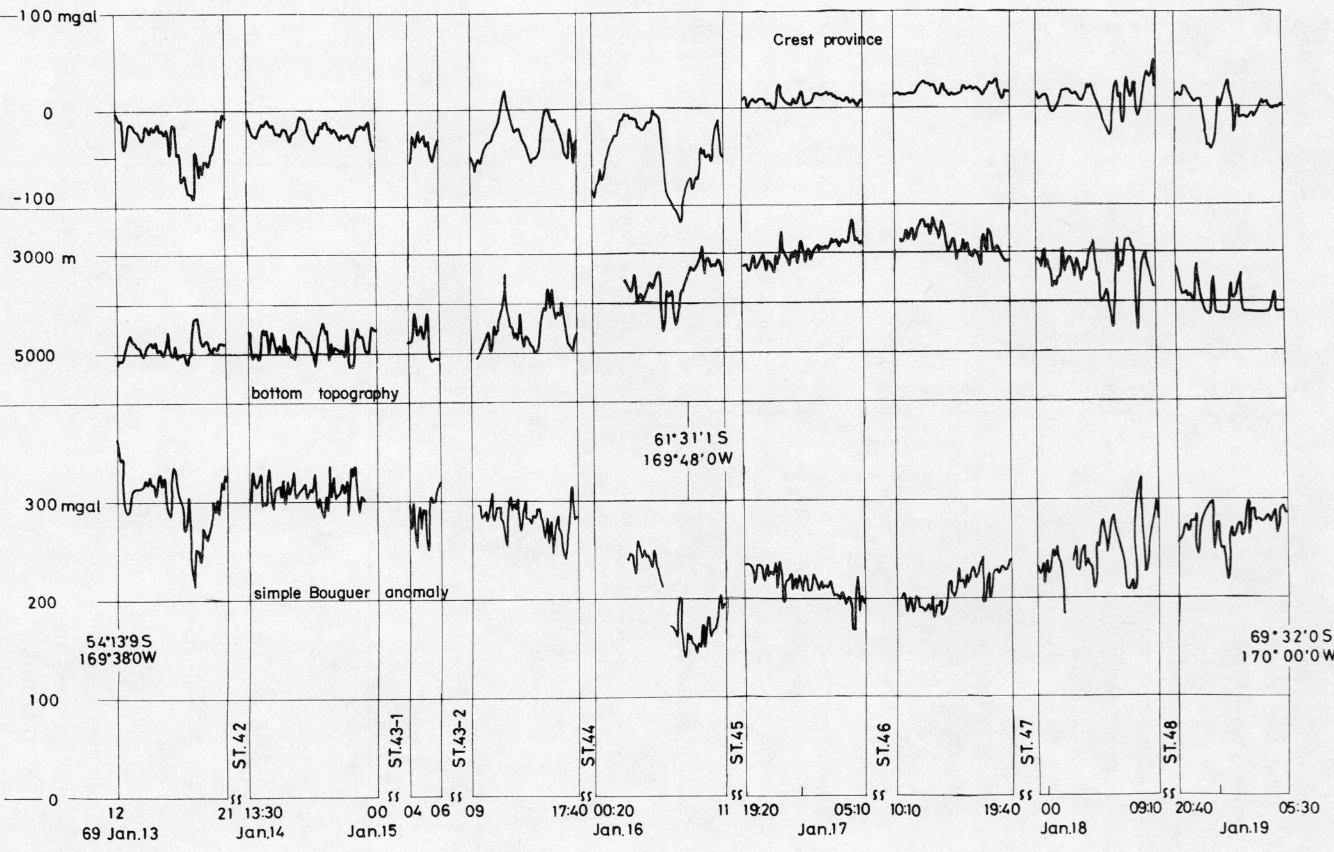

Fig. 9 Free-air Bouguer gravity anomalies of the South Pacific-Antarctic Ridge

This boundary is characterized by a gravimetric 'trough' in which the anomaly is about —50 mgal.

Considering the results of seismic work on the mid-oceanic ridge, the boundary between crest and flank corresponds to the boundary at which the mantle-crust mixing layer disappears (Talwani *et al.* 1965). It is suggested, therefore, that the boundary corresponds to that at which the lithosphere produced at the crest starts to move as a plate and forms ocean floor.

There is an inactive ridge in the North-west Pacific named the Shatsky Rise. The profile of free-air gravity anomalies across the rise (Fig. 10) shows that isostatic equilibrium is perfect (Segawa 1970), and the local magnetic anomaly there is not so very large. It is difficult to identify the crest of the rise by means of this anomaly, a situation similar to that of the Yamato Bank of the Sea of Japan. The problem is whether or not we can find any essential difference between the origin of this rise and an active ridge.

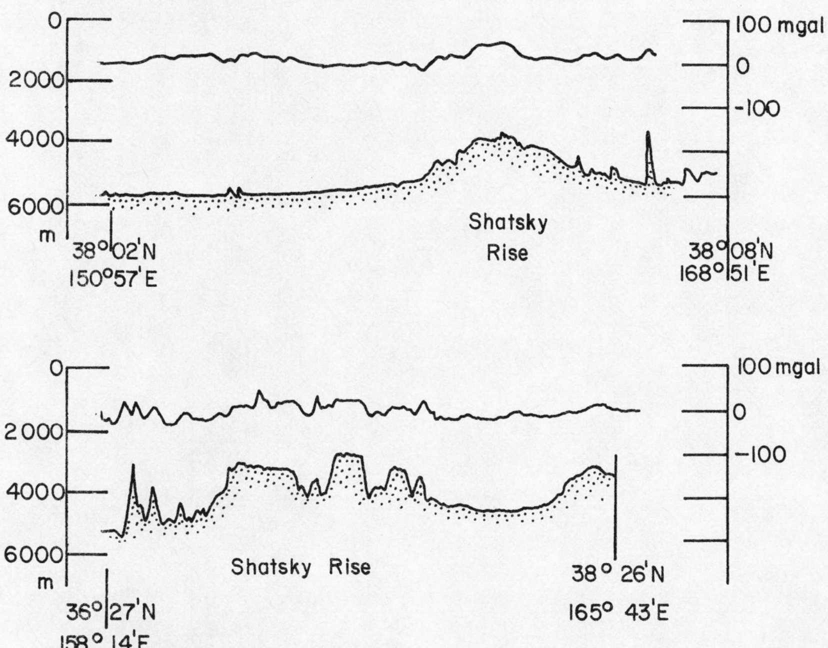

Fig. 10 Free-air gravity anomalies over the Shatsky Rise, North-west Pacific

As already mentioned, if we assume that positive anomalies over a marginal basin are produced by excess mass transported beneath the basin, the origin of the Yamato Bank will be explained. In the same way, the Shatsky Rise may be interpreted as caused by mass excess transported beneath it at an earlier geological time and now in perfect isostatic equilibrium because the mass transport has long ceased.

ORIGIN OF THE WESTERN PACIFIC VIEWED FROM GRAVIMETRIC RESULTS

As a free-air gravity anomaly corresponds approximately to isostatic anomaly if the horizontal extent of anomaly is sufficiently large, the gravity measurements will provide us with information on mass excess and mass deficiency beneath the surface of the earth. Although the gravimetric results are apparently simple, this information will help solve the problem of the origin of the general features of the surface.

In the following discussion, the author will speculate on how the present distribution of mass has been formed in the process of sea-floor spreading.

How are marginal basins formed?

The author accepts that marginal basins have been and are spreading. Their manner of spreading, however, is different from the spreading at mid-oceanic ridges. Although the mechanism of mass supply beneath the crest of mid-oceanic ridge is not yet clear, mass excess in marginal basins is considered to be transported by sinking lithosphere.

When the lithosphere moves horizontally towards a continent and sinks down beneath the margin, an island arc of initial stage will be formed. The mass composing the island arc comes mostly from that carried down by the motion of the lithosphere. At this early stage the material sinking with the plate appears to be raised up just beside the down-going slab.

As the lithosphere sinks further, the island arc will migrate towards the ocean as a result of the excess mass raised between the island arc and the continent. There will be a kind of reflection of mass at the margin of the continent. It is worth noting that the direction of 'reflection of motion' need not be unique, unlike the reflection of light.

For instance, in the distribution of free-air gravity anomalies or, indeed, topographical features, in and around Japan, two different trends can be recognized: one north to south in north-eastern Japan, the other north-east to south-west in south-western Japan and the Sea of Japan. These two trends may possibly correspond to directions nearly perpendicular to the motions of sinking lithosphere and of migration of the Japanese island arc. It could be argued that the island arc of north-south trend extends further to include the Izu-Ogasawara Arc and that south-western Japan, as well as the Yamato Bank in the Sea of Japan, is a product of mass-excess transportation.

Difference between seamounts and island arcs

In seamounts in the central Pacific, the root seems to lie directly beneath its topographic expression. On the other hand, the root of an island arc is offset to its oceanic side (or towards the trench). In the Izu-Ogasawara Arc and the Emperor Seamount Range, their roots are offset but not so much as in the usual island arc.

What is the reason why the root of a seamount is directly beneath it in some instances but is offset in others? If we assume that an island arc is produced at the

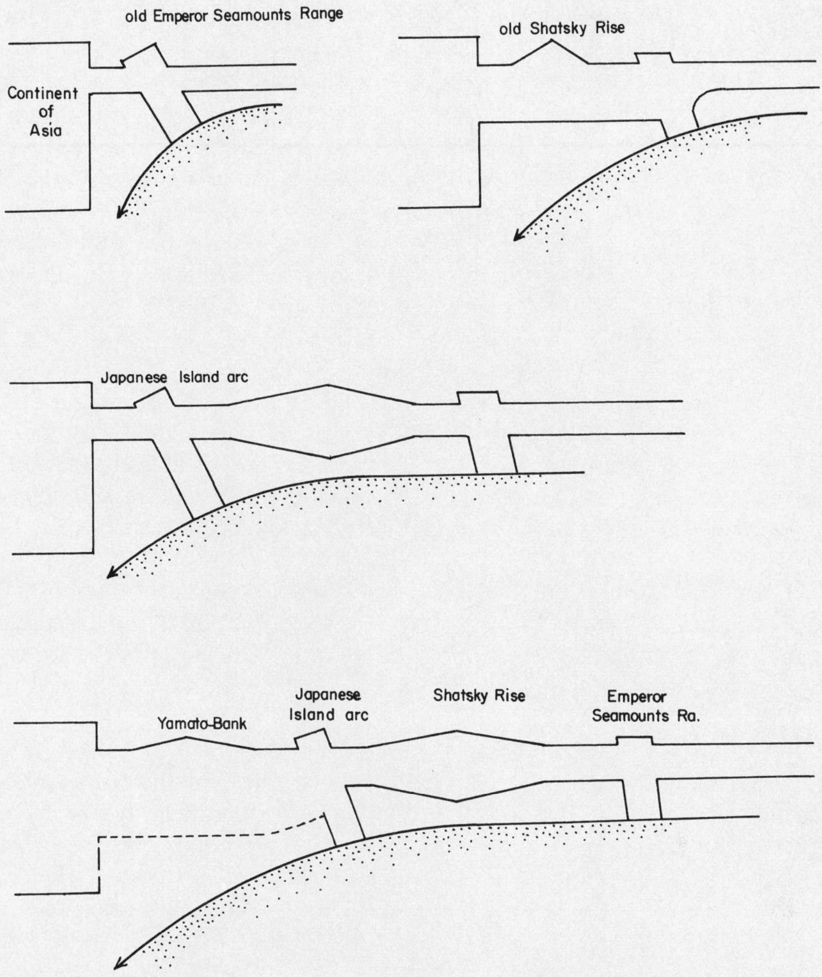

Fig. 11 Schematic diagram of spreading of marginal basins and the migration of island arcs

margin of a continent and continues its existence by maintaining a balance with the horizontal motion of a plate, then the crust will recover to normal isostatic equilibrium when the motion of the plate stops, and the trench and island arc will lose their identity by their buoyancy. Looking at the Emperor Seamount Range from this point of view, it will not be difficult to consider that the seamount chain has migrated eastwards from the east coast of the Asiatic continent. This feature is shown schematically in Fig. 11. In this figure, (*a*) is the initial stage of formation of the Emperor Seamount Range; (*b*) shows the migration of the Emperor Seamount Range and the formation of the palaeo-Shatsky Rise: the rise would have achieved its isostatic equilibrium during a long period of migration; (*c*) suggests that the island arc of Japan and Sea of Japan are being produced by the same process.

According to this concept, the North-west Pacific Basin had a border in the Emperor Seamount Range; at one time the Japanese and Kuril-Kamchatka Arcs were part of a marginal sea like the Sea of Japan. The origin of the Izu-Mariana Island Arc and the Kyushu-Palau Ridge may be interpreted by the same process.

The exact age of formation of the present configuration is beyond the scope of this gravity interpretation and will be decided by other methods.

REFERENCES

Cullen, D. J. 1967. Mantle convection and sea-floor spreading in the south-west Pacific. *Nature*, **216**, 356-7.

Dehlinger, P., Couch, R. W. & Gemperle, M. 1967. Gravity and structure of the eastern part of the Mendocino escarpment. *J. geophys. Res.* **72**, 1233-47.

Dietz, R. S. 1961. Continent and ocean basin evolution by spreading of the sea-floor. *Nature,* **190,** 854.

Hess, H. H. 1962. History of the ocean basins. In *Petrologic Studies, Buddington Volume,* 599-620, Geol. Soc. Am., New York.

Segawa, J. 1970. Gravity measurement at sea by use of T.S.S.G. *J. Phys. Earth,* **18,** 19-49, 203-84.

Talwani, M., LePichon, X. & Ewing, M. 1965. Crustal structure of the mid-oceanic ridges. 2: Computed model from gravity and seismic refraction data. *J. geophys. Res.* **70,** 341-52.

Tomoda, Y. 1967. Continuous Measurement of Gravity and Magnetic Force in the 4th Southern Sea Expedition of the *Umitaka-maru. La Mer (Bull. Soc. franco-japonaise d'oceanographie),* **5,** 175-205.

——— 1968. Geophysical Works of the *Umitaka-maru* in the southern Sea 1964-1965. *J. Tokyo Univ. Fish.,* **9,** 5-11.

——— 1969. West Pacific Ocean viewed from the Magnetic Anomalies. *J. seis. Soc. Japan* (2), **22,** 12-19 (in Japanese).

Tomoda, Y. & Kanamori, H. 1962. Tokyo Surface Ship Gravity Meter a-l. *J. geod. Soc. Japan,* **7,** 116-45.

Tomoda, Y., Ozawa, K. & Segawa, J. 1968. Measurement of gravity and magnetic field on board a cruising vessel. *Bull. Ocean Res. Inst., Univ. Tokyo,* **3,** 1-170.

Tomada, Y. & Segawa, J. 1966. Gravity measurement at sea in the regions; eastern part of the Indian Ocean . . . *J. Tokyo Univ. Fish.*, **8,** 107-31.

——— 1967. Measurement of Gravity and Total Magnetic Force in the sea near and around Japan, 1966. *J. geod. Soc. Japan,* **12,** 157-64.

Tomoda, Y., Segawa, J. & Tokuhiro, A. 1970. Free air gravity anomalies at sea around Japan measured by the Tokyo Surface Ship Gravity Meter, 1961-69. *Proc. Japan Acad.* **46,** 9.

Tomoda, Y. *et al.* 1968. Preliminary Report of the *Hakuho-maru* Cruise KH-68-3 (July-August 1968), North Pacific Ocean. *Publ. Ocean Res. Inst.,* Univ. Tokyo, 1968.

Tsuboi, C., Jitsukawa, A. & Tajima, H. 1956. Gravity survey along the lines of precise levels throughout Japan by means of a Worden gravimeter. *Bull. Earthq. Res. Inst. Tokyo Univ.* Suppl. **4** (9); pts 1-9, 552 pp.

Tectonics of the Pacific Segment of the Earth

YU. M. PUSHCHAROVSKY

Geological Institute, Academy of Sciences of the U.S.S.R.
Pyzhevsky 7, Moscow G-17, U.S.S.R.

ABSTRACT

The Pacific segment of the earth includes the floor of the Pacific Ocean and the circum-Pacific tectonic belt. The latter is a combination of Late Precambrian-through-Cenozoic folded zones and recent geosynclinal zones framing the oceanic floor. The circum-Pacific belt has been developing for a long time and remains highly mobile up till now. The Pacific floor has a complicated structure. Within its limits there may be distinguished the largest areas: the East-Pacific mobile belt and two thalassogens located to the north-west and south-east of it. The term 'thalassogen' is used instead of 'thalassocraton' which is unsuitable nowadays. The analysis and history of development of the Pacific segment of the earth shows that the hypothesis of mobilism is not able to explain the tectonic phenomena in this part of the planet; it must deny the circum-Pacific belt altogether. The same can be said of the hypotheses of 'sea-floor spreading' and 'plate tectonics'.

INTRODUCTION

Tectonic hypotheses of recent times are based on speculative ideas of movements rather than on an analysis of concrete structural forms of the earth's crust. This has led to such hypotheses as 'sea-floor spreading', 'plate tectonics' and 'new global tectonics'.

In this paper the author concentrates on concrete structural forms and zones of the earth crust common to the Pacific area. They are presented on the tectonic map of the Pacific segment of the earth. This map was compiled in the period between the Eleventh and Twelfth Pacific Science Congresses and published at the end of 1970. The map was a result of co-operative work of researchers of the Geological Institute and Institute of Oceanology of the Academy of Sciences of the U.S.S.R.

The task of tectonic maps in general is to summarize concrete data on structural forms of one or another area of the earth's crust. At the same time these maps in principle reveal distributional regularities of structural formations in time and space. Because of this, tectonic maps prove to be a restraining factor for those tectonic hypotheses that are too isolated from reality. If there is no harmonious relation between tectonic maps and hypotheses, then the latter cannot be confirmed by the facts.

The concept of the existence of a tectonically specific Pacific segment of the earth was suggested for the first time by N. S. Shatsky in 1957. This theme, however, had been a subject of interest long before. At first the eastern hemisphere (oceanic) was opposed to the western one (continental). With increasing geological knowledge, certain structural peculiarities of the Pacific area became gradually elucidated. We would recall that about 50 years ago V. I. Vernadsky (Vernadsky 1934) suggested an idea of dissymmetry in extention of the sialic shell of the earth, namely, its absence over the vast space of the Pacific Ocean.

At present, the specific structure of the Pacific hemisphere appears clear to every unprejudiced geologist: it is the greatest of the earth's oceans, occupying nearly 35 per cent of its surface; its floor is surrounded or framed by a rim of Neogaean folded zones and recent geosynclinal tectonic zones. It is evident that any global tectonic concept should consider and explain this grand structure. Forestalling the pending arguments, we must say that none of the existing concepts satisfies this requirement. Moreover, the Pacific hemisphere as an entity is often neglected, since researchers tend to concentrate their attentions on less significant structural phenomena.

Following the discovery of the asymmetry in the Moon's structure (differences in the structure of its visible and invisible sides) it is clear that tectonic opposition of the Pacific side of the planet to its other part is of a primary importance. It is interesting that geologists have approached this most peculiar feature of the earth empirically, piece by piece, by studying actual folded chains, rocks of both the land and oceanic floor, geological and geophysical peculiarities of the peri-oceanic zones.

The Pacific tectonic segment of the earth includes the floor of the Pacific Ocean and the rim of folded zones and recent geosynclinal formations surrounding it (Fig. 1). This rim is interpreted by the author as the circum-Pacific tectonic belt which will be considered below.

CIRCUM-PACIFIC TECTONIC BELT

In the peri-oceanic zones of continents, along their margins and generally parallel to their Pacific coasts, there stretch large areas of heterochronous folded structures, as well as the island systems combined with deep trenches and basins. According to the definition given by the author (Pushcharovsky 1965), these formations in total make up the circum-Pacific tectonic belt. Its outer boundaries are drawn along the margins of intracontinental old platforms, the inner ones along abyssal trenches that are advanced into the ocean. Thus, this is a tectonic belt with definite outlines in space. The outer boundary stretches over 57,000 km, the inner one some 10,000 km less.

Tectonic peculiarities of the Pacific Ocean frame, composing the circum-Pacific belt, were noticed by E. Süess who contrasted the structures of Pacific coasts to those of the Atlantic. Haug introduced the concept of the circum-Pacific geosyncline (Haug 1900). Stille (1945, 1957) and others wrote a great deal about circum-Pacific folded areas and the many peculiarities of the structural development of the circum-Pacific belt. Exceptionally important ideas on structure and areas of metallogenesis

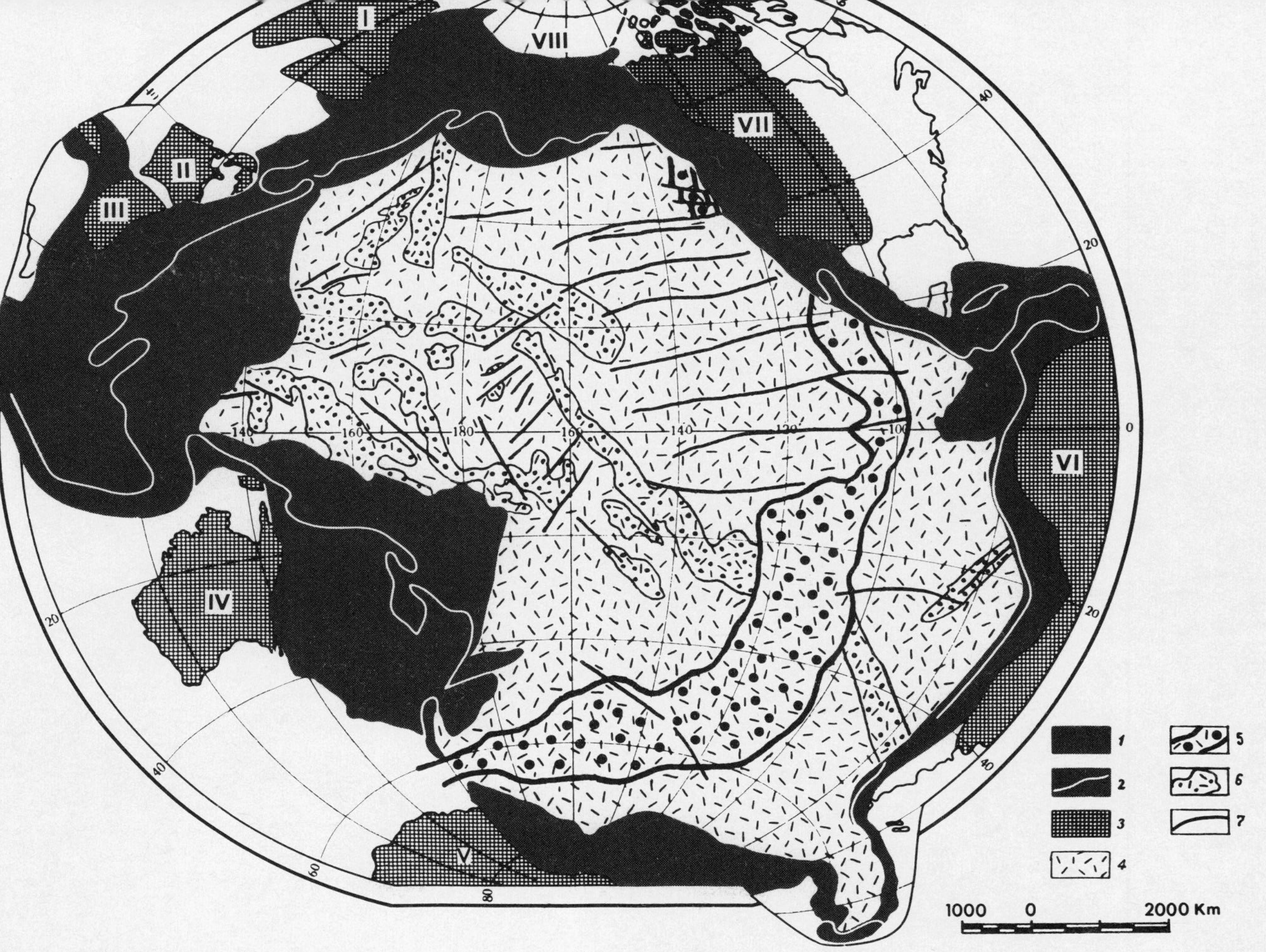

Fig. 1 Pacific tectonic segment of the Earth. 1, circum-Pacific tectonic belt. 2, boundaries of distribution of recent geosynclines. 3, ancient platforms: I, Siberian; II, Chinese-Korean; III, South-Chinese; IV, Australian; V, Antarctic; VI, South American; VII, North American; VIII, hypothetic Hyperborean. 4, Pacific floor. 5, East-Pacific mobile belt. 6, tectonic uplifts of various types. 7, fracture zones.

were suggested by Smirnov (1946). His concepts are in accordance with the author's, especially those concerning the boundaries of the belt. Neither these authors nor others (Shatsky 1960, Kheraskov 1963) doubted that they were dealing with a planetary structure, tectonically uniform, binding the Pacific Ocean.

The structural entirety of the belt is determined not only by its boundaries, as mentioned above, but also by the fact that it is divided into two concentrically located rings, an outer and an inner. The outer ring consists of folded structures, whereas the inner one is of recent geosynclinal structures.

The outer ring includes folded zones dating from the Late Precambrian to the late Cenozoic (Stille's Neogäikum). In order to denote them, it is expedient to use the precise subdivisions of the geochronological scale rather than the names of the European scale of folding epochs (Caledonian, Hercynian and Alpine). This is done because of the considerable variation in time of the formation of folded zones throughout the globe. It would be a mistake to regard the Lachlan zone of eastern Australia, where geosynclinal development ended in the Lower Devonian, as Caledonian; it would be better to name it the middle Palaeozoic, and denote the actual time by an index. In Scotland, for instance, the Caledonian geosyncline had finished its development 40 m.y. earlier.

Study of the geological structure of the outer ring shows that within its limits there were widely developed Late Precambrian and Palaeozoic geosynclines. Pre-Mesozoic folded zones, however, had a restricted distribution. Late Precambrian zones are distinguished in Antarctica, eastern Australia and Korea. Middle Palaeozoic zones occur in eastern Australia and in the south-east of China; late Palaeozoic in eastern Australia, Bolivia, and in certain areas of eastern Asia. Mesozoic folded zones were widely distributed, but Mesozoic geosynclines even more so; the Mesozoic can be divided into early and late zones. Among Cenozoic folded zones, extending over vast areas, there are distinguished early, middle and late Cenozoic zones.

This review shows that the circum-Pacific tectonic belt was highly mobile during geological history. This mobility gave rise to either a long continuous development of geosynclines, or regeneration of geosynclinal conditions. The former development of geosynclines can be observed in the west of North America or in Sikhote-Alin, and regeneration in the Andes, Japan, New Zealand, also perhaps in the east of Australia and in other places. We shall refer again to the mobility of the circum-Pacific belt as a most peculiar feature of its development.

A regular arrangement of folded zones in the circum-Pacific belt is noteworthy. The nearer to the ocean, the younger the zones are. Such a successive change of folded zones of different age is clearly seen on the margins of all the continents. It is especially obvious in Australia and Melanesia (Bogdanov 1967; Brown, Campbell & Crook 1968), where to the east of the old platform stretches the Late Precambrian Adelaidean zone; then follows the middle Palaeozoic zone, still further eastwards; then the upper Palaeozoic, and at last, the Melanesian zone of late Cenozoic folded structures, which, as everywhere within the belt, did not finish their development. The latter zone is in contact with a ring of recent geosynclinal structures adjacent to the oceanic floor. On the margins of other continents heterochronous folded zones are not so abundant; however, as already mentioned, a basically similar picture can be observed.

The phenomenon described expresses the general trend in the development of geosynclinal process in the circum-Pacific belt. It means that in the course of time the geosynclinal process has shifted towards the ocean. If we accept this, we should acknowledge as well that the Pacific Ocean floor has long existed as an independent tectonic area. A Mesozoic age-limit of the floor is certain to be out of the question.

In this connection it would be expedient to concentrate our attention on the problem that has become better known during the last years. We refer to the distribution of old peri-oceanic geosynclines in the circum-Pacific belt. Here there are widely developed volcanogenic, volcanogenic-sedimentary, greywacke and siliceous strata, as well as magmatic rocks, the composition and structure of which testify to their origin under geosynclinal conditions with an oceanic or suboceanic type of crust at the basement. The Franciscan formation in California, greywacke sequences in New Zealand, the lower beds of the section in the Sakhalin, and some others may serve as good examples of such strata. Their oldest components can be attributed to the upper Palaeozoic. To such structural formations belong also a part of the Sikhote-Alin and eastern Australian strata, and the whole eugeosynclinal complex of the North American Cordilleras. Thus, the age of peri-oceanic geosynclines on the periphery of the Pacific Ocean is considerable. It would be logical to conclude that the present-day tectonic relations between the Pacific Ocean floor and the structures of its frame are deeply rooted.

We have mentioned three important tectonic peculiarities of the outer ring of the circum-Pacific folded formations, namely: regular distribution of folded zones in the belt differing in the age of folding, high mobility of the tectonosphere within the ring, and lastly, distribution of rather old peri-oceanic geosynclines.

We may refer now to the inner structural ring of the belt that joins the oceanic floor.

The author believes that this ring is the main recent geosynclinal belt on the globe. We can definitely say that if this is not a geosynclinal belt then there are no young geosynclines on the earth. But this is an opinion seldom expressed. Assuming today's geosynclines, they should be represented, first and foremost, by the systems of island ridges and abyssal trenches lying on the margins of the Pacific Ocean.

Such systems, being lineal, are characterized by rather contrasting tectonic relief, the amplitude may reach several kilometres. They are distinguished by a high degree of tectonic mobility that is especially confirmed by movements in the Late Tertiary and Quaternary. The vast majority of trenches with enormous depths to their basement were formed at that time and a great number of positive structures underwent considerable uplifts. The formation of volcanogenic, volcanogenic-sedimentary and other sediments of geosynclinal and geoanticlinal types is proceeding in these systems. They are characterized by an intense development of recent volcanism (subaerial and underwater) and high seismicity.

As well as these systems, including lineal uplifts (island arcs among them) and their accompanying abyssal trenches and basins, the belt involves various block forms, that is, massifs. These usually display features of a complicated structural development in which processes of structural creation are associated with those of destruction. The lateral massif of Fiji (Dickinson 1967) may serve as an example.

In addition, there are distinguished in the ring marginal zones that are tectonically unstable folded systems, which include among others east Kamchatka, a considerable part of Japan and the Philippines. Like the massifs, they testify to a very complicated course of development of geosynclinal zones expressed in structural reconstructions and changes in crust structure. For instance, the Palaeozoic structures of the Kitakami mountains in Japan are cut by the Japan Trench. Thus, it becomes obvious that the geosynclinal process is not a simple process of successive growth (extension) of the crust in one direction. It is more complicated. This is well shown by examples in the Caribbean region. Here the structures of the recent geosynclinal belt interrupt and cut off earlier structural formations, changing the previous tectonic plan. In the course of reworking of this plan an extension of the crust over some areas took place, as in the Colombian depression located on the strike of the Nicaraguan graben. In other cases fragments of old structures can be involved in vertical movement of the material in deep-seated zones. This is exemplified by granite blocks, weighing up to two tons, uplifted from a depth of about 2,000 m in the region of the southern part of the Aves range (age of the granites is 79 m.y.[1]). A new geosynclinal formation may pull asunder the blocks of the earlier structures, for example, the blocks of the Greater Antilles (the separate blocks of Cuba, of Haiti and Puerto Rico). A certain rotation of blocks may take place (Jamaica).

The other area with similar phenomena is represented by the New Guinea—New Zealand sector. A young geosynclinal process here refabricates the previously formed tectonic plan, the plan of the 'Papuan geosyncline' stretching from New Guinea through New Caledonia to New Zealand. This can be seen especially well in the areas of the Coral Sea and Norfolk Ridge.

Now let us recall the high tectonic mobility of the outer ring of the circum-Pacific belt over a long period of its history. In both instances, outer and inner, the geosynclinal process appeared to be monotypic. Therefore we can make a generalized conclusion that the concept of the simple growth of a 'granite layer' in geosynclines (ruled by a linear law) is erroneous. The geosynclinal process is complicated, even contradictory, with considerable and various changes of crustal structure in the geosynclinal zones. Considerable horizontal movements of tectonic blocks during the geosynclinal process suggests the importance of lateral displacement of deep-seated masses (the 'tectonic flow' of Peive, 1967).

Recent geosynclines occupy a very extensive area within the circum-Pacific tectonic belt. A considerable area is occupied also by late Cenozoic folded zones with development not yet completed. The present stage of development of the belt is characterized by high mobility. The slow formation of folded zones, within the outer periphery of the belt, has up till now been the most characteristic feature of the process. More generally, and over a rather long period (at least since the Late Precambrian), there took place a slow and also uneven displacement of the geosynclinal operation towards the oceanic floor.

During the study of geosynclinal belts, the author also concluded that the classification which distinguished only eu- and miogeosynclines, is too simple. The main classificatory feature of geosynclines, depending on the character of their development, should be the duration of volcanic processes in the course of formation of

[1] *Science News,* **99** (2), 1971.

geosynclinal complexes, but not the presence or absence of ophiolites as is usually adopted. If the latter feature is taken as a basis, such geosynclines as the Andean (rich in volcanics but devoid of ophiolites) are beyond classification. If volcanism persists for a long time (Nevadan belt), such a geosyncline should be named a 'eugeosyncline'. If it does not proceed for more than 10 per cent of the time of development, such a geosyncline is to be regarded as a 'miogeosyncline' (West Sakhalin, Great Valley, and so on). In some instances (roughly from 10-50 per cent) we deal with mixed-geosynclines or, according to the terminology presented by the author, 'mictogeosynclines'). The duration of volcanism manifested is established empirically by the study of geological sections. The numerical indices which can be introduced into the classification make it both more detailed and more objective. A quantitative estimate of volcanic action is an index of such important features of a developing geosyncline as the degree of permeability of the crust and the character of the rocks filling the geosyncline.

OCEANIC FLOOR

Considering the oceans in general, it is easy to single out the mobile belts characterized by higher tectonic activity: in the Atlantic Ocean there is the Mid-Atlantic Ridge; in the Pacific, the East Pacific Rise and its continuation within the Albatross plateau. The East-Pacific mobile belt is not situated in the middle part of the Pacific floor and lacks a central rift valley. The author suggests that a tectonic structure of this type be named a 'thalassoarsis' (Pushcharovsky 1967).

The East-Pacific mobile belt divides the floor of the Pacific Ocean into two regions. The one to the north-west occupies a vast area and is characterized by various structures. The south-eastern region is commensurate in area with the oceanic belt; its structure is more simple. Three large tectonically heterogenous parts can be distinguished within the first area. One of them is in the central north-west of the Pacific. Here there are large uplifts, arch- and block-type, combined with platy structures. It is characterized by an abundance of high volcanic mountains, contrasting forms of tectonic relief, extensive development of guyots and deeply-submerged coral formations. This is the area which Menard distinguished as the Cretaceous 'Darwin Rise', a once dynamic part of the oceanic floor subsequently destroyed by younger tectonic processes. For this area, the supposition of heterogeneity in its structure and material is inevitable in the tectonic sense. Geophysical data, as far as the author knows, confirm this.

Discovery of a complex relief on the Pacific floor was quite unexpected. Equally so was the discovery of gigantic fault zones in the eastern part, which are the most distinguishing tectonic feature of oceanic floor, stretching over the north-east and east. They are well known and do not require consideration. Though known to be numerous, it is noteworthy that their actual number has not been established as yet. They have a complex structure, characterized by a great number of local faults and narrow contrasting forms of structural relief, and testify to the mobility of the oceanic floor.

The third part of the area concerned is the South Pacific plate adjacent to the recent geosynclinal area of Melanesia. Its structure is relatively more simple and is likely to be related to a comparatively young stage in the structural development of this region. This is determined by a combination/interaction of the East-Pacific mobile belt with accompanying subsidence zones, including the South Pacific plate and a subsidence zone corresponding to the south-eastern area of the oceanic floor. The comparatively young age can be explained by a variety of features, in particular the cutting off of the Antarctic structures by the mobile oceanic belt.

The above generalized structural features of the Pacific Ocean floor, along with its tectonic mobility, render the often-used term 'thalassocraton' out of date. The term 'craton' means a certain stable and isometric structure. The oceanic floor does not correspond to this concept, neither in large part nor in whole. Within its limits there should be distinguished the oceanic mobile belts and *thalassogens,* the latter being complicated areas of sea floor lying between the structures of the peripheral frame and the oceanic mobile belts. They exemplify the obvious need for much more detailed tectonic zonation of the crust within the oceans. This should be based on an analysis of structural forms and dynamic portions of the floor. The possibility of such zonation has been already shown in principle, for both the oceanic mobile belts and thalassogens.

Tectonic peculiarities of the Pacific Ocean show that its floor differs considerably from those of other oceans. This could be due to differences in the actual formation of the oceans. The structure of the Pacific floor is in accordance with the conclusion of a long-enduring development of the circum-Pacific belt, as a peri-oceanic belt. It follows that the Pacific segment as a whole is a natural combination of the oceanic floor and the circum-Pacific belt.

The author believes that the structure of the Pacific segment exemplifies special processes and energy-systems in the corresponding parts of the upper layers of the earth. This particular dynamism may be accounted for by a primary heterogeneity of structure and composition of the tectonosphere.

PACIFIC SEGMENT AND HYPOTHESES OF CONTINENTAL DRIFT

What has been said above of the circum-Pacific belt and the Pacific segment is incompatible with the notion of the moving of continents over vast areas. Conversely, we have to say that mobilism in general must largely deny the concepts both of the circum-Pacific belt and the Pacific segment, although as far as the author knows, none of the supporters of mobilism go into this. Can one speak of a belt without acknowledging the regularity in peripheral arrangement of the tectonic zones on the margins of the continents? But mobilism does not recognize this regularity, because it assumes an *independent*, though simultaneous, movement of continents. It must deny a peripheral belt as an actual entity and so is obliged to say that it has no unitary history. To follow on, we have to deny the existence of a volcanic ring around the Pacific Ocean, as well as a seismic ring, since the links of the rings (from the viewpoint of mobilism) occupy an independent and often occasional position.

It can be objected that this latter conclusion is not necessary. In this case the supporters of mobilism must find the reasons for the occurrence of a uniform volcanic or seismic belt on a planetary scale, localized around the periphery of the Pacific Ocean alone, but not of the Atlantic and the greater part of the Indian Oceans; these last two compound the difficulties in providing such reasons.

Compelled to deny the circum-Pacific belt, mobilism must also deny all the spatial and chronological structural regularities as stated on the previous pages of this paper. Mobilism does not recognize either the existence of the ring of Mesozoic granitoid zones surrounding the Pacific (clockwise) from Indonesia and Antarctica, and actually denies the specific character and regularities in the localization of Pacific metallogenesis.

CONCLUSION

All that has been said leads the author to emphasize the difficulties of applying the ideas of mobilism to the Pacific half of the globe. Not less difficult is the use here of the hypothesis of sea-floor spreading and plate tectonics. One tends to think that this hypothesis as also the older hypothesis of continental drift, would not have been developed if real consideration had first been given to a concrete structural analysis of large tectonic systems and areas of the Pacific segment of the earth.

The subject of global tectonics requires new and more comprehensive concepts. Tectonic maps of the future should contribute to the working out of these concepts.

REFERENCES

Bogdanov, N. A. 1967. The Palaeozoic of eastern Australia and Melanesia. *Trans. Geol. Inst. Akad. Nauk SSSR,* **181** (in Russian).

Brown, D. A., Campbell, K S. W. & Crook, K. A. W. 1968. *The geological evolution of Australia and New Zealand.* Pergamon Press.

Dickinson, W. R. 1967. Tectonic development of Fiji. *Tectonophysics,* **4-6,** 543-53.

Haug, E. 1900. Les géosynclinaux et les aires continentales contribution a l'etude des transgressions et des regressions marines. *Bull. Soc. géol. Fr.,* ser 3, **28,** 617-710.

Kheraskov, N. P. 1963. Some generalizations on formation and development of the structure of the earth crust. *Trans. Geol. Inst. Akad. Nauk SSSR,* **91** (in Russian).

Peive, A. V. 1967. Fracturing and tectonic motion. *Geotektonika,* **5,** 8-24 (in Russian).

Pushcharovsky, Yu. M. 1965. Essential features in the formation of the Pacific Ocean tectonic belt. *Geotektonika,* **6,** 19-34 (in Russian).

——— 1967. The Pacific Ocean tectonic segment of the earth's crust. *Geotektonika,* **5,** 90-102 (in Russian).

Shatsky, N. S. 1960. Geotectonic generalizations on the distribution of endogenic ore deposits. *Izv. vissh. ucheb. zaved. Geologiya i razvedka,* **11,** 9-18 (in Russian).

Smirnov, S. S. 1946. The Pacific Ocean mineral belt. *Izv. Akad. Nauk SSSR,* (*Geol.*) **2,** 13-38 (in Russian).

Stille, H. 1945. Die zirkumpazifischen Faltungen in Raum und Zeit. *Geotekt. Forsch.* **7-8,** 261-323.

Stille, H. 1957. 'Atlantische' und 'pazifische' Tektonik. *Geol. Jb.* **74,** 677-86.
Vernadsky, V. I. 1934. *Geochemical essays*, **4.** *Gorgeonefteizdat*. Moscow (in Russian).

Plate Tectonics in the North-east Pacific[1]

TANYA ATWATER

University of California, San Diego Marine Physical Laboratory of the Scripps Institution of Oceanography, La Jolla, California 92037, U.S.A.

ABSTRACT

Marine magnetic anomalies and fracture zones in the North-east Pacific are summarized in Atwater and Menard (1970). Detailed aspects of my interpretation of these anomalies in terms of plate tectonics have been discussed in the references listed. Only a short summary will be given here. Fig. 1 shows the approximate shape of the boundaries between the Pacific plate and the Kula and Farallon plates through time, as delineated by anomalies and fracture zones.

In the North-east Pacific, anomalies and fracture zones from 80-60 m.y. old show the existence of three spreading ridge systems separating three diverging oceanic plates: Pacific, Farallon, and Kula plates (Grow & Atwater 1970, Atwater 1970, Fig. 18). Geometrical extrapolation of the magnetic bight and the Mendocino Fracture Zone backwards in time suggests that this three-ridge configuration originated not earlier than 120 m.y. ago (Atwater & Menard 1970). Before that time there was some different plate geometry in this region. The Kula plate along with its bounding ridges and all anomalies that were formed at those ridges since 60 m.y. ago, have subsequently been subducted at the Aleutian Trench or Alaska. Thus, the Tertiary history of the Kula plate is not known.

Spreading between the Farallon and Pacific plates was normal from 80-60 m.y. From 60-53 m.y. the spreading changed in direction from ESE-WNW to E-W. This changed all of the fracture zone and anomaly trends and created new fracture zones near the magnetic bight (Fig. 1 and Menard & Atwater 1967, 1968; Atwater & Menard 1970). From 53-32 m.y. spreading was normal in the north, but sometime between 48 and 38 m.y. the section of ridge crest just north of the Molokai Fracture Zone jumped eastward 480 km stranding a piece of the Farallon plate within the Pacific plate. The section south of the Molokai jumped westward 100 km deleting a piece from the Pacific plate (Menard & Atwater 1968). This is the most straightforward way to create the 'disturbed zone', since it requires only a relocation of a ridge crest segment. Another model has been suggested to explain this zone, which involves a fundamental breaking and a later rehealing across the entire Pacific plate (Malahoff 1971). If the first model is accepted, all the anomalies formed between 80 and 32 m.y. can be simply explained by the spreading between three rigid plates, the Kula, Farallon, and Pacific plates.

Beginning about 32 m.y. ago, anomaly patterns are less orderly, showing the gradual break-up and disappearance of the Farallon plate as it was subducted beneath North America. In order to work out the geometry of this break-up, the motions of the North American plate with respect to the oceanic ones must be determined. These motions are very poorly known, but a model which assumes that the relative motions were approximately constant explains many

[1] Contribution of the Scripps Institution of Oceanography, new series.

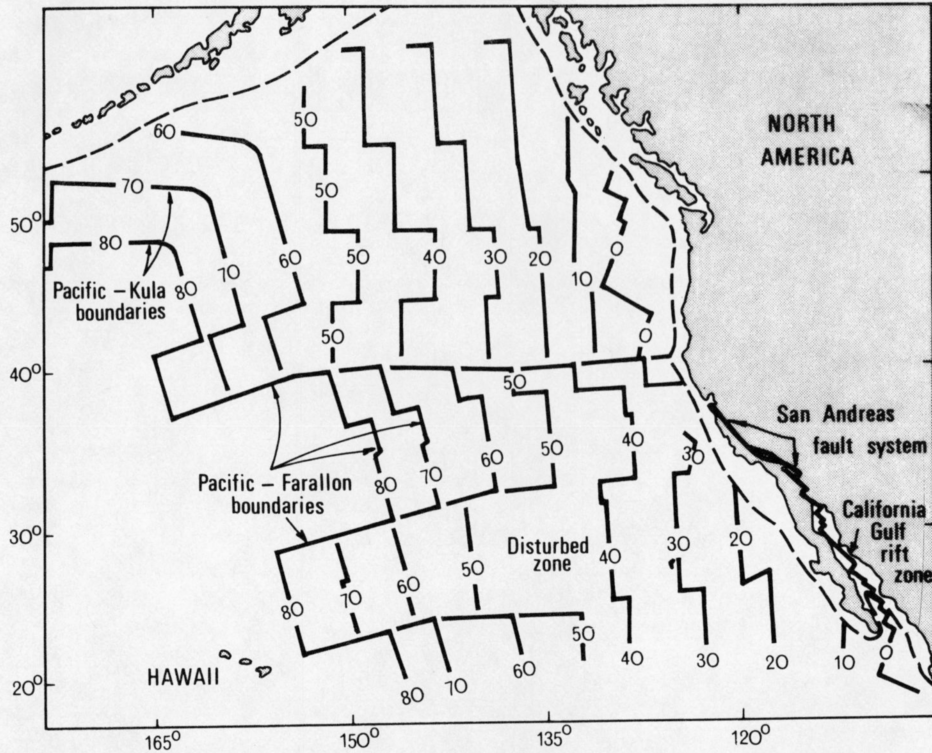

Fig. 1 Approximate shape of boundaries (spreading ridge segments and transform faults) between the Pacific and Kula plates and between the Pacific and Farallon plates through time, as delineated by magnetic anomalies and fracture zones, adapted from Atwater and Menard, 1970, Fig. 1. Time is given in m.y. before present. This timing may change by minor amounts as the magnetic anomaly time scale is refined.

features in the continent (Atwater 1970, Grow & Atwater 1970). However, this model cannot be adopted exactly for times earlier than about 15 m.y. ago (Atwater 1970, Fig. 16; Atwater 1971). The history of the San Andreas Fault and the Gulf of California is crucially dependent upon the model chosen for the relative motion, since these features are presently thought to take up the motion between the North American and Pacific plates (Atwater 1970). A more detailed history of relative motion between the American and Pacific plates must be worked out before the tectonics of western North America can be fully integrated into plate tectonic concepts.

REFERENCES

Atwater, Tanya. 1970. Implications of plate tectonics for the Cenozoic tectonic evolution of western North America. *Bull. geol. Soc. Am.* **81,** 3513.

——— 1971. Evidence from plate tectonics for the age of initiation of deformation on the San Andreas-Gulf of California system. *Geol. Soc. Am., Cordilleran Sect. 67th Annual Meeting, Abstracts with programs*, **3**(2), p. 134 (Abstract).

Atwater, Tanya & Menard, H. W. 1970. Magnetic lineations in the northeast Pacific. *Earth Planet Sci. Letters,* **7,** 445.

Grow, J. A. & Atwater, Tanya. 1970. Mid-Tertiary tectonic transition in the Aleutian Arc. *Bull. geol. Soc. Am.* **81,** 3715.

Malahoff, A. 1971. The Murray Fracture Zone: history, structure, geology and comparison to other Pacific fracture zones. (Abstract). *Proc. Twelfth Pacif. Sci. Congr.* (Abstracts), Canberra 1971, p. 355.

Menard, H. W. & Atwater, Tanya. 1968. Changes in direction of sea floor spreading. *Nature,* **219,** 463.

——— 1969. Origin of fracture zone topography. *Nature,* **222,** 1037.

Seismicity, Focal Mechanisms and the Boundaries of the Indian-Australian Plate[1]

DAVID DENHAM

Bureau of Mineral Resources, P.O. Box 378, Canberra City, A.C.T. 2601, Australia

ABSTRACT

The world-wide distribution of earthquakes defines the zones of tectonic activity that exist between the earth's stable blocks or plates. In this context the seismic activity associated with the major boundary of the Indian-Australian plate is examined.

It is shown that the main ridge system, which defines the southern boundary of the plate and extends from the Arabian Sea triple-junction to the Macquarie Ridge triple junction, consists of a series of spreading centres and fracture zones, with the fracture zones having a considerably higher level of seismicity. Representative focal mechanisms show typical strike-slip solutions at the fracture zones and normal faulting at the ridge crests.

The northern boundary of the plate consists of five main arc-like features which represent the convergence zones. These extend from the Himalayan front to the New Hebrides Arc. Earthquake focal mechanisms obtained from shallow earthquakes in these regions indicate underthrusting along the whole of the northern boundary.

The eastern and western margins of the main plate are defined by the Tonga-Kermadec Arc system and the Owen Fracture Zone. The latter is not very active but the Tonga-Kermadec system represents underthrusting of the Pacific plate.

The New Guinea region is examined in some detail and six different seismic provinces are recognized. It appears that four plates interact in the west New Britain region where the two Bismarck Sea plates, the Australian plate and the Pacific plate meet at an unstable quadruple junction.

In general the distribution of earthquakes and the reliable focal mechanisms presented give a consistent picture of the development of the Indian-Australian plate in terms of plate tectonics even in complicated regions like New Guinea.

INTRODUCTION

Although the ideas behind plate tectonics and sea-floor spreading have been developed only in the last 10 years, the considerable success and rapid acceptance of these concepts have made them fundamental to tectonic considerations of any scale, whether they be restricted to small regions or whether they encompass most of the earth.

[1] Published with the permission of the Director, Bureau of Mineral Resources, Canberra.

The importance of seismological evidence in the development of plate tectonics is fundamental to our understanding of tectonic processes. Earthquakes are direct manifestations of the geodynamic activity currently taking place; their spatial distribution enables delineation of plate boundaries; and studies of the elastic radiation they produce provide clues pertinent to the source mechanisms involved. Unfortunately, unlike astronomers who can currently observe stellar and galactic activity in a time zone extending from the present to many millions of years ago, seismologists can look only through a very restricted time window of at most 50 years in duration, and in terms of high quality world-wide observations only about 10. Nevertheless the seismological studies made in the last few years have provided some of the crucial observations in the development of the concepts of plate tectonics (see for example, Isacks, Oliver & Sykes 1968).

These studies led to ideas which resulted in the representation of the surface of the earth as a relatively small number of plates, and enabled, at least to a first approximation, the determination of their rates of motion and directions of movement (Le Pichon 1968). The applications of the basic principles of plate tectonics proved so successful, that it is now possible to look in detail at some of the smaller geotectonic features and second-order phenomena in efforts to understand further the processes currently taking place near the surface of the earth.

In general, seismology allows us to observe two basic processes. The first and perhaps the most important involves interactions at the plate boundaries, where three types of interaction can be categorized: (1) diverging boundaries as exemplified at mid-ocean ridges; (2) strike-slip boundaries such as are evidenced at transform faults, or fracture zones; and (3) converging or colliding boundaries as seen at island arcs. Some boundaries, particularly those associated with active convergence, such as the Sunda Arc or the Tonga-Kermadec region, indicate interaction between the lithosphere and the asthenosphere, down to at least 700 km from the earth's surface. By analyzing the spatial distributions and the source mechanisms of the earthquakes associated with the plate boundaries it is possible to determine constraints on the geodynamic processes taking place.

The second type of earthquake activity to be taken into account is that occurring within the plates—whether the plates are oceanic or continental. Usually the regions situated away from the plate boundaries are relatively quiescent, but nevertheless major earthquakes having no obvious connection with the main plate movements occur there, and the recent Koyna (India 1967), Meckering (W. Australia 1968) and Lake Mackay (Australia 1970) earthquakes are cited as examples. Do these types of events signify embryonic plate boundaries or are they merely manifestations of the stresses within the plate? Answers to these questions are important to a complete understanding of the situation.

This study, which considers the seismological evidence relating to the development of the Indian-Australian plate is restricted to the major earthquake activity occurring at the main plate boundaries. The earthquakes taking place within the plate itself will not be examined. The evidence presented relies mainly on the publications of the Lamont-Doherty Geological Observatory and the work carried out by the Bureau of Mineral Resources Geophysical Observatory at Port Moresby.

THE MAIN PLATE—GENERAL CONSIDERATIONS

Fig. 1, which is based on the World Seismicity maps compiled by ESSA (Barazangi & Dorman 1969) shows that the boundaries of the main Indian-Australian plate are well defined by earthquake epicentres. The main spreading centres at the southern and western boundaries of the plate extend from the triple junction in the Arabian Sea at about 13° N, 58° E to the junction at the southern end of the Macquarie Ridge located at 62° S, 160° E. The latter junction is poorly located, owing to the complicated seismicity pattern in this region and could be in error by as much as a degree or two. The great circle distance between these junctions is about 107°. A third triple junction, associated with the spreading centres, occurs at 20° S, 65° E, where the main Carlsberg Ridge system bifurcates at the Rodriguez Fracture Zone.

The main convergence zones are also well defined by the distribution of epicentres and consist of five arc-like features extending from the Pamir Knot at 35° N, 71° E to the southern end of the New Hebrides at about 22° S, 171° E. The great circle distance between these points is about 110°, slightly greater than the ridge-system great circle; however, the shapes of these two plate boundaries are very similar.

The main spreading and converging zones are connected by two major tectonic features. At the north-west of the plate this is accomplished by the Owen Fracture Zone and its north-easterly extension. This fracture zone is probably a relatively new feature resulting from the opening of the Red Sea, which is spreading slightly faster than the Carlsberg Ridge system. The connection at the east end of the plate is more complicated because of the influence of the rapidly spreading East Pacific Rise. However the earthquake hypocentres along the Macquarie Ridge and through the New Zealand and the Tonga-Kermadec regions provide a very clear eastern boundary. It extends a distance of about 55°, some 30° longer than the Owen Fracture Zone.

We will now examine the main plate boundaries in more detail.

MID-OCEAN RIDGE SYSTEM

In general the seismic belts associated with the ridge crests are characterized by moderate activity along single, narrow, linear zones corresponding either to ridge crests or active fracture zones. The seismic activity appears to be confined to the crust as all earthquakes located to date in ridge systems have been shallow. Furthermore, the seismic activity associated with the fracture zones appears to be significantly higher than that associated with the ridges themselves. The Indian Ocean ridge system is typical of this pattern. The earthquakes occurring in the section between the Arabian Sea triple junction and the triple junction near the Rodriguez Fracture Zone correspond to the Carlsberg Ridge which is a series of fracture zones striking NE to NNE with crests nearly perpendicular to them. The locations of the epicentres are not accurate enough to determine which part of the feature is a ridge and which is a fracture zone but nevertheless the extent of the seismicity zone is well defined.

Six focal mechanisms (1–6 in Fig. 1) are shown from this section of the ridge. These are taken from Sykes (1968, 1970) and Banghar and Sykes (1968). Earthquakes

1, 4 and 6 give predominantly strike-slip solutions consistent with the mechanisms of sinistral transform faults proposed by Wilson (1965) and identified by Sykes (1967), in the Mid-Atlantic Ridge system. The strike of the preferred fault plane is in accordance with Le Pichon's pole of rotation, located at 26° N, 21° E. Solutions for earthquakes 2 and 5 indicate large components of normal faulting, with the tension axes parallel to the strike of the fracture zones and the strikes of the preferred fault planes for earthquakes 1, 4 and 6. Earthquake 5 is offset slightly from the main earthquake zone but the mechanism solution is consistent with the ridge solution. Earthquake 3 is the only event inconsistent with the general picture as its tension axis is almost east-west. However since the first motion observations only fall in two of the four quadrants this solution may not be very reliable.

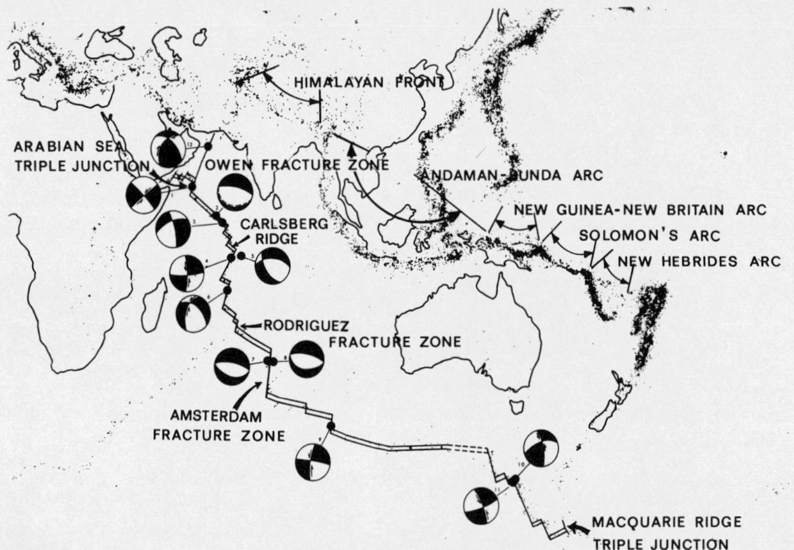

Fig. 1 Regional setting of the main Indian-Australian plate. The main ridge system consists of a series of spreading centres (double lines) and fracture zones (single lines). The convergence zones are represented by the five arc-like features extending from the Himalayan front to the New Hebrides Arc. Focal mechanisms for the ridge earthquakes are shown as equal-area projections of the lower focal hemisphere. The quadrants of compressional first motion are black. All these earthquakes occurred at shallow depth.

At the Rodriguez Fracture Zone the ridge bifurcates at a triple junction. The section striking SE intersects the Amsterdam series of fracture zones at about 80° E. Between the triple junction and these fracture zones the seismicity associated with the ridge is very low and a significant gap in the earthquake epicentres is apparent. Where the fracture zones are encountered, the activity increases considerably and the ridge crest is offset by about 1,000 km. Mechanisms from two earthquakes (7 and 8) in this region have been determined (Banghar & Sykes 1968). Both of these gave large components of normal faulting and suggest that they are located on a piece of ridge within the series of fracture zones. The strikes of the fractures obtained from the earthquake epicentres and the azimuths of the tension axes of these two earthquakes all lie approximately north-south.

South-east of the Amsterdam Fracture Zone the ridge crest strikes almost east-west and a long aseismic section is present between 88° E and 94° E. Earthquake 9 is located at the eastern end of this aseismic section and is presumably associated with a fracture zone. The focal mechanism for this event is one of strike-slip, parallel to the epicentres in the vicinity, and consistent with the polarities predicted by Wilson for transform faults.

East of 95° E the ridge crest continues as a series of long, westerly striking segments, with a section between 128° E and 138° E that is almost completely aseismic. Somewhat surprisingly 'this portion coincides with the most clearly developed morphologic and magnetic pattern of the ridge' (Hayes & Pitman 1970). At the eastern end of the aseismic section the comparatively high seismic activity defines at least three major fracture zones. These extend from about 138° E to the triple junction at the southern end of the Macquarie Ridge, and offset the main ridge crest by about 1,500 km. Two focal mechanisms (earthquakes 10 and 11) from this region indicate strike-slip faulting along the fracture zones with the directions of motion consistent with transform faulting. The strike of the fracture zones at this part of the ridge is approximately north-north-west.

At the southern end of the last fracture zone there is another aseismic section which presumably corresponds to a ridge crest having few cross-fractures.

In summary the main Indian Ocean ridge system consists of ridge crests offset by fracture zones. The ridges appear to be associated with low levels of seismicity, and in several regions they appear to be currently aseismic. The fracture zones are well delineated by the distribution of earthquakes and correspond to the regions of higher seismicity. The strike of the fracture zones changes from NNE in the north-west to NNW in the south-east. This is consistent with the focal mechanisms obtained and could well result from the influence of the south-west branch of the ridge which extends to the southern Atlantic Ocean. If this is actively spreading, which the seismic activity suggests, then an additional rotational movement would be added to the eastern end of the main ridge system.

OWEN FRACTURE ZONE

The north-western boundary of the plate is taken to be the Owen Fracture Zone as far as this discussion is concerned (although it could well be argued that this is an intra-plate feature and the main plate could extend almost to the Mediterranean). Low to moderate levels of seismicity are associated with the fracture zone which extends from the triple junction in the Arabian Sea to the Pamirs. If the spreading rate of the Indian and Arabian blocks were the same, presumably this seismic zone would not exist, but it appears that these units are moving at different rates. The earthquake mechanism for earthquake 12 implies a large component of dextral strike-slip motion.

This suggests that the rate of spreading in the Gulf of Aden is currently greater than that of the Carlsberg Ridge. Evidently more earthquakes should be examined in the zone to clarify the situation.

HIMALAYAN FRONT

South-east of the Pamirs the northern boundary of the Indian-Australian plate is represented by the Himalayan front. Apparently the Indian subcontinent under-rode the plateau of central Asia as it moved northwards. As the densities of both the Indian and Asian continental blocks are lower than the density of the low-velocity channel in the upper mantle, these blocks would not sink into the asthenosphere and a very thick continental crust would result. The distribution of earthquakes in this region is complex, and is presumably symptomatic of a continent-continent collision. However, apart from the well defined arc-like front, with its convex side facing the underthrusting plate, the region possesses little other resemblance to a typical island

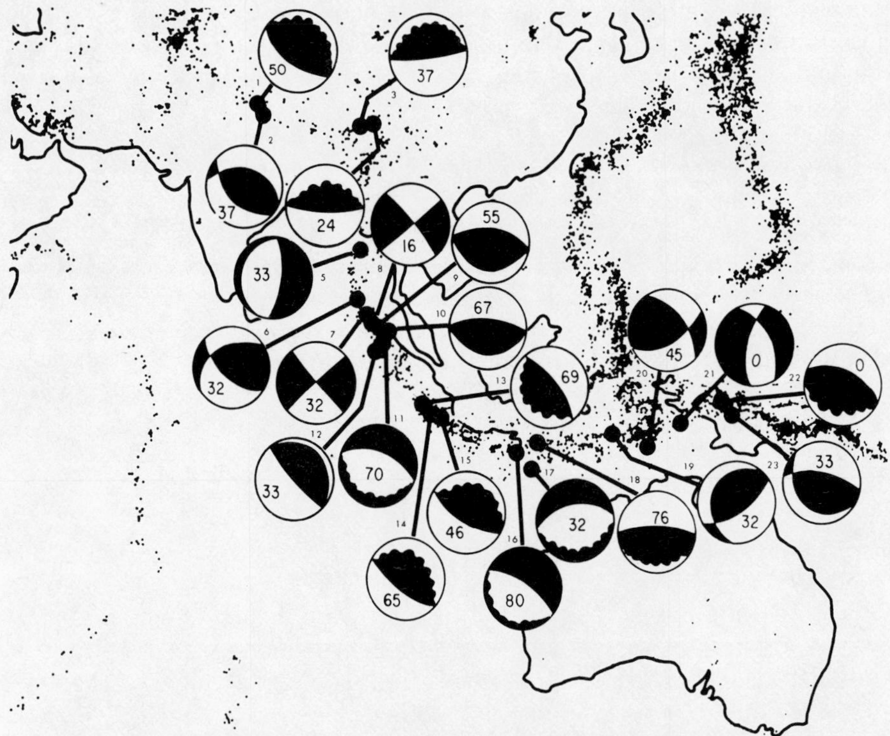

Fig. 2 Representative focal mechanisms for shallow earthquakes from the Himalayan front and the Andaman-Sunda Arc. The numbers on the solutions give the depth of the earthquake in kilometres. Where the locations of the nodal planes are uncertain they are represented by wavy lines. The representations of the mechanisms are the same as in Fig. 1.

arc. There is no Benioff zone and the only earthquakes deeper than 70 km occur at the edges of the front, under the Pamirs in the west and under the Burmese-Indian border in the east. All other events in this region are shallow. Fitch (1970) has published several focal mechanisms for this region. Four typical mechanisms associated with the seismic front are shown in Fig. 2 and are numbered 1, 2, 3 and 4. All these earthquakes are shallow and indicate underthrusting with the strikes approximately parallel to the seismic front. The inferred slip planes are shallow but are not well defined because of the lack of data from seismograph stations immediately to the north of the earthquakes.

ANDAMAN-SUNDA ARC

The northern end of the Andaman-Sunda Arc joins the eastern end of the Himalayan front near the Burmese border. This large arc extends to the Banda Sea region, where it curls tightly to the north. The seismic activity along the arc can be divided into two parts at the Sunda Strait (between Java and Sumatra). To the west of the strait hardly any earthquakes occur at depths greater than 200 km, and the Benioff zone is poorly defined. To the east of the strait the dipping seismic zone is clearly identified and many earthquakes occur at depths down to 700 km, with the usual aseismic gap between 300-500 km. The dip of the seismic zone changes consistently along the arc from about 60° near the Sunda Strait to 85° near the Banda Sea, where the arc curves tightly and terminates.

Nineteen focal mechanisms for shallow earthquakes from this region are shown in Fig. 2. Twelve of these earthquakes can be interpreted as resulting from thrusting (6, 9, 10, 12, 13, 14, 15, 18, 19, 20, 22 and 23) and nine of these are consistent with the concept of underthrusting along the convex side of the Sunda Arc (6, 9, 10, 12, 13, 14, 15, 18 and 20). Mechanisms for three earthquakes located behind the arc suggest strong compressive forces (19, 22 and 23). The mechanism for event 22 is taken from Fitch and 23 from a preliminary solution by Everingham (pers. comm.) for the large West Irian earthquake of January 1971. The similarity between the two solutions is striking and is suggestive of a low angle overthrust striking east-south-east.

Two of the solutions give strike-slip mechanisms (7 and 8). These are similar to some of the earthquakes published in the Wickens and Hodgson catalogue (1967) which contains several strike-slip solutions with the fault plane either parallel or perpendicular to the strike of the arc. Stauder (1968) found similar events in the Aleutians. The mechanisms for this type of earthquake are not completely understood, but events giving strike-slip solutions certainly occur in island arc provinces.

Earthquake 21 gives evidence of tension. Earthquakes of this type have been observed by Stauder in the Aleutians and Ripper (1970) in the New Guinea region. The four remaining earthquakes (5, 11, 16 and 17) give solutions which suggest normal faulting. Mechanisms of this type have also been observed in the Aleutians (Stauder 1968) and the Middle America Trench (Molnar & Sykes 1969) but not in the Tonga-Fiji region (Isacks, Sykes & Oliver 1969). They appear to be connected with the bending or faulting of the plate prior to underthrusting.

Fig. 3 shows some mechanisms for deep and intermediate earthquakes. These are probably better solutions than those for the shallow shocks because the teleseismic stations cover a larger area of the focal sphere. Eight events originating from the depth range 70-200 km are shown (1, 2, 3, 12, 14, 15, 16 and 17). These mechanisms have axes of tension dipping approximately parallel to the dip of the seismic zone, while the pressure axes are close to horizontal. Three earthquakes from the depth range 200-400 km (4, 11 and 29) are shown. They give similar mechanism plots, but in event 4 the *T* axis is nearly horizontal and strikes along the zone, while events 11 and 29 suggest that the *P* axes are horizontal and parallel to the zone. The correct interpretation for these mechanisms is not clear.

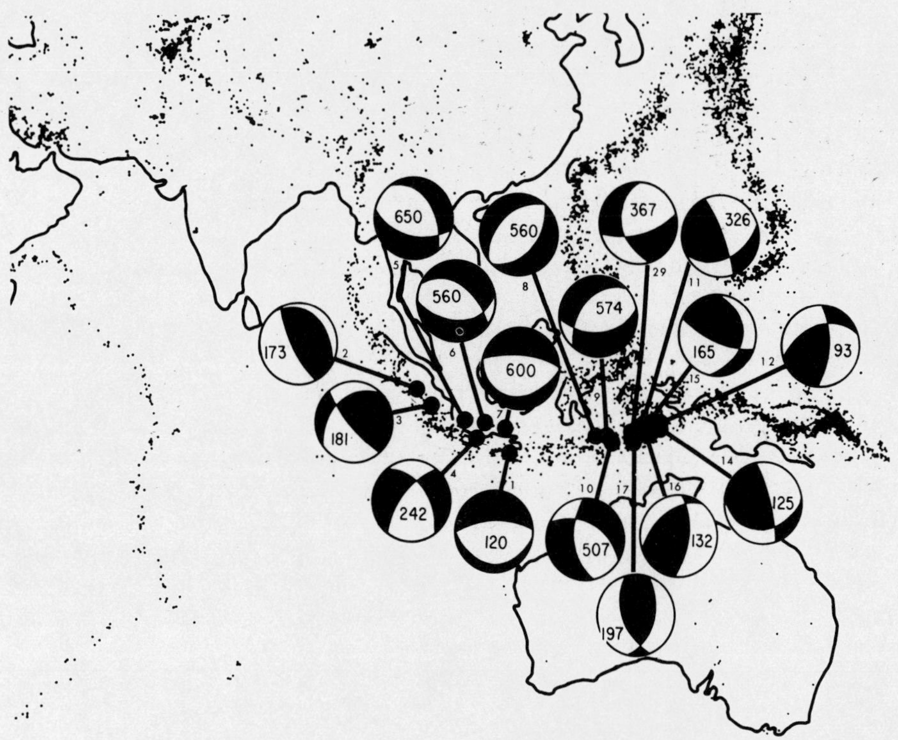

Fig. 3 Representative focal mechanism for intermediate and deep earthquakes from the Andaman-Sunda Arc. The symbols are the same as in Fig. 2.

Six deep-focus earthquakes (5, 6, 7, 8, 9 and 10) are plotted in Fig. 3. They all show similar mechanisms with their pressure axes nearly vertical and the *B* axes close to horizontal and striking parallel to the arc. This implies that the lithospheric slab is in compression in contrast to the situation immediately above the aseismic gap.

In general the picture obtained from the Andaman-Sunda Arc is consistent with a zone of underthrusting as observed at other arcs. The shallow events indicate dip-slip solutions under the arc, the intermediate depth shocks suggest tension along the dip of the seismic zone and the deep earthquakes suggest near-vertical compressive forces. These observations support the model in which gravitational forces play an important part in the behaviour of the underthrusting slab.

The situation in the Banda Sea region is more complex than for the rest of the arc, and the stress axes there, together with the distribution of earthquakes, suggest deformation of the downthrusting slab. East of the Banda Sea, the Sulu Spur and West Irian regions are indicative of the complications resulting from the violent impact of three rapidly moving plates and probably represent a series of small plates which prevent the major units meeting at a point.

NEW GUINEA-SOLOMON ISLANDS REGION

The New Guinea-Solomon Islands region is one of the most complicated boundary zones of the main plate. Fig. 4 shows all the known earthquakes from 1958 through 1970 that have been located by using at least fifteen seismic stations in the hypocentral determinations. The epicentres of these events are considered to be accurate to about $\frac{1}{10}°$ and represent the most up-to-date seismicity map currently available for the area. Denham (1969) has described in detail the distribution of earthquakes in the region in which at least six distinct seismic provinces have been recognized.

The main plate boundary in this region is probably associated with the high level of seismic activity experienced at the northern margins of the Solomon Sea and is manifested by the New Britain and Solomon Islands Arcs.

The New Britain arc contains a typical Benioff zone dipping to the north under New Britain. At the eastern end of the arc the dip is about 50°; several earthquakes have been observed under the Bismarck Sea at depths of at least 500 km. The western end of the arc terminates near the New Guinea mainland at about latitude 145° E. The earthquake zone dips almost vertically in this vicinity; no earthquakes deeper than 300 km have been reported from this region.

West of the New Britain arc there is a separate seismic zone. This extends from the Huon Peninsula to West Irian. There is no Benioff zone associated with this feature but several intermediate depth earthquakes have occurred there and in general it represents a SW-dipping slab which could well be the result of overthrusting caused by a general north-south compression in the New Guinea mainland region.

East of the New Britain arc the main seismicity zone swings through 90° and the main plate boundary is represented by the Solomon Islands Arc which extends from New Ireland to the trench south of San Cristobal Island. Deep earthquakes are commonly reported in the vicinity of Bougainville Island, where the seismic zone dips steeply to the north-east. Between Bougainville Island and Guadalcanal the deep trench disappears, the seismic level is reduced and no deep earthquakes have been observed from this region. From Guadalcanal to the Santa Cruz Islands the trench system is well developed, the level of seismicity increases, and earthquakes at depths exceeding 500 km have been reported.

A zone of minor seismicity which crosses the Solomon Sea from Eastern Papua to the Solomon Islands has been described by Milsom (1970) as a minor spreading

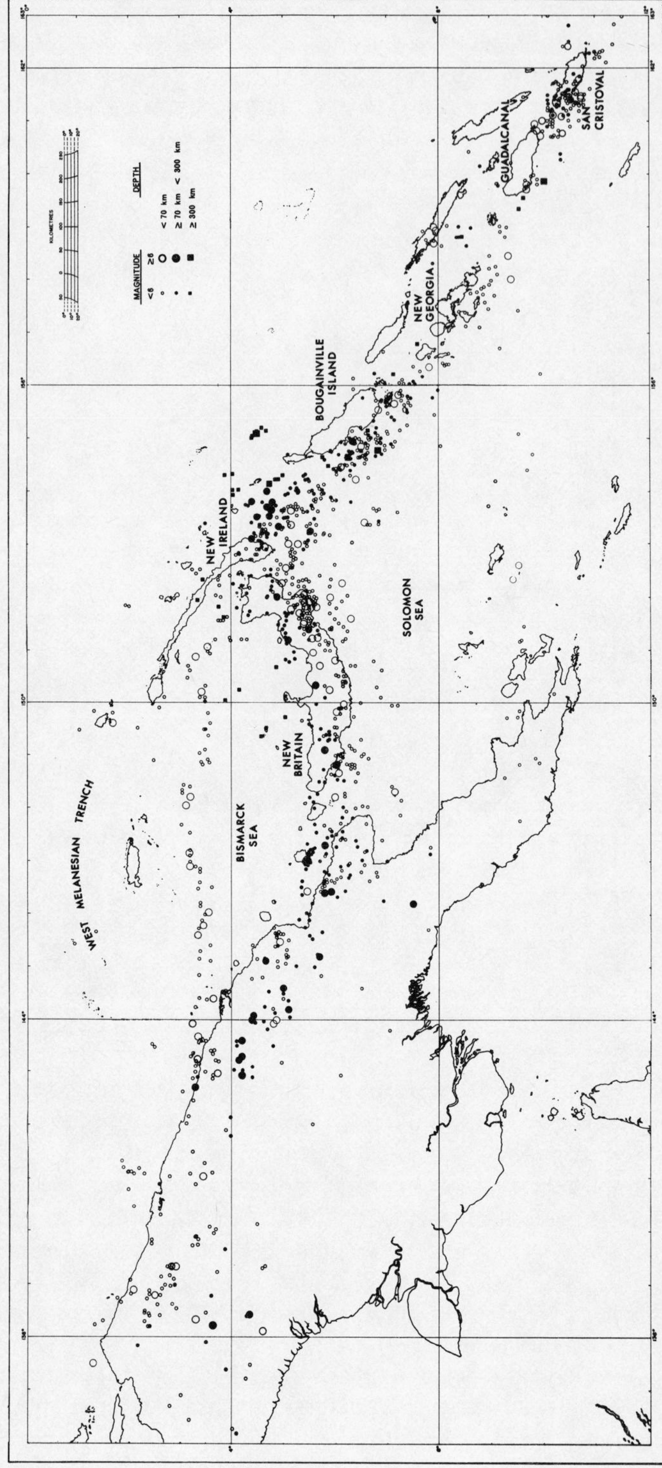

Fig. 4 Earthquake distribution in the New Guinea region for the period 1958-70. At least fifteen stations have been used in locating all the earthquakes plotted.

centre. The evidence for this is rather tenuous because the distribution of earthquakes does not suggest the usual definite lineations associated with ridge systems and fracture zones. It would explain, however, the absence of a trench near New Georgia and also the abrupt increase in seismicity at the southern tip of Bougainville Island.

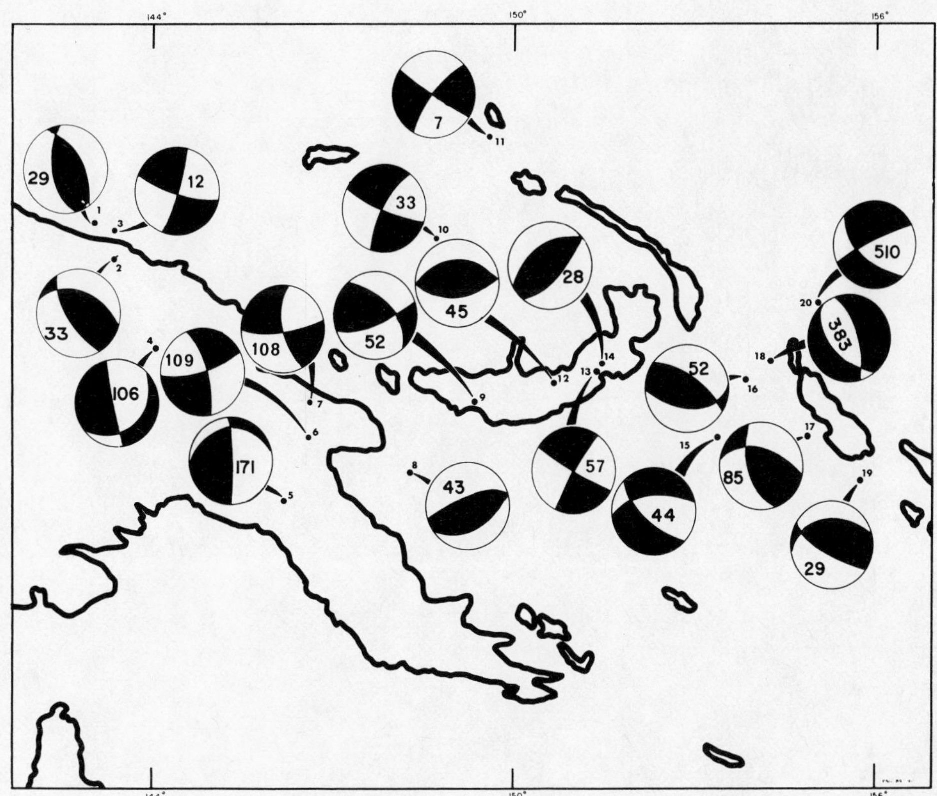

Fig. 5 Representative focal mechanisms for the New Guinea region. The symbols are the same as in Fig. 2.

One of the most remarkable seismic features in the region is the zone of shallow earthquakes extending across the Bismarck Sea at about latitude 3° S. The maximum width of the zone is only about 40 km and it stretches from the south-western end of New Ireland to the New Guinea mainland. As will be shown later it appears that this zone represents a left-lateral strike-slip fault which divides the Bismarck Sea into two small sub-plates. The northern boundary of the northern Bismarck Sea plate is manifested by the West Melanesian arc. The level of seismicity for this boundary indicates that the relative velocity between this plate and the main Pacific plate to the north is very small. Only about ten earthquakes associated with this feature are plotted on Fig. 4.

A representative sample of twenty focal mechanisms for the region are plotted in

Fig. 5. These are taken from Ripper (1970, and pers. comm.) and are probably some of the most reliable solutions obtained to date from island arc provinces because of the good coverage by the local network of seismograph stations and the presence of stations on the trench sides of the arcs.

All the shallow dip-slip solutions associated with the arcs give consistent mechanisms indicating underthrusting of the Solomon Sea. Earthquakes 8, 9, 12 and 14 relate to the New Britain arc and 16, 17 and 19 to the northern end of the Solomon Islands Arc. Solution 15 gives a horizontal tension axis which suggests normal faulting and flexure in the plate before it is underthrust. Earthquake 13 is the only strike-slip solution obtained from this island arc province since the World-wide Standard Seismograph Station network (WWSSS) was established. It coincides with the offset of the epicentres which is shown on Fig. 4 in the same vicinity.

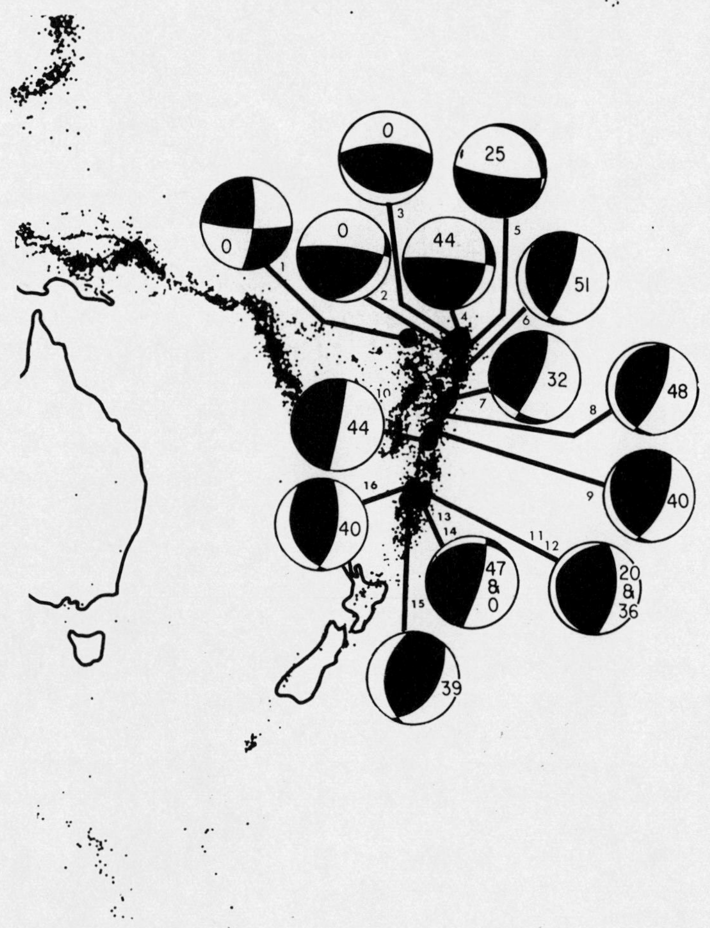

Fig. 6 Representative focal mechanisms for shallow earthquakes in the Tonga-Kermadec region. The symbols are the same as in Fig. 2.

Solutions for earthquakes 3 and 10 suggest that the line of earthquakes across the Bismarck Sea represents left-lateral strike-slip. The pressure axes for these two events are similar to those obtained from earthquakes 1 and 2. However the latter shocks suggest dip-slip solutions indicative of overthrusting and in agreement with events 22 and 23 for West Irian shown on Fig. 2.

The only earthquake associated with the West Melanesia trench is event 11. This suggests right-lateral strike-slip between the main Pacific and the north Bismarck Sea plates.

Two intermediate depth earthquakes (4 and 5) gave solutions for the New Guinea mainland. These could represent either predominantly normal faulting or shallow thrusting. It is not clear which interpretation is correct. Events 18 and 20 represent two deep earthquakes in the northern part of the Solomon Arc. They both give near-vertical pressure axes similar to the deep earthquakes analyzed in the Sunda Arc region.

Perhaps one of the main conclusions that can be drawn from the focal mechanism solutions is that there must be at least one small plate north of New Britain because of the change in direction of the pressure axes between earthquakes 8, 9, 12 and 14, and 16, 17 and 19. If the Solomon Island chain is the main interaction zone between the Pacific and the Australian plates (following Le Pichon 1968) then there should be transform faulting to New Britain, with associated shallow earthquakes. This is clearly not the case, and the maximum pressure axis is perpendicular to the New Britain arc. This means that the Bismarck Sea must be a separate plate interacting with the Solomon Sea, and since the line of E-W earthquakes divides the plate into two sections these can also be regarded as separate plates.

The mainland New Guinea region is clearly in compression and the focal mechanisms suggest overthrusting with possible consequential mountain building. Unfortunately no solutions are available from the zone of earthquakes extending from eastern Papua to New Georgia so the tectonic significance of this feature is at present uncertain.

NEW HEBRIDES REGION

At the time of writing, no comprehensive studies of focal mechanisms in the New Hebrides region have been published although Johnson and Molnar (in prep.) have determined some twenty mechanisms for shallow earthquakes in this region, most of which indicate the expected underthrusting, and Isacks and Molnar (1971) considered deep and intermediate depth events. We will therefore consider only the distribution of earthquakes for this section of the plate boundary. The junction between the Solomon Islands Arc and the New Hebrides region contains a series of shallow earthquakes. These presumably represent a change in mechanism from underthrusting beneath the San Cristobal Trench to transform faulting until the Torres Trench is encountered. This trench is associated with the seismic activity in the northern part of the New Hebrides region. The dip of the zone varies from 75° in the northern part of the region to about 65° in the south. This is at variance with the conclusion of

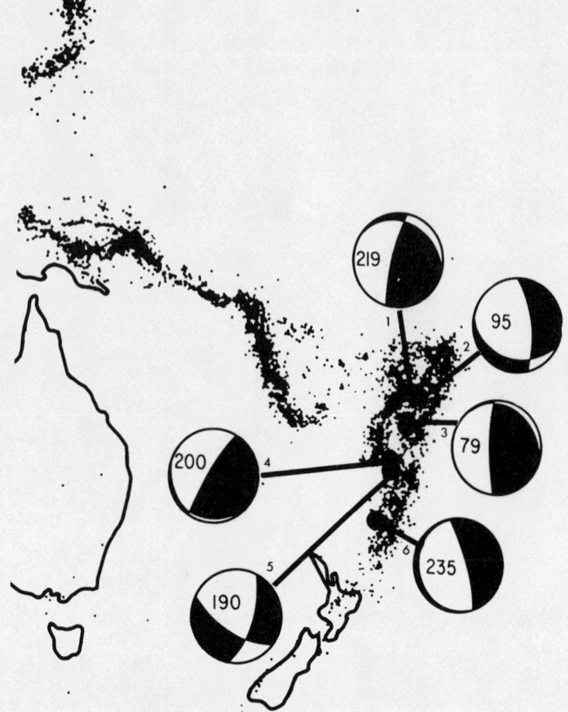

Fig. 7 Representative focal mechanisms for intermediate depth earthquakes in the Tonga-Kermadec region. The symbols are the same as in Fig. 2.

Luyendyk (1970) who showed that in four island arc systems (Sunda, Tonga-Kermadec, Marianas and Kuril) the dip increases as the pole of relative motion is approached. In this example the reverse situation seems to occur, although the change in dip along the zone is not large. The southern end of the New Hebrides Arc marks the end of the convergence zone for the northern edge of the Australian-Indian plate. The zone of seismicity curves round to the north-east and joins the northern edge of the Tonga zone in a series of complex transform faults. The tectonic activity connecting these features cannot be a simple transform fault because deep earthquakes occur along the boundary and interaction of the slabs of lithosphere must take place at depth.

TONGA-KERMADEC REGION

The Tonga-Kermadec region is a very distinct boundary between the Australian and Pacific plates. The great circle to the pole of relative motion between these plates strikes along both the Tonga and Kermadec Trenches, and as can be seen from Fig. 6 the focal mechanisms of the shallow earthquakes can clearly be interpreted as underthrusting from the east, with the pressure axes being nearly east-west. These solutions together with those for the intermediate and deep earthquakes are taken from Isacks, Sykes and Oliver (1969). The mechanisms are very consistent and the dips of the nodal planes from the solutions correspond to the dips of the seismicity zone associated with the arc. The shallow earthquakes at the northern end of the arc, where it bends abruptly, indicate normal faulting with the southern block being downthrust. One earthquake (1) in this region suggests strike-slip faulting along the transform fault.

The intermediate depth earthquakes shown on Fig. 7 occur above the aseismic zone and they represent solutions which are different from those obtained from the shallow events. The pressure axes in all instances are approximately parallel to the dip of the seismicity zone, in the direction of underthrusting. This is in marked contrast to similar earthquakes analyzed from the Sunda Arc discussed earlier, which indicates

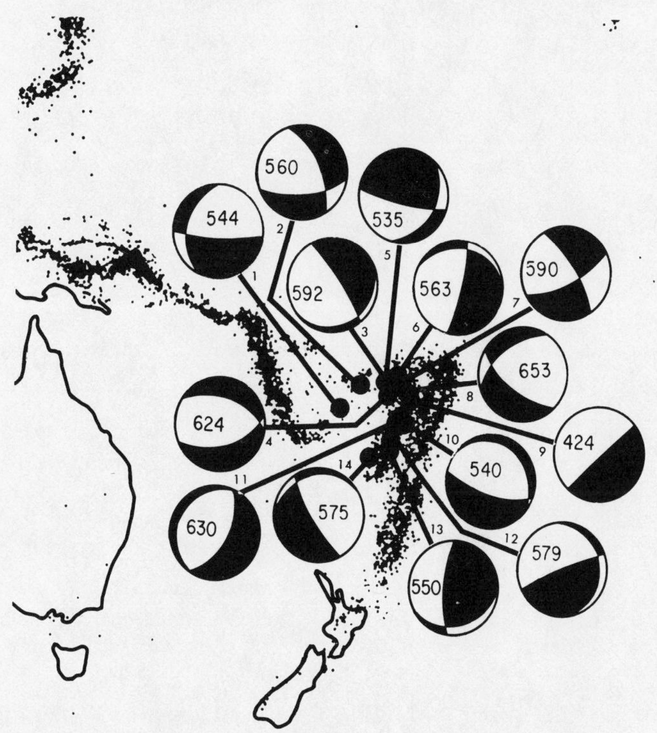

Fig. 8 Representative focal mechanisms for deep earthquakes in the Tonga-Kermadec region

that the tension axes lie parallel to the dip of the seismic zone. The reason for this basic difference is not clear unless it is a function of the underthrusting velocity. Fitch and Molnar (1970) suggest that the predominant force acting on the lithospheric slab in the Sunda Arc at these depths is that due to gravity. However, in the Tonga-Kermadec region the high velocity of the underthrusting may provide the predominant influence on the slab down to greater depths and hence compression along the slab may be the cause of the earthquakes at those depths. The mechanisms published for deep earthquakes are shown in Fig. 8.

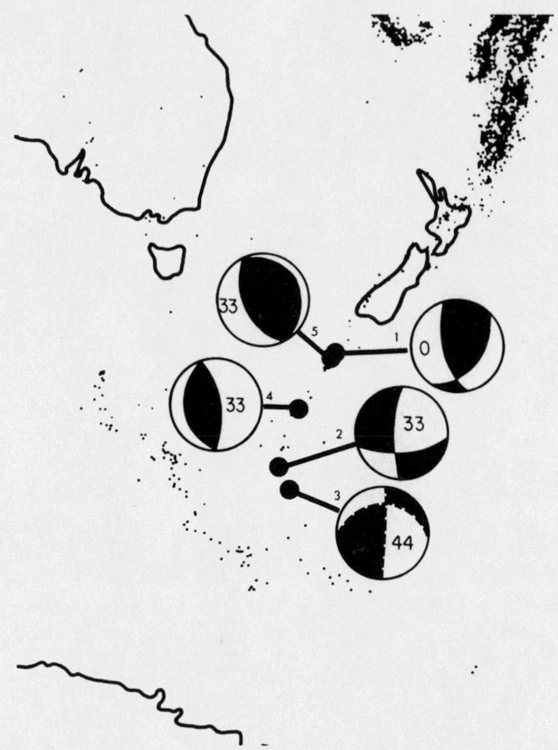

Fig. 9 Representative focal mechanisms from the Macquarie Ridge. The dotted nodal planes on solution 3 represent uncertainties in their positions.

Apart from the predominance of vertical pressure axes, the nodal planes from the mechanisms of the deep earthquakes do not indicate any preferred orientation and it is possible that the different trends of the solutions represent local differences in the stress field at those depths.

Although the Tonga-Kermadec Arc was one of the first to be studied and it provided some of the earliest seismological evidence for underthrusting, it is in some ways anomalous. Firstly, it is not curved like the other arcs, e.g. Sunda Arc and Aleutian Arc, but is almost linear for about 25°. Secondly, most other arcs contain some shallow earthquakes located beneath the axis of the trench that give predominantly horizontal axes of tension nearly perpendicular to the trench. These have been reported by Stauder (1968), for the Aleutian Arc, Fitch (1970*b*) in the Sunda Arc and Philippines, and Ripper (1970) in the New Guinea region. However in the Tonga-Kermadec region no mechanisms of this type have been obtained and very few earthquakes occur on the eastern side of the trench.

Finally, no strike-slip solutions have been obtained for shallow earthquakes in the Tonga-Kermadec region, as have been found in New Guinea, the Aleutians and Sunda Arc.

MACQUARIE RIDGE

The seismicity associated with the Tonga-Kermadec Arc decreases towards the south; the dipping seismic zone disappears, and is not recognized south of the North Island of New Zealand. However a new feature, the Macquarie Ridge complex, becomes evident in the South Island of New Zealand and extends from there to the

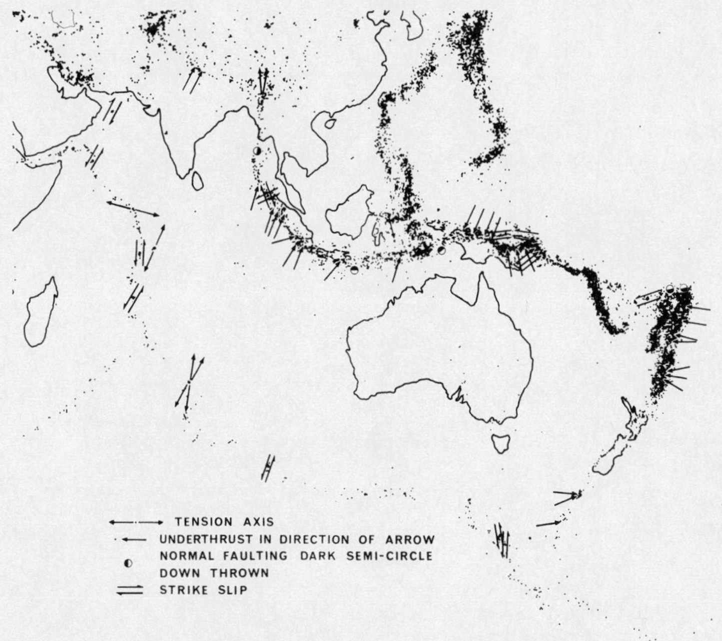

Fig. 10 Representative focal mechanisms for shallow earthquakes at the main boundary of the Indian-Australian plate

triple junction at about 62° S, 160° E. The nature of the Macquarie Ridge has been the subject of speculation and controversy for some time: interpretations range from fracture zone, to mid-ocean ridge, and island arc. Recent marine work by the Lamont group (Hayes, Talwani & Christoffel 1970) suggests that the feature is probably a mixture of the three. In general, these authors maintain that the predominant motion along the ridge is strike-slip with components of underthrusting in the northern sections and tension (ocean ridge area) in the central section.

The focal mechanisms for earthquakes 1, 2, 4 and 5 support this interpretation but 3 (the poorest solution) does not, although there is a significant component of tension perpendicular to the ridge. These solutions are shown in Fig. 9.

We are now back to the Macquarie Ridge triple-junction and have completed the examination of the boundaries of the main Indian-Australian plate.

CONCLUSIONS

Fig. 10 is an attempt to summarize the mechanisms of the shallow-focus earthquakes located at the main boundary of the Indian-Australian plate. The general picture of tension and strike-slip faulting at the ridge system and underthrusting at the northern margins is well represented. A few normal fault events near the trenches indicate downwarping of the lithosphere but on the whole the underthrusting-type mechanisms predominate.

The processes associated with the shallow strike-slip solutions that occur near the trenches are not fully understood. Neither are the deep and intermediate mechanisms although gravitational forces appear to play a large part in them.

The next steps towards our fuller understanding of the tectonic processes taking place, involve the analysis of more mechanisms, so that a better statistical coverage of the main earthquake zones can be obtained. The difficult problem of what happens within the main plate is still to be tackled. It is clear that much more study is required before these problems will be fully solved.

ACKNOWLEDGEMENTS

I would like to thank P. M. McGregor for reviewing the manuscript and the Director of the Bureau of Mineral Resources for permission to publish these results.

REFERENCES

Banghar, A. R. & Sykes, L. R. 1968. Focal mechanisms of earthquakes in the Indian Ocean and adjacent regions. *J. geophys. Res.* **74,** 632.

Barazangi, M. & Dorman, J. 1969. World seismicity maps compiled from ESSA, Coast and Geodetic Survey, epicenter data, 1961-7. *Bull. seism. Soc. Am.* **59,** 369.

Denham, D. 1969. Distribution of earthquakes in the New Guinea-Solomon Islands region. *J. geophys. Res.* **74,** 4290.

Fitch, T. J. 1970*a*. Earthquake mechanisms in the Himalayan, Burmese, and Andaman regions and continental tectonics in central Asia. *J. geophys. Res.* **75,** 2699.

——— 1970*b*. Earthquake mechanisms and island arc tectonics in the Indonesian-Philippine region. *Bull. seism. Soc. Am.* **60,** 565.

Fitch, T. J. & Molnar, P. 1970. Focal mechanisms along inclined earthquake zones in the Indonesian-Philippine region. *J. geophys. Res.* **75,** 1431.

Hayes, D. E. & Pitman III, W. C. 1970. A review of marine geophysical observations in the Southern Ocean. *Proc. SCAR (Scient. Comm. Antarctic Res.), Oslo.*

Hayes, E. E., Talwani, M. & Christoffel, D. A. 1970. The Macquarie Ridge complex. *Proc. SCAR (Scient. Comm. Antarctic Res.), Oslo.*

Isacks, B. & Molnar, P. 1971. Distribution of stresses in the descending lithosphere from a global survey of focal-mechanism solutions of mantle earthquakes. *Rev. Geophys. Space Phys.* **9,** 103.

Isacks, B., Oliver, J. & Sykes, L. R. 1968. Seismology and the new global tectonics. *J. geophys. Res.* **73,** 5855.

Isacks, B., Sykes, L. R. & Oliver, J. 1969. Focal mechanisms of deep and shallow earthquakes in the Tonga-Kermadec region and the tectonics of island arcs. *Bull. geol. Soc. Am.* **80,** 1443.

Johnson, T. & Molnar, P. 1972. Focal mechanisms and tectonics of the New Guinea, New Britain, Solomons, New Hebrides, and Tonga-Kermadec areas, New Zealand and the Macquarie ridge. (In prep.).

Le Pichon, X. 1968. Sea-floor spreading and continental drift. *J. geophys. Res.* **73,** 3661.

Luyendyk, B. P. 1970. Dips of downgoing lithospheric plates beneath island arcs. *Bull. geol. Soc. Am.* **81,** 3411.

Milsom, J. S. 1970. Woodlark basin, a minor center of sea-floor spreading in Melanesia. *J. geophys. Res.* **75,** 7335.

Molnar, P. & Sykes, L. R. 1969. Tectonics of the Caribbean and Middle-American regions from focal mechanisms and seismicity. *Bull. geol. Soc. Am.* **80,** 1639.

Ripper, I. D. 1970. Global tectonics and the New Guinea-Solomon Islands region. *Search.* **1,** 226.

Stauder, W. 1968. Mechanism of the Rat Island earthquake sequence of February 4, 1965, with relation to island arcs and sea-floor spreading. *J. geophys. Res.* **73,** 3847.

Sykes, L. R. 1967. Mechanism of earthquakes and nature of faulting on the mid-ocean ridges. *J. geophys. Res.* **72,** 2131.

——— 1968. Seismological evidence for transform faults, sea-floor spreading, and continental drift. In *History of the Earth's Crust* (Ed. R. A. Phinney). Princeton, New Jersey.

——— 1970. Seismicity of the Indian Ocean and a possible nascent island arc between Ceylon and Australia. *J. geophys. Res.* **75,** 5041.

Wickens, A. J. & Hodgson, J. H. 1967. Computer re-evaluation of earthquake mechanism solutions. *Publs Dom. Obs. Ottawa,* **33,** 1.

Wilson, J. T. 1965. A new class of faults and their bearing on continental drift. *Nature,* **207,** 343.

Tertiary Deep-sea Sediments in the Central Pacific

W. D. NESTEROFF AND C. C. VON DER BORCH

Faculty of Sciences, University of Paris, France; and School of Earth Sciences, Flinders University, Bedford Park, South Australia 5042, Australia

ABSTRACT

In most areas remote from continental margins, the Pacific Ocean floor is characterized by a relatively thin sedimentary cover of some tens to hundreds of metres in thickness. An exception to this general rule is the elongated zone of unusually thick sediment which lies along the equatorial zone in the central part of the ocean, corresponding with a zone of intense biological activity which in turn coincides with the divergence caused by the equatorial current. Drilling during Leg 8 of the Deep Sea Drilling Project verified the biological nature of the sediments of the equatorial region. The sediment column is composed essentially of coccolith and radiolarian oozes. Radiolarian ooze and derived cherts are dominant in Eocene sediments. A distinct hiatus separates the Eocene from the Oligocene and above this hiatus, largely calcareous sediments occur to the beginning of the Miocene. Sediments above the Miocene are composed of alternating thin layers of dominantly calcareous and dominantly siliceous sediments. The variations throughout the sediment column are classified as formations in a stratigraphic context. They are postulated to have been largely controlled by climatic fluctuations during the Tertiary. Drilling in a north-south traverse across the thick equatorial sediments shows a variation in the locus of maximum productivity with time, suggesting either a progressive displacement of the equatorial current during the Tertiary, or a displacement of the Pacific crustal plate to the north-west by sea-floor spreading, or a combination of both processes. The boundaries between the major sedimentary units, or formations, are shown to coincide with major tectonic events in the Pacific area.

REFERENCE

Tracey, J. I., Sutton, G. H., Nesteroff, W. D. Galehouse, J. S., von der Borch, C. C., Moore, T. C., Bilal ul Haq, U. Z. & Beckman, J. P. 1971. Leg 8 Summary. In Tracey, J. I. *et al.*, *Initial Reports of the Deep Sea Drilling Project,* **8,** 17-75. U.S. Govt. Printing Office, Washington, D.C.

Erimo (Sysoev) Seamount and its Relation to the Tectonic History of the Pacific Ocean Basin

Ryuichi Tsuchi and Naoshi Kuroda

Geological Institute, Faculty of Science, Shizuoka University, Shizuoka City, Japan

ABSTRACT

Erimo Seamount is solitary, with summit-depth 3,678 m, and is situated on the slope of the oceanic side of the junction of the Japan and Kuril-Kamchatka Trenches. It has been reported that the seamount might be a guyot, based on a dredge haul of reefal limestone containing Cretaceous nerineid gastropods from a depth of 4,000 m. According to the results of our second survey, however, Erimo Seamount is not a typical guyot, but is probably a submerged volcano with fringing reefs; it seems that the seamount is slanted into the trench. The summit area has a ridge with a gentle slope on the north-west side, changing abruptly to a steep slope at nearly 4,000 m; it is planar and flat on the south-east side at 4,000 m deep.

The nerineid species bears a close resemblance to those of the tropical subgenus *Plesioptygmatis* from the Senonian of Mexico and also of Austria. The geological range of the subgenus is limited to Late Cretaceous. This estimation of the age of the fossils corresponds well to K/Ar ages of the bedrocks which have been estimated at 80 m.y. B.P. In northern Japan, however, no such tropical element has been found in Late Cretaceous sediments.

Bedrocks obtained were olivine-bearing augite dolerite, augite olivine basalt, trachyte and trachyte tuff. Vesicules in the bedrocks suggest an explosive eruption in a shallow sea or on land. As these alkaline rocks are similar to those of Hawaii, it may be considered that the seamount originated in an oceanic basin.

We infer that Erimo was an ancient volcano which arose in a southern oceanic basin and grew to a volcanic isle in Late Cretaceous time. Soon after, it submerged and began its drift north to its present location, and is now being dragged into the trench. The deepening of this part of the Pacific Ocean basin may have commenced just after the cessation of the volcanic activity of Erimo some 80 m.y. ago.

INTRODUCTION

A preliminary report on the discovery of nerineid gastropods from Erimo (or Sysoev) Seamount has already been presented (Tsuchi 1966, Tsuchi & Kagami 1967). In 1969 a second survey of the seamount was made by a research vessel of the University of Tokyo (*Hakuho Maru*—KH-69-2 cruise), which carried out geological and geophysical surveys in the Japan Trench and also in the Japan Sea.

The authors summarize the results of these surveys and relate their data to the tectonic history of the North-west Pacific Basin.

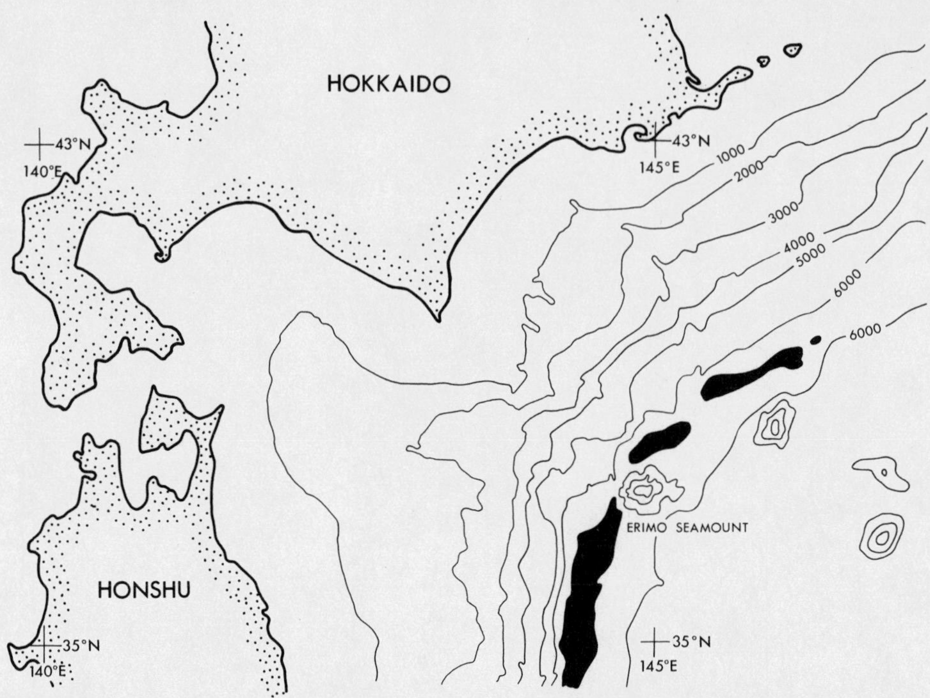

Fig. 1 Location map of Erimo Seamount

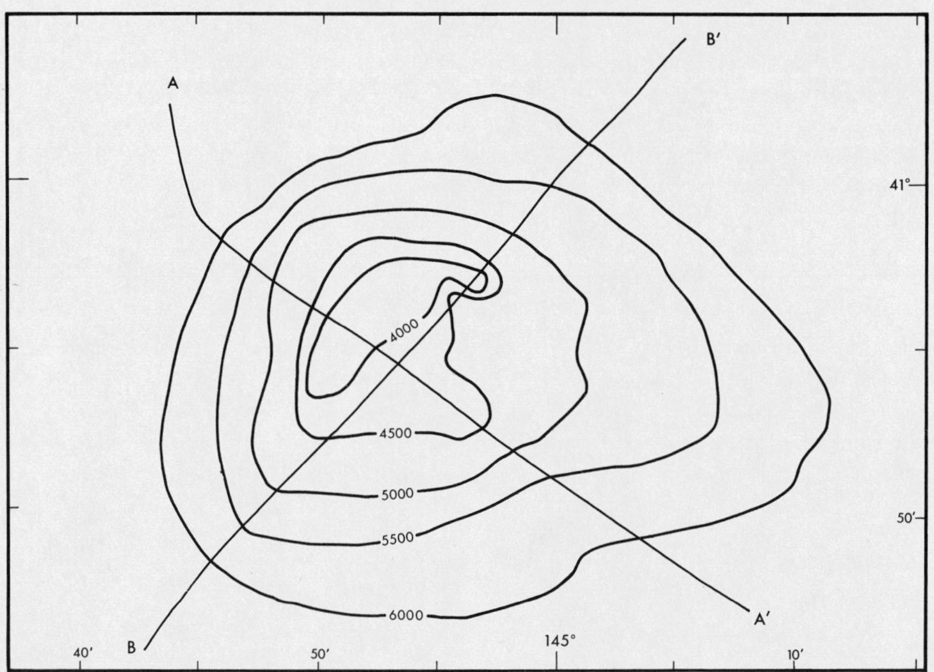

THE TOPOGRAPHY OF THE SEAMOUNT

Erimo Seamount is solitary, located about 300 km east of northern Honshu (Fig. 1), its summit, or shallowest point, being 3,678 m deep. It is situated on the slope of the oceanic side of the junction of the Japan and Kuril-Kamchatka Trenches, and rises about 3,000 m above the floor of the trench, 7,000 m deep.

The bathymetric lines in Fig. 2 are newly drawn from the data of both the second survey and the previous one. The profiles are shown in Figs. 3 and 4, which are traced directly from the echograms along the ship tracks. In the profile from north-west to south-east, the slope of the seamount on the north-west, or trench side, attains 16° inclination, but only 7° on the south-east or oceanic side. It seems, therefore, that the seamount is slanting to the north-west or trench side.

As to the topography of the summit area, a flat area is recognized at 4,000 m on the south-east side, where limestone was dredged at the first survey. On the north-west side, however, a gentle slope from the rounded top, 3° to 4° in inclination, changes abruptly to a steep slope at nearly 4,000 m, where trachytes were obtained during the second survey, though no limestone was found. The bathymetric survey thus discloses that Erimo Seamount is not a typical guyot, but might be a submerged volcano with fringing reefs. The limestone containing the fossils which were collected on the first survey may be a part of these reefs. The abrupt change of the slope at 4,000 m deep on the north-west side of the seamount also suggests a surface that was once near sea-level.

As shown in Fig. 2, the summit area of the seamount has a ridge with north-east to south-west trend, sloping gently to the north-west, and a flat plane on the south-east side. It is reasonable to consider that its south-eastern part was abraded after the cessation of its volcanic activity; the island was submerged soon after and then slanted towards the trench as it appears today. Such configurations, slanting to the trench side, seem to be recognized also on Daiiti-Kashima Seamount in the Japan Trench and Kodiak Seamount in the Aleutian Trench.

NOTES ON *NERINEA*-BEARING LIMESTONE

One of the limestone fragments obtained on the first survey contains many specimens of *Nerinea (Plesioptygmatis) ryofuae* Tsuchi (Ms name). Nerineid mollusca thrived in the Tethyan area during the Jurassic and Cretaceous. They are thick-shelled gastropods, having characteristic inner-structures and are also biostratigraphically important. They have been found frequently in rudistid reefs, associated generally with calcareous algae, larger foraminifera and corals. It is believed that they grew in warm, clear and shallow waters under strong surf conditions.

The matrix limestone is an oolitic calcarenite with rich calcareous algae and

---

Fig. 2 Bathymetric chart of Erimo Seamount. A-A′ and B-B′ indicate the traverses of the seamount, which are shown in Figs 3 and 4.

rounded worn fragments. So far, no large foraminifera, nannoplankton nor corals have been found in them.

The new nerineid species belongs to the subgenus *Plesioptygmatis* (Böse 1906), the type-species of which is *P. burckhaldti*, from the Late Cretaceous (Senonian) of

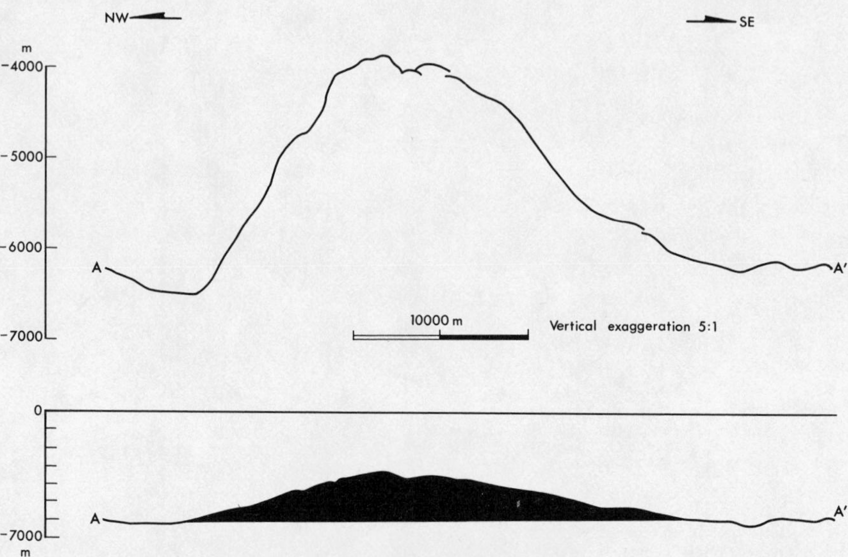

Fig. 3 Topographic profile of Erimo Seamount from north-west to south-east

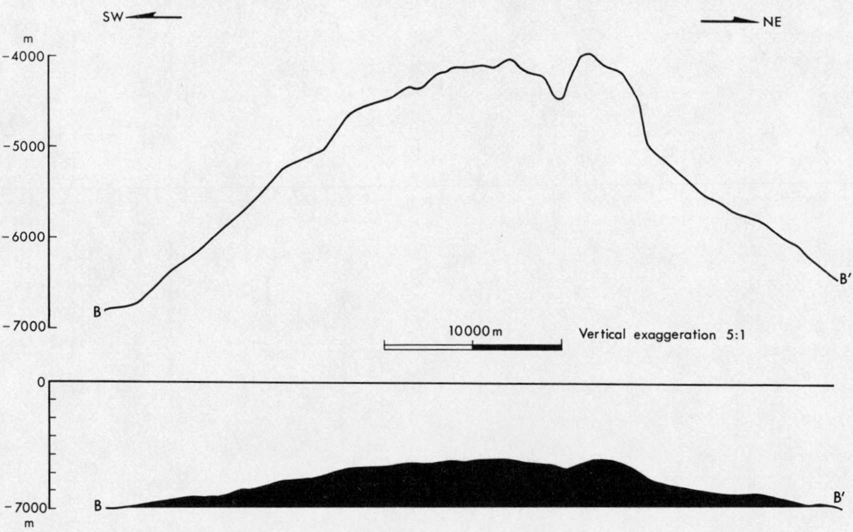

Fig. 4 Topographic profile of Erimo Seamount from south-west to north-east

Mexico. The species also bears a close resemblance to certain species of the subgenus *Simploptyxis* (Tiedt 1958) from Senonian beds of Gosau in Austria. According to some authors, the geological time range of *Plesioptygmatis* is from Cenomanian to Senonian; others would limit it to the Senonian. The range of *Simploptyxis* is Turonian to Senonian. In any case, the age of the Erimo limestone can be assigned to the Late Cretaceous.

In Japan, several Cretaceous nerineids have been described, e.g. *Nerinea rigida* Nagao (1934) from the Aptio-Albian of Miyako on the Pacific coast of north-east Japan, *N. hidakaensis* Fukada (1953) from Aptio-Albian of Central Hokkaido, North Japan, and *N.* sp. from the Cenomano-Turonian of Amakusa, South Japan. All species so far reported from Japan, however, are confined to *Nerinea* s.s., being quite different from *Plesioptygmatis* in the arrangement of the inner-folds. In northern Japan, Aptio-Albian strata comprise calcareous sediments containing tropical elements, such as nerineids, rudistids and orbitolinids, while no such tropical elements are found in Late Cretaceous sediments. From this data, it is reasonable to consider that the Late Cretaceous nerineids of Erimo Seamount belonged to a faunal province different from that of northern Japan.

BEDROCK PETROGRAPHY

The rocks collected around the summit of Erimo Seamount are olivine-bearing augite dolerite, augite olivine basalt, trachyte and trachyte tuff. The exterior surface of these rocks is coated by a thin crust of manganese and/or iron oxides. Though trachyte is believed to be rare among the various volcanic rocks recovered in world-wide submarine dredge hauls, it has been found also from Kodiak Seamount (Forbes 1969).

The olivine-bearing augite dolerite has ophitic texture, and consists mainly of olivine, augite and plagioclase, with subordinate magnetite and apatite. The rock is quite altered, the olivine being replaced by calcite or chlorite, or serpentine, and the augite partially replaced by calcite.

The augite olivine basalt is enriched in glass and has vesicles up to 3 mm in diameter, infilled with calcite, zeolite or opaque minerals. Olivine occurs as phenocrysts and as minute crystals in the groundmass, as also the augite and plagioclase. Both olivines are totally replaced by calcite, chlorite or serpentine. The augite phenocrysts may display zoning. Magnetite occurs as tiny euhedra in the groundmass. Plagioclase phenocrysts are partially replaced by calcite.

The trachyte is nearly aphyric and has flow textures. The compact groundmass is composed of abundant oligoclase ($\alpha_{min}=1{\cdot}538$, An_{20}) laths, and subordinate augite ($2V_z=51°$), magnetite, apatite and glass. The rock contains rare phenocrysts and xenocrysts of amphibole ($2V_x=76°$), plagioclase, magnetite and apatite, from 0·3-1·5 mm in length. Some of the amphibole crystals have semi-opaque rims of fine-grained augite and magnetite. The magnetite may be partially altered to hematite. Some plagioclase crystals have marked reverse zoning around their margins. The marginal plagioclase shows smooth normal zoning so that the crystals have a euhedral outline. The core plagioclase is rounded and displays pronounced resorption. Judging from the texture, this type of plagioclase is probably xenocrystal. Aggregates of this reversely-zoned plagioclase with altered yellowish-brown amphibole, magnetite and apatite occur rarely in the rock. The last three minerals in the aggregates may also be xenocrystal.

The trachyte tuffs are white and pink in colour. They are composed of fine-grained volcanic glass, together with a great many irregular fragments of trachyte, vitreous trachyte, pumice and basalt. Most fragments range in size from 0·4-1·3 mm, but rare ones are larger than 1 cm. The fragments of dark-brown vitreous glass are abundant, have small numbers of minute plagioclase laths and magnetite crystals, and are studded with numerous vesicles, from 0·1-1 mm in diameter. The tuffs contain also a small number of crystals of serpentinized olivine, augite ($2V_z=51°$), amphibole ($2V_x=74°$), plagioclase and apatite. These crystals are less than 1 mm in length. Amphibole is yellowish-brown along *Z*, similar to that of the trachyte. The serpentinized olivine may have come from the augite olivine basalt.

Considering this assemblage in all its aspects, Erimo Seamount is surely a volcano, the summit area of which is composed of alkali volcanics. That numerous vesicles occur in the augite olivine basalt and in the fragments of vitreous trachyte in the

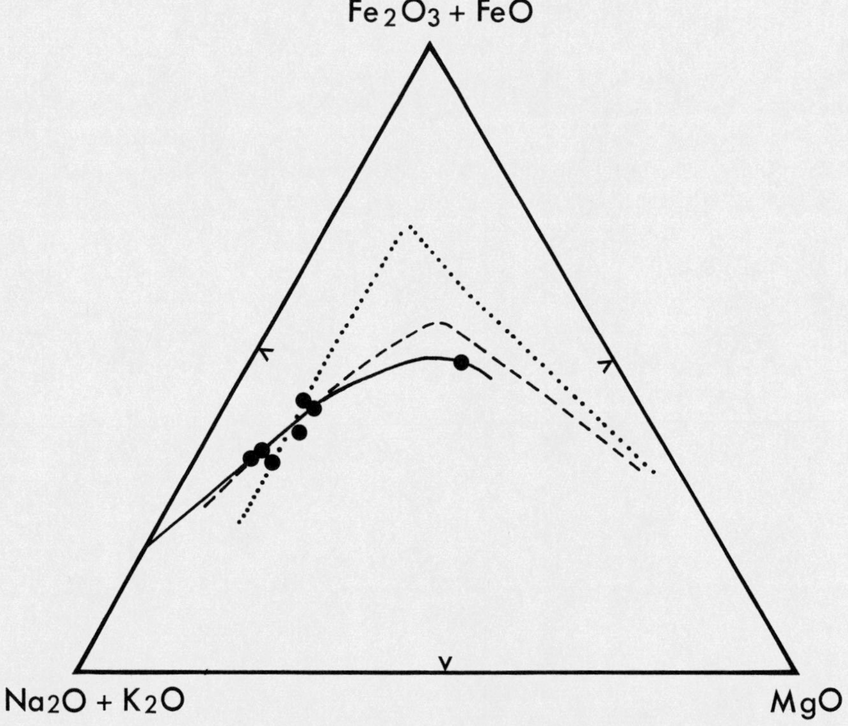

Fig. 5 Differentiation trends of the volcanic rocks of Erimo Seamount and Hawaiian Islands, after Kitano (1970). Solid circles and solid curve: Erimo Seamount rocks; broken line: Hawaiian alkali rock series; dotted line: Hawaiian tholeiitic rock series.

trachyte tuff, and that the exterior surfaces of lavas are free from a thick vitreous crust, are features supporting the notion that Erimo Seamount erupted above sea-level or in shallow water. Vesicular pyroclastics are believed to be formed in subaerial and shallow-water conditions (Verhoogen 1951). This deduction is supported by the other geological and palaeontological evidence. The differentiation trend of the alkali volcanics of Erimo Seamount is similar to that of the Hawaiian alkali volcanics, as shown in Fig. 5 (Kitano 1970).

It is reasonable to deduce, therefore, that Erimo Seamount originated in an ocean basin, different from its present geological environment, and that it was once an oceanic volcanic island.

ERIMO SEAMOUNT AND ITS BEARING ON THE TECTONIC HISTORY OF THE PACIFIC OCEAN BASIN

Data on the topography, fossil-bearing limestone and bedrocks of Erimo Seamount are supported by an absolute age of the bedrocks. K/Ar ages of 80 m.y. for the augite olivine basalt have been recently obtained (Ojima *et al.* 1970). This value corresponds well to the age suggested by the fossil nerineids. Moreover, as the shape of the old volcano shows that it was partly cut by erosion, the age of the volcanics in the latest stage can be regarded as that of the fossils of the fringing reefs.

Comparing the depth and the age of Erimo Seamount with those of other guyots and atolls in the Pacific Ocean, the summit of the seamount is about 2,000 m deeper than the general case. This may be explained by assuming a subsidence of the area which now includes the Japan and Kuril-Kamchatka Trenches. If so, we may infer that Erimo Seamount was a volcanic isle, and its volcanic activity ceased at about 80 m.y. B.P., just prior to the subsidence of the area which now includes the Japan and Kuril-Kamchatka Trenches.

From the palaeontological data, the authors would like to suggest as well that Erimo is an ancient volcano that arose in a more southerly part of the oceanic basin. It grew to a substantial volcanic island by the Late Cretaceous and was then submerged and drifted north to its present location. It is now being dragged into the trench. If this was the case, we may infer that the deepening of the Pacific Ocean Basin commenced just after the cessation of the volcanic activity of Erimo, about 80 m.y. ago. A northerly drift of the Pacific Ocean floor is suggested by palaeomagnetic data from Erimo and other seamounts (Uyeda & Richards 1966, Vacquier & Uyeda 1967).

REFERENCES

Böse, E. 1906. La fauna de moluscos del Senoniano de Cardena, San Luis Potosi. *Boln Inst. Geol. Méx.* **24,** 1-95.

Forbes, R. B. 1969. Dredged trachyte and basalt from Kodiak Seamount and the adjacent Aleutian Trench, Alaska. *Science,* **166,** 502-4.

Fukada, A. 1953. A new species of Nerinea from central Hokkaido. *J. Fac. Sci. Hokkaido Univ.,* Ser. 4, **8,** 211-16.

Kitano, K. 1970. Alkaline basalts from the Erimo seamount. *J. geol. Soc. Japan,* **76,** 399-404 (in Japanese).

Nagao, T. 1934. Cretaceous mollusca from the Miyako District, Honshu, Japan. *J. Fac. Sci. Hokkaido Univ.*, Ser. 4, **2,** 117-278.

Ojima, M., Kaneoka, I. & Aramaki, S. 1970. K-Ar ages of submarine basalts dredged from seamounts in the western Pacific area and discussion of oceanic crust. *Earth Planet. Sci. Letters,* **8,** 237-49.

Tiedt, L. 1958. Die Nerineen der österreichischen Gosauschichten. *Sitzungsberichte, Osterreich. Akad. Wissensch.,* Abt. 1, **167,** 483-517.

Tsuchi, R. 1966. Discovery of Nerineid Gastropoda from Seamount Sysoev (Erimo) at the Junction of Japan Trench and Kurile Trench. *11th Pacific Sci. Congr. Tokyo, Abst., Papers Oceanogr.* **2,** 90.

Tsuchi, R. & Kagami, H. 1967. Discovery of Nerineid Gastropoda from Seamount Sysoev (Erimo) at the Junction of Japan and Kuril-Kamchatka Trenches. *Rec. oceanogr. Wks Japan,* **9,** 1-6.

Uyeda, S. & Richards, M. 1966. Magnetization of four Pacific seamounts near the Japanese Islands. *Bull. Earthq. Res. Inst. Tokyo Univ.* **44,** 179-213.

Vacquier, V. & Uyeda, S. 1967. Palaeomagnetism of nine Seamounts in the Western Pacific and of three Volcanoes in Japan. *Bull. Earthq. Res. Inst. Tokyo Univ.* **45,** 815-48.

Verhoogen, J. 1951. Mechanics of ash formation. *Am. J. Sci.* **249,** 729-39.

Interpretation of Magnetic Anomalies over the Dampier and the Norfolk Ridges, South-west Pacific

M. P. Hochstein

Geophysics Division, Department of Scientific and Industrial Research
P.O. Box 8005, Wellington, New Zealand

ABSTRACT

Magnetic total force anomalies across the Dampier Ridge between 30·5° S and 34° S and across the Norfolk Ridge between 30° S and 36° S, are caused by presumably basaltic extrusions. The magnetic anomalies are controlled by the topography of the ridges. The magnitude of the best fit magnetization lies for most of the profiles in the range of 9–16 Am^{-1}. The directions of the best fit magnetization of the bulk of the Dampier Ridge lie within 20° of the direction of the present geomagnetic field, but greater angular differences of up to 90° have been found for the Norfolk Ridge. From magnetic and seismic profiler data it can be inferred that the upper portions of the Dampier Ridge and the Norfolk Ridge are of Tertiary and Holocene age respectively. A normal magnetization of the Dampier Ridge rather than a horizontal sequence of normally and reversely magnetized bodies is required to explain the magnetic anomalies over this ridge, and hence the hypothesis that the Dampier Ridge is an ancient centre of sea-floor spreading is rejected.

INTRODUCTION

The existence of a system of parallel ridges in the Tasman Sea between Australia and New Zealand, namely the Dampier Ridge, the Lord Howe Rise and the Norfolk Ridge (Fig. 1), has given rise to various speculations about their origin. Not much is known about the structure of these ridges and not many geophysical data are available to put restraints on such conjectures.

A few seismic and gravity measurements have been made over the ridges and the interpretation of the data has shown that a quasi-continental type of crust exists under the Dampier Ridge and the Norfolk Ridge which in part flank the Lord Howe Rise, a much broader and larger feature underlain by continental type crust (Solomon & Biehler 1969, Woodward & Hunt 1971, Shor *et al.* 1971). A layer of presumably Tertiary sediments with a thickness of the order of $\frac{1}{2}$ km has been found on top of the Lord Howe Rise and in depressions of the Norfolk Ridge, but the top of the Norfolk Ridge is free of sediments (Houtz *et al.* 1967, Shor *et al.* 1971). No information is available about the sediment cover on top of the Dampier Ridge.

The most extensive geophysical measurements in the region, however, are magnetic total force measurements (van der Linden 1967, 1969; Taylor & Brennan 1969). It is the aim of this study to show that these magnetic data contain sufficient information to throw some light on the structure of the Dampier Ridge and the Norfolk Ridge.

MAGNETIC ANOMALIES OVER THE DAMPIER RIDGE AND THE NORFOLK RIDGE

Besides some magnetic data published by Taylor and Brennan (1969) and by Woodward and Hunt (1971), most of the magnetic measurements in the Tasman Sea come from studies by van der Linden (1967, 1969).

A look at the magnetic anomaly map of the Lord Howe Rise-Norfolk Ridge area (Fig. 3 in van der Linden 1967) shows that between 30° S and 36° S the Norfolk Ridge is characterized by strong linear magnetic anomalies. A preliminary interpretation of the anomalies over the Norfolk Ridge has been given by Hochstein (1967), using the assumption that the direction of magnetization of the rocks causing the anomalies is parallel or antiparallel to the direction of the present geomagnetic field. It was found that the magnetic anomalies over the Norfolk Ridge are caused by presumably basaltic rocks which have a minimum thickness of about 1-2 km in the axial region.

Marked magnetic anomalies of short wavelength (<30 km) occur over most of the Lord Howe Rise (Taylor & Brennan 1969). It has not been shown yet whether these anomalies are continuous between adjacent profiles. In contrast to the magnetic anomalies over the Norfolk Ridge, the anomalies over the Lord Howe Rise are not controlled by topography (Hochstein 1967).

Broad and relatively smooth magnetic anomalies have been observed over the Dampier Ridge between 30·5° S and 34° S (Fig. 4 in van der Linden 1969). These anomalies have a dominant wavelength which is similar to that of the ridge. From a questionable symmetry of the anomalies, the morphology of the ridge and the absence of seismic activity, van der Linden (1969) inferred the Dampier Ridge to be an ancient centre of sea-floor spreading. In this case the symmetry of the magnetic anomalies would be brought about by a horizontal sequence of vertical-sided blocks of volcanic rocks, each having a different direction of magnetization.

The hypothesis of ancient sea-floor spreading in the Tasman Sea has also been tentatively used by Taylor and Brennan (1969) to explain their observed anomaly pattern, but without stating which specific area they consider likely to be the spreading centre. There is no doubt that the hypothesis of ancient sea-floor spreading is attractive (anonymous 1969), considering the impact which the hypothesis of present day sea-floor spreading has had on various disciplines of earth science. In the case of the Dampier Ridge, however, Cullen (1970) correctly pointed out that van der Linden (1969) has not shown that the presumed symmetry of the magnetic anomaly pattern over the ridge cannot be explained by other models. One important criterion for the hypothesis of sea-floor spreading is, for example, that the magnetic anomalies along profiles perpendicular to the axis of spreading cannot be explained by a more or less homogeneous magnetization of the ridge, although this might be the case for profiles running parallel to the ridge axis (Talwani *et al.* 1971).

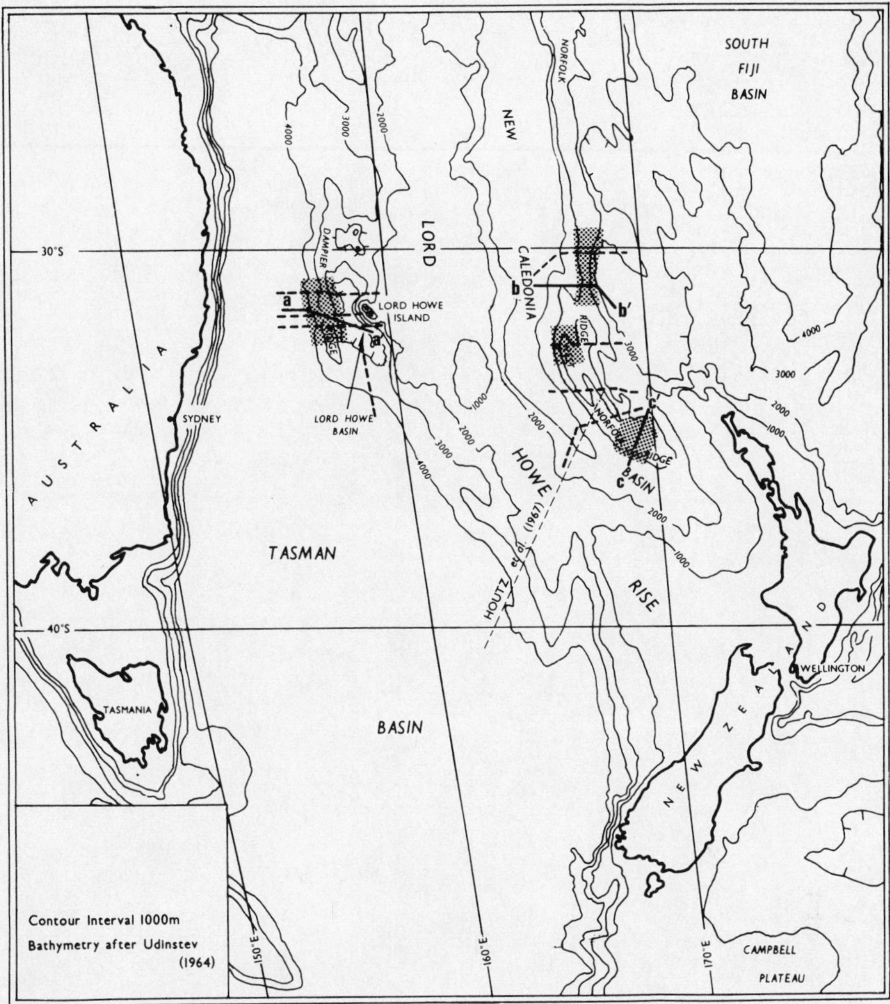

Fig. 1 Bathymetric map of the Tasman Sea (the Tasmantid seamounts are not shown). The magnetic profiles discussed in this paper are shown by broken and solid lines; the profiles marked by solid lines are presented in Figs 2*a*, 2*b* and 2*c*. The profile marked by a-a′ corresponds to the profile shown in Fig. 2*a*, b-b′ to that in Fig. 2*b*, and c-c′ to that in Fig. 2*c*. Shaded areas outline portions of the Dampier Ridge and the Norfolk Ridge, where the magnetic anomalies are dominantly controlled by the topography of the ridge ('goodness of fit' ratio *r* 1·5). A seismic profile line by Houtz *et al.* (1967) is shown by a thin dashed line.

To obtain a convincing argument to explain the origin of the magnetic anomalies over the Dampier Ridge, a quantitative analysis of the magnetic data was attempted. If it could be shown by such an analysis that the observed anomalies can or cannot be produced by a homogeneous magnetization of the ridge, one would have a strong argument either against or for van der Linden's idea. For comparison, the magnetic anomalies over the Norfolk Ridge were included in the analysis since the topographic control of these anomalies had been established by an earlier study (Hochstein 1967). No analysis of the magnetic anomalies over the Lord Howe Rise was attempted.

ANALYSIS OF MAGNETIC ANOMALIES

The method of analysis of the magnetic anomalies over the Dampier Ridge and the Norfolk Ridge was similar to that used by Lumb *et al.* (1972) for the magnetic anomalies around the Cook Islands. It was assumed that the ridges can be treated as two-dimensional bodies which are uniformly magnetized. A best fit magnetization $\mathbf{M}_{\alpha z}$ in profile section was computed using a procedure similar to that of Talwani (1965), with the assumption that the upper boundary of the magnetic body coincides with the sea floor. No seismic reflection data were available to specify more accurately the upper boundary of the magnetic body. The lower boundary was assumed to be horizontal at a depth of 5 km. Theoretical total force anomalies given by the best fit magnetization $\mathbf{M}_{\alpha z}$ and the shape of the ridge were then calculated and compared with the observed anomalies. For this the mean residual $|R|_{av}$ and the ratio of the mean observed anomaly to the mean residual, the 'goodness of fit' ratio r, were computed; a definition of r is given in Table 1.

An attempt was also made to obtain an order of magnitude figure for the thickness of the sediments on top of the ridges. For this it was assumed that the magnetic body is overlain by a non-magnetic layer of constant thickness, and the theoretical magnetic anomalies of models with non-magnetic layers of both 1 and 2 km thickness were also computed and analyzed.

The method of reduction of the magnetic data was the same as that described by Woodward and Hochstein (1970).

RESULTS OF ANALYSIS OF MAGNETIC PROFILES

A total of five magnetic profiles over the Dampier Ridge and six profiles over the Norfolk Ridge were analyzed. The location of these profiles is shown in Fig. 1. The presentation of theoretical best fit and of observed magnetic anomalies was limited to three selected profiles shown in Figs 2*a*, 2*b* and 2*c*, since original magnetic and bathymetric data of most of the eleven profiles have already been published. Results of the analysis of profiles not shown in the figures are given in Table 1 or are summarized in the text.

A surprisingly good match between observed and computed magnetic anomalies was obtained for most of the profiles over the Dampier Ridge. This is illustrated, for example, by Fig. 2*a*. Sections of this profile with poor fits, the lower parts of the western flank of the ridge for example, can probably be explained by differences in shape between the top of the magnetic body and the sea floor rather than by differences in magnetization. There is no significant difference in the degree of symmetry between

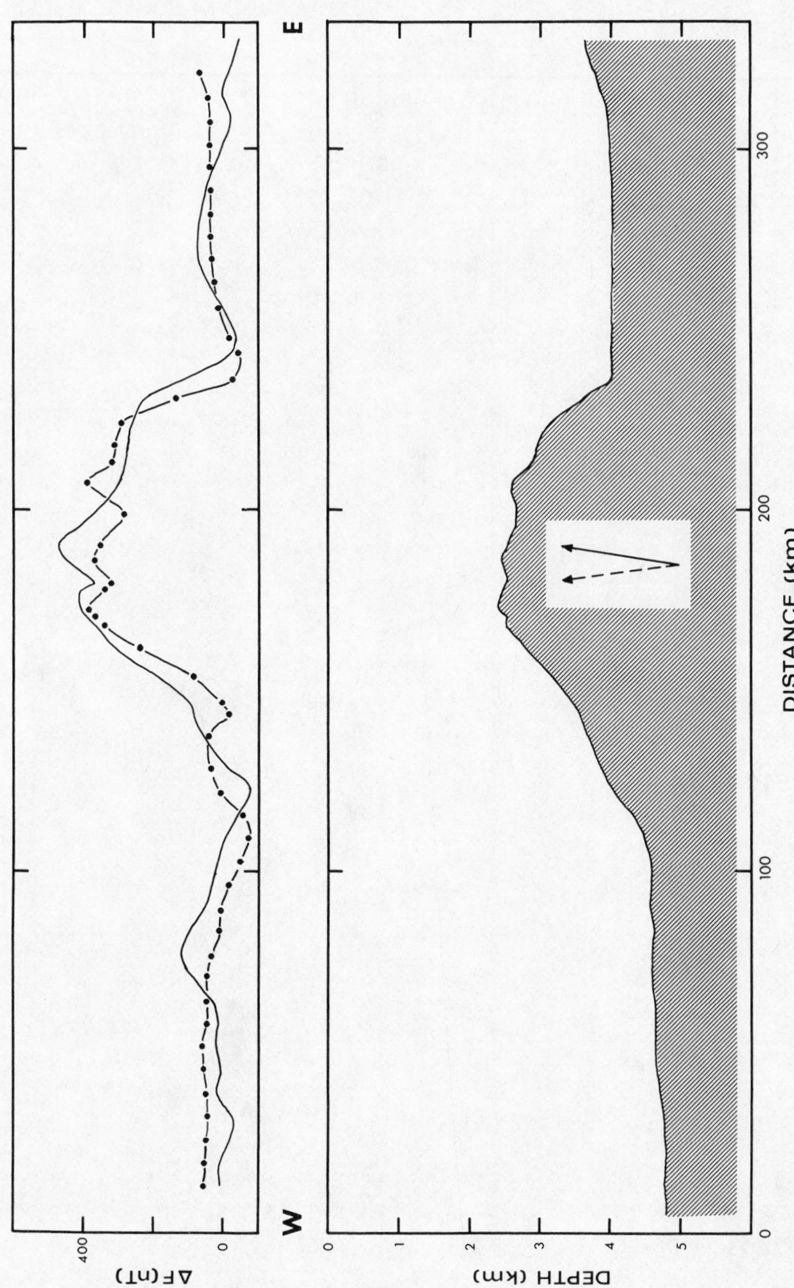

Fig. 2*a* Magnetic and bathymetric profiles of Dampier Ridge between 31·5° S and 32° S. Observed total force anomalies (solid line) and computed total force anomalies (broken line with dots), given by the best fit magnetization, are shown in the upper half of the figure. The bottom topography is shown in the lower part. The direction of the best fit magnetization and of the present geomagnetic field in profile section are shown by a dashed and a solid vector respectively.

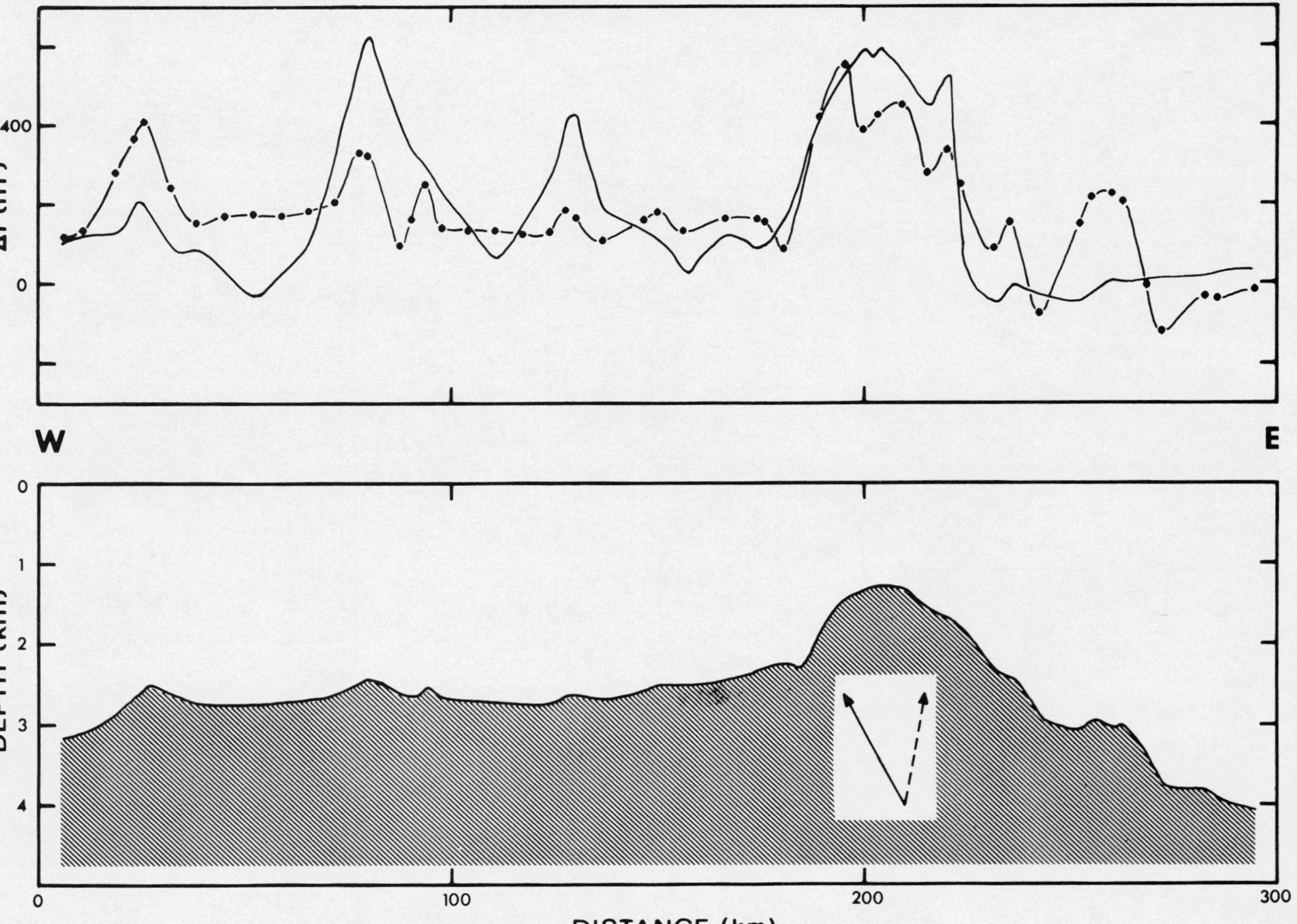

Fig. 2*b* Magnetic and bathymetric profiles of Norfolk Ridge at 30·9° S. Other

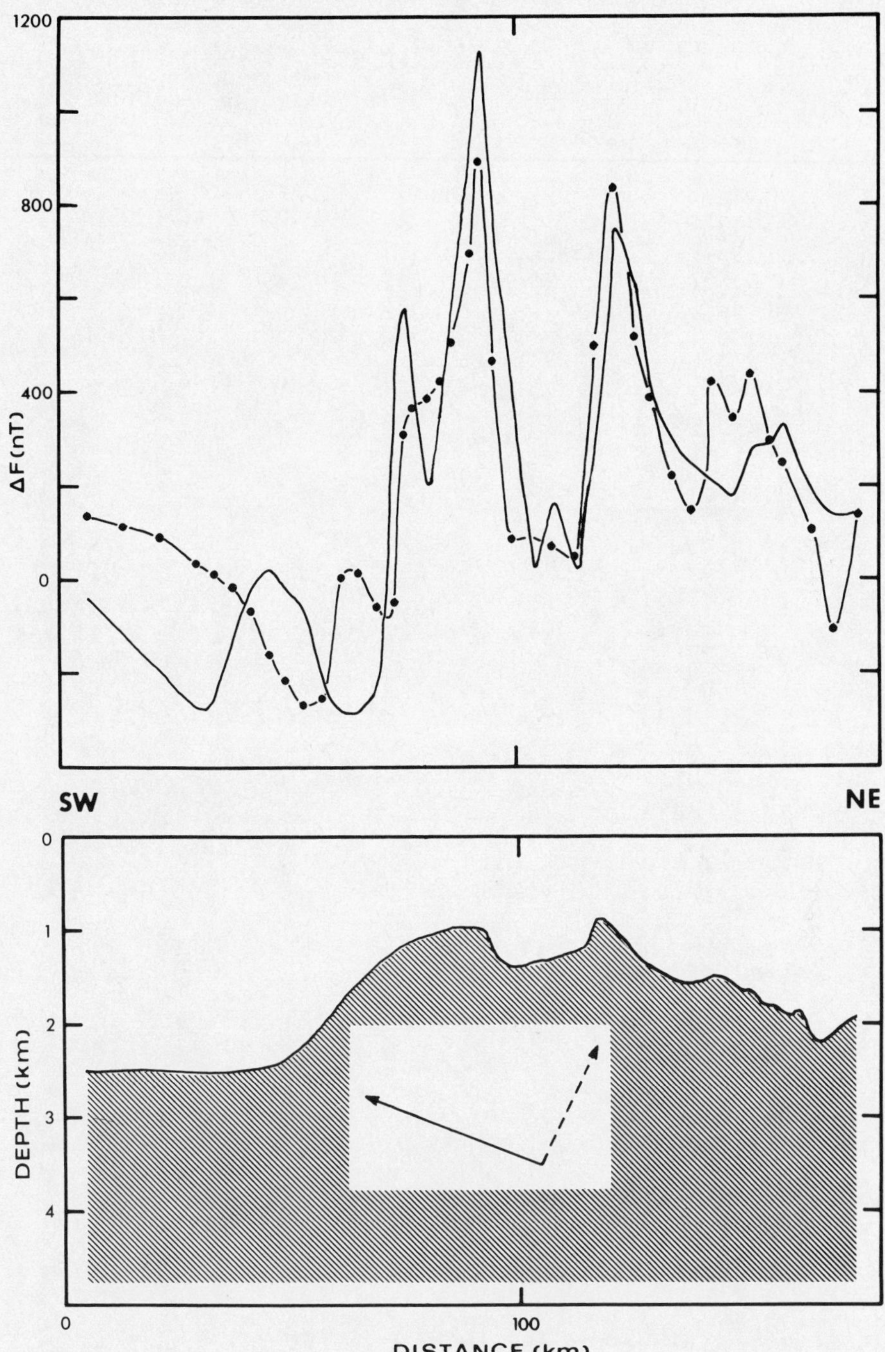

Fig. 2*c* Magnetic and bathymetric profiles of Norfolk Ridge between 34·5° S and 36° S. Other legend as in Fig. 2*a*.

observed and computed magnetic anomalies, a result which also applies to the other profiles.

Results of the analysis of magnetic profiles over the Dampier Ridge are listed in Table 1.[1] An important result of the analysis is that, neglecting polarity, the direction

Table 1

RESULTS OF ANALYSIS OF MAGNETIC PROFILES OVER THE DAMPIER RIDGE

Profile[1]	*Location*[2]		*Best fit magnetization*[3]			*Angular*[4] *difference*	*Fit*[5]	
	Lat. S (°)	α (°)	$\mathbf{M}_\alpha$ (Am^{-1})	$\mathbf{M}_z$ (Am^{-1})	$\lvert\mathbf{M}_{\alpha z}\rvert$ (Am^{-1})[6]	(°)	$\lvert R\rvert_{av}$ (nT)	r
AB	31·1	90	−1·5	−9·1	9·2	19	78	2·44
CD	31·4 to 32·1	110	+1·9	−13·2	13·3	17	78	2·23
EF	31·6	90	+1·5	−12·5	12·6	1	106	1·94
GH	32·0	90	0·0	−3·2	3·2	9	76	1·83
IJ[1]	32·0 to 34·1	172	+3·3	+2·7	4·3	167	73	1·34

Explanation

[1] Notation of profiles follows van der Linden (1969) except for profile *IJ* which has not been published previously.

[2] For exact location of profiles see Fig. 2 by van der Linden (1969). α is the profile orientation.

[3] Directions of components of best fit magnetization are as follows:

$\mathbf{M}_\alpha$ (horizontal component) positive in direction of profile;

$\mathbf{M}_z$ (vertical component) positive downwards.

[4] Angular difference is the difference between the direction of best fit magnetization and that of the normal geomagnetic field in profile section at the centre of the profile.

[5] The mean residual $|R|_{av}$ is defined as

$$\frac{1}{N}\Sigma|R_j|$$

The residual R_j is given by

$$R_j = \Delta F_j - C - \delta T_j = \Delta T_j - \delta T_j,$$

where ΔF_j is the observed anomaly, δT_j the computed anomaly and C a constant found by minimizing ΣR_j^2. The 'goodness of fit' ratio r is defined as

$$r = \frac{\Sigma|\Delta T_j|}{\Sigma|R_j|}$$

[6] SI units are used throughout the paper, unit of magnetization 1 $Am^{-1} = 10^{-3}$ e.m.u., expanded unit of flux density 1 $nT = 1$ gamma.

---

[1] SI units are used throughout this paper, for conversion to c.g.s. units see Table 1.

of the best fit magnetization $\mathbf{M}_{\alpha z}$ is about the same for all the profiles, although the magnitude of $\mathbf{M}_{\alpha z}$ varies from profile to profile and lies in the range of 3-13 Am^{-1}. The angular difference between the direction of $\mathbf{M}_{\alpha z}$ and that of the present geomagnetic field vector projected into the profile section is small ($<19°$). A normal magnetization has been found for the four profiles between 31° S-32° S, but a reverse one for the southernmost profile.

Except for the southernmost profile, the fits of the other profiles given by the 'goodness of fit' ratio $r = 1{\cdot}8$-$2{\cdot}4$ are good if compared with fits of magnetic anomalies in the vicinity of Pacific islands (Lumb *et al.* 1972). The goodness of fit, that is in this case the degree of topographic control, decreases towards the south along the ridge.

For most of the magnetic profiles over the Norfolk Ridge a reasonable fit ($r = 1{\cdot}6$ - $1{\cdot}8$) was obtained. This is illustrated by examples shown in Figs 2*b* and 2*c*. Parameters of the analysis of profiles shown in Figs 2*a*, 2*b* and 2*c* are listed in Table 2. Fits for two adjacent profiles in the vicinity of 34° S are poor ($r < 1{\cdot}2$).

The direction of the best fit magnetization $\mathbf{M}_{\alpha z}$ changes from profile to profile. Whereas the difference between the direction of $\mathbf{M}_{\alpha z}$ and that of the present geomagnetic field in profile section is less than 40° for two profiles between 30° S and 31° S, this difference increases up to 90° for profiles in the south. The values of the magnitude of the best fit magnetization for the six profiles investigated lie in the range of 6-17 Am^{-1}.

Comparing the results of the analysis of magnetic profiles over the Dampier Ridge with those over the Norfolk Ridge, it was found that in both regions the magnetic anomalies of most profiles are controlled by the morphology of the ridge, that is, the upper boundary of the magnetic body causing the anomaly has a shape similar to that of the bathymetric profile. The degree of topographic control, expressed by the goodness of fit between observed and computed anomalies, is greater for profiles over the Dampier Ridge than for the Norfolk Ridge profiles. Reasonable to good fits with 'goodness of fit' ratios $r > 1{\cdot}5$ were obtained for all profiles over the Dampier Ridge between 31° S and 32° S and for most of the profiles over the Norfolk Ridge between 30° S and 36° S. Areas with a reasonable to good fit are shown by shading in Fig. 1.

Although the magnitude of the best fit magnetization $|\mathbf{M}_{\alpha z}|$ varies in both regions from profile to profile, the range is small for profiles with good fits. For three profiles over the Dampier Ridge with fits of $r > 2$ the values lie between 9 and 13 Am^{-1} and for four profiles over the Norfolk Ridge with $r > 1{\cdot}5$ between 11 and 16·5 Am^{-1}. The attitude of the direction of the best fit magnetization, however, is different in the two regions. Neglecting the polarity, this direction is about the same for all profiles over the Dampier Ridge and lies within 20° of the direction of the present geomagnetic field, whereas over the Norfolk Ridge it varies up to 70° between the profiles and is in the extreme case nearly perpendicular to the present field.

For all profiles over the Dampier Ridge the 'goodness of fit' ratio r increases slightly if the top of the magnetic body lies at greater depths, whereas for most of the Norfolk Ridge profiles this ratio is greatest if the top of the magnetic body is at sea-floor level.

Table 2

RESULTS OF ANALYSIS OF MAGNETIC PROFILES SHOWN IN FIGS 2*a*, 2*b* AND 2*c*

Profile	*Location*		*Thickness*[1]	*Best fit magnetization*			*Angular difference*	*Fit*	
	Lat. S (°)	α (°)	(km)	$\mathbf{M}_\alpha$ $(A\,m^{-1})$	$\mathbf{M}_z$ $(A\,m^{-1})$	$\lvert\mathbf{M}_{\alpha z}\rvert$ $(A\,m^{-1})$	(°)	$\lvert R\rvert_{av}$ (nT)	r
aa′ (Dampier Ridge)	31·4 to 32·1	110	0	+1·9	−13·2	13·3	17	78	2·23
	31·4 to 32·1	110	1	+1·9	−14·3	14·3	17	74	2·34
	31·4 to 32·1	110	2	+1·9	−15·2	15·2	16	72	2·11
bb′ (Norfolk Ridge)	30·9	90	0	−5·9	−11·0	12·5	38	144	1·57
	30·9	90	1	−6·7	−12·8	14·5	38	141	1·54
	30·9	90	2	−7·4	−14·4	16·2	39	139	1·52
cc′ (Norfolk Ridge)	34·4 to 36·0	215	0	+15·5	−5·8	16·5	95	208	1·67
	34·4 to 36·0	215	1	+17·8	−7·4	19·3	94	197	1·65
	34·4 to 36·0	215	2	+19·8	−8·7	21·6	93	195	1·60

[1] Thickness of layer of non-magnetic cover; theoretical magnetic anomalies shown in Figs 2*a*, 2*b*, 2*c* have been calculated for the case that the top of the magnetic body coincides with the sea floor (i.e. thickness = 0). For explanation of other columns see Table 1.

DISCUSSION OF RESULTS

The analysis of the magnetic anomalies over the Dampier Ridge and over the Norfolk Ridge has shown that these anomalies are caused by more or less homogeneously magnetized rocks which form the upper portion and probably also the bulk of these ridges. In the case of the Dampier Ridge a horizontal sequence of normally and reversely magnetized bodies is not required to explain the magnetic anomalies. Hence the hypothesis of van der Linden (1969) that the Dampier Ridge is an ancient centre of sea-floor spreading is rejected.

From the magnitude of the best fit magnetization, which is greater than 10 $A\,m^{-1}$ for most profiles over these ridges, it can be inferred that the magnetic rocks are oceanic type basalts (see also Hochstein 1967). The magnitude would be even higher if the basaltic rocks forming the upper portion of these ridges were underlain by similar rocks with opposite magnetization. However, the occurrence of a thick sequence of reversely magnetized rocks, which would lower the resultant magnetization (Lumb *et al.* 1972), is unlikely since values greater than 10 $A\,m^{-1}$ are already very high if compared with magnetization values reported from other similar studies (Francheteau *et al.* 1970). A sequence of normally and reversely magnetized layers probably exists in the southern part of the Dampier Ridge where magnetization values of less than 5 $A\,m^{-1}$ and a reversely magnetized portion of the ridge have been found.

However, results from geophysical studies are not sufficient to deduce with certainty whether basaltic rocks form also the lower portions of these ridges. Neither the relatively low seismic velocity of 4·4 km s^{-1} measured over the Norfolk Ridge (Shor *et al.* 1971) nor the inferred high density of 2·8 Mg m^{-3} of the Dampier Ridge (Woodward & Hunt 1971) can be used as an argument for or against a non-volcanic core. The seismic measurements, for example, were made north of 30° S, where the magnetic anomalies are already much subdued (van der Linden 1967) and the gravity interpretation is based in part on seismic sections of profiles to the east and west of the Dampier Ridge which are outside the area under discussion. At present we favour the interpretation that the bulk of the Dampier Ridge and the Norfolk Ridge is made up of basaltic rocks, an interpretation mainly based on the finding that it is impossible to fit the observed magnetic anomalies, using models consisting of a superficial layer of constant thickness and uniform magnetization (Hochstein 1967).

Assuming that the influence of the induced magnetization can be neglected, in which case the direction of the best fit magnetization coincides with that of the remanent magnetization, and taking into account results from palaeomagnetic studies from Australia (Irving 1964), a recent palaeomagnetic age (Tertiary) can be inferred for the magnetic rocks forming the Dampier Ridge, since the direction of the best fit magnetization $\mathbf{M}_{\alpha z}$ lies within 20° of that of the present geomagnetic field. The much greater angular differences found for profiles over the Norfolk Ridge could indicate a greater palaeomagnetic age for the ridge, although a young age for the upper portion can be inferred from the absence of sediments on the ridge crest (Houtz *et al.* 1967). The angular differences, however, could also be explained by an inhomogeneous magnetization of the Norfolk Ridge as suggested by Hochstein (1967).

Despite uncertainties about what causes the change in direction of the best fit magnetization of the Norfolk Ridge, this study has shown that the Dampier Ridge and the Norfolk Ridge south of 30° S are of volcanic origin and that the upper portions of these ridges are of Tertiary or even younger age. All the available bathymetric data give no evidence that these ridges might be caused by the coalescence of a chain of seamounts. Hence it can be inferred that the basaltic extrusions arose from extensive linear fracture zones similar to those of active mid-oceanic rises. However, the Dampier Ridge and Norfolk Ridge appear to be stable features which were not centres of sea-floor spreading.

ACKNOWLEDGEMENT

The original magnetic and bathymetric data of the profiles discussed in this study were made available by Dr W. J. M. van der Linden, formerly N.Z. Oceanographic Institute, D.S.I.R., Wellington.

REFERENCES

Anonymous. 1969. Ancient Seafloor Spreading. *Nature,* **224,** 1056.

Cullen, D. J. 1970. 'Two-way stretch' of sialic crust and plate tectonics in the South-West Pacific. *Nature,* **226,** 741-2.

Francheteau, J., Harrison, C. G. A., Sclater, J. G. & Richards, M. L. 1970. Magnetization of Pacific seamounts: a preliminary polar curve for the Northeastern Pacific. *J. geophys. Res.* **75,** 2035-61.

Hochstein, M. P. 1967. Interpretation of magnetic anomalies across Norfolk Ridge. *N.Z. Jl Geol. Geophys.* **10,** 1302-8.

Houtz, R., Ewing, J., Ewing, M. & Lonardi, A. G. 1967. Seismic reflection profiles of the New Zealand plateau. *J. geophys. Res.* **72,** 4713-29.

Irving, E. 1964. *Paleomagnetism and its applications to geological and geophysical problems.* Wiley and Sons, New York.

Linden, W. J. M. van der. 1967. Structural relationships in the Tasman Sea and South-West Pacific Ocean. *N.Z. Jl Geol. Geophys.* **10,** 1280-301.

——— 1969. Extinct mid-ocean ridges in the Tasman Sea and in the Western Pacific. *Earth Planet. Sci. Letters,* **6,** 483-90.

Lumb, J. T., Hochstein, M. P. & Woodward, D. J. 1972. Interpretation of magnetic measurements in the Cook Islands, South-west Pacific Ocean. This volume.

Shor, G. G., Kirk, H. K. & Menard, H. W. 1971. Crustal structure of the Melanesian area. *J. geophys. Res.* **76,** 2562-86.

Solomon, S. & Biehler, S. 1969. Crustal structure from gravity anomalies in the South-West Pacific. *J. geophys. Res.* **74,** 6696-701.

Talwani, M. 1965. Computation with the help of a digital computer of magnetic anomalies caused by bodies of arbitrary shape. *Geophysics,* **30,** 797-817.

Talwani, M., Windisch, C. C. & Langseth, M. G. 1971. Reykjanes Ridge Crest: a detailed geophysical study. *J. geophys. Res.* **76,** 473-517.

Taylor, P. T. & Brennan, J. A. Airborne magnetic data across the Tasman Sea. *Nature,* **224,** 1100-2.

Udintsev, G. B. (Ed.) 1964. Bathymetric map of the Pacific Ocean. Institute of Oceanology, Academy of Sciences of the U.S.S.R., Moscow.

Woodward, D. J. & Hochstein, M. P. 1970. Magnetic measurements in the Cook Islands, South-west Pacific Ocean. *N.Z. Jl Geol. Geophys.* **13,** 207-24.

Woodward, D. J. & Hunt, T. M. 1971. Crustal structure across the Tasman Sea. *N.Z. Jl Geol. Geophys.* **14,** 39-45.

Meso-Features of the Pacific Ocean Floor

F. N. SPIESS AND JOHN D. MUDIE

University of California, San Diego, Marine Physical Laboratory of the Scripps Institution of Oceanography, San Diego, California 92152, U.S.A.

ABSTRACT

The Deep Towed Device for the Marine Physical Laboratory of Scripps Institution of Oceanography consists of an instrumented vehicle towed close to the deep sea floor which obtains high resolution records of bathymetry, magnetic field, shallow sedimentary structure and side scan sonar representations of the features within 1 km of the Fish track. Navigation is afforded by an acoustic transponder navigation system which supplies a local reference system with typical position errors of 20 m. The system has been used to study a number of different areas in the Pacific Basin ranging from abyssal fan valleys, abyssal hills, rapid and slow spreading centres and a trench. The more interesting aspects of each of these areas were discussed and mention made of the fine-scale, near-bottom magnetic anomalies which appear to be lineated in the direction of the surface magnetic anomalies and are presumably related to the sea-floor spreading phenomenon.

The bulk of this material was summarized by the authors in the recently published Volume IV of *The Sea* (A. E. Maxwell, ed.). More detailed accounts of work in this field are included in various specific publications as follows:

Atwater, Tanya & Mudie, J. D. 1968. Block faulting on the Gorda Rise. *Science,* **159** (3816), 729-31.

——— 1971. Lineation, symmetry, and small features on the Gorda Rise (Abstr.). *EOS Trans. Am. geophys. Un.* **52** (4), 237.

Grow, J. A., Spiess, F. N. & Mudie, J. D. 1971. Near-bottom geophysical measurements from Aleutian Trench near 173° W (Abstr.). *EOS Trans. Am. geophys. Un.* **52** (4), 246.

Johnson, D. A. 1971. Studies of deep-sea erosion using deep-towed instrumentation. Thesis, Univ. Calif., San Diego, Marine Physical Lab. Scripps Instit. Oceanography, San Diego, California 92152 (SIO Reference 71-21, 1 September 1971).

——— (In prep.) Ocean floor erosion in the equatorial Pacific.

Larson, R. L. 1970. Near-bottom studies of the East Pacific Rise Crest and tectonics of the Gulf of California. Thesis, Univ. Calif., San Diego, Marine Physical Lab. Scripps Instit. Oceanography, San Diego, California 92152 (SIO Reference 70-22, 1 July 1970).

——— 1971. Near-bottom geologic studies of the East Pacific Rise Crest. *Bull. geol. Soc. Am.* **82,** 823-41.

Larson, R. L. & Speiss, F. N. 1970. Slope distributions of the East Pacific Rise Crest. Univ. Calif., San Diego, Marine Physical Lab. Scripps Instit. Oceanography, San Diego, California 92152 (SIO Reference 70-8, 10 March 1970).

Luyendyk, B. P. 1969. Origin of short-wavelength magnetic lineations observed near the ocean bottom. *J. geophys. Res.* **74** (20), 4869-81.

Luyendyk, B. P. 1970. Geological and geophysical observations in an abyssal hill area using a deeply towed instrument package. Thesis, Univ. Calif., San Diego, Marine Physical Lab. Scripps Instit. Oceanography, San Diego California 92152 (SIO Reference 70-14, 1 June 1970).

——— 1970. Origin and history of abyssal hills in the north-east Pacific Ocean. *Bull. geol. Soc. Am.* **81,** 2237-60.

Luyendyk, B. P., Mudie, J. D. & Harrison, C. G. A. 1968. Lineations of magnetic anomalies in the northeast Pacific observed near the ocean floor. *J. geophys. Res.* **73** (18), 5951-7.

Mudie, J. D., Normark, W. R. & Cray, Jr., E. J. 1970. Direct mapping of the sea-floor, using side-scanning sonar and transponder navigation. *Bull. Geol. Soc. Am.* **81,** 1547-54.

Normark, W. R. 1969. Growth patterns of deep-sea fans. Thesis, Univ. Calif., San Diego, Marine Physical Lab. Scripps Instit. Oceanography, San Diego, California 92152 (SIO Reference 69-29, 1 December 1969).

——— 1970. Growth pattern of deep-sea fans. *Bull. Am. Ass. Petrol. Geol.* **54** (11), 2170-95.

Spiess, F. N., Luyendyk, B. P., Larson, R. L., Normark, W. R. & Mudie, J. D. 1969. Detailed geophysical studies on the northern Hawaiian Arch using a deeply-towed instrument package. *Marine Geology,* **7,** 501-27.

Interpretation of Magnetic Measurements in the Cook Islands, South-west Pacific Ocean

J. T. Lumb, M. P. Hochstein and D. J. Woodward

Geophysics Division, Department of Scientific and Industrial Research, P.O. Box 8005, Wellington, New Zealand

ABSTRACT

Total force magnetic anomalies around several of the Cook Islands are fairly simple and bi-polar in form. A group of islands situated on a NW-SE trending ridge exhibit a more complex anomaly pattern which, in part, must have its source beneath the ridge. The virtual palaeomagnetic poles of islands belonging to the first group, and which were calculated from the best fit magnetization, show a large scatter. It is shown that this scatter is most likely to be caused by an inhomogeneous magnetization of the islands brought about by a sequence of normally and reversely magnetized layers. In this case the direction of the best fit magnetization is not representative of that of the mean remanent magnetization and the interpretation of the position of the virtual palaeomagnetic pole in terms of the palaeomagnetic history of a volcanic island is not justified.

INTRODUCTION

Between 1963 and 1969 measurements of the total magnetic force were made around islands in the Northern and Southern Cook Group, South-west Pacific (Woodward & Hochstein 1970, Lumb & Carrington 1971). One of the principal aims of these studies was to obtain information about the mean magnetization of these volcanic islands, and hence some knowledge of their palaeomagnetic history and internal structure. The islands investigated are marked by shaded areas in Fig. 1.

During 1969 some oriented rock samples were collected on two of these islands to find out whether the magnetization of exposed rocks is similar to that calculated for the bulk of the island from sea-borne magnetic data. In this paper all magnetic studies made in the Cook Islands will be summarized; original data of the most recent measurements will be presented elsewhere.

GEOLOGY AND MORPHOLOGY OF THE COOK ISLANDS

The Cook Islands are the summits of extinct volcanoes. Of the eight islands investigated, Aitutaki, Atiu, Mangaia, Mauke, Mitiaro and Rarotonga have exposed volcanic

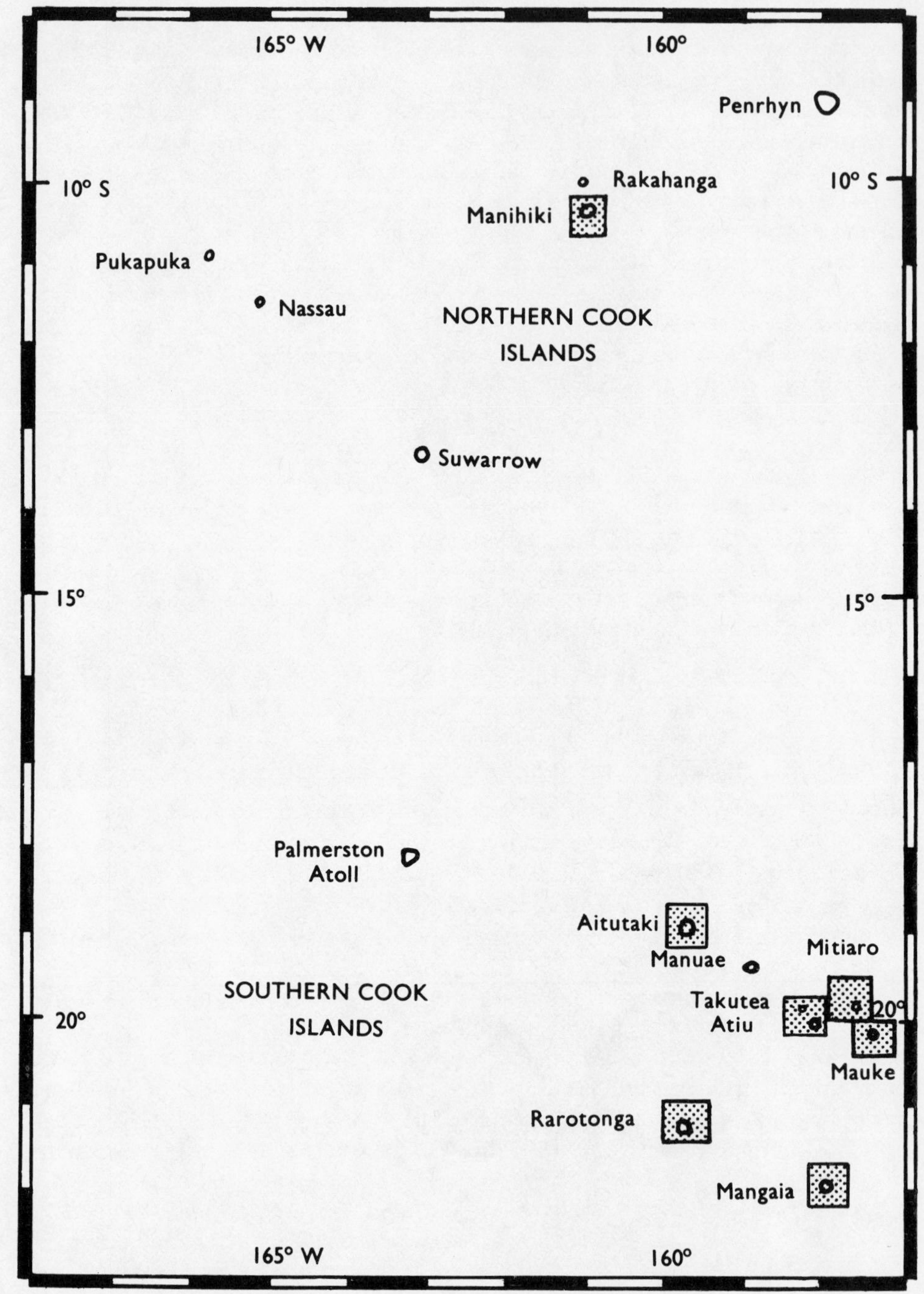

Fig. 1 Map of the Cook Islands. The magnetic measurements discussed in this paper lie within the shaded areas.

rocks surrounded or partly covered by coral, whereas Takutea and Manihiki are completely covered by coral. Samples of exposed volcanic rocks of Aitutaki and Rarotonga have been found by radiometric dating to be of Quaternary and late Pliocene age respectively (Krummenacher & Noetzlin 1966, Tarling 1967). The volcanic activity on Atiu, Mangaia, Mauke and Mitiaro had ceased by the end of the Oligocene; a mid-Miocene age has been inferred for the uppermost volcanic rocks of Manihiki from the thickness of the coral cover (Wood 1967). The islands, therefore, fall into two age groups: young islands (Rarotonga and Aitutaki) and older islands of no later than mid-Tertiary age (Atiu, Mangaia, Manihiki, Mauke and Mitiaro); these ages refer only to the uppermost volcanics of each island. The geology of the islands has been described in detail by Wood and Hay (1970).

The bathymetry of the islands is well known (Summerhayes 1967), and from a morphological point of view the islands discussed here can be classified as: (*a*) isolated islands resting on a flat ocean floor—Aitutaki (?), Mangaia, Rarotonga; (*b*) isolated islands resting on a broad suboceanic plateau—Manihiki; (*c*) islands located on a broad rise of the ocean floor—Aitutaki (?), Atiu, Mauke, Mitiaro and Takutea.

It will be shown later that the magnetic anomaly pattern around the islands is related to the morphological type. The height of the summit of each island above the flat ocean floor at the base is about 4·3–4·7 km for islands in the Southern Group, and about 3·5 km for Manihiki in the Northern Group. The volume of each island above the flat sea floor is of the order of $3–6 \times 10^3$ km^3.

MAGNETIC MEASUREMENTS

The magnetic measurements around the Cook Islands were made along a series of radial profiles. The coverage achieved was similar for most of the islands (7–11 profiles) except for Takutea and Atiu (4–5 profiles). Although detailed magnetic measurements were made on shore on some of the islands, these data were not used in compiling magnetic anomaly maps since it was found that the values were highly variable (Woodward & Reilly 1970). Likewise, sea-borne data were not used if anomalies of short wavelength (<1 km) appeared where the water depth was less than 1 km. The method of reduction of the magnetic data has been described in an earlier paper (Woodward & Hochstein 1970) which also presented maps of total force anomaly around Atiu, Manihiki, Mauke, Mitiaro, Rarotonga and Takutea. Similar maps for Aitutaki and Mangaia, as well as a revised map for Rarotonga, are in preparation. As an example, the total force anomaly map of Manihiki is reproduced here (Fig. 2).

A comparison of the magnetic maps has shown that two types of anomaly pattern occur: (1) a pair of magnetic anomalies of opposite sign—bipolar anomaly—Mangaia, Manihiki and Rarotonga; and (2) magnetic anomalies of irregular shape with no clear relationship to the island—Aitutaki, Atiu, Mauke and Takutea. The anomaly pattern around Mitiaro is of an intermediate type with a secondary magnetic anomaly superimposed on a bipolar anomaly.

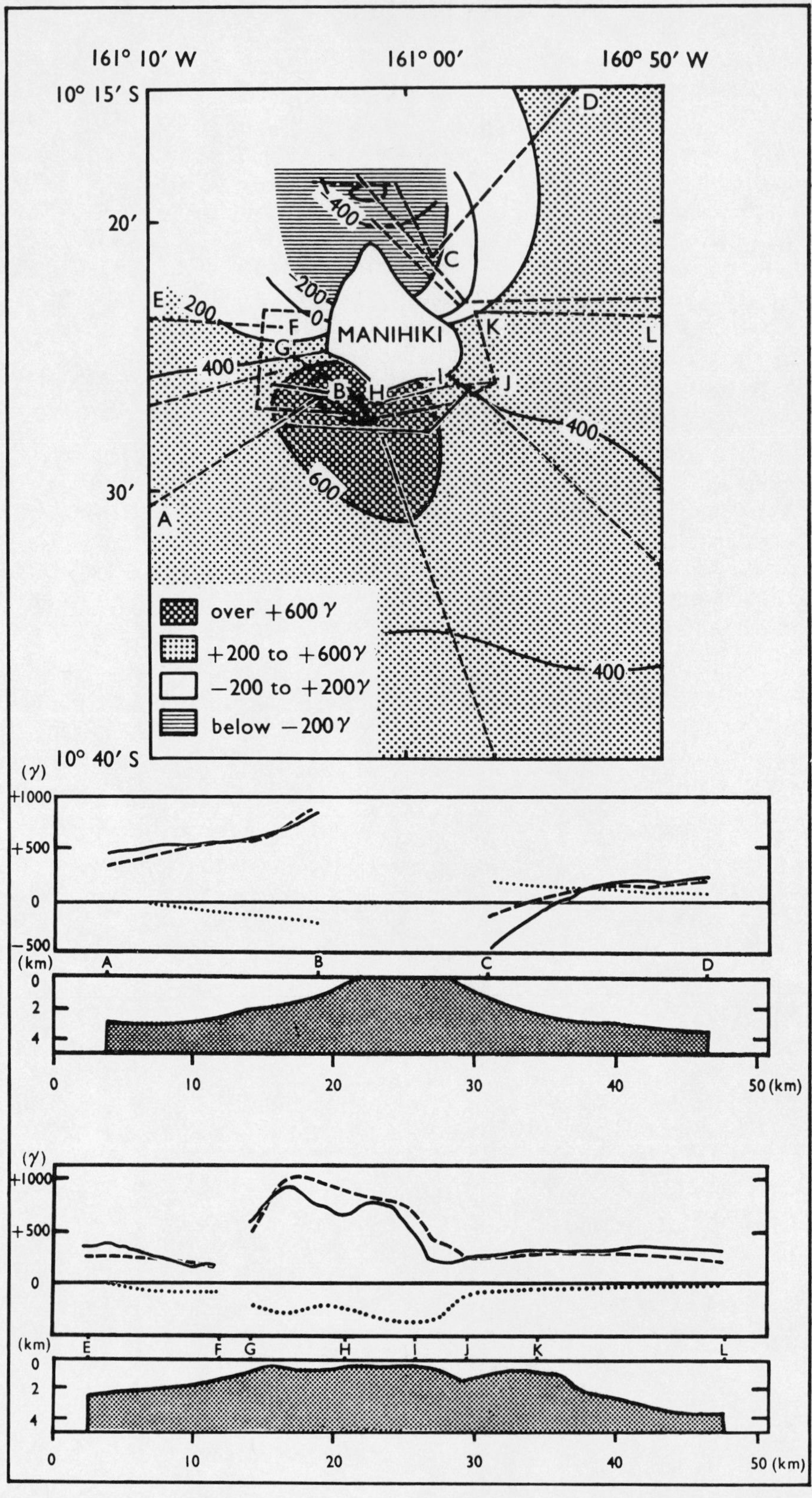
161° 10′ W
161° 00′
160° 50′ W
10° 15′ S
20′
30′
10° 40′ S
MANIHIKI
A
B
C
D
E
F
G
H
I
J
K
L
400
200
0
600
over +600 γ
+200 to +600 γ
−200 to +200 γ
below −200 γ
(γ)
+1000
+500
0
−500
(km)
0
2
4
10
20
30
40
50 (km)

INTERPRETATION OF SEA-BORNE MAGNETIC DATA

For the interpretation of the magnetic anomalies we assumed each island to be uniformly magnetized. This assumption implies that each island was built up during an interval of constant geomagnetic polarity; the implications of the assumption will be discussed later. Firstly, a best fit magnetization vector $\mathbf{M}_m$ was computed employing a modified version of a method first described by Talwani (1965) using bathymetric contours to specify the shape of the volcanic cone. The influence of non-magnetic sediments on the flanks was neglected.

Secondly, theoretical total force magnetic anomalies δT given by $\mathbf{M}_m$ and the shape of the island were calculated for each profile and compared with the observed total force anomalies ΔF. For each island, the mean residual $|R|_{av}$ was computed together with a 'goodness of fit' ratio r defined by Uyeda and Richards (1966). The residual anomaly R is given by:

$$R_j = \Delta F_j - C - \delta T_j = \Delta T_j - \delta T_j,$$

where C is a constant correction to the normal field used in computing the observed anomalies, and is found by minimizing $\Sigma_j R_j^2$. The mean residual $|R|_{av}$ is defined as

$$|R|_{\mathrm{av}} = \frac{1}{N} \sum_{j=1}^{N} |R_j|$$

and the 'goodness of fit' ratio as

$$r = \frac{\sum_{j=1}^{N} |\Delta T_j|}{\sum_{j=1}^{N} |R_j|}.$$

Neither $|R|_{\mathrm{av}}$ nor r are ideally suited to describe the degree of fit since all values of ΔT_j and R_j are given equal weight irrespective of the distance of an observation point from the centre of the magnetic moment of an island (Francheteau *et al.* 1970).

Thirdly, assuming that the induced magnetization $\mathbf{M}_i$ can be neglected, the direction of the best fit magnetization $\mathbf{M}_m$ will coincide with that of the remanent magnetization $\mathbf{M}_r$. Hence, the inferred position of the pole of an ancient magnetic dipole field (the virtual palaeomagnetic pole), can be computed from the direction of $\mathbf{M}_m$. We prefer to use the term *virtual palaeomagnetic pole* (VPP) instead of *virtual geomagnetic pole* (VGP) for reasons stated in Woodward and Hochstein (1970).

Fig. 2 Total magnetic force anomalies around Manihiki. A contoured ΔF-anomaly map is shown in the upper half of the figure; the ship's tracks are indicated by broken lines. Observed anomalies (solid line), anomalies produced by a normal magnetization of the island (dotted line) and anomalies using a best fit magnetization (broken line) along selected profiles are shown in the lower half of the figure, together with the bathymetric section (reproduced from Woodward & Hochstein, 1970, with permission from the *N.Z. Jl Geol. Geophys.*).

Table 1

SUMMARY OF ASSUMED AND CALCULATED PARAMETERS FOR THE INTERPRETATION OF MAGNETIC ANOMALIES AROUND THE COOK ISLANDS

Island	*Location*		*Regional field*[1]			*Best fit magnetization*[2]				*Fit*		*Virtual palaeomagnetic pole*	
	Lat. (S)	*Long.* (W)	F (μT)	D (°)	I (°)	$\mathbf{M}_m$ ($A m^{-1}$)	d_m (°)	i_m (°)	C (nT)	R_{av} (nT)	r	*Lat.*	*Long.*
Group 1: Isolated islands													
Mangaia	21° 54′	157°	41	13	−39	2·5	249	+15	246	71	1·52	22° S	111° E
Manihiki	10° 25′	161° 01′	36	11	−20	5·0	98	+60	232	95	2·78	13° S	111° W
Rarotonga[3] (first set)	21° 12′	159° 46′	41	13	−38	2·4	165	+24	162	76	1·81	73° S	41° W
Rarotonga[3] (second set)	21° 12′	159° 46′	41	13	−38	2·0	141	+45	263	98	1·41	57° S	86° W
Group 2: Islands on a rise of the ocean floor													
Aitutaki	18° 52′	159° 48′	40	13	−35	1·0	25	−19	358	133	1·01	64° N	88° W
Atiu[4]	19° 59′	158° 06′	40	13	−35	2·0	102	−26	23	240	1·10	6° S	51° W
Mauke	20° 09′	157° 21′	40	13	−35	2·2	348	+56	286	179	1·14	31° N	169° W
Mitiaro	19° 51′	157° 43′	40	13	−35	5·9	42	+46	379	166	1·15	28° N	116° W
Takutea[4]	19° 48′	159° 46′	40	13	−35	2·0	102	−26	23	240	1·10	6° S	51° W

Explanation

[1] F is the magnetic flux density ($1 \mu T = 10^{-2}$ gauss, $1 nT = 10^{-5}$ gauss = 1 gamma). D and I are declination and inclination of the present field.

[2] $1 A m^{-1} = 10^{-3}$ e.m.u. of magnetization. d_m and i_m are declination and inclination of the best fit magnetization.

[3] First set of measurements relates to four radial profiles analyzed by Woodward and Hochstein (1970); second set of measurements also includes data of five additional profiles measured more recently (Lumb & Carrington 1971).

[4] Atiu and Takutea were treated as one coherent body.

The procedure described here and the assumptions made are the same as those used by various authors (Uyeda & Richards 1966, Vacquier & Uyeda 1967, Richards *et al.* 1967, Grossling 1967, Schimke & Bufe 1968, Francheteau *et al.* 1970) in the analysis of magnetic anomalies observed over seamounts in the Pacific. The method has not been applied to the analysis of the magnetic anomalies of volcanic islands in deep water except by Woodward and Hochstein (1970). Most of the seamounts studied by the authors listed above stand about 2–3 km in height above the ocean floor and have a volume of the order of $0{\cdot}5$–$1{\cdot}5 \times 10^3$ km^3, i.e. $\frac{1}{4}$–$\frac{1}{6}$ of the volume of the islands in the Cook group. Results of the seamount studies can be compared with our interpretation, bearing the difference in mind.

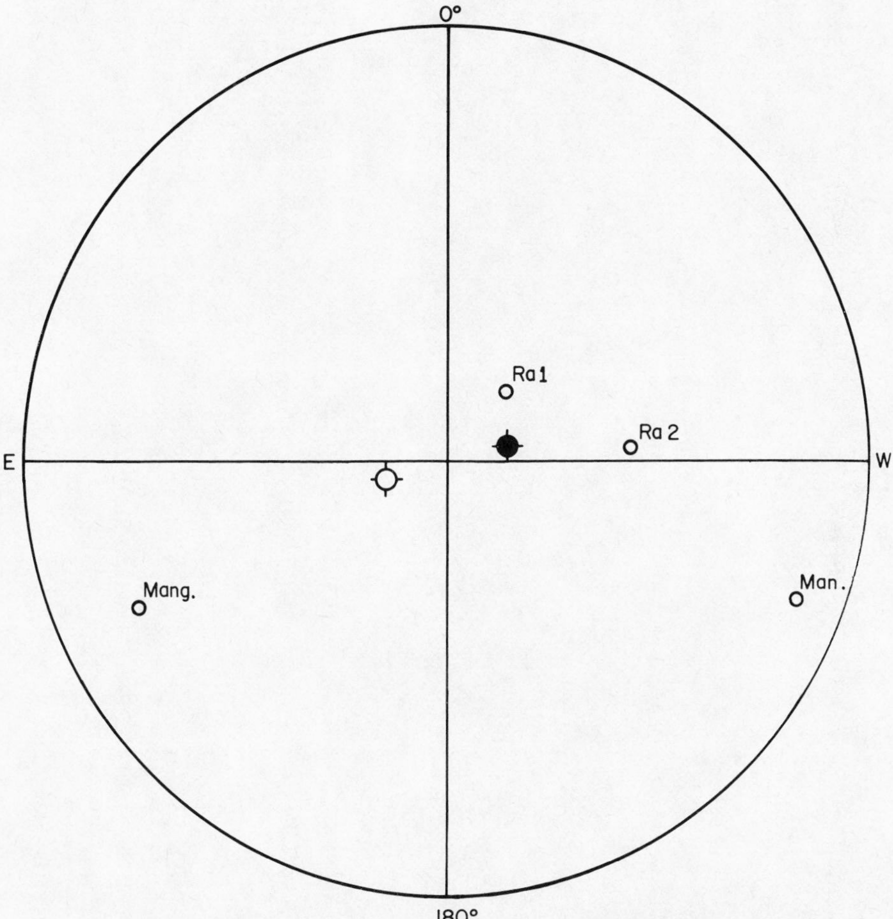

Fig. 3 Positions of virtual palaeomagnetic poles (VPP) for Mangaia (Mang.), Manihiki (Man.) and Rarotonga (Ra) (two sets of data were used for the Rarotonga poles—see Table 1). The solid and open circles with crosses mark the present-day virtual geomagnetic north and south pole, respectively, for Rarotonga. All the virtual palaeomagnetic poles lie in the southern hemisphere. Equal area projection.

A summary of all the parameters derived from the analysis of magnetic anomalies around the Cook Islands is given in Table 1. This table shows that a reasonable fit ($|R|_{av} < 100nT$ and $r > 1{\cdot}4$)[1] has been obtained for magnetic anomalies around Mangaia, Manihiki and Rarotonga, all of which are isolated volcanic cones. The goodness of fit ratios ($1{\cdot}4 < r < 2{\cdot}8$) are comparable with those obtained by Uyeda and Richards (1962) for seamounts near Japan ($r_{av} = 1{\cdot}9$), by Richards *et al.* (1967) for seamounts near Hawaii ($r_{av} = 2{\cdot}3$) and by Francheteau *et al.* (1970) for two groups of seamounts near California and Baja California ($r_{av} = 2{\cdot}3$ and $1{\cdot}8$ respectively). The fit obtained for magnetic anomalies around the islands which lie on a NW-SE trending oceanic rise, i.e. Aitutaki, Atiu, Mauke, Mitiaro and Takutea, is poor ($|R|_{av} > 130\ nT$ and $r < 1{\cdot}15$). At present we believe that the complex anomaly pattern around these islands is caused in part by intrusions beneath the rise. Since little is known of the magnetic anomalies in the vicinity of the rise, no attempt has been made to assess the shape of the intrusive bodies.

The virtual palaeomagnetic poles (VPP) listed in Table 1 are widely scattered and remain so if poles for islands with poor fits (group 2) are discarded (see Fig. 3). In this respect our results are quite different from those of similar studies elsewhere in the Pacific. The VPP of groups of seamounts near Japan, Hawaii, California and Baja California were found to form distinct clusters if plotted on equal area projection maps. The low latitudes of the VPP of Manihiki (13° S) and Mangaia (22° S) are also anomalous if compared with those deduced from the best fit magnetization of about forty seamounts with fits of $r \geq 1{\cdot}5$ (Table 1 in Francheteau *et al.* 1970). In fact, there is only one seamount (Z III-2) near Japan, analyzed by Vacquier and Uyeda (1967), for which a VPP with a similarly low latitude (21° N) has been reported.

A VPP situated at such a low latitude implies either that such a pole existed at the time the island was built up, or that the assumptions upon which the derivation of the pole is based do not hold. In an earlier paper (Woodward & Hochstein 1970) the low latitude of the Manihiki pole was taken as evidence for a pre-Cretaceous age of the bulk of the atoll, an inference based on palaeomagnetic results from neighbouring continents (Irving 1964). In the case of the low latitude of the VPP of Mangaia, we were reluctant to endorse the explanation of a pre-Cretaceous age partly because of the geological evidence (Wood 1967) pointing to a mid-Tertiary age of the uppermost volcanic rocks of the island, although the pedestal might be older. Hence we must examine possible reasons why the best fit magnetization as determined might not adequately represent either the remanent magnetization, or the direction of the earth's field at the time of formation of the island, and thus could be unsuitable for the calculation of a virtual palaeomagnetic pole.

FACTORS CAUSING ERRORS IN THE BEST FIT MAGNETIZATION

The direction of the best fit magnetization $\mathbf{M}_m$ may not be representative of that of the earth's magnetic field at the time of the formation of the island, even if the

[1] SI units are used throughout this paper, a conversion to c.g.s. units is given at the bottom of Table 1.

assumption of a homogeneous magnetization more or less holds, if: (1) the observed field includes the effect of a large intrusion under the flanks; (2) the induced magnetization $\mathbf{M}_i$ cannot be neglected; or (3) the island has been rotated after attaining its magnetization. The direction of $\mathbf{M}_m$ will also differ from that of the magnetic field at the time of the build-up period of the island if: (4) this period embraced large secular variations of the earth's magnetic field, including reversals, i.e. the island is made up of layers magnetized in different, and often opposed, directions; (5) the non-magnetic or weakly magnetic layer on the flanks cannot be neglected.

INFLUENCE OF LARGE INTRUSIONS

A large intrusion beneath the flank of an island, or an extensive flow, with a magnetization significantly different from that of the bulk of the island, would result in the best fit magnetization $\mathbf{M}_m$ not being representative of that of the island alone. However, there is evidence that such disturbances are distinguishable as secondary anomalies, as is the case for Mitiaro (Fig. 3 in Woodward & Hochstein 1970). In addition the fit would be poor, and it is therefore concluded that the scatter of the VPP in Fig. 3 is not caused by large intrusions.

INFLUENCE OF INDUCED MAGNETIZATION

The VPP listed in Table 1 were calculated assuming that the direction of the remanent magnetization $\mathbf{M}_r$ is the same as that of the best fit magnetization $\mathbf{M}_m$, i.e. assuming that the ratio $Q = \mathbf{M}_r/\mathbf{M}_i$ is very large, > 50, say. The direction and magnitude of $\mathbf{M}_r$, however, will differ from that of $\mathbf{M}_m$ if the rocks forming the bulk of an island have an average ratio of $Q \ll 50$. The changes of $\mathbf{M}_r$ as a function of Q have been discussed for a single component of $\mathbf{M}_r$ by Schimke and Bufe (1968). A more general solution of the problem has been used by Lumb (1970) to investigate the influence of Q on $\mathbf{M}_r$ in the case of Manihiki and Rarotonga; the same procedure has been used to calculate the changes of $\mathbf{M}_r$ for Mangaia. The results are presented in Fig. 4 as a plot of the positions of the VPP of Mangaia, Manihiki and Rarotonga for different values of Q. Since the average value of Q is about 11 for forty-seven samples taken on Rarotonga and Aitutaki and even larger values of Q have been reported for rocks from seamounts and the ocean floor (Cox & Doell 1962, Ozima *et al.* 1968), it can be inferred from Fig. 4 that the VPP will change by less than $10°$ if the induced magnetization $\mathbf{M}_i$ is taken into account. Hence the scatter of the VPP in Fig. 3 cannot be explained by the influence of $\mathbf{M}_i$.

ROTATION OF ISLAND

The direction of $\mathbf{M}_m$ would also differ from that of an ancient dipole field if the island had been rotated after attaining its magnetization. Although there is no evidence

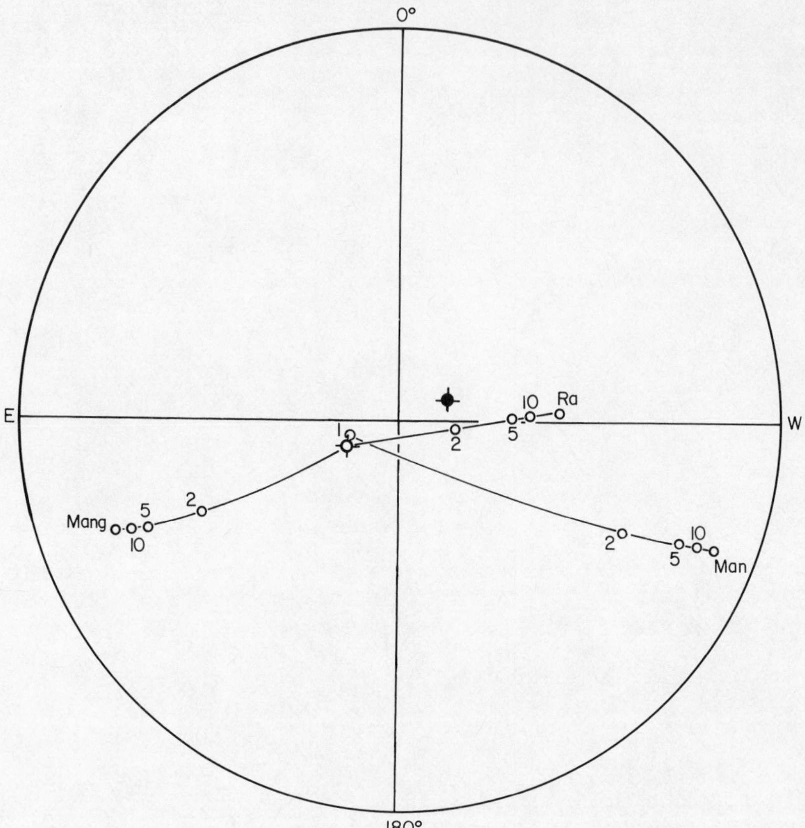

Fig. 4 Positions of virtual palaeomagnetic pole for Mangaia, Manihiki and Rarotonga resulting from different values of Q. The number alongside each point indicates the value of Q. The starting point ($Q = \infty$) is indicated by the abbreviated name of the island. The present-day virtual poles for Rarotonga are shown as in Fig. 3. Equal area projection.

elsewhere that islands have rotated, we looked into the problem of whether the VPP of the three islands under discussion might be brought to coincide with the present geomagnetic poles, assuming that a rotation of each island about the vertical axis took place. The paths which the VPP will take are shown in Fig. 5. It can be seen that a clockwise and anti-clockwise rotation of about 50° of Mangaia and Rarotonga respectively would bring the position of the VPP of these islands within 8°–11° of that of the present geomagnetic south pole. However, the VPP of Manihiki cannot be brought nearer than 33° (by an anti-clockwise rotation of 75°) and this, together with the difficulty of arguing that adjacent islands might rotate in opposite directions, led us to reject the hypothesis that the scatter of VPP in Fig. 3 is caused by rotation of the islands.

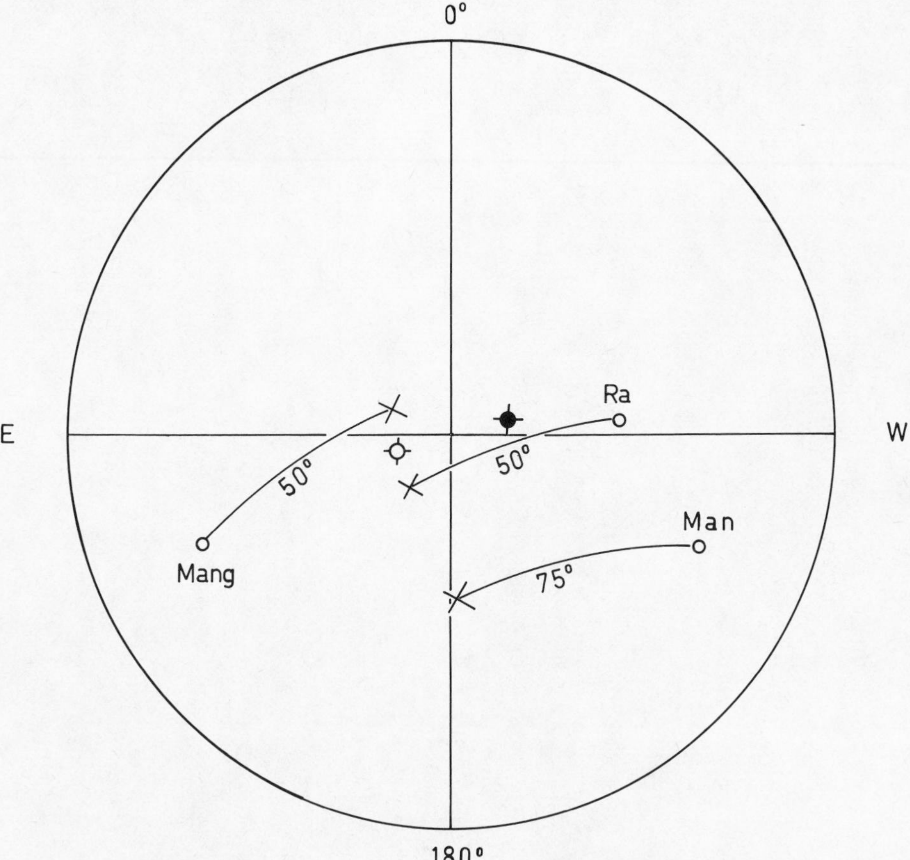

Fig. 5 Paths of the virtual palaeomagnetic pole of Mangaia, Manihiki and Rarotonga caused by a hypothetical rotation of the islands. The figure shows the original virtual palaeomagnetic pole (circle) and its closest position (cross) to the present virtual magnetic south pole as a result of the island's rotation about its vertical axis. The present-day virtual poles for Rarotonga are shown as in Fig. 3. Equal area projection.

INHOMOGENEOUS MAGNETIZATION OF ISLANDS CAUSED BY LAYERS WITH OPPOSITE MAGNETIZATION

Although not much is known about the growth of volcanic islands, the few time estimates published so far point to periods which are longer than those with constant geomagnetic polarity. Taking the total volume of volcanic material discharged during the last 100 years on Hawaii as a representative average, one obtains a discharge rate of about 40×10^3 $km^3/10^6$ yr for this island (cited in Menard 1969). Significantly smaller rates have been reported by Menard (1969), who deduced from the present position of guyots in the North-eastern Pacific, a minimum discharge rate of

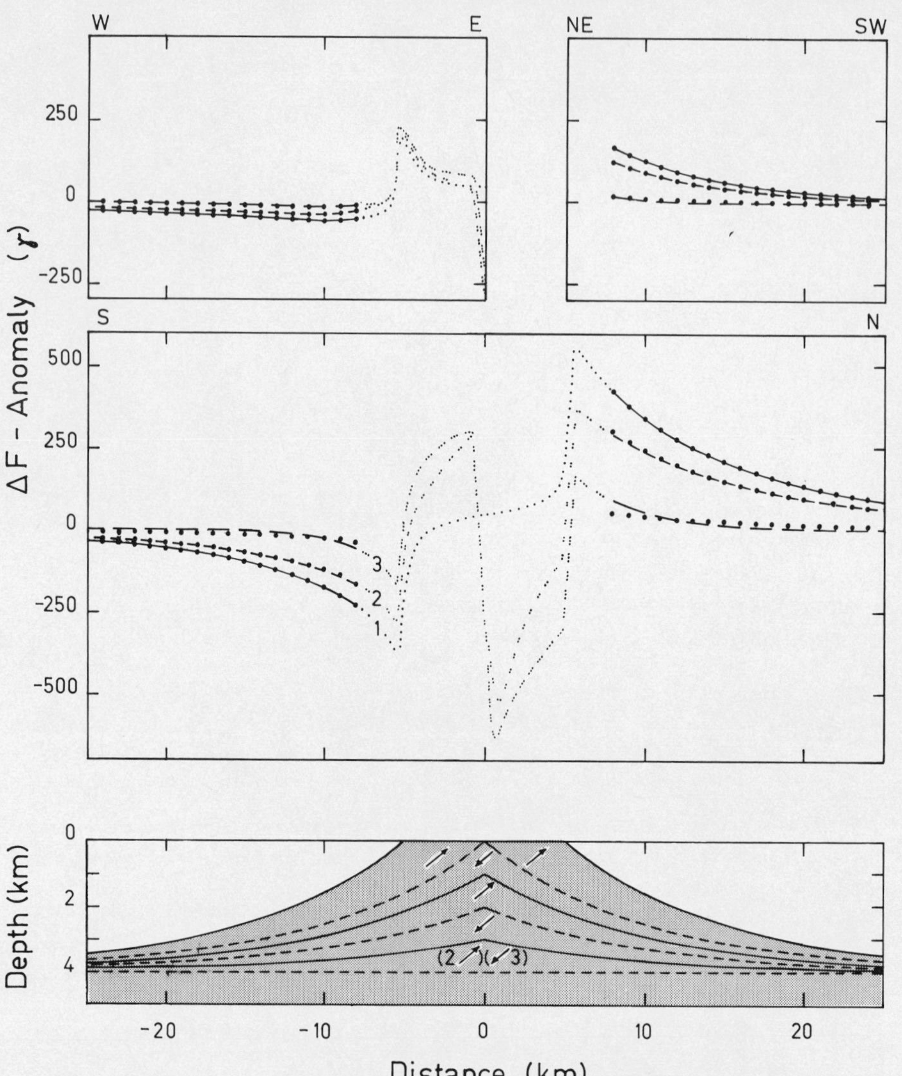

Fig. 6 'Observed' and computed anomalies for ideal island models 1, 2 and 3. The 'observed' anomalies for model 1 (solid line), model 2 (short dashes) and model 3 (long dashes) can be compared with the anomalies computed, using the best fit magnetization (dots). The lower part of the figure shows the sequence of normally and reversely magnetized layers used.

$0{\cdot}14 \times 10^3$ $km^3/10^6$ yr for these features. Hence, 'build-up' periods of 0·1–40 m.y. can be inferred for islands similar in volume to that of the Cook Islands ($3\text{–}6 \times 10^3$ km^3). The average length of intervals with uniform geomagnetic polarity during the last 10 m.y. has been given as $0{\cdot}2 \times 10^6$ yr (Cox 1968), although there is some evidence pointing to a greater length of about 0·5–1 × 10^6 yr of geomagnetic intervals 40–80 m.y. ago (Heirtzler *et al.* 1968). Comparing the time scales of periods of build-up and of constant polarity, it can be inferred that it is quite likely that a series of reversals occurred during the growth of the islands. In this case the islands will be made up of a series of layers of magnetic rocks with opposite magnetization.

In order to check whether the direction of the best fit magnetization $\mathbf{M}_m$ of an idealized volcanic island can be significantly different from that of a hypothetical geomagnetic field which, for example, underwent a series of reversals and secular variations during the time the island was formed, a set of exact input data was computed and subsequently analysed with a similar procedure as had been used for real islands.

Two types of islands were chosen. One type is made up of a series of conical layers, a cross-section of which is shown at the bottom of Fig. 6; the other is made up of a series of truncated conical layers as shown in Fig. 7. The flanks of each layer have a shape which is given by the average shape of volcanic islands as described by Robertson and Kibblewhite (1966). The diameter of the top of each model is 10 km, the water depth at the base, 4 km.

The 'normally' directed hypothetical field was given the direction of an axial dipole field at the latitude of the centre of the Southern Cook Group: $D=0°$, $I=-39°$. Then, by considering a realistic sequence of changes in this hypothetical field, both by reversing the direction of the field and allowing the declination to change by a reasonable value, a series of models was constructed for each island type, with magnetization varying in direction in successive layers. In one model, for example, the direction of magnetization in the top layer is that of the 'normal' hypothetical field, is reversed in the second layer, normal in the third, and so on. The declination in successive layers for this case is 0°, 180°, 0°, 180°, ... For a second model, it was assumed that the declination of the hypothetical field was changed to 20° for the 'normal' direction, but was unchanged (180°) for the 'reversed' direction. The value of 20° for secular variation of declination is not unreasonable (Cox 1962). The declination of the magnetization in successive layers thus becomes 20°, 180°, 20°, 180°, ... Third and fourth models were similar, but with declination sequences of 0°, 160°, 0°, 160°, ... and of 160°, 0°, 160°, 0°, ...

In every model, each layer was assigned a remanent magnetization $\mathbf{M}_r$ of 2·5 $A\,m^{-1}$.

A further modification was brought about by assigning either a normal or a reversed magnetization to the bottom layer of each model. In addition, homogeneously magnetized islands with a declination of magnetization of 0°, 20° and 160° were also considered. In total nineteen different models were studied. To distinguish between the various models a code was chosen which is explained at the bottom of Table 2.

Theoretical magnetic anomalies for each model were computed along four radial profiles. For this purpose a numerical procedure was developed to calculate the magnetic anomalies for the general case of a solid of revolution. The procedure was based on that described by Reilly (1969) for the calculation of the anomalies over a right circular cylinder. The theoretical anomalies were then treated as observed data, and only data at water depths greater than 1 km were used to determine a best fit

Table 2

SUMMARY OF CALCULATED PARAMETERS FOR ISLAND MODELS

Model No.	*Model code*[1]	*Best fit magnetization*[2]				*Fit*[2]		*VPP for magnetizing field*[3]		*Computed pole*[4]	
		$\mathbf{M}_m$ (Am^{-1})	d_m (°)	i_m (°)	*Ang. diff.* (°)	R_{av} (nT)	r	*Lat.* (°)	*Long.* (°)	*Lat.* (°)	*Long.* (°)
1	141	2·3	0	—39	0	0	V. large	89° N	21° E	89° N	21° E
2	045	1·6	0	—40	1	2	42·8	89° N	21° E	88° N	30° E
3	044	0·3	350	—28	14	7	1·69	89° N	21° E	78° N	143° E
4	143	2·0	6	—45	7	25	4·35	89° N	21° E	82° N	24° W
5	144	0·5	343	—15	28	20	0·99	89° N	21° E	69° N	149° E
6	014	0·8	17	—35	22	5	8·46	81° N	101° E	74° N	72° W
7	015	1·3	8	—38	13	2	36·7	82° N	99° E	83° N	65° W
8	113	1·4	12	—42	15	11	6·63	84° N	98° E	78° N	50° W
9	114	0·6	27	—23	35	9	2·71	81° N	101° E	63° N	84° W
10	024	0·8	26	—36	13	5	7·65	81° N	59° W	66° N	67° W
11	025	1·3	22	—39	8	2	38·3	79° N	60° W	70° N	62° W
12	121	2·4	17	—39	2	0	V. large	71° N	62° W	74° N	62° W
13	123	1·4	29	—43	13	2	6·51	77° N	61° W	63° N	55° W
14	124	0·5	33	—26	23	9	2·19	81° N	59° W	58° N	77° W
15	034	0·4	76	—9	81	5	3·12	81° N	101° E	15° N	70° W
16	035	0·6	304	+30	80	2	10·4	79° N	102° E	24° N	141° E
17	131	1·7	335	+39	78	0	V. large	71° N	104° E	42° N	170° E
18	133	0·6	308	+40	87	11	2·40	78° N	103° E	23° N	149° E
19	134	0·5	53	—36	49	9	3·24	81° N	101° E	41° N	60° W
1*a*[5]	141	2·5	0	—39	0	0	V. large	89° N	21° E	89° N	21° E
2*a*[5]	045	1·8	359	—39	1	1	62·1	89° N	21° E	89° N	41° E
3*a*[5]	044	0·5	2	—42	3	6	2·55	89° N	21° E	86° N	14° W
1*b*[6]	141	1·8	4	—39	3	5	21·9	89° N	21° E	86° N	51° E
2*b*[6]	045	1·3	3	—39	2	3	25·4	89° N	21° E	87° N	45° W
3*b*[6]	044	0·3	357	—36	4	7	1·57	89° N	21° E	87° N	131° E
4*b*[6]	143	1·8	4	—41	4	21	5·30	89° N	21° E	85° N	34° W
5*b*[6]	144	0·3	352	—29	12	21	0·95	89° N	21° E	81° N	147° E

Explanation

[1] The model code indicates the following:

First digit gives the model shape—

0 = conical layers (as in Fig. 6).
1 = truncated cones (as in Fig. 7).

Second digit gives the sequence of magnetization of the layers—

1 = top layer normal (declination, $D=0°$), for reversed layers, $D=160°$.
2 = top layer normal ($D=20°$), reversed layers, $D=180°$.
3 = top layer reversed ($D=160°$), for normal layers, $D=0°$.
4 = top layer normal ($D=0°$), for reversed layers, $D=180°$.

Third digit is the number of layers in the model.

[2] Column headings as in Table 1 with the addition that 'Ang. diff.' is the angular difference, in degrees, between the direction of the best fit magnetization and that of the mean magnetizing field. The direction of the mean magnetizing field was computed without regard for polarity, i.e. for the reversely magnetized layers, the opposite direction was used. Each direction was weighted according to the number of layers magnetized in that direction.

[3] The position of the VPP (north pole) given by the direction of the mean magnetizing field.

[4] The position of the VPP (north pole) given by the direction of the best fit magnetization.

[5] Models 1*a*, 2*a*, 3*a* are as 1, 2, 3, but the sampling points are situated on lines having azimuths which differ by 30° from those of the other models.

[6] Models 1*b* to 5*b* are as models 1 to 5, but with a non-magnetic layer mantling the island.

In every case the island was situated at 21° S, 159° W and the regional field elements were: $F=41\mu T$, $D=0°$, $I=-39°$. The model was given a uniform susceptibility of $4\pi\times10^{-3}$.*

* In SI units, the dimensionless quantity *susceptibility* has a value which is 4π times that in the non-rationalized c.g.s. system.

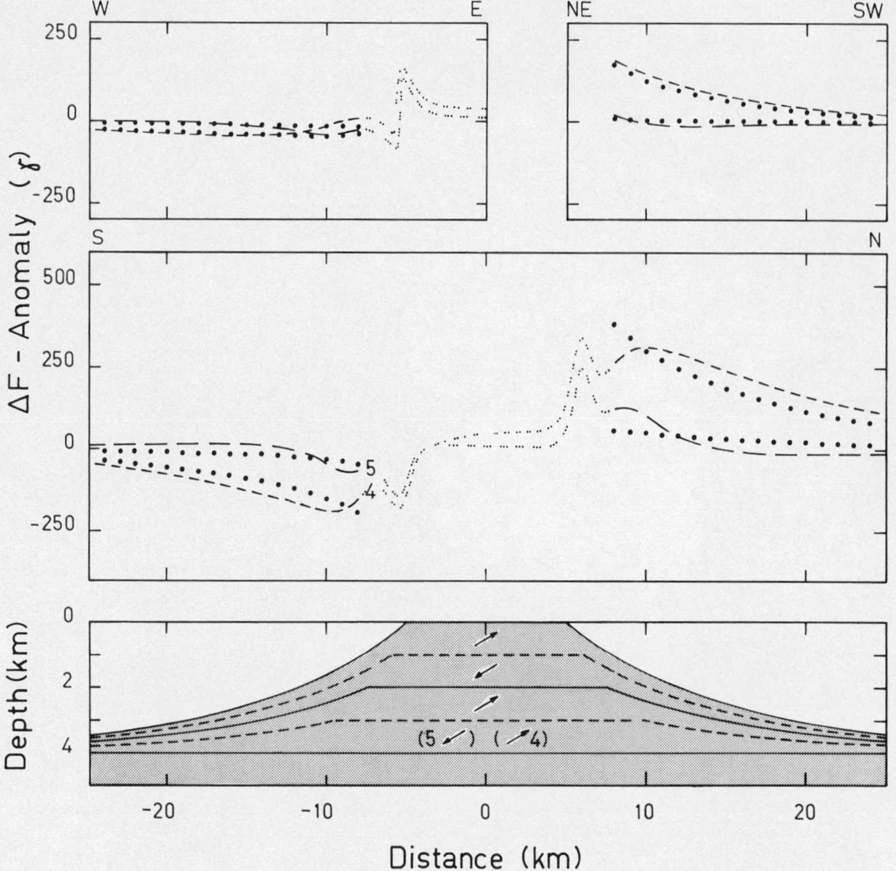

Fig. 7 'Observed' and computed anomalies for ideal island models 4 and 5. The 'observed' anomalies for model 4 (short dashes) and model 5 (long dashes) can be compared with the anomalies computed, using the best fit magnetization (dots). The lower part of the figure shows the sequence of normally and reversely magnetized layers used.

magnetization $\mathbf{M}_m$. For this, the bathymetry of the idealized island was again used to specify the body and the island was assumed to be homogeneously magnetized. The magnetic anomalies resulting from $\mathbf{M}_m$ and the shape of the island were computed, and compared with the 'observed' data by calculating 'goodness of fit' ratios r and average residuals $|R|_{av}$. The 'observed' magnetic anomalies and the anomalies resulting from $\mathbf{M}_m$ are shown in Figs 6 and 7 for the first five models. Best fit magnetization $\mathbf{M}_m$, fits given by $|R|_{av}$ and r as well as the position of VPP resulting from $\mathbf{M}_m$ are listed in Table 2 for all the models investigated.

In order to check whether the sampling procedure chosen might cause an error in $\mathbf{M}_m$, the azimuths of the profiles of models 1, 2 and 3 were changed by 30°. It was found that the limited sampling introduces errors of up to about 10° in the direction of $\mathbf{M}_m$.

A look at Table 2 shows that the direction of the best fit magnetization of models 1–14 does not vary by more than 35° from that of the mean magnetizing field. These changes correspond to changes of up to about 30° in latitude of the VPP. Large deviations in the direction of $\mathbf{M}_m$, however, occur in models 15–19 which all have a reversely magnetized layer on top with a declination of magnetization which differs by 160° from that of the normally magnetized layers. These changes in $\mathbf{M}_m$ correspond to differences of up to 84° between the position of the VPP and that of the pole of the mean magnetizing field, causing a large scatter in the plot of the VPP as is shown in Fig. 8. Hence, it can be concluded that the direction of the best fit magnetization $\mathbf{M}_m$ of real islands which are made up of layers of opposite magnetization can differ significantly from the mean direction of the magnetizing field, especially if the top layer is reversely magnetized. In such cases, the position of the VPP derived from $\mathbf{M}_m$ can likewise differ significantly from the actual position of the pole of the magnetizing dipole field.

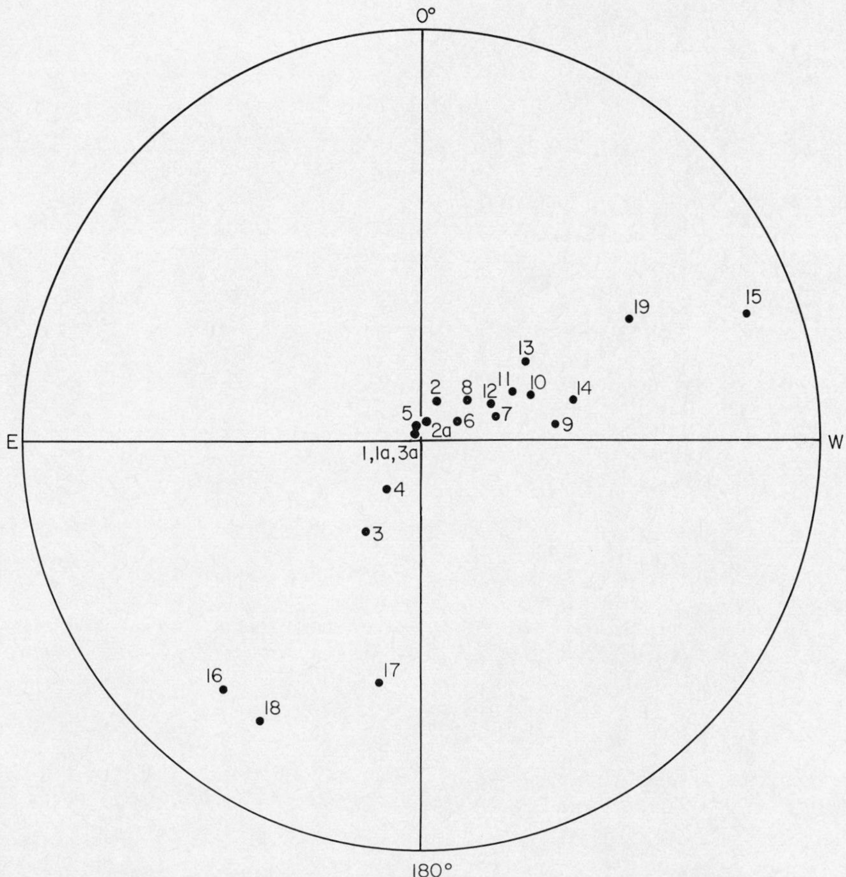

Fig. 8 Virtual palaeomagnetic poles for ideal islands. The numbers refer to the model number in Table 2. Equal area projection.

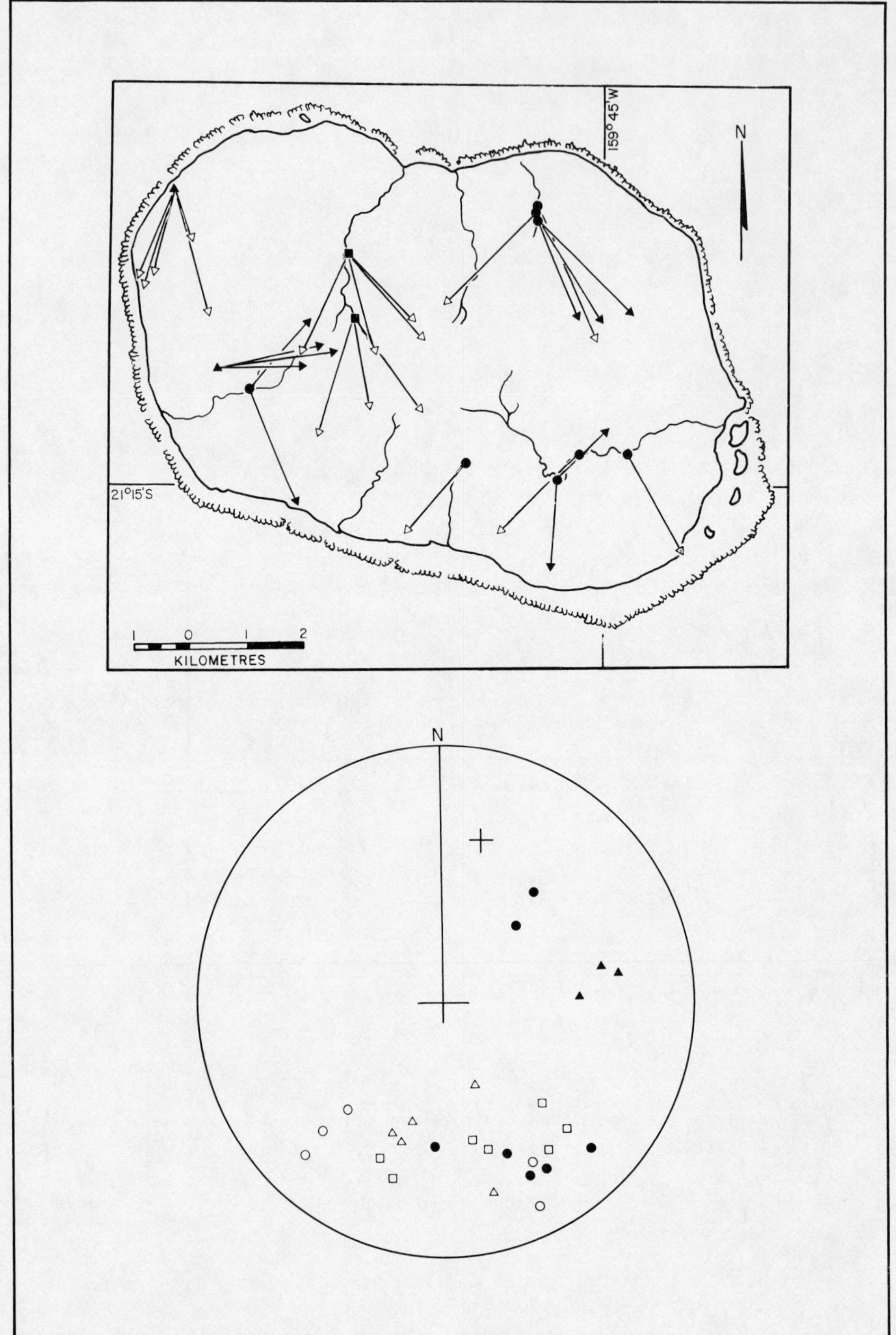

159° 45' W
N
21°15'S
1 0 1 2
KILOMETRES
N

INFLUENCE OF NON-MAGNETIC LAYER ON FLANKS OF ISLANDS

The flanks of the volcanic islands are covered by a layer of presumably weakly-magnetic material made up of talus and coral debris. On Aitutaki, for example, this layer was found by seismic measurements to be up to 1·5 km thick (Hochstein 1967). In order to assess the influence of this layer in determining $\mathbf{M}_m$, the 'observed' anomalies for models 1–5 were taken and the best fit magnetization $\mathbf{M}_m$ was determined for a body similar to that of models 1–5 but with a diameter of 14 km at the top instead of 10 km used previously. This is equivalent to analysing a model with a non-magnetic layer with a thickness of up to 1·5 km on the flanks. The results of the analysis are listed as models 1*b*–5*b* in Table 2 and the models with and without the non-magnetic cover are compared directly in Table 3. It can be seen that the influence of the non-magnetic cover is small and the error introduced in $\mathbf{M}_m$ is about the same as that caused by the sampling procedure. Hence the influence of a non-magnetic layer mantling the island is small and the scatter of VPP in Fig. 3, for example, cannot be explained by the influence of this layer.

MAGNETIC PROPERTIES OF ROCK SAMPLES FROM AITUTAKI AND RAROTONGA

Some oriented rock samples were collected on Aitutaki and Rarotonga to check whether the mean direction of magnetization of exposed rocks is similar to that of the best fit magnetization obtained by the analysis of the magnetic anomalies around the islands. The remanent magnetization of samples collected from five sites on Aitutaki and eleven sites on Rarotonga (Lumb & Carrington 1971) were measured on a spinner magnetometer both before and after stepwise demagnetization in an alternating field, the last step taking place in a field of at least 16 $A\,m^{-1}$ ($\approx$200 *Oe*).

The lower part of Fig. 9 is an equal area plot summarizing the results of the measurements made on rocks from Rarotonga after demagnetization. In this figure each point represents the direction of the magnetization of a single sample and is, in most cases, the mean of the direction of magnetization of several specimens. The upper part of the figure shows the same information but related to sample sites. The

---

Fig. 9 Remanent magnetization directions of samples from Rarotonga. In the upper half of the figure the arrows originating from the sampling site represent the horizontal projection of unit magnetization vectors. The lower half is a plot of the remanent magnetization directions on an equal area projection. In both halves, geological formations are represented by the following symbols: triangles, Raemaru Flows; squares, Avatiu Caldera Complex; circles, Te Manga Group. Solid arrow-heads in the upper part and solid symbols in the equal area projection indicate downward (i.e. positive) inclination. The cross in the lower part of the figure marks the present-day geomagnetic field direction for Rarotonga.

Table 3

COMPARISON OF BEST FIT MAGNETIZATION OF MODELS WITH AND WITHOUT NON-MAGNETIC COVER

Model No.	*Best fit magnetization* without non-magnetic cover $\mathbf{M}_m(Am^{-1})$	$d_m(°)$	$i_m(°)$	*with non-magnetic cover* $\mathbf{M}_m(Am^{-1})$	$d_m(°)$	$i_m(°)$	*Difference in magnetization direction* (°)	*Difference in VPP position* (°)
1,1*b*	2·3	0	−39	1·8	4	−39	3	4
2,2*b*	1·6	0	−40	1·3	3	−39	3	3
3,3*b*	0·3	350	−28	0·3	357	−36	10	9
4,4*b*	2·0	6	−45	1·8	4	−41	4	3
5,5*b*	0·5	343	−15	0·3	352	−29	16	12

direction of magnetization of rocks from Aitutaki are similarly dispersed, although they are all 'reversed', but despite the scatter, the mean magnetization direction for each island is very close to the direction of an axial dipole field. The mean VPP for Aitutaki was found to be situated at 81° S, 82° E, and for Rarotonga it lies at 83° S, 30° E. In the latter case the VPP was computed without regard for polarity, as some samples were normally magnetized.

The pole positions computed from the directions of the remanent magnetization of rock samples are significantly different from those listed in Table 1 which were derived from the sea-borne magnetic data. This difference, together with the large scatter in the directions of magnetization of the exposed rocks, casts further doubt upon the validity of the original assumption that the islands are uniformly magnetized. The magnitude of the natural remanent magnetization is also highly variable. For forty-seven samples from Rarotonga and Aitutaki, this magnitude has a standard deviation of 22·4 Am^{-1} about a mean value of 13·4 Am^{-1}. The mean ratio Q of remanent to induced magnetization, assuming a magnetizing force of 32 Am^{-1} ($\approx$0·4 Oe), is 11·4 (s.d. = 12·4).

The degree of scatter in the directions of magnetization is very large: the circular standard deviations of these directions are 44° and 49° for Aitutaki and Rarotonga respectively. The standard deviations of direction of magnetization within the three geological groups sampled on Rarotonga are similarly high: 32°, 43° and 55° for the Raemaru Flows, the Avatiu Caldera Complex and the Te Manga Group respectively. The names used for the geological units are those used by Wood and Hay (1970). These values are similar to those reported by Tarling (1967) for the Raemaru Flows (s.d. = 20°) and the Avatiu Caldera Complex (s.d. = 47°). A comparison of these results with those of similar studies on other Pacific islands (Tarling 1965*a*, *b*) indicates that this degree of scatter is not uncommon, and, furthermore, it appears that there may be a connection between the magnitude of the scatter and the size of the island[1], but this proposition will be dealt with, in detail, elsewhere.

SUMMARY

Measurements of total magnetic force around most of the Cook Islands have shown that the pattern of magnetic anomalies is somehow related to the bathymetry around each island. Isolated islands resting on a flat ocean floor (Mangaia, Manihiki, Rarotonga—Group 1) exhibit bipolar anomalies, while those islands located on a rise of the ocean floor (Aitutaki, Atiu, Mauke, Mitiaro, Takutea—Group 2) have a more complex pattern.

An interpretation of the magnetic anomalies of each island belonging to the second group in terms of a simple homogeneously magnetized body gives a poor fit between observed and computed anomalies, and it is necessary to invoke further bodies of unknown shape and magnetization to explain the observations. Of this group only Aitutaki has a direction of best fit magnetization which is similar to that of the present magnetic field (19° difference), as might be expected from the young age (0·7 m.y.) of volcanic rocks which outcrop on the island.

The bipolar magnetic anomalies around the first group of islands can be interpreted with the assumption that each island is homogeneously magnetized and the computed anomalies were found to fit the observed ones to an acceptable degree. However, the virtual palaeomagnetic poles calculated from the best fit magnetization for each island have positions which are inconsistent with a Tertiary age for these islands, as has been inferred from geological evidence, and point to more ancient magnetic fields. This inconsistency was tested by investigating whether the direction of the best fit magnetization could be significantly different from that of the resultant remanent magnetization. Of the various factors which can bring about such a difference, for example influence of induced magnetization, non-magnetic cover on the flanks, rotation and non-homogeneous magnetization of the island, only the last factor, i.e. non-homogeneous magnetization, was found to cause differences producing a scatter of pole positions which is similar to that observed.

The influence of non-homogeneous magnetization was assessed by analysing the computed anomalies of model islands composed of a sequence of normally and reversely magnetized layers. Although the range of the models investigated was not exhaustive, the analyses have shown that the greatest differences ($>50°$) between the direction of the best fit magnetization and remanent magnetization occur when the top layer is reversely magnetized and the reversed directions are not exactly anti-parallel to the normal one.

The model study has also shown that low values of the magnitude of the best fit magnetization of composite islands are accompanied by low values of the 'goodness of fit' ratio r. This might explain why most of the eleven seamounts (out of a total of fifty-two) listed by Francheteau *et al.* (1970) with a 'goodness of fit' ratio $r \leq 1{\cdot}4$ also have low values of best fit magnetization in comparison with the average magnetization

[1] In a paper presented at the Congress by Dr E. Winterer the hypothesis was put forward that the islands located on the NW-SE trending rise in the Southern Cook Group are progressively older towards the north-west. Although we do not yet know what causes the scatter in the direction of magnetization of rock samples, the magnitude of the scatter described here indicates that this hypothesis cannot be tested by palaeomagnetic studies.

of the group to which they belong.

Using the results of the model studies as criteria, it can be concluded that the bipolar anomalies of Rarotonga and Mangaia are caused by a non-homogeneous magnetization of these islands brought about by a sequence of normally and reversely magnetized layers. The uppermost part of each island is reversely magnetized and the direction of the best fit magnetization is more likely not representative of that of any ancient geomagnetic field. Hence no conclusion about the possible age of the bulk of these islands can be drawn from the position of the computed virtual palaeomagnetic pole.

It is possible that the same conclusions also apply to Manihiki. However, since the 'goodness of fit' ratio and the value of the best fit magnetization obtained for Manihiki are greater than those obtained for Rarotonga and Mangaia, it is also possible that the direction of the best fit magnetization does not differ too much from that of the mean remanent magnetization. In this case, the position of the virtual palaeomagnetic pole would be indicative of an ancient magnetic field and a pre-Cretaceous age can be inferred for Manihiki.

ACKNOWLEDGEMENT

We wish to thank Mr W. I. Reilly for critically reading the manuscript and for his many helpful comments.

REFERENCES

Cox, A. 1962. Analysis of present geomagnetic field for comparison with paleomagnetic results. *J. Geomagn. Geoelect.* **13,** 101-12.

——— 1968. Lengths of geomagnetic polarity intervals. *J. geophys. Res.* **73,** 3247-60.

Cox, A. & Doell, R. R. 1962. Magnetic properties of the basalt in hole EM7, Mohole project. *J. geophys. Res.* **67,** 3997-4004.

Francheteau. J., Harrison, C. G. A., Sclater, J. G. & Richards, M. L. 1970. Magnetization of Pacific seamounts: a preliminary polar curve for the North-eastern Pacific. *J. geophys. Res.* **75,** 2035-61.

Grossling, B. F. 1967. The internal magnetization of seamounts and its computer calculation. *U.S. geol. Surv. Prof. Pap. 554-F.*

Heirtzler, J. R., Dickson, G. O., Herron, E. M., Pitman, III, W. C. & Le Pichon, X. 1968. Marine magnetic anomalies, geomagnetic field reversals, and motions of the ocean floor and continents. *J. geophys. Res.* **73,** 2119-36.

Hochstein, M. P. 1967. Seismic measurements in the Cook Islands, South-west Pacific Ocean. *N.Z. Jl Geol. Geophys.* **10,** 1499-526.

Irving, E. 1964. *Paleomagnetism and its applications to geological and geophysical problems.* Wiley and Sons, New York.

Krummenacher, D. & Noetzlin, J. 1966. Ages isotopique K/A de roches prélevées dans les possessions françaises du Pacifique. *Bull. Soc. géol. Fr.* (Sér. 7), **8,** 173-5.

Lumb, J. T. 1970. Magnetic properties of rocks from the Cook Islands, south-west Pacific Ocean. Appendix to Woodward and Hochstein (1970). *N.Z. Jl Geol. Geophys.* **13,** 220-4.

Lumb, J. T. & Carrington, L. 1971. Magnetic surveys in the South-west Pacific and rock sampling for magnetic studies in the Cook Islands. *Bull. R. Soc. N.Z.* **8,** 81-9.

Menard, H. W. 1969. Growth of drifting volcanoes. *J. geophys. Res.* **74,** 4827-37.

Ozima, Minoru, Ozima, Mituko, & Kaneoka, I. 1968. Potassium-argon ages and magnetic properties of some dredged submarine basalts and their geophysical implications. *J. geophys. Res.* **73,** 711-23.

Reilly, W. I. 1969. Gravitational and magnetic effects of a right circular cylinder. *N.Z. Jl Geol. Geophys.* **12,** 497-506.

Richards, M. L., Vacquier, V. & Van Voorhis, G. D. 1967. Calculation of the magnetization of uplifts from combining topographic and magnetic surveys. *Geophysics*, **32,** 678-707.

Robertson, E. I. & Kibblewhite, A. C. 1966. Bathymetry around isolated volcanic islands and atolls in the South Pacific Ocean. *N.Z. Jl Geol. Geophys.* **9,** 111-21.

Schimke, G. R. & Bufe, C. G. 1968. Geophysical description of a Pacific Ocean seamount. *J. geophys. Res.* **73,** 559-69.

Summerhayes, C. P. 1967. Bathymetry and topographic lineation in the Cook Islands. *N.Z. Jl Geol. Geophys.* **10,** 1382-99.

Talwani, M. 1965. Computation with the help of a digital computer of magnetic anomalies caused by bodies of arbitrary shape. *Geophysics*, **30,** 797-817.

Tarling, D. H. 1965*a*. The palaeomagnetism of some Hawaiian Islands. *Geophys. J. R. astr. Soc.* **10,** 93-104.

——— 1965*b*. The palaeomagnetism of the Samoan and Tongan Islands. *Geophys. J. R. astr. Soc.* **10,** 497-513.

——— 1967. Some palaeomagnetic results from Rarotonga, Cook Islands. *N.Z. Jl Geol. Geophys.* **10,** 1400-6.

Uyeda, S. & Richards, M. L. 1966. Magnetization of four Pacific seamounts near the Japanese Islands. *Bull. Earthq. Res. Inst. Tokyo Univ.* **44,** 179-213.

Vacquier, V. & Uyeda, S. 1967. Palaeomagnetism of nine seamounts in the Western Pacific and of three volcanoes in Japan. *Bull. Earthq. Res. Inst. Tokyo Univ.* **45,** 815-48.

Wood, B. L. 1967. Geology of the Cook Islands. *N.Z. Jl Geol. Geophys.* **10,** 1429-45.

Wood, B. L. & Hay, R. F. 1970. Geology of the Cook Islands. *Bull. geol. Surv. N.Z.* (n.s. 82), 103 pp.

Woodward, D. J. & Hochstein, M. P. 1970. Magnetic measurements in the Cook Islands, South-west Pacific Ocean. *N.Z. Jl Geol. Geophys.* **13,** 207-24.

Woodward, D. J. & Reilly, W. I. 1970. Note on magnetic vertical force anomalies on Manihiki Atoll, Cook Islands. *N.Z. Jl Geol. Geophys.* **13,** 225-7.

Major Features of the Pacific and the 'New Global Tectonics'

S. W. CAREY

Geology Department, University of Tasmania, Hobart, Australia

ABSTRACT

The central Pacific is indeed pacific in seismicity, vulcanism and tectonism. In contrast with all other oceans, the Pacific rim is concordant, with orogenic grain parallel to the margin, progressing from youngest to oldest from margin into the continents.

The Pacific has both east-west and north-south asymmetry. Along the eastern margin from Arctic to Antarctic the young orogens, the andesite line and the trenches are separated from the continents by oceanic-crust basins hundreds to thousands of kilometres wide. To some these basins represent oceanized continental crust. To others they are disjunctive basins complementary to crustal consumption somewhere else. To me they are disjunctive in a generally dispersive system.

The western Pacific margin has significantly more seismicity and vulcanism than the eastern.

The southern Pacific, along with the associated southern continents, is displaced thousands of kilometres east with respect to the northern Pacific and its associated continents. This movement displaces hemisphere against hemisphere.

Dispersive separation is greater in the south Pacific (and southern hemisphere generally) than in the north.

These asymmetries recur in other geophysical characters—geodetic, magnetic and continental zoning.

As east and west and north and south are born of the earth's rotation, the asymmetries imply a rotational helm in global tectonics, if not a cause. Classical geodynamics has assumed axiomatically a rigid rotating spheroid. Realistic geodynamics must allow for radial and zonal differential motions, both complementary (circulation) and unidirectional (e.g. differential expansion). The consequences in wobbles, differential crustal movements, climates and eustatism are profound.

The nature of the trenches is critical to the fashionable conveyor-belt theory. Trenches do not occur where the theory needs them. Seismic profiles have not revealed the thousands of kilometres of shortening in the trenches which the theory demands, but instead support general expansion.

All crustal polygons (currently renamed 'plates') have increased in area, and each polygon has increased its distance from all other polygons since the Jurassic. This can only mean overall increases in the earth's surface.

Forty years ago geophysicists denied the possibility that continents had separated and most geologists concurred, and would not see the contrary evidence. Those few of us who argued for continental dispersion were repudiated and even scorned and ridiculed. Today geophysicists proclaim the separation of continents but insist that equivalent crust has been consumed in the trenches. Again most geologists concur and will not see the contrary evidence. Earth expansion is repudiated and scoffed at. I believe that the decline of the 'new global tectonics' will be as fast as its rise.

ISLAND ARCS AND RELATED STRUCTURES OF THE WESTERN PACIFIC REGION

Introduction

Patrick J. Coleman,
Geology Department, University of Western Australia,
Nedlands, Western Australia, 6009

This symposium has three parts. The first covers the South-west Pacific and concentrates on the Melanesian arcs; the second the North-west Pacific but includes a foray into the Indonesian system; the third deals with comparisons of island arcs and special topics which do not fit neatly into the first two parts.

The first part gives prominence to the arc systems of the South-west Pacific. Most of the systematic geological work on the Melanesian arcs has been done only over the last fifteen years and the geophysical and geochemical data is still more recent. With the exception of New Zealand and parts of New Guinea and New Caledonia, the intervening areas were largely a geological *terra incognita.* The South-west Pacific deserves emphasis for its own sake, therefore, but I also admit to personal prejudice, for the Outer Melanesian Arcs have been my stamping ground for the past twenty years.

In the 1950s these arcs seemed special, even unique. I speak especially of the Outer Melanesian Arcs, for geologically they were almost wholly at odds with, for example, the Umbgrovian model of an island arc system, by then established as a classic.Most major diagnostic features were in the wrong place, profoundly modified, atypical or altogether absent.

These apparent irreconcilables have been reduced by the great increase in geological and, especially, geochemical and geophysical data gained over the last ten years, and also by the realization that most arcs, or arcs systems (arcs-upon-arcs) are quite individual—thus illustrating the danger of premature adoption of 'classic' models. The notion that young arcs may turn on themselves, so reversing their 'polarity' also helps towards reconciliation. If true, it suggests skittish behaviour by the deep-driving engine: another problem! Nevertheless, I still give the South-west Pacific a particular character, more so than does any article in this book (*pace* Karig) because of the geographical asymmetry and youthful history of its border and the presence in it of such oddities as the Fiji spiral. The geographical distribution of the outer arcs, forming as they do a great angle jutting into the Pacific (what I have termed previously the Melanesian Re-entrant) is more than a superficial pattern; it reflects a difference in behaviour and development of northern and southern Pacific. This can be spoken of either in terms of plate theory or Carey's Tethyan Torsion Zone.

The outer arcs are part of a penumbral border complex (with its Australian hinterland) to the South-west Pacific. This complex is essentially a Tertiary creation and came to occupy its present position well after the Early Cretaceous. Most of the northern Pacific western boundary, with its Asian hinterland, is very much older, going back to at least Triassic times. This disparity between north and south has to do with the Tethys, shadowy concept though that may be. I propose that during the Mesozoic, the Pacific (? proto-Pacific) had a definite north-western and western border. To the south-west it had none but merged with a Tethys which was on the way to dismemberment. Over this merging area, Indonesia/Philippines was the south-east Asian off-shore arc system (excluding Timor which was part of the north-moving Australian complex). The 'Australasian' shift was occlusive, and by the middle of the Tertiary would make an entity of the Indian Ocean (India had by now collided with Asia). Incidentally, although digressive, it can be said that questions on land-animal biodistribution with respect to Asia, the Indonesian 'land-bridge' and Australasia have little point or validity if extended before the Early Tertiary, possibly late Oliogocene. Under sea-floor spreading theory, similar limitations on biodistributional conjectures would extend, of course, to the other continents now separated by ocean basins.

The suggestion of a relatively old north-western and western border for the Pacific but a lack of such to the south-west, at least prior to the Tertiary, is not contradicted by the data presented in pertinent articles in this book.

The second part, which is concerned with the North-west Pacific, contains a small paradox. By and large, such areas as Kamchatka and the Japan Archipelago have been studied in great detail by generations of geologists. But no synthesis had emerged—even along the lines of the early simplistic Indonesian or Sunda type. The combination of an embarrassment of data extending over a considerable part of the geological column and a large number of workers inhibits easy synthesis. It was hoped, in the original programme of proceedings, that this session would give contributors a chance to review their data, old and new, within the light (or rather, the glare) of plate tectonics and sea-floor spreading. In this way we would be spared the presentation of 1950s island arc mutton dressed as 1971 lamb. It was expected that this area would be a scene of confrontation between 'fixist' and 'mobilist' view-points, and so it proved. The reader must judge the relative virtues of both. This is not an easy task, for what appears to be an essentially simple distinction is complicated by thought-processes which are a heritage of older notions. The geosyncline is pre-eminent in this category.

The articles derived from this session in the proceedings reveal the complexities of the north-western systems. One is impressed by the general untidiness of these systems: the notion of a forward-progressing development of arcs, both through time and in space, is severely shaken. It seems clear that arcs may die, e.g. by accretion to a continental mass, then be split off (those marginal seas!) and revivified as part of a newly-developing system—producing arcs-upon-arcs. For the Mesozoic and Cenozoic this process of identity and separation, dormancy and revival, takes on a cyclic character. The difficulty of reconciling this sort of picture, over-simplified though it is, with both geosynclinal concepts and also current versions of plate movements is made manifest by several contributors.

Finally, the articles dealing with the North-west Pacific and Indonesia illustrate the futility of aiming at a single standard island arc model, complete with all ramifications from inception to maturity.

The third part contains papers on such universals as trenches and oceanic crustal layering. It concludes a refreshing geometric approach to the New Zealand region. The final article emphasizes the essential similarities in the younger arcs, with special regard to their spatial configuration and the likely deep processes which produced them.

PART I

Major Features of the New Guinea-Louisiade-New Caledonia-Norfolk Arc System

JACQUES AVIAS

Institut de Géologie, Université de Montpellier, Place Eugène Bataillon, 34 Montpellier, France

ABSTRACT

A tentative synthesis of the structural and geological history of the New Guinea-Louisiades-New-Caledonia-Norfolk system (Inner Melanesian Arc) may be summarized as follows:

The arc system began in the Permian (with dacitic volcanism) as a marginal subsiding zone bordering a sialic emerged stable block of Hercynian age, with further development of a trough, with andesitic volcanism, during the Triassic and beginning of Jurassic times.

A diastrophic phase occurred in the Late Jurassic (equivalent to Rangitatan orogenic phase of New Zealand and Nevadan phase of America) with mainly low-grade metamorphism (greenschist facies).

Stress-release and down-faulting followed, with a Cretaceous transgression (a new subsidence phase with thick sedimentary deposition in angular unconformity on the previous sediments).

A Late Cretaceous-Palaeogene development of a major reverse fault zone (Owen Stanley Fault of New Guinea, Gonord's Accident ouest Calédonien in New Caledonia) gave rise to geanticlinal blocks, bringing to the surface oceanic lavas and sediments—the arching resulted in gravitational sliding, brecciation and some local folding and faulting.

A paroxysmic phase during Oligocene and Lower Miocene times led to the upthrusting westward of the basal layer of adjacent oceanic crust. The upthrusted mass overrode the sialic margin, giving rise to an overthrust slab of ultramafics lubricated by serpentinites and somewhat metamorphosed volcanic-sedimentary formations. Under the overthrust, there was generation of low-grade, greenschist facies metamorphism, with high-pressure minerals (glaucophane-lawsonite). A thermal diapir rose along the shear-heat zone of the Benioff plane, giving birth to a granodioritic magma which injected the whole of the previous sequence and completed the uplift of the whole arc: the uprising generated tensional forces in the adjacent Coral Sea and New Caledonian Basins, with consequent down-faulting.

The end of the uprising phase was followed by stress release, normal faulting producing graben structures (in which a Miocene transgression deposited calcarenites), the stabilization of the whole zone and the death of the arc.

Subsequently, at different times, there have been differential interaction and accommodation movements of the Australian and Pacific plates. In the inner arc, these have resulted in transcurrent faulting and arc-fragmentation with the formation of three main segments: the Norfolk, New Caledonian and New Guinea-Louisiades segments.

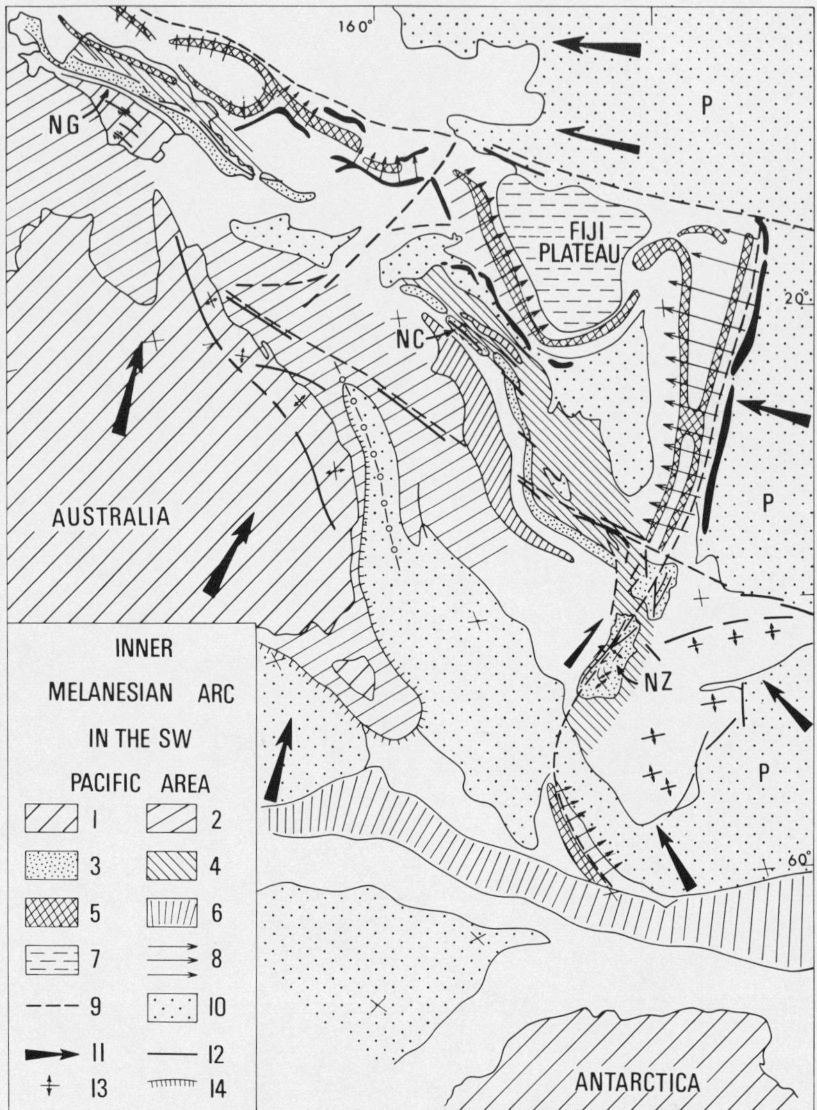

Fig. 1 Island arc systems and related features of the South-west Pacific. NG, New Guinea; NC, New Caledonia; NZ, New Zealand. 1, Australian plate, a.s.l. (Antarctica is similarly hachured); 2, Australian plate, b.s.l.; 3, main chains of the Inner Melanesian Arc; 4, related areas of the Inner Melanesian Arc; 5, Outer Melanesian Arc and related areas; 6, Indian/Antarctic-Pacific/Antarctic Ridge; 7, sialic Fijian mass, both emergent and submerged parts; 8, subduction directions along Benioff planes; 9, megashears or tectonic fault systems; 10, seas, basins and Pacific plate (with P); 11, sea-floor spreading and drift directions; 12, fault zone; 13, anticlinal axis; 14, basinal scarped edge. Trenches in black.

INTRODUCTION

Major recent geophysical and geological data over the last few years, together with previous knowledge of the Norfolk-New Caledonia-New Guinea arc, make possible the generalized, if somewhat tentative, evolutionary account given here.

The Norfolk-New Caledonia-New Guinea morphologic arc (Fig. 1) corresponds to Glaessner's (1950) Inner Melanesian Zone, lying between the New Caledonian and Coral Sea Basins to the west (Fig. 2) and the currently active Bismarck-Solomon-New Hebrides arc to the east (Outer Melanesian Zone). It is essentially a *dead* arc of Alpine age. It includes a northern part, New Guinea and the Louisiade Archipelago, and a southern part, New Caledonia and, for continuity reasons, the submerged Norfolk Ridge, which also constitutes the probable link with the New Zealand Alpine arc.

Born as a marginal trough, after the eastern Australian Hercynian orogenic phase, the following forces are considered to have played an essential part in the development of the system:

(*a*) *differential gravity* forces arising from erosion-sedimentation mass transfers at the end of Palaeozoic, Mesozoic and early Cenozoic times. These occasioned crustal extension, subsidence movements, normal faulting and isostatic readjustments; (*b*) extension-and-compression *tangential* forces linked with the drift of plates or 'polygons' (especially of the Australian and Pacific plates), in turn a part of sea-floor spreading and earth-expansion phenomena resulting perhaps from primary or induced convective currents in the asthenosphere. Consequent interaction at plate edges results in downthrusting of the oceanic plate under the sialic plate margin; (*c*) thermally-generated *expansion* forces linked to *thermal diapirs,* which have their origin mainly as a consequence of *shear heat* in or around Benioff planes, or to internal thermal flow rising up from the interior of the earth at the lithospheric fracture zones of the Pacific or other mid-oceanic ridges. These thermal expansion forces, through phase changes or recrystallization phenomena, result in upward vertical pressures and also tangential expansion phenomena.

The interaction of adjoining plates and differential translation or rotation forces are emphasized and explain transcurrent faulting and rotational movements.

GEOLOGICAL DEVELOPMENT

The structural and geological history of the arc may be tentatively summarized in a succession of major events now described:

1. Due to increasing movement westward of the Pacific plate (or decreasing rift velocity of the Australian plate westward) or to subsidence induced by erosion-sedimentation mass transfer during Permian time, there began a low subsidence along the margin of a palaeo-Australia (an emergent 'Tasmantis' continental mass of pre-Permian folded and metamorphosed formations). This subsidence was accompanied by normal faulting and subaerial dacitic volcanism.

2. Intensification of the preceding processes and increased subsidence to geosyncline proportions during Triassic and Lower Jurassic times, resulted in a mainly

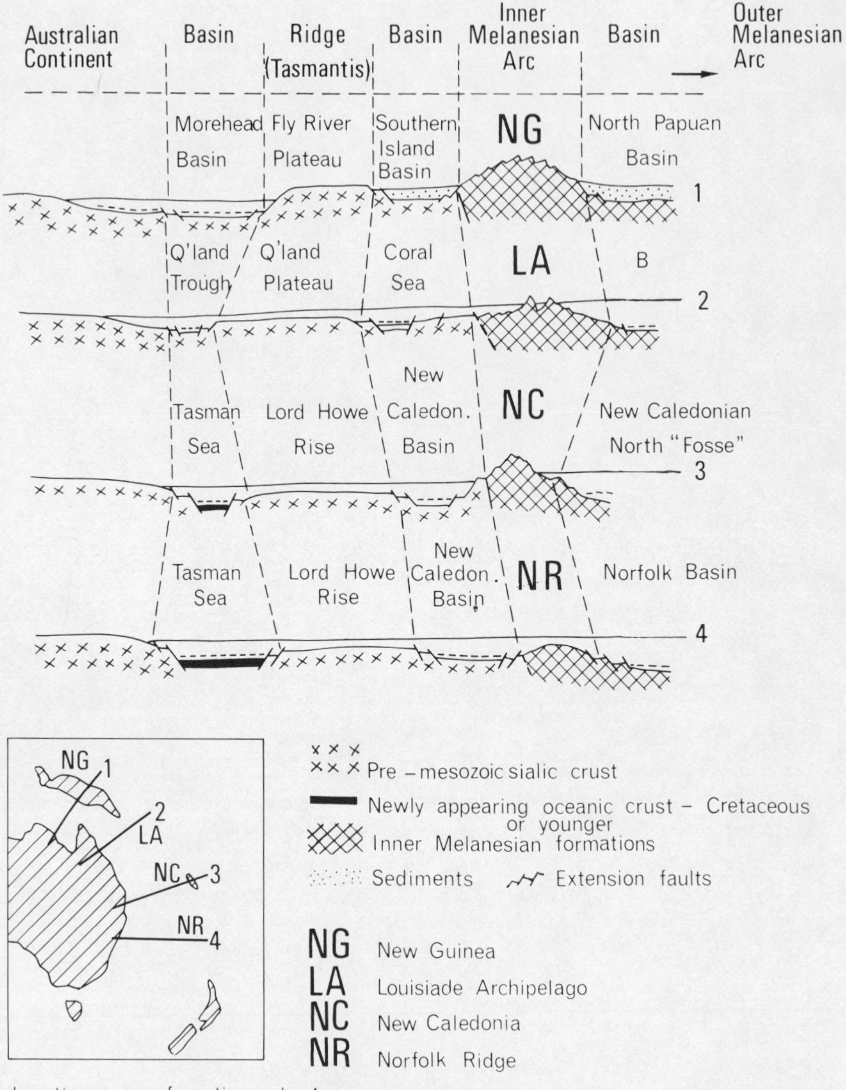

Fig. 2 Four schematic sections which show the comparable relations of different parts of the Inner Melanesian Arc with the Australian continent. Extension structures of the sialic crust are suggested.

detrital sequence (sandstones, conglomerates and greywackes) with abundant turbidity-current and slumping phenomena in the troughs. These may be explained by episodic periods of intense seismic palaeo-activity, linked probably with andesitic (succeeding the dacitic) volcanism of a palaeo-Mesozoic 'Andesite Line' bordering the continental basement.

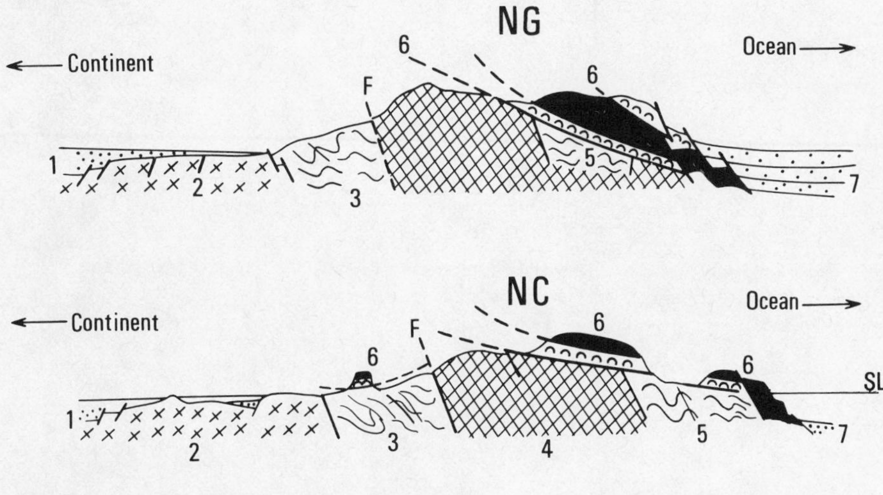

Fig. 3 Comparative schematic sections of eastern New Guinea and New Caledonia (post-Eocene volcanics—present in New Guinea but absent in New Caledonia—are not taken into account).

Unit	*New Guinea*	*New Caledonia*
1 Internal marginal basin	—	—
2 Pre-Mesozoic basement	Fly River Plateau zone	Hugon-Ducas Island zone
3 Internal Folded miogeo-synclinal formations	Southern Highlands and Aure Trough	'Sillon ouest Calédonien'
4 Uplifted metamorphic blocks	Central Highlands	Chaine Centrale
5 External eugeosynclinal folded formations	—	—
6 Ultramafic and associated rocks—overthrust	—	—
7 External marginal basin	—	—

By the end of this stage, several kilometres of sedimentary rocks had accumulated. Subsequent sedimentologic and petrographic evolution testifies to the advanced erosion of a nearby landmass with volcanoes and of the absence of reef-forming organisms suggesting relatively cold sea-water. Then occurred a diastrophism (roughly equivalent to the Rangitatan orogeny of New Zealand, or Nevadan orogenic phase of North America) with uplifting, folding, volcanism and metamorphism (low-grade, generally greenschist to amphibolite facies) of the sedimentary formations of the axial part of the geosynclinal trough. The geological story of the south part of the arc during Permian, Triassic and Jurassic times, was closely similar to that of the New Zealand Alpine Arc, the geological story of the north part of the arc showing some slight differences, in particular a large predominance of sandstones without andesitic debris in greywackes. The folded and metamorphosed rocks resulting from this orogenic phase are found now (Gonord 1970) in the same central position: Central Highlands in New Guinea, Chaine Centrale in New Caledonia.

3. After an emergent phase in the west part of the arc (covering the end of Jurassic and part of Early Cretaceous time) with, in some places, release of stress and down faulting (e.g. in south-western Papua) there was a Cretaceous transgression and the beginning of a new subsidence phase with deposition of mudstones, sandstones, conglomerates, often associated with carbonaceous material. These rested in angular uncomformity on both unmetamorphosed and metamorphosed pre-Cretaceous sedimentary rocks. The transgression was of Upper Cretaceous age (Senonian) in major parts of New Caledonia. This Cretaceous transgression was followed in Eocene times either by marine regression or by locally progressive sedimentation and transgression in subsiding areas with thick Eocene cherts or flysch sequences (Fig. 2).

4. At the end of Cretaceous or in early Paleocene times it is suggested that a major structural feature appeared, namely, a westward major reverse fault zone (a west Owen Stanley Range fault—F1 of Fig. 3) in New Guinea, and in New Caledonia a proven longitudinal fault zone (Gonord's 'Accident ouest Calédonien') of the same significance. These produced uplifted blocks including Mesozoic and pre-Mesozoic metamorphosed substratum rocks (mainly of greenschists facies). Probably linked to these fracturing phenomena, submarine tholeiitic basalt flows and tuffs (with pillow-lavas) were extruded along the whole arc.

At about the same time, due to relative change in latitude by polar or land shift[1] the sea-water became warm enough for reef limestone and foraminiferal development. Along the marginal basement, Eocene algal, foraminiferal and coral limestone lenses (particularly frequent at the transgressive base of chert sequences) grew, and in trough areas, especially in New Guinea, may be found sequences of reddish argillaceous limestones.

5. Later (in the Middle or Upper Eocene), a degree of arching of the ocean floor along the line of the arc initiated more or less intense gravitational sliding and brecciation and, finally, erosion and folding of the sedimentary formations (as shown by detailed studies of Gonord in New Caledonia). Then in the Oligocene occurred an orogenic alpine paroxysmal phase (there is no record of Lower and Middle Oligocene rocks along the whole arc), resulting in further intense imbrication and even overthrusting westwards of previous formations. At the same time, folded rocks of the central zone were metamorphosed or subjected again to metamorphism (alpine phase of metamorphism). The metamorphic grade is generally greenschist facies, but higher in the northern part of New Caledonia and in the d'Entrecasteaux Islands.

This paroxysmal phase was penecontemporaneous with, and linked with, ultrabasic

[1] 'Magnetic lineations south of Australia indicate that the Australian plate has been moving north, away from Antarctica since the early Eocene, 55 m.y. ago (Ringis 1970)' (from Davies & Smith 1970).

overthrust belt emplacement; the 'Papuan ultramafic belt' in New Guinea[2], and the 'Grand Massif Minier du Sud' and 'Massifs Ultrabasiques de la Côte Ouest' in New Caledonia. This emplacement must be considered, in the author's view, to be the last tectonic episode of the Alpine orogeny. For New Guinea the ultramafic belt is thought to be overlying basalts, a slab of oceanic mantle and crust which moved westward and was forced upwards by collision with the sialic core of Papua-New Guinea (Thompson 1967, Davies 1968). In the author's view (Avias 1971), the ultrabasic overthrust may also be the consequence of the separation of the base of the third layer of oceanic crust[3] from the lithosphere at the Mohorovicic discontinuity. This would occur when the down-arching lithosphere collided with the sialic Australian plate margin. The first result was the upthrusting westward of this third layer and part of the second layer (volcanic-sedimentary formations more or less metamorphosed) which have overturned relations in New Caledonia (Fig. 4). At least partially, along the whole arc, remnants of layer two (e.g. pillow lavas) lie beneath instead of above the ultrabasic masses. The second result was folding or refolding of Mesozoic and younger sediments of the geosynclinal trough, which accompanied the overriding by the ultrabasic masses (lubricated by serpentinites and the volcanic-sedimentary formations mentioned).

From the structural point of view, these ultrabasic masses are folded (as shown by studies of petrographic layering in Orloff 1968, Fromager 1968, Guillon 1969) and imbricated, and their base is serpentinized and brecciated. In New Caledonia it is possible that the old Accident ouest Calédonien faulted zone was revived for the emplacement of some of the west coast ultrabasic masses. It is more likely that the primary thrust plane at the base of the eastern ultrabasics carried westwards the present west-coast masses, but to levels now lower than the Accident ouest Calédonien.

Under the overthrust mass, stresses and heat gave rise to a low-grade greenschist metamorphism sometimes rising to albite-epidote-amphibolite facies (or even pyroxene-granulite facies) with the appearance of high-pressure minerals (glaucophane, lawsonite and so on).

Just after the end of this movement, the downthrusting under the sialic crust of lithosphere into the asthenosphere gave birth to shear-induced heat and crystal structural changes. Then arose a 'thermal diapir' with granitization or granodioritic formation in the lower parts of the orogenic uplifted masses and, in some cases, injection of even the upper parts of the ultrabasic thrust sheets. The consequent volume increase resulted in uplift and final stabilization of the arc in Upper Oligocene or Lower Miocene times (Tertiary upper *e*).

6. After this paroxysmal tectonic phase and after the metamorphism and diapiric magmatic consequences, there emerged large subaerial blocks along the whole arc

[2] The age of which could be possibly younger (Upper Cretaceous or Lower Eocene) in New Guinea (Davies & Smith 1970).

[3] In the opinion of the author, these must be basaltic volcanic-sedimentary formations metasomatosed under sea-water by heat and pressure. The result of these metasomatic processes was the development of doleritic spillites, greenschists, serpentinites, amphibolites and finally peridotites, afterwards serpentinized (in the classic meaning) by retromorphosis, when eventually brought close to the surface where reduced temperatures and pressures prevail.

ready to feed subsequent Miocene sedimentation. At the same time, normal faulting occurred, probably linked to release of stress following extension or diapir uplift (Karig 1971) or mass transfer collapse. These faulting processes gave birth to graben structures all along the arc (e.g. Aure Trough in New Guinea, where more than 11,000 m of Miocene and Pliocene sediments accumulated, and the graben of the New Caledonian east and west coasts). In these graben areas limestones and clastic

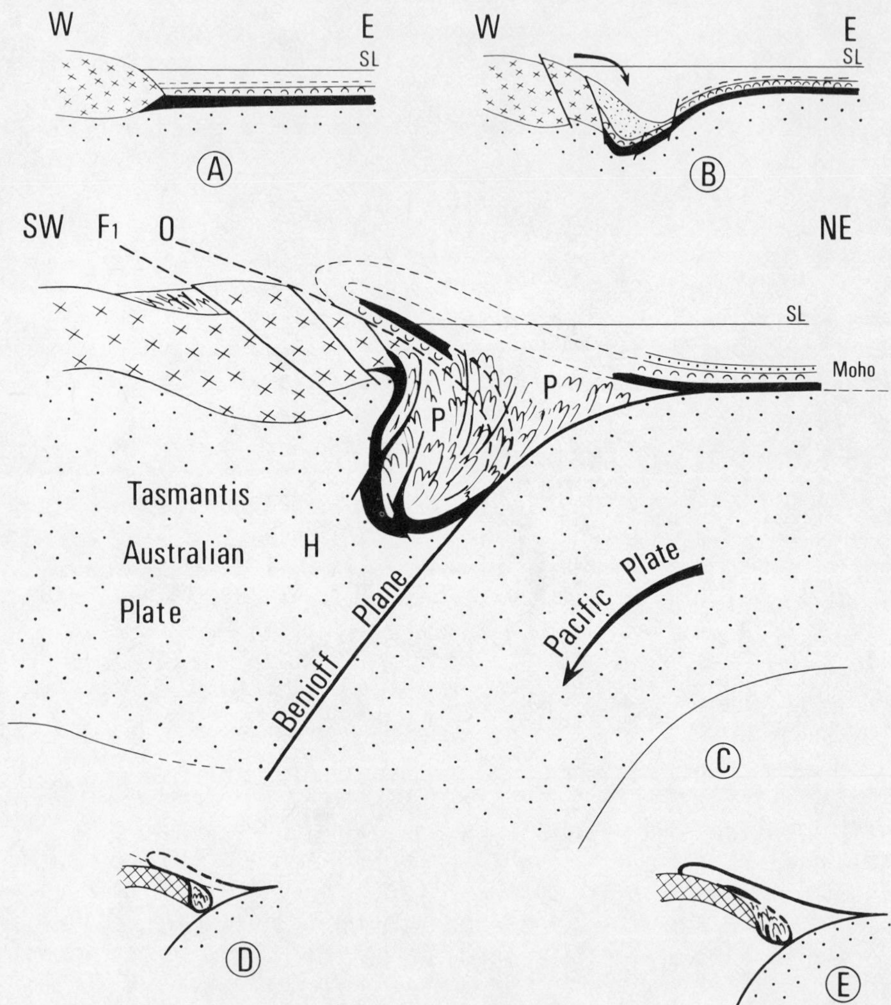

Fig. 4 Proposed formation of the Inner Melanesian Arc: A, Early Permian; B, Triassic/Jurassic; C, D and E, Palaeogene. Symbols: F1—major tectonic fault zone; O, paroxysmal terminal overthrust; H, zones of high heat development, inducing metamorphism, magmatism and volcanism; P, zones of high pressure marked by development of high-pressure minerals. Oceanic crust is layered black with oceanic basalts (∩∩∩) overlying.

sediments were deposited, interlayered in the northern part of the arc, with volcanic lavas and tuffs. Simultaneously, differential adjustments, linked to plate movements between the Australian plate, Pacific plate and possibly smaller intermediary plates (e.g. North Fijian plate) induced strike-slip faults, with dextral or sinistral shearing, resulting in elongation and fragmentation of the arc (Fig. 1). Complex breaks of the arc, with trend changes as between the Louisiade Archipelago and New Caledonia Ridge, and between the Norfolk Ridge and New Zealand Ridge, were probably initiated or emphasized at the same time.

7. In the Upper Miocene and Pliocene further block movements occurred along the whole arc, giving rise to graben and horst structures with consequent drowned or raised terraces. The northern part of the arc (especially New Guinea) was incorporated in a new arc (Outer Melanesian Arc) with block uplifting, tight folding (e.g. of the Aure Trough sediments), and andesitic or acid volcanism; this took place because of the position of this northern part close to the Australian sialic mass, in the vicinity of a triple-plate junction point; perhaps also it had some relation with the rift opening and sea-floor spreading of the axial zone of the Coral Sea (Davies & Smith 1970).

8. During Quaternary and Recent times, in the southern part of the arc, no important tectonic movement has occurred, except relatively slight normal faulting, rifting and block neotectonics linked in part to erosion-sedimentation mass transfers. The Inner Melanesian Arc was consolidated and stabilized: in other words, it was a *dead arc*, and *accreted* to the old Tasmantian and Australian sialic land masses. This does not take into account crust-distension features of the Tasman Sea and New Caledonian Basin. A new orogenic cycle began farther east: new troughs and new arcs, representing processes still proceeding, were born as an 'outer Melanesian zone' (e.g. the New Hebrides area).

For the northern part of the arc, the same new orogenic cycle was proceeding farther north and north-east, giving rise to the Bismarck Archipelago, the Solomons Arc and other outer Melanesian arcs. In Upper Miocene and Pliocene times, however, there existed a strong tendency for the new arc to incorporate not only the northern or north-eastern margin, but the whole of the older Inner Melanesian Arc. This latter, in consequence, was (and is) presently undergoing new fracturing, volcanism and uplifting processes. In Fig. 3 are given comparative schematic present-day sections of New Guinea and New Caledonia, not taking into account—in the case of New Guinea—fracturing and volcanism linked to the growth of the younger Outer Melanesian Arc.

Over recent times the last main event to be noted is the general Flandrian glacio-eustatic transgression, involving the drowning of low coasts, barrier coral reef growth, the features of which testify very accurately to recent neotectonic phenomena (Avias 1969, Coudray 1969) and the delineation of structural trends of the presently emergent parts of the arc.

POSTSCRIPT

As a result of discussion after presentation of this paper, and as a result of other communications and discussions, the following items may be mentioned:

1. The similarity of lithologic facies in the Permian of Australia, New Guinea and New Caledonia has been pointed out by several listeners to this communication.

2. The age of the ultrabasic overthrust in New Caledonia and New Guinea, which until today was given as Oligocene by practically all authors, is now brought into question. Absolute dating of Eocene age for granitic or tonalite intrusives has been demonstrated by J. Guillon in the Massif Minier du Sud (New Caledonia) and by A. W. Webb and R. W. Page in New Guinea. If this absolute dating of the overthrust is correct, and we are really dealing with intrusives and not inclusions, this must lead us to a reconsideration of the age. It is curious, however, that Professor R. N. Brothers announces that he has found an Oligocene age for high pressure metamorphic glaucophanitic schists associated with serpentine intrusions in the northern part of New Caledonia (based on absolute dating of phengite). This has led him to conclude that the northern and north-western ultrabasic masses must be of Oligocene age. For continuity reasons, it would be very odd, in my opinion, if two different ages of overthrust ultrabasic masses occur in New Caledonia.

3. J. Dubois and J. Guillon raised the question of a possible sliding down of the continental crust of New Caledonia *under* the oceanic crust to the east. In my opinion, from geologic and sedimentologic evidence, it seems rather that it was the oceanic crust which overrode the continental material to the west. If so, the lithosphere (at least during Mesozoic time) moved westward or south-westward beneath the sial in consequence of westward pressure by the Pacific plate—JOIDES results show that the Pacific plate has probably moved westward at least from the beginning of the Jurassic, whereas the Australian plate has been moving north away from Antarctica only since the Eocene (Ringis *in* Davis & Smith 1970). The above consideration leads me to conclude that during the New Caledonian orogeny, the Benioff plane was dipping toward the continent (that is, toward Australia).

4. Gonord demonstrated that in New Caledonia the Accident ouest Calédonien (the major fault zone) began in Mesozoic time. It seems to me that a similar major fault zone should exist, of approximately the same age, on the south-west side of the Owen Stanley Range. Its age would be different from the Eocene Owen Stanley fault to the north-east.

5. The complex break between the Louisiade Archipelago and New Caledonian Ridge is a problem. E. Winterer (Scripps Institution) indicates that the bathymetry and structures of this zone are not actually well known. Cullen, however, in his tectonic map of the South-west Pacific (1970) has traced three postulated transverse rift fractures between the two archipelagos and some of the well-known bathymetric trends, especially of the west limit of the Coral Sea, fit well with this assumption. This fits also with the breaks demonstrated for the New Hebrides by D. I. J. Mallick in his paper (this volume).

6. Concerning the age of the Norfolk Ridge, I. M. McDougall's recent work has shown that the basaltic plateau of Norfolk was 2·5 million years old. Limestone clasts in tuffs associated with the basalts are of Lower Miocene age (Coleman & Veevers 1971).

SELECT BIBLIOGRAPHY, INCLUDING REFERENCES CITED

Australasian Petroleum Company, 1961. Geological results of petroleum exploration in Western Papua, 1937-61. *J. geol. Soc. Aust.* **8** (1), 133 pp.

Avias, J. 1953. Contribution à l'étude stratigraphique et paléontologique des formations antécrétacées de la Nouvelle-Calédonie centrale. *Sci. de la Terre.* **1** & **2,** 1-276, Nancy.

Avias, J. 1959. Les récifs coralliens de la Nouvelle-Calédonie et quelques-uns de leurs problèmes. *Bull. Soc. géol. Fr., 7th series*, **1,** 424-30.

——— 1961. On some new points of view adopted concerning the stratigraphic and correlative knowledge of the sedimentary structures of New Caledonia. *Proc. Ninth Pacif. Sci. Congr.* (*1962*). **12,** 325-7.

——— 1967. Overthrust structure of the main ultrabasic New Caledonian massifs. *Tectonophysics*, **4** (4-6), 531-41.

——— 1969. Coral reefs and New Caledonia neotectonic history. *VIIème Congrès INQUA, Paris 1969—Résumés des Communications*, p. 61.

——— 1971. Sur la signification et sur la gènese des grandes ceintures de roches ultrabasiques et roches de leur cortège dans les chaines orogéniques eugéosynclinales. *C.R. Acad. Sci. Paris*, **273,** 667-70.

Avias, J. & Routhier, P. 1962. Carte géologique au 1/100.000eme de la Nouvelle-Calédonie (avec notice explicative). Feuille No. 5: Ponérihouen-Poya, *ORSTOM*, Paris.

Baltzer, F. 1970. Datation absolue de la transgression holocène sur la côte ouest de la Nouvelle-Calédonie sur des échantillons de tourbes à palétuviers. Interprétation néotectonique. *C.R. Acad. Sci. Paris*, **271,** 2251-4.

Baltzer, F., Guillon, J. H., Launay, J. C. & Trescases, J. J. 1967 Geological and geophysical publications on New Caledonia. *N.Z. Jl Geol. Geophys.* **10,** 1275-9.

Benson, W. N. 1924. The structural features of the margin of Australasia. *Trans. N.Z. Inst.* **55,** 99-137.

Brothers, R. N. 1970. Lawsonite-albite schists from northernmost New Caledonia. *Contr. Mineral. Petrol.* **25,** 185-202.

Carey, S. W. 1958. The tectonic approach to continental drift. *Continental Drift—A Symposium.* Univ. Tasmania, Hobart.

——— 1970. Australia, New Guinea and Melanesia in the current revolution in concepts of the evolution of the earth. *Search*, **1** (5), 178-88.

Coleman, P. J. 1967. A possible resolution of the Melanesian Re-entrant. *Upper Mantle Project: 2nd Progress Rept* (*1965-1967*), 192-4 (Ed. A. E. Ringwood). Aust. Acad. Sci. Canberra.

——— 1970. Geology of the Solomon and New Hebrides Islands, as part of the Melanesian Re-entrant, South-west Pacific. *Pacif. Sci.* **24** (3), 289-314.

Coleman, P. J. & Veevers, J. J. 1971. Microfossils from Philip Island indicate a minimum Age of Lower Miocene for the Norfolk Ridge, South-west Pacific. *Search*, **2** (8), 289.

Coleman, R. G. 1967. Glaucophane schists from California and New Caledonia. *Tectonophysics*, **4** (4-6), 479-98.

Coudray, J. 1969. Observations nouvelles sur les formations miocènes et post-miocènes de la région de Nepoui (Nouvelle-Calédonie): précisions lithologiques et preuves d'une tectonique "recente" sur la côte Sud-Ouest de ce territoire. *C.R. Acad. Sci. Paris*, **269,** 1599-602.

——— 1971. Nouvelles données sur la nature et l'origine du complexe récifal côtier de la Nouvelle-Calédonie: études sédimentologiques et paléoécologiques préliminaires d'un forage réalisé dans le récif barrière de la côte sud-ouest. *Quatern. Res.* **1** (2), 236-46.

Coudray, J. & Gonord, H. 1966. Découverte d'une microfaune paléocène dans les formations volcano-sédimentaires de la Nouvelle-Calédonie. *C.R. Acad. Sci. Paris*, **263,** 716.

Cullen, D. J. 1967. The Antipodes fracture zone, a major structure of the south-west Pacific. *N.Z. J. Mar. Freshwater, Res.* **1,** 16-25.

——— 1970. Tectonic map of the south-west Pacific (1/10,000,000). *New Zealand Inst. Cart., Misc. series* **20.**

Davies, H. L. 1968. Papuan ultramafic belt. *23rd Intern. Geol. Congress, Prague*. **1,** 209-20.

Davies, H. L. & Smith, E. 1970. Geology of Eastern Papua. A Synthesis, Rec. Bur. Miner. Resour. Aust. 1970/116 (unpubl.).

Dickinson, W. R. 1962. Petrogenetic significance of geosynclinal andesitic volcanism along the Pacific margin of North America. *Bull. geol. Soc. Am.* **73,** 1241-56.

Dietz, R. S. 1963. Collapsing continental rise—an actualistic concept of geosynclines and mountain building. *J. Geol.* **71,** 314-44.

Dow, D. B. & Decker, F. E. 1964. The geology of the Bismarck Mountains, New Guinea. *Rept Bur. Miner. Resour. Aust.* **76.**

Dubois, J. 1969. Contribution a l'étude structurale du Sud-Ouest Pacifique d'après les ondes sismiques observées en Nouvelle-Calédonie et aux Nouvelles-Hébrides. *Annls Geophys.* **24** (4), 923-72.

Dubourdieu, G. 1968. Sur les forces géologiques en action autour du Pacifique. 62 pp., *Bibl. Collège de France*, Paris.

——— 1970. A propos du mécanisme terrestre. 70 pp., *Bibl. Lab. de Géol., Collège de France*, Paris.

Edwards, A. B. 1950. The petrology of the Miocene sediments of the Aure Trough, Papua. *Proc. R. Soc. Vict.* **60,** 123-48.

Edwards, A. B. & Glaessner, M. F. 1953. Mesozoic and Tertiary sediments from the Waghi Valley, New Guinea. *Proc. R. Soc. Vict.* **64** (2).

Espirat, J. J. 1963. Etude géologique de la région de la Nouvelle-Calédonie septentrionale (Thesis, Clermont University Library.)

Ewing, M., Hawkins, L. V. & Ludwig, W. J. 1970. Crustal structure of the Coral Sea. *J. geophys. Res.* **75,** 1953-62.

Ewing, J. I., Houtz, R. E. & Ludwig, W. J. 1970. Sediment distribution in the Coral Sea. *J. geophys. Res.* **75,** 1963-72.

Falvey, D. A. & Talwani, M. 1969. Gravity map and tectonic fabric of the Coral Sea (abstr.). *Geol. Soc. Am. 1969 Meeting, Abstracts* **7,** 62.

Fleming, C. A. 1967. Biogeographic change related to Mesozoic orogenic history in the S.W. Pacific. *Tectonophysics*, **4** (4-6), 419-27.

Fromager, D. 1968. Nouvelles données pétrographiques et structurales sur les massifs d'ultrabasites et leur contact avec les terrains sédimentaires entre la baie de Canala et la rivière Camboui (Nouvelle-Calédonie). *C.R. somm. Soc. Géol. Fr.* (1968), 83-4.

Gardner, J. V. 1970. Submarine geology of the western Coral Sea. *Bull. geol. Soc. Am.* **81,** 2599-614.

Glaessner, M. F. 1950. Geotectonic position of New Guinea. *Bull. Am. Ass. Petrol. Geol.* **34** (5), 856-81.

——— 1952. Geology of Port Moresby, Papua. pp. 63-86 in *The Sir Douglas Mawson Anniversary Volume*, Univ. Adelaide.

Glasser, E. 1904. Rapport à M. le Ministre des Colonies sur les richesses minérales de la Nouvelle-Calédonie. *Annls Mines Carbur., Paris*, **5,** 503-620, 623-93.

Gonord, H. 1967. Note sur quelques observations nouvelles précisant âge et mode de formation du flysch volcanique sur la côte sud-occidentale de la Nouvelle-Calédonie. *C.R. somm. Soc. Géol. Fr.* (1967), 287-9.

——— 1970. Découverte de formations sédimentaires d'âge éocène C (Eocène moyen à supérieur) dans la chaîne centrale de la Nouvelle-Calédonie. *C.R. Acad. Sci. Paris*, **271,** 1953-5.

Gonord, H. & Bard, J. P. 1971. Découverte d'associations antésénoniennes à lawsonite, pumpellyite et glaucophane dans les 'masses cristallophyliennes' paléozoiques du centre de la Nouvelle-Calédonie. *C.R. Acad. Sci. Paris*, **273,** 280-3 (19 juillet 1971).

Green, D. H. 1961. Ultramafic breccias from the Musa Valley, eastern Papua. *Geol. Mag.* **98** (1), 1-26.

Guillon, J. H. 1969. Données nouvelles sur la composition et la structure du grand massif péridotitique du Sud de la Nouvelle-Calédonie. *Cah. Géol. ORSTOM*, **1** (1), 7-25, Paris.

Harrison, J. 1969. Review of the sedimentary history of the island of New Guinea. *J. Aust. Petrol. Expl. Ass.* **9** (2), 41-8.

Hess, H. H. & Maxwell, J. C. 1953. Major structural features of the S.W. Pacific: a Preliminary interpretation of H.O. 5484 bathymetry chart, New Guinea to New Zealand. *Proc. Pacif. Sci. Congr., Wellington*, **2**, 14-17.

John, V. P. St. 1970. The gravity field and structure of Papua and New Guinea. *J. Aust. Petrol. Expl. Ass.* **10,** 41-54.

Karig, D. E. 1971. Origin and development of marginal basins in the Western Pacific. *J. geophys. Res.* **76** (8).

Krause, D. C. 1967. Bathymetry and geologic structure of the north-western Tasman Sea: Coral Sea-South Solomon Sea area of the south-western Pacific Ocean. *Bull. N.Z. Dep. Scient. ind. Res.*, **183** (*Mem. N.Z. oceanogr. Inst.* **41**), 48 pp.

Lacroix, A. 1942. Les peridotides de la Nouvelle-Calédonie, leurs serpentines et leurs gites de nickel et de cobalt. Les gabbros qui les accompagnent. *Mém. Acad. Sci.* (2nd sér.) **66,** 1-14.

Lillie, A. R. & Brothers, R. N. 1970. The geology of New Caledonia. *N.Z. Jl Geol. Geophys.* **13** (1), 145-83.

Linden, W. J. van der 1967. Structural relationships in the Tasman Sea and South-west Pacific Ocean. *N.Z. Jl Geol. Geophys.* **10** (5), 1280-301.

Manser, W. & Freeman, C. (In press). Bibliography of the geology of eastern New Guinea (Papua New Guinea). *Rep. Bur. Miner. Resour. Aust.* **141.**

Matsumoto, T. 1967. Fundamental problems in the circum-Pacific Orogenesis. *Tectonophysics*, **4** (4-6), 595-613.

McMillan, N. J. & Malone, E. J. 1960. The geology of the eastern Central Highlands of New Guinea. *Rep. Bur. Miner. Resour. Aust.* **48.**

Menard, H. W. 1964. *Marine geology of the Pacific*. McGraw Hill, New York. 271 pp.

Orloff, O. 1968. Etude géologique et geomorphologique des massifs d'ultrabasites compris entre Houailou et Canala. (Thesis, University of Montpellier Library.)

Piroutet, M. 1917. Etude stratigraphique de la Nouvelle Calédonie. Thesis, Protat Fréres, Mâcon, 313 pp.

Rickwood, F. K. 1955. The geology of the Western Highlands of New Guinea. *J. geol. Soc. Aust.* **2,** 63-82.

——— 1968. The geology of Western Papua. *J. Aust. Petrol. Expl. Ass.* **8** (2), 51-61.

Ringis, J. 1970. Magnetic lineations in the Tasman Sea (abstr.). *Intern. Conf. Geophysics of the Earth and the Oceans*, Univ. N.S.W., Sydney.

Roever, W. P. de. 1957. Sind die alpinotypen Peridotitmassen viellicht tektonisch verfrachtete Bruchstücke der Peridotitschale? *Geol. Rundsch.* **46,** 137-46.

Routhier. P. 1953. Etude géologique du versant occidental de la Nouvelle-Calédonie entre le Col de Boghen et la pointe d'Arama. *Mém. Soc. geol. Fr.* **67,** 1-271.

Skwarko, S. K. 1967. Mesozoic mollusca from Australia and New Guinea. *Bull. Bur. Miner. Resour. Aust.* **75.**

Smit, J. A. J. 1964. A review of the relationship between Cretaceous rock and the Kaindi Metamorphics at Snake River, New Guinea. Mines Dept, Territory of Papua & New Guinea, Geol. Invest. Note 64304 (unpubl.).

Smith, E. M. 1966. *Lexique stratigraphique International: Nouvelle Guinée.* **6**: *Océanie, fasc. 3a.* 136 pp. C.N.R.S., Paris.

Smith, J. W. & Green, D. H. 1961. The geology of the Musa River Area, Papua. *Rep. Bur. Miner. Resour. Aust.* **52.**

Thompson, J. E. 1957. The Papuan ultrabasic belt. *Rec. Bur. Miner. Resour. Aust.* 1957/77 (unpubl.).

——— 1967. A geological history of eastern New Guinea. *J. Aust. Petrol. Explor.* **1** (2), 83-93.

Thompson, J. E. & Fisher, N. H. 1965. Mineral Deposits of New Guinea and Papua and their tectonic setting. *Proc. 8th Common. Min. Metall. Congr., Aust.-N.Z.* **6,** 115-48.

Tissot, B. & Noesmoen, A. 1958. Les bassins de Nouméa et de Bourail (Nouvelle-Calédonie). *Revue Inst. Fr. Pétrole*, **13** (5), 739-60.

Wright, J. B. 1966. Convection and continental drift in the south-west Pacific. *Tectonophysics*, **3** (2), 69-81.

The Tectonic Evolution of the Fiji Region[1]

DEREK GREEN AND DAVID J. CULLEN
Fiji Geological Survey, Private Mail Bag, G.P.O., Suva, Fiji, and N.Z. Oceanographic Institute, Box 8005, G.P.O., Wellington, N.Z.

ABSTRACT

Fiji evolved during Tertiary and Quaternary times essentially as a complex volcanic pile built upon a segment of presumed 'quasi-continental' crust. The younger (Pleistocene to Recent) volcanic sequences (beginning with submarine pillow lavas and hyaloclastites, and passing up into subaerial flows) represent the products of numerous volcanic centres distributed along NE-SW and NW-SE structural lines. The extensive development of re-worked and epiclastic deposits has considerably obscured the distribution of the older volcanic centres, developed from the Eocene onwards, but such trends as can be discerned suggest a distribution similar to that of the younger centres and similarly structurally-controlled. The volcanic activity may have begun in relatively deep water, but led to the production of subaerial lava flows, associated with abundant re-worked and epiclastic deposits (unsorted lahar-like and other breccias). This assemblage evidently originated at or near sea-level. The depth of water in which were laid down the marly facies developed distally around volcanic centres, is most commonly estimated at about 50 m. The regional conditions of deposition are thus inferred to have been shallow-water to subaerial. Since up to 10,000 m of strata accumulated under these conditions, deposition must be considered to have been accompanied by subsidence, in a geosynclinal environment. Structural trends revealed by geological mapping in Viti Levu and Vanua Levu, and shown also by the orientation and distribution of the outer islands of Fiji, are thought to be resurgent expressions of the inferred original trends, in the way that would be expected if there had been continuing development of a regional shear pattern during anti-clockwise rotation of the Fiji region. The observed flexure of the 'Wainimala geosyncline' and its associated train of synorogenic intrusions from a presumed linearity to a broad curve striking NW-SE in south-western Viti Levu and ENE-WSW further east is in accord with this hypothesis. Progressive potash-enrichment of the rocks of Viti Levu has been held to imply proximity to an active oceanic trench until 5 m.y. ago; subsequent drifting or rotation then placed Fiji in its present position. However, it is here suggested that an ENE-WSW pattern of post-rotational fractures can be recognized from a study of the submarine morphology of the Fiji Plateau and of the distribution of shallow-focus earthquakes in this area. Hence it is proposed that rotational (as distinct from translatory) movement of Fiji is not continuing at the present day. The crustal movements facilitated by the development of the post-rotational fractures are thought to have led to the extension of the Lau Basin as an 'inter-arc' basin, by increased eastward migration of the Tonga Ridge away from the Lau Ridge, a process that is presumably continuing today.

[1] Published by permission of the Government of Fiji.

INTRODUCTION

This paper provides a review of the geological history of Fiji and a short account of local and regional structural features of both the land and sea floor in the Fiji area. It then goes on to suggest that there has been a considerable anti-clockwise rotation of Fiji. Malahoff's evidence (in prep.) for this concept is supported by the distribution of synorogenic intrusions in Viti Levu, and by interpretation of the fracture pattern in the immediate Fiji region as due to rotational stress. However, it is pointed out that certain ENE-WSW trends, deduced from a study of the bathymetry of the sea floor adjacent to Fiji and apparently related to a local distribution of shallow-focus earthquake epicentres, appear to be post-rotational fractures. From this, it is concluded that rotation ceased some time in the past. Attention is also drawn to the probability of recent opening of the Lau Basins, and the effect this may have had in terminating the development of a NE-SW transform along a line extending from the northern end of the Tonga Trench to the southern end of the New Hebrides Trench.

GEOLOGICAL HISTORY

The discernible geological history of Fiji is restricted to the Tertiary, apparently with the exclusion of the Paleocene and Lower Eocene, for no strata older than Upper Eocene have so far been discovered. The development of Fiji as a landmass appears to have begun with submarine volcanic eruptions along structurally-determined lines, and to have proceeded by the ejection, piling-up, slumping, re-working and lateral transport of fragmental and other volcanic products. Such a process of 'volcano-tectonic lithogenesis' has led to the observed distribution of facies-belts in which the strata become progressively finer-grained outward from volcanic centres. Such facies belts, in fact, largely constitute the lithostratigraphic units which have been geologically mapped (cf. Rickard 1966, Fig. 3; Band 1968, pp. 13-22). It is perhaps worth stressing that the very objectivity of the lithostratigraphic schemes adopted in Fiji, with their multiplicity of local formational names (e.g. Rodda & Band 1967), tends to obscure very considerably the general picture. The authors consider that although considerable variation of detail can be detected in the Fiji stratigraphic succession, the suggested process of accumulation, distribution and re-distribution of volcanic products was basically a simple one leading to a relatively small, oft-repeated, overall range of lithologies. The sequence of events is best known in Viti Levu, of which the stratigraphy will be considered here first.

The oldest rocks known in Viti Levu are all referred by Rodda and Band (1967, pp. 8-10) to the Wainimala Group, although Bartholomew (1960, p. 3) tabulated as pre-Wainimala certain Tertiary *b* strata in the Nandi area. Descriptions of the Wainimala Group rocks have been provided by Houtz (1959, pp. 2-4; 1960, pp. 4-5; 1963, pp. 3-5); Hirst (1965, pp. 9-14) and Band (1968, pp. 9-11). It appears that the Wainimala Group may be described generally as an assemblage of basaltic (spilitic) and andesitic flows, apparently submarine, with pillow lavas and pillow breccias, agglomerates, volcanic conglomerates and volcanic breccias (including both reworked and epiclastic types) as well as arenites, greywackes, mudstones, marls and argillites. Limestones occur at several horizons. They are foraminiferal and their faunas suggest correlation with Tertiary *e-f* (Hirst 1965, p. 13) or *b-f* (Rodda and Band, 1967, p. 8; Houtz 1963, p. 9). The Wainimala Group, at least in its lower part, was affected by folding and low-grade regional metamorphism (e.g. Band 1968, p. 10). However, the unmetamorphosed Singatoka Sedimentary Group, assigned to Tertiary *e-f* by Rodda and Band (1967, p. 10), cannot be everywhere clearly distinguished lithologically from the Wainimala Group which it overlies conformably or unconformably in different localities (Houtz 1959, p. 4). Evidently the sedimentary environment and its immediate lithological products continued to be much the same as in Wainimala times.

The Miocene(?) Savura Volcanic Group (Rodda & Band 1967, p. 12) comprises basalts and later andesite flows and agglomerates, intervening between the Wainimala Group and the Mendrausuthu Group (Tertiary *f-g-h*). The latter, with its various approximate correlatives is virtually equivalent to the 'Suva Group' of Phillips (1965) and comprises an assemblage of mudstones, marls, tuffaceous volcanic 'sandstones', tuffs, volcanic conglomerates and breccias, with andesite flows and pillow lavas. Approximately contemporaneous is the basaltic Mba Volcanic Group, below which the Koroimavua Volcanic Group can be distinguished in western Viti Levu (Rickard 1963, p. 6). Progressive changes in chemical composition with time were noted by Dickinson *et al.* (1968) and Gill (1970), but the lithological contribution of the Mba and Koroimavua Groups to the genesis of Fiji as a land-area, involved the continued distribution and re-distribution of flows, breccias, 'sandstones', tuffs, agglomerates, greywackes and limestones. Andesites and trachyandesites occur as well as basalts while both pillow lavas (of submarine origin) and subaerial flows are present. One of the distal facies of the Mba Group, the Vatukoro Greywackes, has been correlated with Tertiary *g-h* on foraminiferal evidence (Rodda & Band 1967, p. 14). The overlap in time of the Mba Group and the Mendrausuthu Group is clear also from radiometric dating (Rodda, Snelling & Rex 1967, Fig. 3).

The geological history of Vanua Levu apparently began rather later than that of Viti Levu, the oldest known strata being the 'Mount Kasi Volcanics', tentatively ascribed to Tertiary *f* (Bartholomew 1959, p. 9). These, however, have been described by Rickard (1966, reconnaissance geological map) as 'sediments' (mudstones, tuffs, grits and breccias), and since such 'sediments' must have been derived, penecontemporaneously or subsequently, the existence of some older (volcanic) rocks must be assumed. Following a reconnaissance survey of the whole of Vanua Levu, Rickard (1966, pp. 9-23) put forward an essentially lithostratigraphic classification, beginning with the basic-andesite and basalt flows (including pillow lavas) and breccias of the Natewa Group, within the outcrop area of which a number of volcanic centres were tentatively recognized. The sequence was apparently interrupted by the somewhat problematical 'Old Mbua Group' of basalts. Hornblende andesite plugs and various associated breccia formations (Nararo Group) in mid-western Vanua Levu followed during the Miocene and Pliocene; the contemporaneous eruption of dacitic lavas and tuffs, and the formation of breccias and re-worked pumiceous sediments, gave rise to the Undu Volcanic Group in eastern Vanua Levu. Finally, olivine basalts of the

Mbua Basaltic Group were extruded in Pleistocene times.

Rickard distinguished within the volcanic rocks certain 'sedimentary rocks and sediments'. Some of these he clearly regarded (p. 11) as distal facies developed peripherally to volcanic areas, nearer to the centres of which were developed belts of sandstone and of intercalated flows and breccias. It follows that there may be approximately contemporaneous flows, breccias and finer-grained sedimentary rocks at any stratigraphic level, the various distinctive lithostratigraphic formations being diachronous. Hindle (in prep.) has drawn attention to the Miocene-Pliocene fauna of certain hypersthene-bearing marls in mid-western Vanua Levu. These marls are overlain by basalts of the Mbua Volcanic Group on the north-eastern flank of the Mbua volcano which, on geomorphological evidence, Rickard (1966, p. 30) included among the Pleistocene volcanoes of Vanua Levu. Furthermore, it is now known, as a result of archaeological work, that basaltic volcanicity in Taveuni island, to the east of Vanua Levu, continued into historical time (P. Woodrow, pers. comm. 1969).

The conditions under which these various strata were laid down are suggested by Rickard (1963, p. 3; 1966, Fig. 3 and pp. 27-8) and Band (1968, pp. 13-22). Band's demonstration of the evolution of successive facies belts, in which sediments become increasingly fine-grained with increasing distance from volcanic centres, is a convincing proof of the validity of Rickard's concept of a situation in which, around an active volcano 'the boundaries of lithological units that can be delineated in the field cut across the time horizons at a high angle'. Evidently the ancient volcanoes of Fiji were subject to intense erosion, with 'rapid re-working and coalescence, of screes, landslides and lahars' (Rickard 1966, p. 28), giving rise to coarse epiclastic and re-worked breccias, breccio-conglomerates and conglomerates immediately around the volcanic centres. These coarse clastic rocks tend to be intercalated with lava flows on the one hand and on the other pass outwards into belts of mudstone, marl, 'sandstone' and limestone. These latter, peripheral, deposits are usually foraminiferal or otherwise fossiliferous, and palaeontological opinion has often been put forward as to the depth of water in which they were laid down. The estimates (Crespin, Cushman, Todd, Cole, Coleman, Wells, Briggs, Leopold, Sachs, Bayliss, Ladd and Carter, all in unpublished correspondence; Brady 1888) range from 0-400 m, where actual figures have been given. The most commonly quoted depth is 50 m.

PETROLOGICAL CONSIDERATIONS

In the Wainimala Group the 'Tholo Plutonic Suite' includes the apparently subjacent-type intrusions of tonalite, gabbro and diorite. There appear to be no equivalents in Vanua Levu. Houtz (1959, pp. 5-6) envisaged the gabbros in the Lomawai-Momi area of western Viti Levu as the products of contamination of 'granite' and their widespread silicification as possibly late-magmatic. Band (1968, p. 28) referred, however, to two distinct phases of plutonic activity, comprising gabbros followed by tonalites and associated diorites. Stocks and minor intrusions of granodiorite or tonalite, with gabbros and diorites possibly of earlier date, are mentioned by Hirst (1965, p. 28). The relation of the intrusions to the folding of the Wainimala Group rocks is indicated by Band (1968, p. 38) who refers to 'an east-north-east trending anticlinorium, the anticlinal crests of which have been in some cases intruded by stocks of tonalite-diorite and gabbro'. As a specific example of an 'intruded fold' in which the dip of intruded strata increases towards the contacts, the Korolevu anticline is cited. In regarding the Tholo intrusions as synorogenic, Band was followed by Rodda, Snelling and Rex (1967, p. 1253). An implication not mentioned by these authors is that the so-called 'stocks' or 'batholiths' may in reality be laccoliths or phacoliths in the sense of Daly (1933). The importance is stressed in this paper of the fact that in Viti Levu the trend of fold-axes in Wainimala Group rocks, and correspondingly the trend of the belt of outcrops of Tholo intrusions, swings from ENE-WSW to NW-SE. It would appear therefore that although a 'Tholo orogeny' may be supposed to have given rise to a linear folded zone and a corresponding linear distribution of tonalite, gabbro and diorite outcrops, a later deformation must be invoked to account for the observed axial flexure of the folded zone.

In Fiji generally, but more especially in Viti Levu, a progressive change, with time, in the chemical composition of rocks can be discerned to some extent. Discounting the Undu Volcanic Group of eastern Vanua Levu (for which group only a single analysis is available), the trend is one of progressively increasing alkalinity, more especially of potash enrichment. The Eocene to Miocene Wainimala Group rocks can be broadly characterized as basaltic (tholeiitic), andesitic, spilitic and keratophyric. There follows an assemblage of largely andesitic (calc-alkaline) rocks—the Mendrausuthu Group (essentially Pliocene in age)—and finally a sequence of olivine basalt flows and volcaniclastics, the Mba Volcanic Group (Pliocene to Pleistocene). The Koroimavua Volcanic Group, originally described as andesitic (Rodda & Band 1967, p. 13) is subdivided from the base of the Mba Volcanic Group. Rodda (P. Rodda, pers. comm. 1969) emphasized that a previous local usage had included all andesitic rocks in a 'Suva Group', and regarded the upper part of the upper Tertiary in Viti Levu as almost exclusively basaltic. This remains broadly true today and the concept of the successive Wainimala, Suva, Undu and Mba Groups (Phillips 1965) is still a useful one.

Aspects of the apparent petrochemical evolution (of Viti Levu) were emphasized subsequently. Thus Dickinson *et al.* (1968) identified as 'shoshonitic' the lavas of the Koroimavua Group in western Viti Levu, while Rodda (in prep.) demonstrated the alkaline affinities of so-called 'monzonites' intrusive in the Mba Group rocks of central Viti Levu. Gill (1970) considerably elaborated the chemical argument and reached conclusions broadly similar to, and embracing, those outlined above. He recognized three 'periods': a tholeiitic first period (Wainimala and Savura Groups), a calcalkaline (andesitic) second period (Mendrausuthu and Nandi Groups) and an alkali basalt (shoshonitic) third period (Koroimavua and Mba Groups). He went on to suggest (pp. 194-8) that igneous rocks chemically similar to those of Viti Levu can be recognized in certain island arcs ranging from the New Hebrides to the South Sandwich Islands, and to infer that Fiji and these island arcs have in common a process of petrochemical evolution leading from the development of tholeiite to that of shoshonite, with an intermediate calcalkaline stage. He further suggested that this required the proximity of the southern coast of Viti Levu to an 'active oceanic trench' until 4 or 5 m.y. ago, when presumably the shoshonitic volcanism of the Koroimavua and Mba Groups can be regarded as having ceased in Viti Levu.

LOCAL STRUCTURAL FEATURES

Under this heading, it is proposed to take account of the folding and faulting that affected the rocks of the main land-areas in Fiji.

Folding

As might be expected, where a markedly heterogeneous and laterally variable assemblage of volcanic products is concerned, geological maps of Fiji do not necessarily clearly indicate the existence of folds, although, more especially in parts of Viti Levu, attention has been drawn to folding. Rickard (1963, pp. 18-19) described an especially-clear example, the Navala anticline, trending approximately N-S within the central part of Viti Levu Sheet 5 (Fig. 1), and exposing strata of the Singatoka Sedimentary

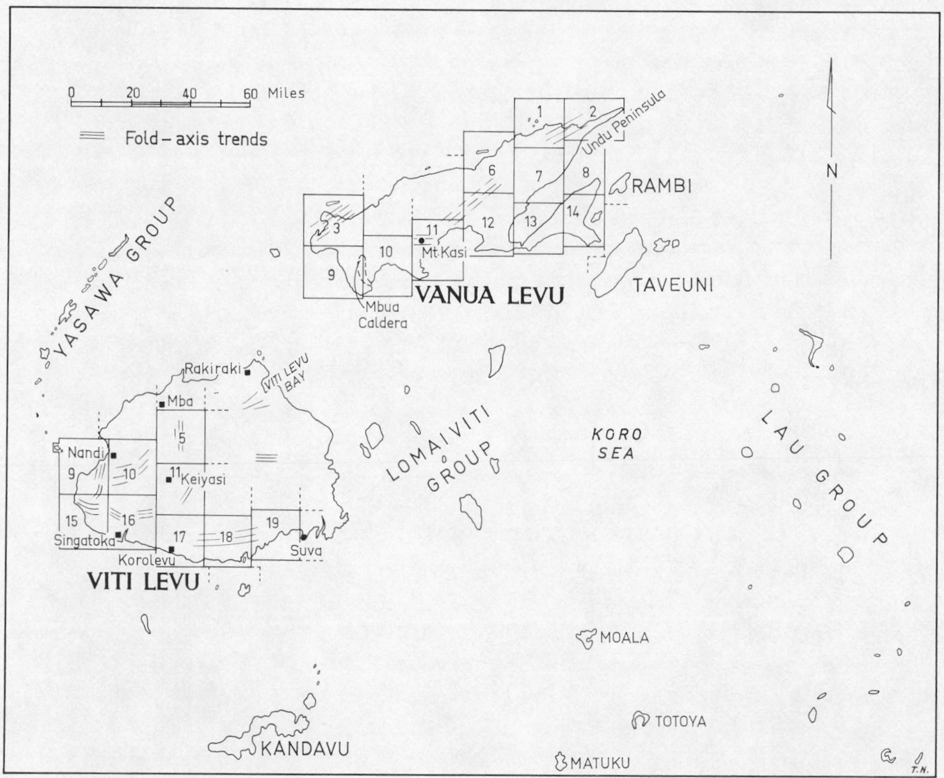

Fig. 1 Map sheet numbers, referred to in the text, for Viti Levu and Vanua Levu (1:50,000 scale series). Fold-axis trends are also shown.

Group (Tertiary *f*) below Mba Volcanic Group rocks (Tertiary *h*). East of Nandi (within the area of Viti Levu Sheet 10) Bartholomew (1960, p. 15) delineated a number of fold-axes trending for the most part approximately E-W, swinging to NE-SW further east, and affecting the marly sandstones of the Nandi Sedimentary Group (Tertiary *g-h*). The area is indeed remarkable for dips commonly between 45° and 90°, the strata in places being vertical or nearly so.

Further south (Viti Levu Sheets 9 and 15) in the Lomawai-Momi area Houtz (1959, p. 3 and geological map) recognized a number of fold-axes trending WNW-ESE in the south and N-S in the north, with an intermediate NW-SE trend in the intervening area, the folds affecting the Wainimala Group (and to some extent the Singatoka Sedimentary Group). Houtz (1960, pp. 14-15) provided a hypothetical discussion of folding, affecting Wainimala and Singatoka Group rocks in the Singatoka area (Viti Levu Sheet 16). The geological map of this area shows trends along WNW-ESE lines in the west, becoming ENE-WSW or E-W in the east. To the east again, in southern Viti Levu (Sheets 17, 18 and 19) Band (1968, p. 38) recognized an anticlinorium trending ENE-WSW in lower Tertiary (Wainimala Group) rocks. However, to the south-west of the Nandrau Plateau of central Viti Levu, in the Keiyasi area (Viti Levu Sheet 11), the trend of fold axes in Wainimala and Singatoka Group rocks, as well as in Navosa Sedimentary Group rocks (Tertiary *g*) is between NE-SW and N-S (Houtz 1963, geological map).

In eastern central Viti Levu (midway between Suva and Rakiraki) Hirst (1965, p. 34) recognized a Middle Miocene deformation producing an E-W anticlinorium in Wainimala Group rocks. He also saw that early Pliocene folding, affecting Upper Miocene Ra Group (sandstones and conglomerates) in the Viti Levu Bay area to the north, has produced fold axes trending NE-SW to NNE-SSW.

There are very few references to folding in Vanua Levu. Bartholomew (1959, p. 18) suggested that there was folding along E-W to ENE-WSW lines in the Mount Kasi area, affecting the 'Mount Kasi Volcanics' (tentatively Tertiary *f*). Rickard (1966, p. 25) referred to probable folding about NE-SW axes in central, eastern and western Vanua Levu, affecting rocks of the Natewa, Undu and Monkey Face Groups.

Faulting

Faulting in the two main islands can be dealt with summarily, as the fault-directions for Viti Levu plotted on the 1:50,000 scale sheets have been conveniently abstracted by Rodda and Band (1967) on to a general geological map at the reduced scale of 1:250,000, while for Vanua Levu, Rickard (1966) plotted photo-lineaments (with some observed faults) on his 1:200,000 scale reconnaissance map. The mapping of eastern Vanua Levu Sheets 6, 7 and 8 (Ibbotson 1969, pp. 32-3) revealed faulting along E-W to NE-SW lines as well as along N-S to NW-SE lines. Rickard (1970, p. 11) plotted mainly photo-lineaments (essentially the same as those on his general reconnaissance map, and with E-W to NE-SW and N-S to NW-SE directions) on Vanua Levu Sheets 1 and 2. Coulson (1971, pp. 35-39) showed that in western Vanua Levu (Sheets 3 and 9) a NNW-SSE trend is especially important. Faults with this direction were also traced by Hindle (in prep.) in the area covered by Vanua Levu Sheet 10, while Bartholomew (1959, p. 17 and geological map) recognized faults aligned NNW-SSE and approximately E-W, within the area of Sheet 11.

Parallel to the known and inferred trends within the two main islands, there exist corresponding trends shown by the orientation and distribution of the smaller islands. This is quite strikingly shown by the linear multi-crater volcanic fissure of Taveuni and by the alignment of the Lomaiviti (the islands of the Koro Sea) as well as of the Yasawas (north-west of Viti Levu). Fig. 2 shows known and inferred fault-directions on land as well as other inferred major structural directions (possibly deep-seated faults) of the immediate Fiji region.

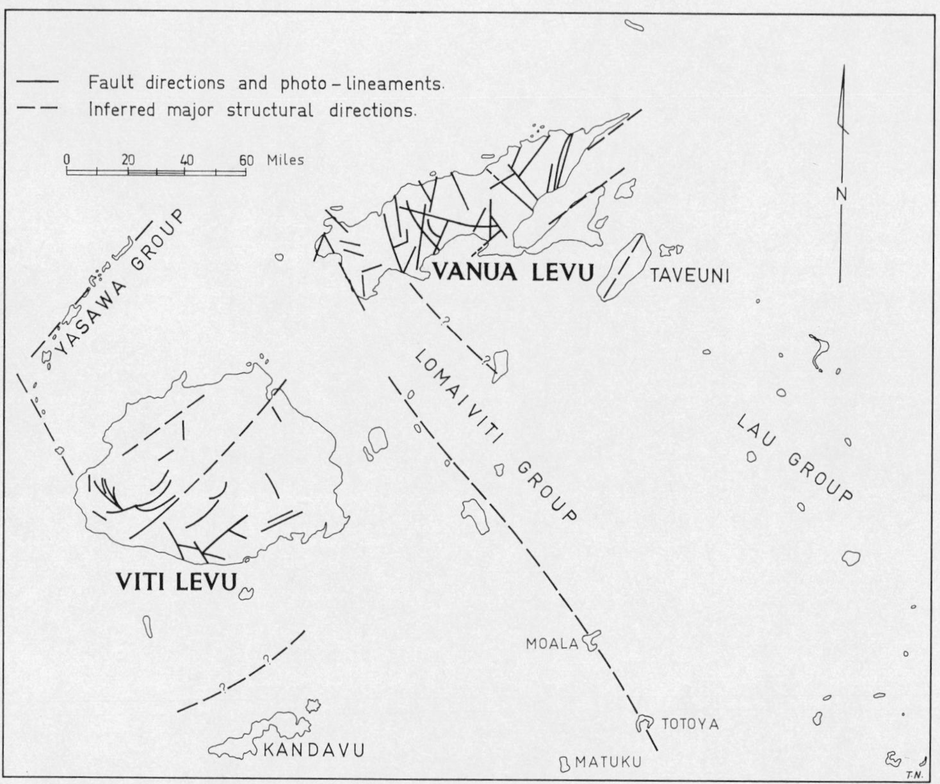

Fig. 2 Structural directions in the Fiji Group

REGIONAL STRUCTURAL CONSIDERATIONS

The structural history of the Fiji region has certain more or less direct links with that of the New Zealand region further south, where Cullen (1967*a* and 1967*c*) and Summerhayes (1967*a*) have accepted the Macquarie Ridge and the Kermadec-Tonga Ridge as island arcs. The latter author indeed (1967*a*, 1967*b*) suggested that the

Alpine Fault, obliquely traversing South Island, might be a concave-arc to concave-arc transform (Wilson 1965, Fig. 2*d*), linking the northern end of the Macquarie Arc to the southern end of the Kermadec Arc. Though Cullen (1967*d*) objected that the Alpine Fault pre-dates the Tertiary arcs in question, it remains possible that it could have provided a pre-determined line of structural weakness for the development of such a postulated transform. The matter evidently has to be considered with reference also to the modes of origin of the associated NE-SW Waipounamu and Antipodes fracture zones (Cullen 1967*b*). It appears reasonable to accept Cullen's (1967*a*, 1967*b*) proposal that there has been a net resultant northward movement of New Zealand and the New Zealand Plateau due to the combined effect of sea-floor spreading from the Indian-Antarctic Ridge, the Pacific-Antarctic Ridge and the East Pacific Rise. This is consistent with an element of dextral movement along the Kermadec and Tonga arc and trench systems (Fairbridge 1961) and evidently could provide an explanation, partially at least, of the mechanism required for the development of the 'Fiji orocline' (Carey 1958).

Fiji stands roughly equidistant from three points defining an equilateral triangle, namely the south-eastern end of the Vitiaz Trench, the northern end of the Tonga Trench and the south-eastern end of the New Hebrides Trench. It seems reasonable to suppose that the tectonic forces responsible for the development of these three features may also have affected the evolution of the Fiji area. More important, however, is the position of Fiji in relation to the line between the northern end of the Tonga Trench and the south-eastern end of the New Hebrides Trench. In this respect, Fiji appears to stand in relation to the New Hebrides and Tonga Arcs much as do the Falkland Islands in relation to the southern tip of South America and the Scotia Arc. This is strikingly apparent from the bathymetric map of the Pacific issued by the Institute of Oceanology, U.S.S.R. (Udintsev 1964). It is here envisaged that Fiji and the Falkland Islands both represent groups of islands similarly placed with reference to sinistral concave-arc to concave-arc transforms. It appears at first sight possible therefore to infer that a major discontinuity delimiting the northern end of the Tonga Trench/Arc extends, or formerly extended, south-east of the two main islands of Fiji, eventually linking-up with the Hunter fracture-zone. This minimizes, but does not necessarily discount, the importance of possible strike-slip faulting along the 'Melanesian border plateau' recognized by Fairbridge (1961) between Samoa and the Vitiaz Trench.

The existence of a simple *transcurrent* fault running NE-SW to the south-east of the two main islands of Fiji (Hess & Maxwell 1953, Fairbridge 1961) was criticized by Cullen (1967*a*, p. 167) on the grounds that the positions of ridge and trench are reversed at opposite ends of such a proposed fault. This sort of reversal, however, is evidently a characteristic of transform faults of the type suggested by Wilson (1965, Fig. 3*d*). Such a displacement within the region between the northern end of the Tonga Trench and the southern end of the New Hebrides Trench may be regarded as a possibility. The development of the 'Fiji orocline' (Carey 1958, Fairbridge 1961), east of Fiji, indicates a far more rapid north-eastward migration of crust beneath the Lau and Tonga Ridges than beneath the Fiji Plateau. Under such conditions, as suggested above, a transform displacement could have arisen. Viti Levu and Vanua

Levu appear to be situated sufficiently near the supposed regional shearing couple to have experienced considerable rotational shear, and even bodily anti-clockwise rotation, as suggested by Malahoff (in prep.).

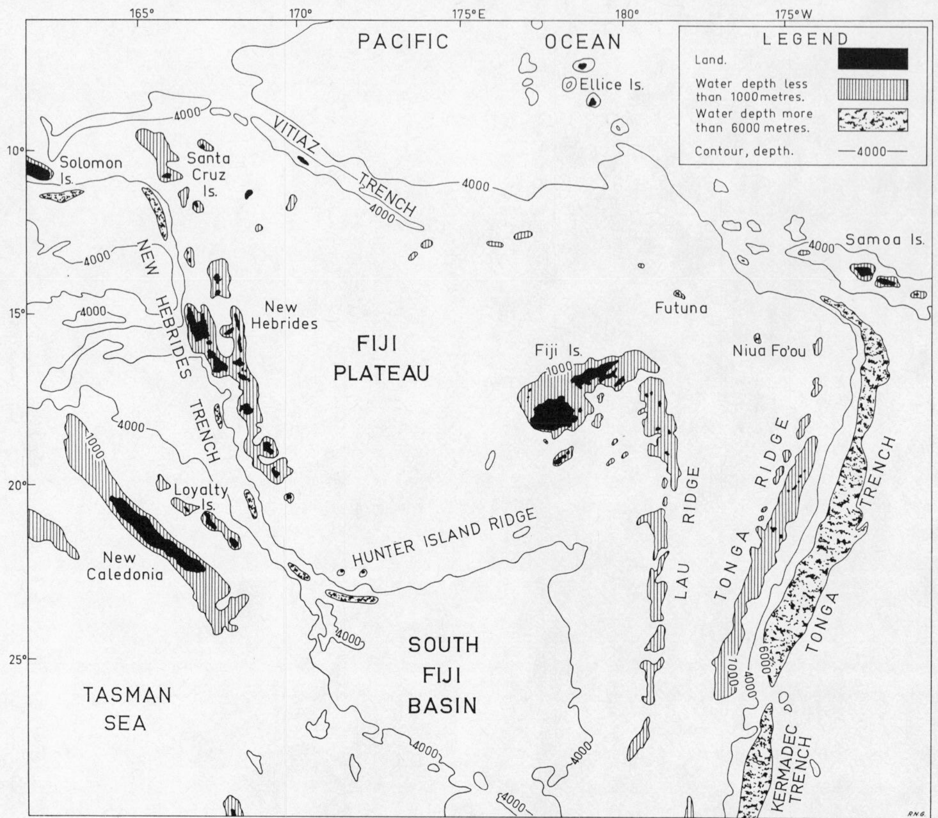

Fig. 3 Physiographic elements in the north-eastern part of Outer Melanesia

Karig (1970, pp. 239-40) regarded the Lau-Colville ridge as a 'third arc', in the sense used by Vening Meinesz (1951), and referred to extension between the 'frontal arc' (in this case the Tonga-Kermadec Ridge) and the 'third arc'. Karig (1970, p. 247) described '. . . meagre sediment fill within the [inter-arc] basin . . .' (i.e. the Lau-Havre Trough) and (*loc. cit.* pp. 249-50 and Fig. 9) westward thinning of a sediment apron deriving from the Lau Ridge and probably including volcanic detritus. Thus it can be inferred that an ancestral Lau Archipelago formed a volcanic chain similar to that of Tonga and that within the last few million years this became extinct and, lagging behind the continued eastward migration of the Tonga Ridge, allowed the opening of the inter-arc basin. These late movements evidently disrupted the north-eastward continuity of the proposed transform displacement referred to above.

POST-ROTATIONAL FRACTURING

The Fiji Plateau comprises an undulating, triangular segment of sea floor north and west of the Fiji islands, lying at depths mainly between 2,000 and 4,000 m, i.e. significantly shallower than the adjacent West Pacific, South Fiji and New Hebrides Basins (Fig. 3). The plateau is bounded to the west and south by the New Hebrides Ridge and the contiguous, arcuate Hunter Island Ridge, and to the north by the Vitiaz Trench. Its eastern margin is less well defined, and in that direction the plateau merges into the northern extremities of the Lau and Tonga Ridges and their intervening trough. Within these limits, the plateau slopes down very gently westwards. Thus, to the north of Fiji, the sea floor lies mainly at depths between 1,500 and 2,500 m, but further west depths between 3,000 and 3,500 m dominate in the Pandora Basin. The intermediate depth and crustal thickness (Raitt 1956) of the Fiji Plateau, its abnormally high heat-flow values (Sclater & Menard 1967), and the occurrence of acid plutonics and volcanics in the Fiji islands themselves (Rodda 1967, p. 1262) all suggest that the plateau is underlain by crust of 'quasi-continental' sialic type. For the present analysis, a detailed bathymetric chart of the central section of the Fiji Plateau has been prepared, at a scale of 1:1,000,000 and with isobaths at intervals of 250 m, from data in the records of the New Zealand Oceanographic Institute. A simplified, reduced version of this chart, showing isobaths every 1,000 m, is reproduced here (Fig. 4) to illustrate the main submarine morphological features of the region.

The surface of the plateau is composed of a complex system of roughly parallel ridges and troughs, averaging some 125 km in length, but mostly less than 20 km across. That this morphology is tectonic in origin seems certain, although the precise mechanisms involved are not known as yet. Malahoff (in prep.) advocates faulting and rifting as an explanation for most of the undulations, in preference to a process involving widespread folding. At about the latitude of Rotuma, however, a series of broader, shallower ridges (the North and South Pandora and North and South Mbulembulewa ridges) divided by a deep continuous trough system (the East and West Rotuma troughs) may well have originated as a fold complex (Fig. 4). This dual ridge system is here considered as a possible faulted and attenuated westward extension of the Tonga Ridge—itself a dual ridge over much of its length.

Two distinct trends dominate the morphology of the central region of the Fiji Plateau. North and north-west of Fiji the ridges and troughs strike between E-W and ENE-WSW, but west of Viti Levu the strike changes abruptly to N-S. The zone of convergence of these two trends extends along the northern margin of the Fiji 'continental' shelf, continuing westwards for some 400 km before curving north-westward to the centre of the Pandora Basin (Figs 4 and 5). North-east of Fiji, the convergence of bathymetric trends is considerably less distinct but can be traced in the area of the Horne Islands. That the bathymetry reflects the existence of an important structural convergence within this zone seems an inescapable conclusion. Two further characteristics distinguish the convergence zone. Where the latter approaches the Fiji shelf from the west there occur two sharply-defined, abnormally deep troughs (the Yasawa and Yandua troughs) each about 125 km long and between 4,500 and 5,000 m deep, with axes approximately parallel to the strike of the convergence.

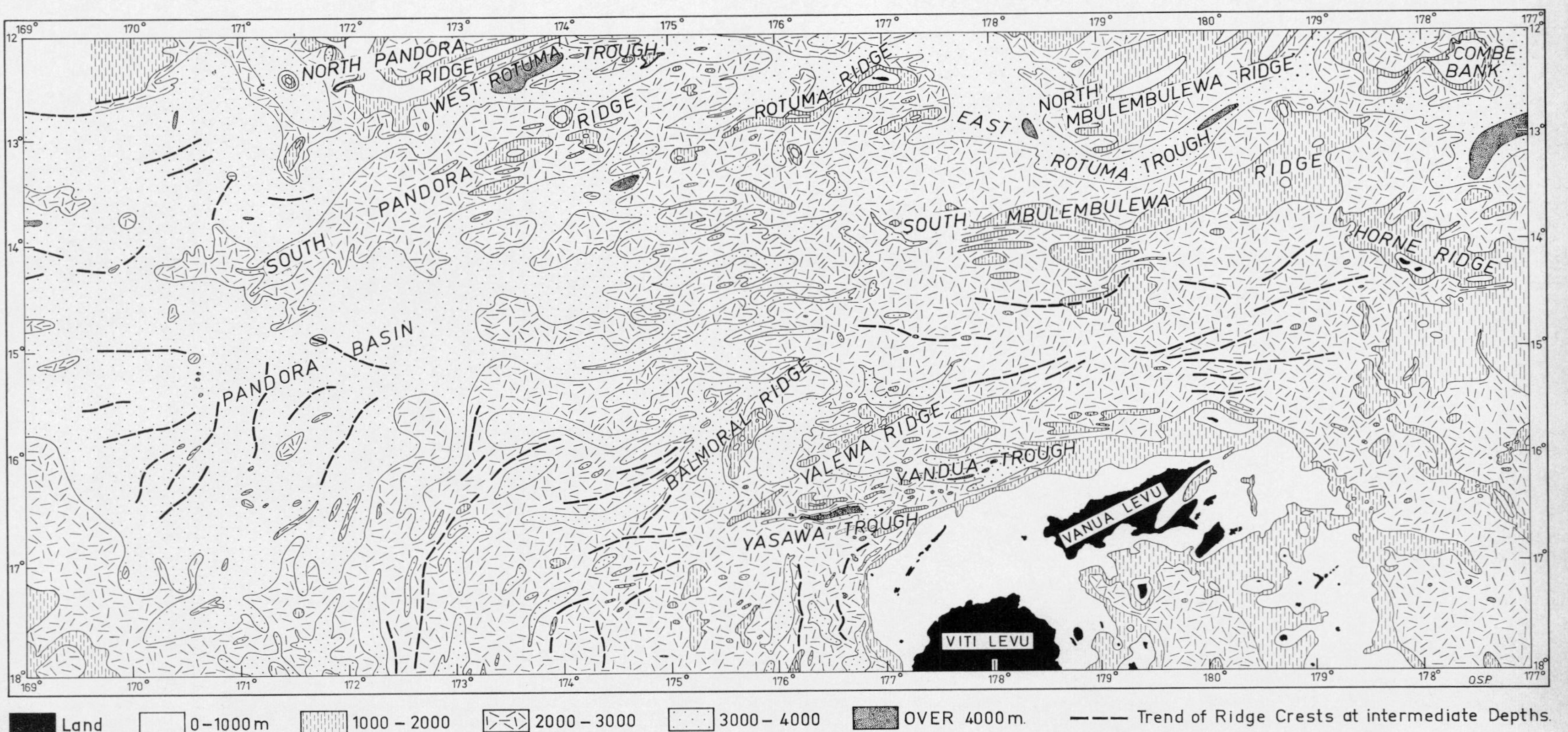

Fig. 4 Detailed bathymetry of the northern part of the Fiji Plateau

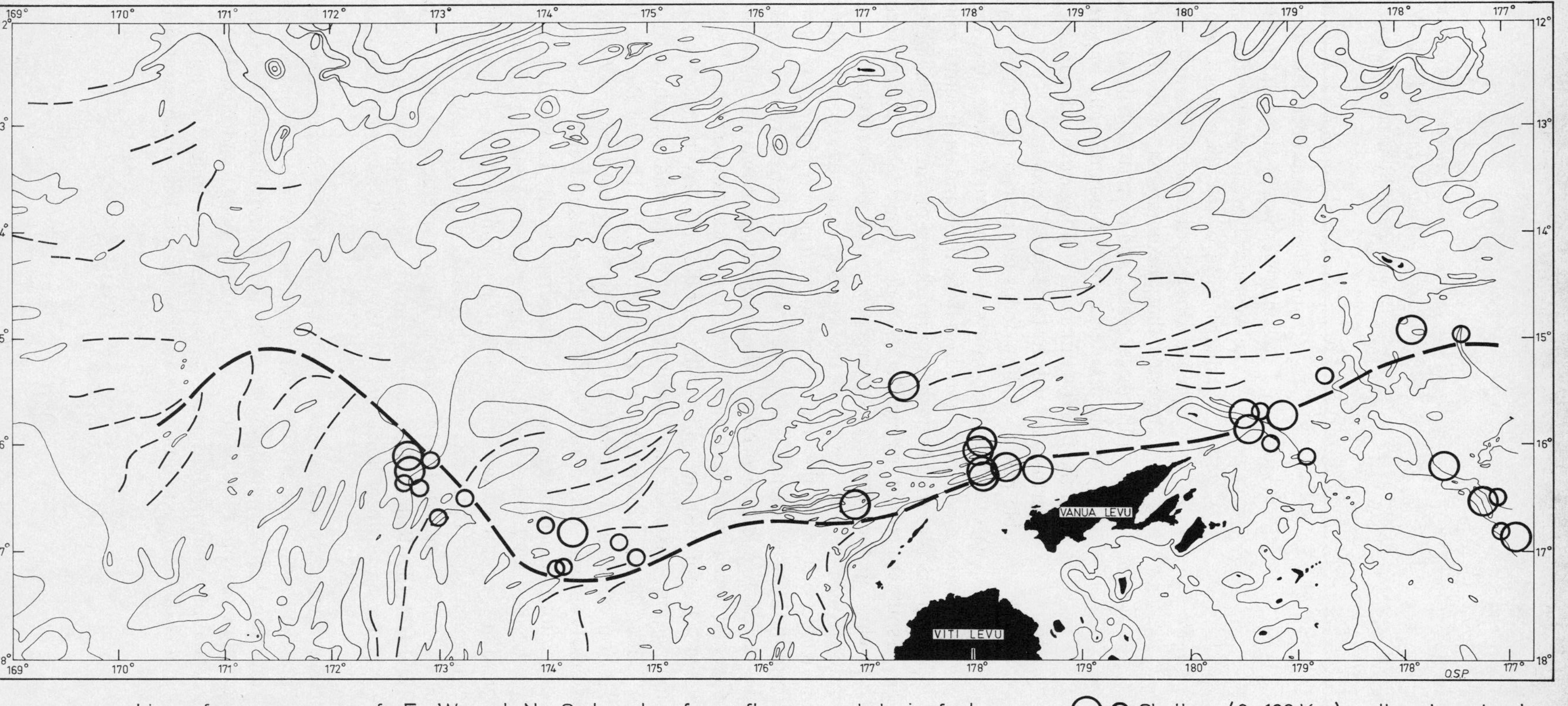

Line of convergence of E–W and N–S trends of sea-floor morphologic features.
Trend of Ridge Crests at intermediate Depths.
Shallow (0–100 Km) earthquake epicentres (After Sykes, 1966).

Fig. 5 Seismic activity in the northern part of the Fiji Plateau

These troughs appear not to be co-axial but to have an *en echelon* arrangement. Interpretation of these troughs as fault-gashes aligned along a broad ENE-WSW fracture zone seems reasonable, and is supported by the second characteristic of the convergence zone—its seismicity.

A belt of predominantly shallow-focus (0-100 km) earthquake epicentres extending westwards from the recurved northern tip of the Tonga Trench has been described by Sykes (1966). The belt appears to continue west-south-westwards along the northern margin of the Fiji shelf, thence swinging to the west-north-west towards the centre of the Pandora Basin (Fig. 5). In fact, the distribution of the epicentres coincides almost exactly with the bathymetric convergence zone described here. This association is undoubtedly significant, and it is suggested that the combination of seismicity, bathymetric (and presumably structural) convergence, and deep trough development within this restricted zone indicates the existence of a fundamentally important crustal dislocation—here named the Fiji fracture zone—along the north flank of the Fiji shelf and extending east-north-eastwards to the Tonga Trench.

Further south, a comparable belt of shallow-focus earthquake epicentres (Sykes 1966), striking east-north-eastwards to the vicinity of Kandavu Passage, may represent another major fracture zone—provisionally named the Kandavu fracture zone—converging on the Fiji fracture zone in the region north-east of Vanua Levu. Detailed bathymetry of the southern part of the Fiji Plateau is not yet available, but this second seismic belt lies close to the expected convergence of the N-S bathymetric trend (already described) west of Viti Levu and the NE-SW trend associated with the Hunter Island Ridge. Certainly, the coastal and submarine morphology of eastern Vanua Levu and the adjacent islands is consistent with control by a swarm of recent NE-SW faults, such as would be expected at the intersection of two major fractures. Undu Peninsula and the adjacent channel (Natewa Bay), Somosomo Strait, Taveuni, and Nanuku Passage, for instance, all exhibit parallel NE-SW trends, while the submarine morphology around Thakaundrove Peninsula and Rambi Island is suggestive of faulted blocks, down-tilted to the east (Fig. 6). The Fiji Plateau thus comprises a region of relatively restricted seismicity, lying between the opposite-facing and intensely seismic Tonga and New Hebrides arc-and-trench systems. The distribution of shallow, intermediate and deep-focus hypocentres in the Tonga region (Gutenberg & Richter 1954, Sykes 1966) indicates a broad Benioff zone inclined gently downward in a general westward direction. It is significant that, at its northern end, the latter terminates abruptly east of the Fiji islands, in the vicinity of the intersection of the Fiji and Kandavu fracture zones. The complementary Benioff zone beneath the New Hebrides Ridge differs in being much narrower, eastward-dipping and, except in the region north of latitude 15° S (Sykes 1966), devoid of deep-focus earthquakes.

Benioff zones are normally regarded as overthrust/underthrust surfaces developing along crustal plate margins, especially where continental crust impinges upon oceanic crust, and it therefore seems appropriate to relate the development of the complex structural pattern of the Fiji Plateau, and the adjoining Tonga and New Hebrides Arcs, to differential movements of adjacent crustal segments. Indeed, by analysis of structural elements in the Fiji region, Malahoff (in prep.) has demonstrated that

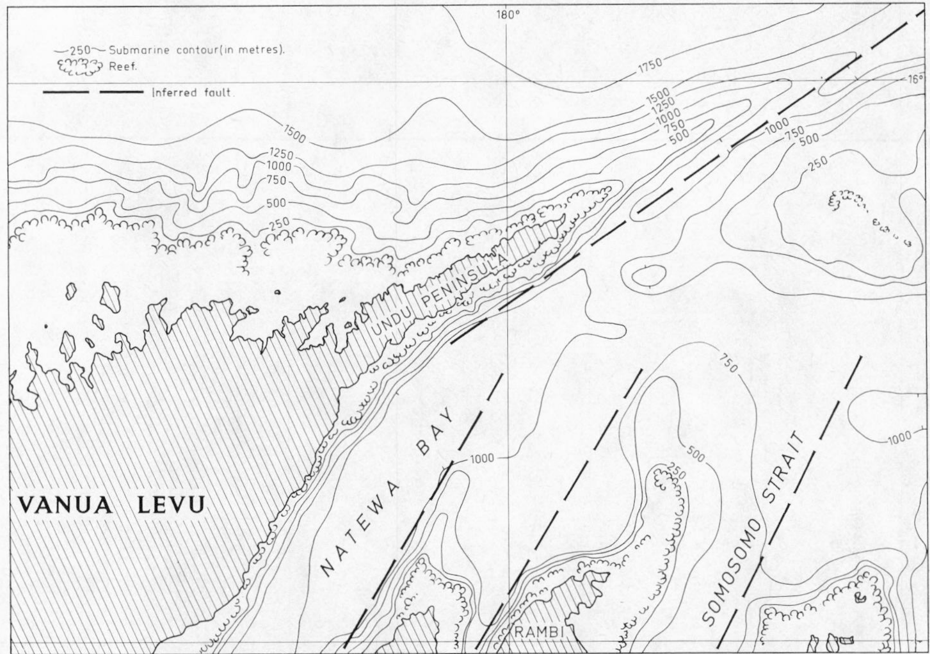

Fig. 6 Structural trends inferred for the area east of Vanua Levu

rotational deformation—which he attributes to different trends and rates of crustal spreading from the Tasman Sea and South Pacific Ocean—has controlled the tectonic evolution of the area, possibly since early Tertiary times.

CONCLUSIONS

By analogy with the observed linearity and linear distribution of younger volcanic centres such as those of Taveuni and the Lomaiviti, the primary volcanic and reworked volcanic materials that built up Fiji as a landmass are considered to have accumulated along and around structurally-controlled linear zones of volcanicity. Shallow-water conditions often prevailed. Considering the estimates of thickness for the Wainimala Group (15,000 ft according to Houtz 1959, p. 9; 30,000 ft according to Band 1968, p. 9) it would appear that during early Tertiary times in the Fiji area deposition took place under typical geosynclinal conditions (cf. Harland 1967, p. 187) quite distinct from those obtaining today in the unfilled oceanic trenches of the South-west Pacific. The extent to which the older formations accumulated around aligned volcanic centres is not known in Viti Levu but Rickard's palaeogeographical reconstruction of Vanua Levu (Rickard 1966, Fig. 1) clearly indicates such an association there. The NE-SW alignment of certain volcanic centres in the Thakaundrove Peninsula is suggested by recent detailed mapping in the area of Vanua Levu

Sheets 12, 13 and 14 (P. Woodrow, pers. comm. 1971). It is possible, therefore, that the geological history of Fiji during the Tertiary was, to a large extent, pre-determined by the inception of critical zones of weakness in the primordial oceanic crust before the Eocene epoch.

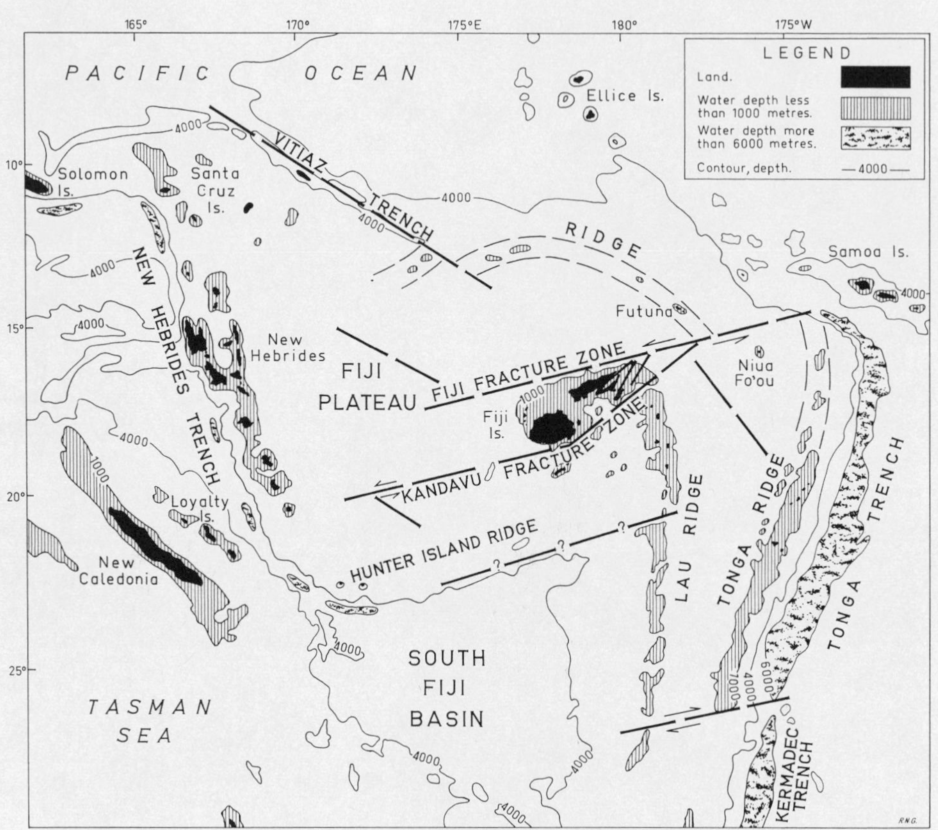

Fig. 7 Major structures, known and inferred, in the north-eastern part of the Outer Melanesian area

The main fault-trends in Fiji are directed NE-SW and NW-SE, while fold axes either trend similarly or strike N-S or E-W. If the belt of synorogenic Tholo plutons originally was linear, and parallel to the length of a Wainimala geosyncline, then the present trend of outcrops is to be explained by subsequent axial flexuring of the folded zone. Flexuring of this type, together with the development of fault and fold patterns related to rotational shear, and other regional structures, is in accord with Malahoff's concept of bodily rotation of Fiji. This concept must be qualified, however, by two other, apparently-conflicting, lines of evidence. Gill's (1970) petrogenetic data suggest that rotation was accomplished within the last 5 m.y. On the other hand, the bathymetric, seismic and related data presented here indicate that rotation ceased some considerable time ago, allowing the development of post-rotational fractures, as discussed above. Malahoff's thesis adequately explains the changes in strike of island chains, and of the ridges and troughs on the sea floor around Fiji, including the differences in trend of bathymetric features north and west of Fiji described earlier. Continued activity of such a spiralling system to the present day as envisaged by Malahoff, however, is not consistent with the occurrence of extensive, parallel, linear and still-seismic fractures such as the Fiji and Kandavu fracture zones, traversing the Fiji Plateau from ENE to WSW. Instead, it is suggested here that anti-clockwise rotation of the Fiji Plateau reached its culmination at some time in the past, and has now ceased. To explain the opening of the Tasman, South Fiji and New Hebrides Basins it is necessary to assume eastward to north-eastward migration of both the Tonga and New Hebrides crustal segments. It is clear, however, that the movement of the Tonga crustal wedge completely outstripped that of the New Hebrides segment, over-riding the Pacific crust, rotating the Fiji Plateau, and forming the intensely seismic Tonga 'salient'. The growth of the salient rapidly reached proportions sufficiently extensive to inhibit the eastward movement of the New Hebrides crust, with the building-up of compressive stresses and the development of a reverse-facing arc-trench system in the New Hebrides region. It is considered significant, in this connection, that the oldest rocks of the New Hebrides Ridge are of Miocene age (in contrast to the presence of Eocene rocks in Fiji itself), and it is proposed that this stage in the evolution of the Fiji Plateau and New Hebrides Arc developed late in the Tertiary period. Subsequent differential movements between the Tonga and New Hebrides Arcs are considered to have been accommodated by the evolution of the Fiji and Kandavu dislocations aligned more or less perpendicular to the New Hebrides Ridge (Fig. 7). The extension of the Lau-Havre trough as an 'inter-arc basin', and the assumption by the Lau Ridge of the role of 'third arc' presumably accompanied the evolution of these fracture zones. In this interpretation, the New Hebrides Arc is regarded as a region of active eastward crustal *under*-thrusting, in contrast to the Tonga Arc, where eastward *over*-thrusting of oceanic by quasi-continental crust is apparent (cf. Isacks, Oliver & Sykes 1968).

ACKNOWLEDGEMENTS

The authors wish to thank Mr O. S. Pahlad and Miss S. Nair, both of the Fiji Geological Survey Department, for their very considerable help in draughting the diagrams and in typing the manuscript, respectively.

REFERENCES

Band, R. B. 1968. The geology of Southern Viti Levu and Mbengga. *Bull. geol. Surv. Fiji*, **15,** 49 pp.

Bartholomew, R. W. 1959. Geology of Savusavu Bay West—Vanua Levu. *Bull. geol. Surv. Fiji.* **5,** 28 pp.

Bartholomew, R. W. 1960. Geology of the Nandi Area—Western Viti Levu. *Bull. geol. Surv. Fiji*, **7,** 27 pp.

Brady, H. B. 1888. Note on the so-called 'Soapstone' of Fiji. *Q. Jl geol. Soc. Lond*, **44,** 1-10.

Carey, S. W. 1958. The tectonic approach to continental drift. *Continental Drift—A Symposium*, 177-355. Univ. Tasmania, Hobart.

Coulson, F. I. E. 1971. The Geology of western Vanua Levu. *Bull. geol. Surv. Fiji*, **17,** 49 pp.

Cullen, D. J. 1967*a*. Island arc development in the southwest Pacific. *Tectonophysics*, **4,** 163-72.

——— 1967*b*. The Antipodes fracture zone, a major structure of the south-west Pacific. *N.Z. Jl Mar. Freshwater Res.* **11,** 16-25.

——— 1967*c*. A note on the regional structure of the southwest Pacific. *N.Z. Jl Sci.* **10,** 813-15.

——— 1967*d*. Mantle convection and sea-floor spreading in the South-west Pacific. *Nature*, **216,** 356-7.

Daly, R. A. 1933. *Igneous rocks and the depths of the earth.* McGraw-Hill, New York and Lond. 598 pp.

Dickinson, W. R., Rickard, M. J., Coulson, F. I. E., Smith, J. G. & Lawrence, R. L. 1968. Late Cenozoic shoshonitic lavas in north-western Vitu Levu. *Nature*, **219,** 148.

Fairbridge, R. W. 1961. Basis for submarine nomenclature in the South-west Pacific Ocean. *Dt. hydrogr. Z.* **15,** 1-15.

Gill, J. B. 1970. Geochemistry of Viti Levu, Fiji and its evolution as an island arc. *Contr. Mineral. Petrol.* **27,** 179-203.

Gutenberg, B. & Richter, C. F. 1954. *Seismicity of the Earth and associated phenomena.* Princeton University Press. 310 pp.

Harland, W. B. 1967. Geosynclines. *Geol. Mag.* **104,** 182-8.

Hess, H. H. & Maxwell, J. C. 1953. Major structural features of the South-west Pacific—a preliminary interpretation of HO 5484, bathymetry chart, New Guinea to New Zealand. *Proc. Pacif. Sci. Congr.* **2,** 14-17.

Hindle, W. (In prep.) The Geology of west-central Vanua Levu. *Bull. geol. Surv. Fiji*, **19.**

Hirst, J. A. 1965. Geology of East and North-East Viti Levu. *Bull. geol. Surv. Fiji* **12,** 51 pp.

Houtz, R. E. 1959. Regional Geology of Lomawai-Momi—Nandroga, Viti-Levu. *Bull. geol. Surv. Fiji*, **3,** 20 pp.

——— 1960. Geology of Singatoka Area—Viti Levu. *Bull. geol. Surv. Fiji*, **6,** 19 pp.

——— 1963. Regional Geology—Keiyasi Area. *Bull. geol. Surv. Fiji*, **10,** 13 pp.

Ibbotson, P. 1969. The Geology of East-central Vanua Levu. *Bull. geol. Surv. Fiji*, **16,** 44 pp.

Isacks, B., Oliver, J. & Sykes, L. R. 1968. Seismology and the new global tectonics. *J. geophys. Res.* **73,** 5855-99.

Karig, D. E. 1970. Ridges and basins of the Tonga-Kermadec island arc system. *J. geophys. Res.* **75,** 239-54.

Malahoff, A. (In prep.) The Fiji plateau, an active spiralling tectonic system.

Phillips, K. A. 1965. A provisional Geological Map of Fiji. *Ann. Rep. geol. Surv. Fiji* (*1964*), 4-6.

Raitt, R. W. 1956. Seismic refraction studies of the Pacific Ocean Basin. Part 1: Crustal thickness of the central equatorial Pacific. *Bull. geol. Soc. Am.* **67,** 1623-40.

Rickard, M. J. 1963. The Geology of Mbalevuto area. *Bull. geol. Surv. Fiji*, **11,** 36 pp.

——— 1966. Reconnaissance Geology of Vanua Levu. *Mem. geol. Surv. Fiji*, **2,** 81 pp.

——— 1970. The geology of north-eastern Vanua Levu. *Bull. geol. Surv. Fiji*, **14,** 13 pp.

Rodda, P. 1967. Outline of the geology of Viti Levu. *N.Z. Jl Geol. Geophys.* **10,** 1260-73.

——— (In prep.) The Geology of northern and central Viti Levu. *Bull. geol. Surv. Fiji*, **13.**

Rodda, P. & Band, R. B. 1967. Part III—Geology of Viti Levu. *Ann. Rep. Geol. Surv. Fiji* (*1966*), 8-16.

Rodda, P., Snelling, N. J. & Rex, D. C. 1967. Radiometric age data on rocks from Viti Levu,

Fiji. *N.Z. Jl Geol. Geophys.* **10,** 1248-59.

Sclater, J. G. & Menard, H. W. 1967. Topography and heat flow of the Fiji Plateau. *Nature*, **216,** 991-3.

Summerhayes, C. P. 1967*a*. New Zealand region volcanism and structure. *Nature*, **215,** 610-11.

——— 1967*b*. Note on the Macquarie Ridge and the Tonga-Kermadec complex—are they parts of the mid-ocean ridge system? *N.Z. Jl Sci.* **10,** 808-12.

Sykes, L. R. 1966. The seismicity and deep structure of island arcs. *J. geophys. Res.* **71,** 2981-3006.

Udintsev, G. 1964. 'Bathymetric map of the Pacific Ocean'. Institute of Oceanology, Moscow.

Vening, Meinesz, F. A. 1951. A third arc in many island arc areas. *Proc. K. ned. Akad. Wet. B* **54** (*S*), 432-42.

Wilson, J. T. 1965. A new class of faults and their bearing on continental drift. *Nature*, **207,** 343-7.

A Summary of the Main Structural Elements of Papua New Guinea[1]

J. H. C. Bain

Bureau of Mineral Resources,
P.O. Box 378, Canberra City, A.C.T., 2601 Australia

ABSTRACT

The Australian Bureau of Mineral Resources 1:1,000,000 scale new geological map of Papua New Guinea has aided the recognition and definition of fourteen main structural and geological elements of Papua New Guinea: the *Fly Platform*, a crystalline Palaeozoic basement veneered with shelf-type Mesozoic and Cenozoic sediments; the *Papuan Fold Belt*, a 50 × 600 km Tertiary fold belt on the uplifted margin of the Palaeozoic basement; the *Kubor Anticline*, uplifted Palaeozoic basement north of the Papuan Fold Belt; the *New Guinea Mobile Belt*, a 100 × 1,600 km mountainous belt north of the Kubor Anticline which contains most of the intrusive, metamorphic, and ultramafic rocks and major faults in mainland Papua New Guinea; the *Papuan Ultramafic Belt*, a 40 × 400 km peridotite-gabbro-basalt complex on the north-eastern side of the Papuan peninsula; two *Palaeogene Volcanic Arcs*, in the New Ireland-Solomons, and New Britain-Finisterre Range areas; the *Torricelli Mountains*. Neogene sediments overlying metamorphic and intrusive rocks of unknown age north of the Sepik River; the Tertiary *Aure Trough*, the Neogene *Cape Vogel Basin*, and the Quaternary *Sepik-Ramu Basin*; the *South-east Papua Tertiary Volcanic Province*, a submarine basalt and chert province; the *Ramu-Markham Fault Zone*, a 10 × 250 km Neogene fault zone; the *Quaternary Volcanoes*, arcuate belts in the Bismarck Archipelago and large irregular fields in eastern Papua and the Papua New Guinea Highlands.

Mainland Papua New Guinea developed from a Palaeozoic nucleus by accretion and subsequent deformation of the products of marginal zones of volcanism and sedimentation migrating north and east from the continent. During the Tertiary, a mobile belt consisting mostly of intrusive, metamorphic, ultramafic, and deformed but unmetamorphosed sedimentary rocks, and deep faults, formed along the outer limit of Palaeozoic basement. A décollement fold and thrust belt formed to the south of the upturned margin of the basement. A northwards movement of Papua New Guinea (which was part of the Australian continent) probably resulted in collision with part of the Palaeogene New Britain-Finisterre island arc and its attachment to the mainland as the Finisterre block. The Papuan Ultramafic Belt is similarly believed to have resulted from interaction between colliding crustal plates.

INTRODUCTION

During the last six years more than 150,000 km^2 of Papua New Guinea have been

[1] This paper is published with the permission of the Director, Bureau of Mineral Resources, Canberra.

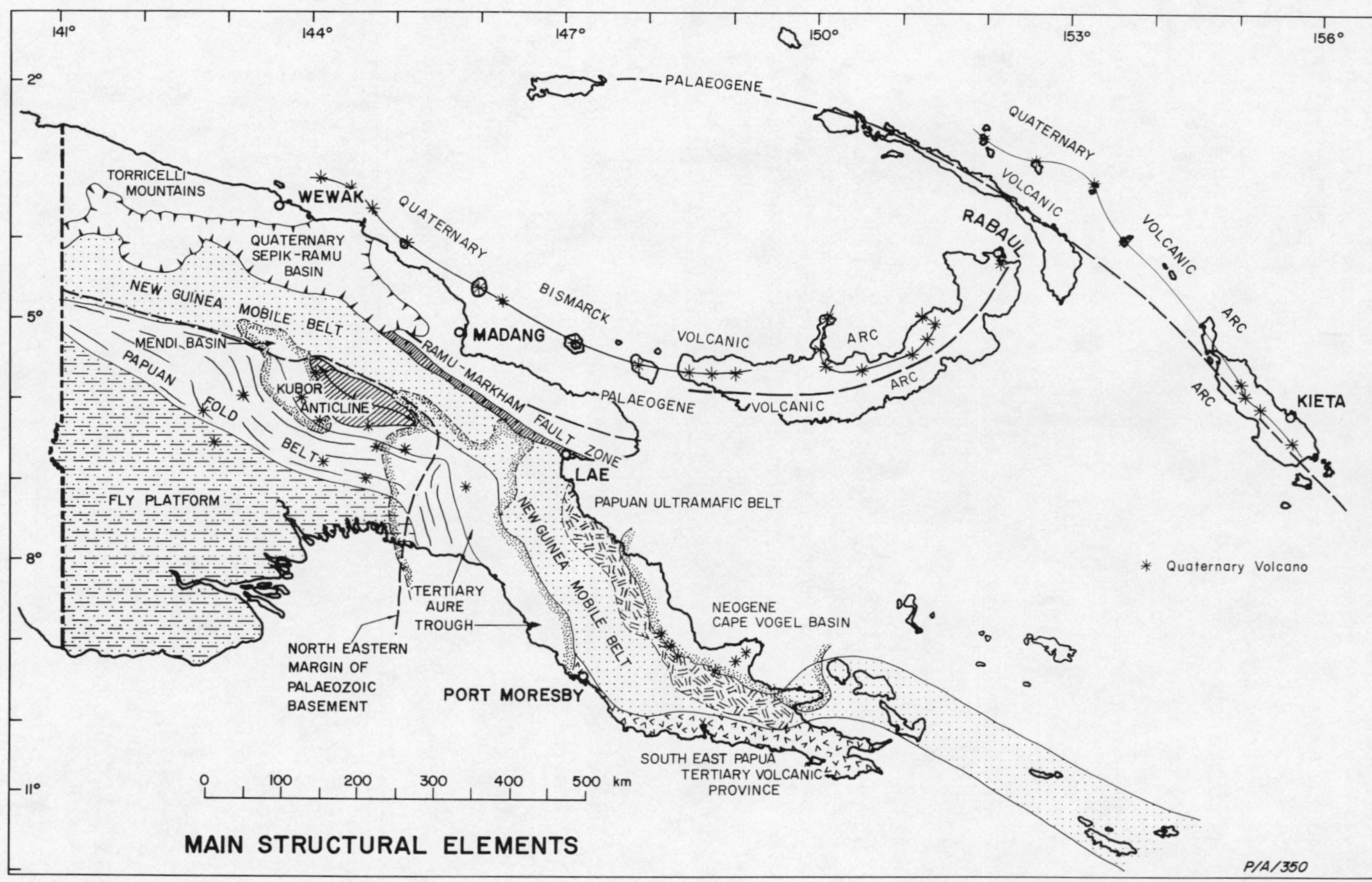

Fig. 1 The primary structural tectonic elements in the area of Papua New Guinea, Louisiade and Bismarck Archipelagos.

mapped at 1 : 250,000 scale by the Bureau of Mineral Resources, and gravity, magnetic and seismic surveys have covered large areas of land and sea. The mapping has progressed so rapidly that most of the information has not yet been published, although it is freely available from the Bureau.

This paper is intended as a summary of the geology to be read in conjunction with the 1 : 1,000,000 scale geological map of Papua New Guinea, which will be published during 1972.

STRUCTURAL ELEMENTS

From the present state of mapping a number of major structural and geological elements in Papua New Guinea can be delineated (Fig. 1).

The *Fly Platform* consists of that part of the rigid, block-faulted, crystalline basement of pre-Mesozoic age (APC 1961) that is overlain by essentially flat-lying Mesozoic sandstone, Neogene shelf limestone and Quaternary sediments (including molasse) and volcanics. The granitic basement is exposed only at Mabaduan on the south-west coast of Papua (9° 40′ S, 142° 40′ E), although several petroleum exploration bores in western Papua have bottomed in granite (APC 1961). The basement extends south beneath Torres Strait and is continuous with the Palaeozoic rocks of north Queensland (Willmott *et al.* 1969). It also extends north and east beneath the Papuan Fold Belt as far as the New Guinea Mobile Belt. The Fly Platform has clearly been part of the Australian continent since at least early Jurassic, and probably late Palaeozoic, time.

The *Papuan Fold Belt* is a belt of subparallel folds and faults (50-70 km wide, 600 km long) which bounds the northern and eastern limits of the Fly Platform and overlies the folded and upturned marginal areas of the crystalline basement (Smith 1965, Jenkins & Martin 1969). The sedimentary succession in the Fold Belt is: 100-5,000 m of Mesozoic marine clastic sediments, thin Palaeogene siltstone, limestone and calcareous sandstone, 200-1,500 m of early Neogene shelf limestone and 100-600 m of late Neogene fine-grained marine and terrestrial clastic sediments. In two places (the Aure Trough and Mendi Basin) the Neogene limestone grades eastwards into flysch-type clastic sediments. The style and state of preservation of the folds varies across the belt: from broad synclines and tight, commonly faulted anticlines in the outer parts (i.e. away from the Fly Platform), to overthrust anticlines and monoclines in the inner parts (Fig. 2). The Tertiary limestone has been considerably shortened within the belt by both folding and overthrusting from the north, or, in the Aure Trough, shortening from the east (Pitt 1966). The outcrop pattern and degree of disturbance of the Mesozoic shales in the anticlinal cores in the outer zone of the belt are suggestive of diapiric folding (Jenkins & Martin 1969). Thrust faults commonly mark a décollement surface between the Tertiary limestone and Mesozoic shales, although some faults clearly extend to considerable depth in the Mesozoic sequence and possibly into the Palaeozoic basement (e.g. Strickland Gorge, R. J. Ryburn pers. comm. 1971). The foreshortening of the sedimentary rocks in the Papuan Fold Belt, therefore, may be due either to diapirism and associated gravity sliding or to north-south compression (east-west in the Aure Trough), or, more likely, to a combination of both.

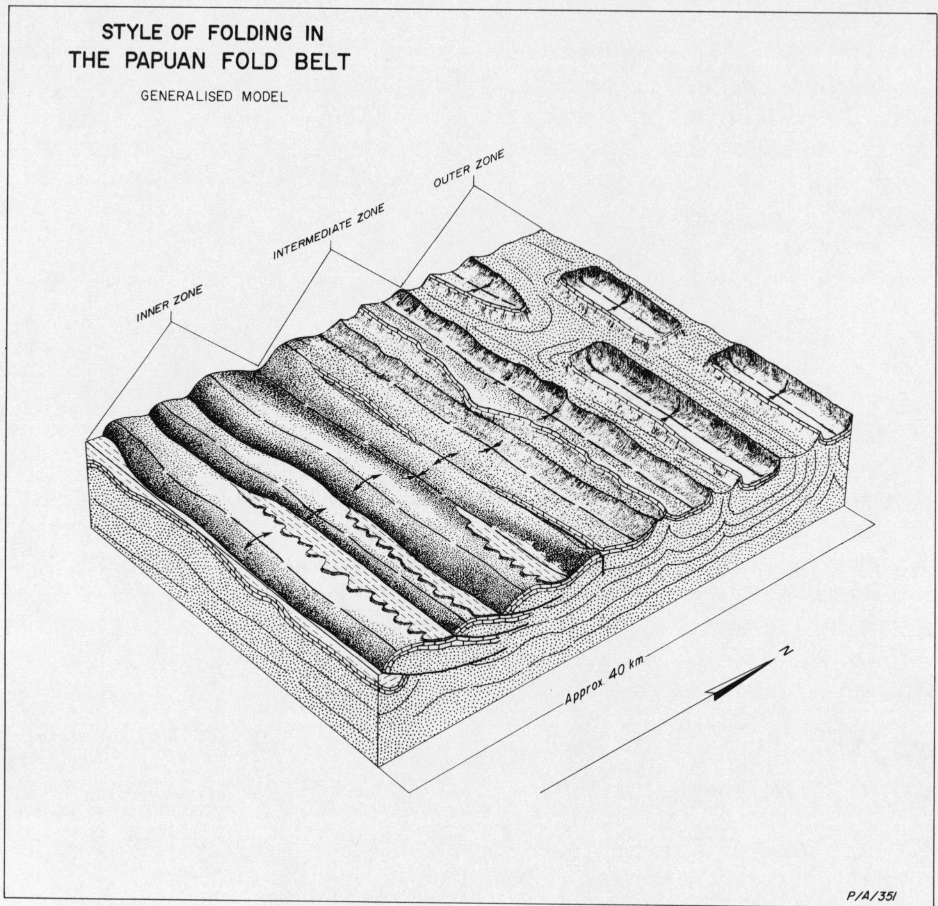

Fig. 2 A generalized model of styles of folding in the Papuan Fold Belt

The *Kubor Anticline*, a 60 × 125 km arch on the north-eastern margin of the Palaeozioc basement, is the largest and easternmost exposure of basement in eastern New Guinea. The core of the anticline consists of low-grade metasediments and minor metavolcanics intruded by Late Permian composite plutons of acid to basic composition. These are overlain by small remnants of Upper Permian to Lower Triassic coralline reef limestone, which are the oldest known fossiliferous rocks in eastern New Guinea (Bain *et al.* 1970). Except for a marine transgression during the Upper Triassic, the crystalline core of the anticline was a landmass from Late Permian time onwards and had a profound influence on sedimentation in the surrounding area. The anticline separates and deflects the two parallel belts of intense deformation—the Papuan Fold Belt and the New Guinea Mobile Belt.

The *New Guinea Mobile Belt* (Dow *et al.* in press, Page 1971) is 50-100 km wide and 1,600 km long, and contains most of the major high-angle faults, and more than

90 per cent of the intrusive, ultramafic and metamorphic rocks of Mesozoic or younger age in Papua New Guinea (excluding Bougainville and the Bismarck Archipelago) (Fig. 3). Deformed but unmetamorphosed volcanic and sedimentary rocks of Mesozoic and Cenozoic age are also present.

The metamorphic rocks are mostly of the greenschist facies, but blueschist, eclogite, and amphibolite are locally present. They were formed during the late Mesozoic to early Neogene by metamorphism of Mesozoic and Palaeogene sedimentary and volcanic rocks.

The intrusive rocks are acid to basic, post-orogenic plutons of Mesozoic to Quaternary age; most are Middle Miocene (12-15 m.y.). They have sharp cross-cutting boundaries, and the larger bodies have deflected major faults. The ultramafic rocks consist of fault-bounded blocks of peridotite, serpentinite, and gabbro emplaced during Palaeogene or early Neogene time.

The faults of the Mobile Belt are anastomosing systems of vertical or steeply dipping major shear zones with long sinuous traces. West of 146° E they have a general west-north-west trend but to the east they trend north and north-north-west. Some of these faults have been active since at least Cretaceous time with vertical movements up to 3,000 m; large lateral movements are indicated but not measurable (Bain *et al.* 1970).

The New Guinea Mobile Belt is situated between the Palaeozoic crystalline basement block to the south and west, and the Torricelli Mountains, Palaeogene Volcanic Arc, and oceanic crust (part of which is the Papuan Ultramafic Belt), to the north and east; it has gradational or obscured contacts to the north and south. The New Guinea Mobile Belt is interpreted as a zone of interaction between opposing plates to the north-east and south-west. By this definition it contains the Papuan Ultramafic Belt which Davies (1971) suggests is the exposed south-western margin of the Solomon Sea oceanic plate. The relationship of the pre-Neogene igneous and metamorphic rocks of the Torricelli Mountains to those of the New Guinea Mobile Belt is not known.

The *Papuan Ultramafic Belt* is a peridotite-gabbro-basalt complex, 40 km × 400 km, dipping oceanwards from the north-eastern side of the Owen Stanley Range in eastern Papua. It consists of an upper zone of 4-6 km of massive and pillow basalt and spilite and minor dacite; a middle zone of gabbro about 4 km thick; and a lowermost zone of ultramafic rocks 4-8 km thick (Davies 1971). Over 90 per cent of the ultramafic zone consists of homogeneous harzburgite, dunite, and enstatite pyroxenite with metamorphic textures; cumulus-textured ultramafics make up the remainder. The complex is bounded by faults, and is intruded by Eocene tonalite at the gabbro-basalt interface. Thompson and Fisher (1965) and Davies (1971) believe the complex may be part of an overthrust sheet of Jurassic-Cretaceous oceanic crust (gabbro and basalt) and upper mantle (ultramafics), which was emplaced during Palaeogene time. If so, the Papuan Ultramafic Belt is the exposed margin of the oceanic crustal plate which underlies part of the Solomon Sea; in any case, it is part of the buffer zone (New Guinea Mobile Belt) between the oceanic and continental plates.

There are two *Palaeogene Volcanic Arcs*. The *Finisterre-New Britain arc* is an

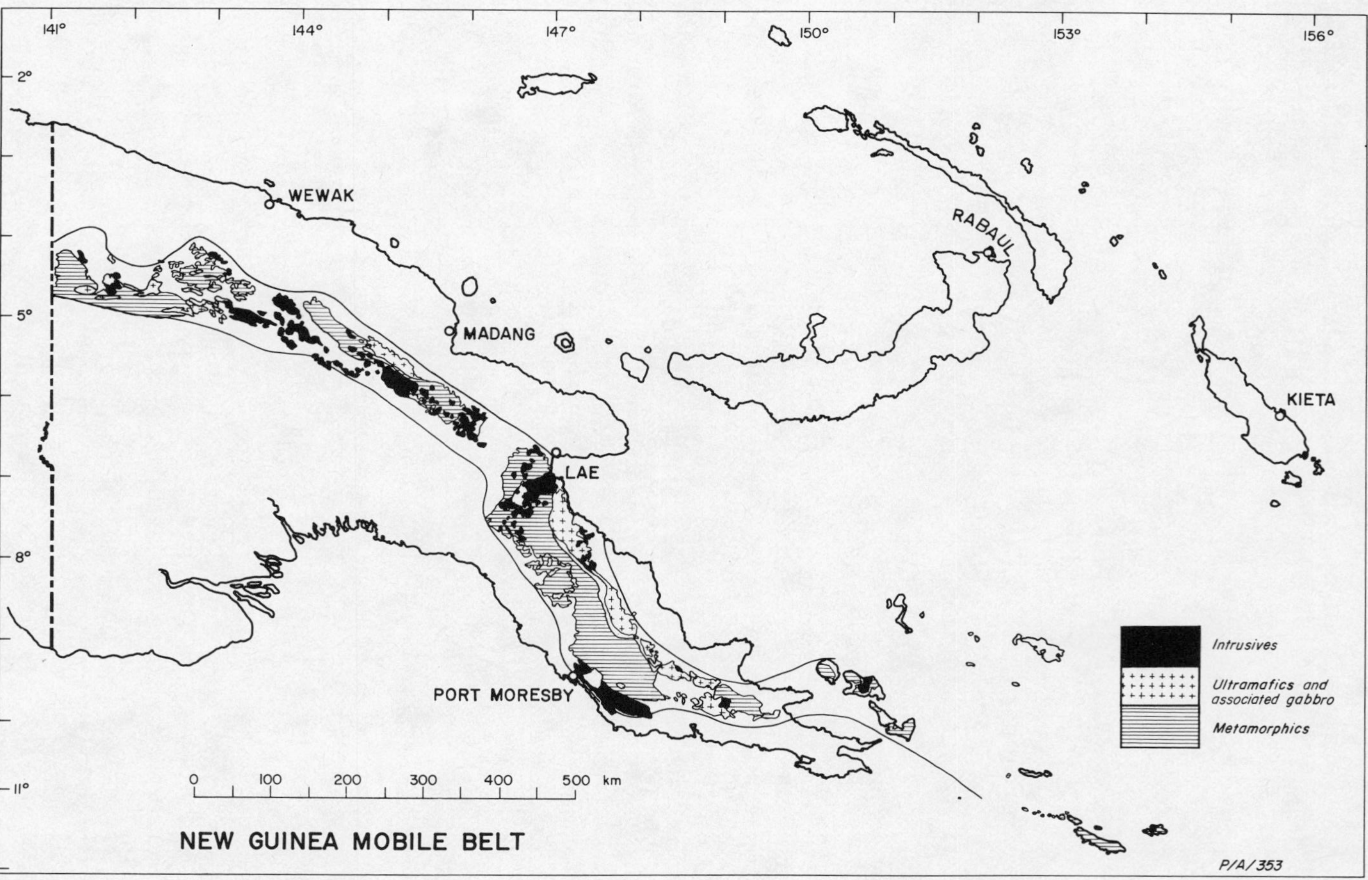

Fig. 3 The New Guinea Mobile Belt, 50-100 km wide and 1,600 km long, the most emphatic tectonic feature of New Guinea

ancient island arc 50-100 km wide and 1,000 km long, composed of andesitic and basaltic marine and terrestrial agglomerate, tuff, and lava, and minor interbedded sediments. The volcanics are mostly altered, incipiently metamorphosed, moderately to strongly folded, and intruded by small acid to basic plutonic and hypabyssal stocks (Mackenzie 1971). Sedimentary rocks are more common in the upper part of the sequence and in the extreme western part of the arc. The arc is extensively overlain by Neogene shoal and reef limestone and minor interbedded sediments. Late Neogene-Quaternary subparallel north-west trending major faults cut the Gazelle Peninsula and southern New Ireland (MacNab 1970). Elsewhere, the island of New Britain has been gently warped about an axis parallel to the length of the island, but not strongly faulted (R. J. Ryburn, pers. comm. 1971). Structural trends in the Finisterre Range are also parallel to the longitudinal axis of the arc. The *Bougainville-New Ireland arc* is a similar but narrower arc, which extends from Manus Island south-eastwards through New Ireland to Bougainville and the Solomon Islands (Blake & Miezitis 1967, Hohnen 1971). The deep structure of New Britain and southern New Ireland is described by Wiebenga *et al.* (this volume).

Although commonly believed to be the north-western extension of the New Britain-Finisterre volcanic arc, the *Torricelli Mountains* are discussed separately because they are not well enough known to be certain of this. The Neogene sediments have been mapped by oil exploration companies, but the igneous and metamorphic rocks are only now being mapped. The main difference between the two areas is that whereas Neogene rocks are underlain by plutonic and metamorphic rocks of Mesozoic (?) age in the Torricelli Mountains, they are underlain by Palaeogene volcanics in the New Britain-Finisterre arc. The absence of Quaternary volcanism from the Torricelli region is another significant difference. Relationships between the Torricelli Mountains and the New Guinea Mobile Belt are masked by the Quaternary sediments of the Sepik-Ramu Basin.

The Quaternary *Sepik-Ramu Basin* consists of low, flat-lying parts of the Sepik and lower Ramu River basins (75×450 km). The basin contains up to 1,500-2,000 m of unconsolidated marine and terrestrial clastic sediments derived from the high mountains that almost completely surround it. Metamorphic rocks, in part overlain by Neogene sediments, underlie most of the basin. Geomorphological evidence suggests that the northern margin of the basin is being elevated and the southern margin depressed; the low-lying parts of the basin are largely covered by swamp.

The Tertiary *Aure Trough*, a 150×400 km flysch basin extending from the central highlands to near Port Moresby (APC 1961) is the largest and deepest clastic basin in Papua New Guinea, and as a structural element includes also the Mendi Basin, from which it is separated by the Kubor Anticline. It adjoins and partly overlaps the New Guinea Mobile Belt to the north and east and overlaps unmetamorphosed Mesozoic rocks to the west, where it thins markedly and grades into shelf limestone and subordinate siltstone. The greater part of the sequence, which has a maximum thickness of 10,000 m, is of Miocene age and contains a large proportion of volcanic detritus (Edwards 1950) derived from the volcanic rocks which crop out along the northern and eastern margins of the basin. Although the axis of the Aure Trough is north-south, most of the post-depositional structural trends are north-north-west

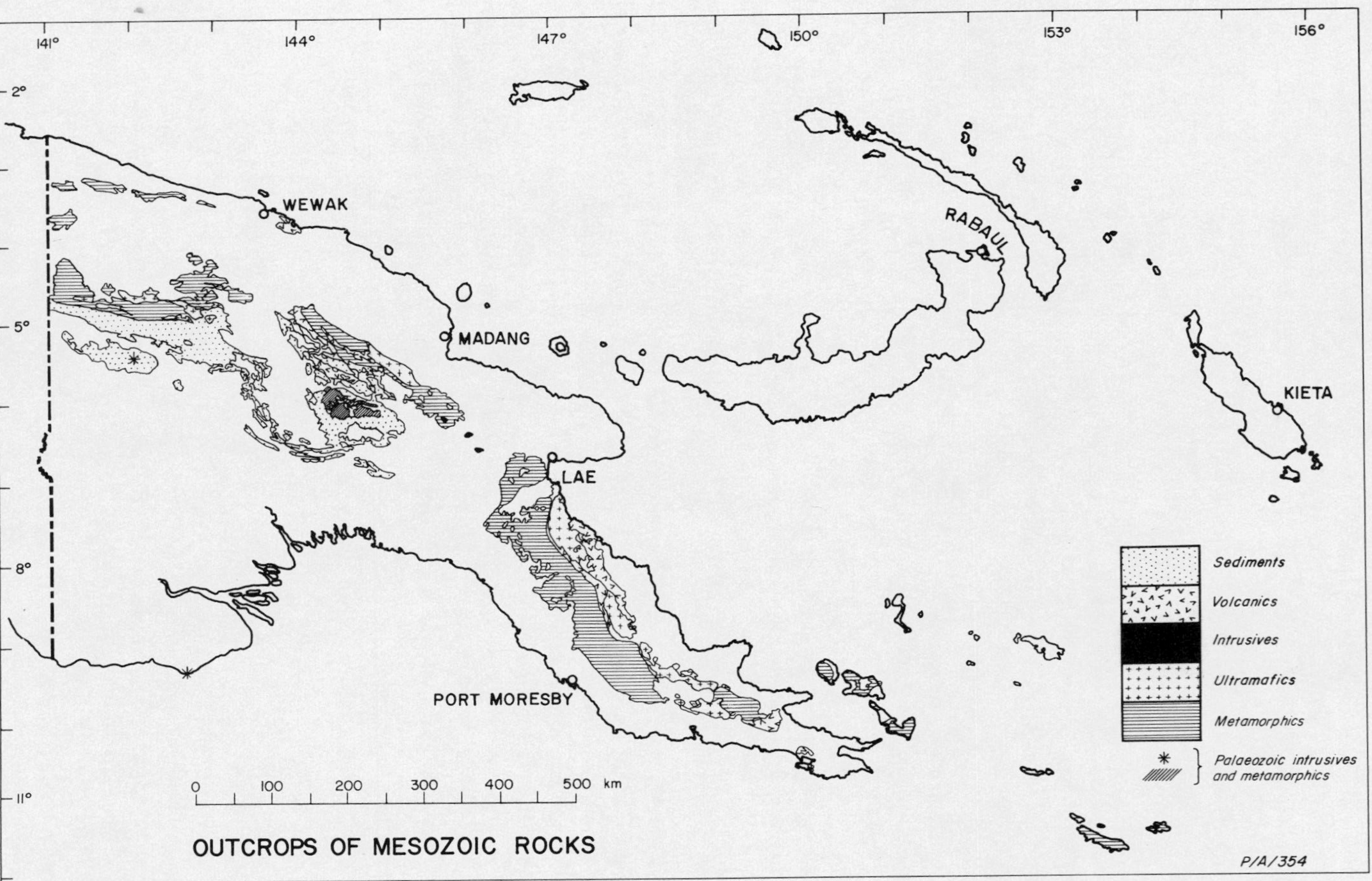

Fig. 4 Outcrop-distribution, as presently known, of Mesozoic rocks (metamorphics, ultramafics, intrusives, volcanics and sediments) in Papua New Guinea. Palaeozoic intrusives are indicated by a star; metamorphics by a patch of right-inclined hachure.

and north-west; in the north-east corner the trends are north-east. Most of the folds and faults (including the part of the Papuan Fold Belt that has been superimposed on the western part of the basin) are believed to be due to east-west compression (Pitt 1966) and uplift along the New Guinea Mobile Belt. The northern embayment of the basin is strongly faulted as a result of vertical and strike-slip movements in that part of the New Guinea Mobile Belt. Deformation occurred throughout the history of the basin and culminated in the late Neogene.

The Neogene *Cape Vogel Basin* (50-100 × 400 km) overlies the Papuan Ultramafic Belt on the north-east side of the Papuan peninsula and contains up to 4,000 m of fine to coarse-grained sedimentary rocks of continental derivation, and subordinate tuff. These are mostly of Middle Miocene to Pliocene age (Davies & Smith 1970). A considerable thickness of Quaternary sedimentary and volcanic rocks covers the Neogene deposits.

The *South-east Papua Tertiary Volcanic Province* (50 × 400 km) overlies the Owen Stanley Metamorphics between Port Moresby and the tip of the Papuan peninsula. It consists mainly of submarine basaltic lavas at least 3,000 m thick, with subordinate lenses of Eocene limestone. West of 148° E the volcanics grade into clastic sediments and then into chert and calcilutite (Yates & de Ferranti 1967). Pliocene shoshonite lavas and agglomerate overlie the Eocene basalts (Davies & Smith 1970).

The *Ramu-Markham Fault Zone* comprises the graben-like south-easterly Ramu and Markham valleys, 10-15 km wide and 250 km long, which separate the Finisterre part of the Palaeogene Finisterre-New Britain volcanic arc from the New Guinea Mobile Belt. The true nature of the zone has not been determined because it is completely covered by Pliocene to Holocene fanglomerate and alluvium. However, it is apparent that vertical movements of more than 1 km and possibly considerable horizontal movements have occurred along the fault zone.

Quaternary Volcanoes, many of them active (Fisher 1957), are found in the Bismarck Archipelago, the Solomon Islands, the central highlands of New Guinea, and eastern Papua (Figs 1 and 7). Rocks of the calcalkaline association predominate, although those of the shoshonite association are common in the central highlands, eastern Papua, and the islands north-east of New Ireland. The distribution and chemistry of the volcanoes is discussed by Johnson *et al.* (this volume).

GEOLOGICAL HISTORY

The Palaeozoic basement (Australia-New Guinea continental crust) of the Fly Platform formed the nucleus for the development of the present landmass of Papua New Guinea. In the Jurassic, Cretaceous, and Upper Paleocene sediments of continental derivation were deposited on this basement. These were overlain by bioclastic shelf limestone in the Palaeogene and lower Neogene, and marine and lacustrine sediments (including molasse) in the upper Neogene and Quaternary (Fig. 7). The Platform was epeirogenically uplifted in the Holocene.

This sedimentary sequence extended and thickened oceanwards, and up to 5 km

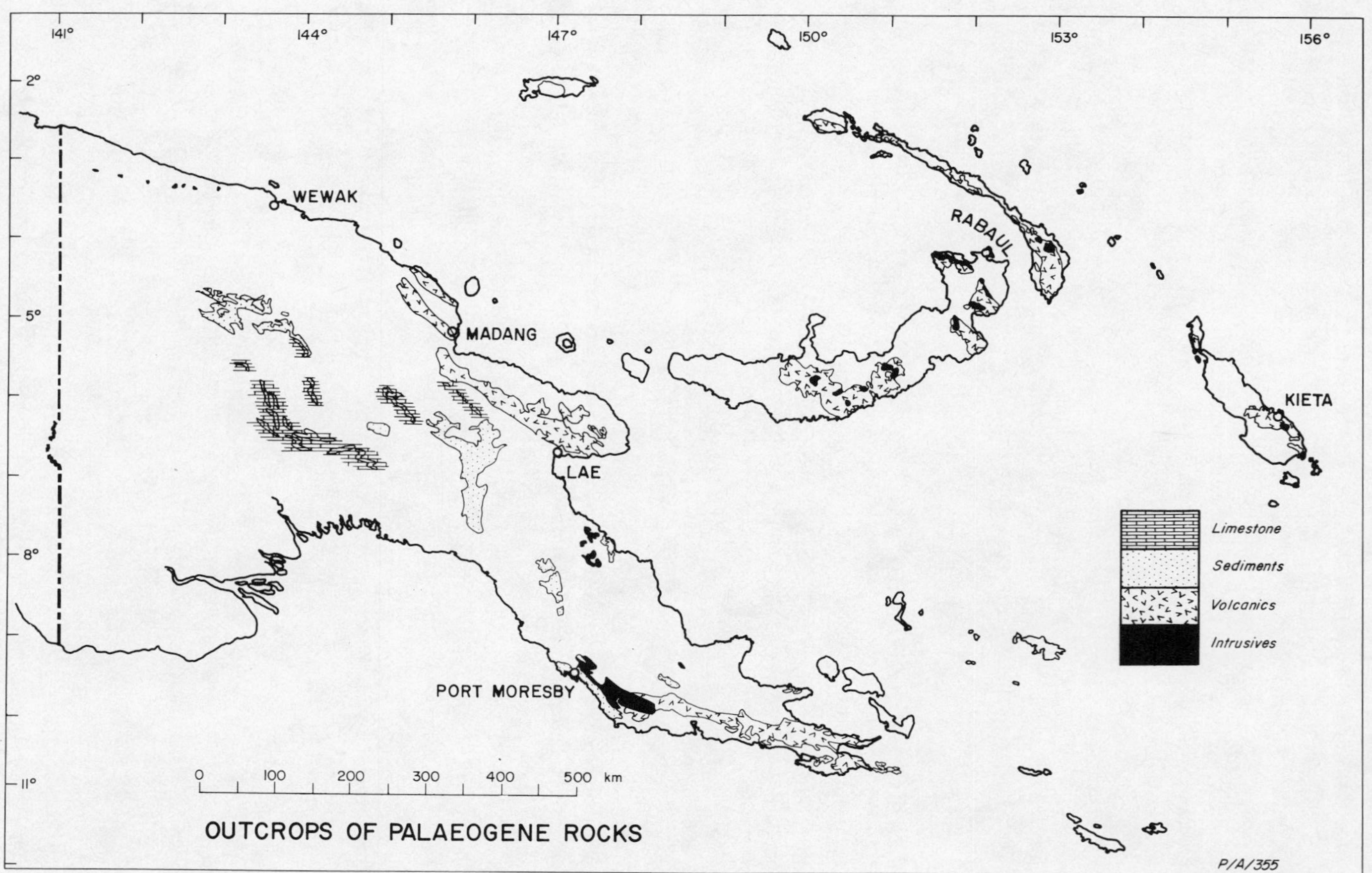

Fig. 5 Outcrop-distribution of Palaeogene (older Tertiary) rocks in Papua New Guinea

of Mesozoic sediments (Fig. 4) accumulated in the vicinity of the Papuan Fold Belt. These sediments were overlain partly by Palaeogene (Fig. 5) and lower Neogene (Fig. 8) shelf limestone, 500-1,500 m thick, and partly by up to 10 km of Tertiary volcanolithic flysch-type sediments and volcanics in the Aure Trough and Mendi Basin (Figs 1, 5 and 6). Marine and lacustrine sediments covered most of the limestone and flysch during the upper Neogene and Pleistocene (Fig. 6).

The Papuan Fold Belt was deformed during the Neogene: in the east probably by east-west compression, and in the west by southerly gravity sliding and diapirism induced by uplift of the northern margin of the Palaeozoic basement, as exemplified by the Kubor Anticline, and by north-south compression consequent on the northward movement of the continental crust.

From Late Permian time onwards the Kubor Anticline was a basement high with a strong influence on the nature of the adjacent Mesozoic and Tertiary sedimentation. The anticline was further arched and elevated to its present position in the late Neogene.

Acid to basic volcanism began on the north-eastern margin of the Palaeozoic basement (Australia-New Guinea continent) in Late Triassic time. Thereafter a great thickness of volcanics and volcanically and continentally derived sediments accumulated on and around the continental margin, and the continent grew oceanwards during the Mesozoic and Palaeogene. The formation of most of the metamorphics and major faults (Figs 3 and 7), and the emplacement of most of the ultramafic and intrusive rocks of Mesozoic or younger age, which characterize the New Guinea Mobile Belt, took place in this marginal zone during the Tertiary. Orogenic uplift occurred in the late Neogene.

The South-east Papua Tertiary Volcanic Province formed in the Eocene when a large volume of basaltic lava was extruded on to the sea floor in eastern Papua immediately south of the New Guinea Mobile Belt. Eocene chert and calcareous clastic sediments were also deposited in this submarine volcanic province. The volcanism may have been connected with opening of the Coral Sea (Davies & Smith 1970). After a period of uplift and erosion in the late Palaeogene and early Neogene, parts of the region were covered by subaerial basic volcanics during the Pliocene.

Rocks of the Papuan Ultramafic Belt formed in the Jurassic and Cretaceous, probably as a part of the oceanic crust of the Solomon Sea. In the Palaeogene or early Neogene they were thrust over the metamorphic rocks of the New Guinea Mobile Belt. Both belts were uplifted during the late Neogene and Quaternary.

The Cape Vogel Basin developed during the Neogene and Quaternary on the north-east flank of the emergent New Guinea Mobile Belt (specifically the Papuan Ultramafic Belt), and was filled with material shed from the belt. The southern margin of the basin was uplifted during the Holocene by continued emergence of the New Guinea Mobile Belt.

Volcanic island arcs developed in the Bougainville-New Ireland-Manus and New Britain-Finisterre areas during the Palaeogene. Fluctuations in the intensity of volcanic activity, and periodic uplift of parts of the arcs, resulted in alternate episodes of essentially reef-limestone growth and volcanic and volcaniclastic sedimentation, which have continued to the present day. Opposing movements of the New Britain-

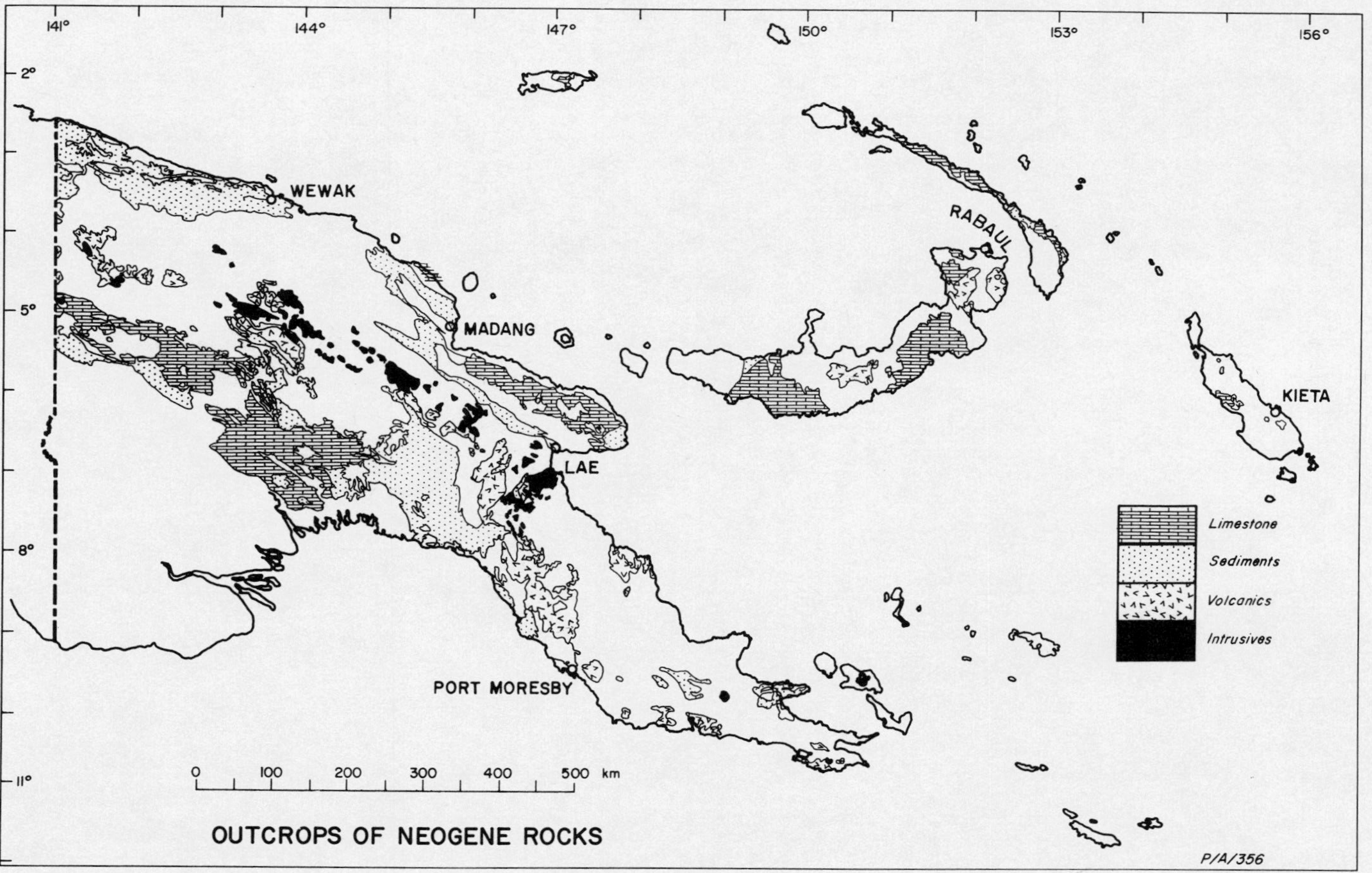

Fig. 6 Outcrop-distribution of Neogene (younger Tertiary) rocks in Papua New Guinea

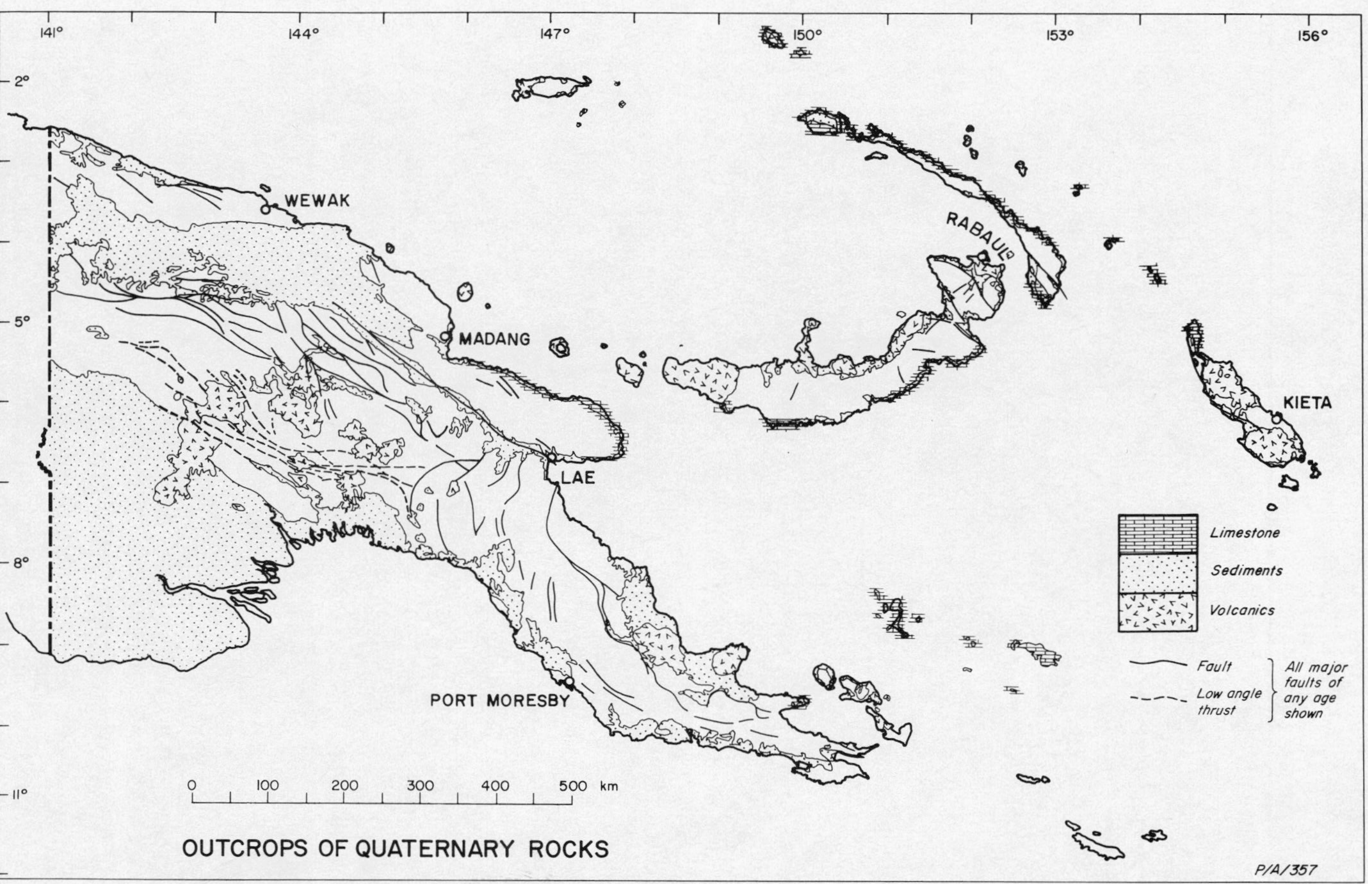

Fig. 7 The broad spread of Quaternary rock outcrops in Papua New Guinea. Major faults (all ages) are also shown.

Finisterre arc and mainland Papua New Guinea probably resulted in attachment of the Finisterre part of the arc to the mainland during the late Neogene. The New Britain arc probably moved southwards with respect to the Bougainville-New Ireland arc, resulting in attenuation of the Gazelle Peninsula and southern New Ireland.

In the Neogene marine clastics were deposited on the presumably late Mesozoic to Palaeogene metamorphic and igneous basement of the Torricelli Mountains. The probable source of the sediments was the emergent New Guinea Mobile Belt and subordinate local volcanism. The region was folded, faulted, and uplifted in the late Neogene or Quaternary, or both.

At that time a large basin (Sepik-Ramu Basin) opened between the Torricelli Mountains and New Guinea Mobile Belt and was partly filled with Pliocene and Quaternary marine and lacustrine sediments.

Interaction between the Finisterre area and the New Guinea Mobile Belt during the Neogene gave rise to the Ramu-Markham Fault Zone, which is now represented by a pronounced graben-line valley along most of its length. The valley floor was covered by fanglomerates and alluvium in the Pliocene and Quaternary.

Numerous volcanoes, many still active, formed on the mainland, on the islands, and in the seas off the north-east coasts of the mainland and New Ireland during the Quaternary.

ACKNOWLEDGEMENTS

I gratefully acknowledge the assistance and encouragement of my colleagues in Canberra and Port Moresby, especially H. L. Davies and R. J. Ryburn. D. B. Dow, D. E. Mackenzie and R. W. Johnson critically read the manuscript and offered valuable advice.

REFERENCES

APC (Australasian Petroleum Co.) 1961. Geological results of petroleum exploration in Western Papua 1937-61. *J. geol. Soc. Aust.* **8,** 1-133.

Bain, J. H. C., Mackenzie, D. E. & Ryburn, R. J. 1970. Geology of the Kubor Anticline—Central Highlands of New Guinea. Rec. Bur. Miner. Resour. Aust. 1970/79 (unpubl.).

Blake, D. H. & Miezitis, Y. 1967. Geology of Bougainville and Buka, New Guinea. *Bull. Bur. Miner. Resour. Aust.* **93.**

Davies, H. L. 1971. Peridotite-gabbro-basalt complex in eastern Papua: an overthrust plate of oceanic mantle and crust. *Bull. Bur. Miner. Resour. Aust.* **128.**

Davies, H. L. & Smith, I. E. 1970. Geology of Eastern Papua: a synthesis. Rec. Bur. Miner. Resour. Aust. 1970/116 (unpubl.).

Dow, D. B., Smit, J. A. J., Bain, J. H. C. & Ryburn, R. J. (In press.) Geology of the South Sepik Region. *Bull. Bur. Miner. Resour. Aust.* **133.**

Edwards, A. B. 1950. The petrology of the Miocene sediments of the Aure Trough, Papua. *Proc. R. Soc. Vict.* **60,** 123-48.

Fisher, N. H. 1957. Catalogue of the Active Volcanoes of the World including solfatara fields. Part V. Melanesia. *Int. volc. Assoc. Naples.*

Hohnen, P. D. 1970. Geology of New Ireland. Rec. Bur. Miner. Resour. Aust. 1970/49 (unpubl.).

Jenkins, D. A. L. & Martin, A. J. 1969. Recent investigations into the geology of the Southern Highlands, Papua. *Econ. Comm. Asia & Far East* (*ECAFE*). 4th Symposium on the development of petroleum resources of Asia and the Far East, Canberra, Australia.

Johnson, R. W., Mackenzie, D. E., Smith, I. E. & Taylor, G. A. M. 1972. Distribution and petrology of Late Cenozoic volcanoes in Papua New Guinea. This volume.

Mackenzie, D. E. 1971. Intrusive rocks of New Britain. Rec. Bur. Miner. Resour. Aust. 1971/70 (unpubl.).

MacNab, R. P. 1970. Geology of the Gazelle Peninsula, T.P.N.G. Rec. Bur. Miner. Resour. Aust. 1970/63 (unpubl.).

Page, R. W. 1971. The geochronology of igneous rocks in the New Guinea region. Ph.D. thesis, Aust. Nat. Univ., Canberra.

Pitt, R. P. B. 1966. Tectonics in Central Papua and the adjoining part of New Guinea. Ph.D. thesis, Univ. of Tasmania, Hobart.

Smith, J. G. 1965. Orogenesis in western Papua and New Guinea. *Tectonophysics*, **2**, 1-27.

Thompson, J. E. & Fisher, N. H. 1965. Mineral deposits of New Guinea and Papua, and their tectonic setting. *Proc. 8th Comm. Min. Metall. Congr.* **6,** 115-48.

Wiebenga, W. A. 1972. Crustal structure of the New Britain-New Ireland Region. This volume.

Willmott, W. F., Palfreyman, W. D., Trail, D. S. & Whitaker, W. G. 1969. The igneous rocks of Torres Strait, Queensland and Papua. Rec. Bur. Miner. Resour. Aust. 1969/119 (unpubl.).

Yates, K. R. & De Ferranti, R. Z. 1967. The Astrolabe mineral field. *Rep. Bur. Miner. Resour. Aust.* **105.**

Crustal Structure of the New Britain-New Ireland Region[1]

W. A. Wiebenga

Bureau of Mineral Resources, P.O. Box 378, Canberra City, A.C.T. 2601 Australia

ABSTRACT

Results of seismic and gravity surveys which were conducted during 1967 and 1969 in the Bismarck Archipelago by the Australian Bureau of Mineral Resources, Geology and Geophysics in association with various universities are described briefly. A correlation between seismic velocities and rock densities is used to support seismic interpretation. The mechanism for trench-forming is described. A lithospheric slab is sagging and sinking under its own weight in a subduction zone underneath New Britain. Tensional, or differential, stresses have fractured the lithosphere to allow the formation of large intrusives and volcanic zones. At the lower part of the crust the common rock type is probably amphibolite. Block faulting, associated with graben formation, was superimposed on the earlier tectonic pattern. Some block faults have an appreciable sinistral component. The mechanism given for the New Britain Trench may possibly be used for the Bougainville trench except that activity started later.

INTRODUCTION

In 1967, and again in 1969, the Australian Bureau of Mineral Resources conducted long-range seismic refraction experiments in the Bismarck Archipelago (Fig. 1). These ventures, which were co-operative programmes with the University of Hawaii, the University of Queensland and the Australian National University, have been the source of much new information bearing on the structure and history of this complex region. Brooks (1971) has described the operational aspects of these surveys and presented the time-distance data, and a detailed interpretation of these data will be published shortly.

Further new geophysical data for the region have been provided by land-gravity surveys, marine magnetic surveys and continuous seismic profiling, carried out in conjunction with the seismic experiments. In addition, the Bureau of Mineral Resources has recently completed a systematic survey of the Bismarck Sea, during which shipboard gravity, magnetic and reflection seismic observations were made.

In view of the current interest in the New Britain-New Ireland region as a possible

[1] Published with the permission of the Director, Bureau of Mineral Resources, Canberra.

site of plate convergence and interaction, it has seemed desirable to attempt to make a synthesis of the recent data in terms of possible large-scale tectonic processes.

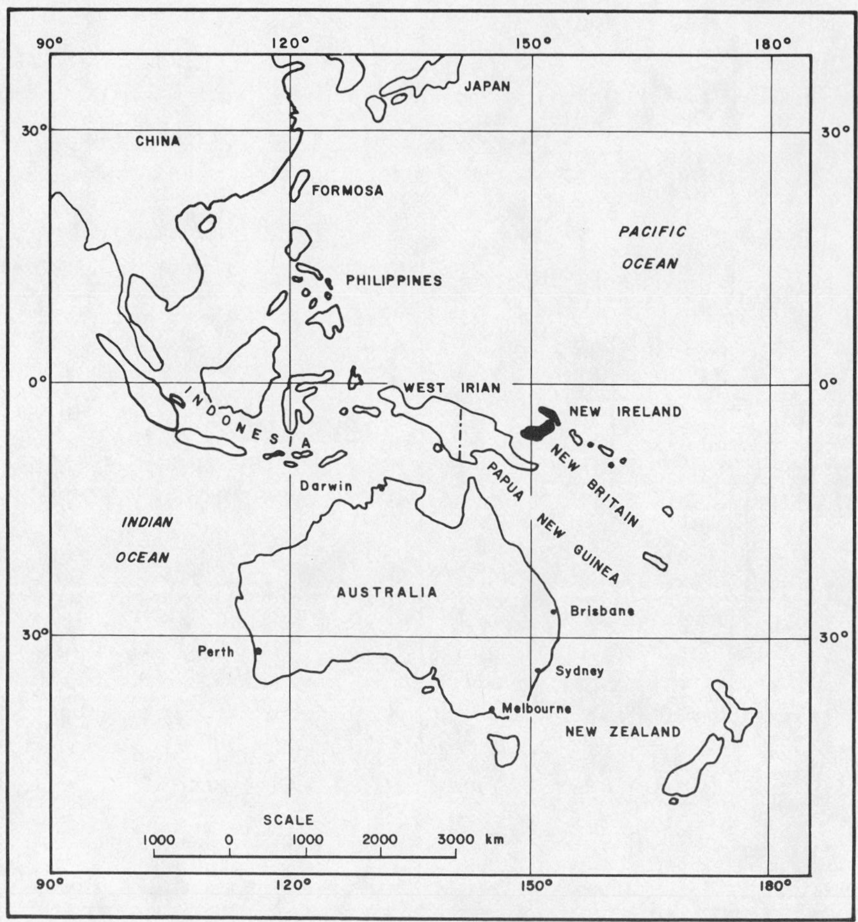

Fig. 1 General locality map of the Bismarck Archipelago (New Britain and New Ireland)

REGIONAL GEOLOGY

New Britain displays many of the features which characterize island arcs (Fig. 2). It has an elongated, arcuate shape, an oceanic trench (New Britain Trench), an inclined zone of earthquake foci dipping steeply beneath the island (Denham 1969), and a belt of volcanism along the north coast. New Ireland, on the other hand, is not obviously associated with a trench, and has no active volcanoes, though there is a chain of volcanic islands parallel to the Pacific coast of the island. The following summary of the geological history of the islands is based on R. J. Ryburn in Brooks (1971).

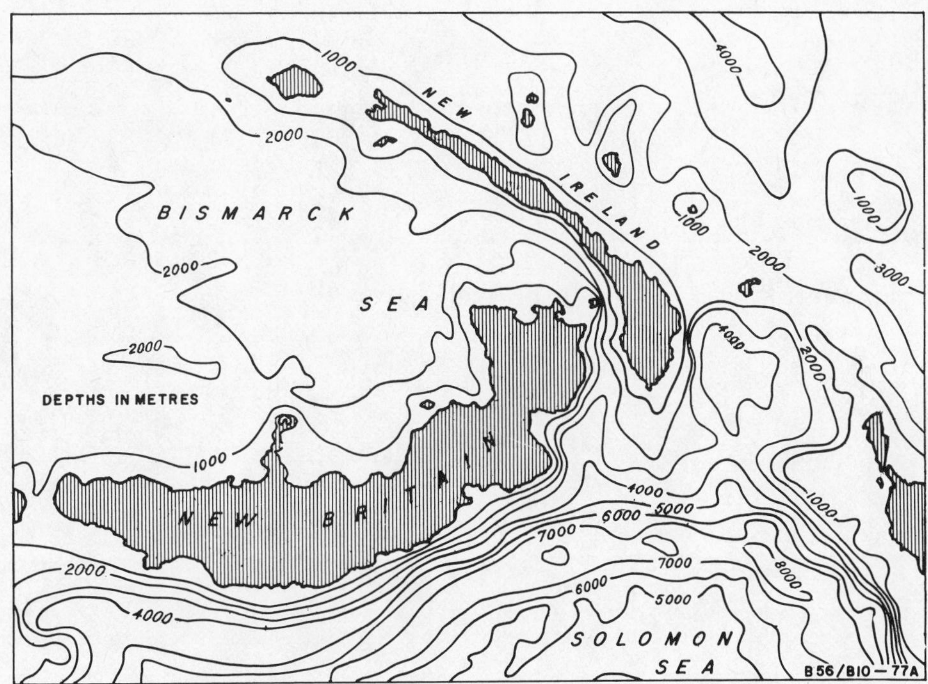

Fig. 2 Bathymetric map of the area of the Bismarck Archipelago. The length of New Britain is approximately 480 km.

The geological evolution of New Britain appears to have started in the Eocene with an episode of island arc volcanism. The resulting volcanic rocks, and derived sediments underlie much of the island, with thicknesses exceeding 2,000 m. These were subsequently subjected to folding, faulting, uplift and erosion in the Lower Oligocene.

Basic to intermediate plutonic rocks were emplaced along the axis of the island in the Upper Oligocene in bodies up to 15 km diameter. Associated volcanism produced pyroclastics, lava, and derived marine and terrestrial sediments which occur in the Wide Bay-Open Bay isthmus and west of the Willaumez Peninsula.

In the Miocene, New Britain underwent a period of slow subsidence during which reef limestones were deposited over much of the island, with thicknesses in places up to 1,500 m. The base of the limestone is early Miocene in western New Britain and becomes progressively younger eastwards to the Gazelle Peninsula, where it is Middle Miocene. Limestone deposition continued into basal Pliocene times in some areas. Intermediate to acid volcanism in the Upper Miocene and Pliocene produced tuffaceous sediments, pyroclastics and minor lava flows on the Gazelle Peninsula and central New Britain.

Much of the present mountainous topography of New Britain is the result of block faulting and regional uplift, which seems to have started in the late Pliocene or early Pleistocene, and probably continues today. This uplift has produced, on the south coast of New Britain and the east coast of the Gazelle Peninsula, a series of raised coral reefs, exhibiting, in some places, as many as six terrace levels. The uplift appears to have been as great as 500 m, but varies laterally. Recently formed reefs, a few metres above sea-level, indicate that this uplift is still active. The north coast shows no evidence of Quaternary uplift, and may, in fact, be subsiding.

Contemporaneous with the renewal of tectonic activity in the late Pliocene or early Pleistocene, volcanism was again active in New Britain. Quaternary volcanic rocks are found in the Gazelle Peninsula at Rabaul, at the western end of the island, and along the north coast, where the Willaumez Peninsula may represent a large fracture at right angles to the major volcanic axis. For the most part, these rocks are the products of central-type volcanoes, many of which are still active. They range in composition from tholeiitic basalt to rhyolite, with the most abundant lava type of intermediate composition, similar to that of the 'andesites' described from several island arcs of the Western Pacific.

New Ireland, like New Britain, is underlain by a sequence of volcanic rocks at least 2,000 m thick, produced by island arc-type volcanism in the Oligocene. Along much of the length of the island, the volcanic basement is intruded by numerous stocks and dykes of gabbro, norite, diorite and tonalite, together with hypabyssal equivalents. These intrusions are probably related to the Oligocene volcanism.

In the Lower Miocene, orogenesis caused intense faulting and tilting of the Oligocene volcanic rocks. This ceased in the late Lower Miocene, and was followed by a long period of intermittent subsidence. Limestones accumulated during this episode, with deposition continuing into the Pliocene, and in some areas into the Pleistocene. The limestones are absent in the central part of the island, where the Oligocene basement is unconformably overlain by up to 500 m of volcanic rocks of Upper Miocene to Pliocene age.

In the late Pleistocene the whole of New Ireland was rapidly uplifted and tilted towards the north-east, so that the extensive plateau limestones now dip at 5°-10° to the north-east.

The Weitin Fault, which trends north-west across southern New Ireland, is a major structural feature, probably at least partly responsible for the strongly linear shape of the south-west coast of the island today. The north-east coast also appears to be fault bounded, at least in part, but the details have largely been hidden by Quaternary deposits.

GEOPHYSICAL DATA

Previous Geophysical Studies

Apart from studies of earthquake distribution, there has been little geophysical work done which bears directly on the problem of the nature and origin of the major structural features of the New Guinea-New Britain area.

During 1966 the Bureau of Mineral Resources carried out preliminary tests to evaluate the usefulness of deep seismic sounding methods in the Rabaul area. This study, reported by Cifali *et al.* (1969), resulted in a tentative model crust for the Rabaul area, consisting of near-surface layers with *P* velocities of 1·5 km/s and 2·8 km/s, and deeper layers with velocities near 5·0 km/s and 7·0 km/s. In the immediate vicinity of Rabaul the depth to the top of the 5·0 km/s layer varied between 1 and 3 km.

Denham (1968), from a study of *P* wave spectra, derived a crustal model for Rabaul showing two discontinuities, one at 14 km depth where the *P* velocity increased to 7·5 km/s, and one at 50 km depth where the velocity was 8·0 km/s. In 1969, from a study of the distribution of earthquake foci with depth, he indicated a north-westerly dipping focal zone beneath New Britain.

Gravity, magnetic and seismic refraction data for the Solomon Sea, obtained by the Hawaii Institute of Geophysics, are reported by Furumoto *et al.* (1970) and Rose *et al.* (1968). A preliminary account of seismic refraction results from the Ontong Java Plateau, to the east of New Ireland, is given by Woollard (1970).

Green and Pitt (1967) have published a tentative interpretation of a small number of palaeomagnetic measurements on New Guinea rocks, which suggests a change in the pole azimuth since the Early Tertiary, indicating an anti-clockwise rotation of New Guinea. Other arguments supporting similar changes in the relative position of New Guinea have been given by Gardner (1970). There is, as yet, no quantitative evidence relating to possible changes in the relative positions of New Britain and New Ireland.

Seismic Refraction Data

Because the details have been given elsewhere (Brooks 1971) it is not necessary to present here a lengthy discussion of the methods of interpretation used in deriving a crustal model from the data of the 1967 and 1969 New Britain-New Ireland seismic experiments. Difficulties which arose during the interpretation should be mentioned, however, in order that certain limitations of the model may be understood.

The two seismic experiments, together, involved recording over 80 shots at nearly 50 stations, so that a very large number of data were available for analysis. However, because the locations of stations, and sometimes those of shots, were determined in varying measure by considerations of logistics, their distribution was far from ideal. One serious shortcoming has been the fact that the stations were, to a large extent, centrally grouped on the land area, with shots in the surrounding seas (Fig. 3), so that it was not always possible to obtain satisfactorily reversed profiles. On the other hand, many stations observed shots at several azimuths, so that by suitably grouping shots and stations a measure of control on the computation of refractor attitude was obtained. For future surveys in this area, it may be useful to consider extending this method of azimuthal profiles along the lines suggested by Brown *et al.* (1971), though implementing it in an area of complex structure may not be easy.

Because of the generally open pattern of shots, near-surface layers were not usually well determined, though this restriction was not as acute in the Rabaul area, where it

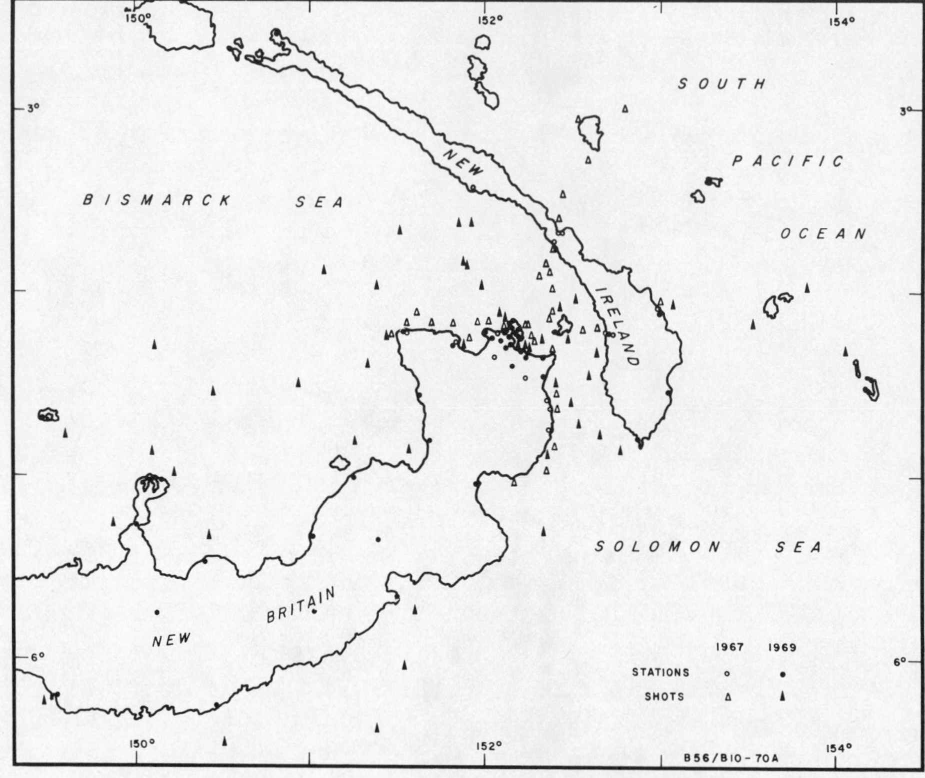

Fig. 3 Localities of seismic shots and stations

was possible to obtain a relatively dense pattern of shots and stations. Despite the difficulty of determining the velocities of the uppermost layers in many areas, it is believed that, in general, computed depths to the Mohorovicic discontinuity are correct to ± 10 per cent of the depth.

The results of the seismic interpretation are shown in Fig. 4, in the form of contours on the surface of the Mohorovicic discontinuity. In preparing this map, use has been made of the Hawaii Institute of Geophysics data for the Solomon Sea (Furumoto *et al.* 1971) and for the area immediately to the north-east of southern New Ireland (Woollard 1970). Also shown are generalized faults and lineaments based on geophysical interpretation, sparker surveys, geology and morphology.

The broad features of the crustal structure represented by Fig. 4 are as follows:

1. A crust of intermediate thickness in the south-east part of the Bismarck Sea, traversed by a west-south-west trending zone of thinner crust between Vitu Island and the north-western extremity of the Gazelle Peninsula;

2. A generally thick (30-40 km) crust below New Britain and New Ireland, with local thinning (15-20 km) in the central part of New Britain and the western portion of the Gazelle Peninsula;

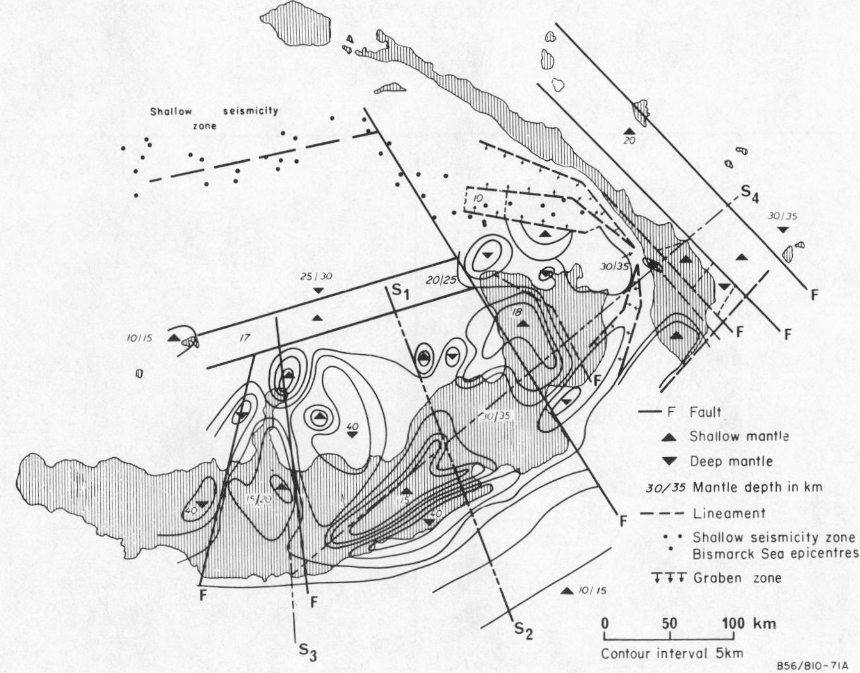

Fig. 4 Moho surface contours for the New Britain area

3. Local thickening (40+ km) of the crust in the vicinity of the volcanic province of the New Britain north coast and the Willaumez Peninsula;

4. Thick crust (40+ km) on the New Britain side of the New Britain Trench, with thinner, oceanic type crust on the Solomon Sea side of the trench;

5. A north-westerly trending zone of thinner (less than 20 km) crust between New Ireland and the thick (30-35 km) crust of the Ontong Java Plateau.

Fig. 4 also shows the location of the pronounced trough between New Britain and New Ireland, reported by Brooks *et al.* (1971). This appears to be a major crustal feature of considerable significance, though its role in the regional tectonics is not known.

Velocity-Density Relationships

Fig. 5 plots *P* velocity against density for a representative suite of rocks obtained from outcrops in New Britain, and for eight samples of ultrabasic rocks from eastern Papua. The densities and *P* velocities, determined in the Bureau of Mineral Resources' Rock Testing Laboratory, are estimated to be accurate to 1 per cent and 2 per cent respectively.

The New Britain samples, twenty-five in number, range in composition from acid volcanic rocks to gabbro, and are believed to be typical of the exposed rocks of the island. The plotted points have been fitted with a smooth curve, and this has been extended linearly to the density and velocity values suggested for rocks at 1 kb pressure.

Fig. 5 suggests that the East Papua and New Britain samples belong to different geological provinces. Using Birch's empirical relation between density, seismic velocity and mean atomic weight (Birch 1961) the mean atomic weight in the East Papua samples would be about 23, in the New Britain samples about 22, suggesting a slightly higher iron content in the Papua samples.

This graph has been used as the basis for assigning density values to the layers

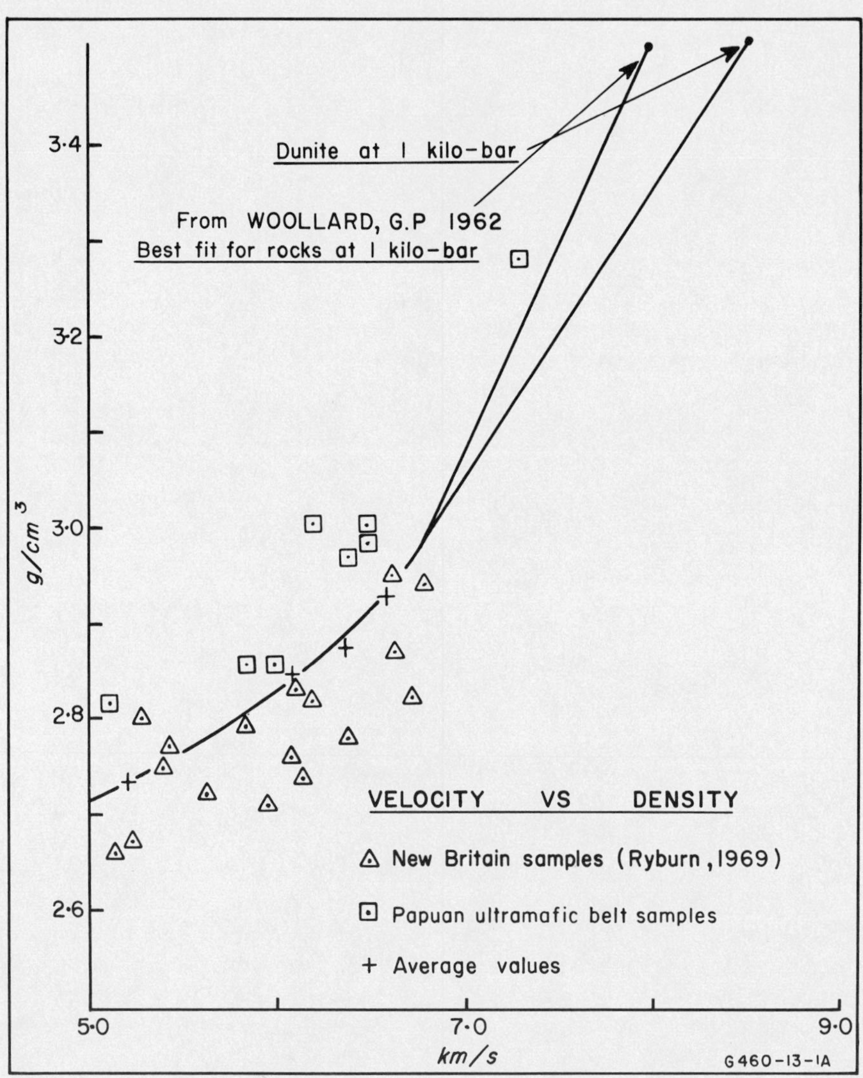

Fig. 5 Velocity/density relationships for a suite of rocks from New Britain and eastern Papua

defined in the seismic model, in turn to permit the computation of gravity anomalies from crustal models.

In accordance with tables published by Clark (1966), summarized by Bott (1971), the velocity/density information can be translated into geological terms, e.g. quartz diorite, gabbro/norite, amphibolite and dunite have mean densities of 2·85, 2·99, 3·12 and 3·28 g/cm^3; mean 1 kb pressure velocities of 6·4, 7·02, 7·17 and 8·20, and mean 10 kb pressure velocities of 6·7, 7·24, 7·35 and 8·31 km/s, respectively.

Transitions between rock types will involve transitions in velocity and density.

A rise in temperature of a few hundred degrees usually corresponds to an appreciable decrease in seismic velocity, e.g. in 'hot' volcanic zone mantle velocities may drop from about 8·1 to about 7·6 km/s, as was observed along the larger part of section S_3 to S_4, Fig. 8.

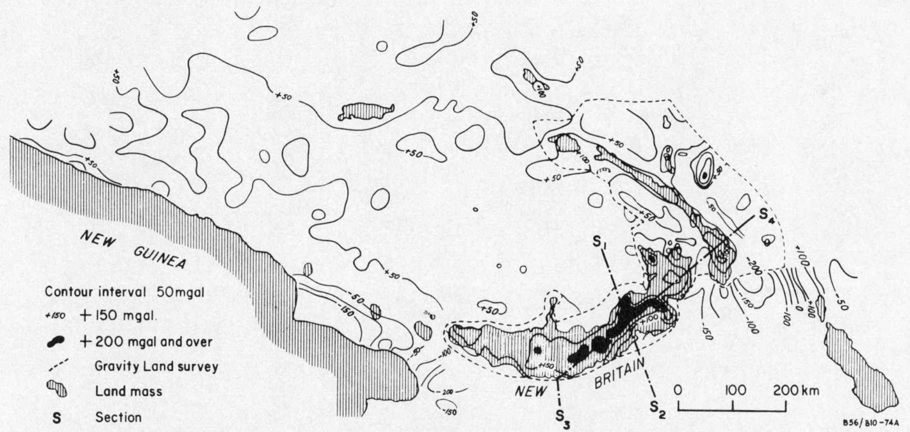

Fig. 6 Free-air gravity anomalies in the Bismarck Archipelago and adjacent areas

Gravity Data

Gravity data in the New Britain-New Ireland and Bismarck Sea areas were obtained by helicopter and marine surveys by the Regional Gravity and Marine Survey Groups of the Bureau of Mineral Resources during 1969 and 1970 (not yet published). Data for the Solomon Sea and neighbouring Pacific Ocean were taken from Rose and Tracy (1971).

Fig. 6 shows the Free Air Anomalies (FAA). For structural computations the FAA in the land areas should be adjusted for terrain. In the centre of New Britain (see Figs 6 and 7) the resulting effect is a reduction of the FAA by about 90 to 100 mgal.

The FAA pattern of New Britain as a whole gives the impression of a giant fracture in the crust through which higher density material has flowed to the surface. Except for the trench areas, and an area between Bougainville and New Ireland, the marine gravity values are moderately high, up to +100 mgal. However, without seismic data it is not possible to evaluate the significance of the gravity patterns.

To check the seismic sections equivalent densities were determined for the seismic velocities (Fig. 4). The section was then subdivided into four-sided two-dimensional blocks, infinite in the third dimension, and of constant density within the block. The gravity effect of the blocks along the profiles were calculated with a Hewlett-Packard calculator using a formula given by Grant and West (1965). Following Woollard (1962) the standard crust for which FAA=0 was taken to have a thickness of 32 km, with crust and mantle densities of 2·9 and 3·3 g/cm^3 respectively. After computation of the gravity effects of the individual blocks, the gravity effects for discrete locations along the section were summed, giving the computed FAA. Discrepancies between the computed and observed FAA were corrected by modifying the section.

In some places large regional discrepancies in the computed gravity values cannot be eliminated by reasonable modifications in crustal structure and density. In such instances a slight change in the mantle density in the 30-100 km depth range was assumed. For instance, in the south-east part of the Bismarck Sea an upper mantle density of 3·33-3·34 gives a good fit. This agrees with the exceptionally high east-west mantle velocities which were recently computed for this zone and which will be discussed in a later paper.

TECTONICS

It is generally considered that compressive stresses have formed island arcs and trenches with a volcanic zone on the concave side of the structure, e.g. Isacks *et al.* (1968). According to this theory a dipping shear plane was developed, lithosphere

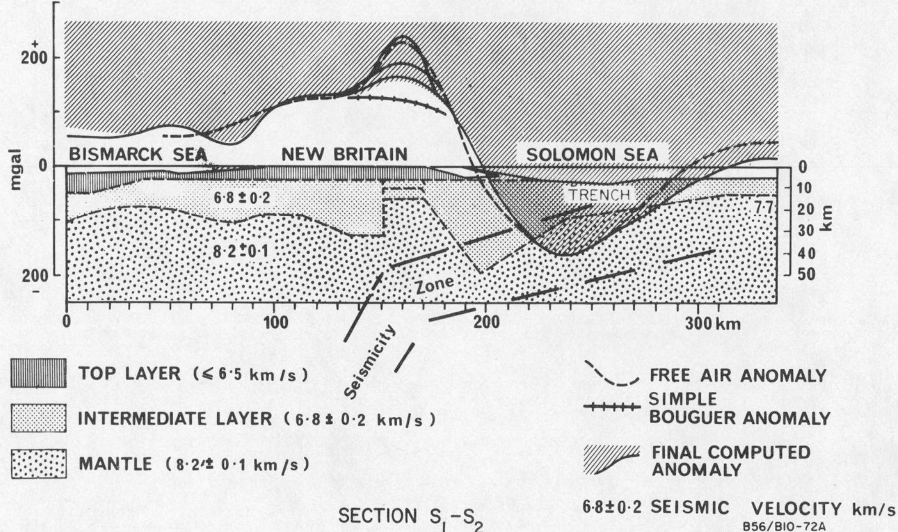

Fig. 7 Profile for section S_1-S_2 (see Fig. 4)

being pushed down underneath the island lithosphere, by way of 'subduction' zone. Focal mechanism studies at the associated seismicity zones are usually taken as proof for this mechanism. However, considerable difficulties exist in explaining the New Britain structure (Fig. 7, supplemented by Fig. 8) as the result of this mechanism because of the following reasons.

(*a*) Following Green (1971), it is postulated that andesitic to basaltic magmas are generated in the lower crust and/or upper mantle (mantle depth 30-40 km in some existing volcanic zones). Before this magma appears as volcanics at or near the surface they have to pass through fractures or fissure zones. In the New Britain area the seismicity zone dips at unusually high angles (50°-90°) and hence it is difficult to see how compressive stresses could cause fractures or fissures on the northern side of the

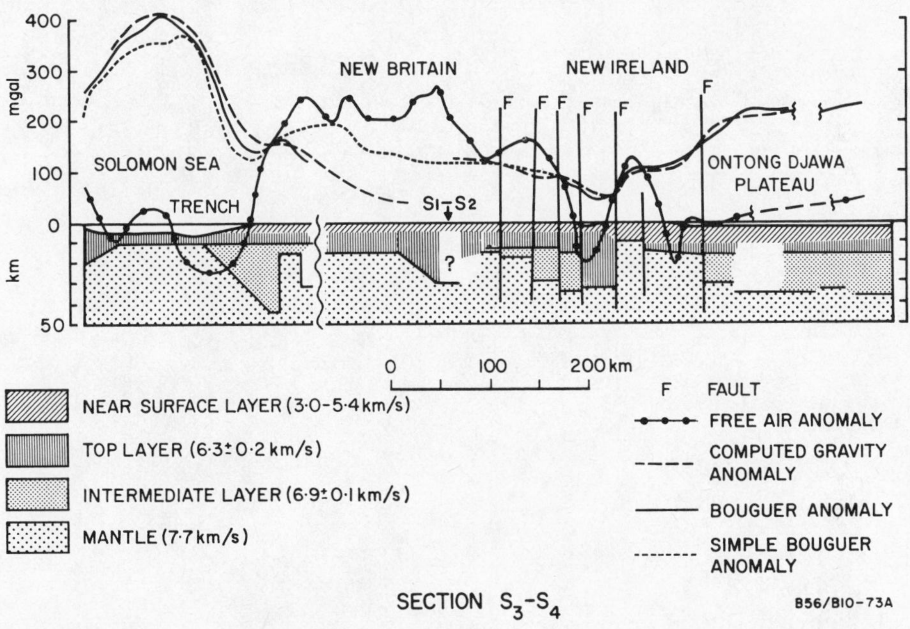

Fig. 8 Profile for section S_3-S_4 (see Fig. 4)

trench. Furthermore, near the subduction zone the lower crust consists of a wedge-shaped body with a seismic velocity of about 6·9 km/s, to be interpreted as metamorphic gabbro or amphibolite. The origin of this body is located in the upper mantle where basaltic magma was formed by partial melting. The same argument as above applies.

(*b*) Fig. 7 shows an intrusion of mantle material (velocity 8·2 km/s) in the centre of New Britain, associated with a volcanic zone at the surface. Various intrusive models with corresponding computed Free Air Anomaly profiles are shown. It is not clear how such a structure can be formed under any compressive stress system in the lithosphere.

(*c*) The Bismarck Sea crust north of New Britain is riddled by an east-west striking fracture system in which the fractures are filled with volcanics resulting in a more or less east-west striking magnetic pattern (to be published in a later paper). These fractures are developed by tensional or shear stresses in a brittle crust, possibly since the beginning of the Tertiary. But how can such east-west fractures exist just north of the trench if the trench zone lithosphere is under north-south compressive stress?

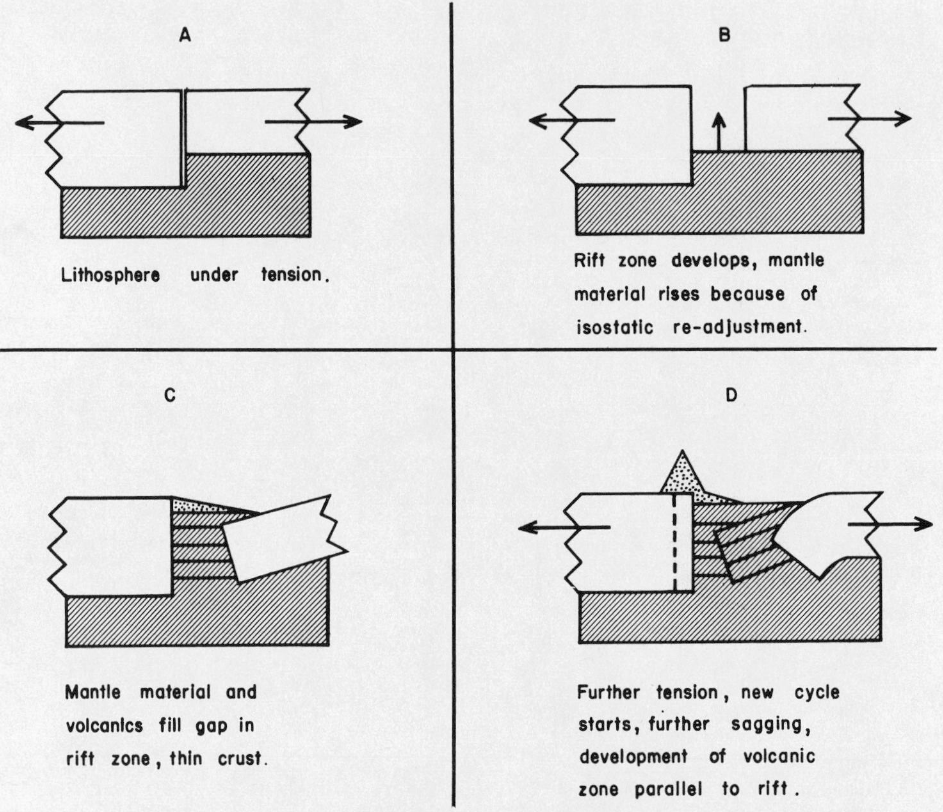

Fig. 9 Diagrammatic representation of a rifting mechanism to explain the formation of structures as shown in Fig. 7

Fig. 9 shows diagrammatically an alternative mechanism for the formation of a structure shown in Fig. 7. In Fig. 9*a*, crust and possibly the lower part of the lithosphere is rifted at the junction of thin and thick crust by tensional stresses; in 9*b* partially molten rock (mainly from underneath the thin crust because of the lower hydrostatic pressure) rises from the lower crust and/or upper mantle into the fracture system; 9*c* represents magma frozen in the rift-zone while the lithosphere with the thinner crust sinks because of the space available by outflow of material, developing simultaneously a trench at the surface. With 9*d* the stress has built up sufficiently to fracture again the crust, and the cycle is renewed. Meanwhile that portion of the lithosphere which has descended into the subduction zone, continues to sink and results in a seismicity zone (Isacks *et al.* 1968, Fig. 14*d*). A volcanic zone on the fresh fracture is indicated.

An important factor in the 'sinking lithosphere mechanism' is the high lithosphere density when compared with the asthenosphere.

The tensional stresses in Fig. 9 may be superimposed on a large regional stress. In that instance the mechanism is worked by differential stresses, and may be applied to a large number of situations.

Fig. 9 presents the formation of an asymmetrical rift zone because of the variation in crustal thickness. There is no reason why in a symmetrical rift zone, sinking of lithosphere should not take place on either side of the rift zone.

Figs 4 and 8 show how the north-easterly striking lineaments, associated with the New Britain Trench and volcanic zone, are cut off by a system of younger north-westerly lineaments which are interpreted as block faults, roughly parallel to the Solomon Islands chain and Bougainville trench. Some of the block faults appear to have important strike slip components. The Weitin Fault in New Ireland is reported to be a sinistral fault. The Gazelle Peninsula may have been off-set some 30 km by strike-slip along an interpreted fault which also coincides with an offset in the seismicity zone in the Bismarck Sea. Associated with the block faulting is volcanism and graben formation. Grabens between New Ireland and New Britain (Brooks *et al.* 1971) suggest that New Ireland is moving away from New Britain. In the Gazelle Peninsula an intermediate layer with 6·9 km/s velocity or more, interpreted above as amphibolite, characterizes the lower crust.

The boundary with the South-west Pacific plate (?) (Ontong Java Plateau in Fig. 8), is an important fault, associated with a string of volcanic islands, where in some places mantle material comes close to the surface.

The South-west Pacific crust (Ontong Java Plateau) is remarkable for its thickness and high average density (3·0-3·1 g/cm^3). In many respects it resembles the Bismarck Sea crust in that it is intensely fractured and rifted, and the fractures are filled with volcanic material. It is suggestive of a tensional stress system, similar to that in the Bismarck Sea (Furumoto *et al.* 1972).

CONCLUSION

As an alternative to the widely held theory that the New Britain Trench and associated structures were caused by compression, this paper suggests that they originated with a tensional or shear-stress pattern, probably early in the Tertiary. Partial melting and outflow of magma towards the surface caused the lithospheric slab to sink under its own weight. Later in the Tertiary (Oligocene) north-easterly striking tensional stresses, resulting in block-faulting, were superimposed on the older tectonic pattern. Probably these later events can be correlated with the appearance of New Ireland. Graben formation suggests a movement of New Ireland in a north-easterly direction. Some of the block faults appear to have left lateral strike-slip components. The boundary with the Pacific Ocean crust is marked by a probable fault zone, dotted with volcanic islands of lower crust or upper mantle composition. It is suggested that the Bougainville trench and Solomon Islands chain are related to the block faulting, and were formed by the same type of mechanisms as those responsible for the New Britain Trench structures.

This is one of a series of papers to be published on the geophysics of the New Britain-New Ireland region.

ACKNOWLEDGEMENTS

Permission granted by the Director of the Bureau of Mineral Resources, Geology and Geophysics to publish this paper is acknowledged.

Thanks are due to Mr B. C. Barlow of the Bureau of Mineral Resources and Dr J. P. Webb of the University of Queensland, who assisted with the paper, and Dr A. S. Furumoto of Hawaii Institute of Geophysics, who contributed in discussions.

The views expressed are the author's own and not necessarily those of the Bureau of Mineral Resources, Geology and Geophysics or of other participants.

REFERENCES

Birch, F. 1961. The velocity of compressional waves in rock to 10K bars (pt 2), *J. geophys. Res.* **66,** 2199-224.

Bott, M. H. P. 1971. The Interior of the Earth, 63-70, 268, Edward Arnold, London.

Brooks, J. A. (Ed.) 1971. Investigations of crustal structure in the New Britain-New Ireland region. Part I: Geophysical and Geological Data. *Rec. Bur. Miner. Resour. Aust.* In press.

Brooks, J. A., Connelly, J. B., Finlayson, D. M. & Wiebenga, W. A. 1971. St George's Channel-Bismarck Sea Trough. *Nature,* **229,** 205-7.

Brown, R. J., Borg, H. & Bath, M. 1971. Strike and dip of crustal boundaries—a method and its application. *Geofis. pura appl.* **88,** 60-74.

Cifali, G., D'Addario, G. W., Polak, E. J. & Wiebenga, W. A. 1969. Rabaul preliminary crustal seismic test, New Britain, 1966. Rec. Bur. Miner. Resour. Aust. 1969/125 (unpubl.).

Clark, S. P. Jr. (Ed.) 1966. Handbook of physical constants, *Mem. geol. Soc. Am.* **97.**

Denham, D. 1968. Thickness of the Earth's crust in Papua, New Guinea and the British Solomon Islands. *Aust. J. Sci.* **30,** 277.

Denham, D. 1969. Distribution of earthquakes in the New Guinea-Solomon Islands region. *J. geophys. Res.* **74,** 4290-9.

Furumoto, A. S., Hussong, D. M., Campbell, J. F., Sutton, G. H., Malahoff, A., Ross, J. C. & Woollard, G. P. 1970. Crustal and upper mantle structure of the Solomon Islands as revealed by seismic refraction survey of November-December 1966. *Pacif. Sci.* **24,** 315-32.

Furumoto, A. S., Wiebenga, W. A., Webb, J. P. & Sutton, G. H. 1972. Crustal structure of the Hawaiian Archipelago, Northern Melanesia, and Central Pacific Basin by seismic refraction method. *Tectonophysics.* In press.

Gardner, J. 1970. Submarine geology of the western Coral Sea. *Bull. geol. Soc. Am.* **81,** 2599-614.

Grant, F. S. & West, C. F. 1965. *Interpretation theory in applied geophysics,* McGraw-Hill, New York.

Green, D. H. 1971. Comparison of basaltic magmas as indicators of conditions of origin: application to oceanic volcanism. *Phil. Trans. R. Soc.* (A) **268,** 707-25.

Green, R. & Pitt, R. P. B. 1967. Suggested rotation of New Guinea. *J. Geomagn. Geoelect.* **19,** 317-21.

Isacks, B., Oliver, J. & Sykes, L. R. 1968. Seismology and the new global tectonics. *J. geophys. Res.* **73,** 5866 and Fig. 14*d*.

Rose, J. C. & Tracy, R. W. 1971. Gravity results in the Solomon Islands region, aboard H.M.S. *Dampier* in 1965. Data Report No. 17, Hawaii Inst. Geophys., Univ. Hawaii.

Rose, J. C., Woollard, G. P. & Malahoff, A. 1968. Marine gravity and magnetic studies of the Solomon Islands. In *The Crust and Upper Mantle of the Pacific Area. Am. Geophys. Un. Monogr.* **12,** 379-410.

Woollard, G. P. 1962. The relation of gravity anomalies to surface elevation, crustal structure, and geology. *Res. Rep. Series No. 62-9,* Univ. Wisc.

——— 1970. *Annual Progress Report,* Contract N00014-70-A-0016-0001, Jan. 1, 1970 to July 31, 1970. Hawaii Inst. Geophys. HIG-70-27.

The Solomon Islands Fractured Arc

BRIAN D. HACKMAN

Geological Survey Department, G.P.O. Box G24,
Honiara, British Solomon Islands

ABSTRACT

The Solomons active primary fractured arc extends from Buka-Bougainville in the north-west to San Cristobal in the south-east. Seven major island groups form a double *en echelon* chain. The limits of the Solomons segment are defined by angular re-entrants in the trench system on the south-west margin. The trenches on the Pacific side are less clearly developed.

The Solomons coincide with an arcuate gravity low on the north-east side of a large Bouguer positive which extends over the Coral Sea.

The fractured arc is considered to have evolved from a series of oceanic welts which started to shoal in the Lower Miocene and sustained rapid uplift until the present day. The oldest rocks, which appear on all the major island groups except Bougainville and New Georgia, form a 'basement' of late Mesozoic basaltic lavas, pelagic limestones and cognate gabbroic intrusives. In the Central Province, which excludes Malaita, the basement rocks have been metamorphosed to greenschist or amphibolite grade and intruded by Alpine-type ultramafics in the axial regions of geanticlinal structures.

The basement is blanketed by a thick sequence of volcanic and sedimentary rocks ranging in age from Oligocene to Recent; in the Pacific Province this sequence has been folded in the Pliocene along axes trending NW-SE.

The pattern of seismicity indicates that the Benioff zone dips towards the Pacific at either end of the Solomons Arc, where the trench system is well developed; elsewhere seismic zonation is not clearly defined. Fracturing of the uplifted oceanic welts under the influence of deep-seated transcurrent faulting may have led to the anti-clockwise rotation of discrete blocks, on which were periodically impressed the effects of a regional NE-SW stress system. The regional structure is discussed in relation to recent plate tectonics models for the South-west Pacific.

The Melanesian archipelagos trend in a general north-westerly direction between Fiji and New Guinea: the Solomons system forms a double *en echelon* chain of seven major island groups, namely Bougainville, Choiseul, Santa Isabel and Malaita, and, in opposition, New Georgia, Guadalcanal and San Cristobal (Fig. 1). There is a trench on the Coral Sea side, interrupted between Guadalcanal and Bougainville, where the Woodlark Rise from Papua abuts against the Solomons Arc. The limits of the Solomons segment are defined by angular re-entrants in the trench system—to the north-west between New Britain and Bougainville, to the south-east between San Cristobal and the Santa Cruz Group. The political boundaries of the British

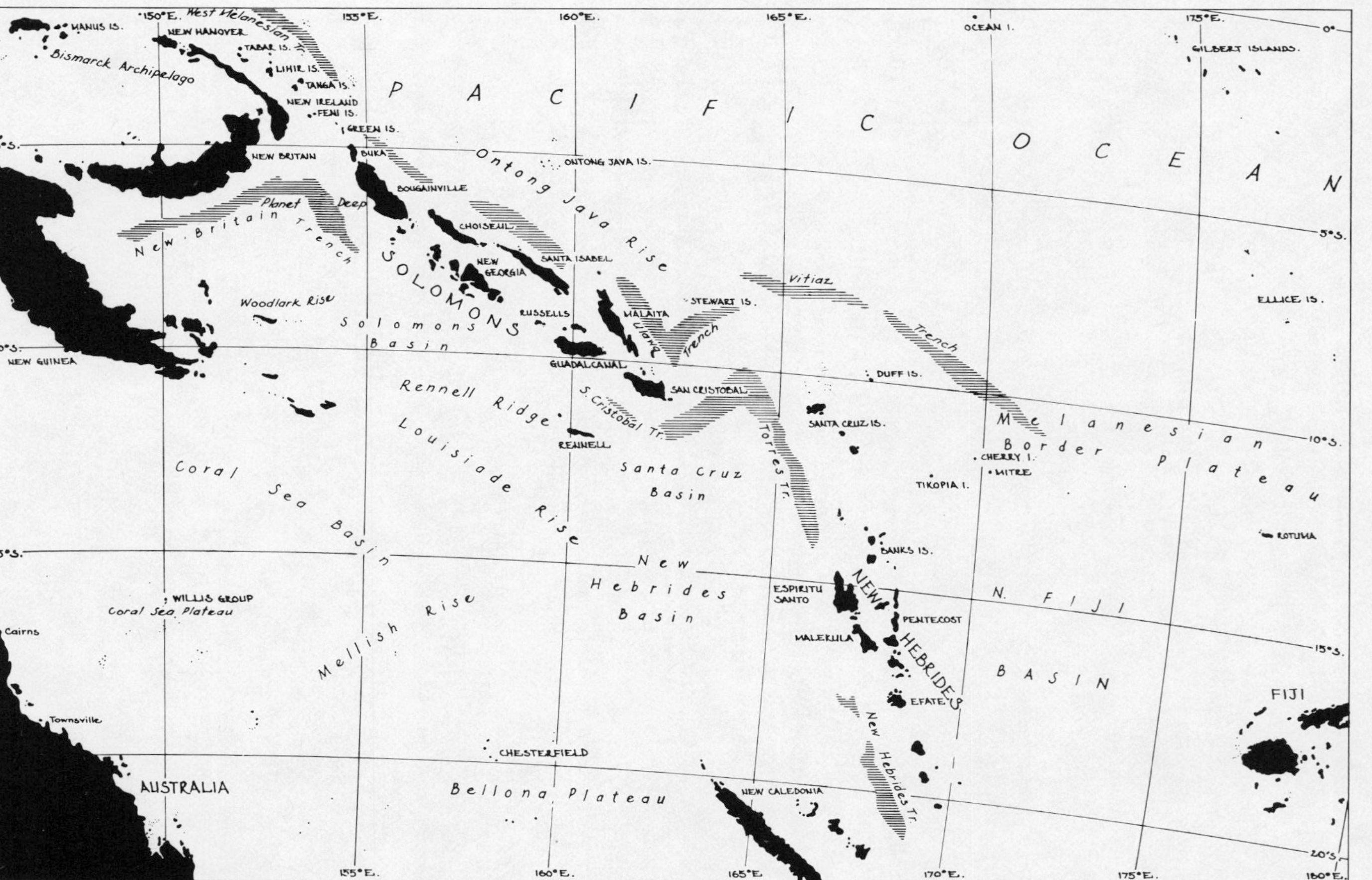

Fig. 1 The Melanesian Archipelagos, South-west Pacific

Solomons exclude Bougainville, but incorporate the Santa Cruz Islands which are structurally a northern extension of the New Hebrides Arc. Wilson (1959) cited the Solomons as an example of an *active primary fractured arc,* which by definition should have a major transcurrent fault running along its axis. The double *en echelon* pattern reflects a system of faulted anticlinal horsts and intervening basins progressively offset by a left-handed sigmoid effect directed towards the north-west.

In the classic sense, the narrow linear orthogeosyncline cannot be identified.

Since 1964 there has been a tremendous increase in the amount of geological and geophysical data obtained from throughout the Solomon Islands. In particular, this began with the land gravity survey of 1965-6 by the University of Wisconsin, assisted by the U.S. Army Map Service (Grover 1968, Laudon 1968). Marine gravity, magnetic and seismic reflection studies were made by the University of Hawaii (Rose *et al.* 1968), and an airborne geophysical survey and photogeological interpretation were sponsored by the United Nations (Aktiebolag Elektrisk Malmletning 1967).

As well as the earlier reconnaissance surveys of the islands, detailed geological mapping on the scale of 1:50,000 has covered nearly three-quarters of Guadalcanal Island; the Santa Cruz Group has almost been completed, and mapping has commenced on Malaita and Florida. Private companies have accelerated their prospecting programmes since 1968.

The Solomons area coincides with a slightly arcuate gravity low which flanks the north-east side of a large composite Bouguer positive which extends over the northern Coral Sea. This feature corresponds with a major bulge in the geoid, which causes deflections of orbital satellites. In the Solomons, the estimated depth of the crust-mantle interface varies between 9 and 30 km. Relatively negative zones coincide with the two axial basins which have up to 2 km of sediment. There are exceptionally steep gravity gradients on the southern flanks of the Indispensable Strait basin, leading up to the highest positive readings of about +250 mgals in the south-east of San Cristobal.

The magnetic pattern shows an E-W grain, interrupted by more complex zones of high magnetic relief which correspond with areas of intense faulting and Miocene to Recent vulcanicity. Magnetic highs tend to correspond with blocks of oceanic basalt, magnetic lows with intervening sedimentary basins.

Coleman (1965, 1970) attempted a summary of the geology of the Solomons in terms of four geological provinces, whose boundaries cut across the outlines of the double *en echelon* chain (Fig. 2).

The Pacific Province is characterized by a basement of Upper Mesozoic oceanic basalts surmounted by about 1,200 m of Cretaceous to Pliocene chalky carbonate sediments, which are folded on axes trending NW-SE; this province is typified by Malaita Island, but also includes north-eastern Santa Isabel.

The Central Province includes San Cristobal, Florida, most of Guadalcanal, Santa Isabel and Choiseul. As in Malaita the basement includes at least 2,000 m of upper Mesozoic lavas and cognate sills, but has been more extensively fractured and metamorphosed. Gabbroic material invaded the lava pile in the Late Cretaceous, and Alpine type ultramafics were emplaced in the axial zones of geanticlinal structures in the Early Tertiary. The basement is overlain unconformably by a pile of up to

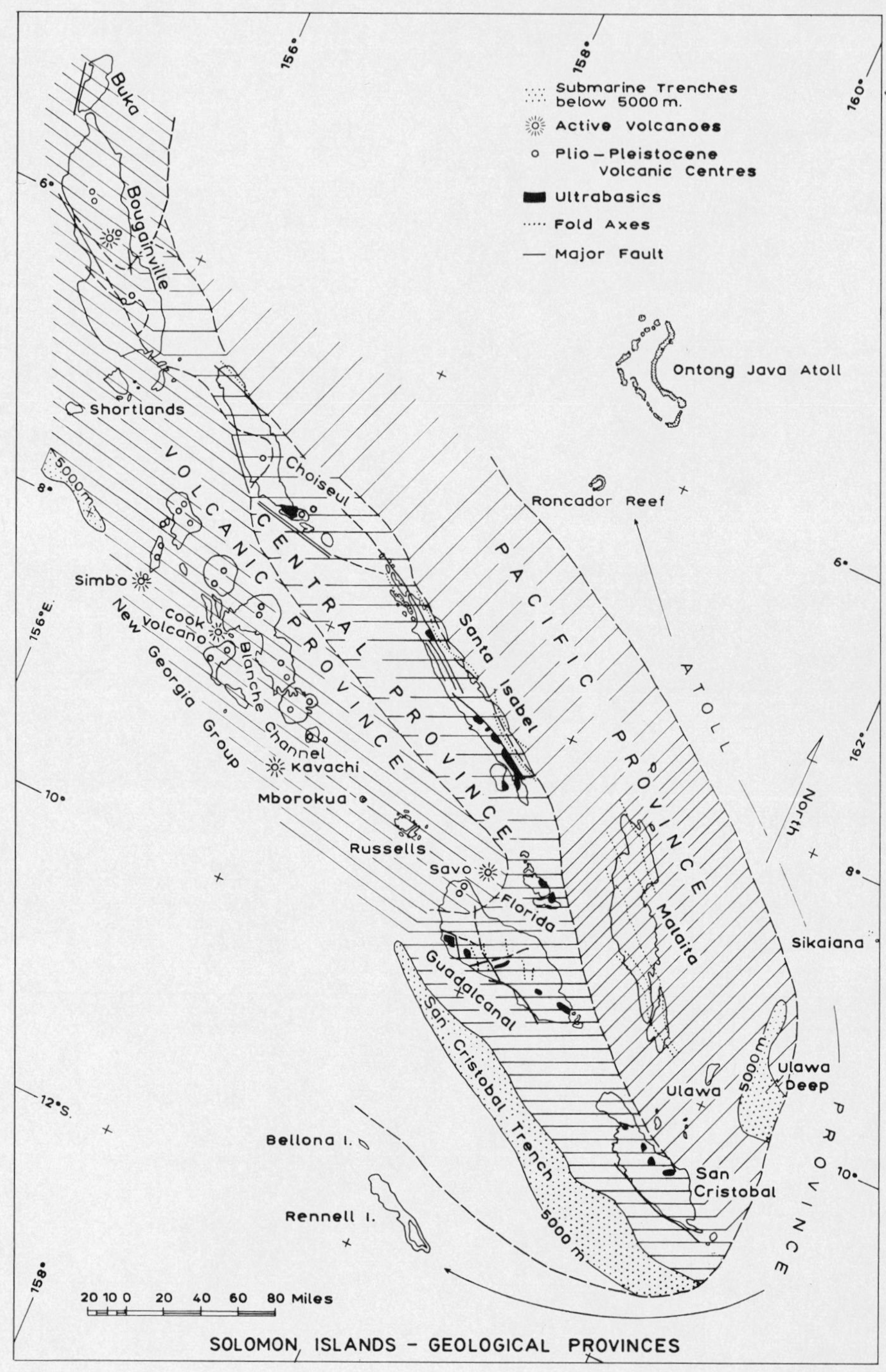

SOLOMON ISLANDS – GEOLOGICAL PROVINCES

5,000 m of varied sedimentary rocks, including Lower Miocene reef limestones and turbidites, also Plio-Pleistocene volcaniclastic material with minor reefs. Recent work by Craig (in press) in the Santa Cruz Group, which is at the northern end of the New Hebrides Arc, shows features comparable with the Central and Volcanic Provinces of the Solomons, although the oceanic basement is not seen.

The Volcanic Province, including Western Guadalcanal, Savo, the Russells and most of Bougainville, is typified by the New Georgia Group, a complex of predominantly andesitic volcanic cones, lagoons and fringing reefs ranging in age from Upper Miocene to Recent. Diorite plugs have been emplaced at depth.

The Atoll Province includes Lord Howe and Sikaiana on the Ontong Java Rise to the north of Malaita. To the south, Bellona and Rennell are uplifted atolls emergent from a sinuous ridge which links New Caledonia with Papua. There are phosphate deposits on Bellona, and the trial mining of 30 million tons of bauxite on Rennell is due to commence in late 1971.

In the Pacific Province the basement consists of at least 1,000 m of basalts, characteristically pillow lavas with hyaloclastite and minor segregations of chert. The lavas are commonly autobrecciated and form pépérite mixtures with the calcareous ooze into which they were extruded.

In the Central Province similar basalts have been metamorphosed to greenschist grade at depth in the axial zones of anticlinal structures. There is every gradation from pillow lava through sheared and brecciated basalt to chlorite-actinolite-schist; locally, two later schistosities have been impressed on an earlier schistosity. Over large areas of the Central Province the basaltic pile has been invaded by uralitized leucogabbro, with affiliated dykes of doleritic material injected while the gabbro was still in a plastic state. In south-east Guadalcanal there are also unusual dykes of basic material with glomeroporphyritic clusters of plagioclase felspar.

Ultramafic material, predominantly harzburgitic with slivers of metagabbro, was emplaced in axial zones, probably in the Eocene and Oligocene, and subsequently serpentinized.

The 'basement' in the Central Province merits close comparison with the Ultramafic Belt of Eastern Papua as described by Davies (1968).

The sedimentary sequence in the Pacific Province includes about 1,200 m of folded deep-water carbonate rocks, of minimum Late Cretaceous age, and subsidiary shales of finely brecciated submarine volcanic material (Coleman 1966); lithified chloritic clays with pyrite concretions are common. Of special interest, but of limited extent, are the alkaline ultramafics including alnöite-breccias, ankaratrites and melanite-ouachitites which underlie the limestones of north-central Malaita; their structural relationships are still unknown. Probable terrigenous detritus appears in the Pliocene part of the sequence. A Pliocene age is suggested for the emergence of Malaita, and for the tectonic episode which folded the limestones and underlying lavas.

In contrast, in the Central Province terrigenous material first appears in the early Lower Miocene; Lower Miocene calcarenites and mudstones unconformably overlie

---

Fig. 2 Geological Provinces in the Solomons area. The Atoll Province (see text) is a geographical expression.

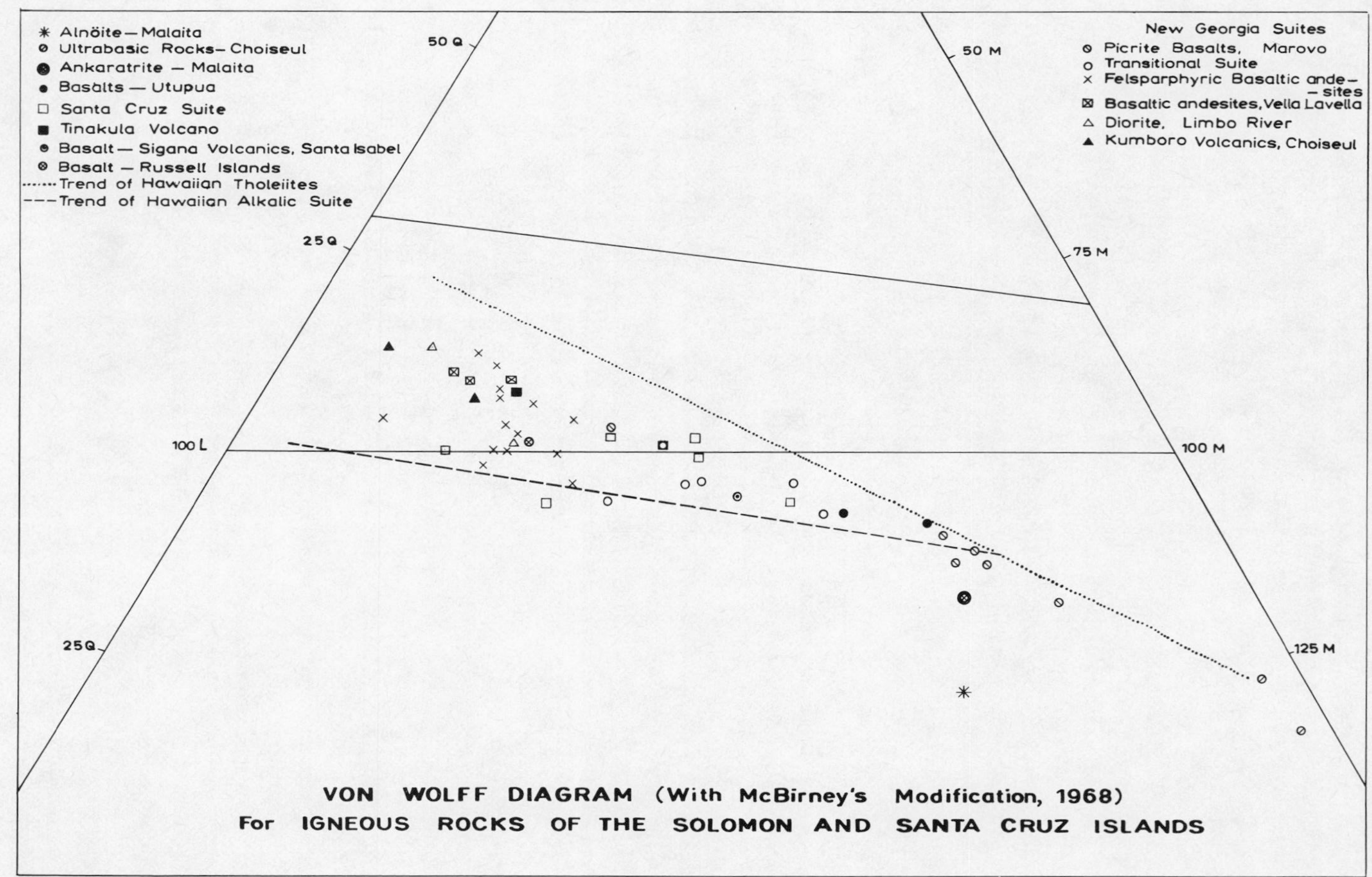

Fig. 3 Von Wolff diagram for igneous rocks from the Solomon Islands. Note that the Santa Cruz group is geologically a part of the New Hebrides Archipelago.

the Mesozoic basement. After the period of uplift which led to shoaling and rapid erosion, a phase of relative stability allowed for the formation of fringing reefs and derived calcarenites. Concomitantly the basement was extensively fractured, with local extrusions of basaltic andesite and associated pyroclastics. The deeper troughs were filled with a well-laminated greywacke facies, for example the Mole Formation of Choiseul (Coleman 1962), the material having been derived from unstable blocks with emergent volcanoes. Chaotic tilloid or paraconglomeratic facies were deposited on the steep submarine slopes of volcanic islands. Poorly sorted fine-grained arenites, with occasional exotic blocks, were laid down in the quieter intervening gulfs such as the Mbokokimbo Basin of eastern Guadalcanal (Hackman 1968, 1971).

The Central Province conditions phase westward into those of the Volcanic Province, as typified by the New Georgia Group today, where a pattern of emergent volcanic islands with fringing and offshore reefs provides an environmental framework for the accumulation of varied sediments of volcaniclastic and biogenic origin. Kavachi submarine volcano is currently (1971) active; there are nearly thirty well-preserved centres and four active or quiescent volcanoes.

It is not possible to delineate within the present-day volcanic zones distinct petro-chemical suites which might tie up with the pattern of seismicity. However, 112 analyses of Solomons igneous rocks are now available, thanks to the assistance of Professor Stanton (University of New England). On a von Wolff diagram (Fig. 3) the pre-Miocene or basement basalts follow a trend intermediate between the oceanic Hawaiian tholeiites and the alkali series of Macdonald and Katsura (1964). In the Oligocene-Miocene island arc, tholeiites were extruded in central Guadalcanal, leading to a calcalkaline trend in the post-Miocene volcanics, which produced the hornblende-andesites and dacites of the volcanic province and diorite plugs at depth. Its most acid end member might be considered to be the shallow Pliocene granodiorite stock of Koloula in southern Guadalcanal. Lodes bearing copper sulphides follow a distinct fracture pattern in the granodiorite, which has been a favoured target for prospecting in recent years as a potential 'porphyry copper' deposit. In the Santa Cruz Group, volcanics are mostly tholeiitic basalts, with some orogenic suite affinities.

The Solomons Arc, it is suggested, originated as a series of geanticlinal welts somewhere to the north-east of the Australian continent towards the end of the Mesozoic era. Initially, basalts were extruded into an oceanic calcareous ooze and cognate dolerites invaded the lava pile. A series of parallel whaleback swells became more distinctive and developed subsequently into a system of fan-profiled anticlinal horsts. Marginal reversed faulting locally imparted a distinct asymmetry to these structures: ultramafic material expanded into the axial zones, where the basic lavas were subjected to low-grade metamorphism. Emergence of one of the geanticlinal ridges in the Oligocene-Lower Miocene gave rise to an embryo 'Central Province' or frontal arc. Biogenic reefs stabilized and marginal basins filled with terrigenous sediments. In the Pliocene a parallel ridge rapidly emerged to the north-east, forming the Pacific Province: the pelagic limestones were buckled into a series of cascade folds whose axes parallel the major geanticlinal trends.

Since the Pliocene the history of the islands has been one of rapid differential block

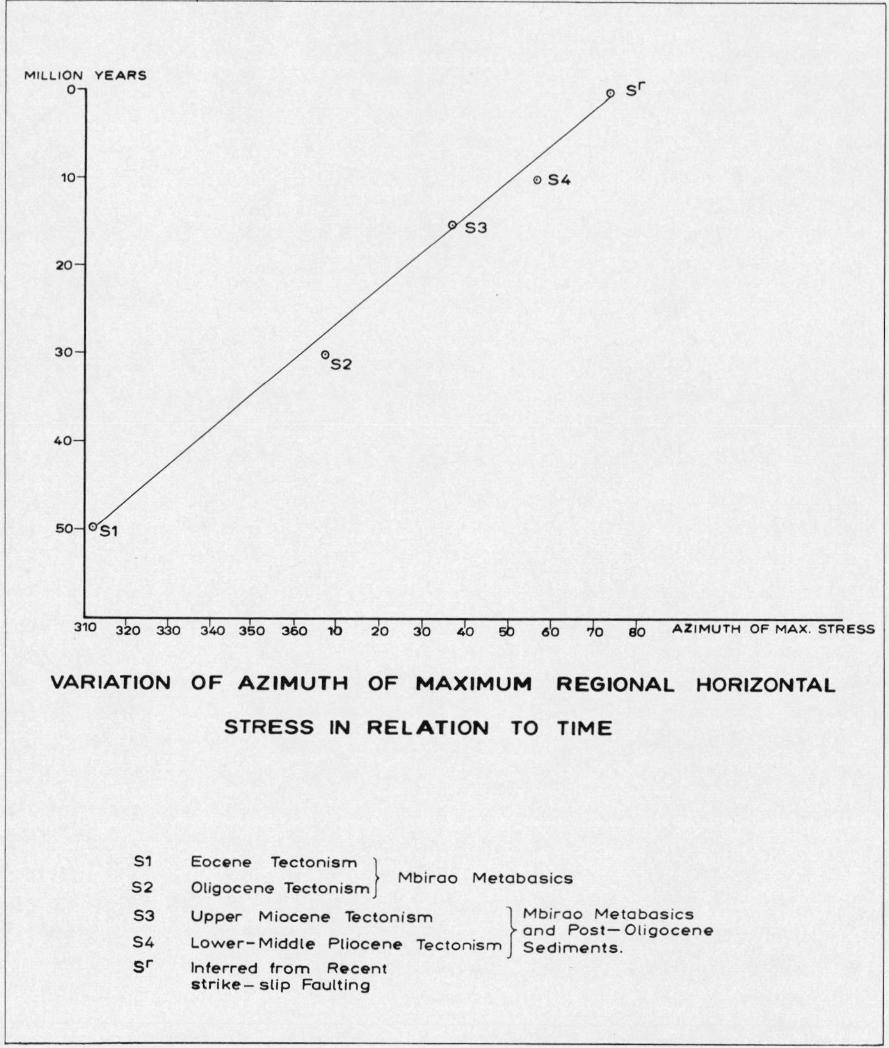

Fig. 4 Suggested clockwise rotation of Guadalcanal during the Tertiary

uplift. Thus Pleistocene surfaces of marine erosion on Guadalcanal are now at 800 m a.s.l. The south side of the frontal arc has been progressivly modified by step-faulting down towards the trench. Behind Honiara, the capital, a beautiful series of terraces bears witness to the interaction of eustatic change and tectonic uplift throughout this period.

At least three sets of metamorphic S-surfaces can be distinguished in different parts of the basaltic 'basement' of the Central Province. These have already been mapped in considerable detail in south-east Guadalcanal (Hackman 1971), and it seems likely that a similar picture could be obtained from eastern Choiseul (Thompson 1960).

In Guadalcanal the first set of S-surface trends generally NE-SW, although the pattern has been somewhat modified by later folding. The second set trends WNW-ESE, and the third set trends NNW-SSE, and is axial to folds which affect the earlier S-surfaces. The third set is also parallel to the major fold axes which affect the sedimentary sequence in Malaita and the pre-Pliocene sediments of Guadalcanal.

If it be assumed that the strike of the S-surfaces was generally parallel to the axes of the major geanticlinal structures, the derived principal horizontal stress has rotated progressively since the beginning of the Tertiary. In fact the plot of the stress direction against time is broadly linear (granted that there may be considerable errors attached to the age determinations), and suggests a clockwise rotation of 2° every million years (Fig. 4).

In Guadalcanal the Alpine type ultramafics have been emplaced in three linear zones (Fig. 5). To the west the Ghausava belt trends NW-SE, to the east the Marau belt trends W-E, but centrally the Suta belt trends NE-SW, at right angles to the main trend of the Solomons chain, and significantly reflecting a left-handed sigmoid bend or small *orocline* in the terminology of Carey (1958). This contrasts with the parallel *en echelon* structures of an island such as Malaita, with its folds trending NW-SE, also with the distinct linearity of an island like Santa Isabel. The situation in central Guadalcanal does, however, merit close comparison with that of eastern Choiseul, where the ultramafics also trend, anomalously, across the axis of the fractured arc.

Thus rotationary stress changes are implied in the angles of the sigmoidal bends, but not in the rectilinear portions of the arc. One possible interpretation is that the regional stress regime has remained fairly constant since the end of the Mesozoic, but, periodically, buckling has accelerated and planar metamorphic S-surfaces have been impressed at depth. At other times stress has been relieved by sinistral transcurrent movement along east-west lineaments combined with the systematic anticlockwise rotation of discrete blocks. Each rotated block would define a small sigmoid flexure: this is in accord with the current notion of van der Linden (1969) of the anti-clockwise rotation of a fragmented Melanesian complex with respect to Australia, superimposed on a translation of the entire area towards the north-east, along the lines of current interpretations of sea-floor spreading.

Fig. 6 shows the generalized pattern of seismicity for the Solomons-Santa Cruz region, based on data obtained since 1962 (modified from Westwood 1970). A broad seismic zonation from deep to shallow focus parallels the New Hebrides-Santa Cruz arc and trench system. In the case of the Solomons Arc, however, the pattern is clearly defined only on the south-west side of Bougainville.

The main trench system to which this seismic zonation is related is on the Coral Sea side, not on the Pacific side of the fractured arc; the Benioff zone dips to the north-east at both ends of the Solomons. However the low level of seismicity across the central part of the Solomons, associated with the absence of a well-marked trench, spoils the pattern and requires some explanation. Many authors have emphasized the importance of transcurrent faulting, especially sinistral shearing on east-west lines across the Solomons area. One example is that of the Pocklington Fault, described by Krause (1962), which forms a very steep feature across the Solomon Sea. In south Guadalcanal recent transcurrent movements of the same trend have

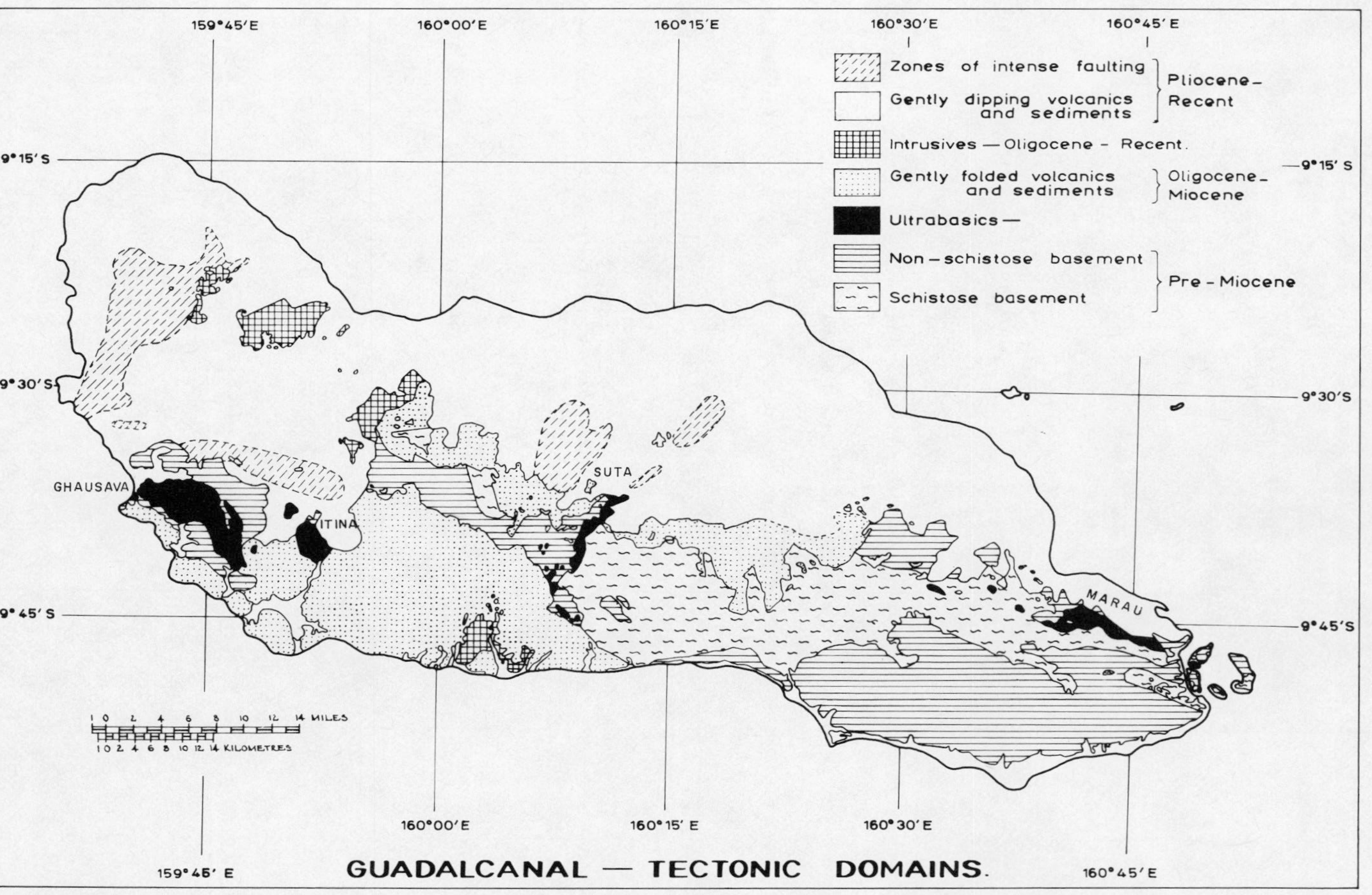

Fig. 5 Essential geology and tectonic domains on Guadalcanal, a key island in the Solomon group

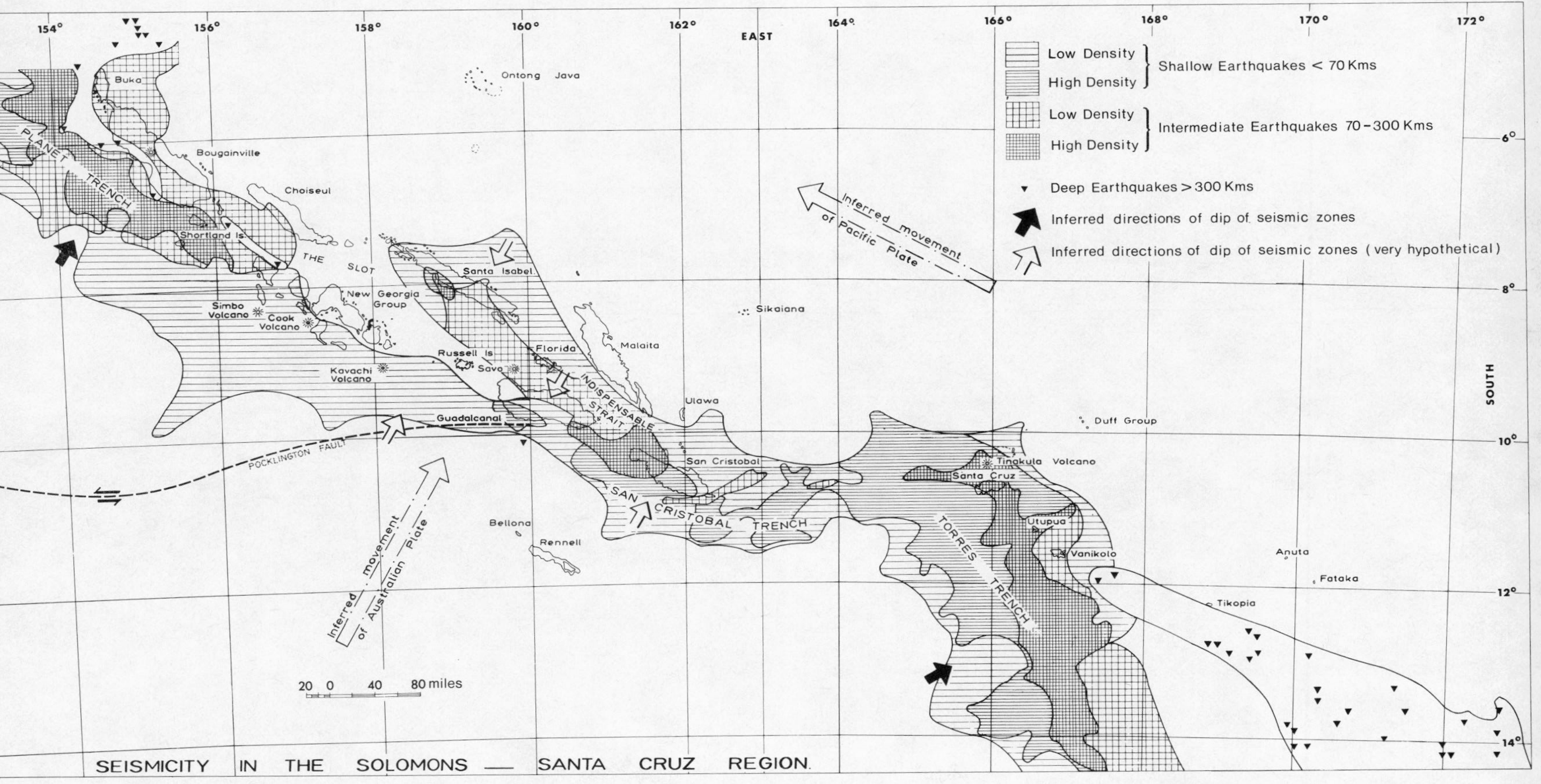

Fig. 6 Seismicity in the Solomons–northern New Hebrides region

visibly displaced river valleys giving a 'shutter-ridge' effect. Possibly a combination of strike-slip shear and rotation of discrete blocks has broken the regularity of seismic zonation in the central Solomons. The high-density patch of shallow to intermediate shocks, which occurs between Guadalcanal and San Cristobal could conceivably fit in with the continued anti-clockwise rotation of a postulated Guadalcanal block.

An alternative explanation of the seismic pattern, in terms of currently propounded 'plate tectonics' models, is that the ill-defined seismic zone in the central portion of the Solomons Arc is near-vertical, due to the imminent 'polarity reversal' of the trench-arc system. Karig (1972, and see also Karig this volume) has suggested that the Pocklington and Woodlark Ridges to the west of the Solomons (Fig. 1) are complex 'remnant arcs' now seismically inactive, the active zone having migrated northwards since the Early Tertiary to its present position along the New Britain-Bougainville arc. The Australian plate is conceived to have formerly underthrust the Pacific plate along the line of the Papuan promontory and the Papuan ridge; following the northward migration of the active zone, however, the arc now approaches a polarity reversal, a new trench forming on the north side of the Solomons in preparation for the overthrusting of the Pacific by the Australian plate and a reversal of the dip of the Benioff zone. This process would have advanced furthest in the central portion of the Solomons Arc, where the seismic zone is ill-defined or possibly vertical.

Seismic refraction data indicate crustal thickening underneath the Ontong Java Rise (Furumoto *et al.* 1970), which could be due to underthrusting of the Pacific by the Australian plate; this suggests that the Solomons Arc has faced south since the early Mesozoic.

However, insofar as the Alpine ultramafic belts locate former tectonic axes, the inclinations of the boundary thrusts suggest polarity changes along the arc. Thus the Marau and Suta ultramafics (Fig. 5) are inclined to the north, whereas the Ghausava body dips southwards (Hackman 1971) as does the ultramafic emplacement of Santa Isabel. If it follows that in eastern Guadalcanal the arc faced south, but in western Guadalcanal and Isabel the polarity was reversed, then a NE-SW transform fault mechanism is required in central Guadalcanal during the Oligocene. Accepting Thompson's (1960) Miocene age for the thrust emplacement of the Isabel ultramafics, it would appear, given the validity of these lines of reasoning, that the polarity alternated along the length of the Solomons Arc even in the mid-Tertiary.

Clearly the Solomons fractured arc, by virtue of its anomalous features, provides a fascinating testing ground for current theories on global tectonics. More work is needed on earthquake first-motion studies, detailed bathymetry and comparative palaeomagnetic determinations to prove or disprove the detailed pattern. Detailed descriptions of petrotectonic assemblages are required, carefully tied to age-determinations to ascertain how far they match with postulated arc polarity reversals. Any regional interpretation must take into account the breaks in seismic zonation and the east-west sinistral megashears which affect the whole Melanesian belt from the New Hebrides north-west to New Guinea. Both vertical and horizontal tectonics must be considered.

If the plate tectonics models for the Melanesian region can be extended to recognize the important role of large scale strike-slip movements and anti-clockwise rotation of discrete blocks within the zone of plate interaction, then we are a step nearer to integrating the observed geology of this complex area into its global context.

REFERENCES

Aktiebolag Elektrisk Malmletning. 1967. Report on an airborne geophysical survey in the British Solomon Islands (Stockholm), 1965-6 (2 vols).

Carey, S. Warren. 1958. *Continental Drift. A Symposium.* pp. 177-355. Geol. Dept Univ. Tasmania, Hobart.

Coleman, P. J. 1962. An outline of the geology of Choiseul, Solomon Islands. *J. geol. Soc. Aust.* **8,** 135-58.

——— 1965. Stratigraphical and structural notes on the British Solomon Islands with reference to the First Geological Map, 1962. *Geol. Rec. Br. Solomon Isl.* **2** (1959-62), 17-31.

——— 1966. Upper Cretaceous (Senonian) bathyal pelagic sediments with *Globotruncana* from the Solomon Islands. *J. geol. Soc. Aust.* **13,** 439-47.

——— 1970. Geology of the Solomon and New Hebrides Islands, as part of the Melanesian Re-entrant, South-west Pacific. *Pacif. Sci.* **24,** 289-314.

Craig, P. (In press.) The Geology of Santa Cruz. *Br. Solomon Isl. Geol. Surv.*

Davies, H. L. 1968. Papuan ultramafic belt. *23rd Int. Geol. Congr.* **1,** 209-20.

Furumoto, A. S., Hussong, D. M., Campbell, J. F., Sutton, G. H., Malahoff, A., Rose, J. C. & Wollard, G. P. 1970. Crust and upper mantle structure of the Solomon Islands as revealed by seismic refraction survey of November-December 1966. *Pacif. Sci.* **24** (3).

Grover, J. C. 1968. The British Solomon Islands: some geological implications of the gravity data, 1966. In *The Crust and Upper Mantle of the Pacific Area. Am. Geophys. Un. Monogr.* **12,** 296-306.

Hackman, B. D. 1968. The geology of east and central Guadalcanal: a preliminary statement, 1966. *Geol. Rec. Br. Solomon Isl.* **3,** 16-25.

——— 1971. The regional geology of Guadalcanal: a contribution to the geology of fractured island arcs. Ph.D. thesis, Univ. W. Australia.

Karig, D. E. 1972. Remnant Arcs. *Bull. geol. Soc. Am.* **83,** 1057-68.

Krause, D. C. 1967. Bathymetry and geologic structure of the north-western Tasman Sea-Coral Sea-South Solomon Sea area of the south-western Pacific Ocean. *Mem. N.Z. oceanogr. Inst.* **41,** 48 pp.

Laudon, T. S. 1968. Land gravity survey of the Solomon and Bismarck Islands. In *The Crust and Upper Mantle of the Pacific Area. Am. Geophys. Un. Monogr.* **12,** 279-95.

Linden, W. J. M. van der. 1969. Rotation of the Melanesian Complex and of West Antarctica—a key to the configuration of Gondwana? *Palaeogeogr. Palaeoclim. Palaeoecol.* **6** (1), 37-44.

Macdonald, G. A. & Katsura, T. 1964. Chemical composition of Hawaiian lavas. *J. Petrology,* **5** (1), 82-133.

Rose, J. C., Woollard, G. P. & Malahoff, A. 1968. Marine gravity and magnetic studies of the Solomon Islands. In *The Crust and Upper Mantle of the Pacific Area. Am. Geophys. Un. Monogr.* **12,** 379-410.

Thompson, R. B. M. 1960. The geology of the ultrabasic rocks of the British Solomon Islands. Ph.D. thesis, Univ. of Sydney.

Westwood, J. V. B. 1970. Seismicity of the Solomon and Santa Cruz Islands, southwest Pacific. *J. geol. Soc. Aust.* **17** (1), 87-92.

Wilson, J. T. 1959. Geophysics and Continental Growth. *Am. Scient.* **47,** 1-24.

Some Petrological and Structural Variations in the New Hebrides

D. I. J. MALLICK

New Hebrides Geological Survey, British Residency, Vila, New Hebrides

ABSTRACT

Petrological variations for the three main periods of volcanism in the New Hebrides, pre-Middle Miocene, Upper Miocene-Lower Pliocene and Pliocene-Recent, are illustrated by Harker diagrams for K_2O. All the basic volcanics of the New Hebrides are of tholeiitic or high-alumina affinities and show transitions to calcalkaline andesites, latites and dacites. In the Pliocene to Recent volcanics there is a common, but not ubiquitous, tendency for alkalinity to decrease with increasing distance from the New Hebrides Trench, giving an anomalous, negative correlation of alkalinity with seismic zone depth. In other cases alkalinity appears to have increased with time. The Upper Miocene-Lower Pliocene volcanic province is too narrow to allow recognition of lateral changes, but there is a marked longitudinal variation from tholeiitic basalts and basic andesites on Maewo and Pentecost, to latites on Efate. Data on the original composition of the pre-Middle Miocene volcanics is more limited, since they have commonly suffered subsequent alteration, but there are indications that representatives on the Eastern Belt of islands are poorer in alkalies than those of the Western Belt, that is, the alkalinity variation is similar to that in more recent volcanics. This suggests that no polarity reversal of the New Hebrides Arc has occurred since the Lower Miocene. It is concluded that the Mohorovicic discontinuity may have controlled magma segregation and thus the composition of the erupted materials.

The high-level structure is dominated by normal faults trending slightly oblique to the axis of the New Hebrides Ridge and by a few important E-W fractures which may be the surface expression of the latitudinal crustal rifts which dominate the deep structure. It is suggested that the opening of the inter-arc basin of the northern New Hebrides involved the westward migration of the island blocks of Malekula and Santo, perhaps over-riding the trench or filling it with epiclastic detritus opposite this section of the ridge.

INTRODUCTION

The area dealt with in this contribution is the New Hebrides Anglo-French Condominium, which lies on the central section of the New Hebrides Ridge. The ridge is linear and trends SSE from its abrupt termination at about 10° S, north of the Santa Cruz Islands, to 22° S near Aneityum, the southernmost island of the New Hebrides. Further to the south, the ridge swings through the two small Recent volcanoes of Matthew and Hunter Islands to run ENE towards Fiji. To the east of the ridge is the small ocean basin of the Fiji 'Plateau' with 2-3 km depth of water. The New Hebrides Trench to the west is divided into two sections, there being no trench off the north-central parts of New Hebrides, where the E-W lineations of the D'Entrecasteaux zone

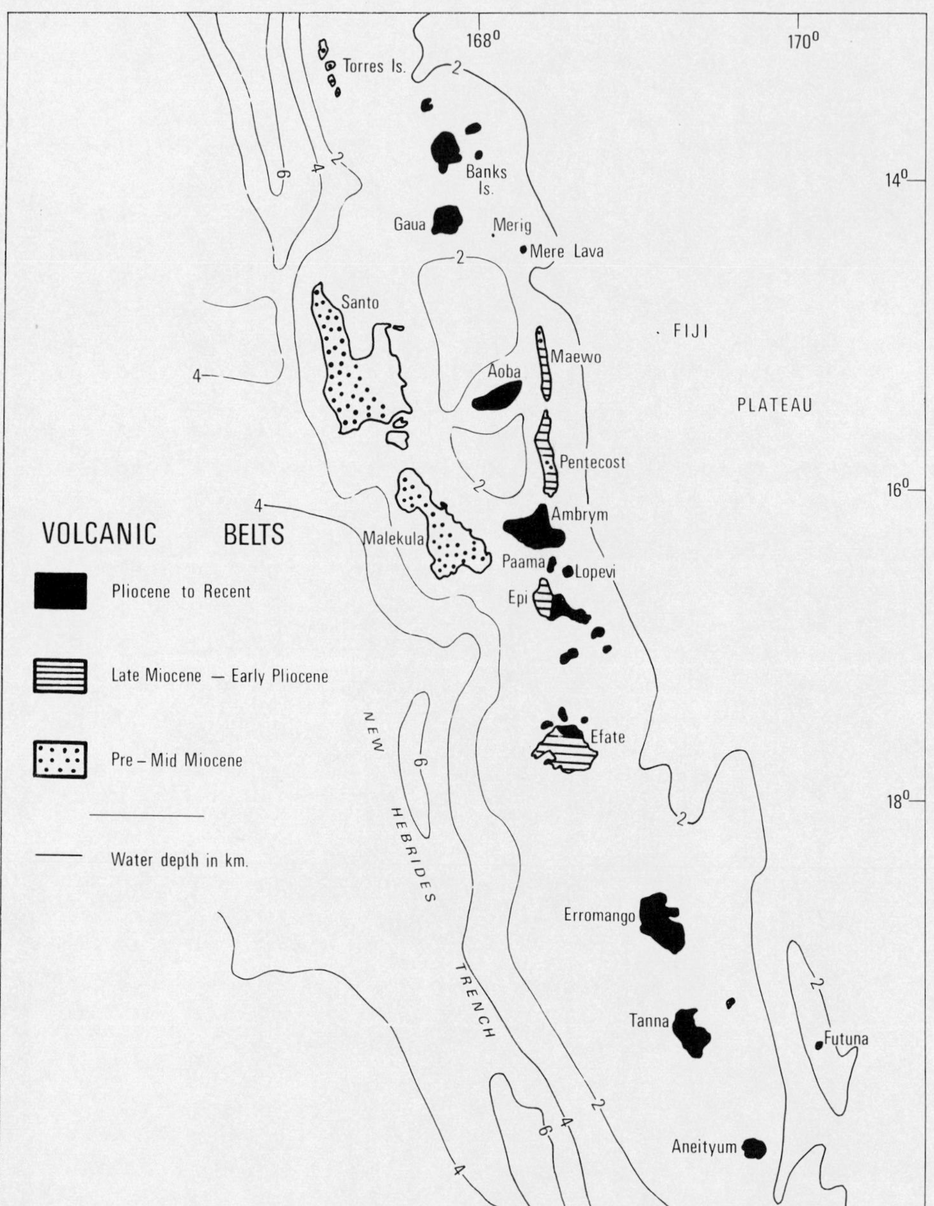

Fig. 1 Distribution of the three volcanic belts of New Hebrides

of the Coral Sea Basin abut against the New Hebrides Ridge. Despite the break in the trench system, the seismic zone is continuous throughout the major SSE-trending sector of the ridge, and dips at approximately 60° eastwards (Dubois *et al*, this volume).

Coleman (1970) showed that there were a number of similar features in the geology and history of the Solomon and New Hebrides Arcs, but that there were also a significant number of differences. Notable among the latter were the relative youth of the New Hebrides, the lack of folded deep-sea pelagic sediments comparable to those of the Pacific Province of the Solomons, the absence of major overthrusts and the possession of a transverse gravity profile with the highest values on the eastern side of the ridge; there is a series of gravity maxima on the southern or trench side of the Solomon Islands.

Recently, Mitchell and Warden (1971) have summarized the general geology and evolution of the New Hebrides in terms of three belts: a Western Belt consisting of the Torres Islands, Santo and Malekula; an Eastern Belt consisting of Maewo and Pentecost; and a Central Chain extending from the Banks Islands in the north to Aneityum in the south (Fig. 1). They showed that there was a small overlap in time of the periods of volcanism in the Eastern and Central Belts and they considered that the rocks of the Western Belt were calcalkaline, those of the Eastern Belt were tholeiitic, while those of the Central Chain were of tholeiitic and high-alumina affinities. The paper also contained the suggestion that the New Hebrides Arc may have reversed its polarity in the past (see also Karig, this volume), and that the ultramafic rocks of Pentecost mark the site of a former trench on the eastern side of the New Hebrides. As a consequence of this, and because the younger volcanoes of the Central Chain lie between belts of older volcanics, a consideration of compositional variations across the three belts was unlikely to be of value in determining the source of the primary magmas.

The purpose of this contribution is to examine further some aspects of subdivision and variation within the New Hebrides to see if there is any detailed evidence to support an arc polarity-reversal and if it offers any constraints on structural evolution and magma genesis.

The data used in this paper come mainly from published and as yet unpublished reports of the New Hebrides Geological Survey, as well as the author's own observations.

BASIC SUBDIVISION

The subdivision used in Fig. 1 is based on the age of the main periods of volcanism. There are three of these: pre-Middle Miocene, Upper Miocene to Lower Pliocene and Pliocene to Recent. In the northern part of the New Hebrides the products of these three periods of volcanism are largely separated, in spatial terms, into the Western, Eastern and Central Belts, respectively. In the southern part of the Central Belt, however, there is a juxtaposition and overlapping of the products of the last two periods. The distribution and general features of the products of the three main volcanic episodes are as follows:

The pre-Middle Miocene volcanism

Pre-Middle Miocene volcanics occur mainly in the Western Belt, but also occur in two small areas on Pentecost and Maewo. The volcanics of the Western Belt are mainly submarine volcaniclastics which range in composition from basalt to hornblende dacite and which accumulated on the flanks of a late Oligocene-early Miocene reef-fringed archipelago. Intrusions into the volcanic piles in the Lower Miocene were mainly of porphyritic andesite and microdiorite, but include a few bodies of coarse-grained diorite and gabbro.

Early Miocene volcaniclastic rocks also occur in the north of Maewo and contain occasional pebbles of quartzphyric dacite (Liggett, in prep.) as well as rare calcarenite clasts containing an Upper Eocene fauna of larger foraminifera (Coleman 1969). In central Pentecost there is a series of lavas of probable Oligocene age which are intruded and slightly metamorphosed by gabbros, and are in fault contact with unmetamorphosed early Middle Miocene volcaniclastics.

The Upper Miocene to Lower Pliocene volcanism

The main mass of volcanics exposed on Maewo and Pentecost are basaltic and basic andesitic submarine lavas and volcaniclastic sediments containing a planktonic fauna free of shallow-water species. The basaltic lavas are commonly pillowed (whereas most of the Lower Miocene lavas of the Western Belt are brecciate).

Fine, reworked tuff horizons at the top of a major unit of pumiceous latite breccias forming most of central Efate have also yielded a planktonic foraminiferal fauna, comparable to the *Globigerina dutertrei* fauna (McTavish 1966) of the Solomon Islands of Upper Miocene-Lower Pliocene age.

The submarine volcanics of western Epi (Warden 1967) on which no age data are yet available, are provisionally included in this Upper Miocene-Lower Pliocene suite; they lie spatially and compositionally between the mainly basaltic volcanics of Pentecost and the latites of Efate.

The Pliocene to Recent volcanism

Volcanics of this age are predominantly subaerial and confined to the Central Chain. Two subgroups may be recognized:

(*a*) a *northern subgroup* consisting of the Central Chain islands northwards from Ambrym which partially fill a deep basin at the crest of the New Hebrides Ridge. They include large shield volcanoes with summit calderas (Ambrym, Aoba and Gaua) as well as small, simple cones (e.g. Ureparapara, Mere Lava). All are youthful, several being still active; no pre-Pleistocene rocks have yet been proved.

(*b*) a *southern subgroup* consisting of the islands southwards from Paama and Lopevi. They are mainly clusters of small volcanic cones, of Pleistocene to Recent age in the Central Islands but somewhat older on the three southern islands of Erromango, Tanna and Aneityum. On Erromango volcanism extended from the late Miocene to Pleistocene but without the spatial separation that occurs in the northern New Hebrides.

In this southern subgroup there appears to have been a general tendency for the eruption foci to migrate eastwards relative to the preceding volcanism; the five centres in the *Catalogue of Active Volcanoes* (Fisher 1957) all lie on the eastern side of the islands at present.

Post-volcanic deposits of the three belts

During the Quaternary the New Hebrides islands have been generally rising relative to sea-level and all but the most recent volcanic islands bear a fringe or capping of raised reef limestones. On most of the islands of the Central Chain there is but a small development of low-altitude raised reefs, although on the slightly older island of Erromango there are five terraces of raised reefs extending up to 300 m altitude.

The Quaternary cappings of raised-reef limstones on the Mio-Pliocene volcanics of Maewo and Pentecost were previously entire; they originally formed patch reefs or atolls. There is a hiatus in the stratigraphic column of these islands in the Pliocene for which few deposits are known; this presumably represents a period of erosion of the volcanic piles, with the debris accumulating in the pelagic apron.

There is an even greater time gap on the Western Belt between the end of the main volcanic period and the beginning of the development of the Quaternary, and possibly late Pliocene, reef limestones. On Santo, Robinson (1969) records that volcanism continued sporadically into the mid-Miocene, and Mitchell (1966) recorded bands of tuff of unknown provenance in the Middle Miocene of Malekula. For the most part, however, the period from Middle Miocene to early Pliocene is represented by thick sequences of fine-grained epiclastic and biogenic deposits which accumulated peripheral to the volcanic structures.

PETROLOGY OF THE IGNEOUS ROCKS

The rocks of the New Hebrides are part of the circum-Pacific andesite-basalt zone, as Lacroix (1940) recognized. The basalts generally contain <1 per cent TiO_2, well below the lower discriminating limit of the oceanic basalts (Chayes 1964). Of more than 200 analyses now available, only a half dozen or so contain a little normative nepheline; this can generally be explained by altered $Fe_2O_3:FeO$ ratio. The remainder of the rocks have normative quartz + hypersthene or olivine + hypersthene and are of tholeiitic, high-Al or calkalkali affinities. Almost all of the rocks are porphyritic, usually markedly so; truly aphyric rocks are rare. With few exceptions plagioclase is the predominant phenocryst phase, the rocks with high alumina contents (20-21 per cent) invariably being rich in plagioclase phenocrysts.

Colley (1969) recognized two types of andesite, an Erromangan type in which amphibole was rarely present and a Malekulan (or calcalkali) type characterized by phenocrysts of hornblende. Wilkinson (1969), however, considered that the differences between these two types were small and that both could be derived from a common parent.

Pliocene to Recent volcanics

Most of the rocks of this age are basalts or basaltic andesites; more basic types (e.g.

picrite basalts on Aoba, Warden 1970) and more acid andesites and possibly dacite also occur, but are uncommon. Colley (1969) suggested that the occurrence of alkali-rich rocks, more common on Ambrym than on Erromango, might be due to Ambrym lying further from the New Hebrides Trench and so deriving its magma ultimately at a greater depth from the Benioff zone—a relation similar to that originally shown by Kuno (1959) for the Japanese arcs. More recent data indicates that this is not so. On the contrary, the alkalinity tends more commonly to decrease with distance from the trench and thus from the Benioff zone.

Unfortunately, the New Hebrides is not ideal for the study of lateral variation, being a very narrow belt of islands—probably the result of the steep dip of the seismic zone. The greatest separation of volcanoes of similar age across the New Hebrides Ridge is in the southern part of the Banks Islands, where there is approximately 60 km between Gaua in the west and Mere Lava in the east, with Merig about half way between. Malahoff (1970) interpreted the magnetic anomaly pattern as indicating that each of the three islands was on a separate crustal rift; they thus constitute three separate sampling points across the ridge.

Gaua is a Pleistocene low volcanic shield composed mainly of basalts but with some basic andesites; it has an active cone in its large summit caldera. Mere Lava is a slightly dissected simple cone of basalts containing conspicuous mafic phenocrysts and occasional coarse-grained meso- and melanocratic nodules. Merig island forms a tiny protrusion from the planed-off top of a volcanic pile and is comparable in age to the older parts of Gaua. It consists of andesitic and basaltic breccias cut by a high-level hypersthene andesite intrusion, itself cut by occasional olivine basalt dykes.

The islands are thus all broadly of comparable age (<2 m.y.) and differ quite notably in their chemistry (Mallick 1971), with alkalinity (and P_2O_5) increasing from Mere Lava to Gaua, that is, towards the trench and contrary to the pattern established for other Pacific island arcs. The clear separation of the high K_2O-high P_2O_5 series of Gaua and the low K_2O-low P_2O_5 series of Mere Lava is shown on the Harker diagram in Fig. 2*a*; the Merig rocks plot in between. A similar separation is obtained using Differentiation Index (Σ normative salics) as abscissa. In addition to the changes in alkalies and P_2O_5, total Fe and the Fe_2O_3:FeO ratio are both consistently higher in the Gaua basalts than in those of Mere Lava and in the Gaua andesites than in those of Merig.

The C.I.P.W. norms indicate that the Gaua basalts extend from the critical plane of silica undersaturation (olivine basalt) through olivine tholeiite to saturated and oversaturated tholeiites. By contrast the Merig and Mere Lava basalts are restricted to olivine and quartz tholeiites which have considerably more normative Hy than those of Gaua.

The consistently higher oxidation ratio of the Gaua basalts suggests that this is a primary feature of the magma and not the effect of secondary alteration. As such it would be wrong to arbitrarily reduce the Fe_2O_3/FeO ratio as suggested by Coombs (1963), a procedure which would displace five of the six Gaua basalts analysed into the alkali basalt field. More data is required on the mineralogy of the opaque minerals to check the origin of the oxidation ratios.

The Fe_2O_3 content of the Gaua basalts is sufficient for all the modal opaque

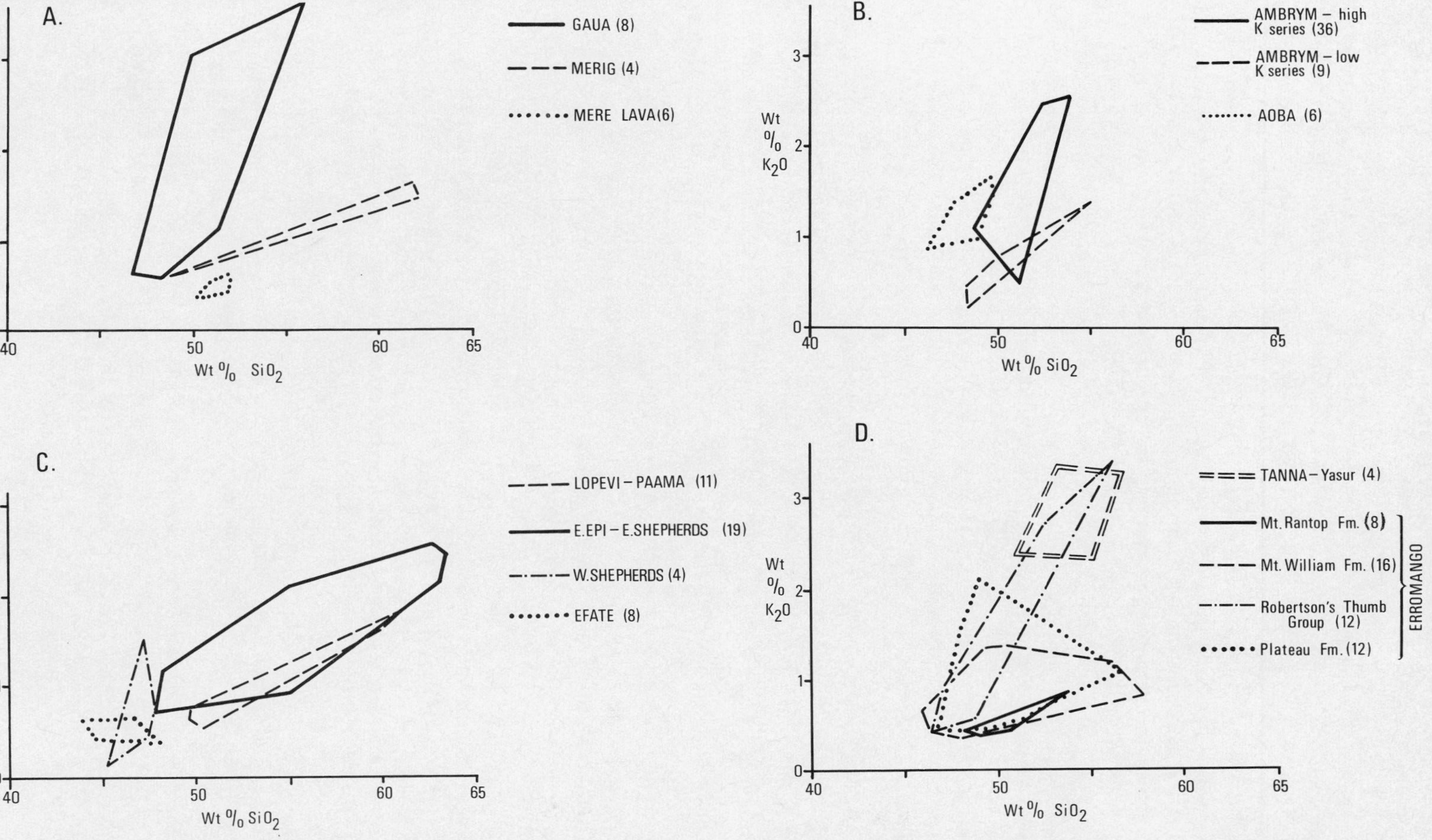

Fig. 2 K_2O-SiO_2 plots for the Pliocene to Recent volcanics: A, Southern Banks Islands (Mallick & Ash, in prep.); B, Ambrym (Stephenson, pers. comm.) and Aoba; C, Central Islands (Warden 1967 & Ash, in prep.); D, Erromango (Colley & Ash 1971) and Tanna. Figures in brackets are numbers of analyses.

material to be magnetite, whereas in some of the Mere Lava basalts it is too low for this to be so.

Mineralogically, there appears to be little difference between the basalts of Gaua and Mere Lava, except that in those of the latter, phenocrysts of olivine and pyroxene are more common and prominent, while some on the former island contain a little interstitial alkali feldspar. In both, however, the predominant phenocrysts are usually of plagioclase, although on Gaua there are some ankaramitic varieties which have phenocrysts only of olivine and clinopyroxene. The few basalts which do occur on Merig are olivine-phyric and similar to those of Mere Lava.

The andesites of Gaua and Merig differ quite markedly. Those from Gaua are basic (55-56 per cent SiO_2) and alkali-calcic ($Na_2O + K_2O > CaO$) and contain a similar mineral assemblage to the basalts—*plag* + *cpx* + *mt* ± *ol*—except that the feldspar tends to be rather more abundant and more sodic. In addition rare scraps of biotite or hornblende occur in the groundmass. The Merig andesites (57-62 per cent SiO_2) are calkalkaline and are characterized by phenocrysts of hypersthene as well as the more abundant plagioclase and clinopyroxene; they also contain common xenocrysts of brown hornblende.

The main conclusion from the southern Banks Islands is that there is a spatial variation in alkalinity within a tholeiitic series of rocks, alkalinity increasing away from the trench, giving a negative correlation of alkali content with depth to the Benioff zone. Available data is inadequate to indicate whether or not it is significant that the youngest lava from Gaua is the least alkalic basalt analysed from that island.

There is a broadly similar tendency for rocks lower in total alkalies, K_2O and P_2O_5, to occur on the eastern side of both the Central Islands and Erromango. In both these instances there are clusters of volcanic centres with little lateral separation. Consequently, there is much more overlapping of the various K_2O fields on Harker plots but, nevertheless, the rocks of the most easterly islands tend definitely to plot on the K_2O-poor side (Figs 2*c* & 2*d*). The spatial variation seems reasonably clear but, as was mentioned earlier, the foci of volcanic activity have tended to migrate eastwards with time. It is consequently uncertain in the southern part of the Pliocene to Recent volcanic province whether the spatial variations are truly due to differences of position or whether they are to an extent time-dependent.

The island of Tanna appears to be anomalous; the only analyses so far available are from the active cone of Yasur which is on the east side of the island but whose products are alkali-rich basalts and basic andesites (Fig. 2*d*).

The large caldera volcanoes of Ambrym and Aoba were fed from magma chambers now represented by small clusters of magnetic source bodies lying on E-W crustal rifts (Malahoff 1970); consequently, it is not surprising that no lateral variation across the islands has yet been recognized. On Ambrym, Stephenson (1971) recognized, however, an older volcanic group characterized by low K_2O and low P_2O_5 and a younger group containing both low K_2O-low P_2O_5 and high K_2O-high P_2O_5 types (Fig. 2*b*); the products of the active volcanoes on the island are of high K_2O type.

Only a few analyses are so far available from Aoba (Warden 1970), but these indicate that alkali-rich rocks similar to the high K_2O-high P_2O_5 series of Ambrym and Gaua are present.

Mineralogically, there appears to be little distinctive variation in the Pliocene to Recent volcanics south of the Banks Islands. Stephenson, for instance, stated that he had no petrographic criterion available to separate low from high K_2O types on Ambrym. The basalts generally have normal tholeiitic mineralogy (*plag* + *cpx* + *mt* ± *ol* ± *opx*) and are predominantly feldsparphyric. Olivine is quite common as a phenocryst, but occurs more rarely in the groundmass. Orthopyroxene is rare in the basalts and pigeonite has not been recognized. In the basic andesites the mineralogy is similar, except that olivine is rarer and orthopyroxene more common; amphibole is rare but does occur in some of the rocks on Erromango (Colley & Ash, 1971).

Late Miocene- early Pliocene volcanics

As a whole the rocks of this province range from basic tholeiitic basalts to latites; they are of moderate alkalinity, lying somewhere between the rocks of Gaua and those of Merig on a Harker plot.

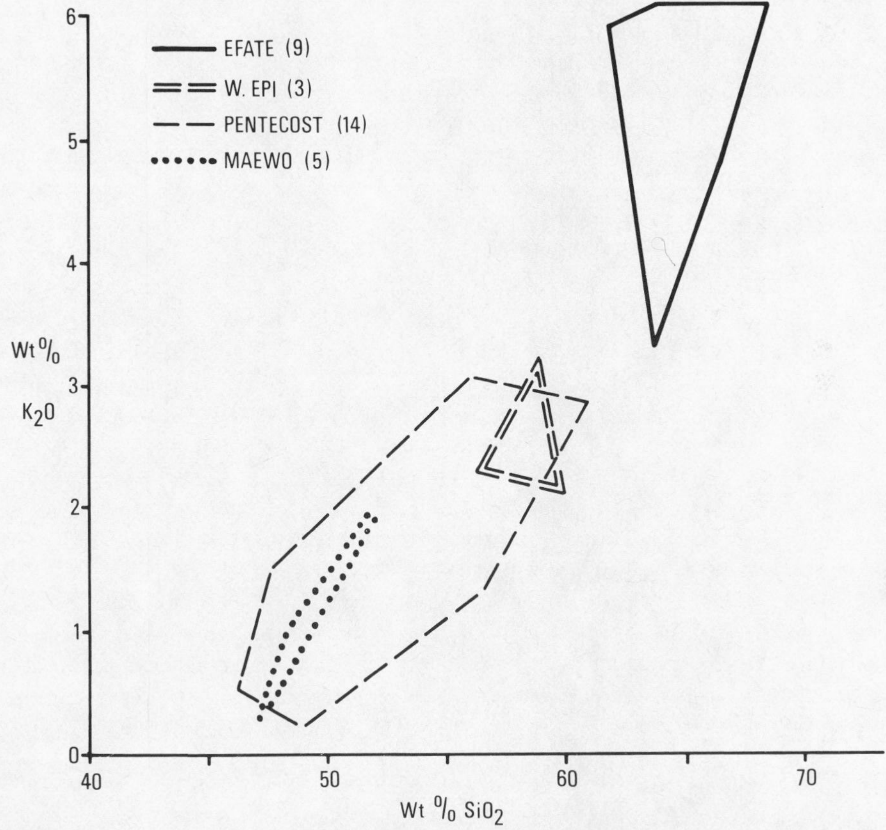

Fig. 3 K_2O-SiO_2 plot for the late Miocene-early Pliocene volcanics. Figures in brackets are numbers of analyses.

As might be anticipated from the province being only about 10 km in width above sea-level no lateral variation across the province can be recognized. There is, however, a marked longitudinal variation in composition (Fig. 3) from tholeiitic basalts on Maewo and Pentecost through basic calcalkali, two-pyroxene andesites on Pentecost and Western Epi to the siliceous latite pumice of Efate.

No variation of composition with time has yet been recognized as the data on the detailed stratigraphy and the number of analyses are, at present, inadequate.

The basalts of Maewo and Pentecost are olivine tholeiites and quartz tholeiites and include both olivine-phyric and olivine-free types. Groundmass olivine is not common, but does occasionally occur, notably in rare types with picritic affinities on Maewo and ankaramitic affinities on Pentecost. P_2O_5 is generally rather low (0·07-0·27 per cent), but modal apatite does appear. The basic andesites of Pentecost (56-60 per cent SiO_2) typically contain the phenocryst assemblage *plag+cpx+opx+mt* in a *opx*-free groundmass which is usually glass-rich. Amphibole is absent.

The basic andesites of western Epi are somewhat similar to those of Pentecost, but contain slightly higher alkalies and P_2O_5 and contain rare xenocrysts of quartz (Warden 1967). They are accompanied by latitic tuffs (unanalysed) which contain occasional quartz and a little biotite.

Pumiceous and perlitic latites (with the phenocryst assemblage *plag+cpx+opx+mt*) and derived from them, poorly reworked pyroclastic breccias and epiclastic sandstones are the main lithologies of central Efate. They contain 62-68 per cent SiO_2 and are very rich in alkalies (8-11 per cent) of which K_2O, ranging from 4·4 per cent to 5·9 per cent in the rocks analysed, is generally more abundant than Na_2O (Ash, in prep.).

Pre-Middle Miocene volcanics

The pre-Middle Miocene rocks of the Western Belt are characterized by the occurrence of primary green hornblende in the more acid members. Primary hornblende is not, however, common in the Eastern Belt.

The volcanic rocks of Malekula, Santo and the Torres Islands range from basalts of probable tholeiitic affinity, through the common calcalkali andesites bearing phenocrysts of green hornblende, to the most acid rock, containing 67·8 per cent SiO_2, described by Lacroix (1941) as hornblende dacite.

Mitchell (1968) pointed out that much of the late Oligocene-early Miocene volcanic succession of Malekula had suffered zeolite facies metamorphism, resulting in chloritization of many of the rocks and changes in the various oxide ratios and in the water content. Consequently, there is appreciable scatter on a simple Harker plot of K_2O. Taking only the less altered rocks, those with $\Sigma H_2O < 2$ per cent, still leaves a wide scatter for the rocks of Santo (Fig. 4) (which are similar to those of Malekula) while very few of those from Malekula fall in this category. Those with $\Sigma H_2O > 2$ per cent from Malekula are added to Fig. 4 to demonstrate the additional K_2O scatter associated with them.

Mitchell (1968) recognized two groups of minor intrusions on Malekula—mesocratic pyroxene-bearing basic andesites and leucocratic hornblende andesites: similar rocks are also found on Santo and the Torres Islands. These intrusives as a whole tend to be rather more Al_2O_3-rich than the lavas, culminating in a leucocratic hornblende diorite from south-west Santo, which has 47·1 per cent SiO_2 and 23·34 per cent Al_2O_3 (Obelliane 1961).

In the Santo rocks with $H_2O<2$ per cent the basalts generally contain about one per cent K_2O and the andesites and dacites about 1·5 per cent K_2O, although some andesites contain almost 4 per cent. As might be anticipated, increased hydration of the rocks is accompanied by decrease in K_2O to below 0·4 per cent in certain basalts and andesites.

Few rocks from the small areas of outcrop of pre-Middle Miocene rocks on Maewo and Pentecost have yet been analysed, but tend to be of very low K_2O content. Liggett (in prep.) has described early Miocene conglomerates from northern Maewo with clasts of quartzphyric dacite, andesite, basalt, microgabbro and microdiorite; only the microdiorite contains hornblende. The dacite, with over 71 per cent SiO_2 and the most acid rock yet recorded from the New Hebrides, contains <2 per cent K_2O.

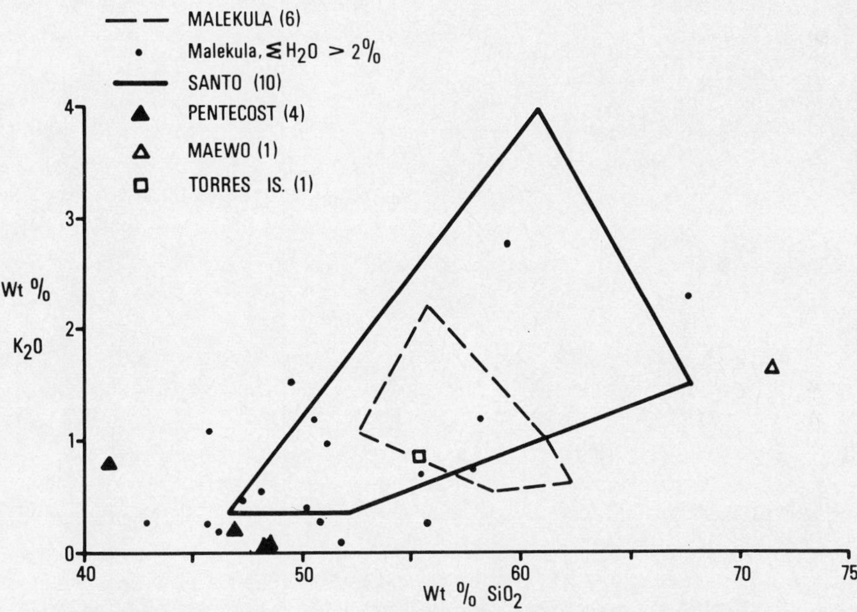

Fig. 4 K_2O-SiO_2 plot for the pre-Middle Miocene volcanics. Figures in brackets are numbers of analyses.

Of the pre-Middle Miocene volcanic province rocks of Pentecost, only the interior of the larger bodies of gabbro are free of metamorphic or metasomatic alteration; they are moderately high in Al_2O_3 (19 per cent—reflecting high modal feldspar) and exceptionally low in K_2O, the two analyses giving K_2O=trace (Obelliane 1961) and K_2O=0·12 per cent (Fig. 4). The marginal facies of the gabbros are amphibolized, the sample plotted with 46·9 per cent SiO_2 and 0·22 per cent K_2O contains no pyroxene but the assemblage *plag + hbl + ilm + sph + act + chl + epid*. The other rock plotted is evidently anomalous; described by Obelliane (1961) as a norite with slight amphibolization of clinopyroxene, it contains only 41·16 per cent SiO_2 and 0·81 per cent K_2O, but has ΣFe as $FeO = 18{\cdot}05$ per cent. With the exception of this anomalous rock, the few other analyses available from Maewo and Pentecost plot on the low K_2O side of those from the Western Belt.

CONCLUSIONS ON VOLCANICS

1. In the Pliocene to Recent rocks of the Central Chain there is a common, but not ubiquitous, tendency for the alkalinity of the volcanic rocks, which are all saturated or oversaturated, to decrease eastwards and thus give an anomalous negative correlation of alkalinity with depth to the Benioff zone. In the case of the southern Banks Islands, it appears that this spatial variation is true for a single limited period of time. A similar spatial variation in the Central Islands and on Erromango is associated with a migration of volcanic foci eastwards with time; it is not yet certain whether or not that variation is dependent mainly on position or on time. The analogy with the southern Banks Islands suggests, however, that position is an important feature. Neither is it yet clear whether the eastward migration of foci is a shift of foci relative to stationary islands or whether the islands are migrating westwards relative to stationary volcanic foci. The latter situation would occur if there were marginal consumption of the edge of the over-riding Fiji Plateau plate at the New Hebrides Trench.

Tanna and Ambrym do not appear to fit the general pattern, for their youngest volcanic products are alkali-rich tholeiites and in the case of Tanna the active cone lies on the east side of the island.

2. No lateral variation in composition is recognized in the very narrow belt of Upper Miocene-Lower Pliocene volcanics, but there is considerable variation along its length. The K_2O variation shows little spread and a trend slightly less K_2O-rich than that of Gaua. If the pattern established for the majority of the Pliocene-Recent volcanics can be applied to earlier volcanicity the compositions of the Mio-Pliocene group indicate that probably they all formed close to the ridge crest. Since Maewo and Pentecost lie well east of it at present, some later movement of these islands is implied.

3. From the limited data available, it appears that the pre-Middle Miocene volcanics of the Eastern Belt are less alkaline, and especially less K_2O-rich, than those of the Western Belt, that is, the alkalinity variation is similar to that of the majority of the Pliocene to Recent rocks. The petrological variations thus give no support to the suggestion that the polarity of the New Hebrides may have changed since the Lower Miocene.

If the pattern of variation established for the Pliocene to Recent volcanics is applicable in detail to the pre-Middle Miocene, then the islands of the Eastern and Western Belts may have formerly been in closer proximity. The testing of this hypothesis must await more data, in particular more analyses and the establishment of whether or not the pre-Middle Miocene rocks of the Eastern and Western Belts are truly comparable in age, as the preliminary data suggest.

4. The lack of the normal positive correlation between alkalinity and depth to the Benioff zone suggests the advent of another factor controlling magma composition. As Green, Green and Ringwood (1967) emphasized, the depths to the Benioff zone are too great to be the depths of magma segregation as Kuno (1959) suggested; they interpreted their experimental work as indicating that magma segregation must have occurred well above the Benioff zone, but at depths proportional to the seismic zone depths. They showed that it was possible to derive quartz tholeiites from an olivine normative parent only above 15 km depth; high Al basalts of either tholeiitic or alkaline affinities, only slightly enriched in silica, are obtained from olivine tholeiite or olivine basalt parents between 15 and 35 km depth; from 35-60 km derivative liquids trend towards alkali basalts. It thus appears that the wholly tholeiitic and over-saturated high-Al series of the New Hebrides must have been derived from close to the 15 km depth, the more alkali-rich varieties being perhaps derived from somewhat greater depths. Since Malahoff (1970) deduced from gravity data that the depth to the mantle varies from 16-20 km for the eastern half of the New Hebrides Ridge, it seems possible that magma segregation and, thus, compositional variation, is governed by the position of the Mohorovicic discontinuity, which becomes shallower eastwards.

STRUCTURE

Coleman (1970) and Mitchell and Warden (1971) have outlined the structure of the New Hebrides, emphasizing the tensional nature of the block faulting which controls the shapes of many of the islands.

The Bouguer gravity anomalies in general increase from west to east across the New Hebrides, culminating at +210 mgals over northern Maewo. Malahoff (1970) interpreted this as indicating that mantle depths increase from the trench to a maximum of about 24 km along the western side of the ridge and then decrease to a minimum of 16 km beneath Maewo on the eastern side. In the southern part of the New Hebrides the maximum depth to mantle lies a little to the west of the islands (a situation similar to that recorded from the southern Kuril Islands by Gainanov *et al.* 1968). The older islands of Santo and Malekula, on the other hand, lie directly above regions of thicker crust, with separate maxima of 24 and 26 km occurring beneath the two islands. This difference from the younger parts of the New Hebrides may indicate a movement of Malekula and Santo relative to the axis of maximum crustal thickness; such evidence of differential movement complements that from the petrological variations discussed above.

The seismicity of the New Hebrides area shows a continuous depth distribution between about 10 and 300 km, defining a Benioff zone dipping at roughly 60° to the east (Dubois *et al.* 1971). A further set with hypocentres in the depth range 550-650 km form a broad band roughly parallel to the Vitiaz Trench system. There is an inhomogeneous distribution of hypocentres along the New Hebrides Ridge. Shallow foci occur throughout, but are concentrated in three areas: (*a*) north of the Santa Cruz Islands, where there is a marked bend in the trench system; (*b*) a little to the north of

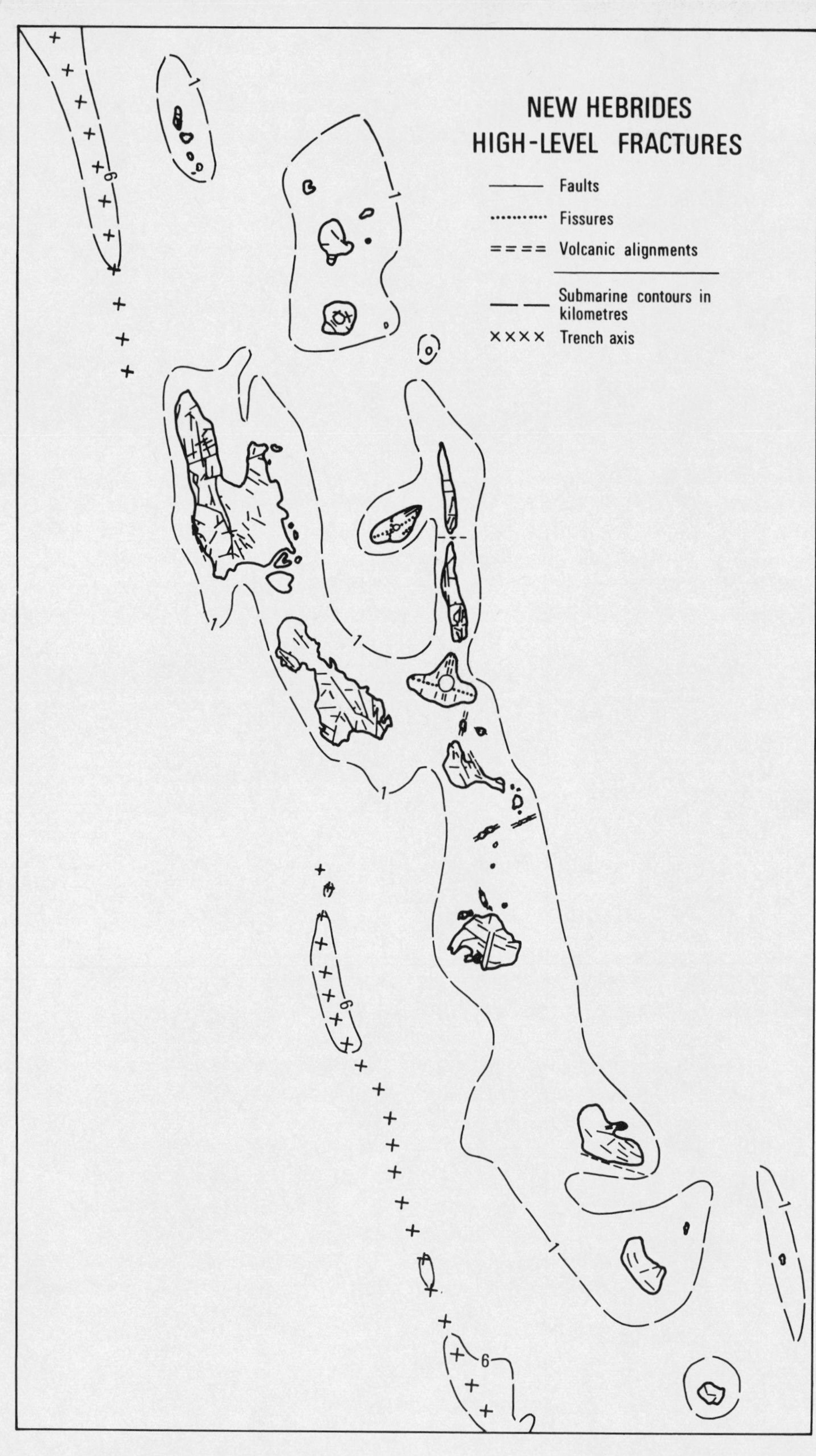
NEW HEBRIDES
HIGH-LEVEL FRACTURES
Faults
Fissures
Volcanic alignments
Submarine contours in kilometres
Trench axis
1
6
1
1
1
1
6
6
1
1

Santo; (*c*) between Efate and south Malekula. The last two areas are where the two separate sections of the New Hebrides Trench system terminate. Earthquakes with intermediate focal depths occur mainly in the area between Aoba and the northern Banks Islands, and in the Tanna area.

The total force magnetic anomalies are bipolar over most of the volcanic centres, and show a predominance of E-W trends. Malahoff (1970) interpreted this as indicating that the New Hebrides Ridge is crossed by a series of mainly E-W crustal rifts on which cylindrical intrusions occur. The latitudinal trends are particularly marked in the central parts of the New Hebrides and appear to mark the continuation of the structural grain of the D'Entrecasteaux zone across the ridge. Some E-W trends also occur further to the north and south, but are there accompanied by important divergent trends.

Of note in Malahoff's interpretation is the general lack of deep structures trending along the ridge. This contrasts with the high-level fracture pattern (Fig. 5) in which directions slightly oblique to the ridge axis and E-W directions predominate. As Mitchell and Warden (1971) emphasized, the high-level structure is dominated by tensional block faulting. Géze (1964) suggested that much of the faulting in the southern New Hebrides was due to gravitational collapse along sector graben. Certainly the Bouguer anomalies of Tanna and Erromango indicate that they are remnants of larger structures (Malahoff 1970).

The youthful volcanoes of the northern part of the Central Chain are relatively little-faulted, but three (Ambrym, Aoba and Gaua) have large collapse calderas (Fig. 5). The fissure systems of Aoba and Ambrym, which parallel their longest dimensions, lie slightly oblique to the deep crustal rifts recognized by Malahoff.

It is on the older islands of the Eastern and Western Belts that longitudinal trends predominate. On Maewo and Pentecost the major faults, such as the central Pentecost faults which form the northern limit of the Basement Complex, trend E-W although the structural grain of the islands is N20° E, slightly oblique to the island axes. This trend is also encountered in the south-east corner of Malekula and even in the alignment of the older (Pleistocene) volcanic cones of Ambrym.

On Santo there are some major E-W faults, but the main ones, as on Malekula, trend more or less along the islands, that is, N10° W on Santo and N30° W on Malekula. Although these two islands have very similar geology, there are a number of structural differences. Differential movement between the islands is indicated by Malekula having suffered greater early deformation resulting, so far as we know, in it alone having deep-water red mudstones of probable pre-Miocene age exposed on its north-west coast (Mitchell 1971). Santo, on the other hand, suffered greater late uplift, its mountains now standing much higher than those of Malekula and lack the extensive fringe of raised reef limestones found on the west side of Malekula. The magnificent west coast of Santo is, in fact, fault-controlled, the faults throwing down to the west; most of the other major longitudinal faults on Santo, like all those on Malekula, throw down to the east. A more recent example of differential movement occurred in 1965

Fig. 5 High-level fracture pattern in New Hebrides

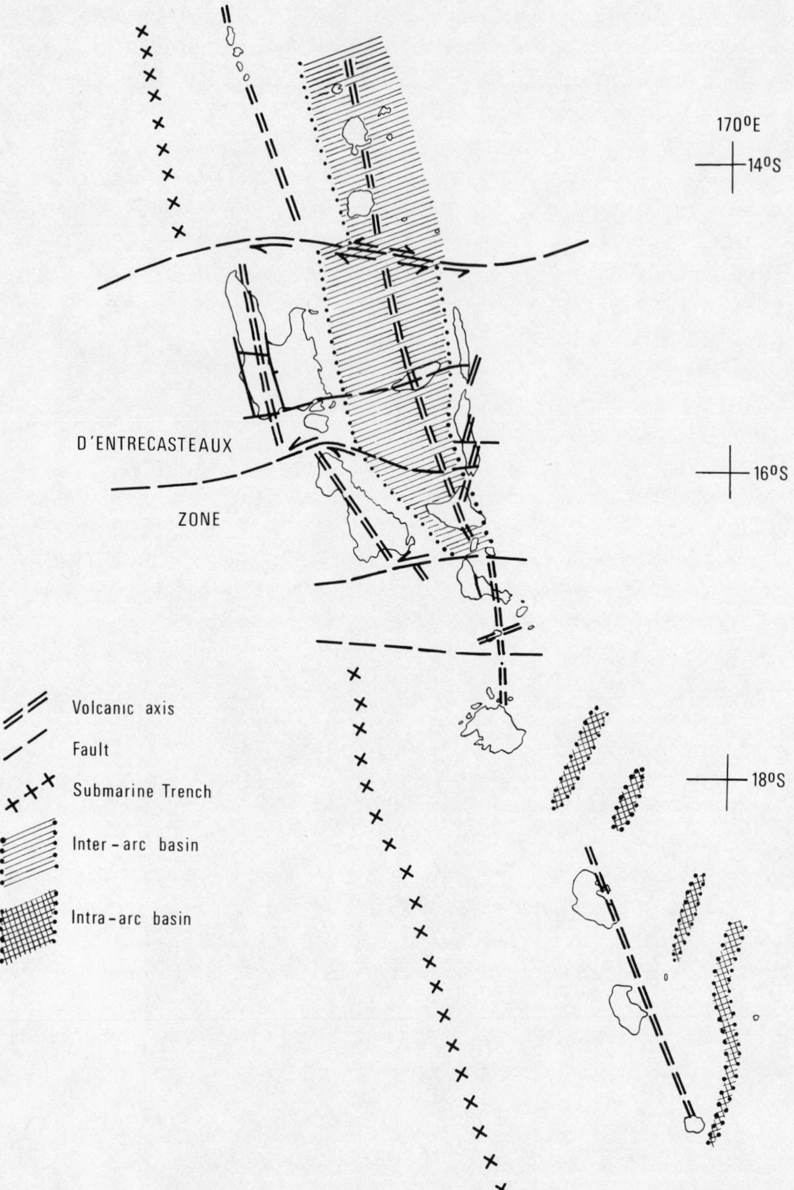

Fig. 6 Speculative interpretation of the structure of New Hebrides

when part of NW Malekula was uplifted by 2 m (Mitchell 1971), whereas Santo was not affected. The different nature of the west coasts of these two islands may, perhaps, be explained by the edge of the island arc block being located well to the west of Malekula, but close to the coast of Santo.

The physiography of the northern part of the New Hebrides, in which Quaternary volcanic structures partially fill a deep basin (3 km of water north of Aoba) at the crest of the ridge, was the primary feature interpreted by Karig (1970) as an inter-arc basin formed by separation of the Eastern and Western Belts, a small-scale analogue of the Tonga Ridge-Lau Basin-Lau Ridge structure. Such separation is now supported by the available petrological data. The inter-arc basin of the northern New Hebrides has margins which must be more or less parallel to the coasts of the islands of the Eastern and Western Belts. This contrasts with the more recent elongate basins shown to exist in the southern part of the New Hebrides, which trend a little east of north across the east flank of the ridge and whose irregular bottom topography suggests that they are not sediment-filled. They are shown as intra-arc basins on Fig. 6, which is a speculative interpretation of the structure of the New Hebrides.

The opening of the main inter-arc basin probably occurred in fairly recent times since only Quaternary materials occur in it. If, however, the volcanic focus has remained stationary with time, this could indicate westwards movement by the Western Belt before the formation of the Eastern Belt at the ridge crest, with subsequent separation leading to the present two-ridges and basin structure.

The opening of the inter-arc basin affects only the northern part of the New Hebrides and implies a rotation of Malekula anti-clockwise by about 20° about an axis off its south-eastern tip, while Santo moved bodily westwards, resulting in a divergence of their long axes. Such movements would imply the opening of an angle on the west between the two island masses in the sea area between Santo and Malekula, where Malahoff (1970) interpreted a salient of shallower-than-average mantle. The westward migration of Santo and Malekula relative to the axis of the New Hebrides Ridge, probably along transform faults, may be at least a factor contributing to the absence of a trench off this sector of the arc; the islands over-rode the trench and shed detritus to fill it.

As a whole, the New Hebrides is thus composed of high-level tensional faulting, much of it of longitudinal character, and deeper E-W crustal rifts. This can be reconciled with lithosphere plunging eastwards beneath the New Hebrides (implying ENE-WSW compressive stresses) if the deep rifts indeed mark planes of shear failure (tear or transform faults) crossing the arch of the New Hebrides Ridge slightly oblique to the main stress. The higher level longitudinal faulting about the ridge axis is due to tensional failure at the crest of the stressed body.

REFERENCES

Ash, R. P. (In prep.) Geology of Efate. *New Hebrides geol. Surv., Regional Rept.*

Chayes, F. 1964. A petrographic distinction between Cenozoic volcanics in and around the open oceans. *J. geophys. Res.* **69,** 1573-88.

Coleman, *w.* J. 1969. Derived Eocene larger foraminifera on Maewo, eastern New Hebrides, and their South-west Pacific implications. *New Hebrides geol. Surv. Rept*, 1967, 36-7 Ed. D. I. J. Mallick).

——— 1970. Geology of the Solomon and New Hebrides Islands as part of the Melanesian Re-entrant, South-west Pacific. *Pacif. Sci.* **24,** 289-314.

Colley, H. 1969. Andesitic volcanism in the New Hebrides. *Proc. geol. Soc. London*, **1662,** 46-51.

Colley, H. & Ash, R. P. 1971. Geology of Erromango. *New Hebrides geol. Surv., Regional Rept.*

Coombs, D. S. 1963. Trends and affinities of basaltic magmas and pyroxenes as illustrated on the diopside-olivine-silica diagram. *Miner. Soc. Am., Spec. Paper*, **1,** 227-50.

Dubois, J., Larue, B., Pascal, G. & Reichenfeld, C. 1972. Seismology and structure of the New Hebrides. This volume.

Fisher, N. H. 1957. *Catalogue of the Active Volcanoes of the World*, **5.** Melanesia. *Int. volc. Assoc.* Naples.

Gainanov, A. G., Zverev, S. M., Kosminskaya, I. P., Tulina, Yu. V., Livshitz, M. Kh., Sichev, P.M., Tuyezov, I. K., Fotiadi, E. E., Milashin, A. P., Soloviev, O. N. & Stroev, P. A. 1968. The crust and upper mantle in the transition zone from the Pacific Ocean to the Asiatic continent. In *The Crust and Upper Mantle of the Pacific Area* (Eds L. Knopoff, C. L. Drake & P. J. Hart). *Am. geophys. Un. Monogr.* **12,** 367-78.

Géze, B. 1963. Observations tectoniques dans le Pacifique (Hawaii, Tahiti, Nouvelles-Hébrides). *Bull. Soc. géol. Fr.* (ser. 7), **5,** 154-64.

Green, T. H., Green, D. H. & Ringwood, A. E. 1967. The origin of high alumina basalts and their relationships to quartz tholeiites and alkali basalts. *Earth Planet. Sci. Letters*, **2,** 41-51.

Karig, D. E. 1970. Ridges and basins of the Tonga-Kermadec island arc system. *J. geophys. Res.* **75,** 239-54.

Kuno, H. 1959. Origin of the Cenozoic petrographic provinces of Japan and surrounding areas. *Bull. volcan.* **20,** 37-76.

Lacroix, A. 1941. Composition minéralogique et chimique des laves des volcans des îles de l'Océan Pacifique situées entre l'equateur et le tropique de Capricorne, le 175° de longitude ouest et le 165° de longitude est. *Mém. Acad. Sci. Paris*, **63,** 97 pp.

Liggett, K. (In prep.) Geology of Maewo. *New Hebrides geol. Surv. Regional Rept* (see also *New Hebrides geol. Surv., Rept* (*1965*), 8-12).

McTavish, R. A. 1966. Planktonic Foraminifera from the Malaita Group, British Solomon Islands. *Micropaleontology*, **12,** 1-36.

Malahoff, A. 1970. Gravity and magnetic studies of the New Hebrides Island Arc. *New Hebrides geol. Surv., Spec. Rept*, 64 pp.

Mallick, D. I. J. 1971. Southern Banks Islands. *New Hebrides geol. Surv. Rept* (*1970*), 12-16 (Ed. D. I. J. Mallick).

Mallick, D. I. J. & Ash, R. P. (In prep.) Geology of the Southern Banks Islands. *New Hebrides geol. Surv., Regional Rept.*

Mitchell, A. H. G. 1966. Geology of South Malekula. *New Hebrides geol. Surv., Rept*, **3,** 42 pp.

——— 1968. Sedimentological and geological evolution of Malekula Island, New Hebrides. Ph.D. thesis, Univ. Oxford.

——— 1971. Geology of northern Malekula. *New Hebrides geol. Surv., Regional Rept.*

Mitchell, A. H. G. & Warden, A. J. 1971. Geological evolution of the New Hebrides island arc. *J. geol. Soc. London*, **127,** 501-29.

Obeliane, J. M. 1961. Contribution à la connaissance géologique de l'archipel des Nouvelles-Hébrides. *Sciences de la Terre*, **6** (*1958*), 139-68, Nancy.

Robinson, G. P. 1969. Geology of North Santo. *New Hebrides geol. Surv., Regional Rept*, 80 pp.

Stephenson, P. J. 1971. Ambrym Island project. *New Hebrides geol. Surv., Rept* (*1970*) (Ed. D. I. J. Mallick).

Warden, A. J. 1967. The geology of the Central Islands. *New Hebrides geol. Surv., Rept*, **5.**

——— 1970. Development of Aoba caldera volcano, New Hebrides. *Bull. volcan.* **34,** 107-40.

Wilkinson, P. 1969. Chemical comparison of New Hebrides with other Pacific volcanism. *Proc. geol. Soc. London*, **1662,** 51-5.

Seismology and Structure of the New Hebrides

J. Dubois, B. Larue, G. Pascal and C. Reichenfeld
Centre O.R.S.T.O.M., B.P.4, Noumea, New Caledonia

ABSTRACT

Study of the seismicity of the New Hebrides area over the last six years has established the existence of a Benioff zone. This can be defined between 0-350 km dipping north-east at angles varying between 45° and 70°. Propagation of body and surface waves along the New Hebrides Arc is abnormal. This is explained by the presence of an anomalous wedge of high-level, low-velocity upper mantle extending from about a depth of 20-150 km and with a width of 120 km.

The O.R.S.T.O.M. (Office de la Recherche Scientifique et Technique Outre-Mer) network of seismological stations in the South-west Pacific has added much data within the last ten years to what is known about the seismicity and structure of the island arc of the New Hebrides.

Eight stations are operated in this network: Noumea (NOU—N.O.A.S. code) and Koumac (KOU) in New Caledonia; Ouanaham (OUA) in the Loyalty Islands; and Port Vila (PVC), Luganville (LUG), Lonorore (LNR) and Lamap (LMP) in the New Hebrides (Fig. 1*b*).

SEISMICITY

Over the length of the New Hebrides Archipelago a belt of great seismic activity extends from 10° S-24° S, and active volcanism is associated with it. The epicentres of earthquakes of magnitude greater than 5 are plotted on Figs 1*a* and 1*b*, determined from 1961-1966 by the International Seismological Centre. The accuracy of epicentres depends on the influence of the nearest stations used in the computation and especially of the New Hebrides stations which are in an anomalous area of seismic wave propagation. This influence was studied for six New Hebrides earthquakes after two computations, one with and one without the use of New Hebrides network data. The differences in the calculated positions of the epicentres vary from 3-20 km (3, 5, 6, 16, 20, 22 km); for three earthquakes the two different epicentres are inside the error ellipse. Given strong shocks and a large number of recording stations with good distribution in azimuth, which we have in this area, the accuracy achieved is better than ± 10 km.

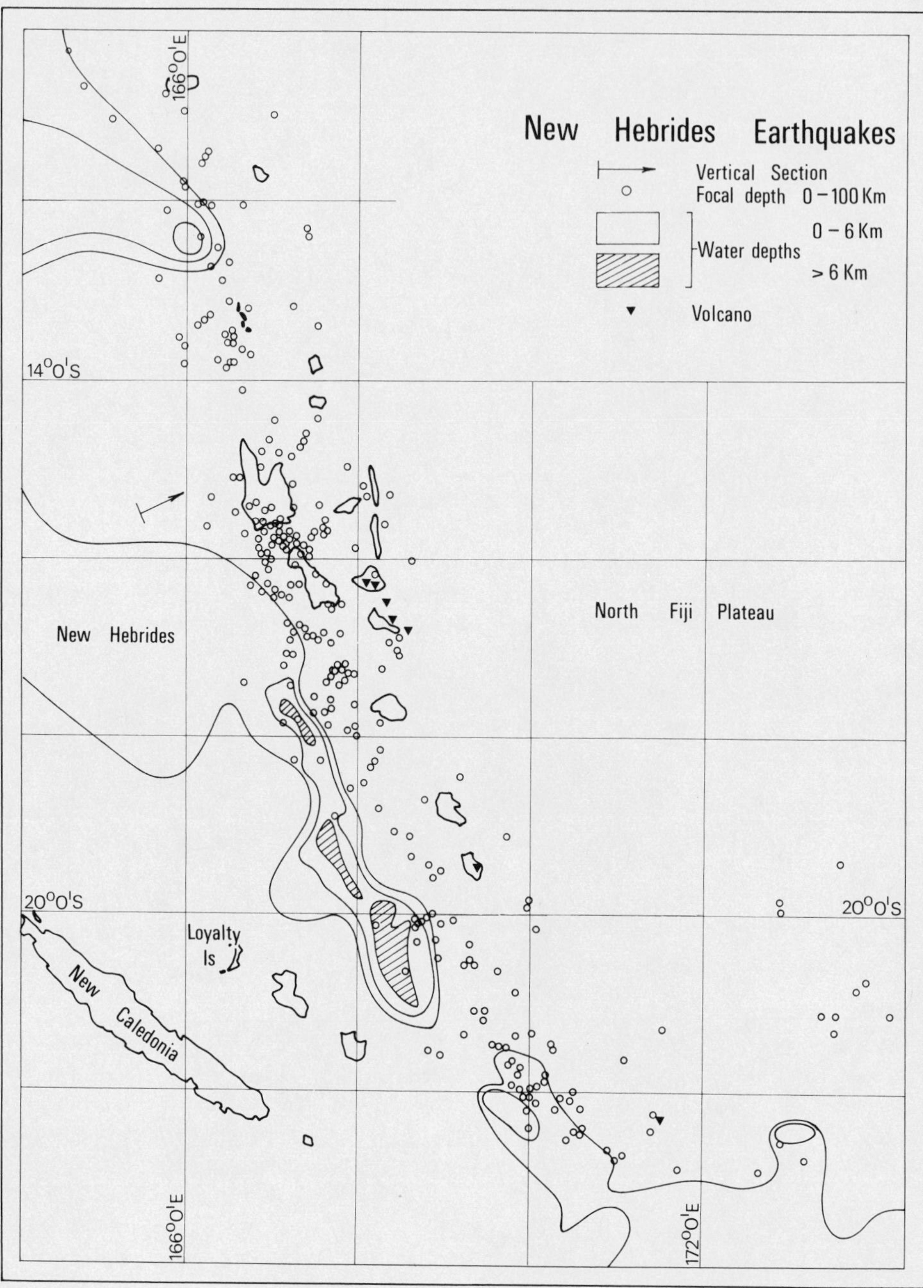

Fig. 1*a* Seismicity in the New Hebrides area, 1961-66, showing epicentres of earthquakes with focal depth 0-100 km. From Dubois, 1971 (by permission of the American Geophysical Union).

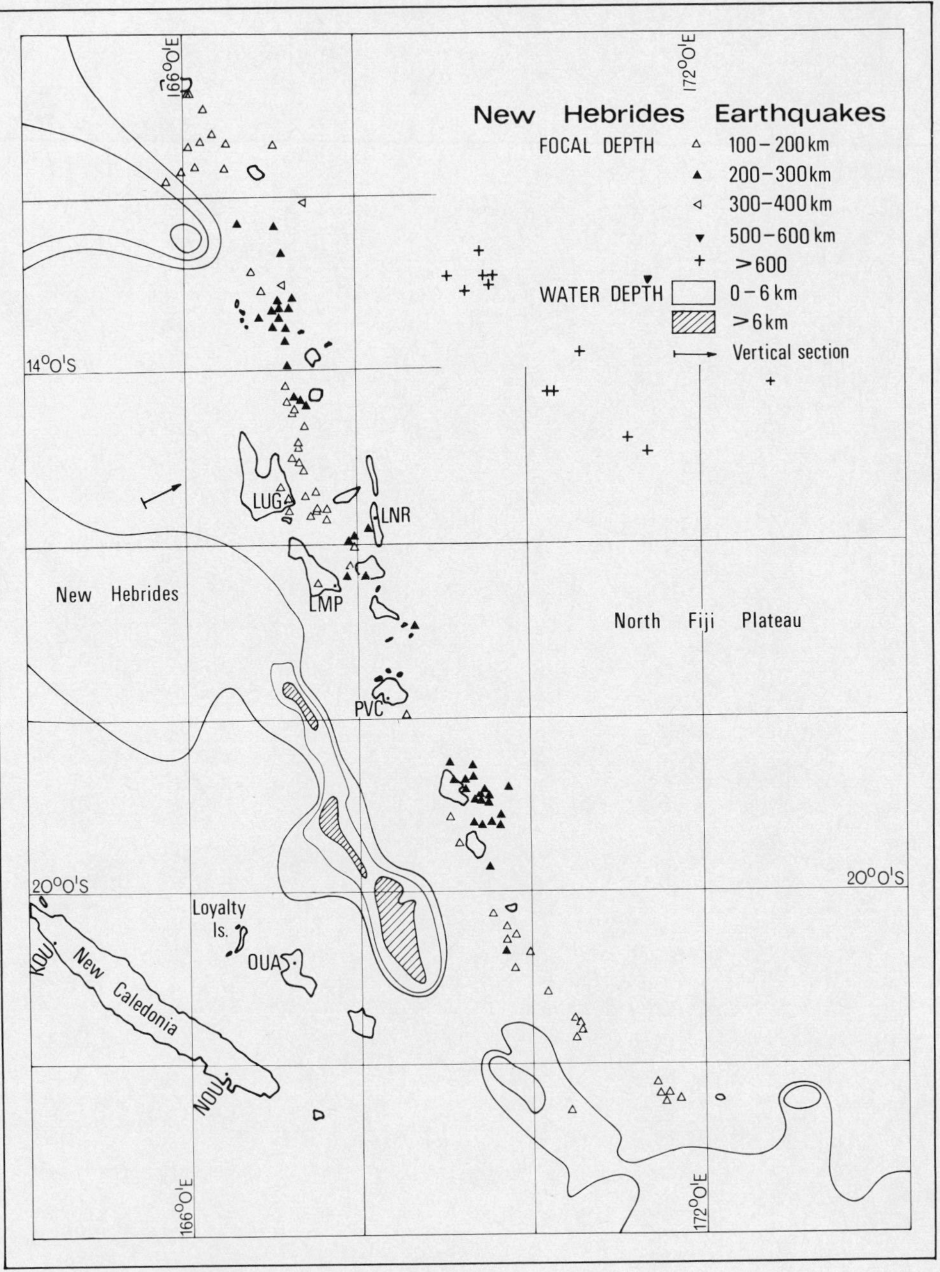

Fig. 1*b* Earthquake epicentres in the New Hebrides area, 1961-66, with focal depth greater than 100 km. O.R.S.T.O.M. seismological stations are shown: Noumea (NOU), Koumac (KOU), Ouanaham (OUA), Port Vila (PVC), Lamap (LMP), Lonorore (LNR) and Luganville (LUG). After Dubois, 1971.

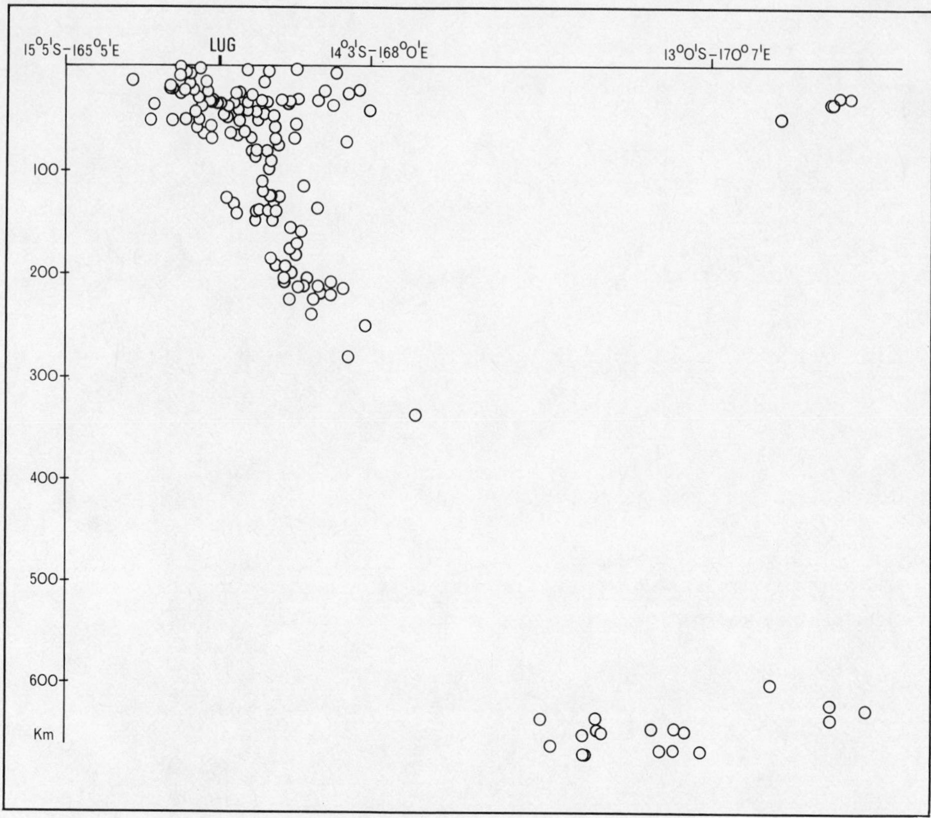

Fig. 2 A typical cross-section of earthquake hypocentres (Luganville, Espíritu Santo profile; see Figs 1*a* and 1*b*). From Dubois 1971, with permission.

Accuracy in depth was studied by using two methods: from *P* and from *pP-P*. The error is less than ±15 km when data from more than twenty stations is used.

The vertical sections (e.g. Fig. 2) show the foci concentrated around a plane dipping north-eastwards beneath the island arc at about 60°, but between it and the earth's surface there is a marked diffusion of shallow and intermediate foci.

This leads us to believe that there exist different 'populations' of earthquakes (Larue 1970). According to the plate tectonic theory (Oliver & Isacks 1967) one set of the shocks would be associated with movements of the sinking lithosphere, the second set would be the result of tectonic readjustments (Benoit & Dubois 1971).

It was possible to determine on ten vertical sections the surface around which the foci are grouped and then to draw the isodepth lines of this surface (Fig. 3). There is a gap in focal depths below 350 km. Deep focus earthquakes are limited to a belt running between 12-15° S and 169-174° E. We cannot assume that these earthquakes are associated with the dipping slab.

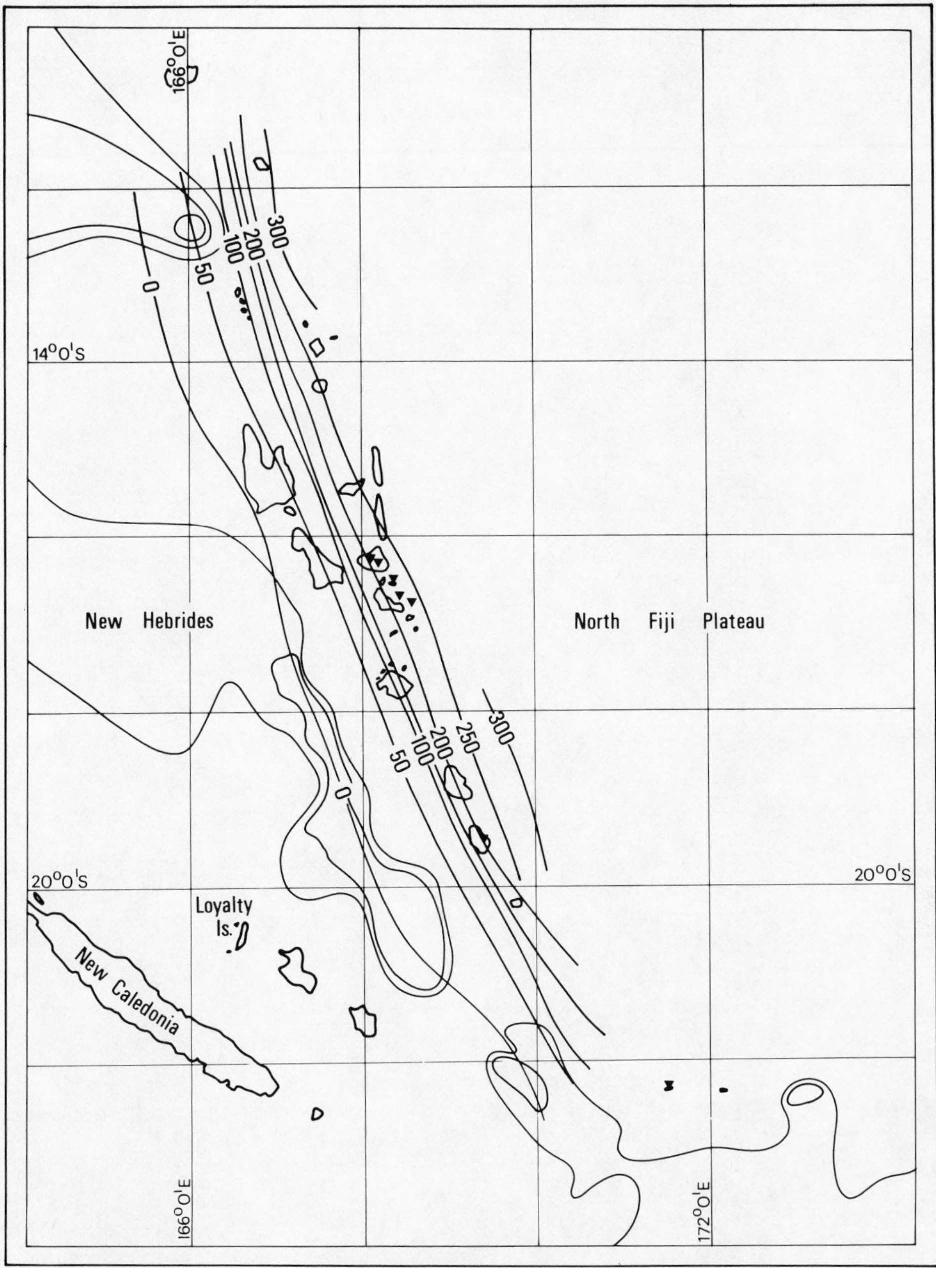

Fig. 3 Map of isodepth lines which define a seismic surface or zone (Benioff zone) dipping to the north-east. Depths in km.

ANOMALIES OF PROPAGATION

The anomalies of propagation of *P* waves and Rayleigh waves along the seismic belt were studied using earthquakes or events from both remote areas and the New Hebrides as recorded in Port Vila, Luganville, Lamap and Lonorore.

From the east, deep-focus Fiji earthquakes produce late arrivals of *P* waves to

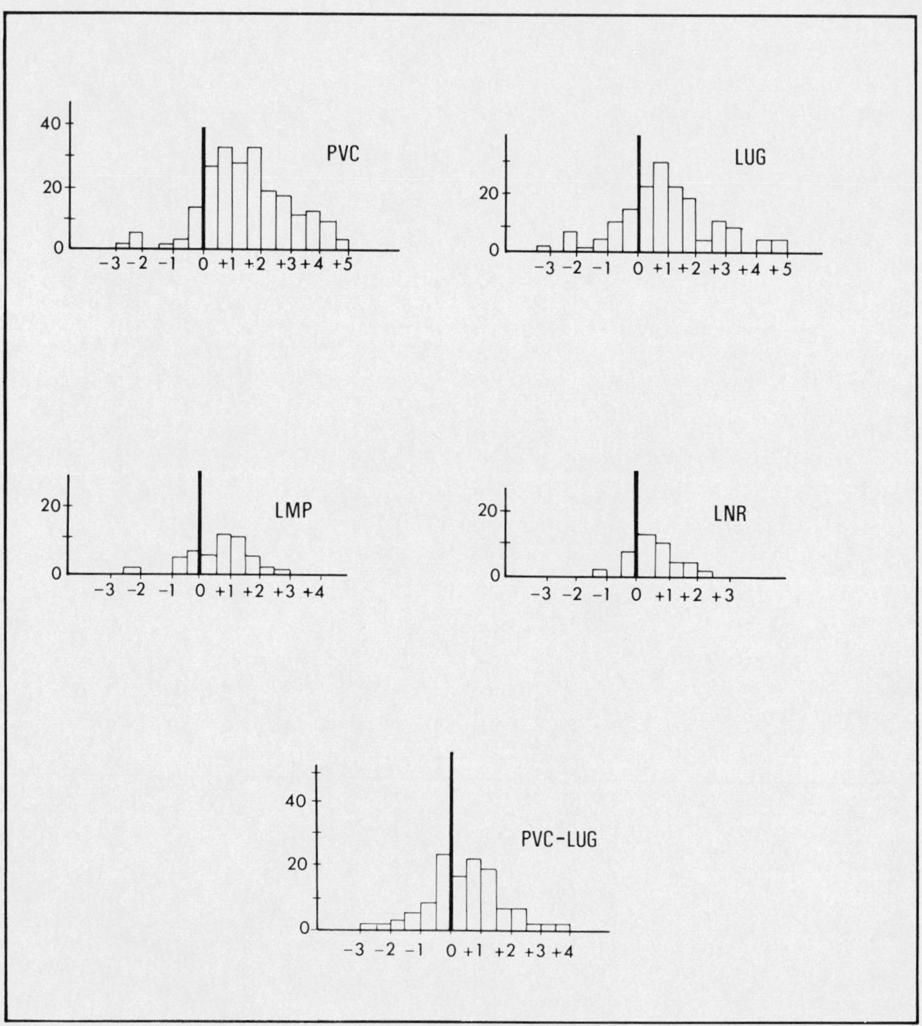

Fig. 4 Histograms of time residuals of *P* waves from Fiji deep-focus earthquakes at New Hebrides stations: Port Vila (PVC), Luganville (LUG), Lamap (LMP), and Lonorore (LNR). Interval of class is 0·5 s. Histogram for station pair PVC-LUG is shown. From Dubois, 1971, in part.

these four stations (Fig. 4). This fact is interpreted as due to the existence of a low-velocity upper mantle. There are local differences inside this area, as it is possible to see on the histogram of arrivals-delay between two stations PVC and LUG; the *P* wave arrivals are later in PVC than in LUG (slab effect under LUG?) and similarly between LNR and LMP.

From a northern direction the Longshot nuclear test gave a very late arrival in LUG. For the same epicentral distance (70°) we find a relative delay of 3·5 s between Melanesia and Australia. These delays may be explained by factors at the source, or under the recording stations, or along the raypath. Davies and MacKenzie (1969) show that a part of it is at the source, as an effect of a plate under the Aleutian Arc; the second part (1 s) between Australia and the New Hebrides is surely under Luganville because it cannot be found in the deep mantle along two very close paths (Dubois 1966).

So then, arrivals of *P* waves from the north and the east are usually late, 1 s and more, this fact probably due to the presence of low-velocity upper mantle in these directions. On the contrary, from the west and the north-west, for shocks in the Solomon, New Britain and New Guinea areas, early arrivals (0·7 s) are observed (Pascal 1970).

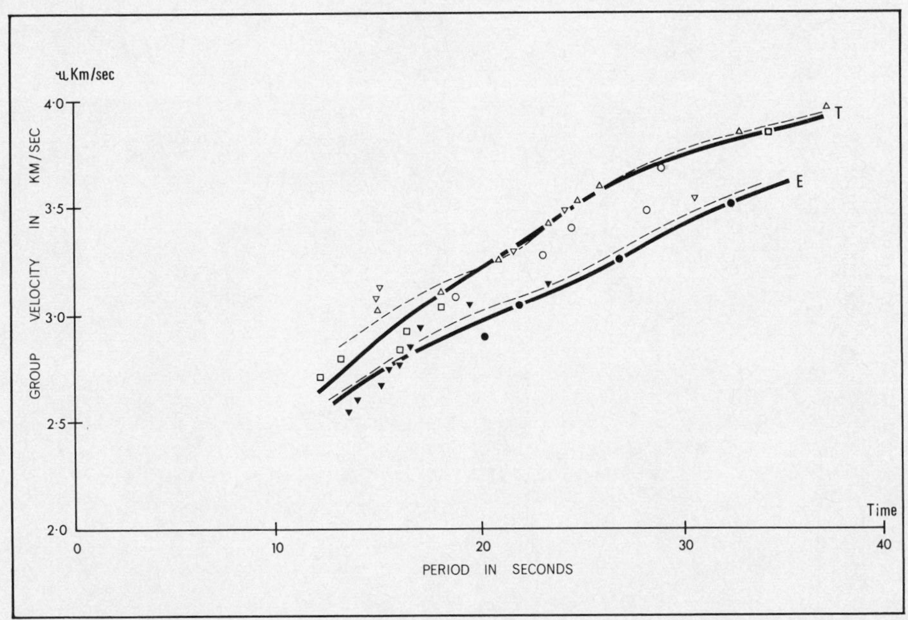

Fig. 5 Group velocity of Rayleigh waves, fundamental mode. Data from trench epicentres (see also Figs 1*a* and 1*b*) are shown in open symbols; from eastern slope epicentres in solid symbol (dashed lines). The theoretical dispersion curves of models T and E are indicated by heavy lines. From Dubois, 1971, with permission of the American Geophysical Union.

Studying the propagation times along the New Hebrides Arc it was possible to compute the apparent velocity between LUG and PVC. The velocity increases with the epicentral distance and, by applying the Herglotz-Wiechert method, a linear gradient is found in the upper mantle: from 7·4 km/s at a depth of 20 km (*P* wave velocity) to 8·1 km/s at a depth of 120 km. The late arrivals in New Hebrides stations from Fiji earthquakes and the Longshot Aleutian event are thus explained.

The propagation of *S* waves was not undertaken, for these phases are very weak on the raypath along the arc, implying a strong attenuation in the anomalous upper-mantle wedge, but it was possible to obtain indications of on the spatial variations of *S* wave velocity by the dispersion of the Rayleigh waves along the seismic belt. The influence coefficients of the different parameters on the phase velocity of Rayleigh waves were used to fit the theoretical curves to the experimental data. (For discussion see Dubois 1971, with Figs 7-11.) The observations for two groups of earthquakes in the Santa Cruz area show little difference between dispersion curves (Fig. 5). The theoretical models corresponding to this dispersion are in good agreement with the model chosen to explain *P* wave propagation, i.e. an upper mantle

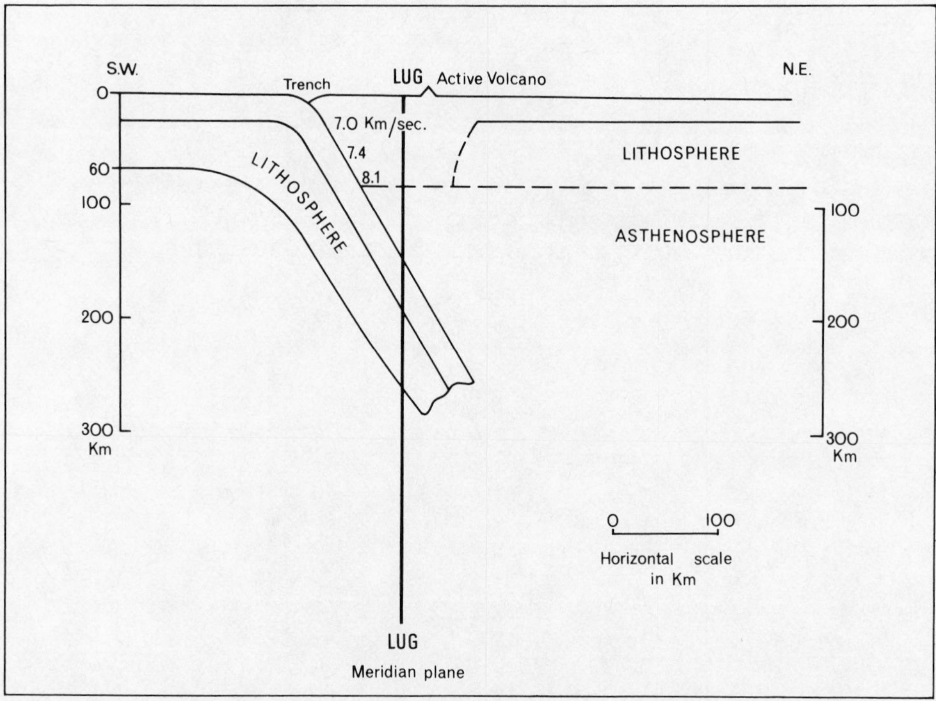

Fig. 6 Schematic cross-section of the New Hebrides Arc. Interruption of the dipping lithospheric slab corresponds to the lack of hypocentres below 350 km. The anomalous high-level, low-velocity mantle wedge is shown (below LUG). From Dubois, 1971, with permission.

with a vertical gradient of parameters α, β, ρ (*P* and *S* wave, velocities and density) from 20-120 km in depth. The little difference between group E (East slope group) and T (Trench group) is attributed to the effect of the differing thickness of the water layer on Rayleigh wave propagation (Dubois 1969).

A verification was done on phase velocity of Rayleigh waves inside the area delimited by LUG, LMP and LNR (Dubois & Reichenfeld 1971).

The first shear mode was also observed on records at PVC and their dispersion curves were compared with a theoretical one. This mode is strongly influenced by the bathymetry profile along the raypath; so for the north-south profiles the Tryggvason correction of sloping interface was applied. The verification after correction is good (Dubois 1971, Fig. 13).

STRUCTURAL IMPLICATIONS

Given the above data on seismicity and body wave and Rayleigh wave propagation we consider that the structure of the New Hebrides Arc may be represented schematically as in Fig. 6 (cf. Mitronovas & Isacks 1971, Barazangi & Isacks 1971, Jacobs 1970; and plate tectonics by Oliver & Isacks 1967).

This structure, which features a seismic surface (Benioff zone) dipping from 0-350 km at an angle varying from 45-70°, arises from a sinking lithospheric slab. The presence of the slab results in early arrival of *P* waves from west and north-west. Finally there is an anomalous wedge of low-velocity upper mantle. This shows a linear gradient in depth of α and β with high attenuation. The wedge extends to a depth of 150 km, with width 120 km, and explains the late arrivals from east and north and the particular nature of propagation along the island arc.

REFERENCES

Barazangi, M. & Isacks, B. L. 1971. Lateral variations of seismic wave attenuation in the upper mantle above the inclined earthquake zone of the Tonga Island Arc: Deep anomaly in the Upper Mantle. *J. geophys. Res.* **76** (35), 8493-516.

Benoit, M. & Dubois, J. 1971. The earthquake swarm in the New Hebrides Archipelago, August 1965. *Recent Crustal Movements, Bull. R. Soc. N.Z.* **9,** 141-8.

Davies, D. & MacKenzie, D. P. 1969. Seismic travel time residuals and plates. *Geophys. J. R. astr. Soc.* **18,** 51-63.

Dubois, J. 1966. Temps de propagation des ondes *P* à des distances épicentrales de 30 à 90 degrés, Région Sud Ouest Pacifique. *Annls Geophys.* **22** (4), 642-5.

——— 1969. Contribution a l'étude structurale du Sud Ouest Pacifique d'après les ondes sismiques observées en Nouvelle Calédonie et aux Nouvelles Hébrides. *Annls Geophys.* **25** (4), 923-72.

——— 1971. Propagation of *P* waves and Rayleigh waves in Melanesia: structural implications. *J. geophys. Res.* **76** (29), 7217-40.

Dubois, J. & Reichenfeld, C. 1971. Sur la vitesse de phase des ondes de Rayleigh aux Nouvelles Hébrides. Rapp. ORSTOM, Paris (unpubl.).

Jacobs, K. H. 1970. Three-dimensional seismic ray tracing in a laterally heterogeneous spherical earth. *J. geophys. Res.* **75** (32), 6675-89.

Larue, B. 1970. Séismicité aux Nouvelles Hébrides, rapport préliminaire. *Rapp. ORSTOM,* Paris.

Mitronovas, W. & Isacks, B. L. 1971. Seismic velocity anomalies in the upper mantle beneath the Tonga-Kermadec arc. *J. geophys. Res.* **76** (29), 7154-80.

Oliver, J. & Isacks, B. L. 1967. Deep earthquake zones, anomalous structures in the upper mantle and the lithosphere. *J. geophys. Res.* **72** (16), 4259-75.

Pascal, G. 1970. Etude des O-C des ondes P de 30° à 100°, Relation avec l'hypothèse des plaques. *Rapp. ORSTOM*, Noumea.

Structural and Other Aspects of the New Caledonia-Norfolk Area

J. Dubois, J. H. Guillon, J. Launay, J. Recy and J. J. Trescases

Centre O.R.S.T.O.M., B.P. 4, Noumea, New Caledonia

ABSTRACT

Seismic data suggests that crustal thickness under the west coast area of New Caledonia is about 20 ± 2 km but is about 35 ± 4 km under its Central Chain. The propagation of Rayleigh waves along the Norfolk Ridge, between New Zealand and Noumea, indicates a crust averaging 20-25 km.

The New Caledonian ultramafic massifs, emplaced probably during the Upper Eocene, are relics of a thick peridotite slab which was originally much more extensive. The massifs rest upon sediments and basaltic rocks of Eocene age.

The sea-level changes of the Pleistocene and Holocene are marked by uplifted terraces and other topographic features. These markers have been dated radiometrically and indicate the existence of relatively high sea-levels resulting from both eustatic and tectonic movements. The hypothesis is put forward that these movements resulted from a positive flexure of the Australo-Tasmantis plate before its descent beneath the oceanic lithosphere.

INTRODUCTION

The Norfolk Ridge runs continuously from the D'Entrecasteaux fracture zone (17° S) to the north of New Zealand (34° S). Its main NW-SE trend in the northern part (essentially made up of New Caledonia and its prolongations) becomes north-south in the central part and then resumes a NW-SE direction toward its southern end. The eastern side of its northern part is bounded by a submarine pluto-volcanic range revealed by the uplifted atolls in the Loyalty Islands. Between New Caledonia and the Loyalties there is a basin with steep walls and with a flat bottom, made up of fine mud and calcareous-siliceous fill. The New Caledonian Arc and that of the New Hebrides converge at a point located around 22° 30′ S, where the Hebrides Trench is contiguous to the southern prolongation of the Loyalty range. South of this point the trends of these two arcs diverge.

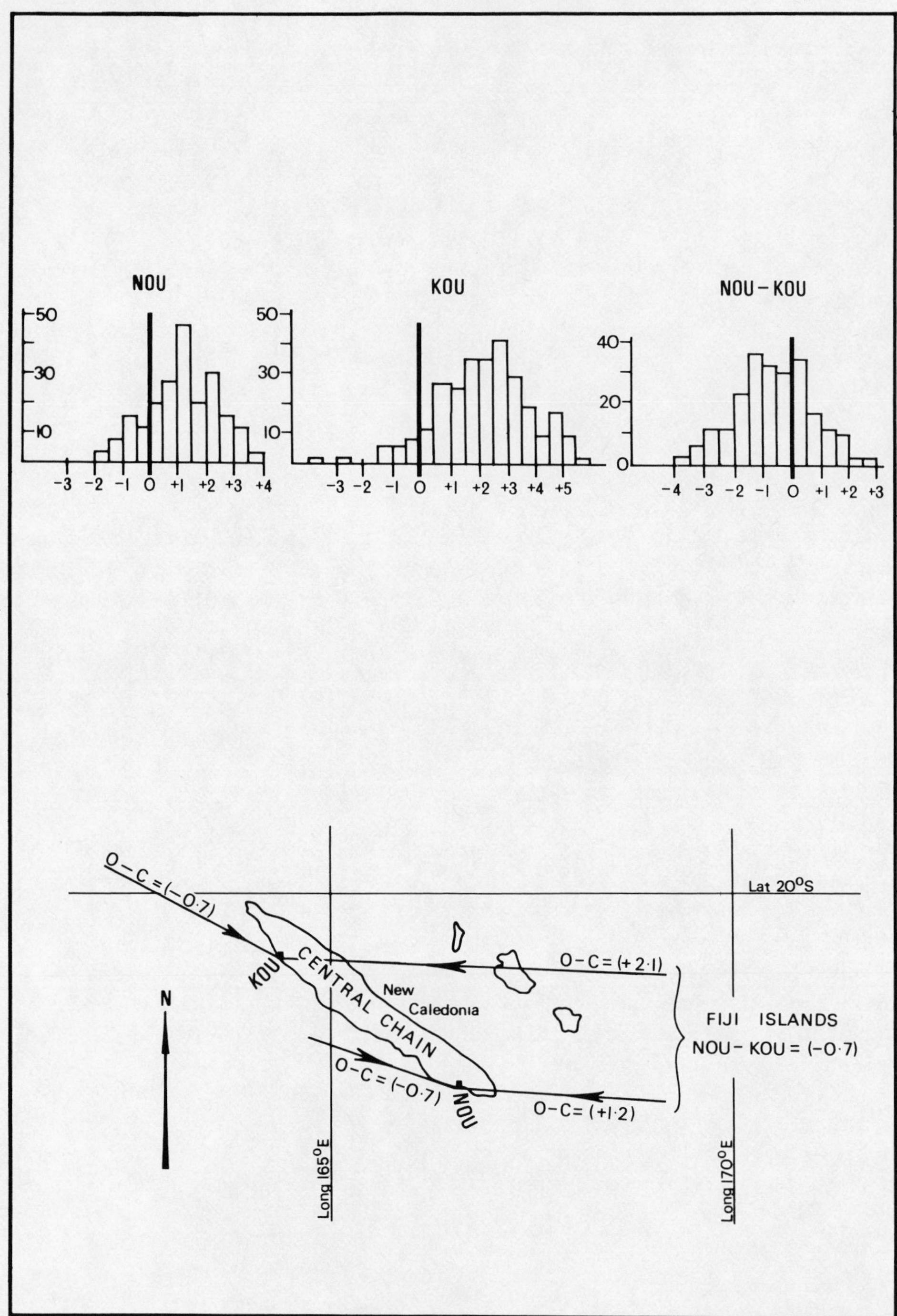
NOU
KOU
NOU - KOU
O-C = (-0·7)
Lat 20°S
KOU
CENTRAL CHAIN
New Caledonia
O-C = (+2·1)
N
FIJI ISLANDS
NOU-KOU = (-0·7)
O-C = (-0·7)
NOU
O-C = (+1·2)
Long 165°E
Long 170°E

DATA ON THE DEEP STRUCTURE OF THE NEW CALEDONIA ARC AND NORFOLK AREA

The study of *P* wave propagation gives information on the deep structure of New Caledonia. From eastern directions, the residuals of *P* wave arrivals (observed *minus* computed arrival times) from deep-focus earthquakes in the Fiji area are positive both in Noumea and Koumac seismological stations; inside the area there are local differences. The arrivals are later in Koumac than in Noumea (Fig. 1).

From the north, the Longshot nuclear test provided interesting data. For the same epicentral distance we find a relative delay of 3·5 s between Melanesia and Europe and 1 s between Australia and Melanesia. These delays may be explained in three ways: as delays at the source, or under the station, or along the ray-path.

Davies and MacKenzie (1969) have shown that a part of this delay is at the source, as an effect of the plate under the Aleutian Arc. The second part, 1 s, between Melanesia and Australia, surely has its source under the stations, because we cannot agree with the third explanation: a delay in the deep mantle between two close ray-paths would imply very marked lateral variations.

We consider that the delay in *P* arrivals from the north, the east and south-east probably arise from a low-velocity upper mantle. Local differences (0·7 s) exist inside this area (i.e. between Koumac and Noumea), which can be explained in terms of topographic effects and the presence of a crustal root under the Central Chain of New Caledonia.

From the west and north-west, however, early arrivals (0·8 s) are observed for New Britain and New Guinea earthquakes.

In a further study, the equation of propagation of *P* waves,

$$T = \frac{\Delta}{v} + a,$$

from New Hebrides normal focus shocks was found to be linear and the values of the constant term of the equation give indications of the thickness of the crust for the rays crossing the Central Chain (for details see Dubois 1969, 1971).

The sum of these data (Fig. 1) provide evidence, first, of a root under the Central Chain of New Caledonia of approximately 15 km; second, of a total crust thickness of about 35-39 km under the central chain but about 22 km under the western coastal area; and, third, of an upper mantle with low *P* wave velocities toward east and north and high *P* wave velocity towards the north-west (the *fossil slab* effect).

The propagation of Rayleigh waves was studied between Noumea and Koumac. It was possible to compute the phase velocity for a seismic path from a Tonga earthquake. In Fig. 2 the correspondence of peaks and troughs on records at Noumea and Koumac was examined. The matrix inversions method of Haskell (1953) was used

---

Fig. 1 Time residuals of *P* waves from Fiji deep-focus earthquakes at New Caledonia stations: Noumea (NOU) and Koumac (KOU). Interval of class is 0·5 s. A histogram for stations pair NOU-KOU is shown. Arrivals are later in Koumac than in Noumea. In part after Dubois, 1971.

to compute theoretical models for different thicknesses of the crust. The best (Fig. 2) corresponded to a thickness of 22 km with a P wave velocity of 6·2 km/s and S wave velocity of 3·6 km/s. There is good agreement in interpretation of body wave and Rayleigh wave propagation data.

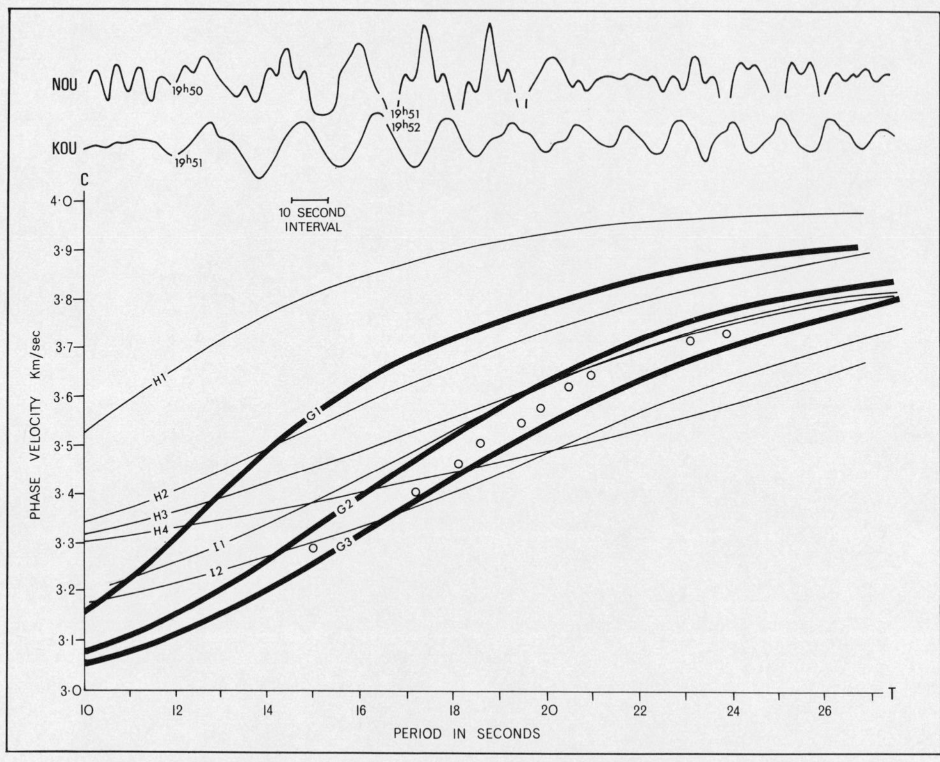

Fig. 2 Correspondence of peaks and troughs (phases of Rayleigh waves) on seismogram records at Noumea and Koumac, following a Tongan earthquake with epicentre on the Noumea-Koumac line. The observed and computed dispersion curves (using Haskell's method) for models I, H and G are shown. After Dubois, 1971.

From the south, an earthquake in New Zealand gave good records in Noumea of P wave propagation along a path following the Norfolk Ridge. From the study of the group velocity of Rayleigh waves on seismogram records in Noumea, it can be seen that the dispersion curve (Fig. 3) is quite intermediary between continental and oceanic dispersion (number 5 in the classification of Saito and Takeuchi 1966), and corresponds to a mean crustal thickness of 25 km along the path. This observation is a proof of the continuity of the New Caledonia and Norfolk Ridge.

Coming back to the deep structure of this arc, it appears that the topography and roots under the Central Chain of New Caledonia can only explain half of the 2 s delay observed between east and west *P* wave arrivals in Noumea and Koumac, respectively. The presence of fossil lithosphere dipping eastward under New Caledonia may explain this difference. A statistical study of residuals and a calculation according to the Davies and MacKenzie (1969) method is to be undertaken later to examine precisely this point.

MAIN GEOLOGICAL EVENTS

New Caledonia is made of sedimentary and metamorphic formations ranging in age from Permian to Miocene. The most prominent are tholeiitic basalts and also huge ultramafic massifs which were emplaced probably in the Upper Eocene (Routhier 1953, Guillon & Routhier 1971).

The emplacement of ultramafic material took place at a later stage of the Alpine orogeny, following the emplacement of the basalt which appears especially on the west coast of New Caledonia. The ultramafic massifs, with an area of 7,000 sq. km, are distributed throughout the length of the island. A great massif covers the southern part of the island; then there is a series of isolated massifs spread along the axis of a syncline parallel to the west coast (Guillon 1971).

The ultramafic massifs generally rest on the basalts, but can also be found lying unconformably on sedimentary formations—mostly those of Cretaceous to Eocene age—tightly folded, imbricated and overturned towards the south-south-west. The floor of the massifs, which show a thick serpentinitic fringe, is either horizontal or dips NNE at an angle of 10°, increasing progressively from south-west to north-east and reaching 50° on the east coast, where strong gravimetric anomalies (170 mgal) are found, corresponding to a thickness of ultramafic material of 8 km (Crenn 1953).

The order of superposition, peridotites-on-basalts, is contrary to that generally found in alpine-arc situations. Because of mineralogical similarities (especially of clinopyroxene) in the basalts and peridotites, it is likely, however, that these rocks are co-magmatic. It is possible they come from the differentiation of a highly-picritic magma of non-alkaline character (Challis & Guillon 1971) and that their respective emplacement has taken place later during the Alpine orogeny.

The ultramafic massifs are mostly harzburgites, dunites and orthopyroxenites, and some chromitic seams. These rocks are disposed in the massifs with regular rhythmic banding, which shows that the ultramafic massifs have the form of broken folds with a large curvature and generally overtilted towards the south-south-west. This layering is strongly discordant on the floor of the massifs which represents, as in New Guinea (Davies 1968), a major structural discontinuity. It is likely that the ultramafic massifs represent a nappe structure, the root of which may be found on the east coast of New Caledonia, and that their emplacement could be the consequence of thrusting of the oceanic plate onto the continental margin.

The emplacement of the ultramafic massifs is followed by the intrusion of granodiorites, adamellites and hornblende-quartz diorites, which appear either in the ultramafic rocks (cutting them discordantly), or in the sedimentary formations. But the granodiorites and diorites are never found far from the contact between the

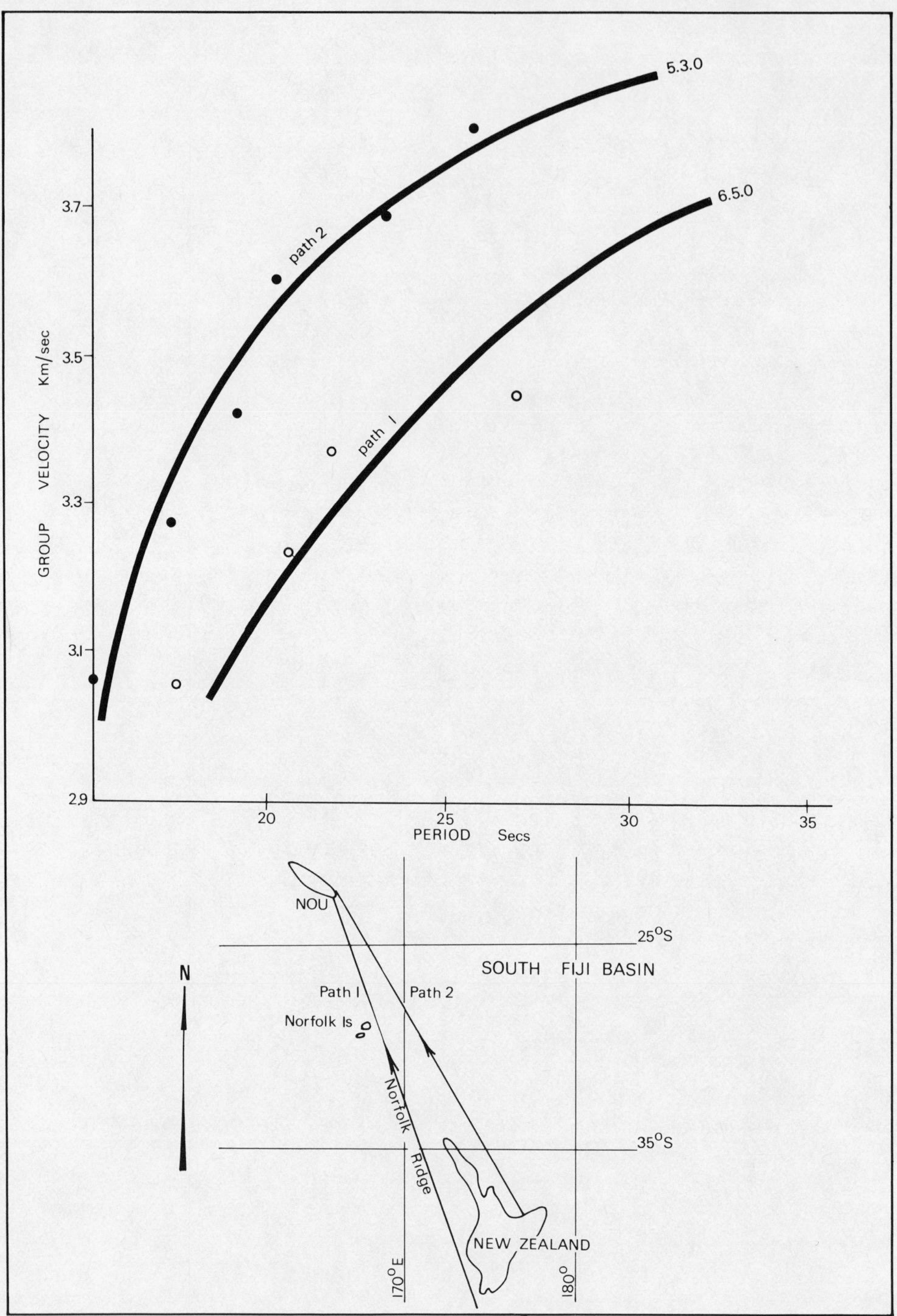

Fig. 3 Dispersion curve of group velocity of Rayleigh waves from a New Zealand

ultramafic massifs and their substratum. The emplacement of these rocks represents the last magmatic occurrence in the geological history.

DYNAMIC ASPECT OF POST-UPPER EOCENE MOVEMENTS OF THE NEW CALEDONIAN AND LOYALTY ARCS

New Caledonian Arc

(*a*) *Upheaval accompanying peneplanations.* The isostatic upheaval of New Caledonia can be traced by making a geomorphological survey of the ultrabasic rock massifs. These peridotites are easily weathered and have been subjected at least since the Miocene to the effects of a tropical to insular subtropical climate. Weathering of the lateritic type has left a residue mainly made up of iron hydroxides which have accumulated in place and by mechanical reworking effects in the depressions. Intensive chemical erosion (at present 28 mm per 1,000 years according to Baltzer and Trescases 1971) and the reworking of residual laterites have caused the lowering and flattening of the topography. Several successive levels, forming tiers or terraces, can be observed along the topographic profiles (Trescases 1969). The ironstones and laterites characterizing these surfaces have enabled them to be at least partially preserved in the landscape. With each resumption in isostatic movement, the state of equilibrium toward which the topography is tending is broken, the surface being formed is uplifted, and erosion begins to destroy it. In this way the highest surface ('peneplain' according to Davis 1925), which is also the oldest, is found at an altitude of more than 1,000 m in the middle of the island and at 300 m toward the edges. The second surface (intermediate level according to Wirthmann 1965) is 150-300 m below the 'peneplain'. The third surface (former piedmonts—Trescases 1969) is 500-600 m below the intermediary level.

The peridotites (with a density of 3·0-3·3, depending on the degree of serpentinization) make up a sheet which once covered a much larger area than that now observed (Routhier 1953, Guillon & Routhier 1971). In particular, large areas in the central zone must have been covered, and now all that remains are relict ultrabasic blocks. The ablation of all or part of such a dense covering layer may have caused the uplift of the island by isostatic compensation. In this case the highest areas would correspond to the most intensive erosion.

The major morphological feature suggests an uplifting in which isostasy probably played the leading role. The slowness of the phenomenon, spread out over several million years, and the fact that the crust is thin on the western and eastern edges of New Caledonia have certainly caused crustal flexures with very short curve radii (*relaxation curve* according to Nadai 1963). The upthrusting phenomenon caused an upswell of crust which is laterally absorbed within a short distance and thus must have been limited to New Caledonia and its edges.

---

earthquake. The dispersion curve corresponds to a mean crustal thickness of 25 km along the path.

(*b*) *Subsidence.* The subsidence phase which follows was first observed by Davis (1925) and later confirmed by Routhier (1953). The longitudinal warping previously observed continued.

(*c*) *Quaternary upheaval.* In New Caledonia the presence of uplifted undercuts, beaches and reefs at different levels has already been described (Avias 1949, 1959; Routhier 1953, Launay & Recy 1970), and various radiometric measurements have recently been published by Baltzer (1970) and Launay and Recy (1971).

The Isle of Pines, south-east of New Caledonia, appears as a massif of lateritized peridotites. It is almost entirely peneplaned with a rim of terraces which represent successively uplifted coral fringing reefs running down to the sea. A coral sample taken from the top part of the oldest reef at 20 ± 3 m altitude was dated by the ionium/thorium method and showed an age of 118,000 ± 8,000 years B.P. On the eastern part of the island, a NNE-SSW trending hill, consisting of cross-bedded coral sand, is 79 m high. The age of this formation is different to that of the coral shelves but is unknown.

On the eastern and western shores of New Caledonia, outliers of coral terraces or shelves at 3 and 6 m altitude show an age between 25,000 and 35,000 years B.P. The formation of these coral outliers may be attributed to the high sea-level period of about 30,000 B.P. (estimated to be somewhat less than 10 m above the present sea-level by Faure and Elouard 1967). The presence of sea-level traces at a higher altitude than the dated levels, in particular near Hienghène, appears to indicate the existence of prior movements in some areas.

An examination of more recent markers has revealed the existence in New Caledonia, since the middle Holocene up to the present, of positive tectonic movements with a mean rate, as calculated on the basis of Shepard's eustatic variation curve, of 1-2 mm per year and often less. The results of these eustatic and tectonic movements indicate a higher relative sea-level between 7,000 and 2,000 B.P. The mechanism resulted in uplifted fossil beaches which are often prolongations of the present beach.

The mean rate of upheaval estimated for the top of the uplifted shelf at the Isle of Pines (118,000 B.P., altitude +20 m), appears to be very slow (i.e. 0·1-0·2 mm per year) as compared with the mean upheaval rates calculated during the middle and upper Holocene in the Isle of Pines, at Dumbea on the south-east coast and Mara on the west coast, if the Shepard and Curray curve is taken as a reference for the eustatic variation. If this observation were to be confirmed by additional radiometric dating, this would lead to the determining of a slow upheaval movement combined with spasmodic positive and perhaps negative oscillations.[1]

Loyalty Arc

The petrographic data we now have on the Loyalty submarine ridge come solely from samples gathered on Ile Maré. The presence of basalts with olivine (oceanic-type volcanism) and of gabbros with olivine, both quite comparable to those we know in New Caledonia, has been established. These rocks are probably the result of the thorough differentiation of strongly picritic parent material. An analysis of a basalt sample from the top of Rawa butte by the potassium-argon method produced an

[1] We succeeded in finding only positive readjustments during the Holocene.

age of 29 ± 4 m.y., i.e. Upper Oligocene or Lower Miocene (Chevalier 1968). At a few localities on top of these basalts there are volcanic tuffs containing reworked organic limestone pebbles with a microfauna of probable Aquitanian age (R. Anglada, C. Froget & J. P. Massé, pers. comm.).

(*a*) *Subsidence phase*. The coral atoll of Ile Maré lies on top of a volcanic substratum. The subsidence of the arc leading to the formation of Ile Maré and other Loyalty atolls is therefore post-Aquitanian. Chevalier attributes a Neogene age, based on examination of the corals, to the oldest parts of the reef complex.

The observation of a Neogene subsidence phase in New Caledonia and the Loyalty Islands does not, at present state of understanding, enable any conclusion to be reached on a possible common origin or perhaps a synchronization of this phenomenon in the two regions.

(*b*) *Recent upheaval phase*. An upheaval movement with decreasing amplitude (following the trend of the arc from SE to NW) brought about the emergence of various atolls. Ile Maré (altitude of 130 m) was uplifted more than Lifou located farther north. Only the south-eastern part of Ouvea atoll emerges, and still farther north Beautemp-Beaupré atoll remains submerged.

The madreporian fauna gathered at the top of the reef ring, and examined by Chevalier revealed a lower Pleistocene age; he suggests, however, that it may be younger.

Radiometric age measurements on three coral samples taken from the lowest terraces on Ile Maré between 2·7 and 3·2 m altitude revealed ages corresponding to a high sea-level period about 30,000 years B.P. (Launay & Recy 1971). Therefore, the upheaval of the southern part of the Loyalty Arc appears to have begun in the Pleistocene and to have continued up to the present.

An upheaval movement appears to have begun in the lower Pleistocene, influencing the south-eastern part of the Loyalty group, while the north-western part remained unaffected; the amplitude diminished from south-east to north-west. Later, a similar movement affected New Caledonia, the amplitude being greatest to the south, but the uplift is clearly less in the southern part of the New Caledonian Arc than in the southern part of the Loyalty group.

The following general aspects may now be stressed. The New Caledonia-Norfolk and Loyalty Arcs are parallel; the New Hebrides Trench is arcuate. Their opposing convexities are tangential at a point located slightly south of Ile Maré. The migration and burial of the Australo-Tasmantis plate underneath the oceanic slab at the level of the New Hebrides Trench may have caused a positive flexure in the plate prior to its downward movement. The stresses were probably greater (because of the warping of the dipping lithosphere) and the flexure correspondingly more marked (Dubois, Launay & Recy, in press) around the tangential area between the opposing convexities of the trench and the New Caledonia-Norfolk system.

On the basis of a recent calculation of the thickness and rigidity of the lithosphere in this area—60 + 5 km and $0{\cdot}7\text{-}10^{12}$ dynes/sq. cm according to Dubois (1968, and unpublished data 1971), the flexural parameter was found to be equal to 150 km (Walcott 1970). Taking Lliboutry's diagram (1969) and using Nadai's relaxation curves (1963), the flexure in the western part of the New Hebrides (cf. Fig. 4) can

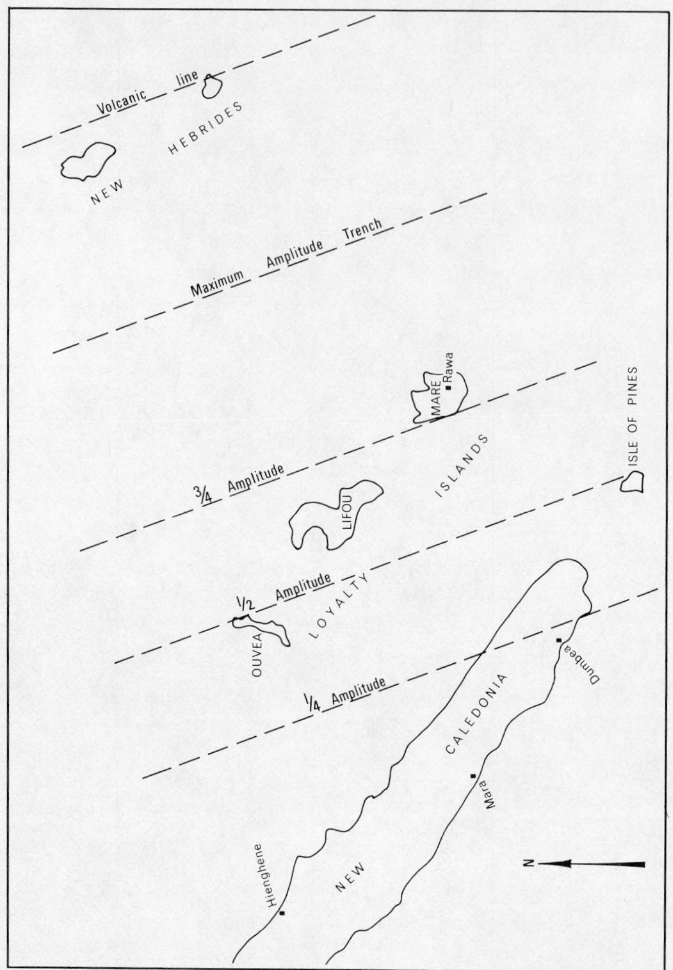

Fig. 4 Pattern of a positive flexure in the Australo-Tasmantis plate, New Hebrides-Loyalty Islands area.

be plotted before it dips underneath the insular arc (expansion from south-west to north-east). This expansion of 5 cm per year (Dubois 1969) shows that the amplitude increases from $\frac{1}{2}$-$\frac{3}{4}$ in the space of 72 km in 1·4 m.y. Between Uvea and Maré there is an altitude drop (over a period of 2·3 m.y.) of about 100 m corresponding to a distance of about 120 km in the direction of expansion. The result of this is an uplifting of the Loyalty Islands by 4·3 cm per 1,000 years (Fig. 4). Geological observations appear to agree with this pattern (Launay & Recy 1971). The pattern is certainly more complex south of the arc as the result of the curvature of the structure. However, this is only a first approximation.

Beginning in the lower Pleistocene (with reference to the age of the corals on the

Maré reef ring) the migration of the plate brought the southern part of the Loyalty Arc into the zone of influence of the flexure. Then in the middle or upper Pleistocene the southern part of the New Caledonian Arc began to be similarly effected. Assuming a flexure-lithosphere interaction, these spatial effects would decrease, beginning at the maximum amplitude line (Fig. 4). Likewise, there would be a difference in time, with the zones furthest away being more recently affected. Observations on Quaternary tectonics appear to conform to both these requirements. Such a flexural upswell of the lithosphere does not exclude the possibility of crustal or local readjustments, as is suggested by the upfolding of the Yaté uplifted shelf and by the Hienghène undercuts.

CONCLUSION

We have attempted to link seismological, petrographic and geodynamic data together in order to propose various structural hypotheses. The seismological data reveal the existence of a continuous ridge with a relatively thin crust along the New Caledonia-Norfolk alignment.

The accumulation of ultrabasic rocks may be explained as a consequence of the movement of the Australo-Tasmantis block dipping underneath the oceanic plate in the area of New Caledonia in the Upper Eocene. This accumulation was accompanied by erosion and shear faulting which generally influenced the structure of the New Caledonian Arc. The mechanical and chemical erosion of a large proportion of the peridotitic cover led directly to peneplanations and then to upheaval movements by isostatic compensation. This phenomenon, which was spread out in time, was probably limited to New Caledonia. As well, there were superimposed eustatic variations which complicated the isostatic readjustments.

The hypothesis of a flexure of the lithosphere (the Australo-Tasmantis plate) before it dips underneath the oceanic plate at the site of the New Hebrides Trench provides an explanation for the Quaternary tectonic observations made in New Caledonia and the Loyalty Islands. The upheaval effects decrease south-westwards.

We cannot yet specify the exact amplitude of these movements, but the pattern proposed, which includes the flexuring of the lithosphere and accompanying isostatic compensations, approximates well to the seismological and geological data so far obtained for the region.

REFERENCES

Avias, J. 1949. Note préliminaire sur quelques phénomènes actuels ou subactuels de pétrogenèse et autres dans les marais côtiers de Moindou et Canala. *C.R. Som. Soc. Géol. Fr.* **277,** 280.

——— 1959. Les récifs coralliens de la Nouvelle Calédonie et quelques uns de leurs problèmes. *Bull. Soc. géol. Fr.*, 7 série, **1,** 424-30.

Baltzer, F. 1970. Datation absolue de la transgression holocène sur la côte ouest de la Nouvelle Calédonie sur des échantillons de tourbe à palétuviers. Interprétation néotectonique. *C.R. Acad. Sci. Paris,* **271,** 2251-4.

Baltzer, F. & Trescases, J. J. 1971. Erosion, transport et sédimentation liées aux cyclones tropicaux dans les massifs d'ultrabasites de Nouvelle Calédonie. Première approche du bilan général de l'alteration, de l'érosion et de la sédimentation sur péridotites en zone tropicale. *Cahiers ORSTOM*, (*Géol.*) **3** (2).

Challis, G. A. & Guillon, J. H. 1971. Etude comparative à la microsonde électronique du clinopyroxène des basaltes et roches ultramafiques de Nouvelle Calédonie. Possibilité d'une origine commune de ces roches. *Bull. Bur. Rech. Géol. Min.* **4** (2).

Chevalier, J. P. 1968. Géomorphologie de l'île de Mare. In *Expédition francaise sur les récifs coralliens de la Nouvelle-Calédonie*, vol. 3. Editions de la fondation Singer-Polignac, Paris. 155 pp.

Crenn, Y. 1953. Anomalies gravimétriques magnétiques liées aux roches basiques de la Nouvelle Calédonie. *Annls Géophys.* **9** (4), 291-9.

Davies, D. & MacKenzie, D. P. 1969. Seismic travel time residuals and plates. *Geophys. J. R. astr. Soc.* **18,** 51-63.

Davies, H. L. 1968. Papuan ultramafic belt. *23rd Intern. Geol. Congr.* Prague, **1,** 209-20.

Davis, W. M. 1925. Les côtes et les récifs coralliens de la Nouvelle Calédonie. *Annls Géogr.* **34,** 244-69, 332-59, 424-41, 521-58.

Dubois, J. 1968. Etude de la dispersion des ondes de Rayleigh dans la région du Sud-Ouest Pacifique. *Annls Géophys.* **24** (1), 359-68.

——— 1969. Contribution à l'étude structurale du Sud Ouest Pacifique d'après les ondes sismiques observées en Nouvelle Calédonie et aux Nouvelles Hébrides. *Thèse, ORSTOM*, Paris.

——— 1970. Etude de la propagation des ondes *S* dans la région Nouvelle Calédonie, Nouvelles Hébrides. *Rapp. ORSTOM* (à diffusion restreinte), Paris.

——— 1971. Propagation of *P* waves and Rayleigh waves in Melanesia: structural implications. *J. geophys. Res.* **76** (29), 7217-40.

Dubois, J., Launay, J. & Recy, J. 1971. Un bourrelet de la plaque australienne avant son plongement sous la plaque oceanique serait à l'origine des mouvements tectoniques Quaternaires observés dans la region Nouvelle Calédonie/Iles Loyautés. *Rapp. ORSTOM*, Paris.

Faure, H. & Elouard, P. 1967. Schéma des variations du niveau de l'océan Atlantique sur la côte de l'Ouest de l'Afrique depuis 40,000 ans. *C.R. Acad. Sci. Paris,* **265,** 784-7.

Guillon, J. H. (In press.) Geology of New Caledonia and Loyalty islands. In *Data for Orogenic Studies*, Geol. Soc. London.

Guillon, J. H. & Routhier, P. 1971. Les stades d'évolution et de mise en place des massifs ultramafiques de Nouvelle Calédonie. *Bull. Bur. Rech. Geol. Min.* **4** (2).

Haskell, N. A. 1953. The dispersion of surface waves in multi-layered media. *Bull. seism. Soc. Am.* **43,** 17-34.

Launay, J. & Recy, J. 1970. Nouvelles données sur une variation relative récente du niveau de la mer dans toute la région Nouvelle Calédonie, Iles Loyautés. *C.R. Acad. Sci. Paris,* **270,** 2159-61.

——— 1971. Variations relatives du niveau de la mer et néotectonique en Nouvelle Calédonie au Pléistocène supérieur et à l'Holocène. *Rapp. ORSTOM*, Paris.

Lliboutry, L. 1969. Sea-floor spreading, continental drift and lithosphere sinking with an asthenosphere at melting point. *J. geophys. Res.* **74** (27), 6525-44.

Nadai, A. 1963. *Theory of flow and fracture of solids.* Vol. 2. MacGraw Hill, New York.

Routhier, P. 1953. Etude géologique du versant occidental de la Nouvelle Calédonie entre le col de Boghen et la pointe d'Arama. *Mém. Soc. géol. Fr.*, **67,** 1-271.

Saito, M. & Takeuchi, H. 1966. Surface waves across the Pacific. *Bull. seism. Soc. Am.* **56** (5),

1067-91.

Shepard, F. P. & Curray, J. R. 1967. Carbon 14 determination of sea-level changes in stable areas. *Prog. Oceanog.* **4,** 283-91.

Trescases, J. J. 1969. Premières observations sur l'altération des péridotites de Nouvelle Calédonie: Pédologie, Géochimie, Géomorphologie. *Cahiers ORSTOM, (Geol.)* **1** (1), 27-57.

Walcott, R. J. 1970. Flexural rigidity, thickness and viscosity of the lithosphere. *J. geophys. Res.* **75** (20), 3941-54.

Wirthmann, A. 1965. Die Reliefentwicklung von Neukaledonien. In *Tagunsbericht und wissenschaftliche Abthandlungen,* 322-35. Deutsch. Geograph. Bochum. Juin.

PART II

Structures and Geological History of the Kuril-Kamchatka Island Arc

M. S. Markov and M. Yu. Khotin
Geological Institute, Academy of Sciences of the U.S.S.R.
Pyzhevsky per. 7, Moscow G-17, U.S.S.R.

ABSTRACT

The Kuril-Kamchatka Arc consists of four structural zones of differing geological history. In this region a gradual rejuvenation of folded zones towards the Pacific is observed, which reflects the general regularity of an advance of island arcs (geosynclinal areas) over oceanic areas. Also, the segments of the peri-oceanic structures, including trenches, appear to have been formed at different periods of time.

The Kuril-Kamchatka Arc consists of four structural zones of different geological history: west Kamchatka, central Kamchatka, east Kamchatka, and Kuril zones. The peninsulas of east Kamchatka appear to be independent structural elements. This paper deals with each of the above zones.

The eastern boundary of the west Kamchatka zone extends from the Okhotsk Sea towards the western coast of Kamchatka, south of Bolsheretsk. It can be traced further along the western boundary of the central Kamchatka depression, parallel to the general trend of the peninsula. This boundary is well pronounced not only geologically, but also geophysically—with both gravity gradient and linear magnetic anomalies (Rivosh 1963, Smirnov 1971). The oldest sedimentary formations of the zone belong to the Albian (Cretaceous) and consist of slightly metamorphosed volcaniclastic deposits. The main part of the Upper Cretaceous of the west Kamchatka zone belongs to the Senonian and is represented by greywacke and subarkosic rocks as thick as 3,000 m (Vlasov 1964). Characteristic of the zone is the wide distribution of times of folding, from the end of the Cretaceous to the beginning of the Palaeogene. The Tertiary formations rest on the folded Cretaceous deposits with a hiatus and sharp unconformity. Peculiarities of sedimentation of the lower parts of the Tertiary section can be clearly seen on the palaeogeographical scheme compiled by Smirnov (Fig. 1). Tertiary deposits are represented mainly by clastic rocks (sandstones, mudstones), frequently with conglomerates and coals. Some parts of the section are characterized by rhythmic flysch alternations. The formational characteristics of the Palaeogene deposits of west Kamchatka are not clear, continental and paralic facies being widely distributed. Typical molasse sediments appear only in the Neogene.

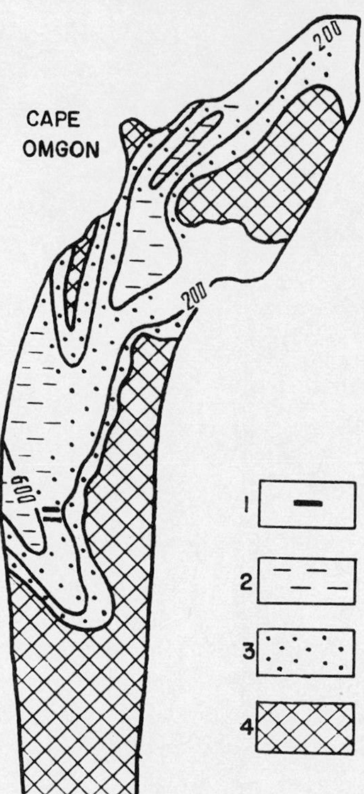

Fig. 1 Palaeogeographic map of western Kamchatka, following Upper Cretaceous orogeny (after L. Smirnov 1971). 1, coal deposits; 2, mudstones; 3, sandstones; 4, land. Isopach lines (200 and 600 m) are shown.

The total thickness of the Tertiary is 10,000 m (Vlasov 1964, Smirnov 1971). Metamorphic rocks of the Sredinny massif offer a special problem. Recent studies have established two complexes of rocks: a lower one in which the rocks underwent metamorphism of a granulitic facies and then were subjected to diaphthoresis; and an upper one, characterized by amphibolitic and greenschist facies of metamorphism. Mesozoic spores and pollen were found in the rocks of the upper complex. The lower complex is evidently of a pre-Mesozoic age, but the exact age cannot be determined. One may think of these rocks as originally melanocratic formations that were later considerably and repeatedly granitized. The last granitization processes (judged by the data of K-Ar determinations) occurred at the end of the Cretaceous and in the Palaeogene. The rocks of the upper complex are, most probably, deeply metamorphosed volcanic formations of an early geosynclinal stage of evolution of an island arc. The Sredinny massif seems to be an area of long-living geanticlinal uplift of the west Kamchatka zone, at its boundary with the central Kamchatka zone.

The central Kamchatka zone stretches from Penzhina Bay in the north to the Sredinny massif and Ganaly projection of metamorphic rocks in the south (Aprelkov

1971). The eastern boundary of the zone is hidden under waters of the Litke Strait in the north and under the deposits of the central Kamchatka depression farther on to the south; only in the southern part of Kamchatka does it coincide with the series of sublongitudinal faults bordering the Valaginsky Range from the west (Vlasov 1964).

This zone is composed of greywacke and volcanogenic-siliceous deposits of the Senonian. Characteristic of the latter is a predominantly andesite-basaltic alkaline basaltic composition of volcanics (Rotman & Markovsky 1968, Baikov & Marchenko 1969) with an abundance of psammitic tuffs, ashy tuffs, and cherts. The total thickness of the Cretaceous deposits of the zone amounts to 5,000-6,000 m. Cretaceous deposits are overlapped with a hiatus by Oligocene-Miocene rocks, the lower part of which is represented by volcanogenic detrital formations and the upper part by andesite-basaltic, andesitic, and dacitic effusives and pyroclastics of terrestrial and shallow-water origin (Rotman 1968, Aprelkov 1971). At the end of the Palaeogene and the beginning of the Neogene the Sredinny volcanic belt began to form, overlapping the boundary with the west Kamchatka zone. The central Kamchatka zone appears to have joined a geanticlinal uplift of the west Kamchatka area since the end of the Cretaceous.

The east Kamchatka zone, which can be traced from Karaginsky Island in the north, through Ozernoy Peninsula and the series of eastern ranges of Kamchatka, to Shipunsky Peninsula in the south, is characterized by thick sections of Cretaceous, Palaeogene and Miocene age. The sequence begins with greywackes replaced upsection by terrigenous-chert formations which are derivatives of subalkaline basaltic volcanism (Fig. 2). Ultrabasic effusives and some manifestations of subvolcanic activity are characteristic of the upper part of the Upper Cretaceous (Erlikh *et al.* 1971). Terrigenous strata occur only in the southern part of the zone. In the north, Cretaceous volcanic formations lie directly on the eroded surface of a basement. Thickness of Cretaceous deposits in the zone is considerable.

Palaeogene deposits are represented by terrigenous-carbonaceous, flysch-like and volcanic-cherty subalkaline rocks and, in the upper part of the section, by black bituminous argillite with intercalations of flint and lenses of pelitic limestone. Thickness of these formations reaches 5,000-7,000 m. Most of the east Kamchatka rocks formed under relatively deep-sea conditions.

These deposits were rumpled into squeezed isoclinal folds at the end of the Miocene, after the flysch strata of the Middle and Upper Miocene accumulated in residual depressions. Since the end of the Pliocene the east Kamchatka zone became the east volcanic belt that stretches parallel to the present-day deep-sea trench.

The metamorphic rocks of a basement are exposed within the central and east Kamchatka zones (Markov 1970). These include heavily metamorphosed rocks of a melanocratic gabbroic composition and can be considered as the rocks of the 'basaltic' geophysical layer. There are good grounds to regard the age of these rocks as pre-Mesozoic.

The Kuril zone includes the southern part of Kamchatka, the Kuril Islands and east Hokkaido. It makes a T-shape junction with the structures of the above-mentioned zones within the area of the Petropavlovsk-Malki dislocation (Fig. 3).

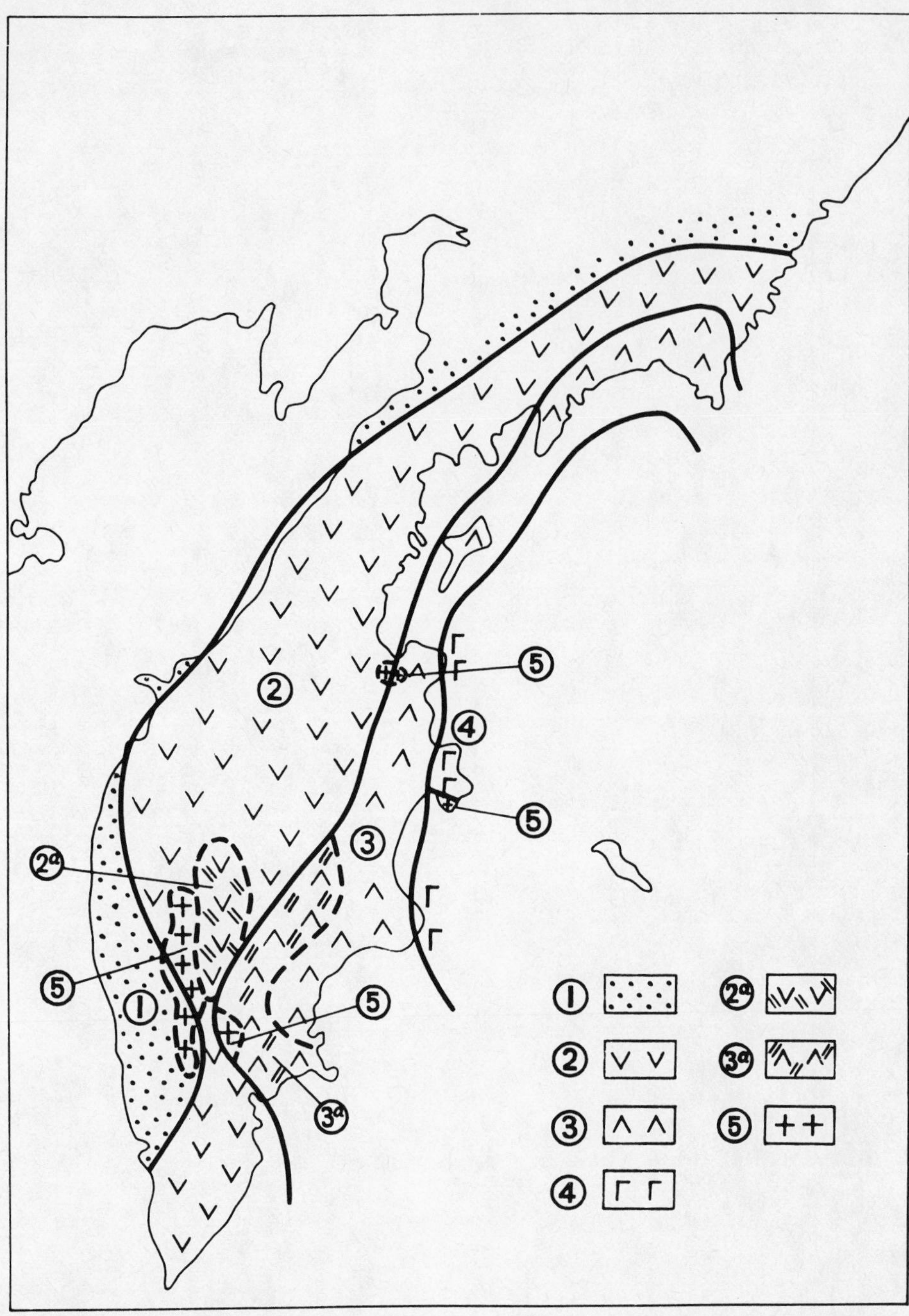

Fig. 2 Structural facies zones of the Late Cretaceous in Kamchatka. 1, zone of terrigeneous deposits; 2, zone of subaqueous andesite-basaltic and alkaline-basaltic volcanics; 2a, subzone of increased alkalinity; 3, zone of deep-sea subalkaline

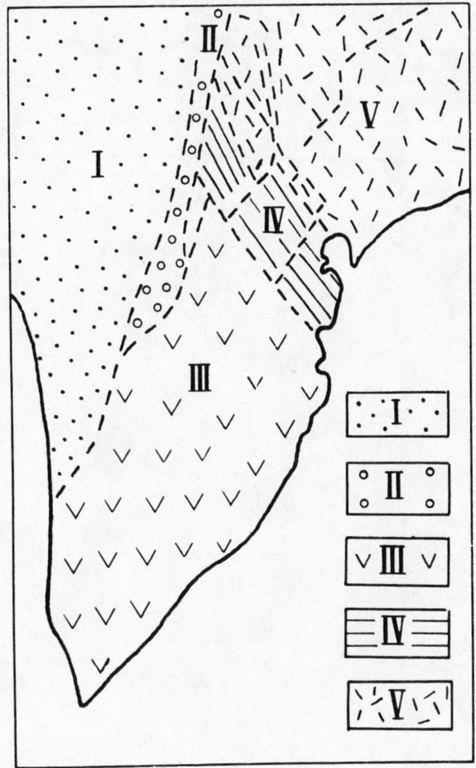

Fig. 3 Structural map of southern Kamchatka. I, zone of western Kamchatka with Upper Cretaceous orogenic movements; II, graben of central Kamchatka; III, zone of southern Kamchatka—gently folded Tertiary volcanic rocks; IV, zone of strongly faulted, dislocated Tertiary deposits; V, zone of eastern Kamchatka with Middle Miocene orogenic movements.

The oldest strata exposed in the zone are Upper Cretaceous. Judging by xenoliths in the lavas, they are underlain predominantly by metamorphic rocks of melanocratic composition—amphybolites, pyroxene gneisses, gabbroids (Rodionova & Fedortchenko 1971). Cretaceous deposits consist of tuffaceous effusives, and, less frequently, terrigenous volcanomictic rocks. The calcalkaline, occasionally alkaline character of the effusives, the peculiarities of composition and lamination of detrital deposits, and epigenetic alterations of rocks, show that the Lesser Kuril ridge existed as an area of uplift since the end of the Cretaceous (Solovyeva 1971). The section of

---

ultramafic and tholeiitic volcanics; 3a, subzone of increased alkalinity; 4, zone of deep-sea (oceanic) tholeiitic volcanics; 5, outcrops of metamorphic rocks (basement complex).

the Lesser Kurils is crowned by practically unaltered Plio-Pleistocene basalts and andesite-basalts.

The Greater Kuril Ridge is composed of Neogene and Quaternary deposits represented by a complicated combination of basalt, andesite-basalt, andesite, volcanomictic conglomerate, sandstone and aleurolite. Both marine and continental facies are present here. Similar deposits occur also within south Kamchatka. Tertiary deposits of this part of the Kuril zone are characterized by a complex combination of effusive and volcanogenic-sedimentary continental, near-shore, and marine facies.

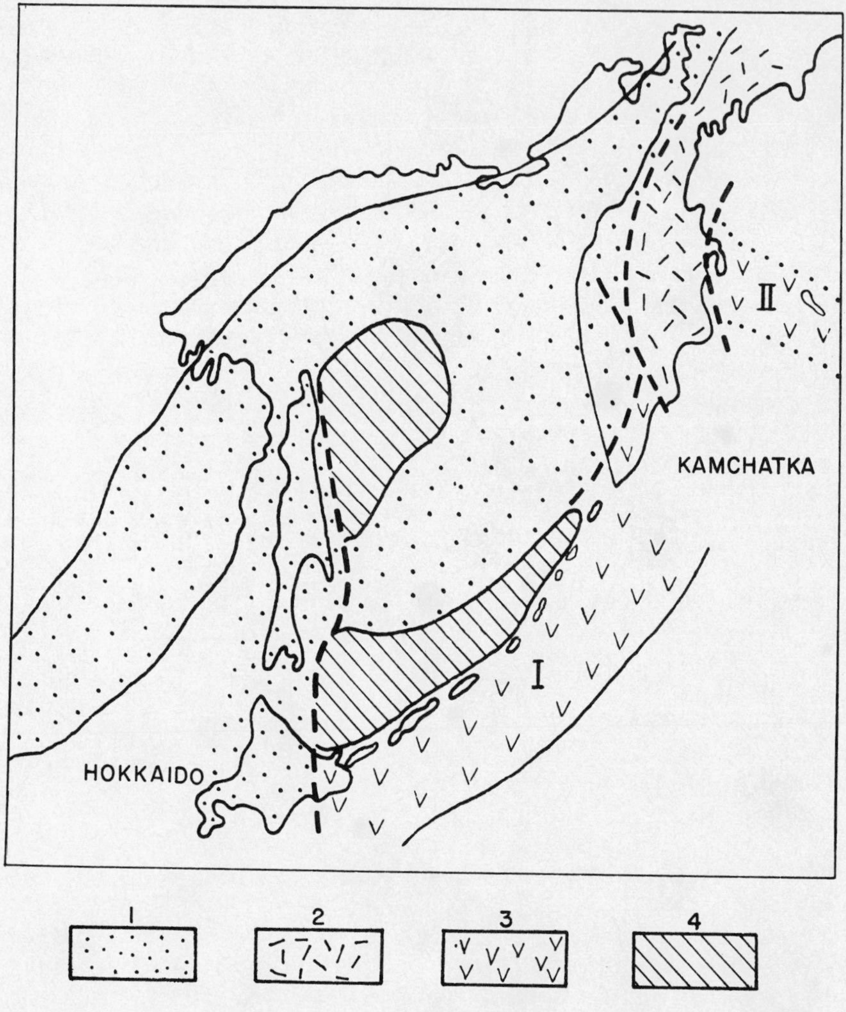

Fig. 4 Tectonic map of the Okhotsk region. 1, zone of the Late Cretaceous orogeny; 2, zone of the Middle Miocene orogeny; 3, zone of unfolded island arcs: I, Kuril Arc and II, Aleutian Arc; 4, basins with suboceanic crust.

A terrigenous component of detrital rocks has been formed mainly at the expense of local sources. This shows that the uplift of the Greater Kuril began since the beginning of the Neogene.

Cretaceous and Cenozoic deposits of the Kuril zone are dislocated, if only slightly, thus distinguishing the zone from the other structural zones of the Kuril-Kamchatka Arc. One might suggest that in this zone fold-forming movements, completing the geosynclinal evolution, are not yet over. In the south-west the structures of the Kuril zone meet the structures of central Hokkaido, forming a T-shaped joint.

The peninsulas of east Kamchatka (Shypun, Kronotsk, Kamchatka Cape) belong to different structural zones. The Shypun Peninsula is a part of the eastern Kamchatka zone. The Kronotsk Peninsula, which has outcrops of Cretaceous and Palaeogene deposits, seems to be a north-west termination of the Emperor Range (of sea-mounts). In the peninsula of Kamchatka Cape, the Upper Cretaceous volcanogenic-cherty rocks rest with a sharp unconformity on the metamorphic basement and are overlain conformably by thin terrigenous subarkose formations, the origin of which is not quite clear. The total thickness of Upper Cretaceous deposits does not exceed 2,000 m. They form gentle folds and are penetrated by ultramafic bodies (Dolmatov & Khotin 1969, Markov *et al.* 1969).

Cretaceous strata are overlain with a hiatus and angular unconformity by flysch-like volcanogenic-terrigenous deposits of Palaeogene age, 10,000-12,000 m thick. The Palaeogene formations are similar to those of the Aleutian Arc and suggest that the Kamchatka Cape peninsula is a western continuation of this arc. Similar strata are, moreover, widely distributed in the Kronotsk and Ozernoy Peninsulas. It is possible that equivalents of the upper part of this Palaeogene section are also present on Karaginsky Island.

Thus, we see that the Kuril-Kamchatka Arc consists of a number of structural zones that are combined with each other in a complicated manner in time and space (Fig. 4). Of considerable importance in these combinations are abrupt T-shaped junctions of structural zones. A gradual rejuvenation of folded zones towards the Pacific Ocean reflects the general regularity of the advance of island arcs (geosynclinal areas) over oceanic areas. At the same time one can see that the segments of the peri-oceanic structures, including trenches, have been formed at different periods of time.

REFERENCES

Aprelkov, S. E. 1971. Tectonics and history of volcanism of Southern Kamchatka. *Geotektonika*, **2** (in Russian).

Baikov, A. I. & Marchenko, A. F. 1969. *On the role of metamorphism and metasomatosis processes in mineralization*. Naukova Dumka, Kiev (in Russian).

Dolmatov, B. K. & Khotin, M. Yu. 1969. Formation of pre-Palaeogene intrusive complexes on Kamchatka Cape peninsula (Eastern Kamchatka). *Sov. Geol.* **5** (in Russian).

Erlikh, E. N., Shantzer, A. E. & Kutiev, F. Sh. 1971. Meimechites of Eastern Kamchatka. *Izv. Acad. Sci. USSR geol. Ser.* **2** (in Russian).

Markov, M. S. 1970. Metamorphic complexes and their place in the evolution history of island arcs. *Geotektonika,* **2** (in Russian).

Markov, M. S., Seliverstov, V. A., Khotin, M. Yu. & Dolmatov, B. K. 1969. On the conjugation of structures of Eastern Kamchatka and Aleutian island arc. *Geotektonika,* **6** (in Russian).

Rivosh, L. A. 1963. On the tectonics of Kamchatka peninsula and the floor of adjacent sea regions (on the basis of geophysical data). *Geol. i Geofiz.* **6** (in Russian).

Rodionova, R. I. & Fedortchenko, V. I. 1971. On some problems of abyssal geology and volcanism on Kurile Island arc. *Geol. i Geofiz.* **2** (in Russian).

Rotman, V. K. 1968. Andesitic arcs and their place in tectonic and magmatic history of the North-West Pacific. In *Volcanism and tectogenesis.* Nauka Publ., Moscow (in Russian).

Rotman, V. K. & Markovsky, B. A. 1968. Fundamental features in the geosynclinal development of the North-West Pacific. In *Volcanism and tectogenesis.* Nauka Publ., Moscow (in Russian).

Smirnov, L. M. 1971. Tectonics of Western Kamchatka. *Geotektonika,* **3** (in Russian).

Solovyeva, N. Z. 1970. The effect of volcanism on the formation of Upper Cretaceous volcano-sedimentary deposits on Lesser Kuril ridge. *Litilogia i poleznye iskopaemye,* **6** (in Russian).

Vlasov, G. M. (Ed.) 1964. *The Geology of the USSR,* **31.** Nedra Publ., Moscow (in Russian).

Deep Structure under the Volcanic Belt of Kamchatka

S. A. FEDOTOV

Institute of Volcanology and Institute of Physics of the Earth,
Academy of Sciences of the U.S.S.R.,
B. Gruzinskaya 10, Moscow D-272, U.S.S.R.

ABSTRACT

New data are described on upper mantle properties, seismicity and volcanism of Kamchatka, obtained in detailed seismological observations. The map of longitudinal wave velocities V_p in the upper-mantle layers under Kamchatka is presented, which shows a band with velocities $V_p < 7{\cdot}8$ km/s. These minimal velocities are observed under the volcanic belt. An approximate map of bodies (magmatic chambers?) screening *P* and *S* waves at depths of 30-100 km under Kamchatka is constructed.

For over ten years detailed seismological observations have been carried out in Kamchatka. They are aimed at studying patterns of seismicity, upper mantle properties, deep processes and their connection with volcanism. A number of recent results are given in this communication which makes clearer the picture of deep processes occurring under island arcs.

Kamchatka is only a little less seismically active than north-eastern Japan. It has a network of seismic stations which enable the recording and locating of the hypocentres of all earthquakes of magnitude, $M \geq 2{\cdot}6$, on Kamchatka itself and of earthquakes $M \geq 3{\cdot}3$ occurring under the adjacent Pacific Ocean floor from the peninsula to the deep-sea trench.

In both general and in detailed terms, the essential picture of Kamchatka seismicity is given in an article by Fedotov (1968). The reader is advised to consult this article and especially its Fig. 1, for a better understanding of the more recent results and conclusions discussed in this paper.

It will be noted that in our Kamchatka work, earthquakes are assigned to energy classes (*K*) rather than simple magnitudes (*M*) so that the energy of short-period *S* waves of earthquake foci is estimated in joules. *K* and *M* are connected thus:

$$K^{\phi\ 68}_{S\ 1\cdot 2} \approx lg\ Ej \approx 4{\cdot}6 + 1{\cdot}5\,M.$$

Class $K = 10$ earthquakes would then have magnitude of about $3\frac{1}{4}$ *M;* class $K = 15$ earthquakes approximately $6\frac{1}{4}$ *M*. For further discussion, especially on the dependence of the dimensions of the focus area on the energy class K, see Bune *et al.* (1969).

Relative seismic calm has characterized Kamchatka over the years 1965-8 (no earthquakes with $M>6\cdot5$). Nevertheless, the current up-dated version of Fig. 1 in Fedotov 1968, is so much more detailed that it cannot be reproduced in this paper.

The basic pattern remains the same. Indeed, an incidental advantage of the absence of strong shocks over the period 1965-8 is that the growing picture of distribution of epicentres has not been distorted by after-shock series. We believe we have a good idea of mean long-term seismicity of Kamchatka and the Commander Islands.

Certain features are worth emphasis.

Isodepths of earthquake foci with mean $h=20$, 90, and 180 km are approximately parallel to each other under Kamchatka (see Fig. 2). This shows that the Pacific focal zone approaches a consistent shape under Kamchatka. It is inclined towards the continent at an angle of approximately 50°, and is parallel to the deep-sea trench and to the belt of active volcanoes.

In the region of the Commander Islands, the western extremity of the Aleutian Arc, there are, however, no earthquakes with depths of more than 100 km. The focal zone is either vertical or inclines a little southward under the Pacific Ocean. Let us note that on these islands there are neither active volcanoes nor extinct volcanoes of Quaternary age. Evidently the character of deep processes changes in transition from Kamchatka to the western part of the Aleutian Arc. The intersection of the Kuril-Kamchatka and Aleutian Arcs seems to be one of those places where most valuable data may be obtained on deep processes under island arcs.

Dense swarms of earthquake epicentres stretching along the coast of Kamchatka show clearly that the area where the Pacific focal zone crops out to the ocean floor (Fig. 2). So many earthquakes with $M\geq2\cdot6$ occur in this area that over a time as short as four years their foci merge into large spots on the map of epicentres. Judging by this map, under almost any point in the area where the Pacific focal zone crops out on the ocean floor, at least one weak or moderate earthquake with $M\geq2\cdot6$ and with accompanying displacement took place at depths of 0-50 km during the last 15-20 years.

It has been pointed out that the belt of active volcanoes of eastern Kamchatka and the band of earthquake epicentres of the Pacific focal zone (with depth foci $h=125$-75 km) coincide with each other very well (Fedotov 1968, with references). This correlation is completely confirmed by the data on earthquakes of 1965-70. The connection of active volcanism with processes occurring in the Pacific focal zone at depths of approximately 125-75 km seems to be beyond doubt.

THE MAP OF *P* WAVE VELOCITIES IN THE UPPER MANTLE LAYERS UNDER KAMCHATKA[1]

Every year fifteen seismic stations in Kamchatka record several thousand near earthquakes. Their co-ordinates are determined with good precision. Many thousands of seismic rays penetrate through the upper mantle and the Kamchatka earth crust

[1] The results presented in this section were obtained with the co-operation and assistance of L. B. Slavina.

in different directions. There are several methods by which we can obtain data from these, on deep structure and seismic-wave velocities in the region through which the ray-trajectories pass. Our first results were obtained by study of residuals of *P* waves from earthquakes near and far to the Kamchatka stations, and by the apparent *P* wave velocities of near earthquakes. These results were published by Fedotov and Slavina in 1968.

A map of *P* wave velocities in the upper layers of the mantle under Kamchatka was compiled by one of several possible methods in 1970.

More than 250 Kamchatka earthquakes with normal focal depths and recorded accurately by the Kamchatka stations were used to construct this map. Apparent longitudinal wave velocities were determined in narrow sectors at epicentral distances $\Delta = 150$-650 km. Since we do not know exactly what is the refraction path of the seismic rays, the measured apparent velocities refer to the area which is between a pair of recording stations and the middle points of seismic ray trajectories. The region under investigation was therefore divided into small squares with a side of 15 km. Each of these squares could be placed within the many different areas for which estimates were obtained of $V_p{}^*$. For the centre of each 15-km square a mean value of $V_p \pm \sigma$ was obtained. From these values maps of $V_p{}^*$ were constructed for epicentral distances $\Delta = 150$-400 km and $\Delta = 400$-650 km. The last version of the velocity map is shown in Fig. 1.

The crustal thickness under Kamchatka does not exceed 35 km, therefore at $\Delta = 150$-650 km, waves passing through the upper layers of the mantle are recorded amongst the first arrivals.

It appeared that for the whole region under investigation, $V_p = 7{\cdot}61$ km/s at $\Delta = 150$-400 km, $n = 159$ (the number of squares, 15×15 km), whereas $V_p{}^* = 7{\cdot}72$ km/s at $\Delta = 400$-650 km, $n = 176$, on the average. These figures show that *P* wave velocities in the uppermost layers of the mantle (depths of 30-40 km) in the region between the Pacific focal zone and the middle Kamchatka range average 7·6 km/s. Similarly, average velocities increase here with depth, up to 7·7 km/s.

The chosen method of compilation allows us to get only smoothed-out maps of $V_p{}^*$ velocities. Still they give an idea of the main peculiarities of $V_p{}^*$ velocities in the upper-mantle layers under Kamchatka. Fig. 1 shows that the velocities $V_p{}^* = 7{\cdot}8$-$7{\cdot}9$ km/s are typical for the upper layers of the mantle under the Pacific focal zone and the north-western half of Kamchatka. A band (100-200 km wide) of low values of V_p velocities in the upper-mantle layers ($V_p = 7{\cdot}3$-$7{\cdot}7$ km/s) is located between them. This is probably the active region of the mantle in which velocities $V_p = 7{\cdot}6$-$7{\cdot}7$ km/s prevail. Areas with velocities $V_p = 7{\cdot}3$-$7{\cdot}5$ km/s are comparatively small and gravitate to the belt of active volcanoes.

So far we have not a good explanation for the fact that very different tectonic structures are located above the region of low velocities in the mantle ($V_p = 7{\cdot}3$-$7{\cdot}7$ km/s). We hope that new, more detailed, maps of longitudinal wave velocities in the mantle of Kamchatka will help us to know more precisely the depths at which the processes leading to the formation of these large tectonic structures occur.

PROVISIONAL MAP OF BODIES, SCREENING *P* AND *S* WAVES, AT DEPTHS OF 30-100 KM IN THE UPPER MANTLE UNDER KAMCHATKA[1]

In investigating the earth crust and mantle structure under volcanoes by seismic methods, attempts have been made to distinguish deep magma chambers, which

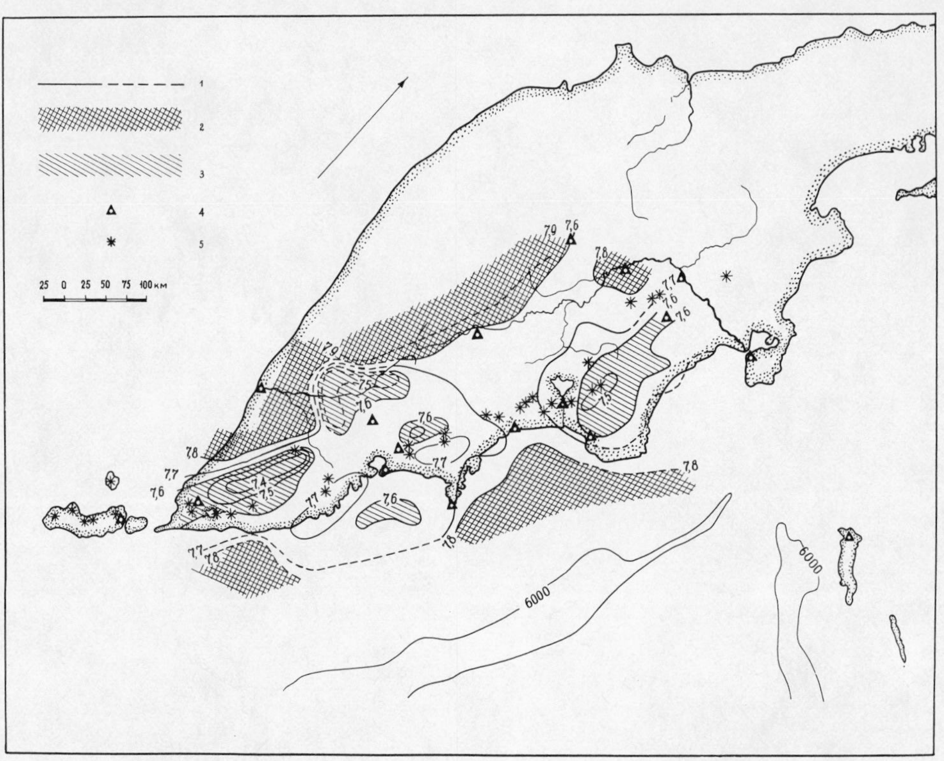

Fig. 1 Map of longitudinal wave velocities V_p in the upper layers of the mantle under Kamchatka. 1, smoothed isolines for V_p; 2, regions where $V_p > 7{\cdot}8$ km/s; 3, regions where $V_p < 7{\cdot}6$ km/s; 4, seismic stations; 5, active volcanoes.

screen *P* and *S* waves from near earthquakes or explosions, at several places in Kamchatka, including the Avachinskaya group and the famous Klyuchevskaya group of volcanoes, located in the depression of the Kamchatka river valley (Fedotov & Farberov 1966, Tokarev & Zobin 1970). Under the Avachinskaya group of volcanoes at depths of 30-60 km a large body, screening seismic waves, was discovered. It appears to have the form of an irregular cone narrowing upwards. Probably it represents an increased concentration of magmatic melts, the deep source of the Avachinskaya group of volcanoes.

[1] The results given in this section were obtained with the co-operation and assistance of O. V. Potapova.

A further object was to make a study of individual hypothetical magmatic chambers and compile maps of such bodies for big areas of Kamchatka. The first result is described in this section.

Anomalously-great attenuation of P and S waves of near earthquakes on the records of some Kamchatka stations led to the effort of locating the possible position of attenuating bodies within the mantle. For this purpose we have chosen more than 400 Kamchatka earthquakes of the energy classes $K_s \geq 8{\cdot}5$ (or $M \geq 2{\cdot}6$) with focal depths 0-100 km and epicentral distances $\Delta < 500$ km.

For all selected earthquakes, station deviations were determined as follows: $\Delta K_p = K_p^i - \bar{K}_p$ and $\Delta K_s = K_s^i - \bar{K}_s$, where K_p^i and K_s^i are energy classes defined by P and S waves at the 'i' station, and $\bar{K}_p$ and $\bar{K}_s$ are the mean values of the same energy classes from the data of all Kamchatka stations. Deviations $\Delta K_p < -1{\cdot}5\sigma = -0{\cdot}6$ and $\Delta K_s < -1{\cdot}5\sigma = -0{\cdot}9$ were considered to be anomalous. 220 anomalous trajectories were obtained for P waves and 170 anomalous trajectories for S waves which comprised five to six per cent of the total number of trajectories. The selected data formed a basis for the schematic map of regions screening P and S waves (Fig. 2). Constructions were made separately for P and S waves.

In the determination of possible positions of screening bodies we proceeded from the following considerations.

While studying the nature of seismic wave attenuation, it has been shown that the seismic shadow behind the Avachinsky volcano is of such a character as to be caused by diffraction of seismic waves on the borders of the magmatic chamber. The shadow behind it is of limited dimensions. Dimensions of the shadow zone were determined by an approximate formula given in the work by Sokolov (1961) for estimation of screen diameter.

$$L = \frac{a^2}{\lambda}\left[1{\cdot}64\sqrt{1-\left(1{\cdot}22\frac{\lambda}{2a}\right)^2}+1\right],$$

where L is the distance from the screen to that receiver, where the shadow converges to a point, that is, the shadow length; a is the screen radius; λ the wave length. The shadow area has the form of a paraboloid. Assume we know only that a certain station is in the seismic shadow and the direction of the seismic ray arrival. In such a case, having assumed that the station is a terminal shadow point, we may find, by the correlation given, the minimum diameter of the screen $2a$ at a fixed λ for each L. Its dimensions must be not less than the cross-section of this area. It was assumed that $\lambda \sim 2{\cdot}5$ km, which corresponds approximately to the frequency of 3 c.p.s. for P waves and 2 c.p.s. for S waves.

As a result we have obtained a dense network of curves of parabolic type. To select the most reliable of them, the frequency of anomalous rays was calculated in each 10° sector. Only those sectors with anomalous trajectories higher than the average (6 per cent) were taken into account, and for these areas were constructed which corresponded to possible positions of screening bodies which we shall call shadows. The correction for the focal depth was not great and was ignored.

Sites located within two and more shadows are shown in Fig. 2. Sites located

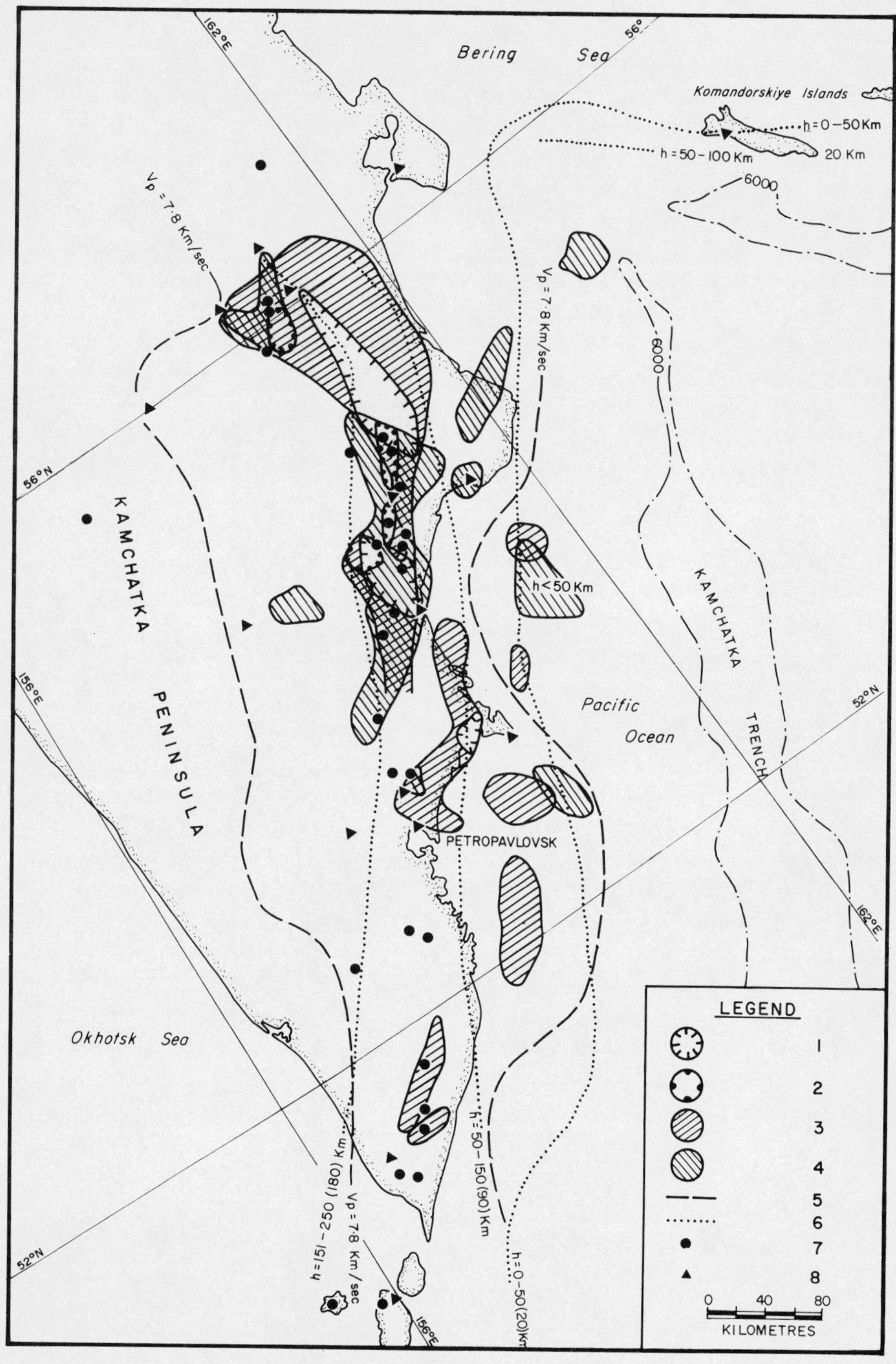
162°E
56°
Bering Sea
Komandorskiye Islands
h=0–50 Km
h=50–100 Km
20 Km
6000
Vp = 7·8 Km/sec
Vp = 7·8 Km/sec
6000
56°N
KAMCHATKA
h<50 Km
KAMCHATKA TRENCH
156°E
PENINSULA
Pacific Ocean
52°N
PETROPAVLOVSK
162°E
Okhotsk Sea
h=50–150(90) Km
52°N
h=151–250 (180) Km
Vp = 7·8 Km/sec
h=0–50(20)Km
156°E
LEGEND
1
2
3
4
5
6
7
8
0 40 80
KILOMETRES

within three and more shadows were considered reliable places of screening bodies. To increase the reliability of the results, additional demands were made of the sites where three and more shadows are intersected: they were to screen not less than two-thirds of the closest surrounding stations. In the opposite case these sections were marked in Fig. 2 as well as the places of double crossing of shadows.

The map obtained as a result of these constructions is the first compilation of a schematic map of screening bodies in the upper mantle at the depths of 30-100 km for the volcanic belt of Kamchatka and the adjacent part of the Pacific Ocean. The position and form of certain screening bodies shown on it are not wholly reliable. Their small number in southern Kamchatka may be simply the result of the fact that the network of seismic stations here is more sparse. Evidently it is not accidental, however, that the most probable places of screening bodies concentrated in Fig. 2 are near the belt of active volcanoes and that they are actually absent westwards of the active volcanic belt. It is also possible that the second chain of probable places of screening bodies, stretching along the Pacific focal zone is not accidental either. Seismic-wave screening may be caused here by great fracturing and heterogeneity of the crust and mantle.

The band of probable places of screening bodies has a width of about 50 km, which corresponds to the belt of active volcanoes and stretches along it. The band is approximately in the middle of a wider (100-200 km) area of low seismic wave velocities in the mantle ($V_p < 7{\cdot}8$ km/s).

CONCLUSION

In the Kamchatka region the oceanic block of crust and upper mantle submerges under the continent along the Pacific focal zone with a velocity of about 1 cm/yr or more. The number of earthquakes in the focal zone quickly decreases with depth and evidently the creep increases rapidly as well. Seismic wave velocities in the oceanic block of the crust and mantle are higher than in the continental block. The structure of the oceanic block is poorly known; it is difficult to say, therefore, whether the 'plate tectonics' scheme is so far true for Kamchatka or not.

Active volcanism and magma formation in the mantle are connected with processes in the Pacific focal zone. The roof of the region of partial magma melting is located under Kamchatka at a depth of about 60 km; the most intensive melting occurs, it is supposed, at depths of 120-200 or 250 km.

Fig. 2 Approximate map of regions which screen P and S waves at depths of 30-100 km in the upper mantle beneath Kamchatka. 1, sites through which P waves propagate badly to three or more near stations; 2, the same sites for S waves; 3, sites through which P waves propagate badly to two near stations; 4, the same sites for S waves; 5, boundaries of the band within which longitudinal wave velocities in the upper mantle layers are $V_p < 7{\cdot}8$ km/s; 6, *isolines*, which show the mean position of earthquake foci with depths 0-50 km ($\bar{h}=20$ km), 50-150 km ($\bar{h}=90$ km) and 150-250 km ($\bar{h}=180$ km), respectively; 7, active volcanoes; 8, seismic stations.

Above this region of the Pacific focal zone, bodies which screen seismic waves in the mantle (magmatic chambers?) are located where seismic wave velocities in the mantle decrease to $V_p = 7{\cdot}3\text{-}7{\cdot}5$ km/s. Here is situated a comparatively narrow (40-50 km) belt of active volcanoes.

There is a band, 100-200 km wide, in which the velocities of longitudinal waves in the mantle, V_p, is less than 7·8 km/s. A volcanic belt stretches along the middle of this band. Under this band intensive mantle differentiation probably takes place. These are probably deep processes because they appear to have no connection with the tectonic structures of eastern Kamchatka.

Kamchatka is a typical part of the chain of island arcs of the Western Pacific. The data given here may be typical as well.

REFERENCES

Bune, V. I. *et al.* 1969. Methods of detailed studies of seismicity. *Trudy Inst. Fiz. Zemli AN SSSR*, **9** (176), 1969 (in Russian).

Fedotov, S. A. 1968. On deep structure, properties of the upper mantle and volcanism of the Kuril-Kamchatka island Arc according to seismic data. In *The crust and upper mantle of the Pacific area.* (Eds L. Knopoff, C. L. Drake & P. J. Hart). *Am. geophys. Un., Geophys. Monogr.* **12,** 131-9.

Fedotov, S. A. & Farberov, A. I. 1966. On screening of transversal seismic waves and on the magmatic chamber in the upper mantle in the region of the Avachinskaya group of volcanoes. In *Vulkanism i glubinnoye stroyeniye Zemli.* Nauka Publ., Moscow (in Russian).

Fedotov, S. A. & Slavina, L. B. 1968. Estimation of longitudinal wave velocities in the upper mantle beneath north-western part of the Pacific and Kamchatka. *Izv. AN SSSR Fizika Zemli*, **2,** 8-31 (in Russian).

Sokolov, B. S. 1961. Defectoscopy of materials. *Gostekhizdat* (in Russian).

Tokarev, P. I. & Zobin, V. M. 1970. Peculiarities of near earthquake seismic wave propagation in the earth's crust and upper mantle in the region of the Klyuchevskaya group of volcanoes of Kamchatka. *Bull. Volcanic Stations, SSSR*, **46,** Nauka Publ., Moscow (in Russian).

The Old 'Inner' Arc and its Deformation in Japan

TOSHIO KIMURA
Geological Institute, University of Tokyo, Hongo, Tokyo 113, Japan

ABSTRACT

In Japan the 'inner' arc of Southwest Japan-Ryukyu meets with the 'outer' arc of Northeast Japan-Bonin-Mariana. The two arc systems were not formed at the same time. The Honshu Arc, involving both Northeast and Southwest Japan, was formed by earth movements beginning in the Silurian. The eugeosynclines and the deformation zones within the Honshu Arc migrated toward the ocean until the Neogene in Southwest Japan but only until the earliest Cretaceous in Northeast Japan. The old Honshu Arc was formed by a successive series of orogenies related to the migration of the eugeosynclines and deformation zones. Such successive migration, which is noteworthy in Southwest Japan, is explained by the successive retreating of the oceanic plate. On the other hand, the younger Northeast Japan-Bonin-Mariana Arcs system began at least in Early Cretaceous time and became fully developed in the Neogene, marked by extensive Neogene volcanism. Landmasses of the old Honshu Arc in Northeast Japan were separated into many massifs, which were rotated and displaced by the movements of the new system. Northeast Japan as a whole was also rotated anti-clockwise, and advanced toward the ocean. Although it is generally thought to be a typical island arc area, its older geologic structures, which were formed before the Early Cretaceous, are complicated because of the later fragmentation.

INTRODUCTION

The migration of eugeosynclines is remarkable in Japan as pointed out by Kobayashi (1956*b*). The basic volcanics in the eugeosynclines were emplaced at the same time as the granite intrusions in the adjacent orogenic zones, as depicted by Matsumoto (1964), which shows that the orogenic movements in eugeosyncline do not occur independently of the movements in the adjacent orogenic zone. In turn, this seems to be intimately related, in terms of 'plate tectonics', to the movement of the oceanic plate in the subduction zone. In this paper I deal with the formation of the old Honshu Arc and the superposition of the younger arc system upon it in Northeast Japan.

MIGRATION OF GEOSYNCLINES AND ZONES OF DEFORMATION IN SOUTHWEST JAPAN

In Southwest Japan, there are eugeosynclines of different ages as shown in Table 1. Among these, only the Chichibu eugeosyncline was at all wide, about 200 km (Figs 1, 2, and 3), comparable to the Alpine or Appalachian. Other eugeosynclines in Japan were very narrow, about 20 km in width. If we can accept the Chichibu geosyncline to be the primary one, the other geosynclines must be secondary.

The *Chichibu* geosyncline began with Silurian acidic volcanism, not basic. The acidic volcanics were as prominent on the southern border, the oceanic side, as they were on the northern border. The volcanics in Devonian time were andesitic. Basic volcanics in the Chichibu eugeosyncline became marked in Lower Carboniferous, Early Permian and Middle Permian times (Kanmera 1971). Information on pre-Silurian basement rocks of the Chichibu geosyncline has been collated from data given by Kanmera and Nakazawa (1968), and Kimura and Tokuyama (1971). Precambrian[1] and Palaeozoic metamorphic rocks have been reported from the continental as well as the oceanic side and from the inner part of the geosyncline. Precambrian zircon is included in the Cretaceous Ryoke granite, and kyanite and staurolite, which are thought to be relict minerals, are found in the Abukuma metamorphics. The Upper Carboniferous strata, to the south of the Hida metamorphic zone, have disconformities within them, accompanied by 'red rocks' which are thought to originate in residual soils (Igo 1961). The late Palaeozoic strata of the Chichibu geosyncline often yield conglomerates with clasts of granite and gneiss; these clasts came from the marginal lands or small landmasses within the Chichibu geosyncline. Some of them yield a Precambrian radiometric age (Shibata *et al.* 1971). The late Palaeozoic strata in the northern half of the Chichibu geosyncline are several thousands of metres thick (Yoshida 1971), far thinner than the granitic layer in the same area.

These records show that a sialic layer was widely distributed below the Chichibu eugeosyncline. However, the basic volcanics in the Mikabu zone (the central part of the Chichibu eugeosyncline) have been derived from the upper mantle (Sugisaki *et al.* 1971). Therefore it is possible that the Chichibu geosyncline was ensimatic only below the submarine volcanic zones.

The Hida gneisses give a Triassic radiometric age generally, although some show Precambrian and Palaeozoic ages. It is clear that the Hida metamorphics have been metamorphosed or re-metamorphosed in Triassic time. However, it is not yet clear that the Hida metamorphics originated from nearby late Palaeozoic mio- or eugeosynclinal strata within the Chichibu geosyncline. The Precambrian pebbles in the late Palaeozoic and the disconformities with the 'red rocks' indicate the presence of landmasses in the Hida zone. The late Palaeozoic strata along the southern border of this zone, however, do not in general show marginal facies characteristic of proximity to a large landmass. It is probable that there was a shelf with exposed small land areas during the development of the zone.

[1] For the radiometric datings in Japan see the bibliography by Matsumoto (1968).

Basic volcanics are absent or very rare in the Upper Permian, where turbidites facies are prominent in some places. The Lower and Middle Triassic strata in the Chichibu geosynclinal area are mostly poor in fossils, except in a few localities. However, recent conodont study (Koike *et al.* 1970) shows that many strata, long thought to be of the Permian, are actually Triassic. The Triassic yields radiolarian cherts, often distributed together with acidic volcanics, but not with basic ones to my

Table 1

TECTONIC ZONES AND EUGEOSYNCLINES IN SOUTHWEST JAPAN

Tectonic zones	*Eugeosynclines*
Hida zone High temperature metamorphic zone. Triassic metamorphics prevail.	Chichibu eugeosyncline (Silurian-Middle Permian)
Sangun-Yamaguchi zone Sangun metamorphics (high pressure) underlying the less-metamorphosed late Palaeozoic and Lower Triassic strata. High pressure metamorphism ended generally before Middle Triassic.	
Ryoke zone High-temperature metamorphic zone. Cretaceous metamorphics prevail.	
Sambagawa-Chichibu zone Sambagawa metamorphics are distributed mostly in the northern part and change gradually into the southern less-metamorphosed Palaeozoic strata. High-pressure metamorphism ended before mid-Cretaceous generally.	
Sambosan zone Upper Permian and Triassic strata; some of them are slightly metamorphosed.	Sambosan eugeosyncline (Upper Permian-Triassic)
Shimanto zone Upper Jurassic-Cretaceous strata; some of them are slightly metamorphosed.	Shimanto eugeosyncline (Upper Jurassic-Cretaceous)
Nakamura zone Palaeogene strata, with some metamorphics.	Nakamura eugeosyncline (Palaeogene)
Tanzawa zone Neogene strata, with some metamorphics.	Neogene eugeosyncline

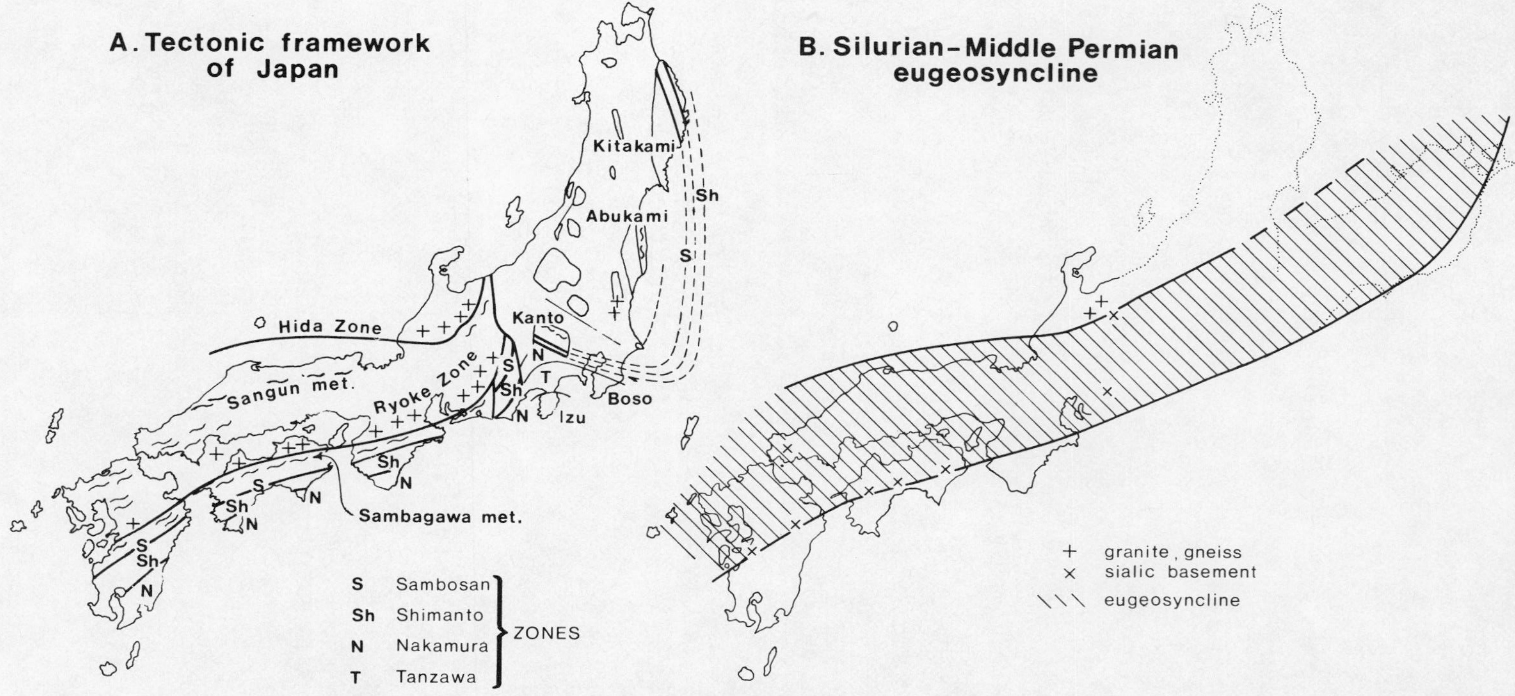

Fig. 1 A, Tectonic framework of Japan; Sangun and Sambagawa metamorphics are distributed in Sangun-Yamaguchi and Sambagawa-Chichibu zones, respectively. B, Silurian-Middle Permian Chichibu eugeosyncline.

present knowledge. These radiolarian cherts may not be a necessary criterion for a eugeosyncline. Triassic basic submarine volcanics have been reported until now only from the Sambosan geosyncline. Moreover, some Upper Triassic sequences, in the northern half of the Chichibu geosyncline, are of molasse facies and shallow shelf facies in the southern half. It is considered, therefore, that the eugeosynclinal stage of the Chichibu geosyncline ended generally before the Upper Permian.

The Upper Jurassic-Cretaceous strata include abundant terrestrial deposits in the northern half of the Chichibu geosynclinal area, the marine miogeosynclinal or mobile shelf stage ending generally before Upper Triassic or Upper Jurassic time. On the other hand, in the southern half, marine shelf facies occurred until the Cretaceous, the Lower Cretaceous miogeosynclinal strata being very thick.

In the *Sambosan* geosyncline the sequences range at least from the Upper Permian to the Triassic (Kanmera 1971) (Fig. 2). The section is characterized by abundant basic submarine volcanics, together with thick chert, extremely thick and bedded sandstone, turbidites and unfossiliferous limestone. The Sambosan zone has long been united with the Chichibu zone, because of the mutual resemblance of their successions.

In the *Shimanto* geosynclinal zone the rocks are mostly Cretaceous (Matsumoto 1953), although some Upper Jurassic strata may be included (Tamura 1961). The Shimanto group in the Akaishi mountains has shale and basic volcanics together with chert in the lowest part, and thick shales and sandstones upon them. Acidic tuffs prevail except for the lowest horizon. Some sandstones are turbidites; those in the northern area have been supplied from the north and those in the southern area from the south, from the oceanic side (Fig. 2). Quartzite pebbles supplied from the south are also reported (Tokuoka 1967). There must have been landmasses or submarine swells on the oceanic side of the Shimanto.

The Shimanto sequences are usually intensely faulted and folded at outcrops, suggesting 'tectonic churning'. Precise study of the geologic structure, however, shows that the major structures are nearly horizontal on a large scale (Kimura & Tokuyama 1971), even though the strata may be generally steep-dipping in outcrop. The strata at the lowest structural level show flow folding, those in the middle show lense folding (Kimura 1968) or shear folding, and in the upper level, flexure folding. There are intermediate styles of folding at the marginal levels. The particular folding style depends principally on the depth at which folding took place. These variations show that the folding has occurred mainly after the deposition of almost all strata of the Shimanto geosyncline, and not during it.

The rocks of the Shimanto geosyncline are not of deep-water origin (Matsumoto & Hirata 1969). During deposition terrestrial sedimentary basins were distributed in the northern half of Southwest Japan and miogeosynclinal or mobile shelf environments to the north of the Shimanto.

The *Nakamura* (Setogawa or Kobotoke) geosyncline (Fig. 3) is usually united with the Shimanto geosyncline in a wide sense. However, the Kobotoke zone in Kanto, the Setogawa zone in the Akaishi (Kimura 1969), the Muro belt in Kii (Matsushita 1971), the Nakamura zone in Shikoku and the area to the south of the Nobeoka-Shibisan tectonic line (Hashimoto 1961) in Kyushu can all be safely

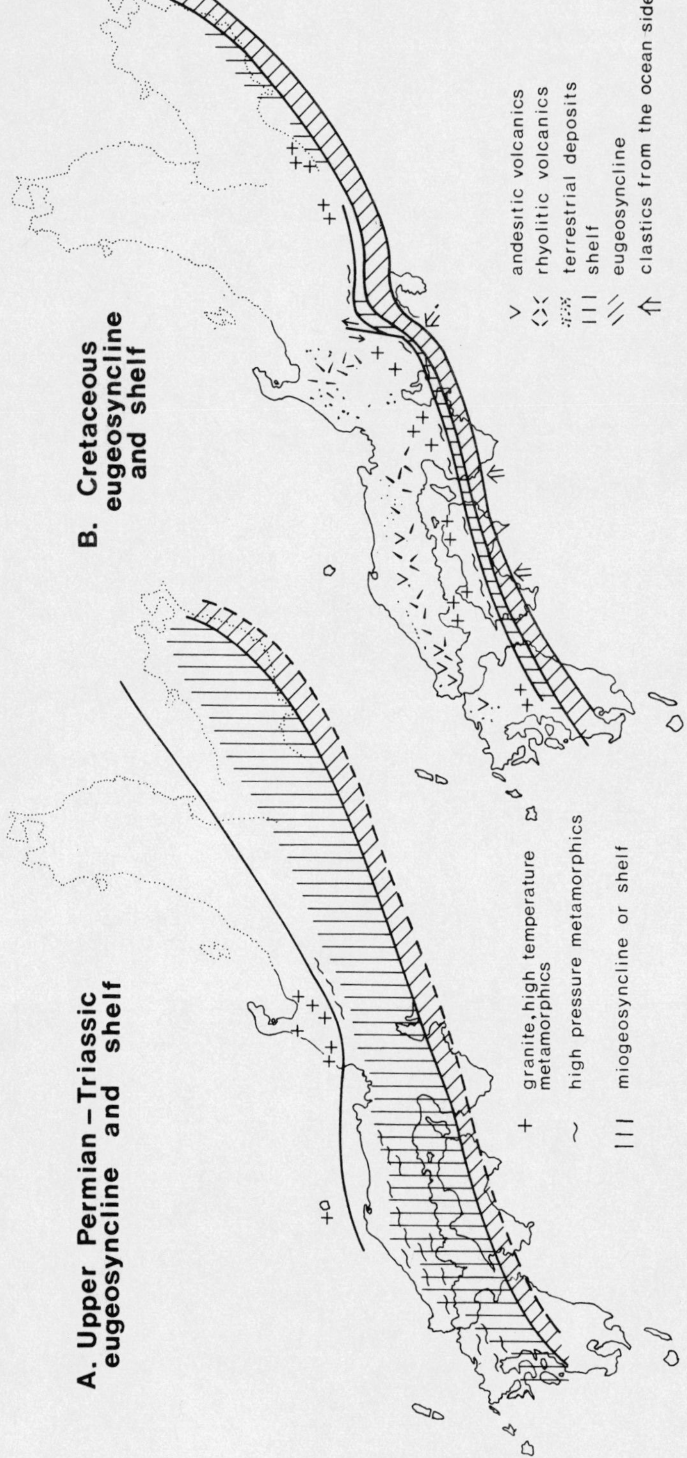

Fig. 2 A, Upper Permian-Triassic Sambosan eugeosyncline and other sedimentary basins. B, Cretaceous Shimanto eugeosyncline and other sedimentary basins.

separated from the Shimanto zone: the strata in these zones yield Palaeogene fossils, in contrast to the Cretaceous fossils of the Shimanto (in the strict sense).

In the Akaishi mountains, the Shimanto Cretaceous strata yield abundant acidic tuffs in the middle and upper horizons. To the south, the Palaeogene strata in the Setogawa zone yield basic volcanics in the lower or middle part, a distinguishing feature. The basic volcanics may occur but do not crop out in Kii, Shikoku and Kyushu.

Sialic clastics were fed into the Nakamura zone from north as well as from south (Shuto 1963), the sedimentary environment not being deep water (Tamura & Harada 1971).

While the Nakamura zone was in the eugeosynclinal stage, the terrestrial sedimentary basins and marine shelf were distributed in rather limited areas within the spread of older Chichibu rocks.

The Neogene *Tanzawa* geosyncline is one of several Neogene geosynclines distributed along the Northeast Japan-Bonin-Mariana Arcs and on the Japan Sea flank of Southwest Japan. There is a Neogene geosyncline running from east to west in the southern part of Northeast Japan, from the Boso peninsula to the Tanzawa mountains. There is another near Shizuoka, which is thought to be the western continuation of the Tanzawa geosyncline beyond the Fossa Magna. Further to the south-west the Neogene geosyncline is thought to have been located offshore of Southwest Japan. The sedimentary basins to the north of the Nankai trough may be the present-day representatives of the geosyncline. Shallow submarine swells to the south of the geosyncline are suggested by the shallow shelf facies of the Neogene formations in the Izu peninsula (Sawamura *et al.* 1970) to the south of Tanzawa.

Neogene shelf facies sediments to the north of the geosyncline are distributed at several localities in the southern part of Southwest Japan.

In summary, there was a wide Silurian-Middle Permian eugeosyncline development in the main part of Southwest Japan. The eugeosynclinal area changed into a miogeosynclinal one, with shallow shelf and terrestrial sedimentary basins formed at first in the northern half and later in the southern half of the older eugeosynclinal area. The Upper Permian-Triassic, Upper Jurrassic-Cretaceous, Palaeogene, and Neogene eugeosynclines were formed successively on the oceanic side of older eugeosynclines, demonstrating a migration toward the ocean. Some geosynclinal strata contain abundant acidic tuffs. At least some sialic clastics have been supplied from the oceanic side. A sialic layer was widely distributed below the Chichibu eugeosyncline. The strata of the Shimanto and Nakamura geosynclines were not deposited in deep water, indicating that they were not deposits carried into the subduction zone by the motion of a conveyor-belt oceanic plate.

MIGRATIONS OF ZONES OF GRANITE INTRUSIONS AND DIFFERENT KINDS OF EARTH MOVEMENTS

In Japan several series of orogenies have occurred. The geosynclines in Japan have not been stabilized by only the one cycle or short-term series of orogenies (Fig. 4).

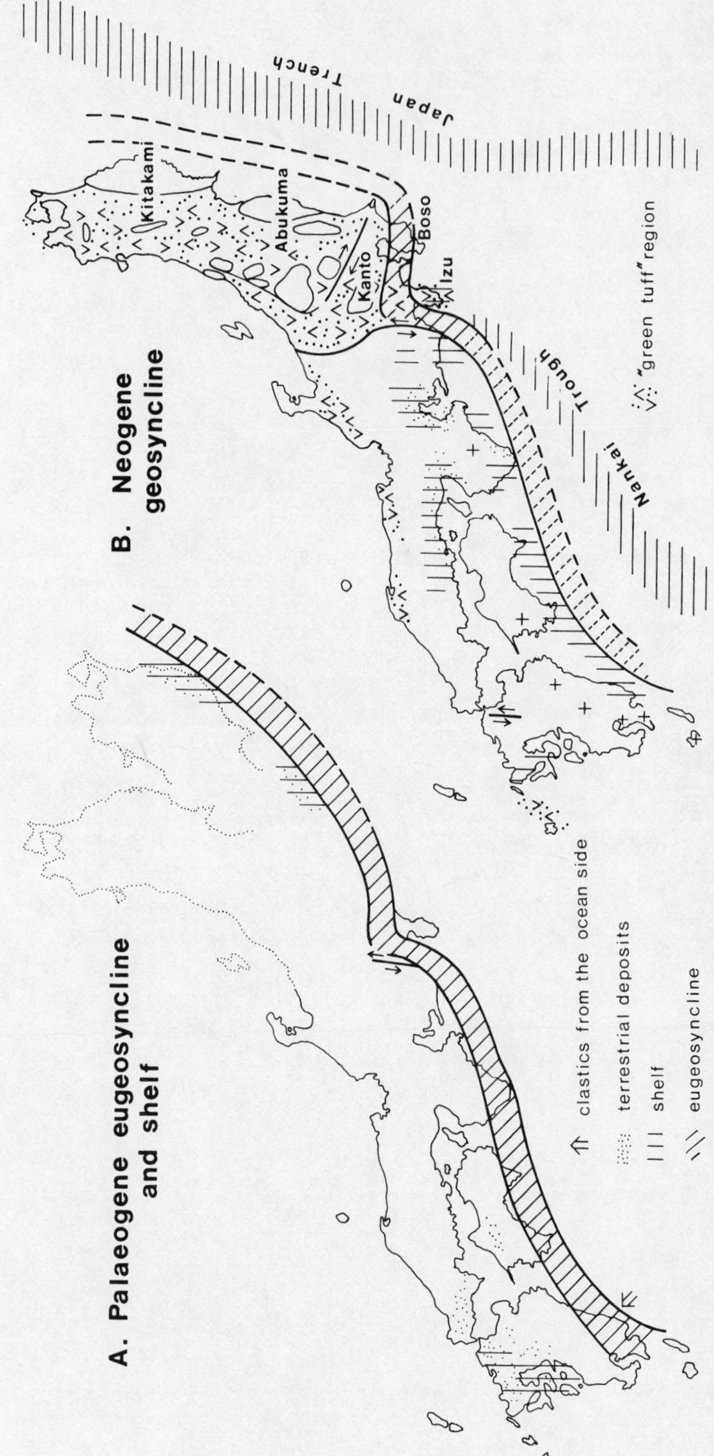

Fig. 3 A, Palaeogene Nakamura eugeosyncline and other sedimentary basins. B, Neogene geosynclines.

Upper Permian-Triassic

The Hida gneisses and granites yield in general Triassic radiometric ages, although some of them show Precambrian and Palaeozoic ages. The Sangun-Yamaguchi terrain was in the stage of intense folding with flow folding in Upper Permian-Triassic time, when the Sambosan zone was in the eugeosynclinal stage. Some Sangun metamorphics give Carboniferous radiometric ages. This means that at least some strata in the northern Chichibu geosyncline were already uplifted and removed from conditions of high-pressure metamorphism in Carboniferous time.

Upper Jurassic-Cretaceous

Ryoke metamorphics and granites in the Ryoke zone as well as in the Sangun-Yamaguchi zone mostly give Cretaceous radiometric ages, although Ryoke high-temperature metamorphism may have begun in the Upper Jurassic (Ono 1961). The Sambagawa-Chichibu zone was in a stage of intense folding with flow folding in contrast to the Sangun-Yamaguchi zone with rather superficial folding (Kimura 1960) in Cretaceous time, while the southernmost part of the Chichibu zone was in the state of a rather mobile shelf or miogeosyncline.

In this way, we see that a zone of superficial folding (the Sangun-Yamaguchi terrain), a zone of high-temperature metamorphism (the Ryoke zone), a zone of upheaval of high-pressure metamorphics and intense folding with flow folding (the main part of the Sambagawa-Chichibu zone), a zone of miogeosynclinal or mobile shelf areas with some folding (the southernmost part of the Sambagawa-Chichibu), and lastly, a zone of eugeosynclinal development (the Shimanto eugeosyncline) were arranged from north to south in Southwest Japan during Upper Jurassic-Cretaceous time.

Palaeogene

The deformation of the Palaeogene strata is rather limited in the Chichibu geosynclinal area. On the other hand, the Upper Cretaceous Izumi group in the Median zone of Southwest Japan shows gentle folds. The Palaeogene strata in the Amakusa islands in Kyushu also show gentle folds as does the Upper Cretaceous. The Cretaceous Shimanto group has been folded intensely prior to the folding of the Palaeogene Setogawa group. Only one radiometric age of Palaeogene granitic rock has been reported from the southern part of Southwest Japan. In the northern part, however, there were noteworthy granite intrusions in the Palaeogene.

Neogene

The Palaeogene Setogawa group shows much more intense folding than the Neogene strata to the south-east of it. In general, the folding occurred prior to the folding of the Neogene strata. Neogene granites are widely distributed in the southern part of Southwest Japan, a large part of which was in the stage of block movements.

In summary, in accord with the notion of migration of eugeosynclines toward the ocean, there also migrated zones of different kinds of deformation, such as the zone of block movements, a zone of folding of 'shallower type', a zone of high-temperature metamorphism and granite intrusion, a zone of uplifting of high-pressure metamor-

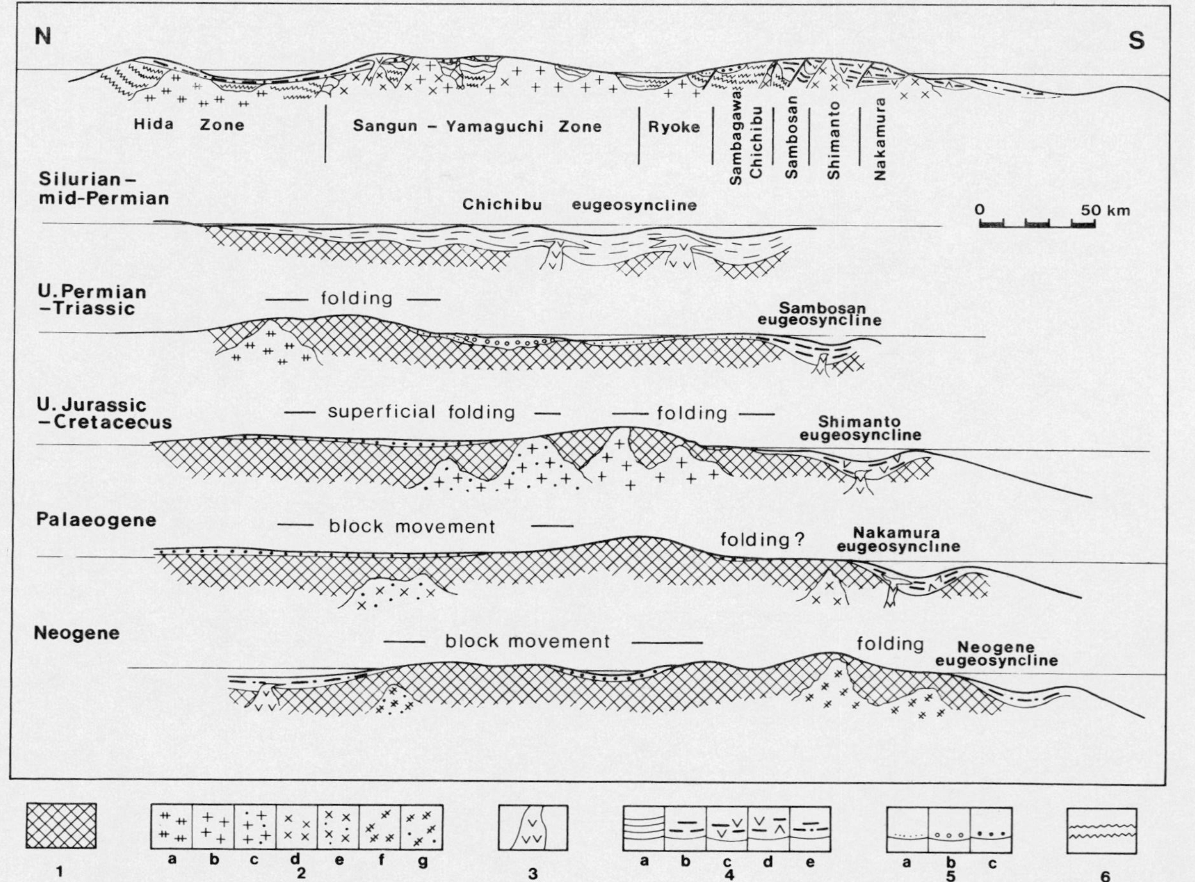

Fig. 4 Schematic cross-sections of Southwest Japan. 1, basement; 2, granites: (a) Triassic, (b) Cretaceous, (c) Cretaceous discordant granites, (d) Palaeogene granites in outer zone, (e) Palaeogene granites in inner zone, (f) Neogene granites in outer zone, (g) Neogene granites in inner zone; 3, basic submarine volcanics; 4, geosynclinal strata: (a) Chichibu, (b) Sambosan, (c) Shimanto, (d) Nakamura, (e) Neogene; 5, miogeosynclinal or shelf facies: (a) Upper Permian-Lower Triassic, (b) Upper Triassic, (c) Cretaceous and later; 6, metamorphics

phics and intense folding, a mobile shelf or miogeosyncline and, finally, a eugeosyncline. Thus a set of zones of deformation was formed at the appropriate time, although some zones may be lacking in part, or may not be especially prominent.

MIGRATION OF GEOSYNCLINES AS WELL AS DEFORMATION ZONES AND OROGENIES

When a set of deformation agencies occurs in the deeper part of the earth's crust or in the upper mantle, a different set of deformational agencies is inferred to operate in the upper part of the crust. Deeper agencies may migrate rather independently of the older deformation zones in the upper crust and so the boundaries of the older deformation zones may not coincide with those of the younger ones. Two different high-temperature metamorphic zones of different ages within the one eugeosyncline of Chichibu show this feature. The Neogene granites in Southwest Japan in general intruded into the Shimanto geosynclinal area, but also into the Chichibu and the Sambosan. The Abukuma metamorphics and the Ryuhozan metamorphics are very similar to the Sambagawa metamorphics in terms of the original sedimentary lithologic facies, but similar to the Ryoke metamorphics in the stage of metamorphism reached (Miyashiro & Haramura 1962).

There is a hypothesis that an ensimatic eugeosyncline is changed into a stabilized zone, part of a sialic mass, through a single orogeny or relatively short-lived cycle of orogenies, and that the deformation in a tectonic zone is related only to the proper agencies confined to that tectonic zone. Such a hypothesis cannot explain the existence of two high-temperature metamorphic zones in a single eugeosyncline. Thus many geologists in Japan (Minato *et al.* 1965) thought that the rocks of the Chichibu geosyncline have been affected principally by the one orogeny in late Palaeozoic or early Mesozoic time. However, radiometric datings show two similar series of deformations of different ages in this one eugeosyncline: the Akiyoshi series in the northern half and the Sakawa series in the southern half (Kobayashi 1941).

Matsuda and Uyeda (1971) also mentioned the migration of belts of orogenies and magmatic fronts, related to plate tectonics. They thought that these migrations have characteristics peculiar to the Pacific-type orogeny.

However, eugeosynclines such as the Sambosan and the Shimanto, which occurred at the same time as the inner high-temperature metamorphic zone (Figs 2, 4), are far smaller than the primary Chichibu geosyncline. Such smaller sedimentary basins in front of the major geosynclinal area are the equivalents of the flysch and molasse basins in the Alps. The migration of orogenic fronts is there supposed by Wunderlich (1966). However, these basins in the Alps are not zones of basic volcanism, because a thick sialic layer probably existed below the basins. The flysch and molasse basins migrated, but toward the older continent of Meso-Europe, which may have stopped their further migration (Fig. 5).

In Japan, on the other hand, facing the Pacific Ocean, new small eugeosynclines were formed successively. According to the migration idea, several series of orogenies occurred. These series are usually very difficult to distinguish one from another,

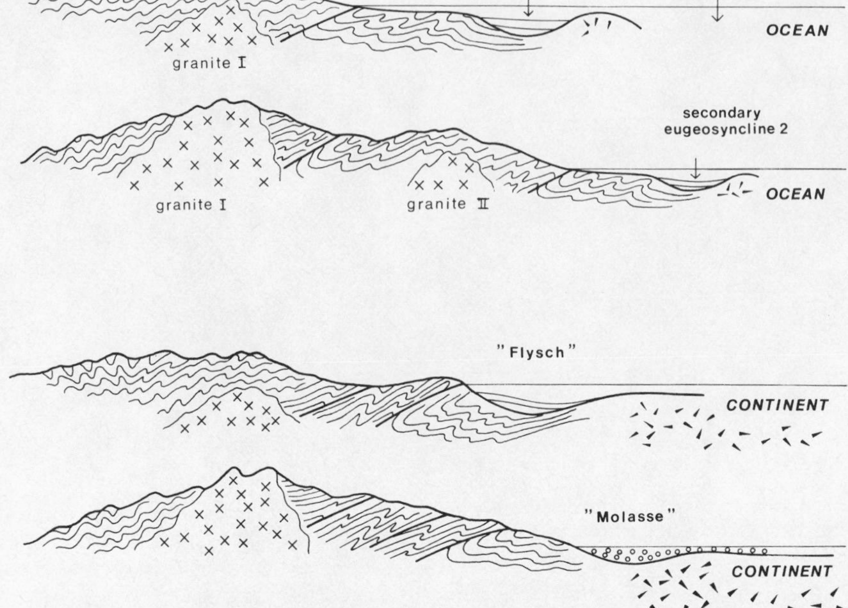

Fig. 5 Migration of secondary eugeosynclines and flysch-molasse basins.

because they are related in space as well as in time. From the viewpoint of stabilization of an orogenic zone, only *one* geotectonic cycle of orogeny, from Silurian to Recent, can be recognized in Southwest Japan.

MIGRATION OF DEFORMATION ZONES AND PLATE TECTONICS

Migration of the geosynclines and deformation zones and series of orogenies in Southwest Japan are well explained by the retreating of the subduction zone of the oceanic plate as in Figs 6, 7 (Kimura & Tokuyama 1971). Matsuda and Uyeda (1971) also have a similar opinion, although the migrations occurred more frequently than supposed by them.

The subduction of the oceanic plate near Japan has occurred at least since the Upper Permian and may, indeed, have occurred also since the Silurian. However, the arrangement of deformation zones is not yet clear for the Silurian-Middle Permian series, although late Palaeozoic earth movements in southern Kitakami (Minato *et al.* 1965) may represent the kind of deformational series to be expected.

The hypotheses, however, that geosynclines are deep sea trenches, or that the strata in eugeosynclines have been carried into the subduction zone by the movements

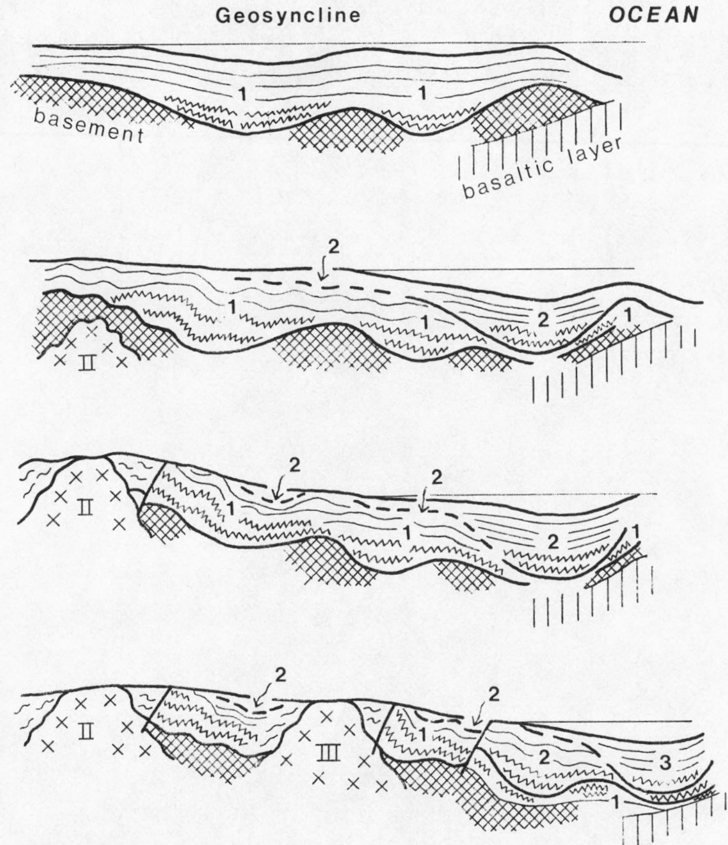

Fig. 6 Migration of geosynclines, metamorphism and granite intrusions. Wavy line: high-pressure metamorphics. 1, 2 and 3: geosynclinal strata. II and III: granite intrusions and high-temperature metamorphics. 2 and 3 are related respectively to II and III.

of the oceanic plate, are not true as tested against Japanese geology. A sialic layer was widely distributed below the Chichibu eugeosyncline; landmasses or submarine swells composed of sialic masses existed on the oceanic side of the Shimanto, Nakamura and Neogene eugeosynclines; the strata in such eugeosynclines have not been deformed by 'tectonic churning' within the subduction zone, although they show complicated minor structures. The eugeosynclinal strata in Japan were not oceanic deposits on an oceanic plate.

There is an opinion that the high-pressure 'metamorphic zone' was the Benioff zone (Takeuchi & Uyeda 1965). This is difficult to reconcile with the observation that when the Hida was undergoing high-temperature metamorphism, the Sangun metamorphics were mostly in the last stage of high pressure conditions. At that time Lower Triassic shelf facies were present in the Sangun 'zone' as well as to the south of it (Nakazawa 1958). Upper Triassic strata in the Sangun'zone' are molassic (Tokuyama 1962). Also, when Cretaceous high-temperature metamorphism occurred in the Ryoke zone, shelf facies of the same age were widely distributed to the south of the Sambagawa zone, the high-pressure metamorphic zone. The Lower Cretaceous Monobegawa group yields abundant pebbles and boulders of granitic rocks supplied from north beyond the Sambagawa (Kobayashi *et al.* 1945). The conclusion is that when high-temperature metamorphism occurred in the Hida and Ryoke zones, the areas of the Sangun and Sambagawa metamorphics were not eugeosynclinal.

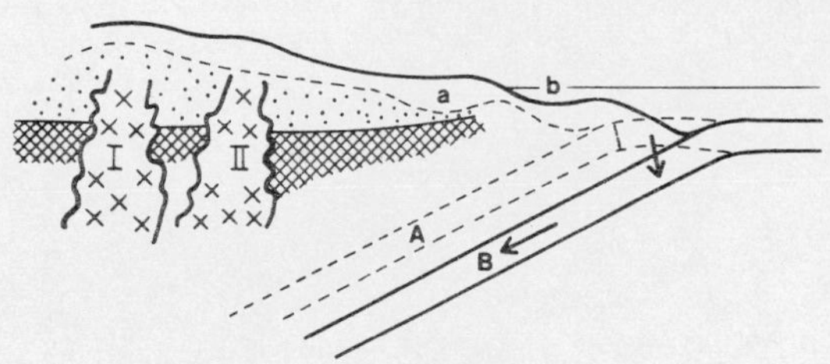

Fig. 7 Retreat of the oceanic plate and migration of eugeosynclines. Plates A and B correspond, respectively, to eugeosynclines a and b, as well as to granite intrusions I and II.

The migration of the deformation zones is well explained by the ideas of plate tectonics. However, the Tertiary granites in Northeast as well as Southwest Japan (on the side of the Sea of Japan) cannot be so well explained by them. These Tertiary granites may be related to the movements which formed this sea.

Finally, several zones of Mesozoic folding and block movements are distributed in the Korean peninsula and in southern Manchuria (Kobayashi 1956*a*), and among them stable belts are intercalated. The histories of sedimentation and the deformation style of these zones are greatly different from those in Japan. The tectonic zones in Southwest Japan are not to be traced into the Korean peninsula, but into the Ryukyu islands (Konishi 1965). Moreover, there is a very wide area of late Mesozoic deformation of the Yenshan in China. The Mesozoic deformational area in eastern Asia on the whole ranges at least 1,000 km in width. Was such a wide deformational area truly formed by the subduction of oceanic plate?

SUPERPOSITION OF NEW ISLAND ARC SYSTEMS ON THE OLDER ONE

Northeast Japan is generally thought to be an area typical of island arcs. A set of deformation zones is not clearly recognized, however, as it is in Southwest Japan. Nevertheless, the pre-mid-Cretaceous strata, distributed now only within massifs, were deposited in similar geosynclines and deformed in similar deformation zones as in Southwest Japan. The Kanto massif is thought by all to be the continuation of the outer zone of Southwest Japan. The Abukuma and Yamagami metamorphics in the Abukuma are correlated to the Ryoke and Sambagawa metamorphics. The Upper Jurassic strata in northern Abukuma are quite similar to those in Southwest Japan. The Iwaizumi and the Taro belts in northern Kitakami correspond, respectively, to the Sambosan and the Shimanto zones (Murata & Sugimoto 1971; Onuki 1969). Thus we can trace the tectonic zones in Southwest Japan into the Northeast.

There are some differences between them. The Middle Carboniferous-Permian strata in southern Kitakami are of shelf facies and do not contain basic volcanics. Much greater differences were manifest in Cretaceous time. The Kitakami massif yields abundant Cretaceous granite, in contrast to its absence in the outer zone of Southwest Japan, the continuation of the Kitakami. This shows the very different conditions in the deeper parts between them. In Southwest Japan eugeosynclines migrated probably until the Neogene. In Northeast Japan, the early Cretaceous strata of the Taro belt (the continuation of the Shimanto zone), yield andesitic submarine volcanics instead of basic ones and are uncomformably covered by the non-folded, Lower Cretaceous Miyako shelf-facies group. No Palaeogene eugeosynclinal areas can be found in the Northeast. We see then that the Northeast developed in a similar way to the Southwest until the lowest Cretaceous. The former was later deformed and separated into massifs which were rotated and displaced. Thus began the new Northeast Japan-Bonin-Mariana Arc system. Volcanism and sedimentation in zones parallel to the new system became prominent from Neogene time. It is usually supposed, therefore, that the new system suddenly formed at the beginning of the Neogene. We can see also similar relations between two arc systems in the Philippines, New Zealand and other regions (Kimura *et al.* 1968). This may indicate a remarkable change of plate systems in the Middle Tertiary or earlier age.

In central Japan, where the superposition of the younger system on the older is well observed (Fig. 8), the change of the systems began even in the Cretaceous. The Sambagawa-Chichibu and other tectonic zones in the Akaishi mountains in the north-eastern end of the outer zone of Southwest Japan run from north to south, although they run from east to west in the other part. The N-S trend has been caused by left lateral movements along great faults (Kimura 1961*a*), related to the formation of the new system. The Sambagawa-Chichibu zone in the Akaishi mountains is much narrower than the same zone in the rest of Southwest Japan (Kimura 1961*b*), although the Cretaceous Shimanto zone has nearly the same width throughout. This means probably that the displacement of the Sambagawa-Chichibu zone in the Akaishi began before the Cretaceous. This is nearly the same age as the beginning of the new system in Northeast Japan as has been mentioned already.

The Cretaceous strata in the Shimanto zone in the Akaishi trend ENE to WSW in general, although they run north to south along the N-S trending strike-slip faults. On the other hand, the Palaeogene strata in the Setogawa zone trend in a NNE-SSW direction. Near and along the western margin of the Setogawa zone, serpentines which are related to the submarine volcanics are aligned roughly north to south. It is probable that the Setogawa zone had a more northerly trend than the Shimanto during the depositional stages. The displacements of the tectonic zones in the Akaishi, therefore, occurred successively, even if rather intermittently. The feature is very similar to that in the Kanto mountains as shown in Fig. 8. These displacements of the Akaishi and the Kanto areas have resulted from the gliding of the upper crust on the lower crust or on the upper mantle (Kimura 1967).

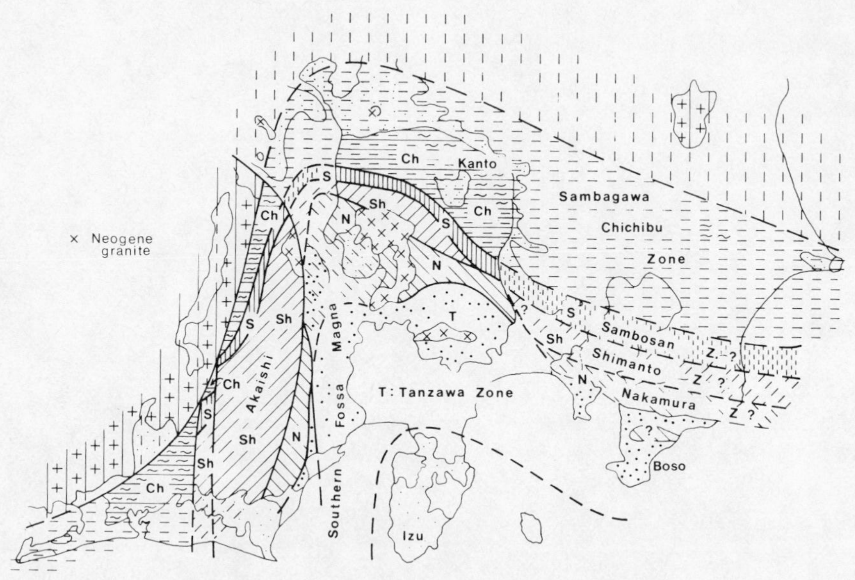

Fig. 8 Tectonic map of southern central Japan.

At the same time as the displacements of the Akaishi and Kanto, the main part of Northeast Japan rotated anti-clockwise as shown from palaeomagnetic data (Kawai *et al.* 1961) and advanced toward the Pacific along a right-lateral strike-slip fault, the Kanto tectonic line (Kobayashi 1941). This great advance of Northeast Japan may be related to the presence of oceanic crust in the north-eastern part of the Japan Sea, although we have little evidence for any corresponding advance of Southwest Japan, at least the western part of it.

In Neogene time, marked volcanism occurred in the zone parallel to the new island arc system. The new system thus became clearly outlined from south to north by the distribution of the volcanic products. However, the Neogene geosyncline and fold zone from the Tanzawa mountains to the Boso peninsula in the southern-most part of Northeast Japan run from west to east—a trend almost at right angles to the trend of the new system. Why does such an E-W trending deformation zone occur within the N-S trending major system? The Neogene volcanism is closely related to the new, *deep-seated* N-S trending system. It may well be that within the upper crustal part were remnants of masses which had been produced by the earth movements in the older system. This inhomogeneity in the upper crustal part may have produced the E-W trending structures, even where movements of the new N-S trending system were taking place. In contrast, the phenomena directly related to the deep-seated agencies, such as the volcanism, developed especially well along the new system.

SUMMARY

There were several eugeosynclines in Southwest Japan: the Silurian-Middle Permian Chichibu, Upper Permian-Triassic Sambosan, Upper Jurassic-Cretaceous Shimanto, Palaeogene Nakamura and Neogene eugeosynclines. Among them the Chichibu is primary and the others are secondary. These eugeosynclinal areas migrated toward the ocean, but have been changed later into miogeosynclinal areas, zones of strong deformation and metamorphism, and later still into zones of block movements. The zones of different kinds of deformation have migrated toward the ocean in accord with the migration of the eugeosynclines.

The migration of eugeosynclines and deformation zones can well be explained by the intermittent retreat of a subduction zone. However, the Chichibu geosyncline was widely underlain by a sialic layer and the rocks in these eugeosynclines were not those carried into the subduction zone by movements of the oceanic plate.

The migration of the eugeosynclines became obscure in Early Cretaceous time in Northeast Japan. Earth movements along the new island arc system of Northeast Japan-Bonin-Mariana began at least in Early Cretaceous time and became obvious in the Neogene, due to the marked volcanism of that time. The superposition of the younger island arc system on the older can be well observed in central Japan as in Northeast Japan.

REFERENCES

Hashimoto, I. 1961. Stratigraphic sequence and geologic structure in the neighbourhood of Nobeoka city, Miyazaki Prefecture. *Rept. Earth Sci., Dept General Educ., Kyushu Univ.* **7,** 37-57 (in Japanese).

Igo, H. 1961. On the disconformity and aluminaceous shales of the Carboniferous Ichinotani formation, Hida massif. *J. geol. Soc. Japan*, **67,** 261-73 (in Japanese).

Kanmera, K. 1971. Palaeozoic and early Mesozoic geosynclinal volcanicity in Japan. *Mem. geol. Soc. Japan*, **6,** 97-110 (in Japanese).

Kanmera, K. & Nakazawa, K. 1968. Review of the history and present status of studies on the Mesozoic and Palaeozoic systems, and some problems of geosynclines in Japan. *Geological Sciences in Japan—Past, Present and Future*, 33-57 (in Japanese). Geol. Soc. Japan (75th Anniv. vol.).

Kawai, N., Ito, H. & Kume, S. 1961. Deformation of the Japanese islands as inferred from rock magnetism. *Geophys. J. R. astr. Soc.* **6,** 124-9.

Kimura, T. 1960. On the geologic structure of the Palaeozoic group in Chugoku, West Japan. *Sci. Papers Coll. General Educ., Univ. Tokyo*, **10,** 109-24.

——— 1961*a*. The Akaishi tectonic line, in the eastern part of Southwest Japan. *Jap. J. Geol. Geogr.* **32,** 119-36.

——— 1961*b*. The lateral faulting and geologic structure of the eastern part of Southwest Japan. *Jap. J. Geol. Geogr.* **32,** 317-30.

Kimura, T. 1967. Structural division of Japan and the Honshu Arc. *Jap. J. Geol. Geogr.* **38,** 117-31.

——— 1968. Some folded structures and their distribution in Japan. *Jap. J. Geol. Geogr.* **39,** 1-26.

——— 1969. The phases and cycles of the orogenic movements. *J. Geogr., Tokyo,* **78,** 299-340 (in Japanese).

Kimura, T. & Tokuyama, A. 1971. Geosynclinal prisms and tectonics in Japan. *Mem. geol. Soc. Japan,* **6,** 9-20.

Kimura, T., Tokuyama, A., Gonzales, B. A. & Andal, D. R. 1968. Geologic structures in the Tayabas Isthmus district, Philippines. *Geology and Palaeontology of Southeast Asia.* **4,** 156-78. Tokyo Univ. Press.

Kobayashi, T. 1941. The Sakawa orogenic cycles and its bearing on the origin of the Japanese Islands. *J. Fac. Sci. Tokyo Univ.* **5,** 219-578.

——— 1956*a*. A contribution to the geo-tectonics of North Korea and South Manchuria. *J. Fac. Sci. Tokyo Univ.* **10,** 133-311.

——— 1956*b*. The shifting of the chert bearing facies caused by the migration of geosyncline. *Konikl. Nederland. Geol. Mijinb. Genoot. Verh.* **16,** 1-11.

Kobayashi, T., Hujita, A. & Kimura, T. 1945. On the geology of the central part of southern Shikoku. *Jap. J. Geol. Geogr.* **20,** 19-45.

Koike, K., Watanabe, K. & Igo, H. 1970. Triassic conodont biostratigraphy in Japan. *J. geol. Soc. Japan,* **76,** 261-9 (in Japanese).

Konishi, K. 1965. Geotectonic framework of the Ryukyu Islands (Nansei-Shoto). *J. geol. Soc. Japan,* **71,** 437-57 (in Japanese).

Matsuda, T. & Uyeda, S. 1971. On the Pacific-type orogeny and its model—extension of the paired belts concept and possible origin of marginal seas. *Tectonophysics,* **11,** 5-27.

Matsumoto, T. (Ed.) 1953. *The Cretaceous system in the Japanese Islands.* Japan Soc. Promotion Sci., Tokyo.

——— 1964. On the age of the geosynclinal volcanism. *Sci Rep. Fac. Sci. Kyushu Univ., Geol.* **7,** 149-59 (in Japanese).

——— 1968. Bibliography of geochronological data in Japan. *Jap. J. Geol. Geogr.* **39,** 1-5.

Matsumoto, T. & Hirata, M. 1969. A new ammonite from the Shimantogawa group of Shikoku. *Trans. Proc. palaeont. Soc. Japan (n.s.),* **76,** 177-84.

Matsushita, S. 1971. *The Kinki district* (in Japanese). Asakura Shoten Co., Tokyo.

Minato, M., Gorai, M. & Hunahashi, M. 1965. *The geologic development of the Japanese Islands.* Tsukiji Shokan Co., Tokyo.

Miyashiro, A. & Haramura, H. 1962. Chemical composition of Palaeozoic slates. *J. geol. Soc. Japan,* **68,** 75-82 (in Japanese).

Murata, M. & Sugimoto, M. 1971. Late Triassic conodonts from the northern part of the Kitakami massif, Northeast Japan. *J. geol. Soc. Japan,* **77,** 393-4 (in Japanese).

Nakazawa, K. 1958. The Triassic system in the Maizuru zone, Southwest Japan. *Mem. Coll. Sci. Kyoto Univ.* Ser. B, **24,** 265-313.

Ono, A. 1969. Geology of the Ryoke metamorphic belt in the Takato-Shiojiri area, Nagano Prefecture. *J. geol. Soc. Japan,* **75,** 491-8.

Onuki, Y. 1969. Geology of the Kitakami massif, Northeast Japan. *Contr. Inst. Geol. Paleont. Tohoku Univ.* **69,** 1-239 (in Japanese).

Sawamura, K., Sumi, K. & Ono, K. 1970. Geology of the Shimoda district (in Japanese), with a sheet map; 1:50,000. *Geological Survey, Japan.*

Shibata, K., Adachi, M. & Mizutani, S. 1971. Precambrian rocks in the Permian conglomerate from central Japan. *J. geol. Soc. Japan,* **77,** 507-14.

Shuto, T. 1963. Geology of the Nichinan area. *Sci. Rep. Fac. Sci. Kyushu Univ.* **6,** 135-66 (in Japanese).

Sugisaki, R., Mizutani, S., Adachi, M., Hattori, H. & Tanaka, T. 1971. Rifting in the Japanese late Palaeozoic geosyncline. *Nature* (*Phys. Sci.*), **233,** 30.

Takeuchi, H. & Uyeda, S. 1965. A possibility of present-day regional metamorphism. *Tectonophysics*, **2,** 59-68.

Tamura, M. 1961. The Torinosu series and fossils therein. *Jap. J. Geol. Geogr.* **32,** 219-77.

Tamura, M. & Harada, S. 1971. Some molluscan fossils from the Shimanto terrain of Kyushu, Japan. *Mem. Fac. Educ., Kumamoto Univ.* **19,** 44-8 (in Japanese).

Tokuoka, T. 1967. The Shimanto terrain in the Kii peninsula, Southwest Japan—with special reference to its geological development viewed from coarser clastic sediments. *Mem. Fac. Sci. Kyoto Univ., ser. Geol. & Min.* **34** (1), 35-74.

Tokuyama, Z. 1962. Triassic and some other orogenic sediments of the Akiyoshi cycle in Japan. *J. Fac. Sci. Tokyo Univ.* Sec. 2, **8,** 379-469.

Wunderlich, H. G. 1966. *Wesen und Ursachen der Gebirgsbildung.* Mannheim.

Yoshida, S. 1971. Significance of *Faltenspiegels* in analysing folds. *J. geol. Soc. Japan*, **77,** 295-300 (in Japanese).

The Structural Relation of the Island of Taiwan with the Ryukyu Island Arc

CHAO-YI MENG

Chinese Petroleum Corporation, 83 Chung Hwa Road, Taipei, Taiwan, China

ABSTRACT

The origin of the geological structures of the island of Taiwan has to be sought in two different regions. The long, narrow Coastal Range of eastern Taiwan, bordering the Pacific Ocean, belongs to the oceanic crust and appears to have been elevated between two major fault systems. Other structures, west of the Longitudinal Rift Valley fault of eastern Taiwan, are assignable to the continental crust and involve the pre-Tertiary metamorphic complex, the folded slightly metamorphosed Palaeogene formations of the Central Range, and the strong and gentle folds in the area of unmetamorphosed Neogene sediments.

As a result of the subduction of oceanic crust and horizontal movements, the deep-seated older formations of the continental crust west of the Longitudinal Rift Valley fault were elevated and distorted and are now represented by the metamorphic rock complex of the Central Range. The combination of compressional stresses and horizontal displacements along fault lines resulted in strongly folded Tertiary formations and numerous over-lapping thrust sheets. During orogenic movements of western Taiwan, folds were developed perpendicular to the east-west trending abutment of the Peikang basement high.

The surface structural trends of the island of Taiwan are essentially north-south; however, recent aeromagnetic data over the Taiwan Strait shows features trending NE-SW or east-west. Thus, it seems that present Taiwan Island structural trends are superimposed or overprinted on a general east-west trend.

The north-south trending structural features of the island lie between the NE-SW trending Ryukyu Island Arc and its extension, the east-west trending basement high (under Peikang, the Penghu Islands, and the Formosan Bank) so producing a very complex structural intersection. It is concluded that the north-south trending structure of the island is of late origin (beginning with the elevation of the Central Range) and that it interrupts or breaks the former westward and south-westward extension of the Ryukyu Arc (Old Ryukyu Arc) now represented by the relict Peikang basement high.

According to age determinations of core samples taken near the Mariana Trench on the east edge of the Philippine Sea on Leg V, Leg VI, and Leg VII of the Deep Sea Drilling Project (DSDP) of 1969, undertaken by the Scripps Institution on the drilling vessel *Glomar Challenger*, the samples from the Philippine Sea Basin appear assignable to Eocene to Oligocene; the age of samples from east of the Mariana Trench indicate

Jurassic or older, the oldest of all bottom samples taken from the entire Pacific (Scripps 1970). These important data, so pertinent to the plate tectonic theory, are found on the Philippine Sea Plate which is adjacent to the island of Taiwan and should be worthy of special consideration in future global tectonic investigations.

The Philippine Basin, with the Japan Trench, the Izu Trench, and the Mariana Trench as its eastern boundary and the Ryukyu Trench, the Taiwan Trough, and the Philippine Trench as its western boundary, may be considered a single plate. The activities of this plate could well influence the origin and history of Taiwan (Katsumata & Sykes 1969).

THE RELATION BETWEEN THE ISLAND ARCS AND THE MARGINAL DEEP SEA TRENCH

Data relating to the oceanic geology of the North-west Pacific are minimal up to the present. Studies of how the origin of island arcs is related to plate tectonics depend mostly on the distribution of deep and shallow foci of earthquakes. For example, earth fractures as determined by the distribution of earthquake foci in the Izu Trench and the Mariana Trench on the eastern edge of the Philippine Plate both dip to the west; similarly, the deep foci near the Ryukyu Trench on the western edge of the plate indicate that this fracture also dips west toward the continent (Katsumata & Sykes 1969).

The distribution of earthquake foci below the deep sea trough east of Taiwan is limited to shallow depths; however, a limited number of deep foci have been recorded near the east coast. The dip of this fracture is decidedly different from that indicated by earthquake foci below the Ryukyu Arc. This is a point to be considered when the origin of the island of Taiwan is treated.

The explanation for the origin of island arcs according to the plate tectonic theory, requires subduction in the deep sea trench adjacent to the island arc. 'Subduction' is also called 'consumption', that is, the oceanic crust is squeezed under a deep sea trench and consumed (Dietz & Holden 1970). For subduction to occur, the oceanic crust must exert compression on the island arc in a direction perpendicular to the strike of the arc, that is, the oceanward side of the arc should be the side receiving the stronger compressional forces. The compressive force sustained is similar to conditions shown in the paper by Katsumata and Sykes: the direction of the compressive force sustained by the Ryukyu Arc is perpendicular to its strike. The direction of the compressive force sustained by the east side of Taiwan, however, is generally toward the north, perpendicular to the NE-SW extension of the Peikang basement high which was connected with the present Ryukyu Arc to form the Old Ryukyu Arc, whose trench differed from the orientation of the present arc.

POSITION OF TAIWAN ON THE MARGIN OF THE PACIFIC

Taiwan is a spindle-shaped large island on the margin of the North-west Pacific, with a north-south length of 380 km and an east-west maximum width of 140 km. On the west it is separated from the eastern edge of continental China by the Taiwan Strait of 200 km width. Among the island arcs that fringe the North-west Pacific, Taiwan is the largest island nearest the Asiatic continent and its northern extremity is the only place where an island arc contacts the continental shelf of the East China Sea. Thus, this island is closely related to the continent of Asia (Fig. 1).

The sea-bottom topography east of Taiwan is very important and shows the Ryukyu Arc, the Okinawa Trough, the Ryukyu Ridge and Trench, arranged concentrically to form an arc system convex to the south-east, but which assumes more of an east-west strike as it approaches Taiwan. The sudden change in direction of the Ryukyu Arc east of Taiwan is the principal factor responsible for the sea bottom topography in this area. With respect to the 2,000 m depth contour, the east-west extension of the Ryukyu Trench turns to a north-south direction off the coast of Taiwan near Hualien (Fig. 1).

The subsea topography around Taiwan and its relation to an underlying basement may now be considered. There are four main aspects to be stressed. First, the trough in the Philippine Sea Basin offshore of eastern Taiwan is very near the coast with almost no intervening continental shelf. This trough is oriented north-south with its northern end cutting at right angles across the Ryukyu Arc. The southern extension of this trench along a bathymetrically low belt should be traceable to the Luzon Trough lying west of Luzon Island. The movement accounting for the origin of this trough must be the source of the main and greatest stress that initiated the rising of Taiwan. This point will be considered later.

Along this trough, east of Taiwan, there are several volcanic islets aligned: from north to south, Agincourt Island, Kueishantao, Lutao, Lanju. These islets were found to have total magnetic intensity anomalies in the aeromagnetic survey conducted by U.S. Naval Oceanographic Office 'Project Magnet' in the seas around Taiwan in 1968 (Fig. 2). From such magnetic anomalies it can be concluded that there must be an active structural line along the north-south trough (Bosum *et al.* 1970). Most of the earthquakes around Taiwan occur within this line.

Second, in the sea north of Taiwan, the sea topography is undulating and the shallow bottom directly connects Taiwan with the continental shelf of the East China Sea. An aero-magnetic survey indicates a strong magnetic anomaly not far north of Keelung which might be due to a volcanic chamber beneath the sea bottom. The area around this magnetic anomaly shows a very gentle magnetic gradient which may indicate a thick sedimentary section. Folds interpretable in this area are all oriented east-west.

Third, the Taiwan Strait lies west of the island and is shallow (20 fathoms) in its northern half, but the southern half is composed of a basement high, extending NE-SW, reflected by the Penghu Islands at its north-east end and the Formosan Bank at its south-western extremity. Between the Penghu Islands and the west coast of Taiwan, the Penghu water-channel extends north-south and widens toward the south, with its steep slope on its west side and forming the eastern edge of the Formosan Bank. This water-channel continues further south into the South China Sea.

Fourth, the total magnetic intensity map surveyed by 'Project Magnet' in 1968

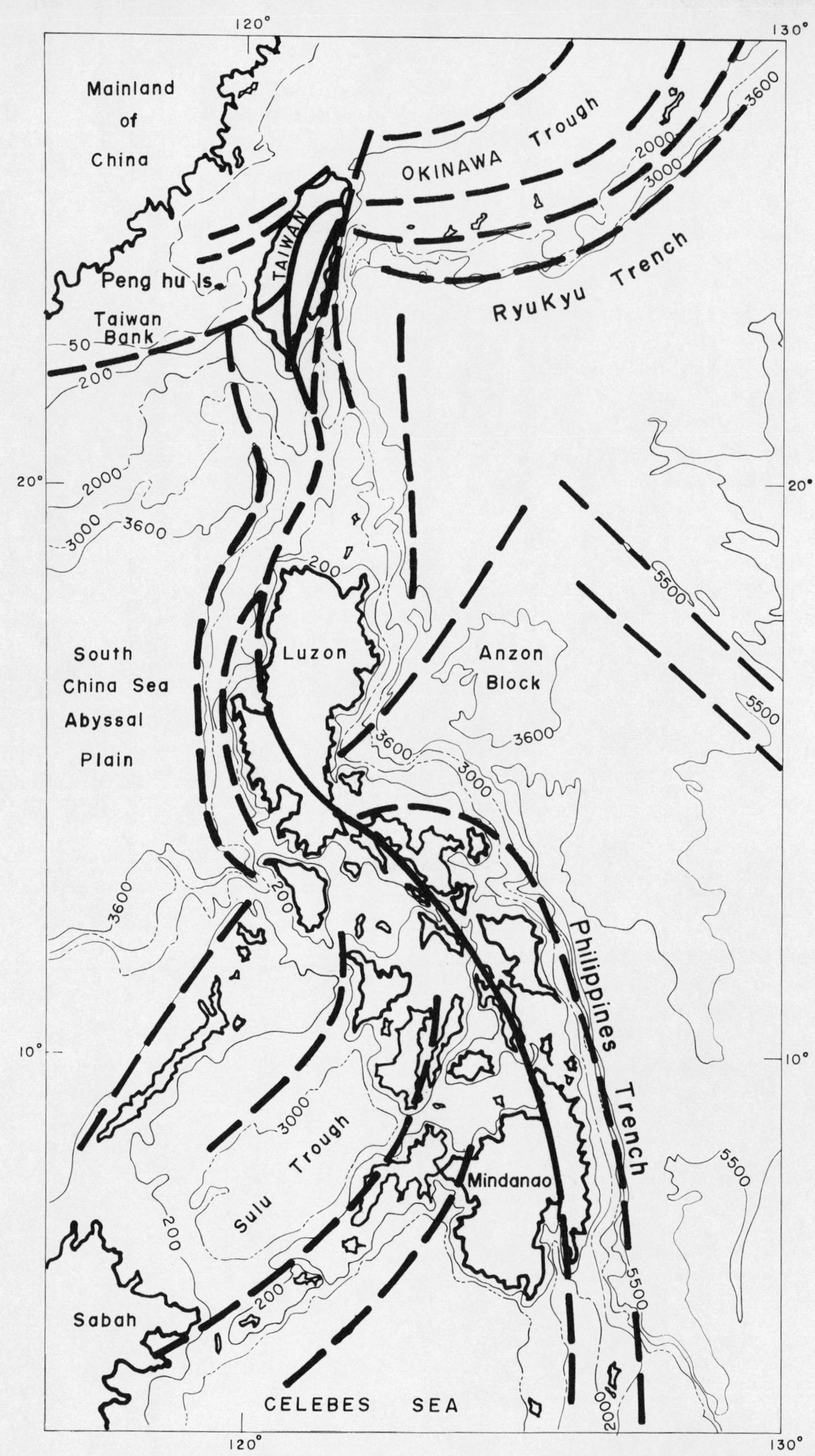
120°
130°
Mainland
of
China
OKINAWA Trough
TAIWAN
Peng hu Is.
Taiwan
Bank
RyuKyu Trench
50
200
2000
3000
3600
20°
South
China Sea
Abyssal
Plain
Luzon
Anzon
Block
5500
Philippines
Trench
10°
Sulu Trough
Mindanao
Sabah
CELEBES SEA
120°
130°

shows that the Peikang basement high extends through the Penghu Islands (Fig. 2). Before the magnetic and gravity survey was conducted on the Penghu Islands it was found that the Bouguer gravity values were very high (+70-80 mgals). A stratigraphic test well, the Tungliang TL-1, was then drilled to find that, although all the isles are covered with basalt, drilling shows this basalt to be slightly more than 80 m thick, and underlain by loose Pleistocene and Neogene sediments. Below 500 m, Miocene strata were penetrated. These Neogene sediments rest unconformably on indurated hydrothermally metamorphosed Mesozoic sandstone and shale.

The magnetic anomaly from the Penghu Islands to the Formosan Bank is shown on the total magnetic intensity map (Fig. 2) and may be interpreted as a NE-SW trending basement high. The trough indicated by the bathymetric chart south of the Formosan Bank may reflect a fault scarp extending eastward to north of Tainan on the coastal plain of Taiwan and so joining the Yichu Fault, or Fault A, discovered from land seismic survey investigations (Fig. 1). The gravity anomaly of the Penghu Islands coincides with the magnetic anomaly and joins with the gravity anomaly indicating the basement high at Peikang. The extension of the ridge-forming basement high in a NE-SW direction from Peikang through the Penghu Islands to the Formosan Bank plays an important role in the development of the structure of western Taiwan.

Based on seismic data, the Paochung PC-1 well was drilled on the Peikang basement high. At 1,677 m below sea-level, this well penetrated indurated, slightly hydrothermally altered quartz porphyry underlain by altered basalt, conglomerate, protoquartzite, subgreywacke, arkose, siltstone, and limestone (Lee 1962). Comparing the strata drilled at Peikang with those encountered in the Tungliang TL-1 well in the Penghu Islands, the stratigraphic position of the latter is higher (Chou 1969).

CONSIDERATION OF THE OLD RYUKYU ARC

It is reasonable to connect the south-western end of the present Ryukyu Arc with the NE-SW or ENE-WSW arc and explain the north-south structural trends perpendicular to this arc as developing during a later movement. This point is not only deducible from the morphological point of view but can be verified from the structural development and palaeogeography.

Deductions from structural development: the surface geologic structures of Taiwan are very young, originating from the Pliocene to as late as the Quaternary and even Recent. Sediments of the Pliocene and post-Pliocene came mostly from the Central Range, thus showing that the present north-south trending structures of the island were deformed subsequent to the Miocene.

Deductions from palaeogeography: in the Tertiary section of western Taiwan, the most prominent lithologic difference occurs between the Miocene sediments of northern and southern Taiwan. In northern Taiwan, the Miocene sediments came

---

Fig. 1 Delineation of the structural trends in the Ryukyu-Taiwan-Philippine area, based on bathymetrical charts of the North Pacific

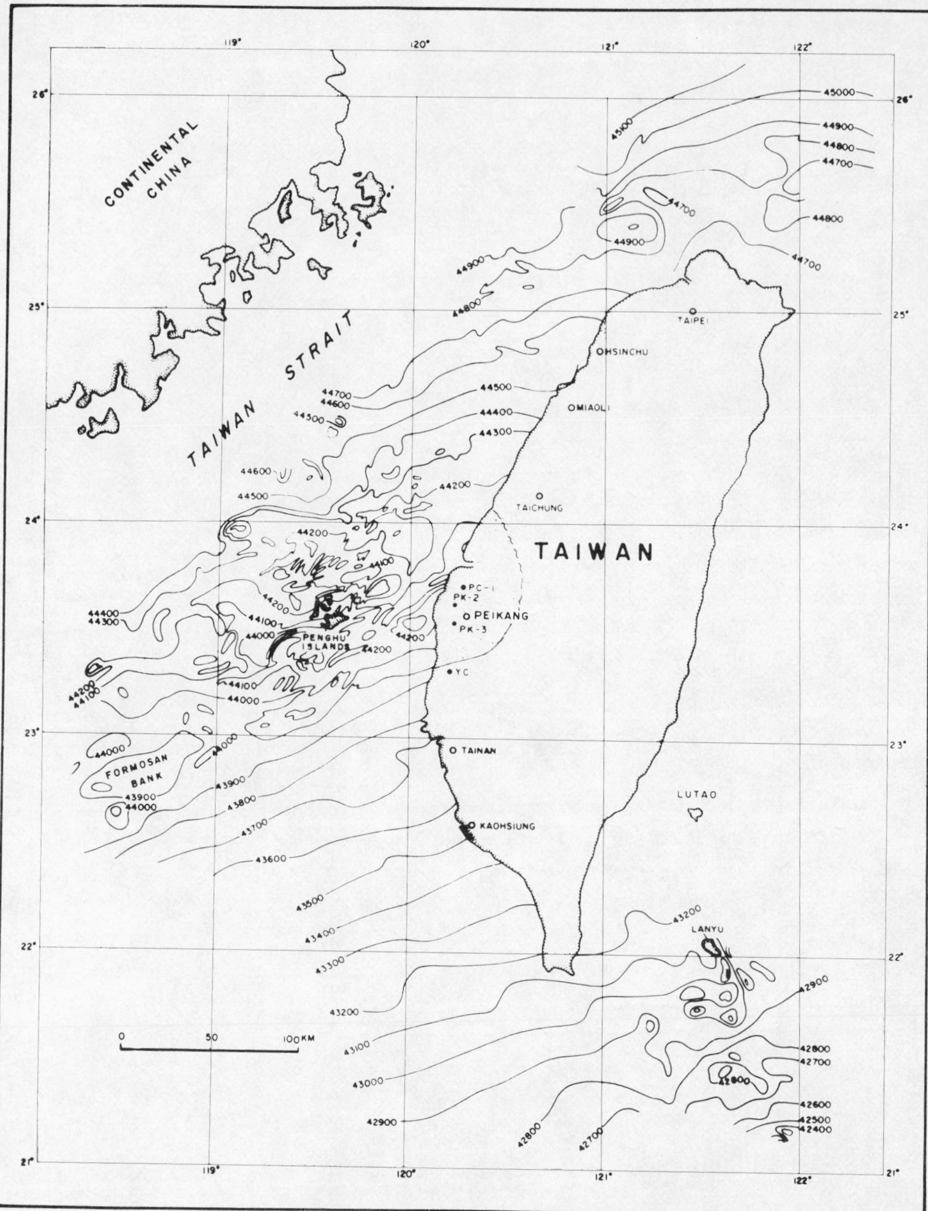

Fig. 2 The total magnetic intensity map of Taiwan Strait in relation to the Peikang Basement High of western Taiwan

from the Chinese mainland and consist of coarse sandstone, coal beds, and alternating deep and shallow marine deposits. In southern Taiwan (south of the Penghu-Peikang basement high) the Miocene sediments consist essentially of mudstone and siltstone.

This difference in sediments of the same age is believed due to the sorting effect of the basement barrier that must have existed during the Miocene and before the north-south trending structures of the island of Taiwan came into existence (Meng 1970) (Fig. 3).

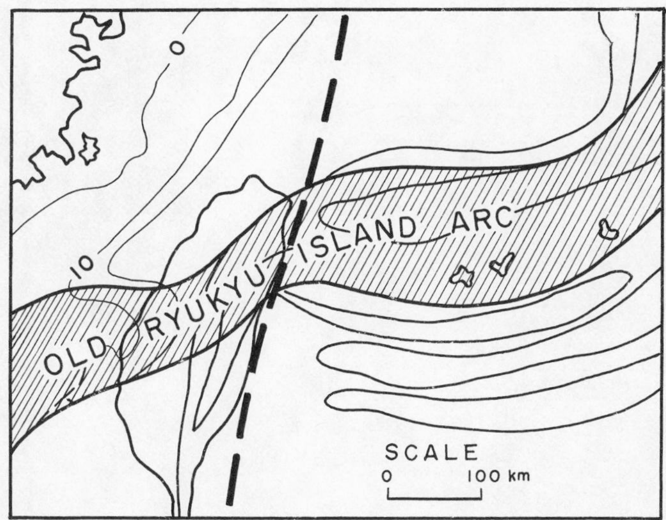

Fig. 3 Hypothetical position of the pre-Pliocene 'Old Ryukyu Island Arc'

Comparison of regional structures: the prominent transcurrent fault of the Philippines runs from Luzon to Mindanao, striking generally north-south. West of this fault, there is a series of parallel faults striking NE-SW: from Palawan to Mindoro; from the Sulu Trough to Negros; and from the scarp on the northern edge of the Celebes Sea across the isthmus of Mindanao. These faults differ in character and direction from the main transcurrent fault through the Philippines; all of them terminate before reaching it. This implies that the parallel faults mentioned above are more or less comparable to the Penghu-Peikang basement high termination at the edge of the foothills of western Taiwan. The fact that the Old Ryukyu Arc has an extension south-west to the south of the China mainland and is paralleled by Palawan, the Sulu Trough, and the Sulu Archipelago (all striking NE-SW) is certainly not brought about by chance (Fig. 1).

The original structural lines in the area from present Taiwan to the Philippines were NE-SW; only by the late Cenozoic did the north-south structural trends of the island of Taiwan become dominant. The north-south trends (transecting the NE-SW trends) are due, therefore, to the latest movement. This new movement was perpendicular to the original NE-SW trends and caused Taiwan to elevate at the structural intersection as a prominent island in the North-west Pacific.

The north-south structural lines are not limited to the island of Taiwan but are also reflected in the off-island submarine topography. One of the best examples is the scarp along the edge of the deep trough, east of Taiwan, which attains a depth of 2,200 m. The scarp extends southward to, and eastward of, the island of Bataan, to the Luzon Trough lying east of Luzon. Another north-south structural line beginning on Taiwan as the Longitudinal Valley (from Hualien to Taitung) also extends southward along the steep coast south of Taitung. A structural line extending from the Longitudinal Valley converges with the deep-trough scarp east of Taiwan. Therefore, the Coastal Range of eastern Taiwan may be considered a narrow fault block having a sharp northern end.

MOVEMENTS BEFORE AND DURING THE ELEVATION OF TAIWAN

The island of Taiwan was not elevated prior to the Pliocene. On the continental margin and off the coast of China, there existed the extension of the Old Ryukyu Arc which crossed the middle part of present Taiwan. The end of this arc near the continent was part of the continental shelf and the portion away from the continent was included within the continental slope.

During and following Pliocene time the oceanic crust on the outer side of the arc pressed northward or north-westward, thus accounting for the east-west or NE-SW fold trends on the continental shelf.

Beginning in Pliocene time, movement occurred along a north-south fracture that intersected the Old Ryukyu Arc. The oceanic crust east of this fracture also moved westward to elevate a narrow strip which now constitutes the Coastal Range of eastern Taiwan. Most of the oceanic crust was subducted under the continental crust, and along the fault trace between the continental crust and the subducted oceanic crust the Longitudinal Valley of eastern Taiwan gradually developed. The subducted oceanic crust plunged below the Longitudinal Valley and pressed against the continental plate to form the major portion of the island of Taiwan west of the Longitudinal Valley.

REGIONAL STRUCTURES OF THE ISLAND OF TAIWAN

The structural development stages of the island of Taiwan are discussed separately (Figs 4-6).

The Coastal Range of eastern Taiwan (A): the Coastal Range mass, consisting mainly of sediments derived from a Pacific Ocean source area, extends under the major thrust resulting from compression by sea-floor spreading. Just east of the thrust trace the sediments are intensely folded and intruded by various igneous rocks.

The Longitudinal Valley of eastern Taiwan (*major thrust*) (T): the block west of the major thrust was forced by the later subduction action to rise along the thrust plane; and the block east of this major thrust, which includes the Coastal Range, plunges under and along the thrust plane.

The pre-Tertiary metamorphic complex on the eastern flank of the Central Range

(B_1): the eastern flank of the Central Range, a belt of complex pre-Palaeogene intensely metamorphosed rocks, is interpreted as deep-seated geosynclinal material that was squeezed to the surface by plastic flow and metamorphosed during later developmental stage of the geosyncline.

The slightly metamorphosed Palaeogene formations of the Central Range (B_2): the west flank of the Central Range, composed of slightly metamorphosed rocks, is

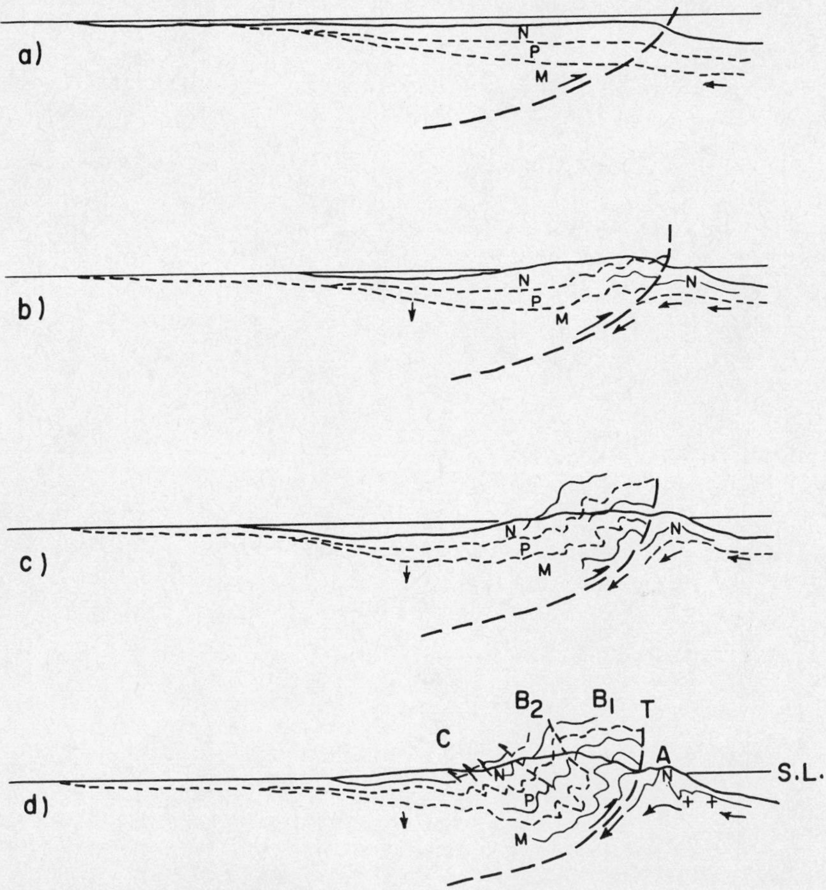

Fig. 4 Sections showing stages in the development of a geosyncline along a continental margin: (a) original position of the low-angle marginal thrust; (b) steepening of the thrust plane as crowding continues; upthrown block warps down and initiates a geosyncline on the continental side; (c) outer margin of upthrown block emerges as newborn islands which supply material for filling the geosyncline; and (d) horizontal compression from crowding causes downwarp of the basement below the geosyncline basin, while the island arc continues to emerge. M, Mesozoic and older rocks; P, Palaeogene rocks ; N, Neogene sediments; for A, T, B1, B2, and C, see text.

interpreted as deep-seated geosynclinal material that was squeezed out during an earlier stage of plastic flow.

The Neogene formations in western Taiwan (C): the western half of Taiwan involves a post-Miocene geosyncline. Although compression-crumpled and shattered in a sedimentary zone close to the Central Range, the folding further west is more gentle and favourable for gas and oil accumulation. The pre-Pliocene structures of Taiwan are overlain by the structures resulting from younger orogenic movements but may still be recognized by geophysical surveys and well drilling. Younger orogenic movements on the island of Taiwan extend westward in the Taiwan Strait but they are of such minor intensity that the structural trends as now recognized probably represent pre-Pliocene movements. Only further investigations can decide this question.

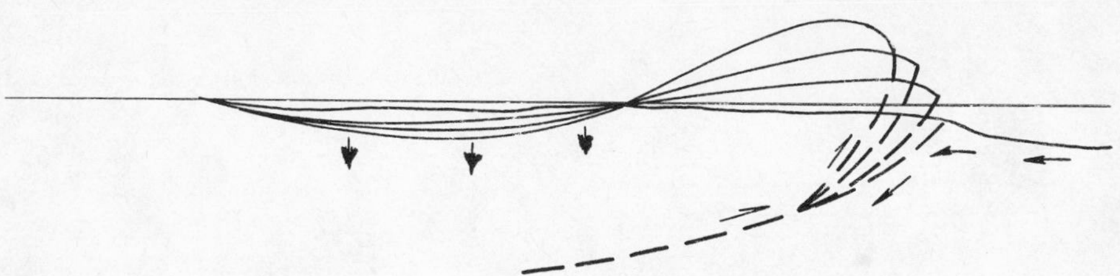

Fig. 5 The cyclic movement of uplift and subsidence along the thrust plane in between the geanticline and the geosyncline.

CONCLUSIONS

1. Before the island of Taiwan originated after the Miocene, the south-western extension of the Old Ryukyu Arc extended through the present position of Taiwan along the Peikang basement high to the Penghu Islands and the Formosan Bank. This arc formed a tectonic dam which blocked the coarser sediments from mainland China. The finer clastics flowed over it and were deposited outside as mudstone and siltstone. This grade-size difference is shown in the Miocene sediments of the northern half and southern half of western Taiwan.

2. After Miocene time there developed a north-south trending earth fracture zone on the west side of the Philippine Basin. The oceanic crustal plate, east of this zone, exerted pressure westward and perpendicular to the fracture, and moved northward along the fracture. The island of Taiwan was gradually folded and elevated because of these two plate movements.

3. Taiwan's origin is attributable to the deeper parts of the oceanic crust being subducted, a process which raised the continental crust, west of the fracture zone, and this in turn gradually became the Central Range of the island. This subduction caused deeply buried formations to undergo pressure and metamorphism and later thrust them to the west. The westward thrusting against the Palaeogene formations

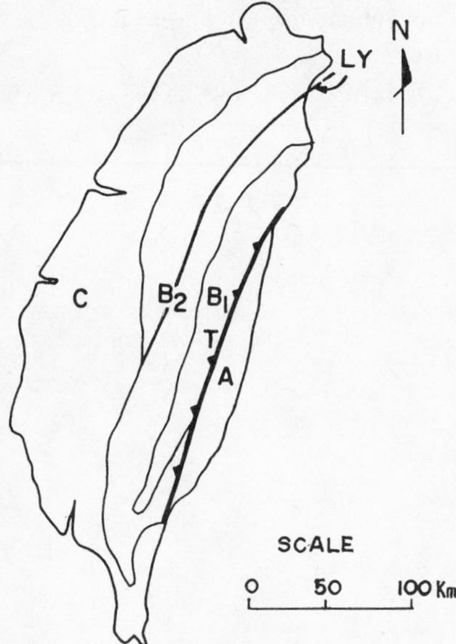

Fig. 6 Sketch of major tectonic elements of the island of Taiwan resulting from orogenic movements after the end of Miocene time. For description of elements A, T, B1, B2, and C, see text.

caused slight metamorphism of these deposits and folded and faulted Neogene formations still further west.

4. In the middle of western Taiwan, and underlying the Neogene formations, is the Penghu to Peikang basement high—a remnant of the Old Ryukyu Arc. When the Neogene formations were subjected to horizontal compression toward the west and also sheared northward by the lateral movement of the Palaeogene formations, deformations varied due to the presence of this basement high.

5. The structural fabric in the Taiwan Strait was little effected by orogenic movements of Taiwan. Surveys of the strait area have just been initiated and interesting results are expected.

6. The Pacific to the east of Taiwan should be an area where many neotectonic problems of the moving western Pacific may be recognized. New information on this area will help not only in understanding the tectonic framework of Taiwan but will also be a contribution to problems affecting current plate tectonic hypotheses.

REFERENCES

Bosum, W. *et al.* 1970. Aero-magnetic survey of offshore Taiwan. *Econ. Comm. Asia & Far East (ECAFE), CCOP, Tech. Bull.* **3,** 1-34. Bangkok.

Chou, J. T. 1969. A petrographic study of the Mesozoic and Cenozoic rock formations in the Tungliang well TL-1 of the Penghu Island, Taiwan, China. *Econ. Comm. Asia & Far East*

(ECAFE), CCOP, Tech. Bull. **2,** 97-115. Bangkok.

Dietz, R. S. & Holden, J. C. 1970. The break-up of Pangaea. *Scient. Am.* **223,** 30-41.

Katsumata, M. & Sykes, L. R. 1969. Seismicity and tectonics of the western Pacific-Izu-Mariana-Caroline and Ryukyu-Taiwan regions. *J. geophys. Res.* **74.** (25), 5923-48.

Lee, P. J. 1962. Mesozoic and Cenozoic rocks of the Paochung well, Yunlin, Taiwan. *Petrol. Geol. Taiwan,* **1,** 75-86.

Meng, C. Y. 1970. A conception of the revolution of the island of Taiwan and its bearing on the development of the Neogene sedimentary basins on its western side. *Econ. Comm. Asia & Far East (ECAFE), CCOP, Tech. Bull.* **3,** 109-26. Bangkok.

Scripps Institution of Oceanography, University of California 1970. *Deep sea drilling project.* News releases.

On Fitting Certain Geological and Geophysical Features of the Indonesian Island Arc to the New Global Tectonics

John A. Katili

Indonesian Institute of Sciences and Bandung Institute of Technology, Djl. Teuku Tjhik Ditiro No. 43, Djakarta, Indonesia

ABSTRACT

The new global tectonics depicts the Indonesian island arcs as the area of interaction between three crustal blocks, the Indian-Australian, the Pacific and the Eurasian plates.

The boundaries of these plates are of a trench and strike-slip fault type west of Sumatra, a trench type south of Java, a strike-slip fault type north of New Guinea and a trench and strike-slip fault type east of the Philippines. The Great Sumatran, the Celebes and Philippine Faults accommodate the south-south-eastward motion of the Eurasian plate, while the Sumatra-Java Trench accommodates the northward motion of the Indian-Australian plate. The Sorong fault-zone in New Guinea and the Philippine Trench accommodate the westward movement of the Pacific plate.

The transition of major strike-slip into large dip-slip faults as observed in the Sumatra-Java arc, the Philippine-Talaud-Halmahera region, the area of central and south Celebes and the region between New Guinea and east Celebes is also in harmony with the postulated north-south and east-west directed regional stress.

Complex overthrust structures and strongly elevated coral reefs of Timor, could be related to the northward drift of Australia.

The peculiar shape of Celebes and Halmahera and the loop-shaped Banda arc, are the result of the northward drift of the Australian continent combined with the westward thrust of the Pacific plate.

Sumatra is characterized by the presence of large active, strike-slip faults, an abundance of Quaternary welded tuff deposits, low volcanic activity during the present time and an absence of deep earthquakes east of this island.

Java on the other hand, typically displays such features as increasing potash content of the andesitic volcanoes towards the hinterland, high volcanic activity, few ignimbrite deposits, deep earthquakes north of this island, and the absence of major transcurrent faults.

This slight discrepancy in the geological and geophysical phenomena of parts of the Sumatra-Java arc, situated north-west and east of Krakatau volcano, respectively, may be partly explained by differential northward movement of the Indian-Australian plate. It is further assumed that the crustal plate presently descending in the Sumatra Trench is at an evolutionary stage which differs from the one descending in the Java Trench, and that past magmatic zones in West Indonesia had a different arrangement.

The apparent irregular zonal arrangement of the active magmatic belt relative to past magmatic zones in Sumatra and Java is due to the difference in dips of the present Benioff zone as compared with the Tertiary and Mesozoic dip.

Temporal changes of location and differing direction and rate of dip of Benioff zones, as well as the existence of parallel opposing subduction zones may be responsible for the complex geological and geophysical features of the Indonesian island arcs.

Other fundamental tectonic problems could be better understood by supposing an interaction of smaller plates in the eastern part of Indonesia.

INTRODUCTION

Since the turn of this century many European geologists have tried to construct small-scale tectonic maps of the Indonesian Archipelago. The tectonic maps and theories have been critically reviewed by Kuenen (1935), Westerveld (1949), Klompe (1957) and Katili (1971). In particular, the theories put forward by Wegener (1922), Smith Sibinga (1933) and Kraus (1951) were ahead of their time, and although they can no longer be fully accepted, such ideas as continental drift and undercurrent processes (now termed subduction or underflow) nevertheless constitute a part of the fundamental basis of the new global or plate tectonics.

This modern concept has been applied to Indonesia by Fitch (1970) and Fitch and Molnar (1970) with respect to seismology, and Hatherton and Dickinson (1969) discussed the petrology of the active volcanoes of Indonesia in relation to the inclined Benioff seismic zone.

Hamilton (1970) discussed how a plate tectonic model could be used as a base to construct a geotectonic map of Indonesia and briefly interprets the evolution of New Guinea, Celebes and Java in terms of plate tectonics.

It is the purpose of this paper to discuss in more detail the geological and geophysical features of the Indonesian island arcs, the Tertiary and pre-Tertiary geology of West Indonesia and approach its problems along similar lines. The difficulties encountered in applying the plate tectonic concept to Indonesia will also be discussed and suggestions will be made for future research.

NEOTECTONIC FEATURES AND PLATE BOUNDARIES IN SOUTH-EAST ASIA

Neotectonics of the Indonesian Archipelago are conveniently grouped by Katili and Tjia (1969) into three types comprising uplift and subsidence, warping and folding, and faulting. In the present map (Fig. 1) the trenches, the active volcanoes, the earthquake epicentres and the axis of negative gravity anomaly have been added to the previous neotectonic maps mentioned above.

The oblong Sumatra-Java Trench varies in depth, while its cross-section is that of a broad and shallow asymmetric gorge. The ground plan is usually curved, tapering towards the end. The trench itself is deepest south of Java (7,000 m). The deepest part west of Sumatra is over 5,000 m. The trench is situated close to the belt of strongly negative gravity anomalies and the seismicity is characterized by shallow earthquakes with hypocentres varying between 30 and 100 km. The trench is interrupted south of the island of Sumba but resumes south of Timor and continues eastward as far as the

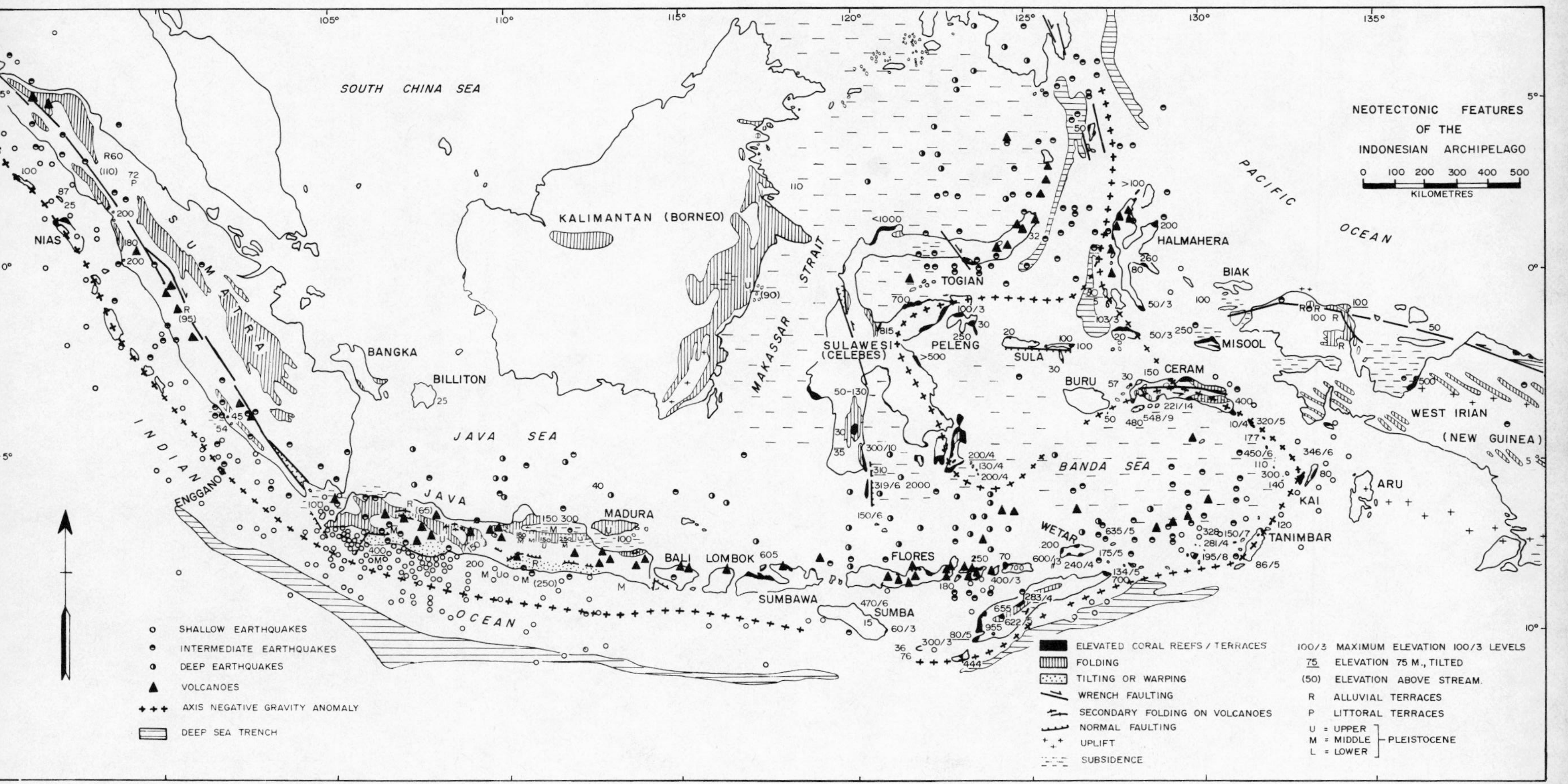

Fig. 1 Neotectonic features of the Indonesian Archipelago

island of Ceram. The break near Sumba could perhaps be ascribed to the presence of a small transform fault. Beside the Philippine Trench, two relatively small trenches east of Minahasa (north Celebes) and west of Halmahera have also been depicted on the map.

Recent volcanoes and the epicentres of deep earthquakes which are located behind the arc, are arranged parallel to the trenches, with some noteworthy deviations.

Dutch geologists had recognized decades ago this systematic relationship of the active tectonic, magmatic and seismic features of Indonesia to the deep submarine trenches. More recently, a number of workers have interpreted various aspects of this system in terms of the plate tectonic theory, e.g. isostatic readjustments (Mitchell & Reading 1971), heat flow and magmatic activity (Oxburgh & Turcotte 1970), lateral variation in the composition of basaltic magmas (Kuno 1966) and K_2O content of volcanics in relation to depths to the Benioff zone (Hatherton & Dickinson 1969).

South of Java, the zone of intense seismic activity (the Benioff zone) has a length exceeding 1,000 km and reaches a maximum depth of 700 km north of Flores. Below the depth of shallow seismicity (0-60 km) a zone of intermediate and deep earthquake dips towards the continent at angles varying between 55° and 70°.

Large transcurrent faults are regional tectonic features prevalent in Southeast Asia. The distribution, physiographic expressions, sense of movements and age of the faulting have been described by Katili (1970). Two groups of large transcurrent faults can be discerned, i.e.: a group trending more or less NW-SE and another one striking approximately east-west. The data presented in that paper tend to support the idea that the Indonesian Archipelago is being protruded south-eastward (Vening Meinesz 1954, Allen 1962, Rodolfo 1969).

The transcurrent nature of the Philippine fault-zone has been described by Allen (1962) using neotectonic evidence. Allen's opinion regarding the Philippine fault-zone has been questioned by some authors. Our experience in the Sumatran fault-zone shows that transcurrent faults in island arcs have a complicated character. Step faulting, movements opposite to the main horizontal motion do frequently occur, albeit on a small scale. As will be seen later, the author supports Allen's opinion that considerable horizontal movement does occur in the Philippines.

The 200 km long NNW-SSE trending Fossa Sarasina in central Celebes has been postulated by Katili (1970) to be a sinistral transcurrent fault. This opinion is supported by a recent investigation carried out in the area by Tjia (pers. comm.). The NNW extension of this fault-zone could be a graben but the bulk of the fault-zone farther to the south-east clearly shows horizontal movement in a sinistral sense (Katili 1971*b*).

Equally strong evidence of dextral horizontal movements has been obtained along the Great Sumatran fault-zone, since the time the author reported his findings at the 11th Pacific Science Congress (Katili & Hehuwat 1967). Aerial photographs covering a distance of about 100 km between Padang Sidempuan and Hutanopan have been analysed and positive right-lateral slip could easily be recognized.

Right lateral motion along certain parts of the Great Sumatran fault-zone may also be inferred from the direction of mountain coulisses, the distribution of granitic bodies and the fold pattern of pre-Tertiary formations, east and south-east of Lake Singkarak (Katili 1971*b*). In his recent field-trip to the Padang Highlands, central Sumatra, Tjia (pers. comm.) observed a buckled bridge near Soemani caused by the heavy 1926 earthquake, demonstrating time and again a right-lateral movement along the fault plane during recent times. Numerous horizontal to sub-horizontal slickensides have also been observed by Tjia along the part of the fault situated between Solok and Alahan Pandjang.

The Sorong fault-zone in West New Guinea as described by Visser & Hermes (1962) is now considered to be a sinistral transform fault between the Tonga-Kermadec and the Philippine submarine trenches (Hamilton 1970). Tjia (pers. comm.) has postulated another sinistral transcurrent fault in the island of Ceram. The Sorong, Sumba, Ceram and probably the Gorontalo fault systems might be considered as belonging to the category of arc to arc transform faults (Wilson 1965).

The neotectonic map of Indonesia prepared by Katili and Tjia (1969), demonstrating the occurrence of large transcurrent faults has been used successfully in delineating plate boundaries in Southeast Asia.

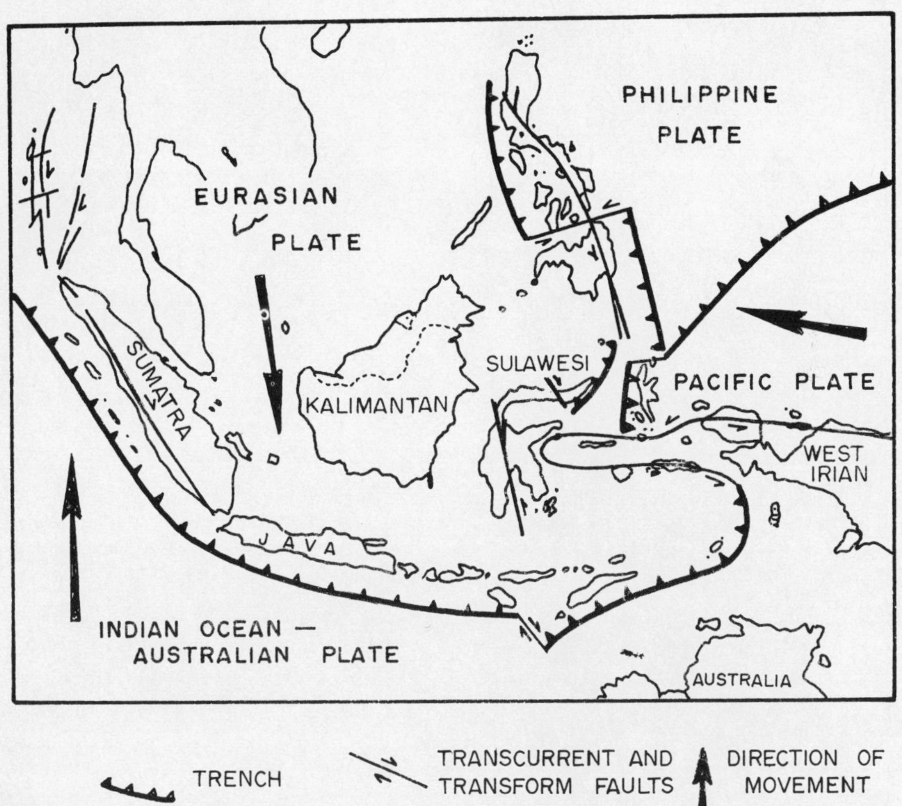

Fig. 2 Present plate boundaries in Southeast Asia

The Sumatra-Java and Timor Trenches accommodate the northward motion of the Indian-Australian plate, while the Philippine Trench accommodates the westward motion of the Pacific plate. The relative motion of Southeast Asia to the south-east is accommodated by the Great Sumatran, Celebes and the Philippine fault-zones.

The physiographic and structural features caused by the interaction of these three gigantic plates and some smaller ones are very complicated. This can be seen on Fig. 2, where the author attempts to delineate the plate boundaries based on our existing structural knowledge of this area. The plate boundaries, defined by Fitch (1970), based on shallow focus seismicity have also been considered in constructing the sketch map. The geology of the eastern part of Indonesia can be understood only by the supposition of interaction of smaller plates.

GEOLOGICAL AND GEOPHYSICAL FEATURES OF WEST INDONESIA, INTERPRETED IN TERMS OF THE PLATE TECTONIC CONCEPT

Following Hamilton (1970) and Dickinson (1971) a plate tectonic model of the Indonesian island arc has been constructed by the author utilizing the excellent

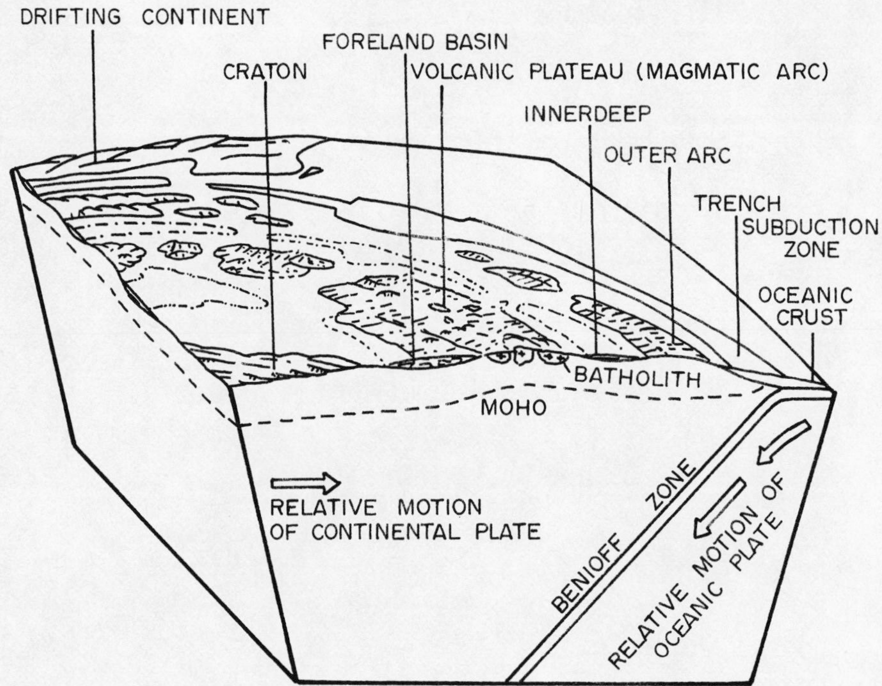

Fig. 3 Plate tectonic model of West Indonesia

scheme of a double island arc drawn by Umbgrove (1949) (Fig. 3).

The structural zones listed in order inland from the trench are: (1) the active subduction zone, (2) the magmatic or volcanic arc, and (3) the foreland basin (Fig. 4). The non-volcanic outer arc and the submarine ridge west of Sumatra and south of Java, respectively, are placed in the arc-trench gap (Dickinson 1971). The characteristic rock assemblage of each belt has been described in detail by Hamilton (1970), Dickinson (1971) and Mitchell and Reading (1971).

The *subduction zone* comprises tectonically chaotic deposits which includes Alpine ultra-mafics, serpentine, gabbro and basalt dominantly of abyssal, tholeiite composition, and also oceanic pelagic sediments consisting of lithified calcareous, siliceous and clayey oozes.

The active *magmatic arc/zone* of Sumatra and Java is marked by intermediate and silicic calcalkaline volcanic products which become systematically more potassic inland. Granitic batholiths, according to Hamilton (1970) are now forming beneath the volcanic belt. Van Bemmelen (1949) has already explained the genesis of the huge

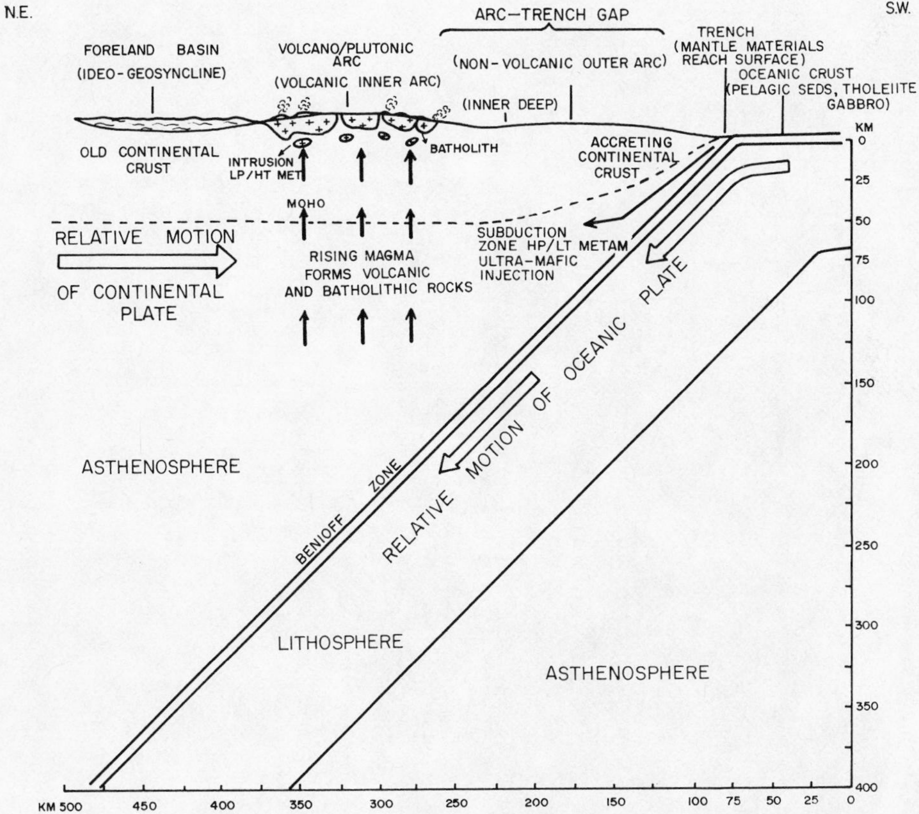

Fig. 4 Diagram indicating relationship of the structural belts to the Benioff zone in the active Indonesian Arc.

Toba ignimbrites of north Sumatra, which occupy an area of 20,000-30,000 square kilometres, in terms of a granitic batholith close to the surface.

The *foreland basin* consists of clastic and volcanogenic sediments derived primarily from the volcanic plateau and formed in a continental or shallow-marine environment.

Using this plate tectonic model we now analyse the Holocene, Tertiary and Mesozoic geology of West Indonesia; many tectonic features can be explained and even predicted.

Although Sumatra and Java are considered a continuous island arc, lateral variations and small discrepancies in the geological and geophysical features occur along this modern arc as demonstrated in the following table.

Table 1

GEOLOGICAL AND GEOPHYSICAL FEATURES OF SUMATRA AND JAVA

Geological and geophysical features	*Sumatra*	*Java*
1. Submarine trench	Max. depth ±5,000 m	Max. depth ±7,000 m
2. Arc-trench gap	Outer island arc	Submarine ridge
3. Volcanic arc	Present	Present
4. Foreland basin	Present	Present
5. Present volcanic activity	Low to intermediate	High
6. Ignimbrites	Abundant	Small occurrence
7. Lateral variation in K_2O content of andesites	Not clear	Very pronounced
8. Shallow and intermediate earthquakes	Present (max. depth 200 km)	Present
9. Deep earthquakes	Not present	Present north of Java (max. depth 700 km)

Sumatra also displays low volcanic activity in comparison with Java and other islands east of Krakatau volcano. Historic paroxysmal eruption accompanied by the formation of calderas are known in Krakatau and Sumbawa but not in Sumatra. These features could be explained by the fact that the dominant tectonic feature in Sumatra is a transcurrent fault while in other islands east of the Krakatau, like Java and the Lesser Sunda islands, dip-slip faults predominate (Tjia 1967).

Volcanism and the depth of seismic activity increase considerably as the structure changes from a predominance of transcurrent faults in Sumatra to largely dip-slip faults in Java and the Lesser Sunda islands. Similar features have already been described by Isacks *et al.* (1968) from the Aleutians, Kamchatka, the Kuril islands and Japan.

Lateral variation in the composition of volcanic rocks, which become systematically potassic in the direction of the hinterland, has been clearly demonstrated in the island of Java (Kuno 1966, Hatherton & Dickinson 1969) but could not be clearly observed in Sumatra. The volcanic belt in Sumatra is relatively smaller than that of Java, and occupies the area bounded by the 200-300 km contour of the inclined Benioff zone.

The model proposed by Hatherton & Dickinson (1969) for andesite production and distribution could very well explain this difference, as earthquake hypocentres deeper than 200 km are not present in Sumatra.

Welded tuff deposits occur abundantly in Sumatra and the deposits around Lake Toba are the largest ignimbrite deposits in this region. In the island of Java and Bali very few acid volcanics occur. This difference could be explained by the fact that the crust in Sumatra is thicker than that of Java. As will be demonstrated later, the plate tectonic model features Sumatra as the location of the Cretaceous, Tertiary and present magmatic arc, while in Java the crust is thinner because of the absence of any Mesozoic magmatic arc. Mitchell and Reading (1971) compare the Sumatra arc to a mountain arc of Andean type.

Isacks *et al.* (1968) have proposed that the deepest earthquakes in a region mark the deepest penetration of a lithosphere and if this assumption is correct the lithosphere appears to have penetrated to a much greater depth east of Krakatau than west of it (Fitch & Molnar 1970). This difference in evolutionary stage of the downgoing slab west of Sumatra and south of Java could thus be held responsible for the discrepancy of the difference in geological and geophysical phenomena described above.

Quaternary and present-day basins which show subsiding tendencies are present along the east coast of Sumatra and the north coast of Java.

Turning to the Tertiary geology of Sumatra and Java we observe again some slight discrepancies although the general picture still demonstrates a continous island arc.

The islands off the west coast of Sumatra are characterized by Miocene and post-Miocene clastic and carbonate sediments, both bathyal and neritic, lying uncomformably upon complexes of clastic sediments, low-grade metamorphic rocks, and subordinate mafic and ultra-mafic igneous rocks. The whole rock assemblage is highly deformed with oceanward thrust structures. Locally the clastic rocks contain lower Tertiary (Oligocene) foraminifera.

Nias, the largest island (40 km by 120 km) is situated in the zone of important negative gravity anomalies, characteristic of an outer island arc. Near Suma-Suma in the south-west coast of this island, pre-Tertiary rocks are composed of schists and phyllitic rocks (van Bemmelen 1949).

The Mentawai islands contain over 5,000 m of folded and faulted flysch-type sediments of Eocene to Miocene age (van Bemmelen 1949) interpreted as a turbidite facies with some tuffs. In the Andaman and Nicobar Ridge similar Lower Tertiary turbidites and tuffs overlie radiolarian cherts which are intruded by serpentines and associated ophiolites (Rodolfo 1969).

A profile across the arc-trench gap, west of Sumatra (Fig. 5) shows the inner deep as consisting of sedimentary series with a maximum thickness of about 6,000 m, comprising Paleogene, Miocene and Pliocene deposits of which the Miocene makes up about 3,000 m. The layers are very slightly folded and the upper part of the section consists of undisturbed Pliocene. A high-angle thrust is directed towards the ocean.

The very thick stratigraphic succession consisting largely of marine turbidites and tuffs distributed in narrow belts can most easily be explained by deposition in ancient

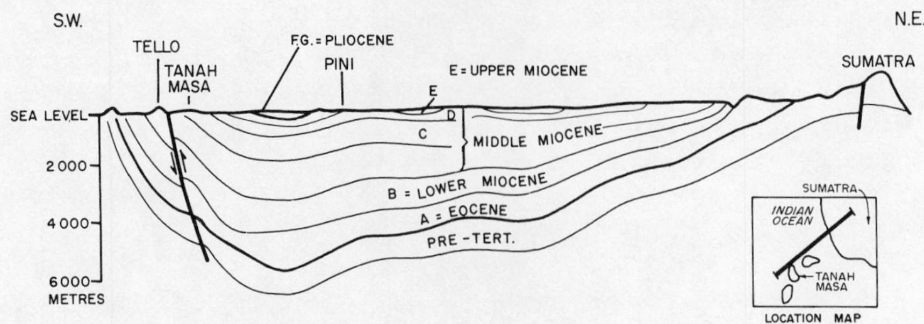

Fig. 5 Schematic sections across the arc-trench gap, West Sumatra

trenches (van Bemmelen 1949, Mitchell & Reading 1971). The islands and the ridge from which they rise are inferred by Hamilton (1970) to consist of subduction complexes that were formed in Early Tertiary time.

No islands are present south of Java, instead a submarine ridge can be found associated with the same negative gravity anomaly as the outer islands off the coast of Sumatra, suggesting an uprising block which coincides with a zone of maximum sedimentary thickness.

The corresponding Tertiary magmatic arc could be found on the west coast of Sumatra and the south coast of Java. In south Sumatra, especially in the Benkulen area, andesites of Oligo-Miocene age are abundantly exposed and intruded by large granitic complexes such as the Benkunat granites which are of intra-Miocene age. The field relationship of the intermediate volcanics and the granites was described by Westerveld (1933). According to this author, the Benkunat plutonic mass has a surface exposure of about 260 km^2 with a core of coarse-grained biotite granite which grades into medium and fine-grained, sometimes porphyritic, biotite or hornblende granodiorites at the edges.

The andesite known in the literature as 'old andesite formation' contains dacite bodies which may attain considerable dimensions. The andesites belong to the same intrusion period as the plutonic masses. This description supports the relation of andesites and granites as envisaged by the plate tectonic model (Hamilton 1970, Dickinson 1970).

Andesites of Tertiary age intruded by intra-Miocene granitic rocks form the bulk of the so-called Southern Mountain of Java, which is a continuation of the Sumatran magmatic belt. These older andesitic rocks are intercalated with Miocene and younger sediments.

As for the Tertiary foreland basins, these are the oil-producing areas of West Indonesia. The stratigraphy of the Neogene fill of the foreland basin in south Sumatra, Java and the Shelf basinal area north of Java has been described by Westerveld (1941), Koesoemadinata (1969), Todd and Pulunggono (1971).

The basin fill thins towards the continent and is deformed by thrusting from the highland side and by folding. In Java, Hamilton (1970) inferred from the literature that progressive formation of basins and migration of the sedimentary axis northward, as folds developed in the south, has occurred.

In conclusion it can be stated that the Tertiary structural zones of West Indonesia can be easily interpreted in terms of plate tectonics. The distance between the subduction zone and the magmatic arc, however, is smaller in comparison with the present system, suggesting that the dip of the Benioff zone was steeper in Tertiary time.

The interpretation becomes more difficult as we move into the Cretaceous system although the broad pattern is nevertheless very simple.

The pre-Tertiary of Sumatra consists mainly of a complex of rock assemblages of Permo-Carboniferous volcanics and sediments and Triassic deposits intruded by plutons, partly overlain by Tertiary sediments. Pre-Tertiary gneisses, limestones and slates, the age of which have not been determined accurately, occur throughout the island. Most of the sediments are deposited in a shallow marine environment. In central Sumatra, the Permo-Carboniferous to Triassic rocks have been intruded by granites. The absolute age of the Lassi-granites in central Sumatra has been found to be 112±24 m.y. which is about mid-Cretaceous (Katili 1962). For south Sumatra the age of granites penetrating the crystalline schists of the Lampong area is about 88 m.y. (Hayase pers. comm.). It is quite obvious that Sumatra during Cretaceous time was a volcanic plutonic arc.

The plate tectonic model requires a Cretaceous subduction zone west of this magmatic arc. This type of rock assemblage could be present in the outer arc, where Cretaceous ultramafic rocks have been mentioned by van Bemmelen (1949). No Cretaceous melange has ever been found in Sumatra.

Java on the other hand possesses no Mesozoic granites. Instead, the pre-Tertiary is characterized by a complex of old rocks which has been interpreted by Hamilton (1970) to be a subduction melange of Late Cretaceous age. The pre-Tertiary rocks of Java are beautifully exposed in the Lokulo area and have been described by Harloff (1933), Loth and Zwierzycki (1926) and Tjia (1966).

It could be predicted from the model that granitic rocks of Cretaceous age should be present off the coast of north Java. This assumption has been verified by the determination of the ages of pre-Tertiary basement rocks off the north coast of Java.

Table 2

AGE OF PRE-TERTIARY GRANITIC AND OTHER ROCKS, WEST INDONESIA

Rock type	*Location*	*Age*
Lassi granites	Central Sumatra	112 ±24 m.y.
Lampong granites	South Sumatra	±88 m.y.
Offshore granites	NE of Djakarta, West Java	±100 m.y.
Offshore granitic rocks	North of Madura	99·7±7 m.y.
Offshore schist	North of Madura	100·9±5·1 m.y.
Offshore tuffs	North of Rembang (Java)	116·1±5·8 m.y.
Offshore conglomerate	North-east of Madura	109 ±3 m.y.

The granitic rocks average 100 m.y. and it may be concluded that north of Java the rocks were involved in a low grade orogenic/metamorphic event of about the same age.

Table 2 shows the absolute ages of pre-Tertiary granitic and other rocks which belong to the Sumatran Cretaceous volcanic plutonic arc.

It is concluded that the Cretaceous volcano-plutonic zone so clearly present in Sumatra does not continue into Java, but passes north of it, running however parallel

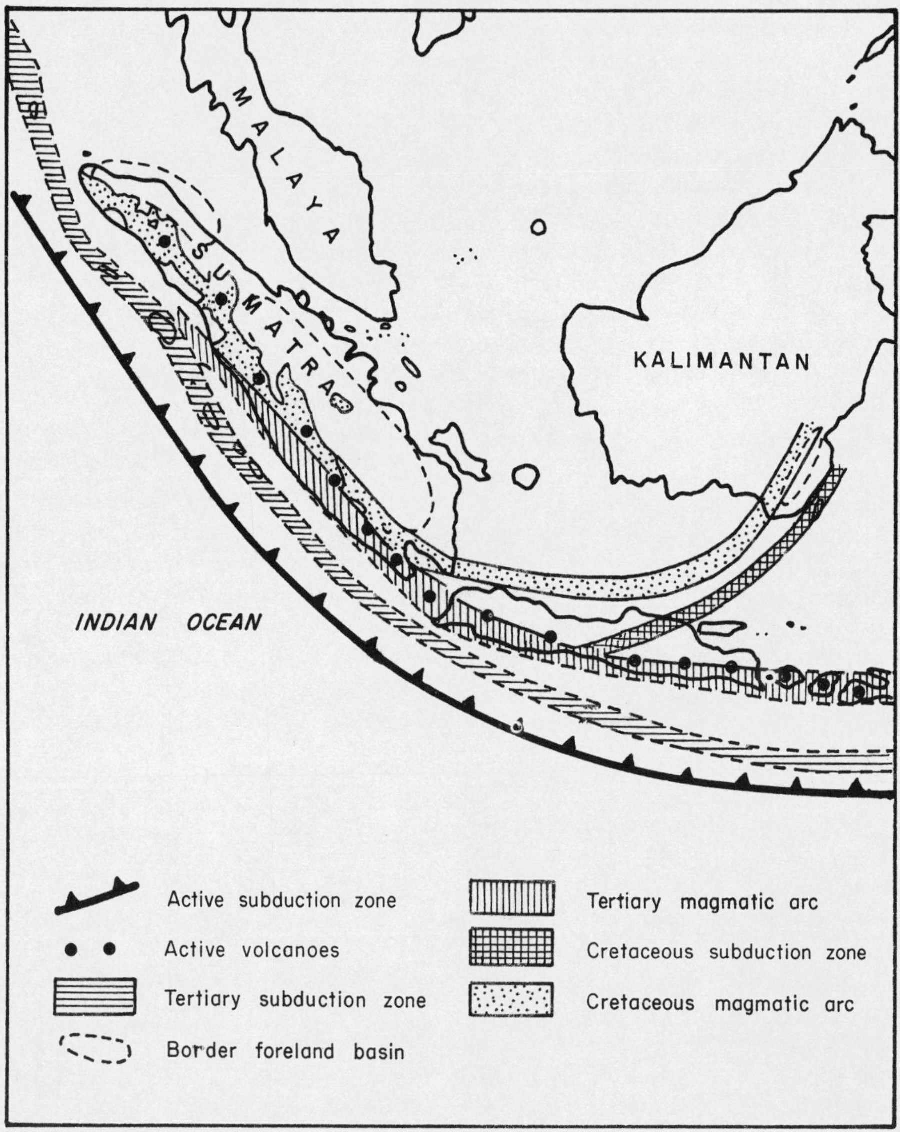

Fig. 6 Subduction zones and volcano-plutonic arcs of West Indonesia

to the Cretaceous subduction zone of Java (Fig. 6). These two zones merge in the Meratus Mountains of south-east Kalimantan, where Cretaceous ophiolites and radiolarite occur side by side with acid plutonic rocks. The geographic arrangement of this fossil subduction zone and magmatic arc is also in accordance with the plate tectonic model in which the granites occur west of the ophiolite complex.

The dip of the Cretaceous Benioff zone must have been considerably steeper than the Holocene and Tertiary seismic zones, but also inclined towards the Asian continent.

Schematic sections across Sumatra and Java summarize the geology of these islands interpreted in terms of the plate-tectonic model (Fig. 7).

The subduction zones have moved systematically farther away from the continent towards the ocean; older subduction zones occur closer to the continent, while the younger ones are situated nearer to the ocean. The magmatic zones also show a zonal arrangement but the ages of the volcanics and granitic zones do not necessarily become younger towards the ocean. Thus the Tertiary magmatic zone of Sumatra occurs on the west coast but the present-day and the Cretaceous zones are located farther east and form the backbone of Sumatra. The Tertiary magmatic zone of Java occurs on the south coast while the present volcanic zone forms the axis of the island; the Cretaceous magmatic zone occurs to the north, off the coast of Java (Fig. 6).

This irregularity in the zonal arrangement has posed problems to previous geologists in postulating the theory of concentric arrangements of orogens and consequently that of accretional continental growth (van Bemmelen 1949, Westerveld 1952, Klompe 1957). This peculiarity is now easily explained by the supposition that the dips of the Holocene, Tertiary and Cretaceous Benioff zones differed one from another.

The difference in dip of the present-day Benioff zones is not an uncommon feature in the Indonesian Archipelago as has been mentioned (Hatherton & Dickinson 1969).

We conclude that the difference in the geological and geophysical phenomena of Sumatra and Java and the surrounding areas is intimately related to the location of the past and present subduction zones and to the inclination of the past and present Benioff seismic zones.

GEOLOGICAL AND GEOPHYSICAL FEATURES OF EAST INDONESIA

Large vertical and horizontal movements have already been recognized in the area between the straits of Makassar and West New Guinea by Dutch geologists such as Brouwer (1925), Kuenen (1935), Umbgrove (1949), van Bemmelen (1949) and others. Uplift and subsidence, warping and folding, horizontal displacements and other neotectonic features have recently been described and summarized by Katili and Tjia (1969), Katili (1970), and Katili and Soetadi (1971).

It is in this area that the actual interaction of the three gigantic plates is taking place. In the discussion regarding plate boundaries we have proposed the existence of smaller plates in this area, bounded by submarine trenches and transform faults.

This part of Indonesia is characterized by subduction zones with submeridional

Structural Zones (Hamilton, Dickinson)	Structural Zones (van Bemmelen)	Sumatra Section		Java Section	
INDIAN OCEAN–AUSTRALIAN PLATE	FORELAND			CHRISTMAS IS.	LOWER TERTIARY VOLCANO
ACTIVE SUB-DUCTION ZONE	FORE-DEEP (TRENCH)				
ARC-TRENCH GAP	NON-VOLCANIC OUTER ARC	MENTAWAI ISLANDS	PRE-YOUNG MIOCENE WITH SW THRUST, CRET. OPHIOLITE COMPLEX (?)		
	INTERDEEP		EOCENE, MIOCENE AND PLIOCENE SEDIMENTS		
MAGMATIC ARC	VOLCANIC INNER ARC	SEMANGKO FAULT BKT. MESURAI TAMBESI-RAWAS MTS.	MIOCENE GRANITES MIO-PLIOCENE SEDS. RECENT VOLCANOES CRETACEOUS GRANITES MESOZOIC SLATES	MALABAR BANDUNG BKT. TUNGGUL	MIO-PLIOCENE, LOWER MIOCENE GRANITES BASALT-ANDESITIC VOLCANOES
FORELAND BASIN	BACK DEEP (OIL BASIN)	DJAMBI	NEOGENE SEDIMENTS	JAVA SEA	NEOGENE SEDIMENTS OVERLYING CRETACEOUS GRANITES
CRATON	HINTERLAND	SINGKEP	PERMIAN AND TRIASSIC SEDIMENTS AND METAMORPHIC ROCKS INTRUDED BY JURASSIC GRANITES.	KARIMUNDJAWA	PERMO-TRIASSIC SEDIMENTS AND METAMORPHIC ROCKS

JAVA SECTION
A
B
JAVA
INDIAN OCEAN
INCLINED BENIOFF ZONE
RELATIVE MOTION OF OCEANIC PLATE
MOHO
RELATIVE MOTION OF CONTINENTAL PLATE

SUMATRA SECTION
A
B
SUMATRA
INDIAN OCEAN
INCLINED BENIOFF ZONE
RELATIVE MOTION OF OCEANIC PLATE
MOHO
RELATIVE MOTION OF CONTINENTAL PLATE

trend in the north, like the Philippine, Halmahera and the Minahassa Trenches and sublatitudinal trend in the south, like the Timor Trench, which are accommodating respectively the westward motion of the Pacific plate and the northward motion of the Australian plate.

The number of transcurrent faults in this region is considerably larger than in West Indonesia and their trend also varies one from the other. As with western Indonesia the changing nature of the past subduction zones account for the complicated geological and geophysical features of East Indonesia.

Foreland basins are not present behind the modern arcs of East Indonesia, e.g. the Banda and Celebes Arcs. This has relevance to the topical discussion on the rôle of plate tectonics in the development of deep-sea basins or marginal seas behind island arcs.

Hamilton (1970) has briefly interpreted the evolution of New Guinea and the Celebes in terms of plate tectonics. He pointed to the complicated active and past tectonic pattern which demonstrates the shifting and swirling zones along which the motion of the plates has been accommodated. Old belts have been deformed and fragments have been swept against unrelated terrains.

Other features which could be related to the northward motion of the Australian plate and the westward movement of the Pacific plate are the loop-shaped Banda Arc, the peculiar shape of Halmahera and the Celebes, the overthrust structures and highly-elevated coral reefs in many parts of Eastern Indonesia.

The author has no intention to go into detail on the interpretation of the geological features as this has already been done, although broadly, by Hamilton (1970).

CONCLUDING REMARKS

From the discussion presented above it is concluded that the new concept of plate tectonics featuring the Indonesian island arcs as the place of interaction of two or more crustal plates provides an excellent basis to explain the various physiographical, geological and geophysical phenomena already described. In West Indonesia the plate tectonic model can be used even to predict the distribution and age of granitic rocks.

The regular zonal structure of the western part of Indonesia is the result of accreting continental crust at the inner side of the present and past subduction zones (see also Dewey & Horsfield 1970). The crust of the arcs was built up by the scraping-up of oceanic sediments and the accumulation of a thick pile of basalts, andesites and their acid derivatives.

Large transform faults, submarine trenches, and the occurrence side by side of structural belts with unrelated geology in East Indonesia, point to large horizontal movement suggestive of continental drift.

Two apparently controversial theories, those of continental accretion and continen-

---

Fig. 7 Schematic sections across West Indonesia interpreted according to the plate tectonic model

tal drift find application in western and eastern Indonesia, respectively, and are thus compatible and found to be complementary with the plate tectonic concept.

As in every model which tries to explain so many features at once, some difficulties were encountered in applying this theory, but they are not difficulties of principle and can mainly be ascribed to lack of detailed field data.

An example is the existence of a Permian volcanic-sedimentary sequence known as the Silungkang formation (Katili 1969), which is widely distributed throughout Sumatra. In central Sumatra, the volcanic rocks consist of flows of hornblende andesites, augite andesites and tuffs with intercalation of limestones and silicified shales.

The plate tectonic model requires the existence of Permian granites in Sumatra. Palaeozoic granites in Sumatra have never been proven positively, although Musper (1930) considered the granites of Sumpur located in central Sumatra to be of Palaeozoic age. A subduction zone in Sumatra must have existed in late Palaeozoic time which points to one of the earliest episodes of lithosphere descent beneath an existing island arc. It also suggests that since this period the margin of some lithospheric plates has remained near the side of a present island arc (Mitchell & Reading 1971). A Permian melange has not been encountered in or west of Sumatra.

Permian andesites and basalts have been described by Klompe *et al.* (1961) from Malaya and West Borneo; this points to the existence of another volcano/plutonic arc in West Indonesia during Permian time, parallel to and east of the Sumatran Permian arc described above. The Permian subduction zone of this arc might be found north of the plutonic arc in the so-called Danau formation (Klompe *et al.* 1961), an ophiolite-radiolarite rock assemblage having an age ranging from Permo-Carboniferous to Cretaceous which could be considered as a melange deposit. The inferred dip of the fossil Benioff zone in this case is in the direction of the ocean probably opposite to that of the Permian Benioff zone of Sumatra.

The existence of a *double* volcano/plutonic arc during Permian time and the possible difference in direction towards which the corresponding Benioff zones dip, make the reconstruction of the subduction zones somewhat complicated.

The occurrence of Jurassic granites in Malaya and the Indonesian tin islands requires corresponding subduction zones to the west, if the Benioff zone was inclined towards the continent. Some Mesozoic ophiolites have been described by Musper in the Gumai mountains of South Sumatra, but their exact age is not really known.

The occurrence of Late Cretaceous granitic rocks in Anambas, Bunguran and Tembelan (Haile 1971), situated east of the Malayan-Indonesian tin belt, points to the presence of another magmatic arc than the one previously mentioned in Sumatra. The existence of another Cretaceous subduction zone should then be postulated possibly east of the corresponding magmatic arc. The Danau formation occurring in Serawak has a Cretaceous age and might be considered as a Cretaceous subduction zone indicating a west and southward dip of the Benioff zone, similar to that described for the Permian in the Borneo region. A possible ophiolitic suite has been reported by Haile (1970) on Natuna island.

The ages of the volcanic plutonic arcs and trench deposits and the inferred ages of Benioff zones in West Indonesia suggest that episodes of lithospheric descent in this region took place during Permian, Jurassic, Cretaceous, Miocene, and from Pliocene to the present day. The Benioff zones to which the older arcs were related lay in a position different from that of today's Benioff zone. The occurrence of two magmatic arcs and two subduction zones of the same age with different dips in different directions makes the situation more complicated.

Other topics of future research in Indonesia could be suggested, based on the plate tectonic concept.

The island of Sumba situated in the area of the Tertiary subduction zone possesses a geology similar to that of the island of the inner magmatic arc. The mobilistic concept makes it possible to consider Sumba as being moved to the south presumably along a transform fault. Further investigation is required.

The isolated volcanic island of Una-Una on the gulf of Gorontalo, Central Celebes (Katili *et al.* 1960) produces a medium alkaline series of rocks which usually occur in the hinterland. How could this be related to the tectonic setting of Celebes in terms of the plate tectonic model?

As mentioned above, two small subduction zones with opposing Benioff zones occur west of Halmahera and east of Minahassa (north Celebes). Between these trenches a submarine ridge (Maju ridge) possessing a very high negative gravity anomaly occurs. Is the ridge, which is supposed to be rising, also spreading at the moment?

The Early Tertiary geology of East Borneo and the west-arc of the Celebes shows many similarities. Could this part of the Celebes, probably a part of Borneo, have drifted away relatively to the east, indicating spreading of the floor of the Makassar Strait?

Despite these and many other problems to be encountered in applying plate tectonics to Indonesia, nevertheless, the dispositions presented above and elsewhere (Katili 1971*a*) show encouraging signs that the plate tectonic concept may explain many diverse geological and geophysical features and could simplify our view of this geologically complex region of the globe.

ACKNOWLEDGEMENTS

The author wishes to extend his deepest appreciation to Mr Michael W. Kontz, Indonesia Gulf Company, for the valuable assistance and suggestions he gave during the preparation of this paper.

The results of radiometric age dating of the basement rocks off the coast of north Java were kindly provided by Indonesia City Service Company, to whom the author wishes to express his gratitude.

REFERENCES

Allen, C. R. 1962. Circum-Pacific faulting in the Philippine-Taiwan region. *J. geophys. Res.* **67,** 4795-812.

Brouwer, H. A. 1925. *The Geology of the East Indies.* MacMillan, New York, 160 pp.

Dewey, J. F. & Horsfield, B. 1970. Plate tectonics, orogeny and continental growth. *Nature*, **225,** 521-5.

Dickinson, W. R. 1970. Relations of andesites, granites and derivative sandstones to arc-trench tectonics. *Rev. Geophys. Space Phys.* **8** (4), 813-60.

——— 1971. Plate tectonics in geologic history. *Science*, **174** (4005), 107-13.

Fitch, T. J. 1970. Earthquake mechanisms and island arc tectonics in the Indonesian-Philippine region. *Bull. seism. Soc. Am.* **60,** 565-91.

Fitch, T. J. & Molnar, P. 1970. Focal mechanisms along inclined earthquake zones in the Indonesian-Philippine region. *J. geophys. Res.* **75,** 1431-44.

Haile, N. S. 1970. Notes on the geology of the Tambelan, Anambas and Bunguran (Natuna) Islands, Sunda Shelf, Indonesia, including radiometric age determinations. *Econ. Comm. Asia & Far East* (*ECAFE*) *CCOP*, *Tech. Bull.* **3,** 55-90.

——— 1971. Confirmation of Late Cretaceous age for granite from the Bunguran and Anambas islands, Sunda Shelf, Indonesia. *Geol. Soc. Malaysia*, *Newsletter*, No. 30, 6-8.

Hamilton, W. H. 1970. Tectonic Map of Indonesia, a progress report. *U.S. Geol. Surv.*, Denver, Colorado, 29 pp.

Harloff, C. E. A. 1929. Voorlopige mededeling over de geologie van het Pratertiair van Loh Oelo in Midden Java. *De Mijningenieur*, **10** (8), 172-7

Hatherton, T. & Dickinson, W. R. 1969. The relationship between andesitic volcanism and seismicity in Indonesia, The Lesser Antilles, and other island arcs. *J. geophys. Res.* **74,** 5301-10.

Isacks, B., Oliver, J. & Sykes, L. R. 1968. Seismology and the new global tectonics. *J. geophys. Res.* **73** (18), 5855-99.

Katili, J. A. 1962. On the age of the granitic rocks in relation to the structural features of Sumatra. In *Crust of the Pacific Basin. Am. Geophys. Un. Monogr.* **6,** 116-21.

——— 1969. Permian volcanism and its relation to the tectonic development of Sumatra. *Bull. volcan.* **33** (2), 530-40.

——— 1970. Large transcurrent faults in South-east Asia with special reference to Indonesia. *Geol. Rundsch.* **59** (2), 581-600.

——— 1971*a*. A review of geotectonic theories and tectonic maps of Indonesia. *Earth Sci. Rev.* **7,** 143-63.

——— 1971*b*. Additional evidence of transcurrent faulting in Sumatra and Sulawesi. *Bull. Nat. Inst. Geol. Mining*, **3** (3), 15-28. Bandung.

Katili, J. A. & Hehuwat, F. 1967. On the occurrence of large transcurrent faults in Sumatra, Indonesia. *J. Geosci., Osaka City Univ.* **10,** 5-17.

Katili, J. A., Kartaadiputra, L. & Surjo. 1960. Magma type and tectonic position of the Una-Una island, Indonesia. *Bull. volcan.* **26,** 431-54.

Katili, J. A. & Soetadi, R. 1971. Neotectonics and seismic zones of Indonesia. *Bull. Proc. R. Soc. N.Z.* **9,** 39-45.

Katili, J. A. & Tjia, H. D. 1969. Outline of Quaternary tectonics of Indonesia. *Bull. Nat. Inst. Geol. Mining*, **2** (1), 1-10. Bandung.

Klompe, Th. H. F. 1957. Pacific and Variscian Orogeny in Indonesia, a structural synthesis. *Proc. 9th Pacif. Sci. Congr.* **12,** 76-115.

Klompe, Th. H. F., Katili, J., Johannas & Soekendar. 1957. Late Paleozoic-Early Mesozoic volcanic activity in the Sunda Land area. *Proc. 9th Pacif. Sci. Congr.* **12,** 204-17.

Koesoemadinata, R. P. 1969. Outline of the geologic occurrence of oil in Tertiary basins of West Indonesia. *Bull. Am. Ass. Petrol. Geol.*, **53** (11), 2368-76.

Kraus, E. 1951. *Vergleishende Baugeschichte der Gebirge*. Akad.-Verlag, Berlin, 588 pp.

Kuenen, Ph. H. 1935. Geological interpretation of the bathymetrical results. Sci. Results

Snellius Expedition Eastern Pt (East Indian Archipelago), 1929-30. **5** (1), 124 pp.

Kuno, H. 1966. Lateral variation of basalt magma type across continental margins and island arcs. *Bull. volcan.* **29,** 195-222.

Le Pichon, X. 1968. Sea-floor spreading and continental drift. *J. geophys. Res.* **73** (12), 3661-97.

Loth, J. E. & Zwierzycki, J. 1926. De Kristallyne schisten op Java ouder dan Kryt. *De Mijningenieur*, **2** (2), 22-5.

Mitchell, A. H. & Reading, H. G. 1971. Evolution of island arcs. *J. Geol.* **79** (3), 253-84.

Morgan, W. J. 1968. Rises, trenches, great faults and crustal blocks. *J. geophys. Res.* **73** (6), 1959-82.

Musper, K. A. F. R. 1930. Beknopt verslag over uitkomsten van nieuwe geologische onderzoekingen in de Padangse Bovenlanden. *Jaarb. Mijnw. Ned. Ind., Verh.* (1930), 261-331.

Oxburgh, E. R. & Turcotte, D. L. 1970. The thermal structure of island arcs. *Bull. geol. Soc. Am.* **81,** 1665-88.

Rodolfo, K. S. 1969. Bathymetry and marine geology of the Andaman Basin, and tectonic implications for South-east Asia. *Bull. geol. Soc. Am.* **80,** 1203-30.

Smith Sibinga, G. L. 1933. The Malay double (triple) orogen 1, II and III. *Proc. K. ned. Akad. Wet.* **36,** 202-10, 323-30, 447-53.

Tjia, H. D. 1966. Structural analysis of the pre-Tertiary of the Lokulo area, Central-Java. *Bandung Inst. Techn., Contribs. Dept. Geol.* **63,** 110 pp.

——— 1967. Volcanic lineaments in the Indonesian island arcs. *Bull. volcan.* **31,** 85-96.

Todd, D. F. & Pulunggono, A. 1971. The Sunda basinal area, an important new oil province. *Oil Gas J.*, June 14, 104-10.

Umbgrove, J. H. F. 1949. *Structural history of the East Indies.* Cambridge Univ. Press, 64 pp.

Van Bemmelen, R. W. 1949. *The geology of Indonesia.* Govt. Printing Office, The Hague, 732 pp.

Vening Meinesz, F. A. 1954. Indonesian Archipelago; a geophysical study. *Bull. geol. Soc. Am.* **65,** 143-64.

Visser, W. A. & Hermes, J. J. 1962. *Geological results of the exploration for oil in Netherlands New Guinea.* Govt. Printing Office, The Hague, 265 pp.

Wegener, A. 1922. *Die Entstehung der Kontinente und Ozeane.* Viehweg, Braunschweig, 144 pp.

Westerveld, J. 1933. Toelichting bij blad 3 (Bengkoenat), Geol. Kaart Sumatra 1:200.000. *Dienst Mijnb. Ned. Ind.*

——— 1941. Three geological sections across South Sumatra. *Proc. K. ned. Akad. Wet.* **44,** 1131-9.

——— 1949. Fasen van gebergtevorming en ertsprovincies in Nederlands Oost-Indie. *Ingenieur*, 1-25.

——— 1954. Phases of mountain building and mineral provinces in the East Indies. *Intern. Geol. Congr.* 1952, *Rept 8th Session*, pt 13, 245-55.

Wilson, J. T. 1965. A new class of faults and their bearing on continental drift. *Nature*, **207,** 343-7.

Geotectonic Development of the Philippines

F. C. GERVASIO
National Research Council of the Philippines, Manila, Philippines

ABSTRACT

The geotectonic development of the Philippines involves at least two long-term and several short-term cycles of crustal reorganization traceable from Palaeozoic to Recent.

The long-term cycles, the Palaeozoic and the Mesozoic-Tertiary geotectonic cycles, are manifested by the reorganization of the pre-existing crustal plate into geosynclinal systems and/or mobile belts and their gradual transformation into platforms. The gradual change into platforms, which involved a series of short-term cycles, is apparently characterized, particularly along mobile belts, by continuing crystallization at depth of primary magma generated during the initial geosynclinal stage.

The short-term cycles are demonstrated by the cyclic occurrences of transgression/ sedimentation followed by regression and orogenic movement yielding mountain systems and/or elements of island arcs and emplacement at near surface of quasi-solid plutons, usually within a geosyncline/platform background.

The span of time covering the better known Mesozoic-Tertiary geotectonic cycle is about 100-130 m.y. while that of the Palaeozoic seems much greater. The short-term cycles, on the other hand, involved periods of 10-60 m.y. becoming shorter from geosynclinal to platform stage.

The development of these various cycles of activity are considered to be effects of reorganization in the earth's interior region—effects with a coeval relationship to the earth's orbital movement around the centre of the Milky Way galaxy. The Mesozoic-Tertiary geotectonic cycle at least seems to correspond with the known period it takes the earth to travel from perigee to apogee position of the galactic orbital path of our sun (under its present radius of orbit about the centre of the Milky Way). Such travel would necessarily involve passing from a stronger to a weaker gravitational field, and so the development of such cycles may be due essentially to fluctuation of gravity.

The essential differences in crustal development between the Palaeozoic and the Mesozoic-Tertiary geotectonic cycles may also be premised on the possible differences—in orbital radius and speed of travel of the earth—during the two cycles. The Milky Way, being a spiral galaxy, has member bodies apparently being drawn in time towards the central region, where the population density is much greater, and a stronger field of interaction between bodies can be expected.

The recognized formation of Barrovian-type metamorphics and granites during the Palaeozoic, being of an earlier orbital cycle, could have been due to weaker gravitational-field setting and slower pace of orbital travel of the earth: conditions conducive to more pronounced magmatic differentiation, anatexis and regional metamorphism, even at shallow depths, were developed, in the presence of strong contractive forces and greater hydrostatic pressure.

INTRODUCTION

Since the Eleventh Pacific Science Congress in 1966 much additional geological data on the Philippine area have been compiled. These include more knowledge about Permian rock formations, Lower and Upper Cretaceous sequences, nature of the Tertiary-Cretaceous boundary, Eocene-Oligocene keratophyre sequences, some Miocene spilites, Quaternary tectonics and sea-level changes.

Many of the current contributions come from the work of the personnel of the Bureau of Mines Geological and Petroleum Survey Divisions, especially by palaeontologists P. P. Andal, E. Espiritu, E. P. Ordoñez and M. V. Reyes; geologists D. Andal (deceased), F. E. Miranda, J. Fernandez, H. Fernandez, E. Vallesteros, R. Santos, D. Almogela, G. Balce, R. Zerda, R. Peña, M. Garcia, P. Caleon, A. Baptista, B. Vargas, C. Samonte and L. Raval: all with whom the writer worked up to April 1970; and also from the work of the Oriental Petroleum and Mineral Corporation geologists headed by E. Tamesis and C. Reyes, who made recent studies of northern Palawan. V. V. Gervasio, also of the Bureau of Mines, provided petrographic studies of the basement metamorphics and the keratophyres. A wealth of geological data were secured from the results of exploration by several local private mining companies at the close of the decade.

The author wishes to acknowledge very much the whole-hearted co-operation of the above group of earth scientists.

SUMMARY OF THE REGIONAL GEOLOGICAL FEATURES OF THE PHILIPPINES

The metamorphic basement and associated Palaeozoic rocks

The metamorphic basement rocks, as previously reported by the author (1964, 1967), consist essentially of a basal sequence of basic amphibolite schist and/or quartz-feldspar-mica-gneiss to quartz-albite-mica-hornblende schist; a thick upper sequence consists of greenschists from the biotite zone to phyllites which are sometimes intercalated with strongly foliated meta-spilite, meta-tuff, meta-conglomerates, wackes, slates and marble. They outcrop in areas around the Sulu Sea, in Palawan, Mindoro, Zamboanga and Tawi-Tawi Island; along the median zone of the mobile belt in Romblon Island group; on Cebu, Leyte, Bohol and north central Mindanao; and along the eastern Pacific sea-board in Sierra Madre; Atimonan, Quezon; Bicol Region and Samar, and finally in Surigao, eastern Mindanao (see Fig. 1). Chloritoid- and cordierite-bearing schists are also recognized in northern Mindoro and Caramoan Peninsula of the Bicol region but seem to be limited to schists in contact with quartz-diorite intrusives.

The reported glaucophanitic schist in Antique, Panay Island, exists mainly as exotic fragments associated with mylonites, thrusted and crushed serpentinite masses, chert and metavolcanics along the N-S trending broad shear zone or melange zone considered part of the radian lineament of the convex Visayan Arc (F. C. Gervasio 1964). Tectonic movements along the zone have caused severe folding and thrusting even of the Mio-Pliocene clastics and tuffs. It is doubtful whether such glaucophane schist is part of the basement metamorphics. Possibly, it is local and of Tertiary development.

The age of the metamorphic basement remains vague beyond pre-Permian in the western and median belts, and pre-Cretaceous in the eastern belt. In general, the upper pelitic greenschist and marble are considered as of Carboniferous age. C. Reyes (pers. comm.) reported a recent discovery of a trilobite in the slaty sedimentary sequence in northern Palawan.

Quite extensive Middle Permian clastics and limestone together with probable Lower Permian sequences were recently recognized in northern Palawan and the Calamian Island group (Busuanga, Culion and Linacapan) by Tamesis and colleagues (Geology of northern Palawan by Tamesis, in prep.) (see Fig. 1). Confirmed fusulinid genera in the limestone are: *Neoschwagerina, Verbeekina, Agathammina, Endothyra* and *Millerella* (Ordoñez & Reyes, pers. comm.).

This probable Lower Permian formation, designated as the Bacuit Chert, consists of a basal subgreywacke or proto-quartzite and a thick sequence of thin interbeds of red chert, quartzite, siliceous shales and sandstone and, in the north island of Busuanga, with interbedded siliceous manganese ore. The sequence is intensely folded along a NW-SE trend from near Cuyo Island to Busuanga, according to C. Ramos (Bureau of Mines Geological Survey), but is sharply bent along N-S to SE trends at western Busuanga and then extends south-westward to the western part of northern Palawan. The NW-SE flexure trend of the chert sequence is strongly discordant with the N-S to NE-SW flexures of the metamorphic basement, which suggests different periods of deformation and divergent stress fields.

The Middle Permian formations, essentially molasse-type deposits, consist of moderately dipping beds of dark-grey mudstone, shales, sandstone and conglomerate overlain by thick-bedded fusulinid limestone. The sequence is known to overlie unconformably the more intensely folded Bacuit Chert and contains clasts of the chert. In Carabao Island, north of Panay, similar clastic sequence which underlies the fusulinid limestone contains some silicic pyroclastic components.

The Mesozoic sequence

Information on the early Mesozoic remains limited to the still questionable Triassic Wasig Formation and the well-published Jurassic Mansalay Formation of southern Mindoro Island. Search for similar sequences in other parts of the archipelago have been fruitless.

The suspected Triassic foliated molassic sediments in Tuuyan, Mindoro (with poorly preserved molluscs, brachiopods and crinoids) was studied by Hashimoto and Sato (1968) and was considered by them as part of the overlying Eocene. Additional study is deemed necessary, however, as the N-S to NE-SW slaty cleavage, well developed in this considered Eocene sequence, is not recognizable in the proximate well-established Jurassic shale and mudstone beds found on the same island.

Part of the thick eugeosynclinal greywacke sequence of the Pandan Formation of central Cebu, was confirmed to be of Lower Cretaceous age. Similar rock sequences were identified in Catanduanes Island, in southern Davao, southern Negros and in Casiguran, Sierra Madre of Luzon, overlain unconformably by Upper Cretaceous

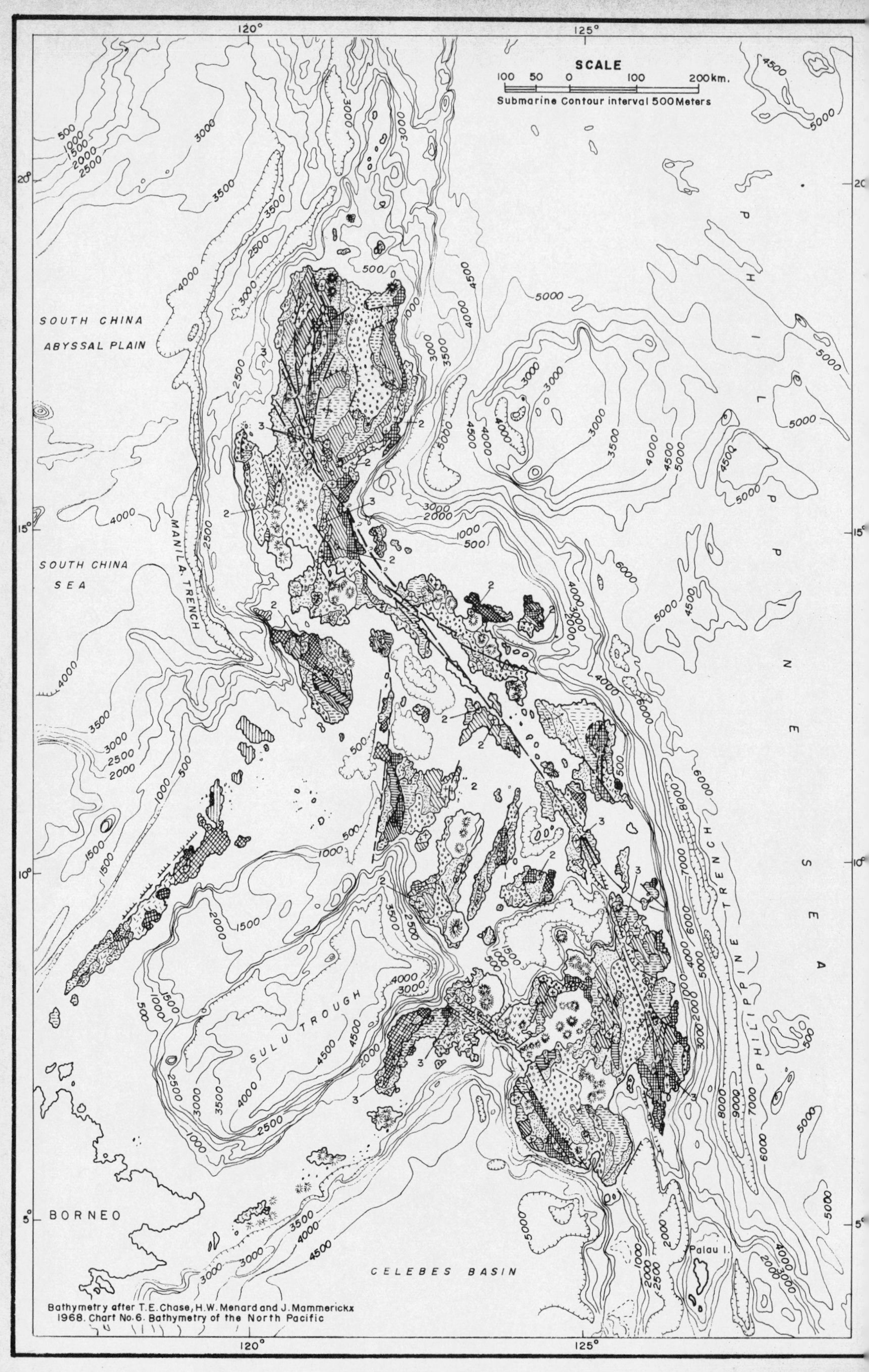

SCALE
100 50 0 100 200km.
Submarine Contour interval 500 Meters
SOUTH CHINA
ABYSSAL PLAIN
SOUTH CHINA
SEA
MANILA TRENCH
SULU TROUGH
BORNEO
CELEBES BASIN
PHILIPPINE TRENCH
PHILIPPINE SEA
Palau I.
Bathymetry after T.E. Chase, H.W. Menard and J. Mammerickx
1968. Chart No. 6. Bathymetry of the North Pacific
120°
125°
20°
15°
10°
5°

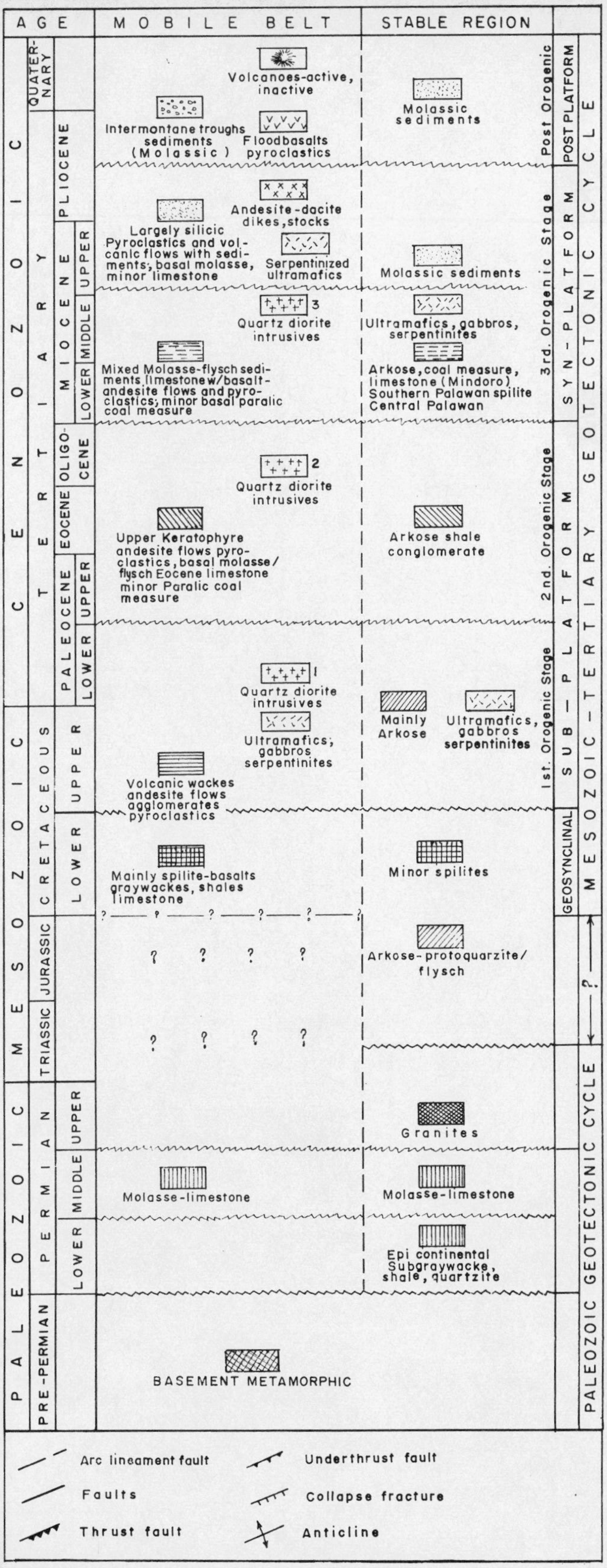

AGE		MOBILE BELT	STABLE REGION		
CENOZOIC – TERTIARY	QUATERNARY	Volcanoes-active, inactive		Post Orogenic	POST PLATFORM
	PLIOCENE	Intermontane troughs sediments (Molassic); Floodbasalts pyroclastics	Molassic sediments		
	PLIOCENE / MIOCENE UPPER	Andesite-dacite dikes, stocks; Largely silicic Pyroclastics and volcanic flows with sediments, basal molasse, minor limestone; Serpentinized ultramafics	Molassic sediments	3rd. Orogenic Stage	SYN-PLATFORM
	MIOCENE MIDDLE	Quartz diorite intrusives 3	Ultramafics, gabbros, serpentinites		
	MIOCENE LOWER	Mixed Molasse-flysch sediments limestone w/basalt-andesite flows and pyroclastics; minor basal paralic coal measure	Arkose, coal measure, limestone (Mindoro) Southern Palawan spilite Central Palawan		
	OLIGOCENE	Quartz diorite intrusives 2		2nd. Orogenic Stage	SUB-PLATFORM
	EOCENE / PALEOCENE UPPER	Upper Keratophyre andesite flows pyroclastics, basal molasse/flysch Eocene limestone minor Paralic coal measure	Arkose shale conglomerate		
	PALEOCENE LOWER	Quartz diorite intrusives 1	Mainly Arkose; Ultramafics, gabbros serpentinites	1st. Orogenic Stage	
MESOZOIC	CRETACEOUS UPPER	Ultramafics; gabbros serpentinites; Volcanic wackes andesite flows agglomerates pyroclastics			
	CRETACEOUS LOWER	Mainly spilite-basalts graywackes, shales limestone	Minor spilites		GEOSYNCLINAL
	JURASSIC	? ? ? ?	Arkose-protoquarzite/flysch		?
	TRIASSIC	? ? ? ?			
PALEOZOIC	PERMIAN UPPER		Granites		PALEOZOIC GEOTECTONIC CYCLE
	PERMIAN MIDDLE	Molasse-limestone	Molasse-limestone		
	PERMIAN LOWER		Epi continental Subgraywacke, shale, quartzite		
	PRE-PERMIAN	BASEMENT METAMORPHIC			

MESOZOIC-TERTIARY GEOTECTONIC CYCLE

Arc lineament fault — Underthrust fault
Faults — Collapse fracture
Thrust fault — Anticline

Fig. 1 Tectonic map of the Philippines and legend

sequences and/or by Cretaceous spilites. Generally, they measure as much as 3,000 m thick, but laterally they are not persistent and are hard to follow. Furthermore, individual beds do not show systematic regional orientation. For example, the sequences in southern Davao trend NW-SE and are generally overturned. In Cebu, they are steeply folded and trend about N10-40E (as in the Mananga River section). In Catanduanes, the sequence trends N-NW and is structurally separated from the greywacke-spilite-chert sequence by a thick mylonite-schist zone. The sequence in Casiguran, Sierra Madre, is essentially of vertical beds that trend about N30E. In Marinduque, similar sequences trend nearly E-W, also dipping vertically. The degree of disturbance induced by the later outpour and intrusion of the spilitic lavas remains almost unknown. Lack of persistent outcrops, even in just one island, suggests lack of continuity and/or the fragmented nature of such formations.

The above intercalated greywacke-spilite sequence is usually overlain unconformably by a thick sequence of massive spilitic pillow lavas and agglomerates, which in many places constitute the more persistent inlier formations of most Tertiary orogenic belts. In central Cebu, such massive flows are also intercalated with Lower Cretaceous limestone lenses, thus suggesting the occurrence of an intra-Lower Cretaceous disturbance of some sort.

The Upper Cretaceous has been recognized in at least six localities and is generally moderately to severely folded as in Tanay, Rizal. A regional unconformity is often expressed between the Upper and the Lower Cretaceous. The usual assemblages include volcanic wackes, shale, pyroclastics and tuffs together with intercalated coralline, chalky and/or cherty limestone. They seem to belong to a different geotectonic stage of development, compared to the earlier sequence. The change involved not only occasioned renewed sedimentation but also a change from essentially basic submarine effusive activity into generally eruptive and more silicic volcanic activity (a dacitic phase is indicated).

Late Cretaceous orogeny and intrusive activities

The K-Ar dating of the quartz porphyrite mass in the Atlas Mine, Toledo, central Cebu, gave an age of $59{\cdot}7 \pm 1{\cdot}2$ m.y. The intrusive masses, generally of small dioritic stocks, formed a N20-30E trending belt and cut through a broadly-folded spilitic lava sequence and the underlying greywackes.

Along the western edge of the mobile belt in Zambales, Mindoro and Zamboanga and along the eastern border of Sierra Madre, Bicol Region, Samar and eastern Mindanao, layered ultramafics with intrusive gabbro and/or serpentinized peridotites were emplaced (see Fig. 1). The largest mass, the Zambales ultramafic-gabbro complex, consists essentially of NE-SW trending, folded and layered dunite-saxonite, and troctolitic and noritic gabbro, intruded by discordant masses of serpentinized dunite, gabbro, diabase dikes and anorthosites. Xenoliths of volcanic rocks are indicated. In other localities contacts with other rocks are in the form of sheared, mylonitized zones typical of cold or diapiric intrusions.

The Cretaceous-Tertiary boundary and the Early Tertiary

In addition to the discovery of *Globorotalia velascoensis* (Samaniego 1964) in samples from southern Palawan, and of *Distichoplax biserialis* (Dietrich) in samples from Palawan, Mindoro, Cebu, Albay and Caramoan by Villavicencio and Andal (1964), some Paleocene localities were discovered recently. These are in Pinugay, Tanay, Rizal, and in the Caramoan Peninsula (by F. Miranda, Bureau of Mines Geological Survey in 1969 and 1971). The Paleocene beds are found structurally and lithogenetically related to the Eocene formations in these localities. Unconformity is generally expressed between the Upper Cretaceous and overlying Upper Paleocene, but not between the Upper Paleocene and Lower Eocene. The faunal break indicated in Tanay, Rizal, covers Upper Maestrichtian to Lower Paleocene (Ordoñez & Reyes 1971, in press). The beds consist of volcanic wackes and shale with associated lenses of limestone.

The Eocene sequence found within the mobile belt consists of basal conglomerates and mudstone, in places with paralic coal measures, which are succeeded by transgressive volcanic wackes, shales and biohermal or nummulitic limestone, thence by an unfossiliferous upper sequence of thinly-bedded clastics with thin lenses of argillaceous silty limestone intercalated and succeeded by thick and extensive sequence of andesitic and keratophyric flows, tuffs and agglomerate. Thin layers and/or lenses of gravel and red mudstone are sometimes interbedded with the upper sequence of thick flows and/or welded tuff, together with boulder-size fragmental volcanic blocks which suggest subterrestrial conditions in many localities of keratophyre deposition. Light-coloured volcanic chert and highly silicified flows, tuffs or agglomerates commonly feature in the uppermost part of the deposits. The thick unfossiliferous upper part of the sequence (2,500 m in places) is generally considered of early Oligocene age.

Within the stable region in Palawan and southern Mindoro, thick sequence of arkose and subgreywackes together with limestones were deposited. Presence of much detrital perthitic feldspar, quartz and mica in arkose and subgreywacke suggests granite provenance.

Intra-Oligocene orogeny and intrusive activity

Intra-Oligocene orogenic movement and intrusive activities seem confined within the mobile belt. Broad to moderate folding along NE-SW to nearly E-W trends of the Eocene clastics and keratophyres, together with the intrusions of quartz diorite and diorite porphyry took place after the keratophyre-volcanic chert deposition. The areas involved include: the Baguio district and Sierra Madre of north Luzon, Iloilo, Panay, Masbate, and Guimaras Island. In Catanduanes Island intense N-S to NE-SW folding and intrusions of diorite dikes, sills and stocks are noted. In southern Negros the trend of the intra-Oligocene quartz diorite intrusive belt is NW-SE.

Broad and extensive positive areas of relatively low relief, however, appear to have developed as a result of this orogeny. No Upper Oligocene or Te_{1-3} sequence has been recognized so far and regional unconformity is known to exist between the keratophyre sequence and Lower Miocene (Te_{4-5}) sequence.

Early Miocene transgression, sedimentation and volcanic activity

Marine transgression and formation of many intra-orogenic belt and open-sea fringe basins were manifested during Lower Miocene (Te_{4-5}) within the mobile belt.

Generally some cobbly and pebbly molasse and/or paralic coal measures were deposited. In other places, as in the Baguio district, thick basaltic and andesitic pyroclastic and agglomerates were formed. As transgression continued, generally thick bioclastic and biohermal limestones were deposited together with volcanic wackes, shales and intercalated layers of marine basaltic and andesitic flows, agglomerates and tuffs. The manifested activity was, in a way, quite similar to that which occurred during Lower Cretaceous, except for the comparatively small volume of basaltic flows and more intermittent nature of effusive activity.

A regressive stage appears to have started sometime during later Middle Miocene (Tf_{1-2}) with intermittent but markedly reduced basaltic and andesitic effusions. Similarly, relatively brackish and thinly bedded limestones were deposited in many areas.

In the stable region, arkose, subgreywackes and limestones were continuously deposited in southern Palawan; spilitic pillow lavas and volcanic chert were laid down in central Palawan; mixed arkose and wackes, together with coal measures, were deposited in southern Mindoro, and thick conglomerates, arkose, shale, limestone as well as basaltic flows were laid down in southern Zamboanga. Transgressive sedimentation continued in northern Palawan until late Miocene.

Intra-Miocene orogeny and intrusions

Following deposition of the Middle Miocene sequence, large quartz diorite masses in the form of stocks and batholiths were intruded in many places within the mobile belt. They include later granodiorite, dacite and andesite porphyry in the form of stocks and dikes. Generally the Miocene cover was broadly warped into N-S to NW-SE trending belts. The pre-existing NE-SW trending Oligocene fold belt of the Baguio district suffered refolding along this N-S trend. More detailed study has not been made in other places.

In central Palawan and in central Mindanao diapiric intrusions of serpentinized ultramafics were emplaced and/or intruded. In southern Mindoro and southern Palawan, the Miocene beds were folded along NW-SE and NE-SW trends, respectively, but there are no indications of dioritic intrusions.

Generally the intra-Miocene orogeny continued to build up the mobile belt into a platform, while the stable region of the Sulu Sea and the adjacent part of the South China Sea along the west could have started to subside, as also part of the Philippine Sea along the east of the mobile belt and, probably, areas presently occupied by big inter-island sea basins.

Upper Miocene-Pliocene activities

Upper Miocene beds in the form of coarse molassic sediments were initially deposited along the fringes of the Miocene orogenic belts in Luzon, Visayas and Mindanao and along the flanks of the folded belts of southern Mindoro. Thicknesses of these deposits reach over 2,000 m in places, and detrital components indicate erosion and/or truncation of the upper sections of quartz-diorite batholiths in many localities of the mobile belt.

The initial post-platform molasse is generally succeeded by a thick and extensive sequence of andesitic to dacitic tuffs and tuffaceous clastics, in places with ass andesitic and dacitic flows and agglomerates. Along major intermontane mixed molasse and pyroclastics were deposited. In western Palawan, there i any noticeable change in the nature of sediments deposited since the Lower Miocene.

The highly eruptive and siliceous volcanic activity extended to the early Pliocene, and appears to have been culminated by a period of intrusion of small masses of andesitic and dacitic stocks, volcanic plugs and pipe breccias in the central Cordillera of Luzon and eastern Cordillera of Mindanao. Stupendous isostatic uplifts to as much as 2,000 m above sea-level of the two Cordilleras, inducing decollemente folding of the Upper Miocene-Pliocene beds, are evidenced. In many other localities horst block movement together with diapiric intrusions of serpentinized ultramafics and folding of the Upper Miocene-Pliocene beds are observed. In other places along the mobile belt, cone volcanoes started to form.

Plio-Pleistocene to Recent activities

Plio-Pleistocene to Quaternary deposits include extensive shallow marine to subterrestrial molasse deposits formed along major intermontane troughs; thick and extensive shelf coralline and bioclastic limestones along island margins, volcanic piedmont deposits around volcanic cones; and in places, as in Antipolo, Luzon and in central Mindanao, extrusions of plateau basalts. Marine and fluvial terrace sediments are also formed and several stranded levels of deposition from a few metres to as much as 250 m above the present sea-level are indicated. Late Pleistocene undeformed tuffaceous beds are also manifested, especially around the Manila area. Present sea transgression is in general indicated.

STRUCTURAL FEATURES

The structural features of the islands have already been described by the writer in 1964 and so it would be repetitious to cite most of them again in this paper.

Essentially, the Philippines are divided structurally into two regions, namely: the mobile belt which covers Luzon, Visayas and Mindanao; and the stable region which embraces Palawan, parts of Mindoro, the Sulu Sea and parts of Zamboanga and the Sulu Archipelago.

The mobile belt, about 300 km wide in the northern part and widening to more than 600 km to the south, consists of two convex and two concave arc segments or arc blocks (with respect to the Pacific), alternately disposed from north to south. Both arc blocks possess the usual structural elements of island arcs but arranged in opposite directions. Thus the convex Visayan arc block has an arcuate deep trench along the east, followed westward by an arcuate peridotite belt and frontal-thrust structural zone, and progressively to the west, by a complex series of Tertiary orogenic belts, and linear zones of active and recently inactive volcanoes with intervening zones of intermontane basins. The concave south Luzon arc block has the Manila Trench at the western edge followed similarly by a peridotite chain along an arcuate frontal thrust zone (Zambales-Mindoro structural zone) in a complex with a Tertiary intrusive

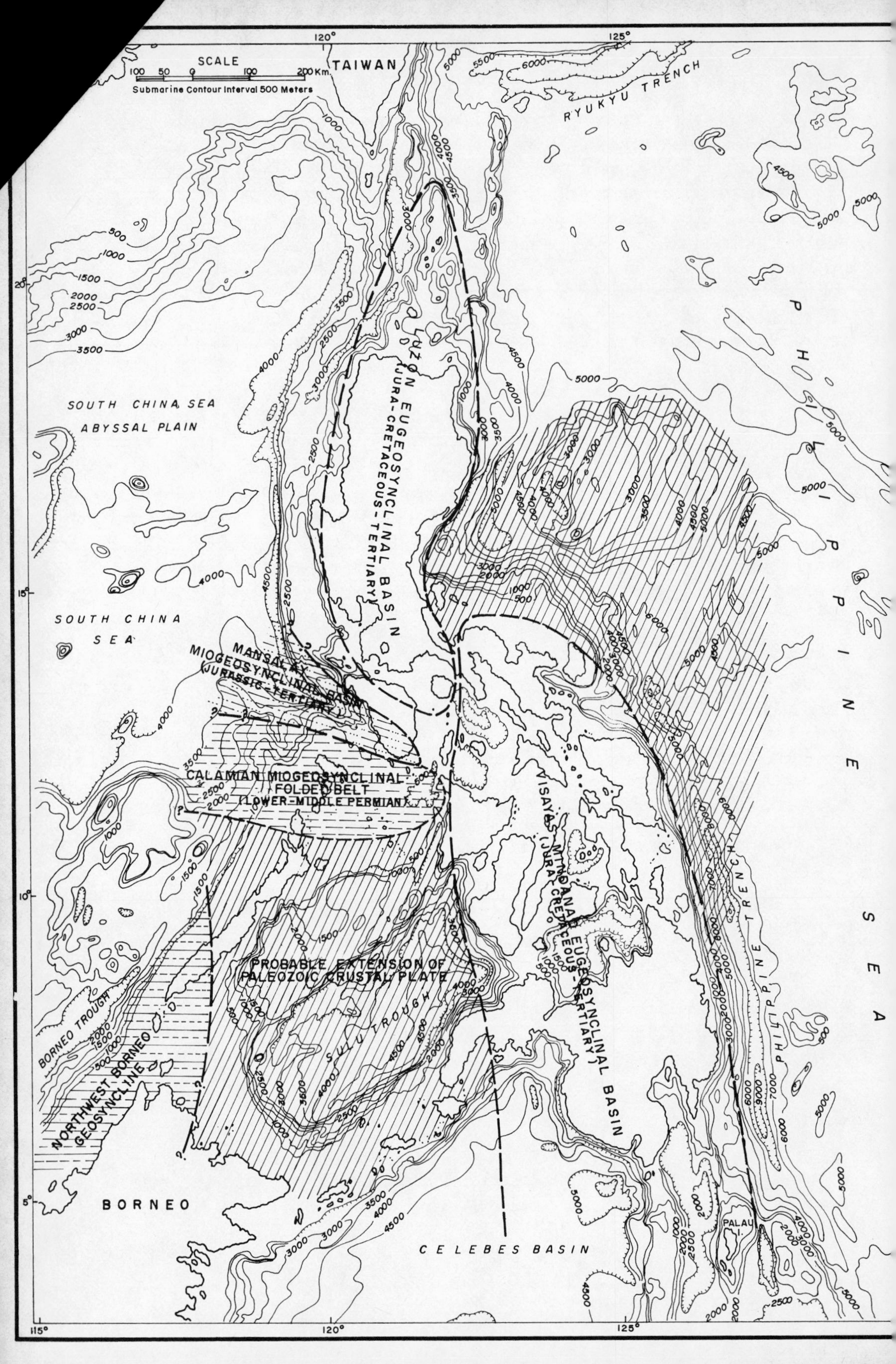
SCALE
100 50 0 100 200 Km.
Submarine Contour Interval 500 Meters
TAIWAN
RYUKYU TRENCH
120°
125°
115°
20°
15°
10°
5°
SOUTH CHINA SEA
ABYSSAL PLAIN
SOUTH CHINA
SEA
LUZON EUGEOSYNCLINAL BASIN
(JURA-CRETACEOUS-TERTIARY)
MANSALAY
MIOGEOSYNCLINAL BASIN
(JURASSIC-TERTIARY)
CALAMIAN MIOGEOSYNCLINAL
FOLDED BELT
(LOWER-MIDDLE PERMIAN)
PROBABLE EXTENSION OF
PALEOZOIC CRUSTAL PLATE
SULU TROUGH
BORNEO TROUGH
NORTHWEST BORNEO
GEOSYNCLINE
BORNEO
CELEBES BASIN
VISAYAS-MINDANAO EUGEOSYNCLINAL BASIN
(JURA-CRETACEOUS-TERTIARY)
PHILIPPINE TRENCH
PHILIPPINE SEA
PALAU I.

belt and linear zones of volcanoes, then the intermontane basin (central Luzon basin) and the Tertiary orogenic belt of Sierra Madre and Marinduque (Fig. 3).

Steeply-dipping transcurrent (strike-slip) faults, considered as lineaments of the arc system, separate the blocks. Along the zones of the Lingayen-Dingalan Lineament, the Antique-Tablas Lineament and the Mindanao Lineament, Tertiary dioritic intrusives, serpentinites, volcanoes and volcanic plugs are localized together with exotic blocks of different rock formations (melange zones?). Rock formations as young as Mio-Pliocene were usually affected by intense shearing, folding and/or brecciation due to recurrent movement along these zones. The structures also controlled evidently the emplacement of some Tertiary intrusives and volcanic activities.

The Philippine fault has been described by several authors (e.g. Alcaraz 1947, Alvir 1941, and Allen 1962) but much still remains to be studied. Strong indications of lateral movement are manifested especially where the said fault passes through the islands of Leyte and Mindanao. Measurement of displacement of a Miocene sedimentary facies in Mindanao along the fault (by a Mobil Company exploration team in 1963) is said to indicate about 28 km left-lateral movement. Reconstruction of the displaced Miocene volcanic ridge in Central Leyte also suggests about 30 km left-lateral displacement. Along Dingalan Valley, in Luzon, study of the supposed extension of the fault zone by Rutland (1968) also suggests possible left-lateral movement during the Cretaceous (?), but no important strike-slip movements appear to have occurred since the Miocene. Some splits of the fault which cut through a Pliocene fold belt of La Union and Ilocos Sur, however, can be seen in aerial photographs and clearly indicate several hundred metres of sinistral displacements.

It is possible that the various prominent fault splays considered part of the Philippine rift system within the Cordillera Central are not essentially part of it, but rather a separate fault system that may have been produced by an eastward subduction (?) movement at the Manila Trench; this in turn may have caused crustal spreading and eastward drifting of the north Luzon block (see Fig. 3).

PHASES OF GEOTECTONIC DEVELOPMENT

In summary, the regional geology of the Archipelago tends to indicate the following phases of geotectonic development:

1. So far as is known, a basement crust formed largely of schists, possibly with associated granite, existed during the Palaeozoic. It apparently represents deeply-

---

Fig. 2 Paleogeographic map showing possible extent of various geosynclinal basins and landmasses (Palaeozoic crustal plate-inclined hachure) during the Lower Cretaceous. Named elements (clockwise from the north) are: Luzon Eugeosynclinal Basin (Jur-Cretaceous-Tertiary); Visayas-Mindanao Eugeosynclinal Basin (Jur-Cretaceous-Tertiary); probable extension of Palaeozoic crustal plate; North-west Borneo Geosyncline; Calamian Miogeosynclinal Folded Belt (Lower-Middle Permian); Mansalay Miogeosynclinal Basin (Jurassic-Tertiary).

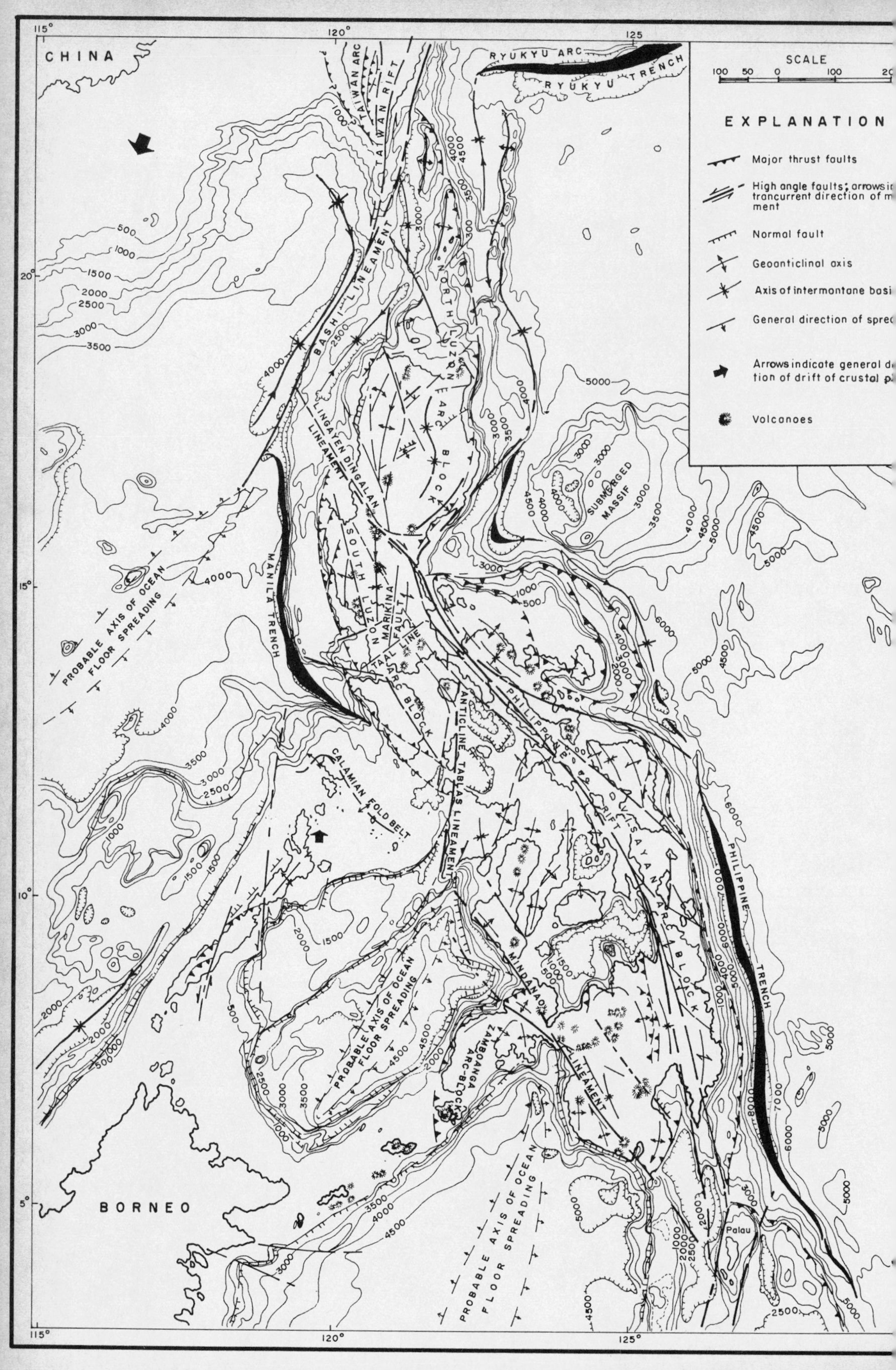
CHINA
RYUKYU ARC
RYUKYU TRENCH
SCALE
100 50 0 100
EXPLANATION
Major thrust faults
High angle faults; arrows i
trancurrent direction of m
ment
Normal fault
Geoanticlinal axis
Axis of intermontane basi
General direction of spre
Arrows indicate general d
tion of drift of crustal p
Volcanoes
TAIWAN ARC
TAIWAN RIFT
BASHI LINEAMENT
NORTH LUZON ARC BLOCK
LINGAYEN DINGALAN LINEAMENT
SOUTH LUZON
MARIKINA FAULT
TAAL LINE
ARC BLOCK
SUBMERGED MASSIF
MANILA TRENCH
PROBABLE AXIS OF OCEAN FLOOR SPREADING
PHILIPPINE RIFT
VISAYAN ARC BLOCK
ANTICLINE TABLAS LINEAMENT
CALAMIAN FOLD BELT
MINDANAO LINEAMENT
ZAMBOANGA ARC-BLOCK
PHILIPPINE TRENCH
BORNEO
Palau
115°
120°
125°
20°
15°
10°
5°

eroded NE-SW fold/orogenic belts extending from the Palawan-Sulu Sea area across the archipelago to the present Philippine Sea. Presumably, it was part of the Sunda shield or continental core of Borneo, if not a separate continental plate (see Fig. 2).

2. Restructuring of this crustal plate into a fold belt trending roughly E-W to NW-SE occurred during the Permian by the superposition of the Calamian geosyncline and its accompanying tectogenesis.

3. A Middle Permian synplatform cycle of transgression, molasse-limestone deposition, followed by orogenesis with granitic intrusions, presumably established a platform; this ended the Palaeozoic geotectonic cycle and converted the region into mostly positive areas that lasted through the Triassic.

4. Jurassic to Cretaceous times involved major reorganization of the region into a new geosynclinal system. A belt of nearly N-S eugeosynclinal basins (Luzon and Visayan geosynclines) developed along the Pacific side; a NW-SE miogeosynclinal basin (Mansalay geosyncline) formed along the west, adjacent to the eugeosynclinal belt, while at the south and south-west the North Borneo Geosyncline, extending to southern Palawan (Wilson 1962) was formed. Still another basin covered eastern Kalimantan. Intermittent, but progressively intensifying upwelling of spilites and basalts, attending geosynclinal sedimentation in most basins during Early Cretaceous, suggest growing internal unrest with progressive fracturing of the crust. Such unrest ended in the re-structuring of the eastern eugeosynclinal zone into a mobile belt, which apparently was climaxed by massive upwelling of spilites and basalts and tearing apart of portions of eugeosynclinal floors. In other parts of the region, uplift, shifting of geosynclinal axes and local folding occurred.

5. The Late Cretaceous geotectonic phase mainly involved cannibalistic sedimentation and further filling of most geosynclinal basins plus the development of plutono-volcanogenic activity (continued magmatic crystallization at depths) within the mobile belt.

6. An orogenic movement at the close of Cretaceous to early Paleocene started the first stage of transformation of geosynclines and mobile belt into a platform. In general, it involved folding and thrusting or crustal shortening and thickening.

Along the mobile belt, such disturbance was climaxed by the formation of island arc structures, with arcuate thrust zones formed along both sides of the belt; and perhaps by quasi-solid emplacement of ultramafics (layered and alpine types), and gabbro along the arcuate thrust zone, and of small masses of diorite porphyries along the central section, as in central Cebu (Atlas Mine porphyry).

7. The Palaeogene was marked by another cycle of regional gradual subsidence and sedimentation (Upper Paleocene to Eocene), followed by regression, which was ended by another orogenic event (second phase of platform development) during the Oligocene. In general there was folding and westward shifting of the western geosynclinal basins and thrusting of the basement crust. Along the mobile belt the orogenic phase was initially characterized by intermittent to intensive keratophyric volcanism,

---

Fig. 3 Schematic plate tectonic framework of the Philippines.

followed by crustal folding and reactivation of island arc structures; and finally by emplacement of quartz diorite stocks and dikes along reactivated island arc structures and developed fold belts at the inner zones of the arcs. Extensive positive areas were developed, which prevailed until late Oligocene. From recent knowledge about the Philippine Sea (Fischer *et al.* 1970), it appears that the developed landmass extended farther east to the Philippine Sea area. Geosynclinal conditions apparently still prevailed in western Borneo and southern Palawan, but in general there was marine regression in most areas.

8. The Miocene phase of activity involved a period of major re-organization of the region as a whole, although it did not significantly affect the ongoing third-stage cycle of platform development within the mobile belt and geosynclinal zone. Regional subsidence, fracturing and upwelling of spilites and basalts took place during early Miocene. The long standing crust of the Sulu Sea area underwent progressive oceanization from east to west. Part of the South China Sea and the Celebes Sea could similarly have undergone ocean-floor spreading (see Fig. 3). Temporal transgression occurred regionally, even along the developing platform areas, but subsequently orogenic movement, with accompanying emplacement of batholithic masses of quartz diorite re-elevated the orogenic belts and finally converted the mobile belt area into a platform.

9. A protracted cycle of orogenic activity from late Miocene to Pliocene involved a brief but rigorous cycle of erosion and molasse deposition, followed by intensive eruptive volcanism of acidic type materials and finally, at the close of Tertiary, an orogenic *coup de grace* raised, *en bloc,* the Miocene batholithic belts including the intra-orogenic belt and adjoining peripheral basin areas; in places the uplift was nearly 2,000 m. Some broad fold belts of Upper Miocene beds developed along the flanks. The development of young fold belts, in areas south of Manila, are generally accentuated by overthrusts and quasi-solid injections of serpentinized peridotites. Areas surrounding the mobile belt platform, in general, apparently continued to subside.

10. The Pliocene-Quaternary to Recent cycle has so far involved generally *en bloc* isostatic adjustment of the area, with an apparent tendency to break apart the Miocene established framework, through the formation of horsts and graben, recurrent movements of transcurrent faults and possible sea-floor spreading (see Fig. 3). Periodic activation of igneous activity along the mobile belt is manifested by formation of numerous volcanoes; in some places by basaltic effusions. There is a recognized trend among the active volcanoes to erupt more basic effusives. Regional fluctuation of sea-level is well recognized, with general regression during the Plio-Pleistocene and transgression in more recent times.

CONCLUSIONS

On the basis of observable geological features and recognized sequence of events, it is clear that the geotectonic development of the Philippines includes both short-term and long-term cycles of crustal reorganization.

The short-term cycles, apparently involving a frequency of 10-60 m.y. (growing shorter towards the platform stage) are demonstrated by the interplay of: (1) periods of crustal subsidence and sedimentation with (2) periods of orogeny. The former is usually accompanied by gradual marine transgression, often advancing into zones of previously established orogenic belts; while the latter is generally preceded by a transition stage characterized by gradual marine regression, followed by folding and/or thrusting of the crust, and culminating in the formation of a new mountain system. Along the mobile belt or plutono-volcanogenic zones, the regressive stage is generally characterized by intensive volcanic eruptions; and the end phase, by the formation of elements of island arcs and emplacement of fracture-oriented quasi-solid intrusives, of bulk composition usually slightly more basic than their penecontemporaneous eruptives.

The long-term cycles, apparently involving a frequency of 100-130 m.y., are manifested by the development of large eugeosynclines and/or mobile belts prevailing in a background of several short-term cycles, gradually changing into platforms. In the Philippine mobile belt, the long-term cycle is apparently characterized, at depths, by a more or less ongoing fractional crystallization of magma, sustaining progressively silicic stages of synorogenic igneous activity.

The occurrence of massive upwelling of spilites/basalts as an anticlimax to eugeosynclinal expansion and formation of mobile belts, suggests an intimate relationship of cycle development to changes occurring in the earth's interior region. In this context we can consider the colossal outpourings of lavas in many other parts of the globe during the particular Cretaceous geosynclinal stage, e.g. the Deccan trap of India, Stormberg lavas of South Africa, Parana basalts of South America, Spitzbergen basalts of the Arctic region, spilites of Borneo, northern New Zealand and elsewhere (Turner & Verhoogen 1960). These outpourings amounted to millions of cubic miles of materials moved out from the depths. Such global occurrences cannot be due simply to upwelling currents nor to any conceivable development at surface or near-surface. More likely, it is due to a significant change of gravity value which could have accentuated, if not triggered, substantial phase changes and volume expansion of the more sensitive portions of the earth's interior region, such as the transition zone between the upper and lower mantle. The dilatation effect on the rigid upper mantle could have resulted in the gradual incision of dilatation fractures, while the crust initially underwent stretching, thinning and fracturing, regional oceanization and geosynclinal formation. Later, as the dilatation fractures became accentuated, a free avenue for escape of activated mantle materials could have been effected, accounting for such colossal outpourings on the surface.

On the other hand, the generally manifested orogenic movements, the nature of their associated deformation, the systematic sequence of emplacement of igneous intrusives during a particular geotectonic cycle—ultramafics, gabbro-diorite during the first orogenic phase, diorite-quartz diorite during the second, and largely quartz diorite-granodiorite during the platform stage—and the formation of island arc structures in general, are still adequately explicable by the classical notion of crustal compression.

It can be presupposed, following the generally temporal behaviour of global tectogenesis, that expansion of the interior region is a temporary activity, and that, as the dilatation stress subsides, an opposite reaction would set in. Either it would be due to isostatic compensation, considering previous material loss from the interior region, and/or due to actual contraction, as the earth eventually moved out from the influence of a stronger gravitational field.

The rigid upper-mantle layer, to accomplish necessary shortening of its circumference, was possibly partly thrusted along pre-existing dilatation fracture zones. The crust, in response to such movement, equally shortened its circumference through folding and thrusting; became depressed where the upper mantle layer was underthrusted, or tossed to great elevations where mantle was overthrusted. It is not necessary for a mountain to be in isostatic equilibrium with the adjacent crust when they may both be supported by the upper mantle itself.

Entrapped activated mantle materials along dilatation fracture zones below the crust—and crystallizing as a primary magma when compressed during periods of contraction—are likely to develop intense hydrostatic stress. The quasi-solid and/or viscous crystalline fractions are forced out (as in the action of a hydraulic press), leaving behind the more silicic liquid fractions. Thus, upon reaching platform stage when the remaining residual fractions of the magma would have largely crystallized, it is relatively more silicic in bulk composition and emplaced in quasi-solid forms.

The course of the earth's orbit around the Milky Way galaxy, of which we know so little, could contain the reason for expansion or contraction. We are familiar with the fact that the earth, in its present position, would take about 225 m.y. to complete one revolution around the centre of the Milky Way, and as a general system of motion of planetary bodies, at least once in every cycle the earth is placed in apogee or perigee position. The perigee to apogee time-span appears to correspond in length of time to the long term cycle or geotectonic cycle, which, as mentioned earlier, is about 100-130 m.y.

However, from the viewpoint that the Milky Way is a spiral galaxy, and its member bodies are moving inward in time towards the centre, where the population density is markedly concentrated and the gravity field is very much stronger, then indeed, in agreement with Carey, 1958 (and as earlier suggested by Halm in 1935), the earth has essentially expanded. Now there is possibly renewed expansion, as manifested by current ocean-floor spreading and general sea transgression.

REFERENCES

Allen, C. R. 1962. Circumpacific faulting in the Philippines-Taiwan region. *Philipp. Geol.* **16,** 122-45.

Amato, F. L. 1965. Stratigraphic paleontology in the Philippines. *Philipp. Geol.* **19,** 1-24.

Andal, D. R., Esquerra, J. S., Hashimoto, W., Reyes, B. P. & Sato, T. 1968. The Jurassic Mansalay formation, southern Mindoro, Philippines. *Geology and Palaeontology of Southeast Asia,* **4,** 179-97 (Eds T. Kobayashi & R. Toriyama). Univ. Tokyo Press, Tokyo.

Andal, P. P. 1966. A report on the discovery of Fusilinids in the Philippines. *Philipp. Geol.* **20,** 14-22.

Beloussov, V. V. 1960. Tectonic map of the earth. *Geol. Rundsch.* **50,** 316-24.

——— 1961. Development of the earth and tectogenesis. *Philipp. Geol.* **15,** 27-58.

Carey, S. W. 1958. The tectonic approach to continental drift. *Continental Drift Symposium, Univ. Tasmania*, 177-355. Hobart.

Christian, L. B. 1964. Post-Oligocene tectonic history of the Cagayan basin, Philippines. *Philipp. Geol.* **18,** 114-47.

Corby, G. W. *et al.* 1951. Geology and oil possibilities of the Philippines. *Dept. Agric. & Nat. Resources Tech. Bull.* **21.** Manila.

Espiritu, E. A. *et al.* 1968. Biostratigraphy of Bondoc Peninsula, Quezon. *Philipp. Geol.* **22,** 63-90.

Fernandez, J. C. & Pulanco, D. H. 1970. Reconnaissance geology of north-western Luzon. *Min. Eng. Mag.* **21,** 14-28. Manila.

Fernandez, N. S. 1960. Notes on the geology and chromite deposits of the Zambales range. *Philipp. Geol.* **14,** 1-8.

Fischer, A. G., Heezen, B. C., Boyce, R. E., Bukry, D., Douglas, R. G., Garrison, R. E., Kling, S. A., Krasheninnikov, V., Lisitzin, A. P. & Pimm, A. C. 1970. Geological history of the Western North Pacific. *Science,* **168** (3936), 1210-14.

Fitch, F. H. 1963. Geological relationship between the Philippines and Borneo. *Philipp. Geol.* **17,** 41-7.

Gervasio, F. C. 1964. A study of the tectonics of the Philippine Archipelago. *22nd Intern. Geol. Congr., New Delhi, 1964, Proc.* **4,** 582-607.

——— 1967. Age and nature of orogenesis of the Philippines. *Tectonophysics,* **4,** 379-402.

Grey, R. R. 1967. Time-stratigraphic correlation of Tertiary rocks in the Philippines. *Philipp. Geol.* **21,** 1-21.

Gutenberg, B. & Richter, C. F. 1954. *Seismicity of the Earth and Associated Phenomena.* Princeton Univ. Press, Princeton, New York.

Hashimoto, W. 1951. Submarine morphology of the Philippine Archipelago and its geological significance. *Philipp. J. Sci.* **80,** 55-88.

——— 1969. Paleontology of the Philippines. *Geology and Palaeontology of Southeast Asia,* **6,** 293-329 (Eds T. Kobayashi & R. Toriyama). Univ. Tokyo Press, Tokyo.

Hashimoto, W. & Sato, T. 1968. Contribution to the geology of Mindoro and neighbouring islands, the Philippines. In *Geology and Palaeontology of Southeast Asia,* **5,** 192-210 (Eds T. Kobayashi & R. Toriyama). Univ. Tokyo Press, Tokyo.

Irving, E. M. 1952. Geological history and petroleum possibilities of the Philippines. *Bull. Am. Ass. Petrol. Geol.* **36** (3), 437-76.

Matsumoto, T. 1967. Fundamental problems in the circum-Pacific orogenesis. *Tectonophysics,* **4,** 595-613.

Ordoñez, E. & Reyes, M. V. 1970. Upper Cretaceous smaller foraminifera of the Philippines. *J. Geol. Soc. Philipp.* In press.

Parke, Jr., M. L., Emery, K. O., Szymankiewicz, R. & Reynolds, L. M. 1971. Structural framework of continental margin in South China Sea. *Bull. Am. Ass. Petrol. Geol.* **55,** 723-51.

Rutland, R. W. 1968. A tectonic study of part of the Philippine fault zone. *J. geol. Soc. London.* **123,** 293-325.

Samaniego, R. M. 1964. The occurrence of *Globorotalia velascoensis* in the Philippines. *Philipp. Geol.* **18,** 65-74.

Santiago, P. D. 1963. Planktonic Foraminifera species from west side of Tarlac Province, Luzon Central Valley. *Philipp. Geol.* **17,** 69-99.

Santos, P. J. 1968. Geology and section measurements in Iloilo Basin Panay Island, Philippines. *Philipp. Geol.* **22,** 1-62.

Smith, W. D. 1924. *Geology and Mineral Resources of the Philippine Islands*. Bureau of Printing, Manila, 1924.

Turner, F. J. & Verhoogen, J. 1960. *Igneous and Metamorphic Petrology*. 2nd ed. McGraw-Hill, New York.

Villavicencio, M. L. & Andal, P. P. 1964. *Distichoplax biserialis* (Dietrich) in the Philippines. *Philipp. Geol.* **18,** 103-14.

Wilson, R. A. M. 1962. Geology of the region (Borneo). *Br. Borneo geol. Surv. Ann. Rept* (1962), 17-19.

PART III

Tectonic Development of Trenches in the Western Pacific

N. A. Bogdanov

Geological Institute, Academy of Sciences of the U.S.S.R.
Pyzhevsky per. 7, Moscow G-17, U.S.S.R.

ABSTRACT

Oceanic trenches can be traced all along the island arcs of the Western Pacific. They have similar morphological and geophysical features, are characterized by thick, unconsolidated and undeformed sediments, mainly turbidites of greywacke composition. Turbidites are deposited both on the ocean-basalt floor and on pelagic sediments. Accumulation of turbidites in a number of trenches commenced in the Eocene and has continued up to recent times, that is, over the last 50 m.y. In their structure, trenches are similar to thalassogeosynclines, and it is likely that their cycle of development proceeded between stages of folding. Analysis of the structure of sediment thickness does not permit the supposition of a 'subduction' process under island arcs. It is more likely that the trenches appeared in a time of folding as a result of extension at the front of arcs. Later, during the geosyncline cycle, they accumulated sediments. In subsequent times of folding, the underthrusting of the oceanic crust under the continental one occurred, and formation of overthrust and melange zones along oceanic coasts of island arcs took place.

In the western part of the Pacific Ocean oceanic trenches run parallel to and alongside the chains of island arcs (see the frontispiece map). In fact, trenches form a nearly continuous strip, stretching from Alaska to the North Island of New Zealand. They are narrow, do not exceed 50-80 km in width and are up to 8-10 km in depth; relative depth of the axial part of trenches, with respect to the ocean bed, is about 4-5 km. As a rule, coastal trench slopes are steeper (8°-15°) on the side of the continent than on the oceanic side (3°-8°). The slope angles increase as the depth increases and the central part of a trench has a V-shaped form. The actual bottom is relatively flat. From the morphological point of view trenches are basically similar—their only difference lies in their depth and length (see Fig. 2 in Raitt *et al.* 1955).

On the average, sediment thickness in the recent trenches ranges from 1-3 km; only at the ends does the thickness reach 4 km. In addition to trenches which are clearly seen in the sea-bottom structure, there are trenches actually filled with sediment—near Tierra del Fuego (Scholl *et al.* 1970), at the south-eastern coast of Alaska (Shor 1966) and near the South Island, New Zealand. In such cases, sediment thickness amounts to 6-8 km. Unconsolidated sediments, according to the dredging data, are represented by greywacke sands, red and black clays and in some cases by volcanogenic formations. They contain radiolarian and planktonic foraminiferal oozes, but sometimes also fragments of shallow-water fossils, thrown into the trench by turbidity currents from the continental slope. Both turbidity and bottom currents pass the sediments along the trench and that is why upper sedimentary layers may consist of turbidites.

In some places (Tonga-Kermadec and Mariana Trenches) turbidites cover directly rocks of the 'basalt' layer. In other places (Alaskan, Kuril and Chilean Trenches) they are underlain by pelagic sediments in layers parallel to the sea floor. This pelagic slime is usually much less than turbidite thickness and does not exceed several hundred metres.

The whole thickness of undeformed trench sediments unconformably adjoins the oceanic and continental slopes in the same manner as the fill of graben structures does the more ancient formations of the graben sides. Fig. 5 in Scholl *et al.* shows well this and other trench features.

The rocks of trench slopes differ greatly from trench sediments. Among the lithologies raised as a result of dredging at depths down to 2,500 m, volcanic and volcanogenic formations (lava and tuff of basalt and andesite) are dominant. They are of the same age as those volcanic rocks which in large part form island arcs. Down the slope in the Mariana Trench (Karig 1971 and this volume), in the Tonga-Kermadec (Fisher & Engel 1969, especially Fig. 2) and in the New Hebrides Trenches (Udintsev & Dmitriyev 1971) there are metabasalts, greenstone, tuffs, gabbroic rocks and amphibolites. Diabases can also be found in these places. Besides volcanic rocks, there are arenites and clays, of Tertiary and Late Cretaceous age, on the slope.

On the oceanic slope, the main sediments found by dredging are Recent pelagic; in the Tonga-Kermadec Trench ultrabasic rocks (serpentinous pyroxenites and dunites) were also found. According to R. Fisher the lower 2 km of trench slope consist of these formations with trench turbidities adjoining them.

From the gravity point of view, trenches are characterized by negative gravity anomalies, the values of which range within 170-250 mgl (Bowin 1966). Heat flow ranges within 0·3 and $0{\cdot}5.10^{-6}$ cal/s.cm^2. This is almost three times less than the measurements of heat flow in the oceanic bed and four times and a half less than heat flow of island arc areas (Lee, Uyeda & Taylor 1966). Island arcs are considered to be the most seismic structures in the world and the hypocentres of many deep-focus earthquakes are located under them. Epicentres of shallow-focus earthquakes (depth of focus 0-200 km) which are located below trenches, make up no more than 3-5 per cent of the total number of the same type, recorded within the arc region. The majority of earthquake hypocentres concentrate along focal planes, the Benioff zones, which dip towards island arcs from the trench axes at an angle of about 45° to depths of up to 650 km. According to Mitronovas and others (1969) the Benioff zone thickness does not exceed 50-100 km (Fig. 1).

The structure of the earth's crust in trench locations has some specific peculiarities. As already mentioned, sediment thickness in the trenches amounts to 2-3 km. As a rule, trenches lack the metamorphosed and dense sediment layer. Very often the sediments occur directly on the second layer (velocity 5·0-6·0 km/s) with thickness of up to 1-2 km. The 'basalt' layer in the limits of a trench is usually not more than 3-4 km (6·6-6·8 km/s velocities). Thus, an average thickness of the earth crust beneath trenches reaches 6-10 km, which is somewhat less than usual oceanic crust: the crust beneath trenches has thicker sediment but a lesser thickness of the second and 'basalt' layers. Kuril-Kamchatka profiles, given by Weizman (1966), show these features well.

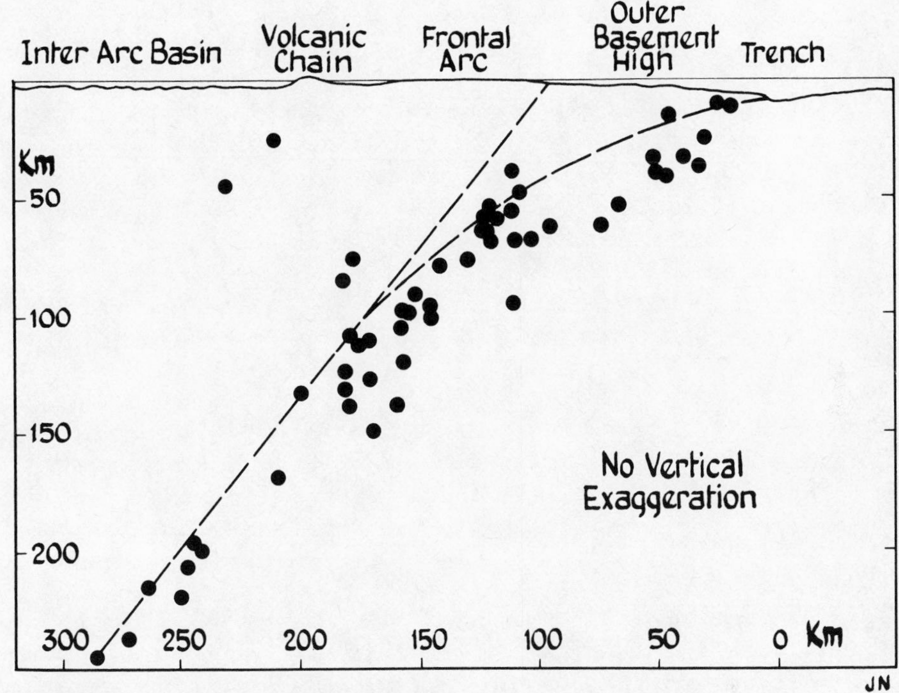

Fig. 1 Cross section of the Benioff zone beneath the Tonga Islands. The dashed lines are added primarily to emphasize the change in dip beneath the volcanic chain (after Mitronovas *et al.* 1969).

As is known, the present trenches are of Miocene and, seldom, Eocene ages, that is, they were formed in post-Cretaceous time. The tectonic zones, which occur among structures along the continental margins, may well be the trenches of the Mesozoic and Palaeozoic. After their filling with volcanogenic and sedimentary material they were joined to the continents as a result of tectonic activity. This type of eugeosyncline we have called thalassogeosynclines (Bogdanov 1969). They have been found in California, Hokkaido and Sakhalin, the Koryak Mountains and the South Island of New Zealand (Bogdanov 1967, 1970).

The complex of volcanogenic and sedimentary rocks of such areas has long attracted the attention of many geologists. About 90 per cent of the total volume consists of greywackes, bearing evidence of turbidite flows. These formations are weakly expressed in lateral extension, have very inconsistent stratification and contain volcanic rock fragments. Fine-grained material, represented by mudstone and schists, are similar in their composition to the coarse-grained formations. It is a characteristic that the greywackes contain quartz and rare feldspar, brought from the adjacent area of the continental and subcontinental type of crust. It seems that such areas represent former island arcs. However, the monotony of the basic part of the mineral composition of the trench-fill, is witness that both its sides were made of similar formations. Some portion of material, mainly fine-grained from which greywackes and schists were formed at a later time, was deposited by the erosion of the sides. Coarse-grained material was brought mainly from the continental slope. Later, the sedimentary material was redistributed by turbidite flows along the trench extension.

Volcanic rocks, pillow lavas and their tuffs, as well as siliceous schists and jasper have been found among the greywackes as separate interlayers. With them lenses of limestone may be associated. All these sediments are likely to be accumulated near the centres of volcanic activity.

Enormous masses of greywackes, up to 15-20 km in thickness, were accumulated in such trenches during 50-100 m.y. So then, we should accept that trenches are long-existent structures. For comparison we can indicate that some of today's trenches, e.g. the Puerto Rico and Alaskan ones, have existed from the Eocene, that is, about 50 m.y. Sedimentation of greywackes took place not only on the basalt layer but also on the pelagic sediments of the oceanic crust, as has been found in California by Bailey and others (Bailey, Blake & Jones 1971). In this respect also, there is a similarity between thalassogeosynclines and recent trenches. Again, in the trenches and in the thalassogeosyncline as well, there is no evidence of high temperatures; even in the folded areas of thalassogeosynclines the formation of granitoid rocks has not occurred (Fig. 2).

In almost all the areas where thalassogeosynclines have been found, their masses were thrust under the respective island arc as a result of tectonic activity at the end of the Lower Cretaceous and during Upper Cretaceous. Horizontal displacements reach 100-200 km.

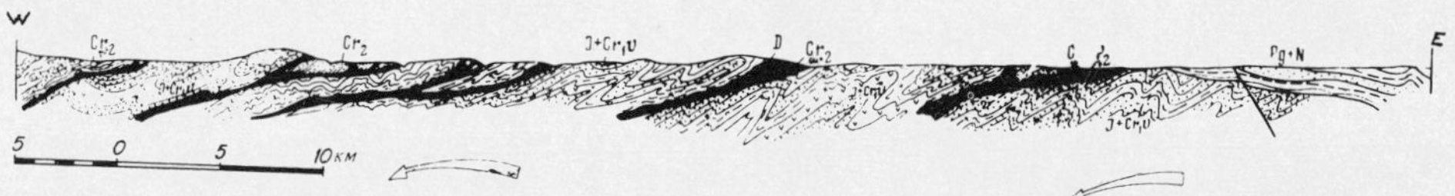

Fig. 2 Geological cross-section of the eastern Koryak Mountains: a thalassogeosynclinal sequence lacking granitoid rocks.

As a result of this kind of displacement, 'tectonic covers' were formed on the oceanic slope of the arc, and melange and 'basalt' layer structures appeared at the surface (Peive 1969, Peive *et al.* 1971). Judging by the nature of dislocation of the strata, which cover the greywacke pile, horizontal displacement occurred during a short period of geological time, commensurate with the period of orogenesis, and did not recur.

The sum of these data suggest that present-day trenches should not be considered as areas of continuous absorption of the oceanic crust along Benioff zones. If absorption occurred along trenches, two variants in depositional character of the sedimentary pile should be observed. In the first, the thickness of sediments would be increased on account of squeezing in front of the island arc; the sequence of accumulation would never be observed, and the whole area of the trenches would be characterized exclusively by complicated dislocations even in the recent deposits. The result would be the formation of a melange several kilometres in vertical thickness. We have not observed examples of this in any trench.

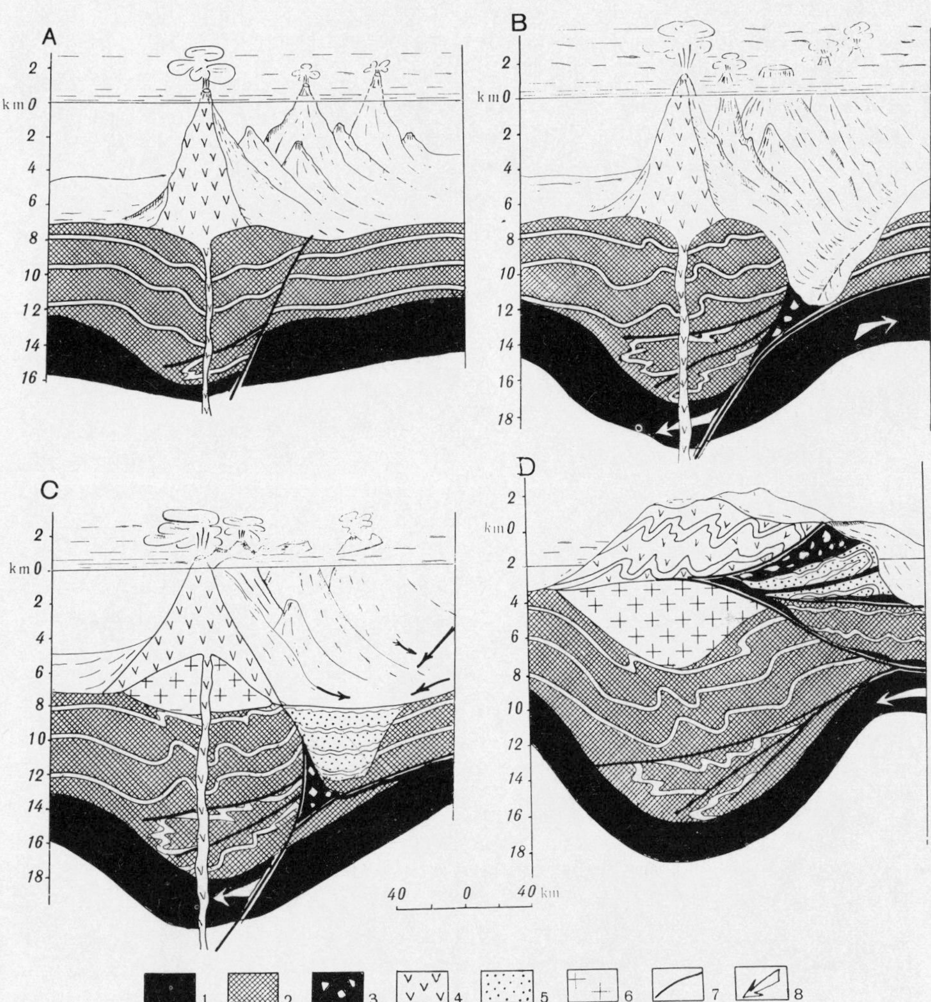

Fig. 3 Hypothetical cross-sections of a trench at various stages of its development. A, formation of a volcanic range; B, formation of a trench; C, filling with sediments; D, underthrust of simatic crust beneath continental one. 1, upper mantle; 2, 'basalt' layer; 3, serpentine melange; 4, volcanic rocks of island arc; 5, turbidite trenches; 6, melanocratic gneisses and metamorphosed rocks; 7, tectonic breaks; 8, direction of movement of the crust.

In the second variant, it is supposed that all the sediments of the oceanic plate, together with its margins, were subducted under the island arc. Squeezing does not occur in the trench, and the character of sediments and their thickness will be similar to those of the oceanic plates. However, all the known trenches differ in their sediment from those of the oceanic bed.

There is a final significant inconsistency of geological data with the hypothesis of crustal subduction: with continuing subduction the formation of melange in front of the island arc occurs over the duration of many millions of years (at least 50), not within a single period of orogenesis or folding. Examples of this are not known in any known folded area. We suggest a hypothesis for another mechanism of trench formation, which, in general, is similar to that of Worzel (1966).

It begins with the formation, along the ocean margins, of deep or abyssal fracture zones which involve both the oceanic crust and upper mantle. The formation of these zones, bordering ocean plates, is likely to have occurred only in definite tectonic epochs, for example, in the West Pacific, in the Lower Cambrian, Late Ordovician, Lower Permian and Lower Cretaceous. Following fracturing, the reduced vertical pressure is compensated by side pressure and one can observe squeezing of 'basalt' layer structures. The initial roots of a volcanic range are thus formed. Further decrease in vertical pressure causes melting of the upper-mantle rocks and under-water eruption of volcanoes (Fig. 3*a*). With continuing volcanism the accumulation of great masses of basalt and volcanogenic and sedimentary rocks takes place in the range area, and a depression (probably with no clear contours as yet) begins to form near the range. The following stage is isostatic compensation of the volcanic arc and movement of third, and probably second layer material as well, from under the depression. As a result, thick 'basalt' roots are formed under the range and the thickness of the second layer reaches 15-20 km, whereas under the depression it decreases to 3-5 km (Fig. 3*b*). At the same time, a narrow zone of 5 km depth is formed on the ocean floor, that is, a trench. In front of the arc, on the trench slope, an ophiolite belt and melange zone are formed because of the displacement of the ocean bed formations (Knipper 1971, Peive *et al.* 1971).

Under this hypothesis, therefore, trenches are formed as a result of spreading or tectonic and mechanical displacement of third-layer material towards the arc.

During further stages of the geological history, the trench is filled with volcanogenic and terrigeneous material similar to that of the Alpine complex of New Zealand, the Franciscan complex of California and of the Piculney complex of the Koryak Mountains (Fig. 3*c*).

With the trench filled with sediments, masses of simatic crust again underthrust the island arc as a result of consequential spreading or of displacement of the third-layer formations in the limits of the ocean. This arises from a period of general orogeny affecting most of the earth surface. In this way, the covering layers, well known in the South-west Pacific, are formed (Fig. 3*d*).

If we assume that crustal subduction has occurred gradually along the Benioff zone, then great thicknesses of sediments would never have accumulated in the oceanic trenches. The geologist would not have the opportunity, as indeed he has, to study known sequences of such sediments. This is an intriguing paradox.

REFERENCES

Bailey, E. H., Blake, M. C. & Jones, D. L. 1970. On-land Mesozoic oceanic crust in California Coast ranges. *U.S. geol. Surv. Prof. Pap.* **700-**C, 70-81.

Bogdanov, N. A. 1967. Paleozoic geosynclines of the western part of the Circum-Pacific belt. *Tectonophysics,* **4** (4-6), 581 (abstr.).

——— 1969. Thalassogeosynclines of the Circum-Pacific belt. *Geotektonika,* **3** (in Russian). (Eng. trans. *Geotectonics,* **3,** 141-7.)

——— 1970. Some aspects of tectonics of eastern Koryak Mountains. *Dokl. Akad. Nauk SSSR,* **192** (3) (in Russian).

Bowin, C. 1966. Gravity over trenches and rifts. In *Continental margins and island arcs. Geol. Surv. Pap. Can.* 66-15, 430-9.

Fisher, R. L. & Engel, C. G. 1969. Ultramafic and basaltic rocks dredged from the nearshore flank of the Tonga Trench. *Bull. geol. Soc. Am.* **80** (7), 1373-8.

Karig, D. E. 1971. Origin and development of marginal basins in the Western Pacific. *J. geophys. Res.* **76** (11), 2542-61.

Knipper, A. L. 1971. History and evolution of the serpentinitic melange of Lesser Caucasus. *Geotektonika,* **6** (in Russian).

Lee, W. H. K., Uyeda, S. & Taylor, P. T. 1966. Geothermal studies of continental margins and island arcs. In *Continental margins and island arcs. Geol. Surv. Pap. Can.* 66-15, 398-414.

Markov, M. S. 1970. Metamorphic complexes and their place in the evolution history of island arcs. *Geotektonika,* **2** (in Russian). (Eng. trans. *Geotectonics* **2,** 1970.)

Mitronovas, W., Isacks, B. & Seeber, L. 1969. Earthquake locations and seismic wave propagation in the upper 250 km of the Tonga Island arc. *Bull. seism. Soc. Am.* **59** (3), 1115-36.

Peive, A. V. 1969. Oceanic crust in past geological time. *Geotektonika,* **4** (in Russian). (Eng. trans. *Geotectonics,* 1969, **4,** 210- 24.)

Peive, A. V., Schtres, N. A., Knipper, A. L., Markov, M. S., Bogdanov, N. A., Perfil'yev, A. S. & Ruzhentsev, S. V. 1971. Oceans and the geosyncline process. *Dokl. Akad. Nauk SSSR,* **196** (3) (in Russian).

Raitt, R. W., Fisher, R. L. & Mason, R. C. 1955. Tonga Trench. *Spec. Publ. geol. Soc. Am.* **62,** 237-54.

Scholl, D. W., Christensen, M. N., von Huene, R. & Marlow, M. S. 1970. Peru-Chile Trench sediments and sea-floor spreading. *Bull. geol. Soc. Am.* **81,** 1339-60.

Shor, G. G. Jr. 1966. Continental margins and island arcs of Western North America. In *Continental margins and island arcs. Geol. Surv. Pap. Can.* 66-15, 216-21.

Udintsev, G. B. & Dmitriyev, L. V. 1971. Evolution of the oceanic lithosphere and geological-geophysical investigation in the western part of the Pacific Ocean. *Vest. Akad. Nauk SSSR,* **11** (in Russian).

Weizman, P. S. 1966. On the deep structure in the Kuril-Kamchatka region. In *Continental margins and island arcs. Geol. Surv. Pap. Can.* 66-15, 244-51.

Worzel, J. L. 1966. Structure of continental margins and development of ocean trenches. In *Continental margins and island arcs. Geol. Surv. Pap. Can.* 66-15, 357-75.

New Zealand Fault Zones and Sea-floor Spreading

H. W. Wellman

Geology Department, Victoria University of Wellington, Wellington, N.Z.

ABSTRACT

From the position of fault zones and from the direction of relative horizontal fault displacements, a microplate and three zones of copolar faults are inferred for New Zealand for the last 10,000 years: a southern zone (southern part of Alpine Fault Zone); two western zones (W. Nelson and Volcanic Fault Zones); and an eastern zone (northern part of Alpine Fault Zone). The three Eulerian poles for these zones, being effectively instantaneous, lie on a great circle. The southern (55° S, 180° E) is that of the Melanesian Geosuture of which the New Zealand fault zones make up a small part. The Melanesian Geosuture extends south from New Zealand to a triple-point-junction (62° S, 162° E) with the South Pacific Geosuture and with the South-east Indian Ocean Geosuture. From sea-floor spreading data the Eulerian pole for the South Pacific Geosuture is at 70° S, 120° E. The Eulerian pole for the Melanesian Geosuture is adopted from the New Zealand data. The Eulerian poles are first considered as being instantaneous, and fixed relative to each other. The pole for the South-east Indian Ocean Geosuture then lies on the great circle through the pole for the South Pacific Geosuture and the pole for the Melanesian Geosuture, and is inferred to be at about 10° S, 150° W from sea-floor spreading data. From the adopted Eulerian pole positions and the sea-floor spreading data, the full Eulerian equatorial relative rotation rate for the Melanesian Geosuture is inferred to be about 154 mm per year. The Alpine Fault Zone is 12° from the pole of the Melanesian Geosuture and its instantaneous dextral displacement is thus about 35 mm per year, a value in close agreement with that inferred from New Zealand data for the last 10,000 years.

Sea-floor spreading data indicates that the Eulerian poles are not relatively fixed, but that the pole for the Melanesian Geosuture is moving away from the southern end of the Alpine Fault Zone at 60 mm per year. The relative rotation rates for the poles of the three geosutures have, however, probably been about the same for the last 10 m.y. The rate of dextral displacement on the Alpine Fault Zone is thus probably accelerating, and the instantaneous rate will be substantially valid for the last few 10 m.y. only. Total displacement on the Alpine Fault Zone is about 450 km. Allowing for the acceleration, 300 km of displacement probably took place in the last 10 m.y., and less certainly 400 km in the last 2 × 10 m.y.

INTRODUCTION

As interpreted here the basic concept of sea-floor spreading is concerned with relative horizontal displacement only. It is first assumed that the earth's radius has not changed appreciably during the last few 10 m.y., and hence the crustal shortening equals crustal extension (spreading). It is then assumed that the crust of the earth consists of a limited number of macroplates that are moving horizontally relative to each other and are separated by boundaries here termed geosutures. Geosutures range in width from almost zero to several hundred kilometres or more and terminate at the junction of two other geosutures at triple point junctions.

Hence the sea-floor spreading concept deals only with the 'relative horizontal displacement' part of crustal deformation. It thus neglects vertical displacement but has the great advantage that for any particular interval of time the relative horizontal displacements for the whole or any part of the earth can be analyzed and integrated.

In a small region, such as that of New Zealand, the earth's curvature can be neglected and the relative horizontal displacement of any two adjoining plates can be represented by the displacement of one sheet of paper relative to one below, that is by the cutting and sliding of maps. For two such sheets, each considered to have a centre, and each considered to be unlimited in extent, there is always one point that is not displaced, the non-displaced point being the point around which each sheet has been rotated relative to the other. For the flat situation the point of rotation may be very distant from the centre of the sheets.

In a large region, because of the inevitable map distortion, this simple method cannot be used. However, according to Euler's theorem, for any particular geosuture there are always two antipodal poles defined by the axis of relative rotation for that particular geosuture, and one of the poles must be 90° or less from any point on its geosuture.

The antipodal poles are here termed 'Eulerian' in order to distinguish them from the geographical poles; and for any geosuture, unless both are on the equator, one is in the northern and the other in the southern hemisphere. For any particular interval of time the axis of relative rotation is fixed relative to each of the two crustal plates that adjoin the geosuture, but in general it has a different position for other time intervals.

In contrast with those within the continents and at the continental margins, the oceanic geosutures are extremely narrow zig-zag features consisting of lines of active spreading connected by strike-slip faults at right angles to them. Together, the spreading lines and strike-slip faults constitute active transform tectonic systems (Wellman 1971*b*). With respect to the Eulerian poles (EPs) for any particular active oceanic geosuture, the spreading lines approximate to segments of great circles, and the strike-slip faults to segments of small circles.

Continental and continental-margin geosutures are wider and more complex than those of the oceans. They are up to several hundred kilometres wide and are generally curved and not zig-zagged like those of the oceans. Relative horizontal fault displacement is generally partly compression and partly strike-slip. A further complication is the existence of micro-plates within such geosutures.

The Melanesian Geosuture (MG) is defined here (Figs 1 & 2) as the belt of rapid relative horizontal displacement that extends from a triple point junction some 2,900 km south-east of New Zealand to a triple point junction some 6,000 km north-east of New Zealand. As shown later, the southern Eulerian pole for the Melanesian

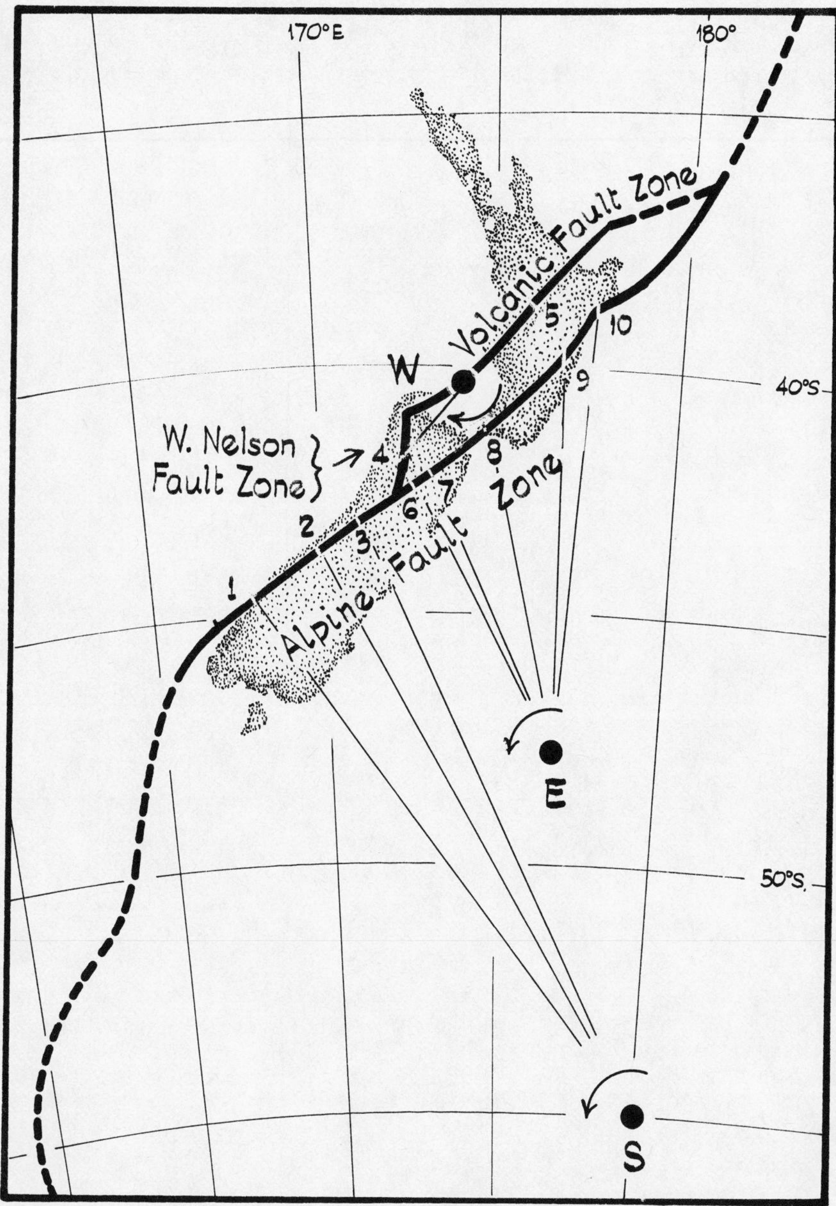

Fig. 1 Sketch map of New Zealand, showing inferred directions of relative horizontal displacement (DRHD) inferred from faulting and from geodetic re-observations. Locality numbers are those in Table 1. The normalized DRHD directions in the table are taken from this figure. The three copolar fault zones (S, E & W) are defined by the ends of the lines radiating from their poles. The arrows near the three poles indicate the sense of rotation of the eastern relative to the western side of the three copolar fault zones.

Geosuture is only 1,300 km south-south-east of the middle of New Zealand, and its axis of relative rotation can be more accurately defined from New Zealand data than it can from data to the north of New Zealand, or from SFS (sea-floor spreading) data.

NEW ZEALAND DATA

Within New Zealand the Melanesian Geosuture is represented by three zones of active faulting that were first recognized, but not named, by Henderson in 1937: the north-east-trending Alpine Fault Zone; the north-east-trending Volcanic Fault Zone; and the north-trending West Nelson Fault Zone. The three fault zones are here considered to enclose a micro-plate which lies within the Melanesian Geosuture. As shown later, the direction of relative horizontal displacement (DRHDs) of the plate boundaries within New Zealand define three Eulerian poles (Fig. 1): one for the two fault zones on the western side of the micro-plate; one for that part of the Alpine Fault Zone on the eastern side of the micro-plate; and one for that part of the Alpine Fault Zone to the south of the micro-plate. In Fig. 1 the poles are shown accordingly as W, E, and S. It should be noted that the Volcanic Fault Zone and the micro-plate are probably only a million or so years old but other microplates probably existed earlier.

The parts or combinations of the fault zones having the same Eulerian poles are here termed copolar, and the individual faults within each of the three copolar fault zones are themselves considered to be approximately copolar.

Hence the DRHD for faults within the zones of copolar faults (ZCFs) that are not more than a few tens of kilometres apart are considered to be approximately parallel. The parallelism applies to the DRHDs of the faults and not to their strikes. As is mentioned later, for faulting during the Hawke's Bay earthquake, if the strike of two faults that form a boundary between two blocks is different, their nature will differ, but their DRHD will be the same.

The DRHD data used to define the position of the three Eulerian poles is from active faulting during the last 10,000 or so years, and from geodetic resurveys, which cover an interval of about 40 years only. Earthquake faulting for the last 90 years provides an important part of the information on active faulting.

New Zealand data on DRHD is set out in Table 1. The entries are grouped according to copolar fault zones, the first group being the southern, the second the western, and the third the eastern. Data are classified under geomorphic (Gm), earthquake (EQ), and geodetic (Gd); the first being displaced topographic features, the second ground displacement during historical earthquakes, and the third geodetic resurveys. 'Slip angle' listed in the table is the direction of fault displacement measured on the plane of the fault, 000° being used for pure normal faulting, 090° for pure dextral faulting, 180° for pure reverse faulting, and 270° for pure sinistral faulting. Intermediate slip angles indicate an intermediate kind of faulting. Observed DRHDs are calculated from the fault data, and the normalized DRHDs, given in the last column, are taken from Fig. 1 by measuring the direction normal to the lines from Eulerian poles.

Table 1

DIRECTION OF RELATIVE HORIZONTAL DISPLACEMENT (DRHD) DATA FROM NEW ZEALAND

Locality number	*Name of fault*	*Nature of data*	*Copolar fault zone*	*Lat. S*	*Long. E*	*Dip of fault*	*Strike of fault*	*Slip angle of fault*	*Observed DRHD*	*Normalized DRHD*
1	S. end Alpine on land	Gm	S	44·5	167·9	c90	52	090	232	232
2	Alpine near Mt Cook	Gm	S	43·5	170·0	c60	56	135	266	240
3	Alpine near Hokitika R.	Gm	S	43·0	171·0	c60	60	110	250	257
4	White Ck, 1929 E.Q.	EQ	W	41·8	172·1	60	00	203	310	310
5	Lake Taupo, 1922 E.Q.	EQ	W	38·6	175·9	c60	52	000	135	142
6	Glenwye, 1888 E.Q.	EQ	E	42·5	172·6	c90	75	090	255	244
7	Av. pure dextral faults	Gm	E	42·0	173·0	90	70	090	250	244
8	Wellington Fault	Gd	E	41·3	174·8	—	45	—	245	257
9*a*	Hawke Bay E.Q. Fault 1	EQ	E	39·8	176·7	20	45	130	261	266
9*b*	Hawke Bay E.Q. Fault 2	EQ	E	39·8	176·7	?75	90	070	266	266
9*c*	Hawke Bay E.Q. Fault 3	EQ	E	39·8	176·7	20	45	130	261	266
9*d*	Hawke Bay E.Q. Geodetic	Gd	E	39·5	176·5	—	38	—	264	266
10	Wairoa E.Q. BB Fault	EQ	E	39·0	177·5	c70	45	160	275	274

No single account exists of the active faulting and geodetic resurvey data for the whole of New Zealand, and the following is a summary of the published and unpublished accounts from which the data set out in Table 1 was taken.

All relevant data known to the writer is used, and at all places fault dip is less well known than fault strike.

The south end of the Alpine Fault near Milford Sound was described by Clark and Wellman (1959) and the fault considered to be steeply dipping and essentially dextral. Air photographs recently examined by the writer indicate that the fault is the same at Kaipo Valley 12 km to the north-east.

The Alpine Fault at places from near Mt Cook to near Hokitika River has been described by Wellman (1953) and by Suggate (1963). Dip is flat on the interfluves and steepens when traced into the valleys. The maximum dip observed is about 60° but it may be even steeper at depth. Displaced river terraces (Wellman 1953) indicate that dextral displacement equals throw near Mt Cook and greatly exceeds it to the north. Slip angle is listed accordingly in Table 1.

On the West Nelson Fault Zone the unambiguous faulting at White Creek during the 1929 earthquake was described by Henderson (1937) and others. Displacement was recorded on two faults after the Inangahua earthquake of 1969 (Lensen & Otway 1971). The faults are part of the West Nelson Fault Zone and their DRHDs are about the same as that for the 1929 earthquake.

In the Volcanic Fault Zone, faulting at the north end of Lake Taupo in 1922 was briefly described by Grange in 1932. He mentioned tensional features and made no mention of strike-slip displacement. The faulting is considered here to have been pure normal. Both cores examined by the writer from the nearby Wairakei geothermal project have slickensides that indicate predominantly dip-slip displacement, which is assumed to be normal and not reverse. Along the Volcanic Fault Zone to the north-east there are numerous active faults that have been closely examined without any definite strike-slip displacement being recorded. Displacement is thus assumed here to be essentially normal for the whole length of the Volcanic Fault Zone.

The faulting at Glenwye (on what is now known as the Hope Fault) during the 1888 earthquake was the first fault displacement in New Zealand to be clearly described (McKay 1892). Displacement was almost pure dextral.

The Hope Fault is one of a series of sub-parallel north-east striking faults that branch off from the Alpine Fault proper as it is traced north. According to displaced river terrace edges (Wellman 1953) they are almost pure dextral near the 173° longitude line. The strike adopted for the faults in Table 1 is an average for the strikes at the points where the faults cross the longitude line, the strikes being weighted according to the inferred rate of dextral displacement of their faults for the last 10,000 years.

The Wellington geodetic quadrilateral extends over the Wellington Peninsula and across the Wellington Fault. The angular changes for the last 40 years have been given by Lensen (1970) and are consistent, 100° being the direction of relative horizontal shortening for the quadrilateral. Lines parallel to the Wellington Fault are assumed to have not changed in length and the DRHD for the fault is calculated accordingly. The annual rate of dextral shear ($0{\cdot}5 \times 10^{-6}$) is used later to estimate a rate of relative horizontal displacement across the southern end of the eastern copolar fault zone, that is across the middle of the Alpine Fault Zone.

Earth movements during the Hawke's Bay earthquake of 1932 were described by Henderson (1933). The main feature was an elongated asymmetrical uplifted dome with a long axis striking at 035°. Faulting probably took place along the whole length of the steep south-east side of the dome, but most of the length is covered by the water of Hawke Bay or by uncompacted alluvium, and faulting showed only in the solid rocks near Poukawa 38 km south-east of Napier. Displacement was well defined for three faults only. The faults join to make an elongated N-shape boundary between two blocks and are reverse-dextral, dextral, and reverse-dextral in nature, each fault having the same DRHD.

After the earthquake nine geodetic triangles covering the earthquake area were resurveyed. The differences in the three angles of each triangle have been expressed as lines in the direction of relative shortening for that triangle, each line having a length proportional to the amount a right-angle facing in that direction would have changed (Wellman 1970). The directions for the six southern triangles, which have a fairly consistent shortening direction, were averaged, individual values being weighted according to their amount of shortening. Lengths in the direction of the long axis of the uplifted dome were then considered unchanged, and the calculated DRHD is shown in Table 1.

During the 1932 earthquake at Wairoa, displacement took place on the north-east striking BB Fault. Upthrow of the south-east side by 1·4 m was described by Ongley (1937), and dextral displacement of 0·4 m (determined by geodetic reobservations) by Walshe (1937). The fault is older than the earthquake, and on air photographs it appears to dip north-west at about 70°. Thus on total information the faulting is considered to have been reverse-dextral, and is so shown in Table 1.

The faulting and geodetic information outlined above indicates that the Alpine Fault Zone is dextral in the south, and dextral-reverse in the north; that the Volcanic Fault Zone is reverse-sinistral. In terms of the three copolar fault zones into which the fault zones themselves are grouped: the southern is dextral; the western reverse-dextral in its southern part and normal in its northern part; the eastern changing from dextral to reverse-dextral as it is traced north.

The total displacement for 10,000 years, the total time interval considered, is small relative to the distance from the copolar faults to their poles. The three poles are thus effectively 'instantaneous' and must lie on a great circle, that is, on a straight line on Fig. 1.

The observed DRHDs were plotted on Fig. 1 and the intersections used to find the most probable position of the three Eulerian poles. That the three poles must lie on a great circle (straight line on Fig. 1) was a useful restraint for controlling the adopted pole positions now given: western zone of copolar faults (West Nelson and Volcanic Fault Zones)—40° S, 174° E; eastern zone of copolar faults (northern part of Alpine Fault Zone)—47° S, 177° E; southern zone of copolar faults (southern part of Alpine Fault Zone)—55° S, 180° E.

It should be noted that the pole of the southern zone of copolar faults is that of the Melanesian Geosuture itself, that the ratio of the relative rotation rates of the three poles is proportional to the sine of the angle between them, and hence that if the

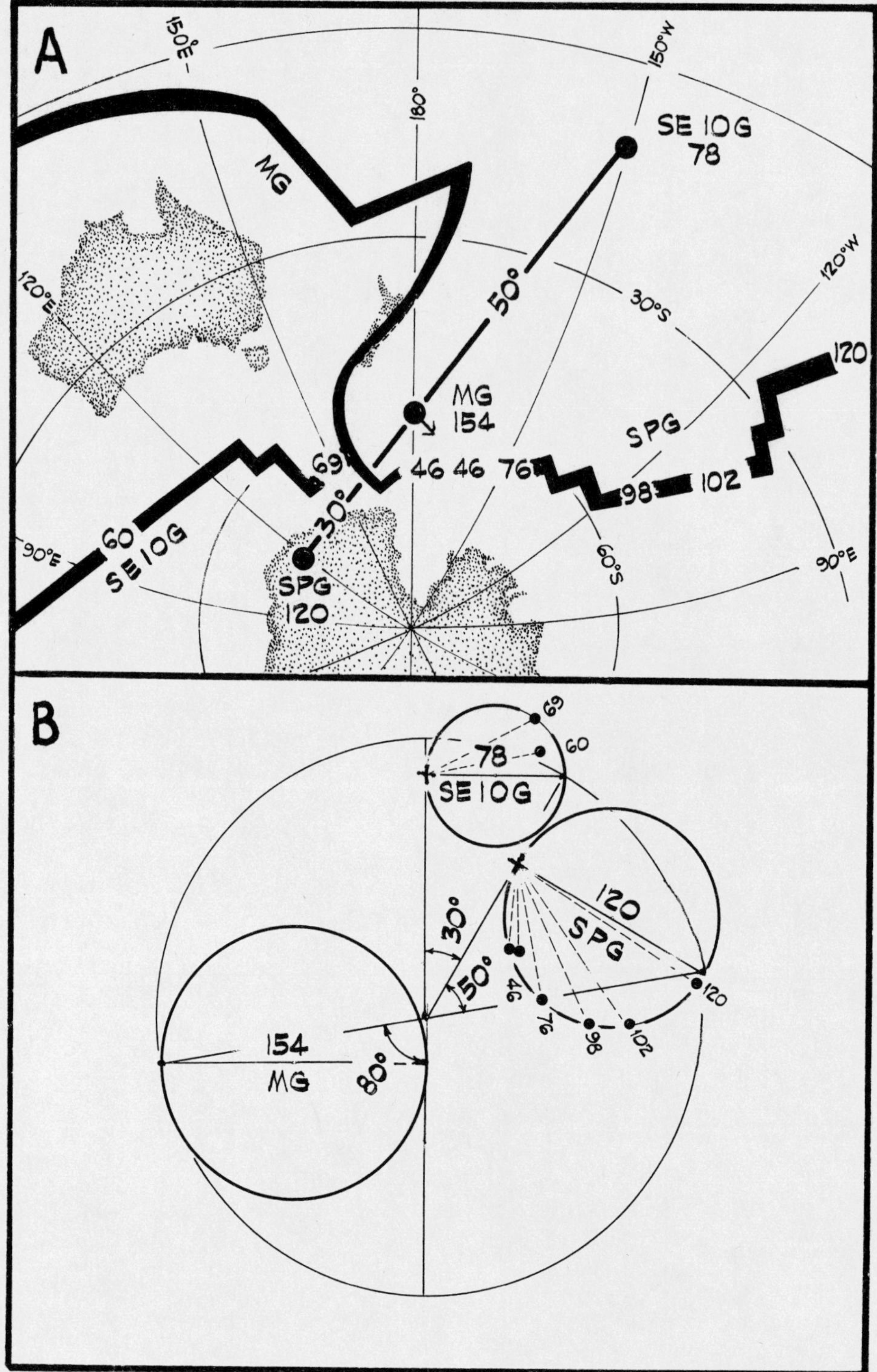
A
150°E
180°
150°W
SE 10G
78
MG
120°E
50°
30°S
120°W
120
MG
154
SPG
69
46 46 76
98
102
30°
60
SE 10G
90°E
SPG
120
60°S
90°E
B
69
60
78
SE 10G
120
SPG
30°
50°
94
76
98
102
120
154
MG
80°

relative rotation rate of one is known that of the other two can be calculated. The angular distances between the poles is less than 20° and the sines of the angular distances are thus almost proportional to the angular distances themselves.

The middle pole, that for the eastern copolar fault zone, is about mid-way between the other two, and its rotation rate is thus about twice that of the Melanesian Geosuture. The rotation rate for the other pole, that of the western copolar fault zone, is about the same as that of the Melanesian Geosuture.

SEA-FLOOR SPREADING DATA

When traced south the Melanesian Geosuture (MG) ends at a triple point junction near 62° S, 162° E, where it joins the end of the South-east Indian Ocean Geosuture (SEIOG) and the end of the South Pacific Geosuture (SPG). The three geosutures and the position of their inferred Eulerian poles are shown on Fig. 2. As already mentioned, the relative rotation rates of the three poles for the boundaries of any three adjoining plates is proportional to the sines of the angles between the poles; the relation is shown diagrammatically by Fig. 2*b*. According to New Zealand data, the present day (instantaneous) pole of MG is at 55° S, 180° E. With this pole fixed, an attempt is now made, using sea-floor spreading data, to define the position of the poles of the two oceanic geosutures. The three poles are considered to be instantaneous and they thus lie on a great circle through the pole for MG. If the position for the other two poles were known, and the relative rotation rate known for any one of the three poles, the rotation rates would then be known for all three poles. Alternatively, if the position were known for one of the other poles, and the relative rotation rate for both of the others, then the position and relative rotation rates would be known for all three poles.

The first attempt at a solution was made by Christoffel in 1971. He used two models. In his second, and most geologically reasonable, he assumed that the Alpine Fault and its southern continuation to the triple point junction approximated to a small circle with respect to the pole of MG. In the present paper an attempt is made to improve on Christoffel's estimate.

The position adopted here for the pole of SPG (70° S, 120° E) is determined from the intersection of the line that gives the best fit with the sea-floor spreading rates on the SPG with a great circle normal to the strike-slip fault on SPG at 65° S, 180° E.

Fig. 2 A, sketch map of region around pole of Melanesian Geosuture (MG) on a central orthomorphic projection centred on pole of MG. Full spreading rates shown in mm per yr. Relative rotation rates for poles are equatorial full-spreading rates. B, diagram to illustrate sine relation between relative rotation rate of poles of the three geosutures and angles between poles. Dots on circles for SEIOG and SPG are spreading rates plotted in polar co-ordinates from tangent points (crosses) according to their angular distance from their poles.

The fault as determined from earthquake epicentres (Barazangi & Dorman 1969) is inferred to strike at about 140°. The inferred position for the pole of SPG is 30° distant from the inferred position of the pole of MG. Having inferred the position for the pole of MG and the pole for SPG, the instantaneous pole for SEIOG must lie on the great circle that passes through them. The adopted position (10° S, 150° W) is 50° from the pole of MG, but according to the spreading values shown on Fig. 2*a* the angle could be as large as 60° or as small as 40°. In Fig. 2*b* a 50° angle is adopted and the equatorial relative rotational rate for MG is 150 mm per year. For 40° the rate is 167, and for 60° 137. The rate for MG is thus almost independent of the position adopted for the pole of SEIOG provided it lies within the above range.

From the triple point junction north to about the middle of the Alpine Fault Zone, MG is about 12° distant from its pole, and the present day (instantaneous) rate of dextral displacement on the Alpine Fault Zone is inferred from SFS data to be about 35 mm per year.

PRESENT RATE OF DEXTRAL DISPLACEMENT ON THE ALPINE FAULT ZONE

It is shown later that New Zealand and sea-floor spreading data indicate that the rate of dextral displacement on the Alpine Fault Zone has probably increased with time, but the rate has probably not changed by more than 10 per cent during the last 3 m.y.

According to the positions adopted for the poles of the three zones of copolar faults in New Zealand (Fig. 1), the rate of dextral displacement is about the same for all lines across the Alpine Fault Zone from its southern end as far north as Wellington.

The Alpine Fault Zone is unusual and tectonically important in that it is possible to observe its rate of dextral displacement and then to compare the rate observed with that inferred from sea-floor spreading.

Estimates that can or have been made are set out below, with values in mm per year:

1. Christoffel, Model 1 (1971), sea-floor spreading data	69
2. Christoffel, Model 2 (1971), sea-floor spreading data	40
3. This paper, sea-floor spreading data	35
4. Fault age 25 m.y., gradual increase of rate with time, 450 km total	40
5. Total dextral displacement of 300 m for 10^4 years	30
6. Wellington geodetic quadrilateral $0{\cdot}5 \times 10^{-6}$ years, 60 km wide F.Z.	30
7. Fault age 100 m.y., gradual increase of rate with time, 450 km total	9

Estimates 1, 2 and 3 are from sea-floor spreading data. In 4 it is assumed, according to observations on the west coast of the South Island, mentioned later, that the rate of faulting was zero 25 m.y. ago (mid-Cenozoic), that the rate has since increased uniformly with time, and that a total of 450 km displacement has taken place in the last 25 m.y. (Wellman 1971). In 5 it is assumed (Wellman, in press) that a total dextral displacement of 256 m has taken place on the faults of the Alpine Fault Zone at the north end of the South Island in the last 10,000 years. The 10,000-year time interval is inferred from earth movements at the south end of the North Island. At Turakirae Head, on the upthrown side of the Wairarapa Fault, there are five uplifted marine beach ridges. At Waiohine River, 60 km to the north-east the fault displaces seven river terraces. From the uniformity of the ratio between the uplift of the beach ridges and the vertical faulting of the river terraces the five beach ridges are correlated with the five youngest river terraces. The ratio uniformity is attributed to uplift and faulting having taken place during five major earthquakes each with about the same epicentre and focal depth. The river terraces as well as the beach ridges are thus considered to be a result of the earthquake uplifts. From eustatic sea-level curves the oldest beach ridge is inferred to be about 6,300 years old, and by assuming a uniform average rate of faulting, the oldest terrace, which is an aggradational surface, is inferred to be about 10,000 years old. The rate of horizontal displacement is 12 mm per year for the Wairarapa Fault alone, and probably about twice as much for all the dextral faults of the south end of the North Island. The dextral faults of the north end of the South Island displace aggradational surfaces that are correlated with the surface at Waiohine River, the total horizontal displacement being about 256 m, and the total rate about 26 mm per year. In 6 it is assumed that the shear rate for the Wellington Quadrilateral is representative of an effective width for the Alpine Fault Zone of 60 km. The effective width cannot be defined to better than 20 per cent until geodetic resurveys are extended. In 7 the method used is analogous to 4 except that faulting is assumed to have started some 100 m.y. ago in the mid-Cretaceous (Suggate 1963).

Except for estimates 1 and 7 the values are consistent, and indicate a present rate of dextral displacement for the Alpine Fault Zone of between 30 and 40 mm per year.

AGE OF THE ALPINE FAULT

The total displacement of the Alpine Zone is well defined in the South Island and is about 450 km, and the age of the fault is assumed to be the time of the start of the 450 km displacement. Age estimates range from (100 m.y.) mid-Cretaceous (Suggate 1963) to (25 m.y.) mid-Cenozoic (Wellman 1971*b*).

It is generally accepted that a reversal of faulting took place on several north or north-north-east striking faults in the north-west of the South Island during the mid-Cenozoic, the early Cenozoic faulting being normal and the late Cenozoic reverse. The reverse faulting is consistent with dextral displacement taking place on the north-east striking Alpine Fault Zone, and the normal faulting with sinistral displacement. Because of the straightness of the Alpine Fault proper, and because of the Cenozoic strata that are infaulted in a major fault that appears to be offset by the Alpine Fault (Wellman 1971) it is assumed here that the fault came into being in the mid-Cenozoic. The start of movement is unlikely to have been sudden, and as the simplest model using pure geological data, the rate of displacement is assumed to have increased regularly with time from 25 m.y. ago. If the total displacement is 450 km, then the

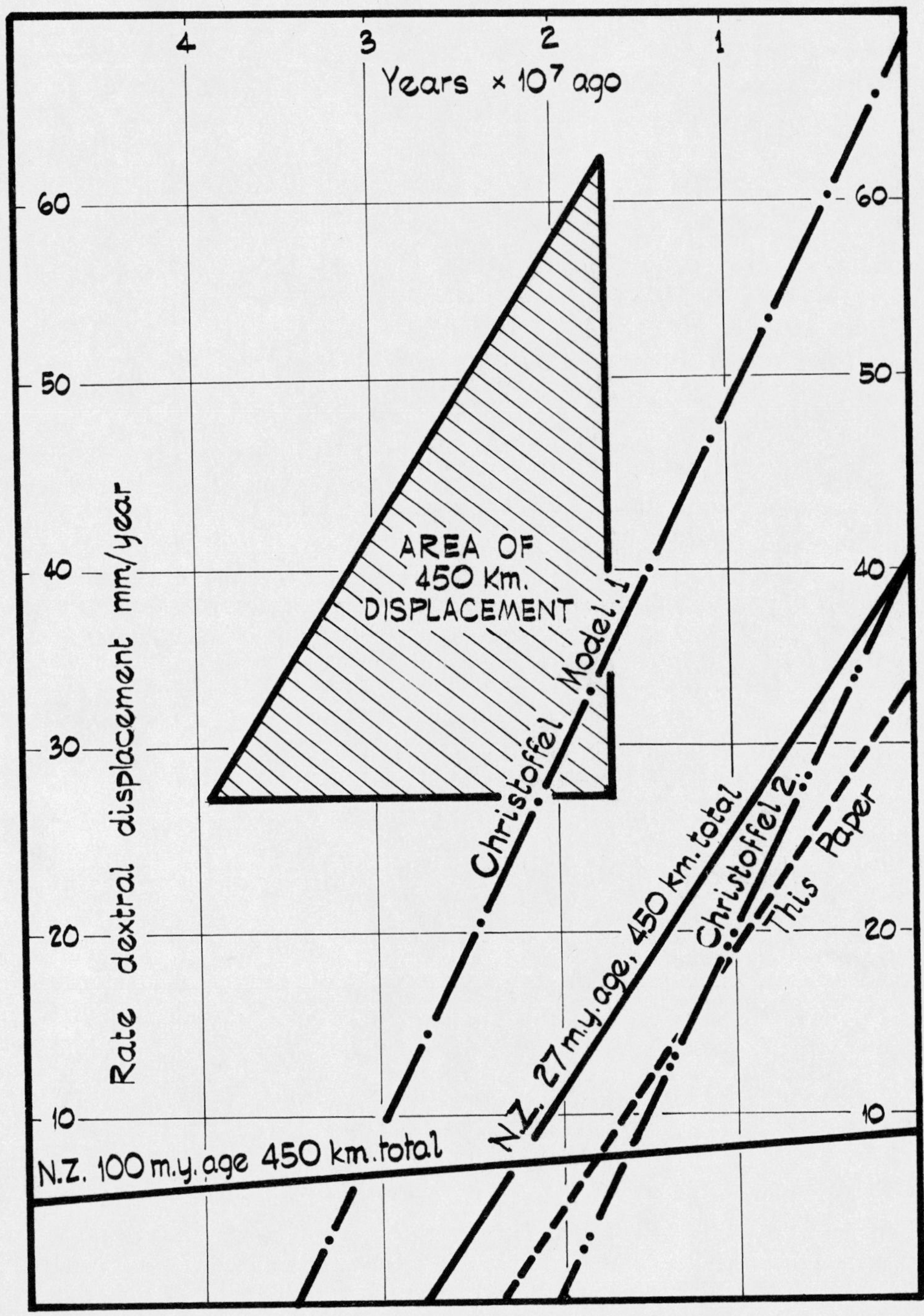

4
3
2
1
Years × 10⁷ ago
60
50
40
30
20
10
60
50
40
20
10
Rate dextral displacement mm/year
AREA OF
450 Km.
DISPLACEMENT
Christoffel Model. 1
N.Z. 27 m.y. age, 450 km. total
Christoffel 2.
This Paper
N.Z. 100 m.y. age 450 km. total

present rate of displacement will be 40 mm per year (Fig. 3).

According to sea-floor spreading data the poles for SPG and SEIOG have been fixed relative to their plates and to each other for the last 10 m.y. at least. If this is the case, then the pole for MG is moving away from the south end of New Zealand in a direction at right angles to the great circle through the three main poles. The rate of movement is well defined and about 60 mm per year, and being largely determined by the 69 mm per year spreading rate near the triple point south of New Zealand, is almost independent of the position adopted for the three main poles. If the rotation rates for the poles of SPG and SEIOG have not changed appreciably during the last 10 m.y., and this is generally accepted, then the rate of dextral displacement on the Alpine Fault Zone will have regularly increased during the last 10 m.y. and present rates cannot be used to estimate the time needed to produce the 450 km total displacement on the Alpine Fault Zone.

The relation between the inferred changing rates of displacement and the total displacement is shown by the sloping lines in Fig. 3 for the models that have been proposed. The slope of a line represents its change in rate, and the area between a sloping line and any two vertical time-lines the total displacement that would have taken place between those times.

The sea-floor spreading data used here is valid for the last 10 m.y. only, and rates and poles may have been different earlier. Consequently, it cannot be used to infer an age for the 450 km displacement. However, for the model adopted here and for Christoffel's (1971) Model 2 the displacement is 300 km for 10 m.y. and 400 km for 20 m.y. The fault is thus older than 10 m.y. and probably older than 20 m.y. Christoffel (1971) inferred an age of 10 m.y. but he did not allow for the accelerating rate of displacement.

CONCLUSIONS

The sea-floor spreading data indicates that most of the 450 km displacement on the Alpine Fault Zone has taken place during the last 20 m.y., that is during the late Cenozoic, but it does not give a definite age for the commencement of the 450 km displacement. It indicates a present rate of displacement of about 35 mm per year. The results are in excellent agreement with geological data from New Zealand described by Wellman (1971). Sea-floor spreading data from the South Pacific and the South-east Indian Oceans is thus confirmed by New Zealand data.

Fig. 3 Diagram showing inferred change in rate of dextral displacement on the Alpine Fault with time according to models proposed. The age of the fault (number of years ago when rate was zero) is shown by the intersection of the rate lines with the time scale at bottom of diagram. Total displacement for each model is given by area of triangle formed by its rate line and lines at right and bottom of diagram. Area equal to displacement of 450 km shown by shaded triangle.

ACKNOWLEDGEMENTS

I wish to thank Prof. D. A. Christoffel for educating me in the concept of sea-floor spreading, and Dr R. Fraser for improving the final draft of this paper.

REFERENCES

Barazangi, M. & Dorman, J. 1969. World seismicity maps compiled from ESSA, Coast and Geodetic Survey, epicentre data, 1961-7. *Bull. seism. Soc. Am.* **59,** 369-80.

Christoffel, D. A. 1971. Motion of the New Zealand Alpine Fault deduced from the pattern of sea-floor spreading. Recent Crustal Movements. *Bull. R. Soc. N.Z.* **9,** 25-30.

Clark, R. H. & Wellman, H. W. 1959. The Alpine Fault from Lake McKerrow to Milford Sound. *N.Z. Jl Geol. Geophys.* **2,** 590-601.

Grange, L. I. 1932. Taupo earthquakes, 1922. Rents and faults formed during earthquakes of 1922 in Taupo District. *N.Z. Jl Sci. Technol.* **19,** 65-144.

Henderson, J. 1932. Earthquakes in New Zealand. *N.Z. Jl Sci. Technol.* **14,** 129-39.

——— 1933. The geological aspects of the Hawke's Bay earthquakes. *N.Z. Jl Sci. Technol.* **15,** 38-75.

——— 1937. The West Nelson earthquakes of 1929. *N.Z. Jl Sci. Technol.* **15,** 38-75.

Lensen, G. J. 1970. Elastic and non-elastic surface deformation in New Zealand. *Bull. N.Z. Soc. Earthquake Eng.* **3,** 131-42.

Lensen, G. J. & Otway, P. M. 1971. Earthshift and post-earthshift deformation associated with the May, 1968, Inanqahua earthquake, New Zealand. Recent Crustal Movements. *Bull. R. Soc. N.Z.* **9.**

Le Pichon, X. 1968. Sea-floor spreading and continental drift. *J. geophys. Res.* **73,** 3661-97.

McKay, A. 1892. On the geology of Marlborough and South-East Nelson. *N.Z. Geol. Surv. Rep. geol. Explor. 1890-1,* 1-28.

Ongley, M., 1937. The Wairoa earthquake of 16th September, 1932. 1—Field observations. *N.Z. Jl Sci. Technol.* **18,** 845-51.

Suggate, R. P., 1963. The Alpine Fault. *Trans. R. Soc. N.Z.* (*Geology*), **2,** 105-29.

Walshe, H. E., 1937. The Wairoa earthquake of 16th September, 1932. 2—Earth movements in Hawke's Bay District disclosed by triangulation. *N.Z. Jl Sci. Technol.* **18,** 852-4.

Wellman, H. W., 1956. Data for the study of Recent and Late Pleistocene faulting in the South Island of New Zealand. *N.Z. Jl Sci. Technol.* **B34,** 270-88.

——— 1970. In 'Tour Guide of North Island N.Z.' for Recent Crustal Movement Meeting. Feb. 1970. *Misc. Publs R. Soc. N.Z.*

——— 1971*a*. Reference lines, fault classification, transform systems, and ocean-floor spreading. *Tectonophysics*, **12.**

——— 1971*b*. Age of Alpine Fault, New Zealand. *Proc. Sec. 4 22nd Intern. Geol. Congr.* India 1964.

——— (In press.) Rate of faulting in New Zealand, *Nature.*

'Basaltic' Layer of the Crust in the West Pacific

A. V. PEIVE AND M. S. MARKOV

Geological Institute, Academy of Sciences of the U.S.S.R.,
Pyzhevsky per. 7, Moscow G-17, U.S.S.R.

ABSTRACT

Metamorphic and metasomatic basic rocks make up the base of the volcanic-sedimentary sequence of a number of the island arcs of the West Pacific. These rocks can be correlated with the geophysical 'basaltic' layer of the crust. Similar rocks are known in mid-ocean ridges and eugeosynclinal zones of continents. This type of basement and, with it, abyssal, pelagic argillaceous-siliceous-carbonate deposits are characteristic of the early oceanic stage in the evolution of eugeosynclines.

The problem of the basement of island arcs, which are regarded by many scientists as present-day geosynclinal systems, is most important for theoretical tectonics. A comparative study of sequences in the folded zones of continents, on island arcs and in the deeper parts of the oceans gives us a chance to establish relations existing between oceans and continents.

Recent research in the island arcs of the West Pacific indicated that peculiar metamorphic and metasomatic basic rocks occur at the base of the sequence (Fig. 1). By their physical properties (density, seismic velocity) these rocks can be compared with the geophysical 'basaltic' layer of the crust. Here are some examples.

In the Ganalsk ridge on Kamchatka the base of the sequence is a metamorphic complex consisting of a mass of amphibolites, garnet amphibolites, pyroxene-amphibole-plagioclase schists with distinctly subordinate bands of biotite-plagioclase schists and quartzites (Markov 1970). A study of these rocks shows that they have been subjected to a lengthy evolution. Initially they were metamorphosed to a granulitic and eclogitic facies of metamorphism (in some varieties relics of typically eclogitic mineral associations have been found). Later these rocks have been partly feldspathized and locally granitized with the formation of plagio-granitic gneisses; also, they have been in part altered into greenschists.

Above these rocks occurs a complex of less-metamorphosed basalts and greywackes containing spores and pollen of a Mesozoic aspect, which warrants an assumption that the underlying amphibolites are Mesozoic, at least. This less-metamorphosed complex is overlain by Upper Cretaceous volcanic-siliceous rocks.

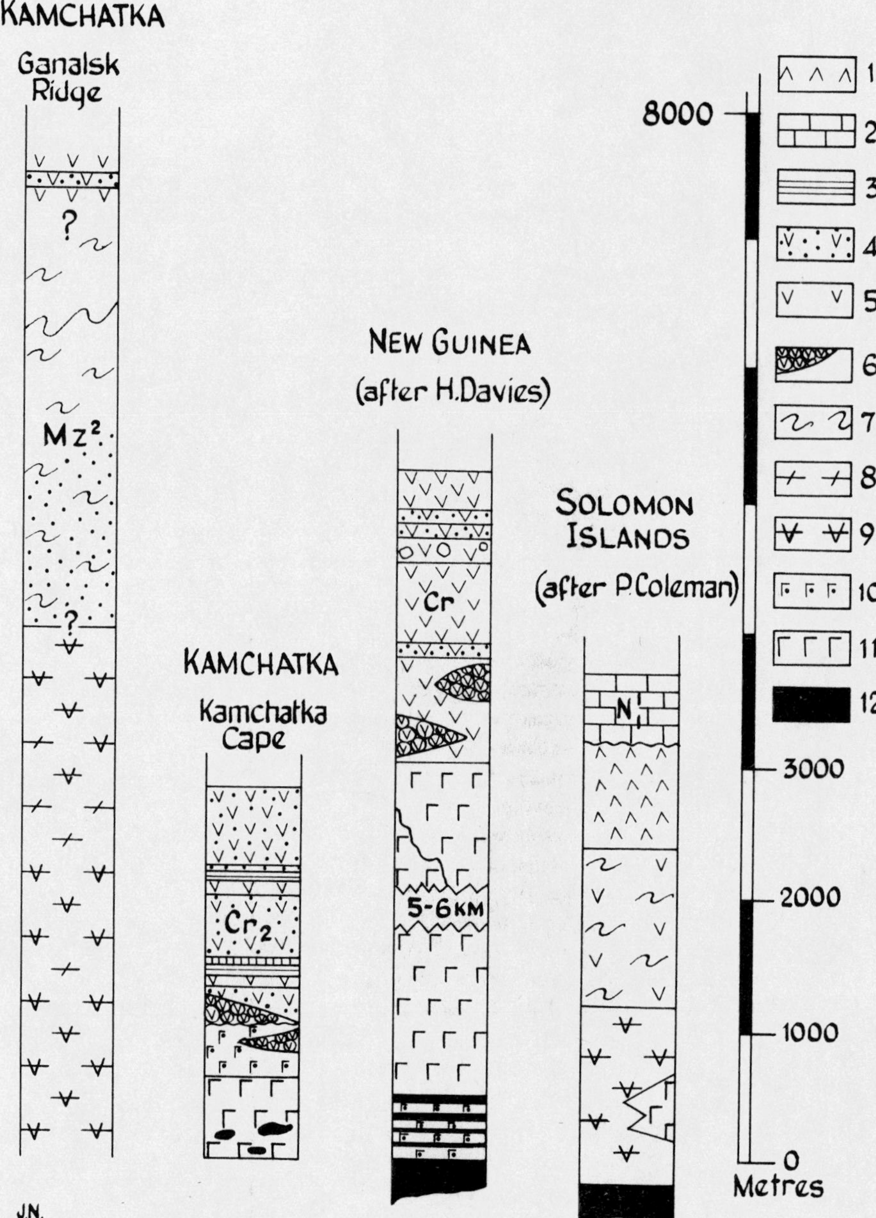

Fig. 1 Situation of melanocratic basement in sections of selected island arcs. 1, andesites; 2, limestones; 3, cherts; 4, basalts/tuffs; 5, basalts; 6, pillow lavas; 7, greenschists; 8, plagiogneisses; 9, amphibolites; 10, gabbro-diabases; 11, gabbro, norites, anorthosites; 12, ultrabasic rocks.

A different type of basement is known on the peninsula of Kamchatka Cape. Here a volcanic-siliceous series of Cretaceous age overlies, with a gap, a complex of metasomatic gabbroic rocks. A study of the basal part of the latter has shown that this was formed by the metasomatic alteration of ultrabasic rocks. Apparently, these ultrabasics were originally enstatitic dunites in which the enstatite was later replaced by diallage. In the marginal parts of the ultrabasic bodies their subsequent and gradual saturation with plagioclase extended even to the formation of lenses and bands of pure anorthosites.

The study of analogous forms in the Urals has also shown that such rocks result from a metasomatic processing of ultrabasic rocks involving an abundant supply of calcium and silica (Efimov & Efimova 1967, Morkovkina 1962).

The top part of the gabbroic complex of Kamchatka Cape represents metamorphosed and recrystallized basalts and dolerites altered into gabbro-diabases with lenses of medium- and coarse-grained gabbros (Dolmatov & Khotin 1969, Markov *et al.* 1969).

One can accept as pre-Cretaceous the age of the metabasic complex of the basement on Kamchatka Cape. Equivalent rocks occur as xenoliths in lavas in eastern Kamchatka and the Kuril Islands, so that one can speak of a general development of a metabasic basement in this territory.

Metamorphic rocks of a basic composition are reasonably well known by now in island arcs of the West Pacific. Where they can be observed, they are located stratigraphically higher than the ultrabasics and underlie a complex of geosynclinal sediments.

In Japan, these rocks are known in the Kurosegawa structural belt, where they are squeezed out along faults together with ultrabasics. They are represented here by amphibolites, epidote-garnet amphibolites and epidote-actinolitic schists (Minato *et al.* 1965).

On Yap Island, located in the junction zone of the Mariana Arc and the Caroline Islands, metamorphic rocks have been exposed at the base of the sequence, and are represented by amphibolites, garnet-amphibolites, greenschists, gabbros and minor bodies of serpentinites and peridotites (Yap Formation). Unconformably above them occurs a mass of sedimentary breccia and conglomerates with bands of sandstones and argillites, which are of Lower Miocene age. Judging from their description, this rock mass greatly resembles the olistostrome formations in geosynclinal zones; in the composition of its clastic material there is a predominance of metamorphic rocks of the Yap Formation.

In New Guinea, in the south-eastern part of the island, the basement within the Papuan ultrabasic belt, consists of ultrabasics, among which, just as on Kamchatka Peninsula, there is a predominance of enstatitic olivinites. According to Davies (1968) processes of silica metasomatosis are developed in the ultrabasics. Davies points out that there are no proofs of a magmatic origin of the ultrabasic rocks in this zone, the latter probably represented by rocks of the upper mantle formed as a result of a selective basalt fusion from a primary pyrolite.

Stratigraphically above the ultrabasics are rocks of a gabbroic complex. Transition zones are recorded locally, in which there is an intercalation of basic and ultrabasic rocks. As a rule, in the bottom part of such bedded members there are hypersthene-diopside pyroxenites, which higher in the sequence are replaced by gabbros and then by anorthosites.

In thin-sections of rocks from the transition zone exposed in coastal scarps south of Salamaua it is possible to see that the plagioclase was formed at a late stage and shows poikilitic inclusions of pyroxene. In many thin-sections one can see that the formation of the plagioclase took place after the serpentinization of these rocks. It is easy to see that the gabbroic rocks that make up the basement of this part of New Guinea, together with its ultrabasics, are very similar to the basement rocks from eastern Kamchatka.

Above the gabbros there is a pile of volcanogenic and volcanogenic-siliceous rocks of a Cretaceous(?) to Eocene age. The nature of contact between the gabbros and Cretaceous rocks is not clear. The age of the melanocratic basement in this part of the Pacific is, apparently, pre-Upper Cretaceous.

Our observations made in New Guinea in 1971 fully confirm Davies's data.

In the Solomon Islands, according to Coleman (1970) and Coleman *et al.* (1965), amphibolites and amphibolitic schists occur in the general sequence and, possibly younger than them there are greenstones, altered basalts and dolerites on Guadalcanal Island. With the rocks of the metamorphic complex are associated ultrabasic rocks, the exposures of which are spatially associated with zones of large faults. In the central structural-facies zone, these rocks are covered by Oligocene(?) volcanics and their fragments are known in Lower Miocene deposits.

Amphibolites and gabbroic rocks have been dredged during the forty-ninth voyage of the *Vitiaz* in 1971, in a graben north of Malaita Island, which indicates the existence of an analogous melanocratic basement in the Pacific structural-facies zone as well, and located beneath Upper Cretaceous abyssal sediments.

We see that in the island arcs of the West Pacific—below volcanic, volcanic-siliceous and greywacke formations—there occur basic metamorphic rocks underlain by ultrabasics. By their stratigraphic position, between ultrabasics and typical geosynclinal sediments, they occupy the place of the geophysical 'basaltic' layer.

Similar rocks have been found also within the former eugeosynclinal zones of the continents and even within the deeper parts of the oceans, which makes it possible to look for analogues between these categories of structures (Knipper 1970, Peive 1969, Peive *et al.* 1971).

In the Mediterranean Alpine belt, in the Palaeozoides of Siberia, Kazakhstan, the Urals and in other folded structures, the eugeosynclinal stage of development is divided by us into two phases—oceanic and transitional (Dergunov *et al.* 1971). The oceanic phase is characterized by a gabbro-amphibolitic basement overlain by spilites, diabases, siliceous and carbonate-argillaceous abyssal rocks; frequently there are large massifs of reef limestones palaeogeographically corresponding to zones of oceanic islands.

In the majority of geosynclinal areas, deposits of the oceanic phase become replaced by andesitic and greywacke-flyschoid masses characteristic of the transitional phase in the development of the crust.

During this phase, an intense tectonic piling-up of eugeosynclinal material and growth of the 'granitic' layer of the crust takes place. It is apparent that the transitional phase in the development of geosynclinal areas of the geological past is very similar with the system of island arcs and marginal seas in the West Pacific. The crust of the system of island arcs and marginal seas is characterized by an intermittent development of the 'granitic' layer and a thick layer of unconsolidated sediments. Many geophysicists describe such a type of crust as transitional to continental crust.

In the Pacific Ocean, the oceanic stage is replaced by a transitional one not only in time, but spatially as well. For the Alpine orogenic cycle, the boundary lies approximately along the Andesite Line. West of it we see a typical transitional zone with a wide development during the Tertiary period of flyschoid and andesitic formations. East of the andesite line, Tertiary deposits are replaced by oceanic basaltic volcanics with bodies of reef limestones laterally giving way to abyssal pelagic argillaceous-siliceous-carbonate deposits. Such formations are characteristic of the early oceanic stage in the development of ancient eugeosynclines. If we assume also that the ultrabasic-gabbro-amphibolitic association of rocks of the geological past corresponds to the third and in part fourth layer beneath present-day oceans, the evolution of oceanic crust and its transformation into continental crust will become much clearer.

REFERENCES

Coleman, P. J. 1970. Geology of the Solomon and New Hebrides Islands, as part of the Melanesian Re-entrant, South-west Pacific. *Pacif. Sci.* **24,** 289-314.

Coleman, P. J., Grover, J. C. & Stanton, R. L. 1965. A First Geological Map of the British Solomon Islands. *Rec. geol. Surv. Br. Solomon Is.* **2** (1951-62), 16-17.

Davies, H. L. 1968. Papuan ultramafic belt. *23rd Sess. Intern. Geol. Congr.* **1,** 209-20.

Dergunov, A. B., Zaitsev, N. S., Mossakovsky, A. A. & Perfil'yev, A. S. 1971. Hercynides of Mongolia and the Palaeotethys problem. In *Problems of theoretical and regional tectonics.* Nauka Publ., Moscow (in Russian).

Dolmatov, B. K. & Khotin, M. Yu. 1969. Formation of pre-Palaeogene intrusive complexes on Kamchatka Cape peninsula (Eastern Kamchatka). *Sov. Geol.* **5** (in Russian).

Efimov, A. A. & Efimova, L. P. 1967. *Kytlym platinum-bearing massif.* Nedra Publ., Moscow (in Russian).

Knipper, A. L. 1971. Gabbroic rocks of the ophiolitic 'formation' in the geological record of the oceanic crust. *Geotektonika,* **2** (in Russian).

Markov, M. S. 1970. Metamorphic complexes and their place in the evolution history of island arcs. *Geotektonika,* **2** (in Russian).

Markov, M. S., Seliverstov, V. A., Khotin, M. Yu. & Dolmatov, B. K. 1969. On the conjugation of structures of Eastern Kamchatka and Aleutian island arc. *Geotektonika,* **6** (in Russian).

Minato, M., Gorai, M. & Hunahashi, M. (Eds) 1965. *The geologic development of the Japanese Islands.* Tsihiji Shokan, Tokyo.

Morkovkina, V. F. 1967. *Metasomatic transformation of the ultrabasic rocks of Polar Ural.* Nauka Publ., Moscow (in Russian).

Peive, A. V. 1969. Oceanic crust in past geological time. *Geotektonika,* **4** (in Russian).

Peive, A. V., Schtreis, N. A., Knipper, A. L., Markov, M. S., Bogdanov, N. A., Perfil'yev, A. S. & Rugenzev, S. V. 1971. Oceans and the geosyncline process. *Dokl. Acad. Sci. U.S.S.R.* **196** (3) (in Russian).

Comparison of Island Arc-Marginal Basin Complexes in the North-west and South-west Pacific

D. E. KARIG

Department of Geological Sciences, University of California, Santa Barbara, California 93106

ABSTRACT

A fully-developed island arc system is made up, front to rear, of a trench, mid-slope basement high, frontal arc, volcanic chain, inter-arc basin and third arc. It has normal polarity if the trench lies closer to the ocean basin than does the volcanic chain; if the reverse applies, it has reversed polarity.

The most variable unit is the mid-slope basement high. It divides the landward slope of the trench into an upper sediment-covered section and a lower actively deforming section. If the sediment on the downgoing plate is thick, then the basement high may be thickened by folded sediment and actually reach sea-level, forming the outer or non-volcanic arc of other terminologies. Basalts and ultramafics may be emplaced into the mid-slope basement high and sediments from the frontal arc accumulate on it. The distance between the trench and the volcanic chain and the degree of flattening of the Benioff zone is related to the growth of the basement high.

As new crust accretes on to the basement high, other crustal material may be rifted from the rear edge of the frontal arc as a result of extensional opening of the inter-arc basin. The rifted fragments form remnant arcs.

The creation of a series of marginal basins and remnant arcs results in simple migration of the active arc system out from the continent. There should be a decrease in basin age, across a series of marginal basins and remnant arcs, towards the active basin. This is borne out, for example, by the age relations across the basin series of the Philippine Sea.

The processes responsible for island arc formation appear to be episodic, marked by pulses of volcanic activity. This suggests separate pulses of subduction with concomitant adjustments in the behaviour of the trench to allow for the relatively constant spreading rates measured at all major oceanic spreading centres.

Polarity reversal and horizontal shear parallel to the arc trend are secondary tectonic processes, which may modify the appearance of active arc systems. The first entails abandonment of a trench and creation of a new trench on the opposite side of the system, with opposite dip. It appears to be a current feature of South-west Pacific arcs. The reversed trench consumes marginal basin crust and may cause collision of the system with remnant arcs or continents. The second involves crustal displacement parallel to the arc trend either within the inter-arc basin, by way of *en échelon* ridges and troughs, or by way of discrete strike-slip faults. Both forms of lateral displacement appear to be the result of oblique underthrusting in the associated trench.

The North-west Pacific appears to have more arcuate systems of normal polarity and with simple basin patterns. The South-west Pacific has straighter arc systems, several with reversed polarity and with internal complexities. Close observation, however, shows that these differences

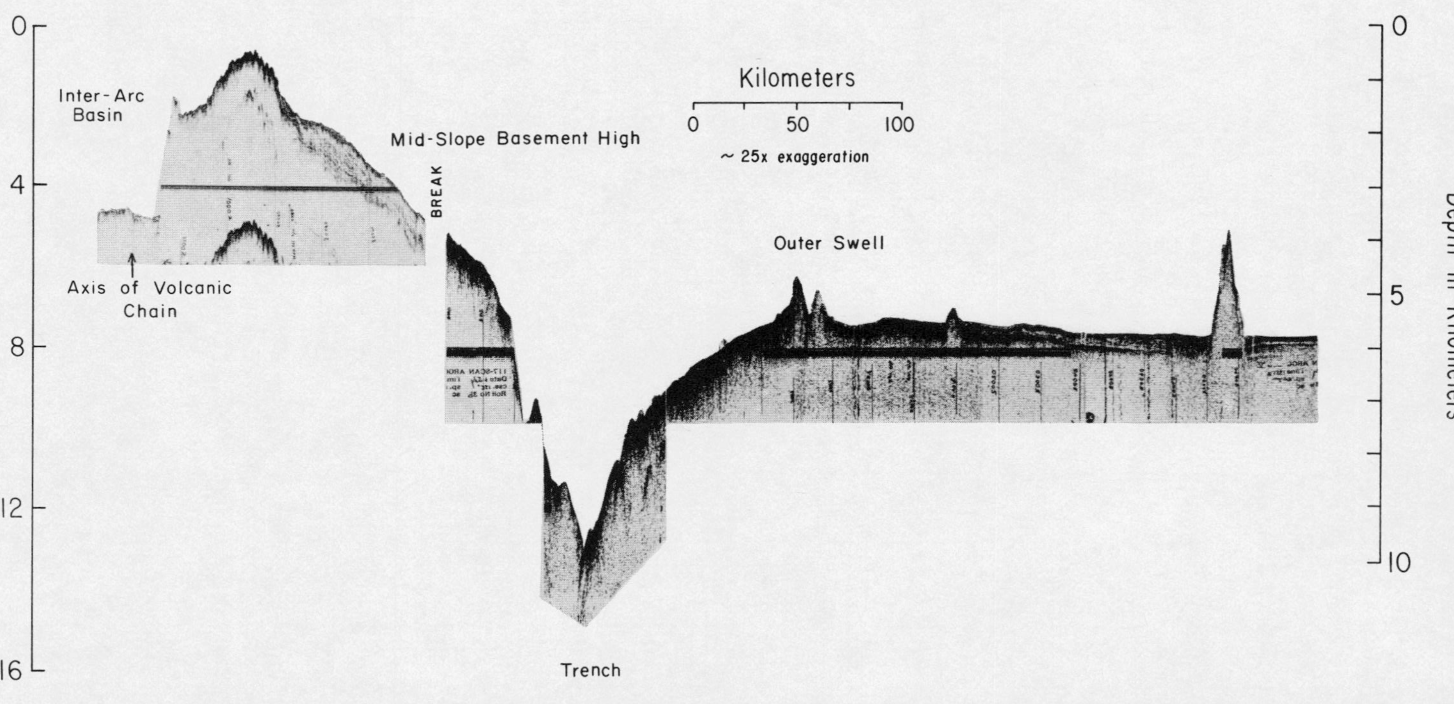

Fig. 1 Seismic reflection profile across most of the Mariana island arc system near the island of Guam (after Karig 1971). No active volcanic centre exists along the profile but the position shown is extrapolated from centres to the north and south. Not shown on the profile are most of the inter-arc basin and the third arc.

are more apparent than real. The variations within any one of several particular regions appear to be just as great as those which appear to distinguish the broader areas of the North-west and South-west Pacific arc systems, respectively.

INTRODUCTION

Recent marine geological and geophysical studies in the Western Pacific suggest a rather simple tectonic pattern to which all active island arc systems conform. Moreover, the processes responsible for the origin of the island arc systems and the marginal basins of the region appear to be intimately related. The differences in character among the arc systems reflect variations in activity of a relatively few second order processes, but the many possible combinations of these variations cause a very wide range in overall arc system patterns.

DISCUSSION

The group of ridges and troughs undergoing deformation along converging plate boundaries is termed an active island-arc system (Karig 1970, 1971*a*). From front to rear, the units of a fully-developed active arc system are: trench, mid-slope basement high, frontal arc, volcanic chain, inter-arc basin, and third arc. Descriptions of these units are given in Karig (1970, 1971*a*). A seismic reflection profile through the Mariana area illustrates most of these units (Fig. 1). Related to the arc system is the outer rise or swell, a low-amplitude tectonic arch on the oceanic plate in front of many trenches (Fig. 1).

An active arc system is said to have normal polarity if the trench lies closer to the main ocean basin than does the volcanic chain, and reversed polarity if the opposite relationship exists.

The most variable and intriguing unit, and the least understood, is the mid-slope basement high. This feature, which divides the landward slope of the trench into a deeper, actively deforming section, and an upper, sediment-covered section, varies in size, configuration, and apparently in composition among Western Pacific arc systems. In arc systems where the present trench has just been activated (as in the New Hebrides arc system), the mid-slope basement high is absent, or extremely poorly developed (Karig & Mammerickx, in press). In older arc systems, where the sediments on the downgoing plate are thin, the mid-slope basement high appears as a bench or break in slope (Fig. 1, also Karig 1970). In these areas, basalts and ultramafic rocks are dredged from the acoustically opaque lower slope (Petelin 1964, Fisher & Engel 1969). In arc systems in which the sediment cover on the descending plate is greater, the mid-slope basement high is often a strongly developed ridge, at times reaching sea-level. This is the tectonic, outer, or non-volcanic arc of other terminologies. Seismic reflection records in these areas show that the sediment cover of the downgoing plate is folded against the inner wall of the trench (Fig. 2, and Chase & Bunce 1969). These folds can be traced up the inner wall to the crest of the mid-slope basement high, tightening as they rise. Chase and Bunce postulate landward-dripping thrust fault between the fold packets. Refraction data agree with the reflection data in demonstrating that the mid-slope basement high in these areas is comprised largely of deformed sediments (Raitt 1967, Ludwig *et al.* 1966, Ludwig 1970). The mode of emplacement of the mafic-ultramafic suite into mid-slope basement highs in areas with less sediment feed is not yet apparent.

Both types of mid-slope basement high grow with time, but the material accreted and the rate of growth differ, at least in the shallow levels. Sediments from the frontal arc build an apron on top of this basement, often forming a substantial trough or basin. Sediments on the outer edge of these troughs often participate in the deforma-

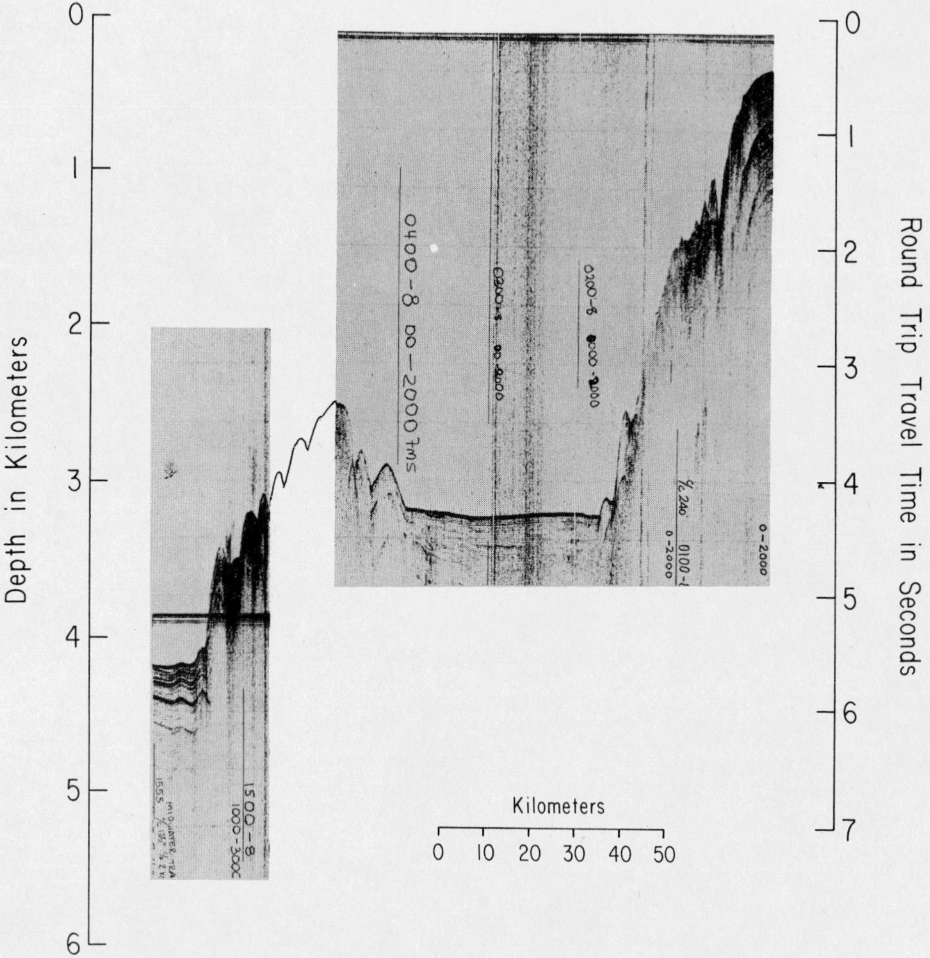

Fig. 2 Seismic reflection profile across the Manila Trench near 19° N, showing folding of sediments at the trench axis and deformation of trench and upper-slope apron sediments on the mid-slope basement high. A low-speed profile across this area shows better the continuity of the trench sediments with those underlying the mid-slope basement high.

tion of the mid-slope basement high.

The distance between the trench and volcanic chain and the amount of flattening of the Benioff zone beneath these two features appear to be largely a function of the growth of the mid-slope basement high (Karig & Mammerickx, in press). Over the longer time span, there may also be a migration of the volcanic chain trenchward (e.g. Oxburgh & Turcotte 1971), especially in areas where sediment accretion and flattening of the upper section of the Benioff zone is greater. However, the volcanic chains of the Mariana and Tonga-Kermadec arc systems have not migrated trenchward appreciably through the Tertiary.

While new crust is accreted at the mid-slope basement high, other crustal material is rifted from the rear edge of the frontal arc during the extensional opening of inter-arc basins. Crustal extension within the inter-arc basins is assumed to be responsible for the creation of most Western Pacific marginal basins. The ridge fragments rifted from the frontal arcs form remnant arcs (Karig 1972), which separate marginal basins of different ages.

The depths of inter-arc spreading centres are approximately equal to those of main ocean basin spreading centres, but because inter-arc basins are flanked by ridges, they do not appear as positive features. The inter-arc basins of the Mariana system and the Tonga system are wide enough to show that the axial area is often shallower than the basin flanks, but the resultant axial high has no median valley. Very limited investigations in these areas suggest that the locus of spreading is distributed over several tens of kilometres across this axial high (Karig 1971*a*).

The magnetic field produced by spreading in inter-arc basins remains unexplained. Linear anomalies are present (Karig 1970*a*, 1971*a*, Sclater *et al.*, 1972), but no symmetry was detected in the inter-arc basins of the Mariana or Kermadec systems. Although these cases could be explained by low inclinations of the field vector and a narrow spreading zone, no identifiable magnetic stripes have been reported from any marginal basin of the Pacific (see also Hilde & Wageman, this volume).

The few chemical analyses of inter-arc basin basalts (Hart *et al.* in press, Sclater *et al.* 1972) indicate that these differ slightly from oceanic abyssal tholeiites in containing more K, Rb, Cs, and other large cations. Hart *et al.* (in press) suggest a lower percentage partial melt of mantle material than at oceanic spreading centres.

Mantle material almost undoubtedly upwells beneath interarc basins (Karig 1971*b*, Oxburgh & Turcotte 1971; Packham & Falvey 1971; Barazangi & Isacks 1971); the arguments now concern the cause and source of this mantle upwelling. It is not clear whether the material passively rises to fill a gap created by some other extensional process, or whether diapiric mantle can cause surficial extension when hydrostatic forces within the diapir overcome forces of regional compression. Nor is it clear whether the material which rises is derived from the asthenosphere behind the arc system or from the downgoing slab.

Simple migration of the active arc system outward from a continent with creation of a series of marginal basins and remnant arcs should result in a decrease in basin age toward the active basin. With the coring of Eocene sediments from the West Philippine Basin (unpublished Scripps Institution core data), the predicted age relationships across the basin series of the Philippine Sea are established. Accompanying the outward decrease in basin age are a decrease in basin depth and an increase in crustal heat flow (Karig 1971*b*, also J. G. Sclater, pers. comm.). Both characteristics

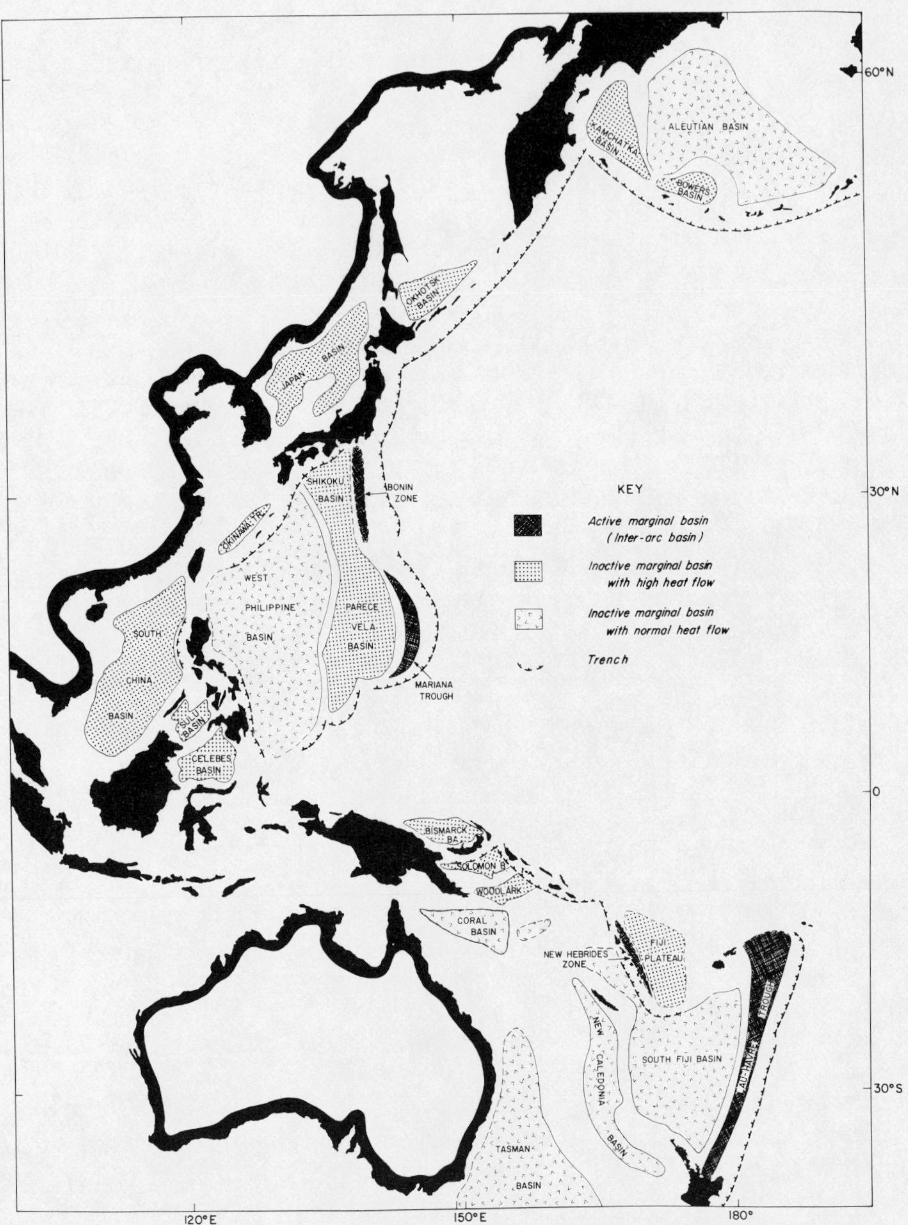

Fig. 3 Classification of marginal basins in the Western Pacific, updated from Karig (1971). Unexplored and filled basins are not shown.

are attributed to the cooling and densification of the diapiric mantle beneath the basin after active extension has ceased. The marginal basins of the Western Pacific for which data are available are shown in Fig. 3 and are divided on the basis of tectonic activity and heat flow. Active marginal basins, the inter-arc basins, show recent crustal extension. Inactive marginal basins with high heat flow opened during the Late Tertiary. The inactive marginal basins with normal heat flow are assumed to be older than mid-Tertiary (Karig 1971*b*).

In addition to the differences reflecting the age of marginal basins, there are differences in size and in the thickness of sediment fill. Basin size is thought to reflect the duration of the formative spreading period and the rate of extension. The quantity of sediment within marginal basins is primarily a function of available source areas and only secondarily one of age (Karig 1971*b*, p. 2546).

The active arc systems separated from continents by several marginal basins show much fewer continental affinities than do those separated from continents by a single basin. In addition, there is evidence that the earlier-formed arcs in a series, which lie closest to the continents, are larger and more continental than later ones. Yamato Rise, western New Caledonia, and the Lord Howe Rise (if this feature is a remnant arc) are Pacific examples of larger, continental remnant arcs.

Both the geologic record on islands of arc systems and the series of discrete marginal basins and remnant arcs suggest an episodicity of the processes responsible for island arc features. However, such episodicity remains poorly tested and must be viewed in consideration of the relatively constant spreading rates measured at all major oceanic spreading centres, at least throughout the Tertiary. Episodic arc activity is compatible with constant spreading if subduction can be accommodated along different plate boundaries at different rates at different times. This might represent minor plate readjustments. It has also been suggested (Sleep & Toksoz 1971) that the series of marginal basins represent cyclic readjustment of Benioff zone dips, with the implication that rate of subduction remains relatively constant.

Data from the Mariana Arc system indicates that the Parece Vela Basin extension ceased in early Miocene and extension of the currently active inter-arc basin began in late Pliocene (Karig 1971*a*). Sediments both on the islands and in the Parece Vela Basin indicate the volcanism continued until late Middle Miocene (Fischer *et al.* 1971), then ceased or was very greatly reduced until sometime in the Pliocene. From these data, one draws the conclusion that the two basins represent two pulses of volcanic activity, and the relationship of island arc volcanism with active Benioff zones further suggests separate pulses of subduction.

Still to be resolved is the behaviour of the trench during such an assumed episode of arc activity. Because active trenches are commonly assumed to be dynamically depressed crustal areas, it is logical to suppose that the topographic contrast between the trench and frontal arc decreases during periods of no underthrusting. Indeed, this appears to be the case in areas where underthrusting should have occurred until recently. However, such gravitational adjustment must be translated into structural geologic terms.

Two secondary tectonic processes which greatly modify the appearance of active arc systems are the reversal of arc system polarity and horizontal shear parallel to the arc trend. Polarity reversal is suggested by geologic features and regional geometries in the New Hebrides-Solomon area (Karig & Mammerickx, in press) but probably has also been an important factor in the development of the Philippine and Indonesian arc complexes. Polarity reversal occurs without collision of arc systems. It entails the abandonment of a trench in its previous position and activation of a new trench on the opposite side of the arc system with the opposite dip. Trench reversal is accompanied by changes in position of other arc system units to conform with the new polarity. The reasons for polarity reversals are still unclear, and the process itself requires further documentation.

Subduction in a reversed trench consumes marginal basin crust and ultimately causes the collision of the active arc system with remnant arcs or continents. It is suggested that many of the ultramafic-mafic complexes which have been emplaced on continental-type crust represent such collisions (Karig 1972).

Arc polarity reversals also cause the bending and offset of arc systems where reversed and normal arc systems meet along trend. The Philippines, New Zealand, and the Fiji area presently show such deformations.

Crustal displacements parallel to the arc trend can take place within the inter-arc basin or along discrete strike-slip fault zones. Within the inter-arc basin, this strain is added to the extensional strain to produce ridges and troughs which strike at angles to the general arc trend. The perpendicular to the ridges and troughs is in the direction of the vector sum of displacements between a small wedge of lithosphere extending from the trench to the inter-arc basin and the main plate to the rear. The Bonin, New Hebrides and Tonga-Kermadec arc systems all display oblique extensional trends.

In arc systems without active marginal basins, strike-slip faults parallel the arc trends but lie between the volcanic chain and the trench (Allen 1965). The Alpine Fault in North Island, New Zealand and the Philippine Fault are examples of this type in the Pacific. The cause of both forms of lateral displacement appears to be oblique underthrusting in the associated trench.

Because of the low dip and temperature along the shallow Benioff zone, it has been suggested (Karig & Mammerickx, in press) that strike-slip motion preferentially occurs along vertical surfaces beneath the weak crust and mantle of the inter-arc basin. If an inter-arc basin is lacking, it appears that horizontal breakage will occur closer to the trench. Oblique extension and strike-slip faults in arc systems requires that this motion must be added to the underthrusting in the trench to obtain a true displacement vector between the two major plates.

CONCLUSIONS

At first glance, the arc systems and marginal basins of the North-west Pacific appear to differ markedly from those of the South-west Pacific. The North-west Pacific has more arcuate systems, most having normal polarity, and the basin patterns look much simpler. The South-west Pacific has straighter arc systems, many of which have reversed polarity and internal complexities.

Upon closer observation, however, these differences diminish. The North-west

Pacific has reversed arcs in the Philippine area, in the Bering Sea (Kienle 1971), and probably along Hokkaido and Sakhalin (Miyashiro 1961, p. 299). The arc systems in the Philippine area are as complex as those in the New Guinea-Solomon area and the basin patterns equally confusing. Although most presently active arc systems in the North-west Pacific have smaller radii of curvature than does the Tonga-Kermadec system, the Philippine arc system and remnant arcs within the Philippine Sea are as straight. Shearing along the arc trends occurs in arc systems of both regions.

The variation in the characteristics of arc systems and marginal basins within each region appear to be at least as great as the differences between arc systems and basins of the North-west and South-west Pacific. The younger arc polarity reversals along the northern margin of the South-west Pacific give that region its unique character, whereas the two-trench pattern in the Philippine Sea is unique to that region. However, these differences could well be ephemeral.

REFERENCES

Allen, C. R. 1965. Transcurrent faults in continental areas. In *A symposium on continental drift. Phil. Trans. R. Soc.* **258,** 82-9.

Barazangi, M. & Isacks, B. 1971. Lateral variations of seismic wave attenuation in the upper mantle above the inclined earthquake zone of the Tonga Island Arc: Deep anomaly in the upper mantle. *J. geophys. Res.* **76,** 8493-516.

Chase, R. L. & Bunce, E. T. 1969. Under-thrusting of the eastern margin of the Antilles by the floor of the western North Atlantic Ocean, and origin of the Barbados ridge. *J. geophys. Res.* **74,** 1413-20.

Fischer, A. G., Heezen, B. C., Lisitzin, A. P., Pimm, A. C., Garrison, R. E., Boyce, R. E., Kling, S. A., Bukry, D., Krasheninnikov, V. & Douglas, R. C. 1971. Initial reports of the Deep Sea Drilling Program. *U.S. Government Printing Office*, **6.** 1329 pp. Washington.

Fisher, R. L. & Engel, C. G. 1969. Ultramafic and basaltic rocks dredged from the nearshore flank of the Tonga Trench. *Bull. geol. Soc. Am.* **80,** 1373-8.

Hart, S., Glassley, E. E. & Karig, D. E. (In press.) Basalts and sea-floor spreading behind the Marianas island arc. *Earth Planet. Sci. Letters.*

Karig, D. E. 1970. Ridges and basins of the Tonga-Kermadec island arc system. *J. geophys. Res.* **75,** 239-55.

——— 1971*a*. Structural History of the Mariana island arc system. *Bull. geol. Soc. Am.* **82,** 323-44.

——— 1971*b*. Origin and development of marginal basins in the Western Pacific. *J. geophys. Res.* **76,** 2542-61.

——— 1972. Remnant Arcs. *Bull. geol. Soc. Am.* **83,** 1057-68.

Karig, D. E. & Mammerickx, J. (1972). Tectonic framework of the New Hebrides Island arc system. *Marine Geology* **12,** 187-205.

Kienle, Jurgen. 1971. Gravity and magnetic measurements over Bowers Ridge and Shirshov Ridge, Bering Sea. *J. geophys. Res.* **76,** 7138-80.

Ludwig, W. J. 1970. The Manila Trench and West Luzon Trough—III. Seismic refraction measurement. *Deep Sea Res.* **17,** 553-71.

Ludwig, W. J., Ewing, J. I., Murauchi, S., Den, N., Asano, S., Hotta, H., Hayakawa, M., Asanuma, T., Ichikawa, K. & Nagurchi, I. 1966. Sediments and structure of the Japan Trench. *J. geophys. Res.* **71,** 2121-37.

Miyashiro, A. 1961. Evolution of metamorphic belts. *J. Petrology*, **2,** 277-311.

Oxburgh, E. R. & Turcotte, D. L. 1971. Origin of paired metamorphic belts and crustal dilation in island arc regions. *J. geophys. Res.* **76,** 1315-27.

Packham, G. H. & Falvey, D. A. 1971. An hypothesis for the formation of marginal seas in the western Pacific. *Tectonophysics* **11,** 79-109.

Petelin, V. P. 1964. Hard rocks in the deep-water trenches of the southwestern part of the Pacific ocean. *Int. Geol. Congr. 22nd Session, Doklady* (by the Soviet geologists), 78-86.

Raitt, R. W. 1967. Marine seismic studies of the Indonesian island arc. *Trans. Am. geophys. Un.* (abst.) **48,** 217.

Sclater, J. G., Hawkins, J. W., Mammerickx, J. & Chase, C. G. 1972. Crustal extension between the Tonga and Lau ridges. Petrologic and geophysical evidence. *Bull. geol. Soc. Am.* **83,** 505-18.

Sleep, N. & Toksoz, M. Nafi. 1971. Evolution of marginal basins. *Nature*, **233,** 548-50.

MARGINAL AREAS
OF THE WESTERN PACIFIC

Introduction

LARIC V. HAWKINS

School of Applied Geology, University of New South Wales,
P.O. Box 1, Kensington, N.S.W. 2033, Australia

The announced title of this symposium was the Evolution of the Continental Margins of the Western Pacific. However, due to other pressing commitments arising at a late stage in the organization of the symposium, a number of distinguished speakers, who were to present papers on the continental shelves and margins, had to withdraw. This left the main theme of this particular symposium as Marginal Areas of the Western Pacific.

As convener of the symposium, I was quite happy to have this change of emphasis, for it bridged and related well to the other symposia of Section D. Further, and more importantly, an understanding of the significance of the existence and development of the marginal areas is vital to a wider understanding of the geodynamic processes and evolution of the region, including that of the continental margins.

At a time when the evolution of the ocean basins and of continent distribution is beginning to be understood in terms of sea-floor spreading and plate tectonics, marginal seas present something of an enigma. They appear to be high-energy areas of relatively young sea floor, intimately related to zones of subduction and are a very prominent feature of the Western Pacific.

That island arc systems have, at least in some cases, migrated outwards over the Benioff zone into the ocean basins with the generation of sea floor behind the arc appears reasonably well established at this time. The precise geodynamic relation of the marginal sea to the process of sea-floor spreading and to the subducting plate is imperfectly understood. So too is the question whether the existence of a marginal sea behind an island arc infers that migration of the arc from a continental margin has occurred and, again, if reversal of the direction of such migration can occur, what is its possible significance within the orogenic process?

I believe that the existence of the marginal sea, as it occurs in the Western Pacific, is highly significant in the evolution of continental margins in this area, and in the orogenic process generally. We can expect a considerable focusing of attention on this problem within the international Geodynamics Programme now being initiated.

A Speculative Phanerozoic History of the South-west Pacific

G. H. PACKHAM

Department of Geology and Geophysics,
University of Sydney, Sydney, N.S.W. 2006, Australia

ABSTRACT

The South-west Pacific is a region of great tectonic complexity. During its history, from the Cambrian to the Jurassic, there was a progressive stepwise development of new continental crust accreted on to the continental margin. Major episodes of growth occurred in the Devonians, Permian and Jurassic. The continental margin was mostly of an Andean type with only occasional development of marginal seas. Volcanic zones were the loci of granitic intrusion in all three major phases, but granites were not entirely confined to the zones.

During the subsequent history of the region, there was fragmentation of the continental margin and splitting off of the Lord Howe Rise, Campbell Plateau and Norfolk Rise from the Australian continental margin in the Cretaceous. This was probably synchronous with the development of new sea floor along the margin of this rifted block. With the commencement of rifting of Australia from Antarctica, the Melanesian arc system was formed either out in the oceanic crust, or as a volcanic margin which migrated outward by the development of new sea floor behind it. The lack of evidence for subduction along part of the arc requires there to have been a spreading axis in the Pacific, with greater activity east of Melanesia.

Rearrangement of stresses took place in the Oligocene or earlier, and part of the oceanic plate was thrust over the continental margin in New Guinea and New Caledonia.

About the mid-Miocene, the northern part of the Melanesian arc became part of the Pacific plate as a result of the change of locations of trenches, from the northern to the southern sides of the arcs in the areas where they had previously existed, with the probable development of a new one south of the Solomon Islands. This change was responsible for a renewal of volcanic activity. Subsidiary spreading in the Fiji Plateau and along the length of the Kermadec Arc has further modified the pattern of tectonic features.

INTRODUCTION

The South-west Pacific region has been the site of continuous orogenic activity throughout the Phanerozoic. The changes which took place in the sea-floor spreading patterns subdivide the tectonic history into three major phases.

Eocene-Recent. With the rifting of Australia from Antarctica at about 50 m.y. (probably anomaly 21; Weissel & Hayes 1971), spreading on the Indian-Antarctic Ridge and the East Pacific Rise was responsible for interaction along the Pacific-Australia plate boundary. The pole of rotation of the Australian plate, with the position of Antarctica constant, was located in the vicinity of 145° W and 10° S and the motion was clockwise. The Pacific plate was rotated anti-clockwise about a pole 110° E and 70° S (Weissel & Hayes, in press). This pattern was probably complicated by spreading along a possible north-westerly trending spreading axis (Herron 1971) and the subsidiary development of new sea floor within the major plates, e.g. the marginal basins within the Australian plate, the Fiji Plateau and the Caroline Basin.

Upper Cretaceous-Eocene (*c.* ?90 m.y.-50 m.y.). Prior to the commencement of rifting of Australia and Antarctica, rifting had commenced south of New Zealand and along the north-westerly trending axis mentioned above. The oldest datable anomaly (No. 32) in the system of Pitman *et al.* (1968) dated at about 78 m.y. is about 300 km from the foot of the continental slope of the Campbell Plateau (Christoffel & Ross 1970). Assuming the half-spreading rate of 2 cm/yr, the oldest sea floor would be around 90 m.y. (early Upper Cretaceous). The pole of opening of the East Pacific Rise at that time was considerably to the north-east of the present pole, since old fracture systems south of the Campbell Plateau are 45° clockwise from fractures associated with spreading from the present day to anomaly 18 (46 m.y. B.P.) (Christoffel & Ross 1970). In what seems to be part of the suggested north-west trending anomaly system, anomaly 32 has been identified (Herron 1971). Both this system and the system south-east of the Campbell Plateau were operating simultaneously (Figs 5 and 6).

Cambrian-Upper Cretaceous. Prior to the rifting of the Campbell Plateau from Antarctica, and the Lord Howe Rise-New Zealand from Australia, they together formed a single continent facing the old Pacific. A reconstruction of this continent has been attempted. The fit of Australia and Antarctica used is that of Sproll and Dietz (1969). The fitting of Antarctica and the Campbell Plateau and Lord Howe Rise is more difficult. With the use of known poles of rotation it is possible to reconstruct the approximate position of the Campbell Plateau at anomaly 21 (Fig. 5), but poles for this time are not well established. Control on the rotation of the Campbell Plateau back to its position against Antarctica has been on the basis of best fit of the 2,000 m isobaths. This rotation involves the location of a pole at around 55° S and 175° E, a position consistent with the fracture trend found by Christoffel and Ross. In reconstructing the position of the Lord Howe Rise, the sigmoidal curvature of the New Zealand Geosyncline and the Alpine Fault has been removed. In addition, the region of the islands of New Zealand has been lengthened slightly in order to compensate for the additional crustal thickening which appears to have taken place. The Lord Howe Rise has been restored to its position along the Australian coast by rotation about a pole at approximately 165° E and 40° S (this is the assumed location of the Upper Cretaceous-Eocene pole of opening of the Tasman Sea).

PHASE 1—CAMBRIAN TO EARLY CRETACEOUS

During this phase, there was an outward stepwise accretion of the continental margin. Substantial areas of crust were stabilized as the result of a complex series of tectonic events which had climaxes in the Late Ordovician, mid-Devonian, mid-Permian and

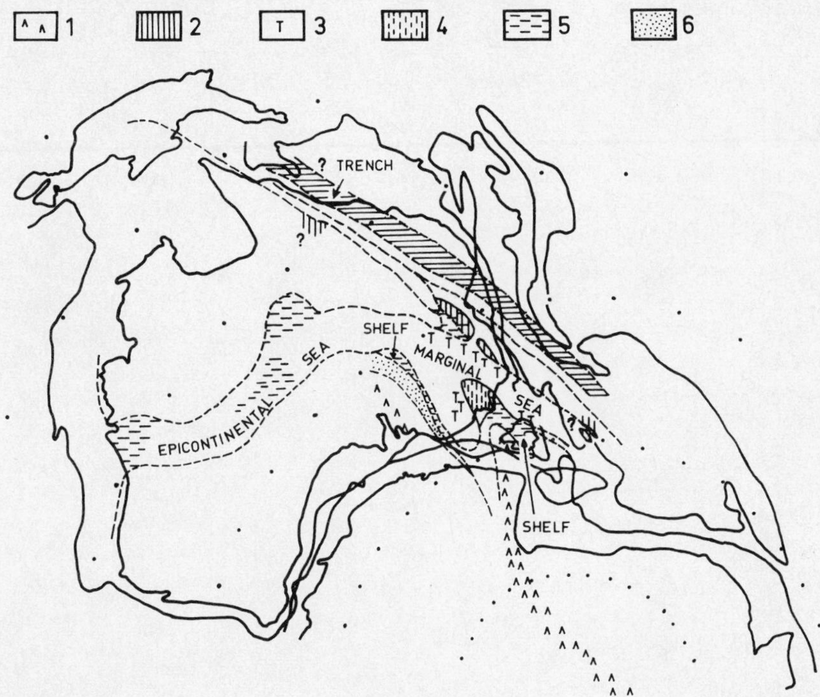

Fig. 1 Restored Ordovician palaeogeography. Legend: 1, Cambrian-basal Ordovician fold belt; 2, intermediate to acid volcanics; 3, black shales and turbidites; 4, marginal plateau; 5, shallow marine; 6, non-marine. In this and subsequent figures, 2-6, the fit between Australia and Antarctica is after Sproll and Dietz, 1969. The 1,000 m submarine contour is shown for continents and 2,000 m for micro-continental blocks. Dots are 10° lat./long. points, based on present pole position.

Late Jurassic. The postulated patterns of tectonic elements were varied, as can be seen from an examination of Figs 1, 2, 3 and 4. These figures assume that the plate tectonic model can be validly applied. Precambrian basement rocks are confined to the western margin of the geosyncline in New South Wales, Tasmania and the margin of the geosyncline in northern Queensland.

The Cambrian record, although sparse in the mobile belt, comprises both volcanics and sediments. In north-west Nelson (New Zealand) a dominantly volcanogenic (basaltic-andesitic) sequence contains large clasts of Precambrian rocks. In Victoria basic volcanics are found in several faulted axes (Singleton 1965). To the south in Tasmania a greywacke-volcanic sequence on the west coast between two Precambrian zones (Spry & Banks 1962) may represent an extensional rift which was compressed at about the end of the Cambrian. This is also the time when the shelf Proterozoic-Cambrian Adelaide Geosyncline (Parkin 1969) and the Antarctic sequence of similar age was folded (Harrington 1965).

The Ordovician sedimentation following this orogeny is known to be widespread in south-eastern Australia and extends into New Zealand (Fig. 1). Sediment was deposited over a wide area in turbidite facies possibly as an extensive submarine fan supplied by rivers flowing from the south-west. These sediments appear to have been partially ponded by the volcanic arc to the east. There is some stratigraphic evidence for an eastward progradation of the zone of maximum deposition. Probably little sediment reached the fore-arc region. The Ordovician rocks are not known to occur in eastern Queensland.

Orogenesis from the end of the Ordovician to mid-Silurian resulted in a broad regional high temperature/low pressure metamorphism west of the volcanic arc (Vallance 1967). This deformed region is one which had high heat flow and was interpreted by Packham and Falvey (1971) as having been a marginal sea. No evidence is available for the high pressure/low temperature zone which presumably lay to the east, although deformation of the Ordovician rocks of the south coast of New South Wales, for example at Narooma (Wilson 1969) is suggestive of subduction (melange) tectonics (but vesicularity in the associated basalts is less in keeping with a deep-sea environment). The compression of the mobile belt could have been the result of trench failure and the consequential coupling of the continental margin region to sea-floor spreading which was taking place at the time.

The orogenesis was accompanied by a hiatus in volcanism till about the middle of the Silurian. Following the hiatus, a complex series of minor orogenic movements (continuing until the mid-Devonian), granitic intrusions and acid to intermediate volcanism occurred in a zone lying along the old Ordovician volcanic zone (Packham 1969). It is presumed that this new regime was related to the establishment of a new subduction zone to the east of it. The region of the suggested Ordovician marginal sea after deformation formed low-lying land or remained submerged. The crust was presumably not thickened sufficiently to cause mountain range formation. Quartz-rich sediment continued to be supplied to this zone from the west and south-west. The Melbourne Trough in central Victoria contains a conformable Ordovician-Silurian sequence (Singleton 1965). The trough may be underlain by a Precambrian basement and the Ordovician deposits could be interpreted as being laid down on a submarine plateau marginal to Tasmania (Fig. 1).

After the Late Ordovician orogenesis, the Melbourne Trough remained generally low-lying relative to the zones of the crustal thickening adjacent to it to the east and west. The uplifted zones of Cambrian volcanics may mark its boundaries.

Within the Silurian to Lower Devonian volcanic zone, some of the sediment is quartz-rich and could have been derived either from the remote westerly source or from the recycling of the quartz-rich detritus of the Ordovician strata after the folding. The remainder of the Silurian to Lower Devonian sediment is volcanogenic with minor contributions of biogenic carbonates. There are two deep troughs (the Cowra and Hill End Troughs of Packham 1969) within the volcanic zone. These may have originated by rifting processes possibly accompanied by the formation of new sea floor beneath them. The Cowra Trough could be as old as Late Ordovician, but the Hill End Trough was probably formed in the mid-Silurian.

During the complex orogenic episode of the Silurian to mid-Devonian interval, massive granites were intruded into the basins, and foliated granites into the highs. To the north, the relict arc region seems to pass into an active continental margin in southern Queensland which apparently lacked marginal seas behind it, but in northern Queensland another trough (the Hodgkinson Trough) of possibly analogous type was formed, perhaps as early as the Silurian with the east-west rift-like structure (the Broken River Embayment) feeding sediment into it (Hill & Denmead 1969). To the west of the trough lies the Chillagoe Shelf—a region of carbonate sedimentation on a Precambrian basement. The associated volcanic arc (if present) would lie to the east on the now submerged Queensland Plateau. The Hodgkinson Basin appears to have persisted into the Early Carboniferous.

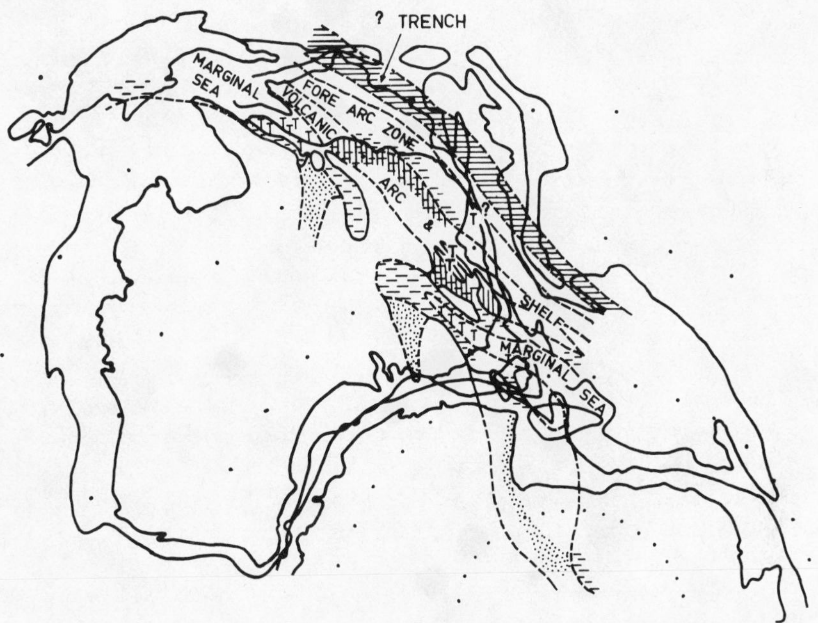

Fig. 2 Restored Lower Devonian palaeogeography. Legend as in Fig. 1.

In the east along the coast of Australia there outcrops a sequence of greywackes and shales which extend from Rockhampton in Queensland to Port Macquarie in New South Wales. These sediments are unfossiliferous except for rare traces of plant remains. They have frequently been regarded as lower to ? middle Palaeozoic, and could represent the deposits laid down beyond the volcanic arc on either the fore-arc region or in the trench itself. Chaotic deformation and local blueschists have been found in the Brisbane area, where the oldest rocks exposed are basaltic volcanics (Roxburgh Greenstones) (Hill & Denmead 1960). This belt of rocks may lie further to the east of the volcanic arc than at the time of its formation: there is the possibility of later rifting and development of a volcanic arc and possibly new oceanic crust within the New England Mobile Belt which developed east of the lower Palaeozoic volcanic arc. If this sequence is younger than thought (i.e. middle to upper Palaeozoic), it could have similar significance to that suggested, but be part of the middle to upper Palaeozoic New England Mobile Belt.

The Lower Devonian complex orogenic phase resulted in a near-stabilization of the western part of the mobile belt (Lachlan Geosyncline, of Packham 1969) (Fig. 2). The subsequent sediments in the Lachlan Mobile Belt (as I now prefer to call it) in the Upper Devonian and Lower Carboniferous are fluvial to shallow-water marine. They are extremely quartz-rich except for local basal arkose, molasse-like sequences, *but* the bulk of the sediment was derived from the west and south-west, not from the orogenic belt.

In the middle to late Palaeozoic New England Mobile Belt there are only minor occurrences known of pre-Devonian rocks. The first rocks of volumetric significance are Devonian. Early Devonian spilitic volcanic rocks are found in the Tamworth district, associated with shallow-water coralline limestones (see Packham 1969). Vallance (in Packham 1969) has shown these spilitic rocks to have been originally basaltic. It is not until the mid-Devonian that intermediate to acid volcanism became established, but once established, continued until the end of the Palaeozoic in the south (Branagan 1969) and into the early Mesozoic in the north (Paine 1969). The main site of this volcanism was on the western side of the New England Mobile Belt extending from Bowen in Queensland to the Newcastle-Forster area in New South Wales. The abundance of these volcanics diminishes to the south. East of the volcanic zone is a zone of predominantly clastic rocks constituting the Yarrol Basin in Queensland (Hill & Denmead 1960) and the Tamworth Trough in New South Wales (see Packham 1969). The principal zone of upper Palaeozoic serpentinites is located east of these clastics. To the east of the Yarrol Basin is the unfossiliferous greywacke sequence mentioned previously, but in New South Wales there is a broad zone of upper Palaeozoic rocks apparently representing a considerable variety of environments. They include greywackes, cherty sediments, pebbly mudstones and occasional limestones outcropping throughout the central part of New England and extending to the coast. Unconformities have been reported between Carboniferous and Lower Permian beds in the central part of this zone (Olgers & Flood 1970).

The complexity of the orogenic history of the northern part of the region in the volcanic zone is indicated by unconformities between Middle and Late Devonian rocks, Early and Late Carboniferous rocks and Late Permian and Triassic rocks (Paine 1969). Granitic intrusions of a variety of ages extending from the Devonian to early Mesozoic have been dated radiometrically by Webb and McDougall (1968). All of the igneous rocks of this region, according to them, have strontium isotope ratios consistent with a possible subcrustal source. In the southern part of the zone the plutons occur within the zone of complex stratigraphy east of the Tamworth Trough. An older group near the centre of the zone is associated with regional metamorphism, locally reaching high grade, while the larger ones are slightly younger and crosscutting. The first group is Early Permian, while the second is Late Permian and cuts the Peel Thrust that contains the serpentinite bodies. Early Permian crustal shortening appears to have taken place. It is possible that the complex zone represents a region that had undergone crustal extension in the Carboniferous and that the serpentinite bodies represent relicts of the new lithosphere formed at that time, thrust up through the sedimentary cover and blueschist metamorphism which occurs locally associated with them. If this does represent an extensional zone with high heat flow, rather than a 'fore-arc' zone, then relicts of the old volcanic arc may be found near the coast.

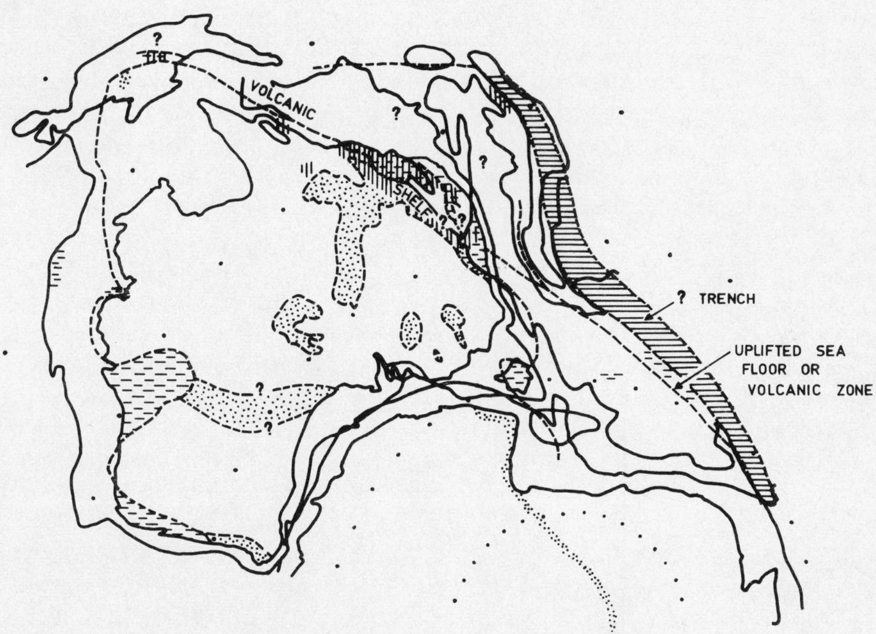

Fig. 3 Restored Lower Permian palaeogeography. Legend as in Fig. 1.

The history of the volcanic zone has parallels with that of the volcanic zone of the Lachlan Mobile Belt, in that it was a zone of intermittent granitic intrusion and orogenesis. The later Permian orogenic activity led to formation of a significant source of sediments deposited in the Permo-Triassic Sydney and Bowen Basins. These troughs have molasse-like characteristics. The New England Mobile Belt continued to be a significant sediment-source throughout much of the Mesozoic.

Although the middle to late Palaeozoic mobile belt is well represented in Australia, no such zone occurs in New Zealand between the early Palaeozoic zone and the Permian-Jurassic New Zealand Geosyncline. The only possible equivalent is the basement of the western zone of the New Zealand Geosyncline which is exposed in the South Island of New Zealand south-west of the Southland Syncline. It is composed of volcanic rocks which are predominantly basic, but with some keratophyres and andesites intruded by large masses of gabbro and norite (Wood 1966).

A reconstruction of possible Early Permian palaeogeography is given in Fig. 3.

One of the difficult points in this diagram is that the Permian of New Caledonia contains dacite and rhyolite lavas and tuffs (Lillie & Brothers 1970), giving the mobile belt a great width in the Queensland-New Caledonia region. It is possible to interpret the section in Australia as being close to the continental margin, and as mentioned above, it appears that the middle to late Palaeozoic mobile belt is very doubtfully represented in New Zealand. Further, the contact between the older Palaeozoic zone and the basement of the western zone of the New Zealand Geosyncline is a faulted one (Wood 1962). A number of explanations are possible, but the two most likely are that (*a*) the great width in the north is the result of large-scale strike-slip motions, moving the part of the section which formerly lay against the older Palaeozoic in New Zealand northwards; or, (*b*) that the Lord Howe Rise in the north has been very considerably extended by later crust, so that New Caledonia once lay very much closer to the Queensland coast. The reconstruction of the mid-Jurassic palaeogeography (Fig. 4) presents the same problem, except that it does appear that plutonic rocks of Mesozoic age occupy a broad belt. Assuming that the reconstruction is basically correct, then the event responsible for the great width of the magmatically active zone occurred after the mid-Jurassic.

The New Zealand 'Geosyncline' is a Permian to Jurassic orogenic belt marginal to the Pacific Ocean (Fleming 1970), in which there are two facies developed—the marginal facies on the west, and the axial facies on the east. Much of the marginal

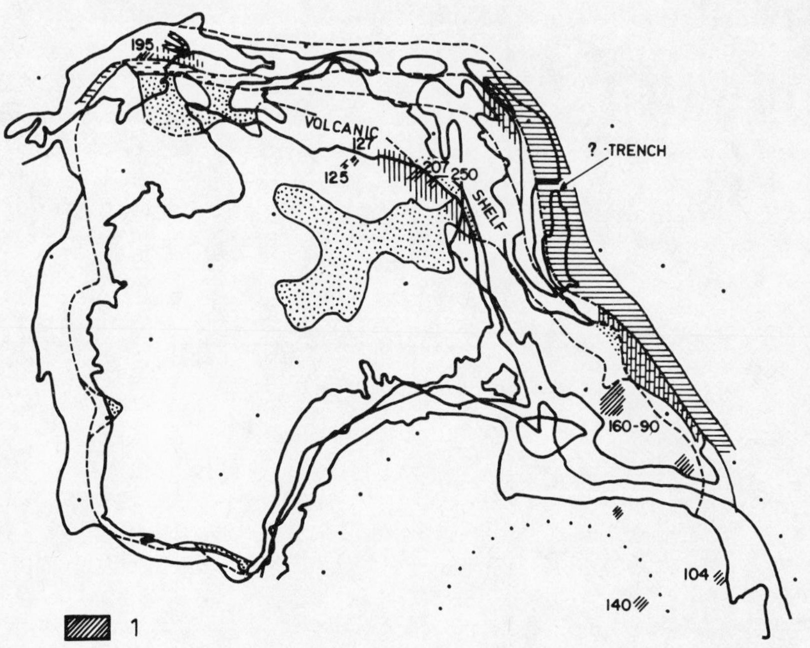

Fig. 4 Restored mid-Jurassic palaeogeography. 1, Plutonic masses with radiometric dates. Other legend as in Fig. 1.

facies was laid down in shallow water; it is gently folded, and its only known basement is composed of volcanic and plutonic, predominantly basic, rocks. The axial facies has no known basement, the rocks are shales, greywackes, basic volcanics and rare limestones and conglomerates, widely disrupted by planes of movement more or less parallel to the bedding, producing widespread lenticularity of the lithological layering on all scales. The western part of the outcrop of this facies is metamorphosed into schists with the grade of metamorphism dropping off towards the dislocation which marks the junction between the two facies. The outcrop of these facies has been disrupted by the Alpine Fault which is a later major strike-slip feature. It has been suggested that the axial facies of the New Zealand Geosyncline represents a trench assemblage (Dickinson 1971), and that the Dun Mountain melange which separates the Permian Putaki volcanics on the west from the axial facies to the east represents a westward-dipping subduction zone (Blake & Landis 1971). Rocks of comparable ages and facies are also found in New Caledonia (Lillie & Brothers 1970).

In eastern Australia shallow-water deposition with intermittent tectonism, andesitic volcanism and plutonic intrusives continued into the Cretaceous in a region generally east of the middle to upper Palaeozoic mobile belt. The folding which terminated the geosynclinal phase (the Rangitata Orogeny), as with the early Palaeozoic orogenesis, did not involve sufficient crustal shortening to form a mountain range, since again no molasse deposits of any magnitude were developed.

The folding movements of the Late Jurassic to Early Cretaceous during which the New Zealand Geosyncline and the remainder of the mobile belt were deformed, marked the end of a long period of continental accretion. The subsequent tectonic activity was of a different style, leading to fragmentation of the margin of the continent.

PHASE 2—UPPER CRETACEOUS TO EOCENE

During this interval, there appears to have been two active ridge systems in the far south-western Pacific region, the South Pacific Rise (south of the Campbell Plateau) and a second system, as yet very little known, approximately at right angles to and extending from the South Pacific Rise north-west across the Pacific Ocean (Herron 1971). It is also suggested that the Tasman Sea opened at this same time (Fig. 4 indicates the general style of the presumed spreading pattern). Considerable mobility in the mantle under the fold belt could have still persisted following the Rangitata Orogeny. This may have contributed to the rifting off of the Lord Howe Rise from Australia, rather than the spreading axis rifting Australia from Antarctica as it was to do later. Incipient rifting is indicated along the south coast of Australia by the development of a basin trending east-west in the Early Cretaceous. A consequence of this suggested pattern of sea-floor spreading is that much of the bending of the New Zealand 'Geosyncline' took place between the Upper Cretaceous and Eocene.

Cretaceous sea floor appears to be widespread in the general region. Pelagic sediments are found resting on basaltic basement in the Solomon Islands on Malaita and Santa Isabel (Coleman 1970), south-eastern Papua (Davies 1971) between the Line Islands and Gilbert and Ellice Islands, and east of the Marianas Trench.

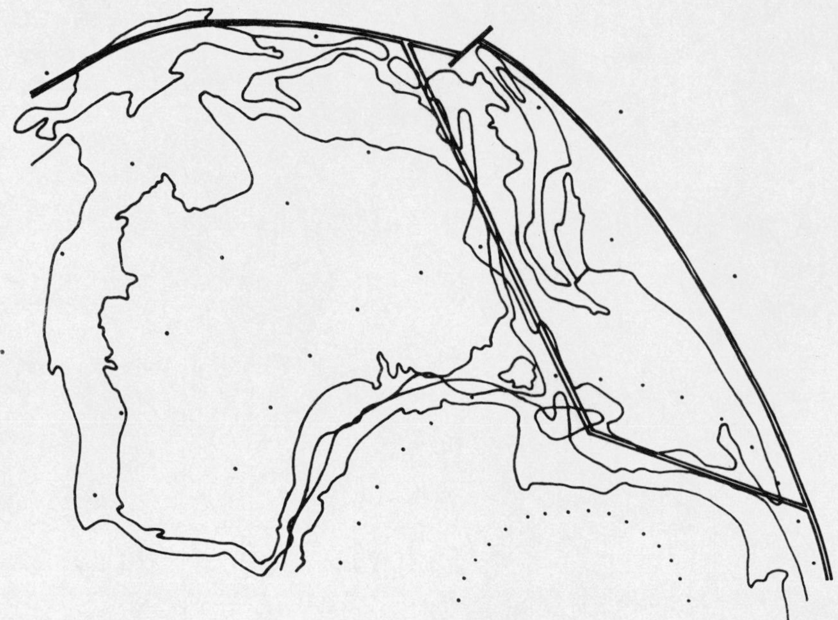

Fig. 5 Postulated Upper Cretaceous spreading axes.

The crust of the Ontong Java Plateau is Eocene or older (Winterer *et al.* 1969). Anomalies identified by Herron extend back to 32 (Upper Cretaceous) on the eastern side of the Eltanin Fracture Zone. These ages are younger than the crust indicated as Jurassic in the Shatsky Rise region and south-west of the Hawaiian Islands by Hayes and Pitman (1970). This Jurassic crust is shown to have been formed by spreading off the North Pacific Rise and the ridge now lost in the Aleutian Trench. The younger spreading system appears to have trended in a north-west direction and was probably responsible for the formation of the crust north of Melanesia. In the absence of evidence of subduction along the edge of this part of Gondwanaland, it is suggested that the ridge formed at the edge of the continent and migrated northwards during the Cretaceous and Eocene (Figs 4 and 5). The spreading axis may have extended further west into the Indian Ocean and been responsible for the rifting of continental crust from the north-western part of Australia out of the *Sinus Australia* of Dietz and Holden (1971) driving it north into Asia (D. A. Falvey, pers. comm.). This new spreading ridge could also have rifted off into the Pacific the outer parts of the upper Palaeozoic to Mesozoic geosyncline north-west of New Caledonia. The axis could have been established soon after the Rangitata Orogeny which was a strongly compressional event.

The nature of the continental margin of Gondwanaland between the Upper Cretaceous and early Eocene was apparently of Atlantic type, calcalkaline volcanics being absent or rare.

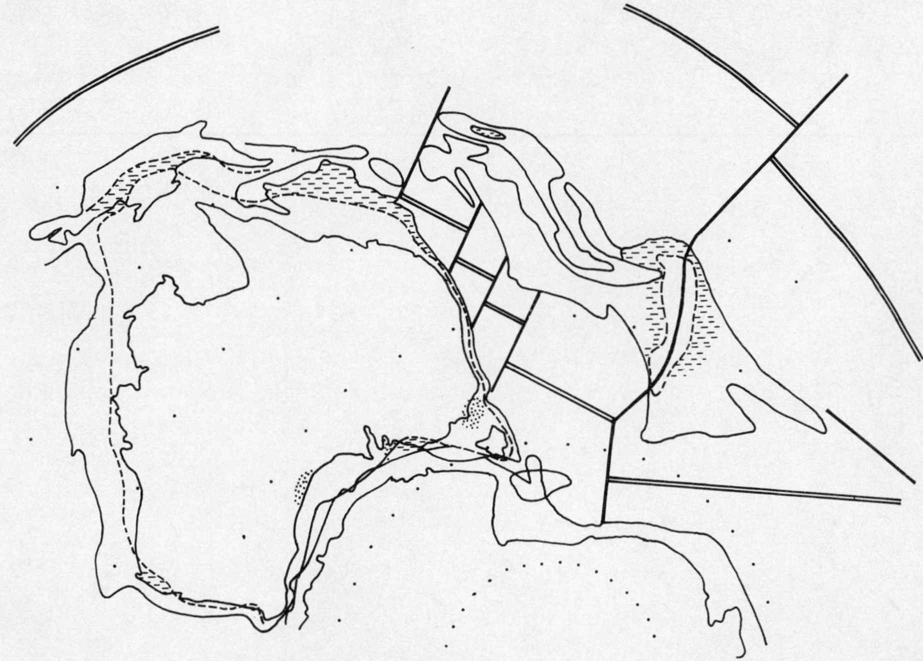

Fig. 6 Postulated spreading pattern in Paleocene time (approx. 55 m. y. ago), just prior to rifting of Australia from Antarctica. Legend as in Fig. 1.

The spreading pattern shown in Figs 4 and 5 does not require any subduction to have taken place between New Zealand and New Caledonia, along the continental margin, if the complex zone of fracture and compression intersecting the New Zealand region also intersects the spreading axis paralleling the coastline. At this stage the region would have been composed of four plates: Australia-Antarctica, Pacific, Tasman, and Campbell.

PHASE 3—EARLY EOCENE TO THE PRESENT

The complex structure of Melanesia appears to have formed during this phase. Rearrangements of plate boundaries are evidenced by the splitting of Australia from Antarctica about anomaly 21 (50 m.y. ago) (Weissel & Hayes 1971), and spreading on the South Pacific Rise on both sides of the Eltanin Fracture Zone (Herron 1971). The crucial question of the duration of spreading on the postulated north-west spreading axis cannot be established at present because of the lack of data. From the locations of anomalies indicated on Herron's map, it appears that spreading could have continued at least until anomaly 7 (in the uppermost Oligocene according to the time scale of Heirtzler *et al.* 1968). Until the location and duration of spreading on this supposed axis can be determined, geometric solutions to the Melanesian structure are not possible. With cessation of spreading on the axis, the Pacific plate would have become very much enlarged, incorporating the region from the East Pacific Rise to the Marianas Trench.

If no spreading had occurred on the north-west trending axis from anomaly 21 time, then about 3,000 km of the Pacific plate north of Australia and Melanesia would have been consumed during the northward movement of Australia since the early Eocene. In the absence of geophysical data, the interpretation has to depend on geological observations, and in particular, the recognition of the dates and locations of calcalkaline volcanism in the Melanesian region. These are taken as indices of subduction and crustal consumption. Unfortunately, more recent data have indicated that the dating of the volcanics and the determination of the petrographic suites to which they belong have frequently been erroneous. The problem of identification has been rendered more difficult by the low-grade (zeolitic or greenschist) metamorphism which frequently occurs in the basement rocks of these islands.

In summary the geology of the principal island groups is as follows:

(*a*) *Tonga-Kermadec Arc.* A pre-Eocene volcanic basement is followed by a sedimentary sequence with uplift in the late Miocene to early Pliocene and Late Tertiary to Quaternary volcanism of a variety of types including tholeiitic and calcalkaline suites (Karig 1970, Brothers 1970, Ewart & Bryan 1971).

(*b*) *Fiji.* Upper Eocene to early Miocene volcanics, intrusives and sediments including basalts, some hornblende and hypersthene andesites, rhyolites and basic to acid intrusives are overlain unconformably by mid-Miocene to Upper Pliocene andesitic volcanics and sediments followed unconformably by Upper Pliocene andesitic volcanics and these unconformably by still further volcanics, dominantly basaltic, with sediments still mainly within the Upper Pliocene (Rodda 1967, Gill 1970).

(*c*) *New Hebrides.* In the western chain of islands, on Malekeula, there are possible pre-Miocene red mudstones faulted against Lower Miocene volcanics and on the Torres Islands andesitic rocks have been dated as early Oligocene. Early Miocene basic and andesitic volcanics and sediments are intruded by hornblende andesites and diorites. These are overlain unconformably by late Miocene turbidites and rare tuffs. These in turn were block-faulted prior to a Pliocene transgression. In the eastern belt of islands, undated (but probably early Miocene) basalts and andesitic lavas are intruded by gabbros and norites and followed by the emplacement of serpentinites containing amphibolite blocks. This was succeeded by the eruption of basaltic pillow lavas and breccias in the late Miocene to early Pliocene. The central islands comprise Pliocene to Recent basaltic and andesitic volcanics; Pliocene to Quaternary reefal limestones occur in all these provinces (Mitchell & Warden 1971).

(*d*) *British Solomon Islands.* The basement rocks are late Mesozoic tholeiitic basaltic lavas overlain by pelagic limestones. These rocks in the central province of the islands (that is, excluding northern Santa Isabel and Malaita) have been metamorphosed to greenschist and amphibolite grade in the Early Tertiary and intruded by Alpine type ultrabasics possibly in the Oligocene. The basement in the central province is overlain by Oligocene to Recent volcanics and sediments with little volcanism in the Miocene. Clastic sediments become increasingly abundant in the northern (Pacific) province from the Upper Miocene onwards and the province was folded along north-west trending fold axes probably in the Upper Miocene. Shallow-water deposits are common in the central province from the Miocene onwards. The Pliocene-Pleistocene volcanics are concentrated on the south-western edge of the chain and are of calcalkaline affinities, while those of the Oligocene-Miocene are basaltic andesites (Coleman 1970, Hackman 1971).

(*e*) *Bismarck Archipelago and Bougainville.* The basement rocks are older than mid-Miocene, extending back to Eocene on New Britain and Oligocene on New Ireland. They include andesitic volcanics on Bougainville and they are intruded by plutonic rocks ranging from gabbros to tonalites on New Britain and New Ireland. There is a mid-Miocene hiatus during which limestones were deposited. This was followed by a renewal of volcanism in the Late Tertiary and Quaternary (Bain *et al.* 1971, Blake & Miezitis 1967). Much of the more recent volcanism is tholeiitic (Jakeš & White 1969).

(*f*) *Eastern Papua.* Upper Cretaceous to Eocene pelagic limestones and cherts are overlain in the Aure Trough on the west of the peninsula by Miocene turbidites and Pliocene to Pleistocene paralic sediments derived from the east. On the eastern side of the peninsula a slab of oceanic crust and mantle has been thrust on to a westerly sequence of Cretaceous and ?older sialic metamorphics. This slab comprises harzburgites, dunites and pyroxenites at the base, gabbros above and an upper layer of basalts and pelagic limestones of Cretaceous age. These are intruded by tonalite bodies overlain by Miocene to Recent andesitic volcanics and sediments with folding occurring in the Pleistocene. The overthrusting occurred in the Eocene to Oligocene. High pressure/low temperature metamorphic assemblages occur at the base of the thrust sheet and the rocks to the east have suffered metamorphism and been intruded by granodiorites (Thompson 1968, Davies 1971).

(*g*) *Northern New Guinea.* The history of this region is analogous in general features to that of eastern Papua except that the deposition of clastics after the Oligocene orogenesis took place to the north of the large mafic and ultramafic bodies such as those that occur in the western Central and Bismarck Ranges. The deformed volcanic basement and Cretaceous to Oligocene pelagic limestones that occur to the north in the coastal ranges are succeeded in most places by thick sequences of clastics with some reef limestones. Orogenesis appears to have continued intermittently resulting in shifting patterns of environments but progressively reducing the areas of deposition until the end of the Pleistocene (Harrison 1969).

(*h*) *New Caledonia.* The late Lower Cretaceous to Upper Cretaceous beds which rest with an unconformity on the older Mesozoic sequence, contain a variety of lithologies including conglomerates, coals, sandstones, shales and a few rhyolite flows. The sequence is mostly marine. The overlying Eocene section is in place conformable with the Cretaceous but elsewhere rests on Triassic greywackes. Two lithological assemblages are found in the Eocene, a regularly bedded sandstone, shale, limestone succession and a foraminiferal limestone-chert sequence. These pass laterally into and are overlain by a sequence of tholeiitic basaltic flows with red shales and radiolarian rocks, but pillow lavas are rare. These are overthrust from the east according to Avias (1967) by the large ultramafic bodies which occupy about one-

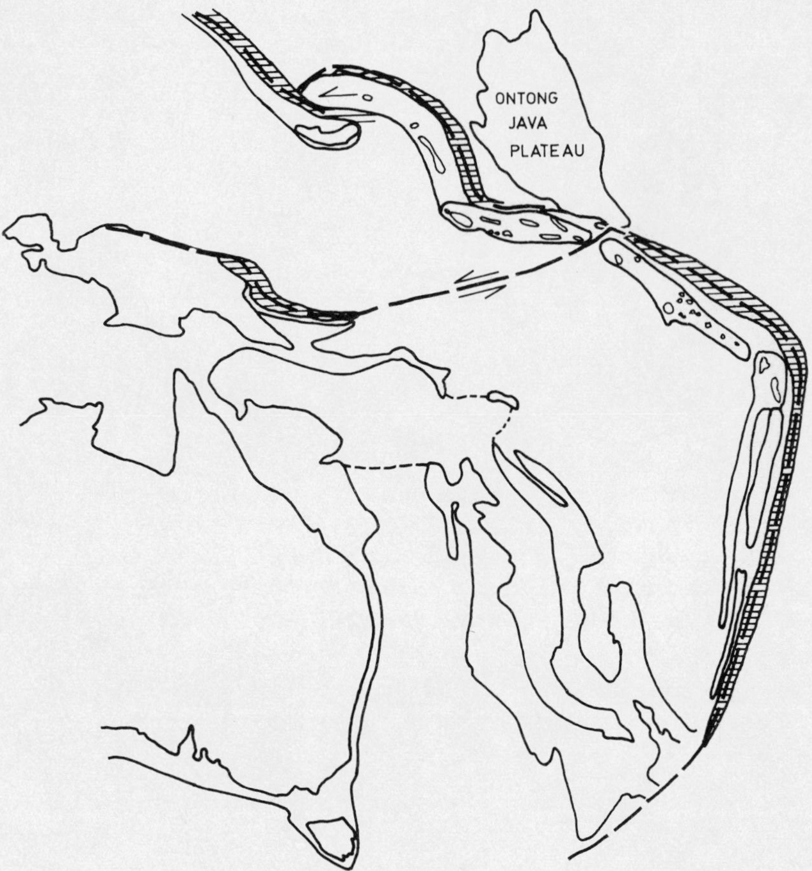

Fig. 7 Postulated distribution of trenches and arcs in early Middle Miocene. Trenches (20 m.y. ago) are indicated by horizontal ruling.

third of the island. The base of the sheet is serpentinized and some of the underlying rocks contain high pressure/low temperature assemblages. The ultramafics are predominantly harzburgites and dunites. Overlying them are horizontal to gently dipping Lower Miocene coralline limestones. Since the Eocene sedimentary sequence extends into the Upper Eocene, the date of emplacement of the ultramafics is generally taken as Oligocene (Lillie & Brothers 1970).

It was suggested above that spreading on the postulated north-west to south-east ridge in the Pacific continued until at least late Oligocene (Fig. 6). It also appears from the discontinuity in ages of sea floor at the northern margin of the Carolina Basin (Fischer *et al.* 1969, Winterer *et al.* 1969) that some new spreading system existed there in the Oligocene to Lower Miocene. Two alternative general hypotheses for the history of the region are possible within the framework of these assumptions. *Either* as Australia moved northwards, the spreading was such that the suggested Cretaceous

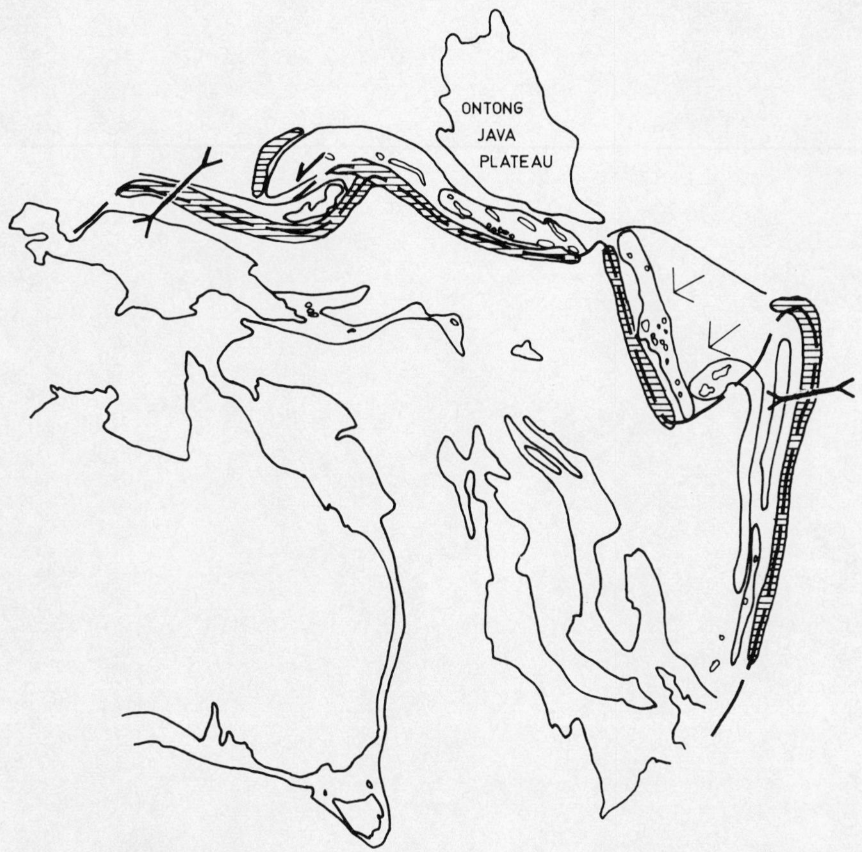

Fig. 8 Postulated distribution of trenches and arcs in the Upper Miocene (10 m.y. ago). Trenches are indicated by horizontal shading, and bars indicate vectors of compression, assuming present spreading pattern.

to Eocene crust outside the margin of the Australian continent formed the sea floor behind the Melanesian arcs. Along the Tonga-Kermadec line and at some locations along the northern edge of the arc, subduction took place with little or no spreading north of the arc, but spreading rates were greater to the east of the Tonga-Kermadec Trench; *or* spreading took place behind the arcs forming new sea floor during the Early Tertiary as the arcs migrated outwards (Coleman 1967), and spreading occurred in the adjacent Pacific east of the Kermadec Trench.

In the former case the crust of the South Fiji Basin would be mainly Cretaceous and in the latter case Eocene to probably Oligocene.

The Eocene dates of shallow-water limestone on Fiji, the metamorphism in the Solomons and the Eocene of New Britain are suggestive of the formation of a ridge at approximately the time of commencement of movement of Australia northwards. The location of this ridge, at its time of formation cannot be determined; however, the tholeiitic nature of the basement rocks of the Solomon Islands and the absence of andesites until the Miocene suggests that the ridge may have been formed well out from the margin of Australia, and that the former hypothesis that the arc originated on old sea floor is the more likely (see Postscript).

The Oligocene dates of mafic overthrusting in New Caledonia, eastern Papua (see Postscript) and possibly northern New Guinea involves the presence of a plate boundary along the Australian continental margin and can be explained by:

(1) a shifting of a plate boundary from the outer side of this arc to the continental

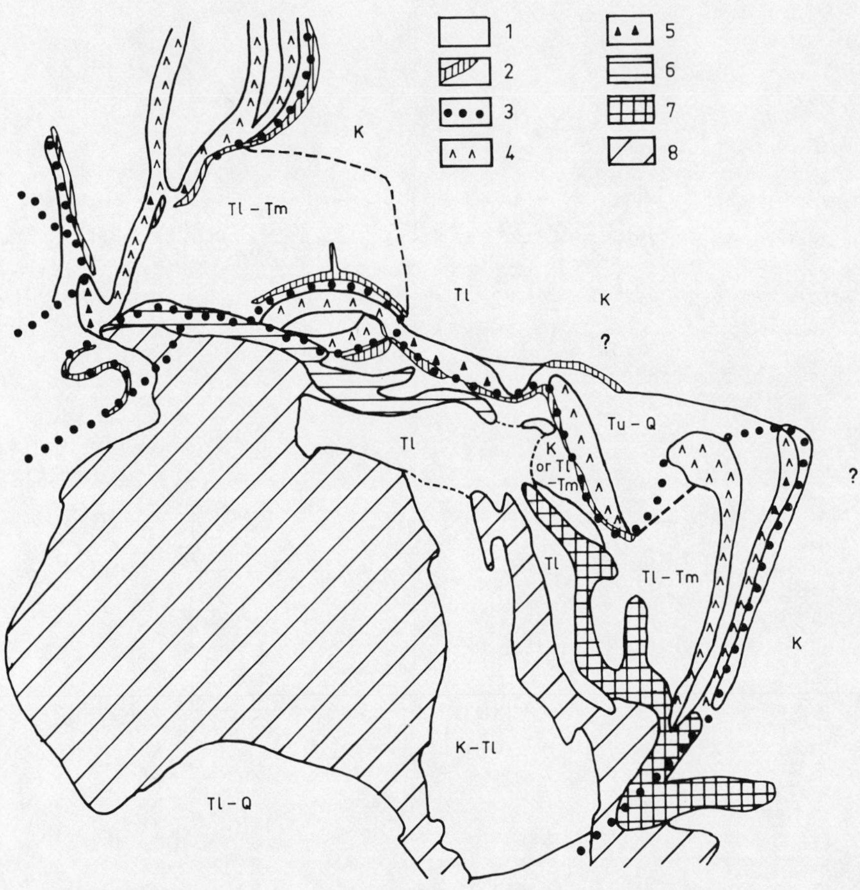

Fig 9 General structure of Melanesian arcs with postulated ages of sea floor. 1, sea floor: K, Cretaceous; Tl, 'Lower Tertiary' (65-40 m.y.); Tm, 'mid-Tertiary' (40-20 m.y.); Tu 'Upper Tertiary' (20-2 m.y.); Q, Quaternary). 2, Trenches and deeps. 3, seismic lines. 4, Tertiary volcanic arc. 5, Tertiary volcanic arc with metamorphosed basement. 6, Tertiary fold belt. 7, Mesozoic fold belt. 8, Pre- Mesozoic continental crust.

margin due to the cessation of subduction in the outer trenches;

(2) spreading behind the outer arc driving both margins of the new plate outwards towards the Pacific to the north-east and Australia to the south-west; or,

(3) spreading behind the continental margin opening the Coral Sea and the New Caledonia Basin in agreement with Gardner's (1970) suggested post-Upper Eocene age for the formation of the Coral Sea floor (see Postscript).

The overthrusting in New Caledonia may have resulted, in conjunction with the motions suggested above, from collision of New Caledonia with the Loyalty Islands; no such arc is apparent in the vicinity of Papua or northern New Guinea, unless it is to be found in the Bismarck Archipelago. The formation of Solomon Sea crust would then post-date the overthrusting.

The Neogene history is a little less obscure. Figs 6 and 7 (for 10 m.y. and 20 m.y. ago) have been constructed using poles of rotation of Australia relative to Antarctica, and the Pacific plate relative to Antarctica from Weissel and Hayes (in press).

The early to mid-Miocene marks a time of orogenesis throughout the arc with unconformities occurring in Fiji, the New Hebrides, Bougainville and the Solomons followed by a hiatus in volcanic activity especially apparent west of the New Hebrides. It is suggested that this was the result of the transfer of the trenches on the northern side of the arc to the southern side (see Fig. 8). The change was followed by the renewal of volcanism in the Upper Miocene to Recent. A change of locus of volcanism is apparent in the Solomons and New Hebrides. Mitchell and Reading (1971) have suggested a reversal of trench location at about this time in the New Hebrides. If this reversal did occur, then prior to it the New Hebrides would have behaved as part of the Australia plate and not part of the Pacific plate as they are at present, consuming the sea floors which were previously behind them. 'Collision' of the arc with the thicker crust of the Ontong Java Plateau (Figs 7 and 8) may have been a cause of the reversal.

The pattern has been modified by subsidiary spreading in the Late Tertiary to Quaternary in the Fiji region east of the New Hebrides. This is indicated by the abnormally thin sediment cover in the Fiji Plateau region (Shor *et al.* 1971) and the high heat flow (Sclater & Menard 1967). At the same time, extension has also occurred on the Tonga-Kermadec Arc splitting it along its length (Karig 1970). Fig. 9 shows the ages of the various sea floors and arcs as proposed in this paper.

POSTSCRIPT

Since this paper was written, new information materially affecting the interpretation of the Late Cretaceous to Tertiary history of the region has become available. Davies and Smith (1971) have reassessed the date of overthrusting of the Papuan Ultramafic Belt as early Eocene. Hayes and Ringis (1972) have established, on the basis of magnetic anomalies, that the opening of the Tasman Sea commenced before 80 m.y. (anomaly 32) and ended at about 60 m.y. (anomaly 24). Spreading was symmetrical about a mid-ocean ridge; the anomalies trend at about 330°.

The results of deep-sea drilling by the *Glomar Challenger* on Leg 21 in the region are also available (Andrews *et al.* 1972). This drilling programme established that (1) deposition commenced in the Lau-Havre Trough at about the end of the Miocene (Site 203); (2) the South

Fiji Basin was probably formed in the Oligocene. At Site 205, near the western side of the basin the deepest rock intersected was finely crystalline basalt intruding late Oligocene deep-water sediments; (3) a drill hole in the centre of the New Caledonia Basin (Site 206) ended in mid-Eocene oceanic sediments without reaching basement; (4) the Lord Howe Rise was submerged at the southern end to bathyal depths at the end of the Cretaceous (Site 207) and possibly a little earlier in the north (Site 208); (5) the oldest sediment penetrated at Site 210 in the Coral Sea was mid-Eocene. The sediments are oceanic and basement was not reached.

Some of the implications of this information are:

(1) The Tasman Sea floor was formed at about the time suggested; when spreading ceased in the Tasman, there was a short hiatus and then the rifting of Australia from Antarctica took place.

(2) The Coral Sea is older than suggested by Gardner (1970) but so too is the latest suggested date of overthrusting. The time relationship between the formation of the Coral Sea floor and the overthrusting cannot be determined on present data, but it is close in time to the rifting of Australia from Antarctica.

(3) The formation of the New Caledonia Basin (mid-Eocene or earlier) predates the mafic overthrusts in New Caledonia (Oligocene) but the age relationship of the New Caledonia Basin to the Coral Sea and Tasman Sea Basins are at present indeterminate.

(4) Drilling results from the South Fiji Basin suggest that the basin was formed in the Oligocene by the formation of new sea floor behind the arc system rather than being an area of old sea floor cut off from the Pacific, assuming that the intrusive basalt is close in age to the time of the formation of the basin.

(5) A very young age for the Lau-Havre Trough has been confirmed by drilling. The formation of the trough commenced at about the end of the Miocene.

REFERENCES

Andrews, J. E., Burns, R. E., Churkin, M., Davies, T. A., Dumitrika, P., Edwards, A. R. Galehouse, J. S., Kennett, J. P., Packham, G. H. & Lingen, G. J. van der. 1972. Deep sea drilling project: leg 21, Tasman Sea-Coral Sea, preliminary results. *Int. Symp. on Oceanography of the South Pacific,* Wellington, N.Z.

Avias, J. 1967. Overthrust structure of the main ultrabasic New Caledonian massifs. *Tectonophysics*, **4,** 531. See also this volume.

Bain, J. H. C., Davies, H. L. & Ryburn, R. J. 1971. Regional geology of Papua-New Guinea: some new concepts (abst.) *12th Pacific Sci. Congr. Rec. Proc.* (Abstracts), **1,** 450. See also Bain, this volume.

Blake, D. H. & Miezitis, Y. 1967. Geology of Bougainville and Buka, New Guinea. *Bull. Bur. Miner. Resour. Aust.* **93.**

Blake Jr, M. C. & Landis, C. A. 1971. The Dun Mountain Melange—a proposed western margin of the Torlesse terrane in northeast Nelson (abst.). *Symp. on Torlesse Supergroup, Vict. Univ. Wellington,* **29.**

Branagan, D. F. 1969. Palaeovolcanology in New South Wales: a stratigraphic summary. *Spec. Publs geol. Soc. Aust.* **2,** 155.

Brothers, R. N. 1970. Petrochemical affinities of volcanic rocks from the Tonga-Kermadec Island arc, Southwest Pacific. *Bull. volcan.* **34,** 308.

Christoffel, D. A. & Ross, D. I. 1970. A fracture zone in the south west Pacific Basin south of New Zealand and its implications for sea-floor spreading. *Earth Planet. Sci. Letters,* **8,** 125.

Coleman, P. J. 1967. A possible resolution of the Melanesian Re-entrant. *Upper Mantle*

Project, 2nd Aust. Prog. Rept (*1965-7*), 192-4 (Ed. A. E. Ringwood). Aust. Acad. Sci. Canberra.

——— 1970. Geology of the Solomon and New Hebrides Islands, as part of the Melanesian Re-entrant, South-west Pacific. *Pacif. Sci.* **24,** 259.

Davies, H. L. 1971. Peridotite-gabbro-basalt complex in eastern Papua: an overthrust plate of oceanic mantle and crust. *Bull. Bur. Miner. Resour. Aust.* **128.**

Davies, H. L. & Smith, I. E. 1971. Geology of Eastern Papua. *Bull. geol. Soc. Am.* **82,** 3299.

Dickinson, W. R. 1971. Clastic sedimentary sequences deposited in shelf, slope and trough settings between magmatic arcs and associated trenches. *Pacific Geol.* **3,** 15.

Dietz, R. S. & Holden, J. C. 1970. The break-up of Pangaea. *Scient. Am.* **223,** 30-41.

Ewart, A. & Bryan, W. B. 1971. Geology, petrography and geochemistry of the volcanic islands of Tonga (abst.) *12th Pacific Sci. Congr. Rec. Proc.* (Abstracts), **1,** 454. See also this volume.

Fischer, A. G. & Heezen, B. C. 1969. Deep sea drilling project: Leg 6. *Geotimes,* **14,** 13.

Fleming, C. A. 1970. The Mesozoic of New Zealand: Chapters in the history of the Circum-Pacific Mobile Belt. *J. geol. Soc. London,* **125,** 125.

Gardner, J. 1970. Submarine geology of the western Coral Sea. *Bull. geol. Soc. Am.* **81,** 2599.

Gill, J. B. 1970. Geochemistry of Viti Levu, Fiji, and its evolution as an island arc. *Contr. Mineral. Petrol.* **27,** 179.

Hackman, B. D. 1971. The Solomon Islands fractured arc. *12th Pacific Sci. Congr. Rec. Proc.* (Abstracts), **1,** 366. See also this volume.

Harrington, H. J. 1965. Geology and morphology of Antarctica. *Monographiae Biologicae,* **15,** 1.

Harrison, J. 1969. Review of the sedimentary history of the island of New Guinea. *J. Aust. Petrol. Expl. Ass.* **9,** 41.

Hayes, D. E. & Pitman, W. C. 1970. Magnetic lineations in the north Pacific. *Mem. geol. Soc. Am.* **126,** 291.

Hayes, D. E. & Ringis, J. 1972. The early opening of the central Tasman Sea (abst.) *Int. Symposium on Oceanography of the South Pacific,* Wellington, N.Z.

Heirtzler, J. R., Dickson, G. O., Herron, E. M., Pitman, III, W. C. & Le Pichon, X. 1968. Marine magnetic anomalies, geomagnetic field reversals, and motions of the ocean floor and continents. *J. geophys. Res.* **73,** 2119.

Herron, E. M. 1971. Crustal plates and sea-floor spreading in the southeastern Pacific. *Antarct. Res. Ser.* **15,** 229.

Hill, D. & Denmead, A. K. 1960. The geology of Queensland. *J. geol. Soc. Aust.* **7.**

Jakeš, P. & White, A. J. R. 1969. Structure of the Melanesian arcs and correlation with distribution of magma types. *Tectonophysics,* **8,** 223.

Karig, D. E. 1970. Ridges and basins of the Tonga-Kermadec island arc system. *J. geophys. Res.* **75,** 239.

Lillie, A. R. & Brothers, R. N. 1970. The geology of New Caledonia. *N.Z. Jl Geol. Geophys.* **13,** 145.

Mitchell, A. H. & Reading, H. G. 1971. Evolution of island arcs. *J. Geol.* **79,** 253.

Mitchell, A. H. & Warden, A. J. 1971. Geological evolution of the New Hebrides island arc. *J. geol. Soc. London,* **127,** 501.

Olgers, F. & Flood, P. G. 1970. An angular Permian/Carboniferous unconformity in south-eastern Queensland and northeastern New South Wales. *J. geol. Soc. Aust.* **17,** 81.

Packham, G. H. 1969. The geology of New South Wales. *J. geol. Soc. Aust.* **16,** 1.

Packham, G. H. & Falvey, D. A. 1971. An hypothesis for the formation of marginal seas in the western Pacific. *Tectonophysics,* **11,** 79.

Paine, A. G. L. 1969. Palaeovolcanology of central eastern Queensland. *Spec. Publs geol. Soc. Aust.* **2,** 183.

Parkin, L. W. 1969. Handbook of South Australian geology. *Publ. geol. Surv. S. Aust.* Adelaide.

Pitman, W. C., Herron, E. M. & Heirtzler, J. R. 1968. Magnetic anomalies in the Pacific and sea-floor spreading. *J. geophys. Res.* **73,** 2069.

Rodda, P. Outline of the geology of Viti Levu. *N.Z. Jl Geol. Geophys.* **10,** 1260.

Sclater, J. G. & Menard, H. W. 1967. Topography and heat flow of the Fiji Plateau. *Nature,* **216,** 991.

Shor, G. G., Kirk, H. K. & Menard, H. W. 1971. Crustal structure of the Melanesian area. *J. geophys. Res.* **76,** 2562.

Singleton, O. P. 1965. Geology and mineralization of Victoria. *8th Common. Min. Metall. Congr.* **1,** 440.

Sproll, W. P. & Dietz, R. S. 1969. The morphological fit of Australia and Antarctica. *Nature,* **222,** 345.

Spry, A. & Banks, M. R. (Eds) 1962. The geology of Tasmania. *J. geol. Soc. Aust.* **9** (2), 107.

Thompson, J. E. 1967. A geological history of eastern New Guinea. *J. Aust. Petrol. Expl. Ass.* **7,** 83.

Vallance, T. G. 1967. Palaeozoic low-pressure regional metamorphism in southeastern Australia. *Meddr dansk geol. Foren.* **17,** 494.

Webb, A. W. & McDougall, I. 1968. The geochronology of the igneous rocks of eastern Queensland. *J. geol. Soc. Aust.* **15,** 313.

Weissel, J. K. & Hayes, D. E. 1971. Assymetric sea-floor spreading south of Australia. *Nature,* **231,** 518.

——— (In press.) Magnetic anomalies in the southeast Indian Ocean. *Antarct. Res. Ser.*

Wilson, C. J. L. 1968. Geology of the Narooma area, N.S.W. *J. Proc. R. Soc. N.S.W.* **101,** 147.

Winterer, E. L. & Riedel, W. R. 1969. Deep sea drilling project: leg. 7. *Geotimes,* **14,** 12.

Wood, B. L. 1962. Notes accompanying *Geological Map of New Zealand Sheet 22* Wakatipu. N.Z. Geol. Surv., Lower Hutt.

——— 1966. Notes accompanying *Geological Map of New Zealand Sheet 24* Invercargill. N.Z. Geol. Surv., Lower Hutt.

Some Basic Problems of Structure and Tectonic History of the North-western Segment of the Pacific Mobile Belt

V. E. Khain and K. B. Seslavinsky

Geological Department, Moscow State University, Moscow V-234, U.S.S.R.

ABSTRACT

A survey of existing data from the north-western segment of the Pacific mobile belt shows that this segment has had a long and varied geological history, beginning in the Archaean. It was part of a primary continental craton well before the Proterozoic. The craton split and geosynclinal belts began their development by Late Proterozoic, with a proto-Pacific to the east. These geosynclines developed on continental crust during the early Palaeozoic, reaching their maximum in the middle and late Palaeozoic. The overall trend was towards the accretion of continental crust by way of successive tectonic cycles of reactivation and rejuvenation. By the middle Mesozoic the formation of oceanic crust took place within linear troughs along the whole of the segment, the Pacific Ocean further developed and many older structural zones were re-shaped. Towards the end of the Mesozoic the geosynclinal systems shifted east and the sub-oceanic marginal seas were formed. During the Tertiary these seas, the island arcs and deep-sea trenches took on their present outlines. This complex history cannot be reconciled with simplistic schemes either of continental accretion at the expense of oceanic crust or of absorption of continental crust by the oceanic.

INTRODUCTION

If the north-western segment of the Pacific belt is considered a natural unit of the latter, we should begin by defining the boundaries of this segment. It can be done most easily in its northern part, where the boundary is a longitudinal fault (noted by Yegiazarov) running through the Bering Strait. The south-west boundary may be drawn, more or less hypothetically, through the Yellow and East China Seas towards the northern termination of the Ryukyu Island Arc and the junction of the Izu-Bonin and Mariana Arcs. In the west the segment abuts against ancient crystalline massifs of Korea, of Khanka Lake, and of the Bureia, Aldan, Okhotsk, Omolon, and Taigonos massifs. In the north it joins the Chukotka folded system of the Arctic (peri-Arctic) mobile belt distinguished by Kheraskov. In the mouth of the Amur, the Pacific belt joins the Mongol-Okhotsk system of the Central-Asia belt and along both sides of the Okhotsk massif it joins the Verkhoyansk-Kolyma system which connects the Pacific and Arctic belts (Yegiazarov 1961).

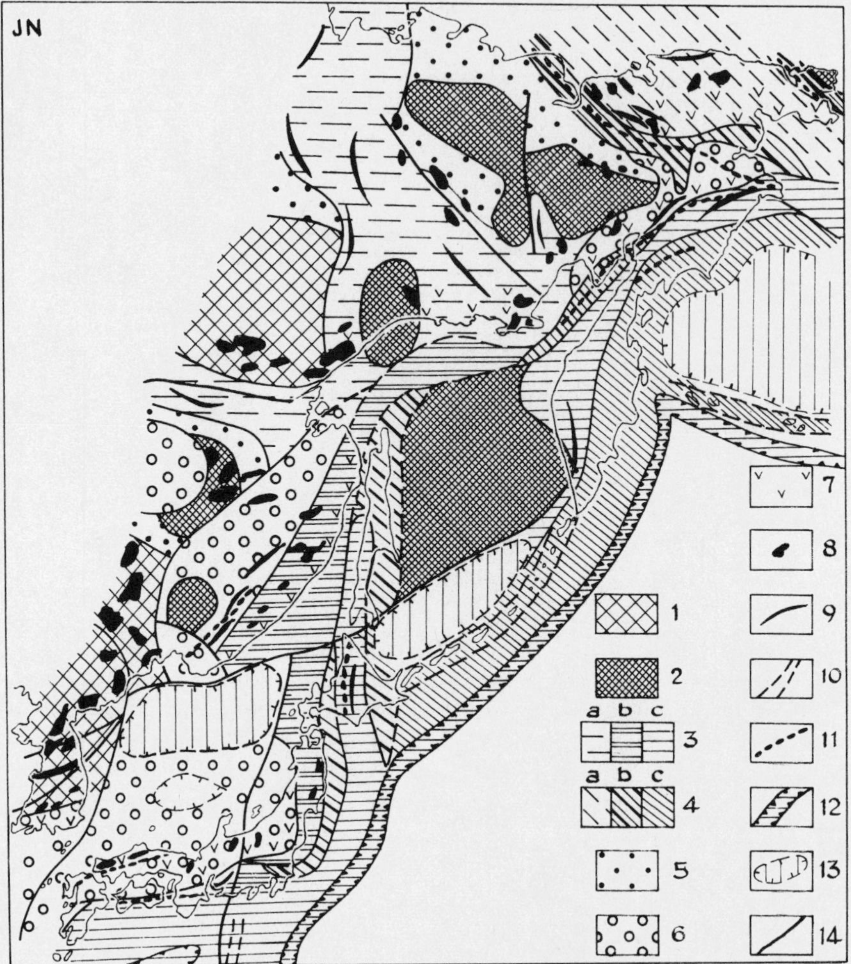

Fig. 1 Main structural features of the north-western segment of the Pacific belt. The area covered is the same as in Fig. 2. 1, crystalline shields of ancient cratons; 2, crystalline massifs in geosynclinal areas; 3, folded geosynclinal systems and troughs of external miogeosynclinal type: (a) Cimmerian, (b) Laramide (Early Alpine), (c) Late Alpine; 4, folded geosynclinal systems of eugeosynclinal type: (a) Cimmerian, (b) Laramide (Early Alpine); 5-6, marginal and intermontane troughs: 5, of Cimmerian folded zones and 6, of Alpine folded zones; 7, Okhotsk-Chukotka volcanic belt; 8, granite plutons; 9, axes of main anticlinoria; 10, axes of geanticlines; 11, ultrabasic belts; 12, deep trenches; 13, basins with crust of suboceanic type; 14, deep faults.

This segment of the Pacific belt has a very complex history and extremely heterogenous structure (Fig. 1). We cannot dwell here on all of even the main features, to say nothing of details, therefore it is reasonable to discuss only those questions which are of fundamental importance. These are: the character of basement on which this segment originated; the main stages and regularities of the evolution of the belt in the Phanerozoic; and the origin of the present structure of the belt and its main features, such as marginal seas with oceanic crust, island arcs and deep-sea trenches. The influence of the tectonic evolution of the region upon its present deep structure will also be discussed.

Our review is based entirely on literature sources, the latest works on geology and geophysics of Soviet geologists especially, such as Belyi (1966), Bersenev (1970), Bogdanov (1969), Chikov (1970), Gainanov (1968), Kosminskaya (1968), Krasny (1966), Markov (1967), Merzlyakov (1971), Milashin (1970), Pushcharovsky (1968, 1969), Smirnov (1964), Tillman (1962), Vlasov (1969), Yegiazarov (1969) and of others; also the works of several Japanese scientists such as Gorai (1968), Matsumoto (1968), Minato (1965), Murauchi (1967) and others. Nevertheless, the authors bear the responsibility for the conclusions expressed herein.

PRECAMBRIAN BASEMENT ROCKS

Proto-Riphean rocks which are exposed along the southern margin of the Pacific segment under review, from Korea to Taigonos and Chukotka, are entirely Early Precambrian, locally proved Archaean, and are characterized by metamorphism of amphibolite or granulite facies. Late Precambrian (Riphean) formations overlying the proto-Riphean in the Sino-Korean and Aldan shields, and in the Okhotsk, Kolyma(?) and Omolon massifs, belong to the platformal cover, which proves that these areas were consolidated at least by the beginning of the Late Proterozoic. The predominant trend of the Early Precambrian structures is NNW-SSE, as may be observed in the Aldan shield and the Okhotsk massif, but at the boundary of the Pacific belt it changes to north-east, parallel to the belt, as seen in Korea, in the Khanka and, particularly, in the Taigonos massifs. The trend of the Early Precambrian structural complex, unconformable with respect to the Pacific mobile belt and to the outline of the oceanic trench, in itself allows us to suppose that originally this complex occupied nearly the whole area of the region under review and might have been a single south-convex arc coeval with formations of the North American craton trending WSW into the Cordillera. But as early as in the Late Archaean the southern part of the Aldan shield was thoroughly reactivated and recycled and the Djugdjur-Stanovoi E-W system was formed, this being the initial stage in the formation of the Mongol-Okhotsk link of the Central-Asia belt of the same trend.

Blocks of the Early Precambrian basement may also have been preserved to the east of the continental part of the region. Geophysical data prove the existence of an ancient median mass in the southern continuation of the Okhotsk massif, though now separated from the latter by a W-E mobile zone, the present north Okhotsk depression. It is most probable that the basement of this massif is built up of Early Precambrian rocks reworked during subsequent tectogenetic, magmatic and metamorphic cycles, in particular during the Baikalian cycle. Another region where a relic of the ancient continental crust might have been preserved is the Yamato Rise in the Sea of

Japan, in which direction Early Precambrian formations of the Korean peninsula continue, to judge from magnetic anomalies.

In many areas of the region the original Early Precambrian continental crust was completely rejuvenated and/or stretched. Later, beginning with the Early Proterozoic, it was replaced by oceanic (secondary) crust. This process was manifested most strongly in the area of the Pacific depression itself and in the external part of the Pacific belt,

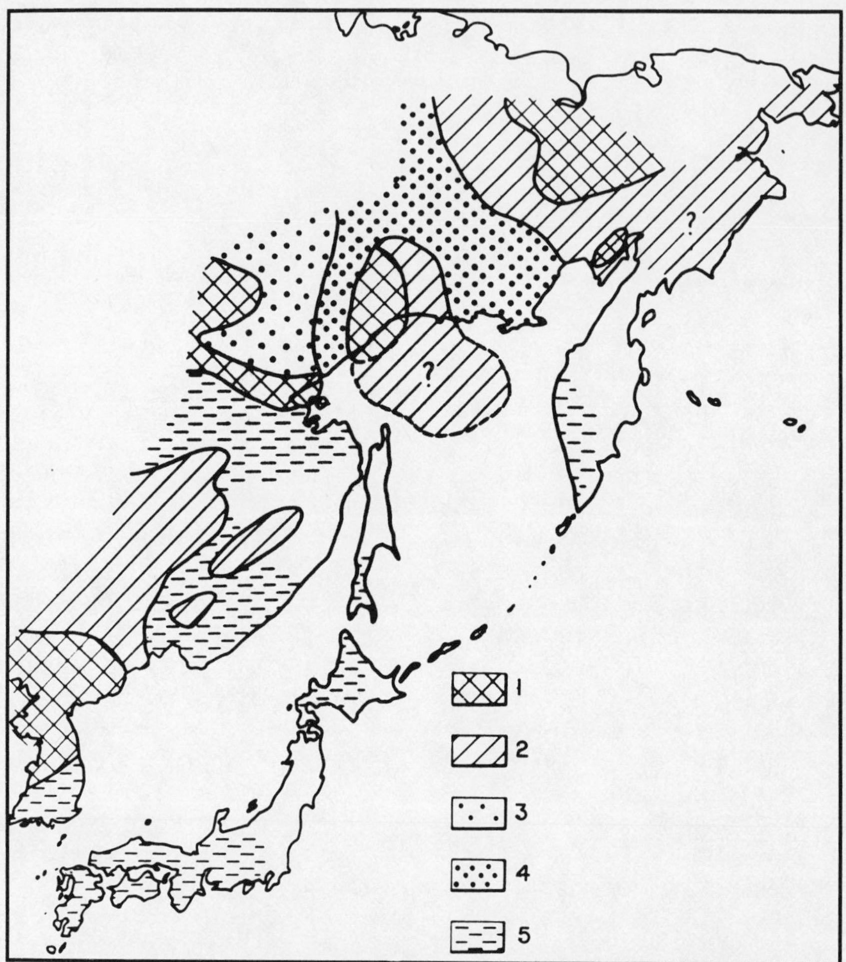

Fig. 2 Palaeotectonic scheme of the Baikalian stage. Combined legend for Figs 2 through to 7. 1-2, block of ancient crystalline basement: 1, more stable and 2, less stable. 3-7, areas of subsidence: 3, of platform type; 4, of parageosynclinal type; 5, of miogeosynclinal type; 6, of eugeosynclinal type (for Baikalian stage 5, of orthogeosynclinal type, non-differentiated); 7, of foredeeps and intermontane basins. 8, zones of regional metamorphism and granitization. 9, ultrabasic belts. 10, island arcs: (a) volcanic, (b) non-volcanic. 11, Okhotsk-Chukotka volcanic belt. 12, marginal basins with crust of suboceanic type.

where geosynclines of Stille's Neogäikum were already being formed on the oceanic crust. The geosynclinal systems of the interior peri-continental regions of the belt and those along its periphery (the Sikhote-Alin, Mongol-Okhotsk, Sakhalin, Verkhoyansk-Kolyma, and Chukotka systems) at first only cut the primary continental platform into separate blocks preserved as cratons (e.g. the Sinian and Siberian), or median masses, like the Khanka, Sea of Okhotsk, or, less probable, Sea of Japan. These median masses may not be regarded as nuclei of early consolidation (e.g. Gnibidenko 1969) as their boundaries are evidently secondary and not primary. The above-mentioned geosynclinal systems originated at different times, as also the climaxes of their development.

GEOSYNCLINAL DEVELOPMENT

The first stage of geosynclinal development in the Neogäikum should be considered *Baikalian* (Fig. 2). Within the continental part of the Pacific belt proper, geosynclinal formations of this age are known in north-eastern Korea and along the western margin of the Khanka and Bureia massifs, as well as in the periphery of the belt (the Mongol-Okhotsk and Tukuringra-Djagdy Ridges; and the Verkhoyansk-Kolyma and South Verkhoyansk downwarp systems). Composition of the sediments suggests their miogeosynclinal nature, and in the South Verkhoyansk downwarp, even parageosynclinal. Sediments in the latter were practically unmetamorphosed; in the other systems they are metamorphosed to greenschist facies.

Metamorphic complexes of the median ridge of Kamchatka (partly), of the West Sakhalin ridge (the younger Palaeozoic age is not excluded), the Hokkaido Islands (the same), and of the interior zone of south-eastern Japan (Khida, Sangun) may be considered as metamorphic geosynclinal formations. Radiometric age-data in the last of these regions clearly prove repeated subsequent rejuvenation and reactivation.

The Baikalian age of these complexes being assumed, one comes to the conclusion that in the Late Proterozoic the geosynclinal belt may have trended eastwards, at least into the interior zones of Kamchatka and the Japanese Islands. Its continental part developed, apparently, on the sialic crust and the rest on the simatic one. Farther to the east a proto-Pacific oceanic depression might have been developed, though it is not proved for certain.

It is reasonable to distinguish an independent *Caledonian stage* (Fig. 3) in the development of the north-western segment only in its north-western periphery. Here, in the southern frame of the Kolyma-Omolon massif, thick Ordovician and Silurian geosynclinal sediments are developed.

Within the south-western periphery of the Kolyma massif (the Moma Ridge) and in the south-eastern Cis-Kolyma uplift, eugeosynclinal complexes of the above-mentioned age were recently recognized, which form zones with an apparent NW trend. These formations are overlain, with a break and structural unconformity, by Devonian red molasse with younger orogenic volcanics.

Orogenic development embraced central areas of the Kolyma and Omolon massifs as well, and here downwarps of a fore-deep type were developed. They were filled

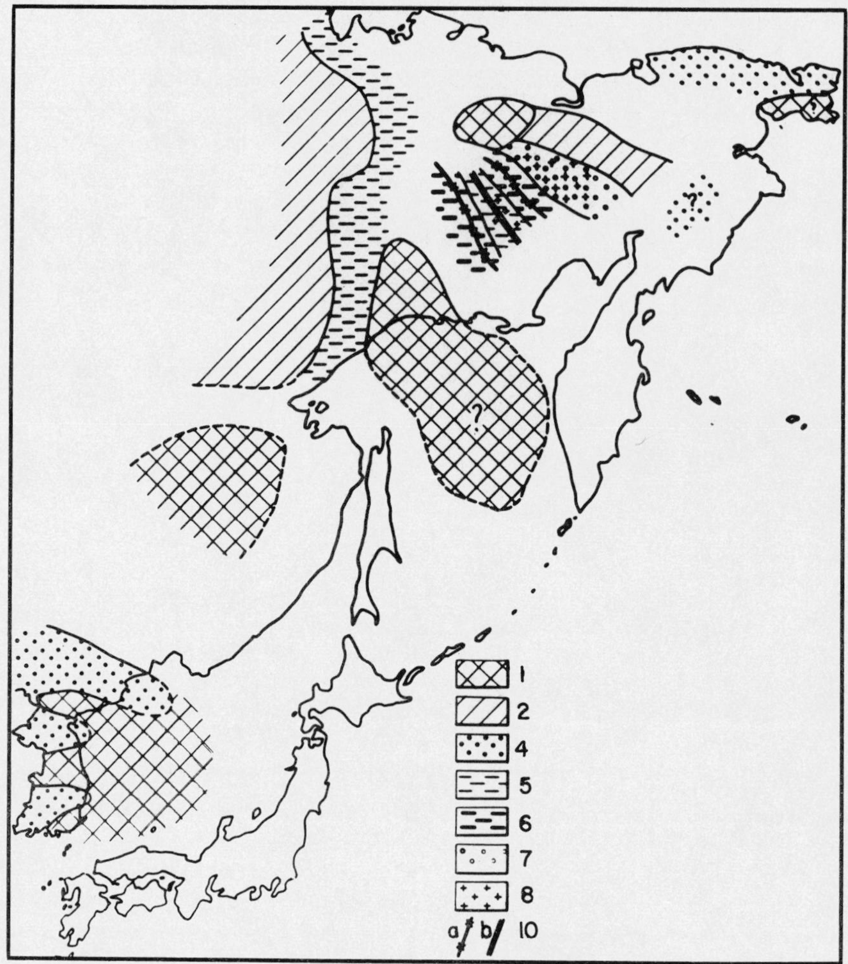

Fig. 3 Palaeotectonic scheme of the Caledonian stage (for legend, see Fig. 2)

with extremely diverse deposits, including volcanogenic, and sedimentation rates often approximated geosynclinal.

The orogenic stage of development of the Caledonides was accompanied by granitization and metamorphism, which is proved by early Palaeozoic granitoids of the Omolon massif (the Abkitsky complex) and of the Cis-Kolyma uplift. Pebbles of these granites occur throughout the Devonian molasse (Tillman 1962). The Caledonian metamorphic zones were recently recognized in the southern Cis-Kolyma uplift (Shishkin 1971).

A similarity between the early Palaeozoic history so far described and that observed in central regions of Alaska is remarkable.

The Caledonian development of the southern part of the region differed essentially from that of the north, adjacent to the Arctic belt. In the peripheral zone the Baikalian geosynclinal development continued in Early Cambrian and was finished by weak orogenesis in Middle-Upper Cambrian. Ordovician-Silurian sediments are scanty here, and belong rather to the Hercynian stage of development. In the exterior and, especially, in the interior zones the Baikalian tectogenesis was more intense and began earlier, hence both the Cambrian and Ordovician are absent and the Silurian marks the beginning of Hercynian sedimentation. There are no reasons to distinguish a separate Caledonian complex in the south, since the lowermost Palaeozoic belongs to the Baikalian complex and the Ordovician, and particularly the Silurian, to the Hercynian one.

The Hercynian stage (Fig. 4) is also displayed differently in different geosynclinal

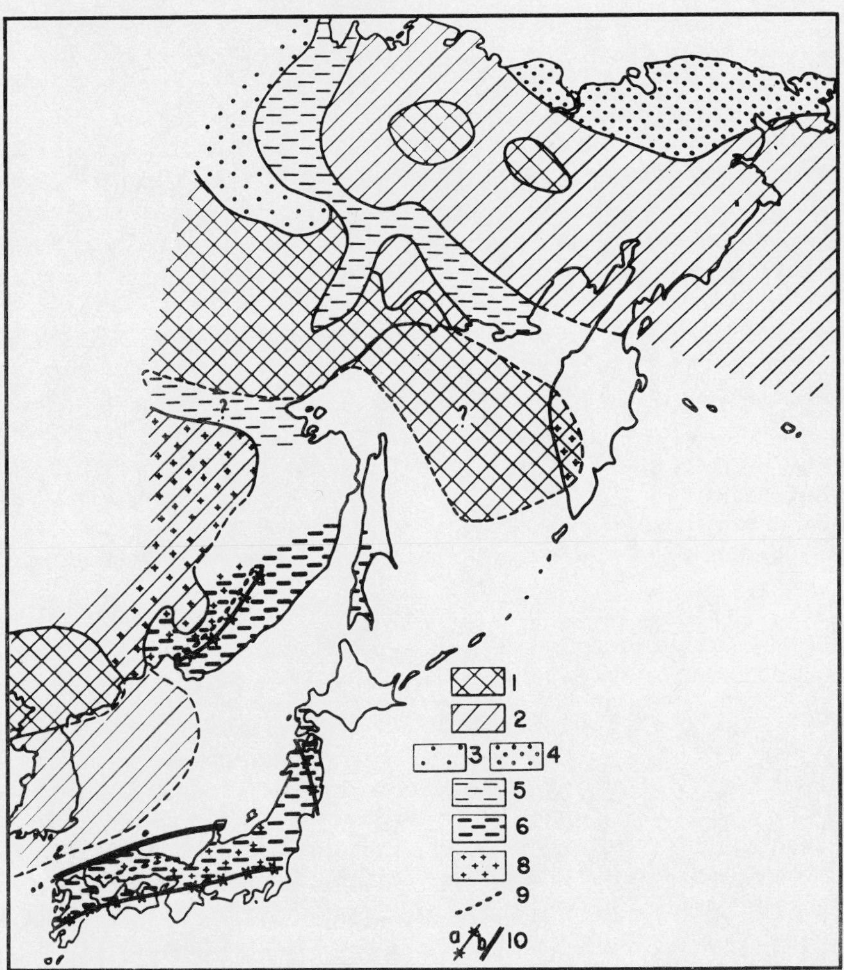

Fig. 4 Palaeotectonic scheme of the Hercynian stage (for legend, see Fig. 2)

systems. In the Verkhoyansk-Kolyma system during the first half of its development parageosynclinal conditions prevailed (in the sense of weak or 'slack' geosynclinal) and the Kolyma and Omolon massifs remained relatively elevated. Only with the middle of Early Carboniferous did the main geosynclinal subsidence begin; it continued up to Middle Jurassic and is, therefore, as much Cimmerian as Hercynian. In the western Verkhoyansk region uplifts persisted until the end of the Palaeozoic. The Palaeozoic history of the Chukotka system is not yet quite clear. The early and middle Palaeozoic sequences are apparently geosynclinal, while uplifts predominated in the late Palaeozoic. Data are scanty on the Palaeozoic history of the Anadyr-Koriak, Penzhina and Taigonos regions. Nearly all Palaeozoic outcrops are wedges in thick, late Mesozoic geosynclinal formations. The lithology of proven Palaeozoic rocks shows they accumulated under rather stable (quasi-platformal) conditions (Sereda 1971).

The Hercynian orogenesis so strongly displayed in the west, in the Trans-Baikal region (outside the discussed area), weakens in the Mongol-Okhotsk system and almost dies out eastwards, giving place to nearly concordant marine Permian and Triassic. The main orogenesis here was also Cimmerian.

In the Sikhote-Alin, especially in its southern areas, on Sakhalin and in the interior zone of the Japanese Islands, the Hercynian movements played an important role. Downwarps of eugeosynclinal character are filled with sedimentary-volcanic sequences many thousands of metres thick, and there are granite intrusions as well. In Japan and probably on Sakhalin and Kamchatka (?) similar sequences experienced regional metamorphism (the Khida and Sangun complexes). But the Hercynian cycle should not be considered here, since molasse is poorly developed and subsidence readily recommenced. Nevertheless, during the Hercynian several structures were consolidated and geosynclinal downwarps were shifted east towards the ocean.

The majority of Hercynian geosynclinal troughs, judging by the nature of their fill and weak magmatism, developed on the continental crust, except the Sikhote-Alin, Primorie and the Japanese Islands. On the whole, neither the Caledonian nor Hercynian tectono-magmatic processes played an important role in the formation of the present structure of the region, especially as compared with later stages.

The Cimmerian stage (Fig. 5) began as early as Palaeozoic, but subsidence climaxes were in the Triassic. This stage was the determinant in the formation of the Verkhoyansk, Chukotka and Mongol-Okhotsk folded systems. The first of these is characterized by exclusively terrigenous sediments and by gradual development of subsidences in the southern part of the Kolyma-Omolon massif, the comparatively independent Inyali-Debin downwarp being formed in the early Mesozoic. The geosynclinal regime gave way to an orogenic one throughout most of the area of the Verkhoyansk-Kolyma system by the middle of the Jurassic. Main elements of the fold structures were formed by that time; some time later granitization centres sprang up. In the periphery of the Kolyma massif a marginal system of downwarps (Moma-Zyrianda) and troughs of a resonance-tectonic type (Pushcharovsky 1969) were developed.

The initial stage of development of the Chukotka folded system is characterized by basic magmatism (gabbro-diabase intrusions) which impart to it an eugeosynclinal

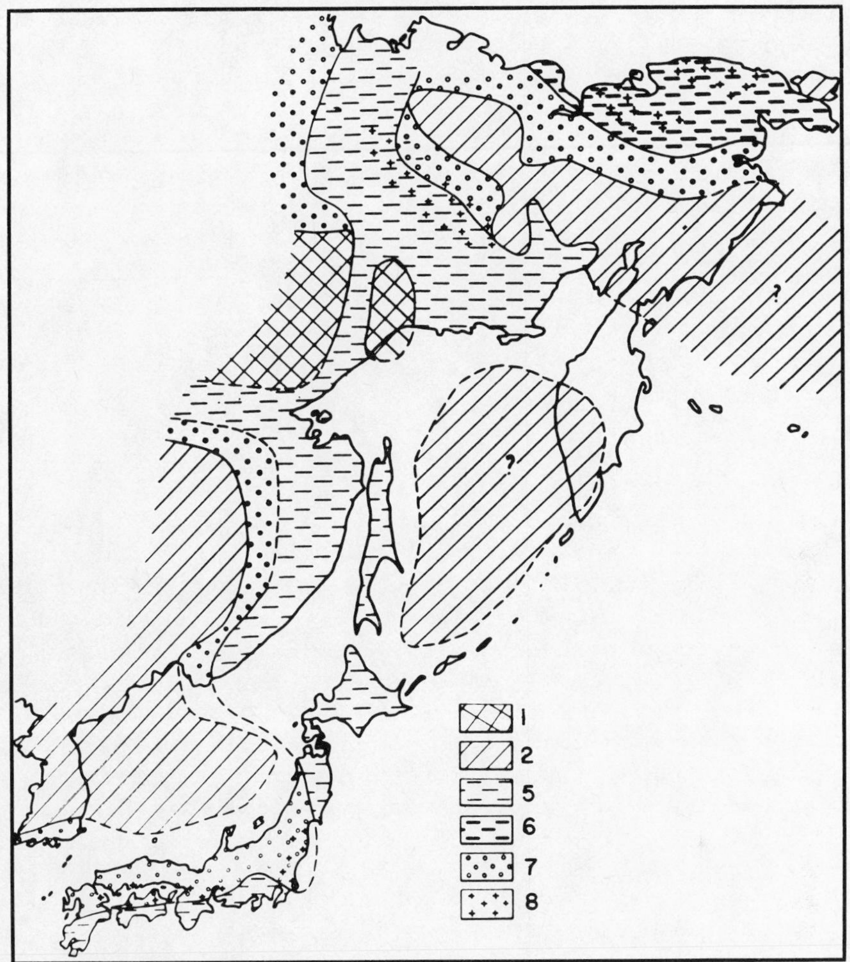

Fig. 5 Palaeotectonic scheme of the Cimmerian stage (for legend, see Fig. 2)

character. It should be pointed out that in the Chukotka system geosynclinal development proper was shorter, compared with the Verkhoyansk region, subsidence in the former having begun as late as Early Triassic, while in the Liassic uplifts predominated nearly everywhere and marine molasse-type sediments accumulated in relic downwarps. The orogenic stage was accompanied by significant granitoid plutonism. In the north-eastern margin of the Omolon and, probably, the Kolyma blocks a resonance-tectonic Oloy marginal system was formed during the Cimmerian development in Chukotka, the depressions being filled with molasse and volcanics.

The Cimmerides of the Verkhoyansk-Chukotka folded area are contemporaneous with Nevadan structures of the North American Cordillera, in particular, of Alaska. There are more and more reasons to suppose that the Chukotka system was once directly connected with the Nevadan structures of northern and southern Alaska (through the Koriak Upland area) and that later, in the Early Cretaceous, it was substantially reactivated (Akramovsky 1970, Sereda 1971). The Khatyrka anticlinorium structure retained its NW trend. The Cimmerides of north-eastern Siberia and of southern Alaska probably formed a single arc convex to the south, which was later disturbed by a shift along the Bering Sea fault and by formation of an oceanic depression in the Bering Sea area.

The Cimmerian geosynclinal complex in southern areas of the segment (Primorie, Sakhalin, Japan) is less pronounced, miogeosynclinal formations predominating (exclusive of Sakhalin). Subsidence here was rather changeable, but similar to north-eastern Siberia, with molasse-filled depressions (marginal systems) forming on adjacent consolidated massifs. Early Mesozoic granitization and metamorphism in Japan (the Rioke and Sambagawa belts, the Abukuma and Kitakami mountains) is probably connected with the final stage of Hercynian orogenesis.

During the *early Alpine stage* (Fig. 6), the beginning of which should be attributed to Late Jurassic times, quite a new evolutionary stage of the north-western segment of the Pacific belt began. Large areas of crust formed earlier were essentially reactivated and recycled; locally, they were subject to tension and filling of troughs of eugeosynclinal type (thalassogeosynclinal—after Bogdanov 1969), developed on the secondary oceanic crust. To this type of formation belong Late Jurassic-Early Cretaceous ensimatic volcanogenic-siliceous rocks, associated with contemporaneous hyperbasite intrusions, in south-western and north-eastern Japan, eastern Sakhalin, on Taigonos peninsula, in the Penzhina and Khatyrka regions, and in western and eastern Chukotka. The almost synchronous arising of an extraordinary long geosynclinal belt is indicative of an origin of global scope. It should be pointed out that eugeosynclinal troughs along the western coast of California, in the Philippines, in the western Indonesia Archipelago and in some other regions of the Pacific belt were formed in the Late Jurassic. This time seems to be of great importance in the formation of the present-day structure of the whole of the Pacific hemisphere. Apparently, it is not by chance that ancient rocks in the sedimentary layer of the Pacific Ocean proper are Upper Jurassic.

Geosynclinal troughs of the early Alpine stage are characteristically linear and their zones are comparatively narrow. The time of formation of these structures was not long, because the main uplifting and folding began in the Aptian-Albian and was finished by the beginning of the Palaeogene. Thus, folded structures of this age are contemporaneous with Laramides of southern Alaska and they once formed a single belt.

The abrupt junction of the Taigonos-Khatyrka and Alaska segments of the belt under discussion is, most probably, the main cause of penetration of geosynclinal conditions into the consolidated Cimmerian block in north-eastern Siberia, along a weakened zone of the north-west boundary of the Omolon massif. The South-Aniuy suture trough was formed here (Seslavinsky 1970). This can be traced along strike almost up to Novosibirskie Ostrova. The Upper Jurassic-Cretaceous structures of Chukotka are apparently of the same type of structure and development.

A remarkable feature of the early Alpine belt is the eruption of huge volcanic masses

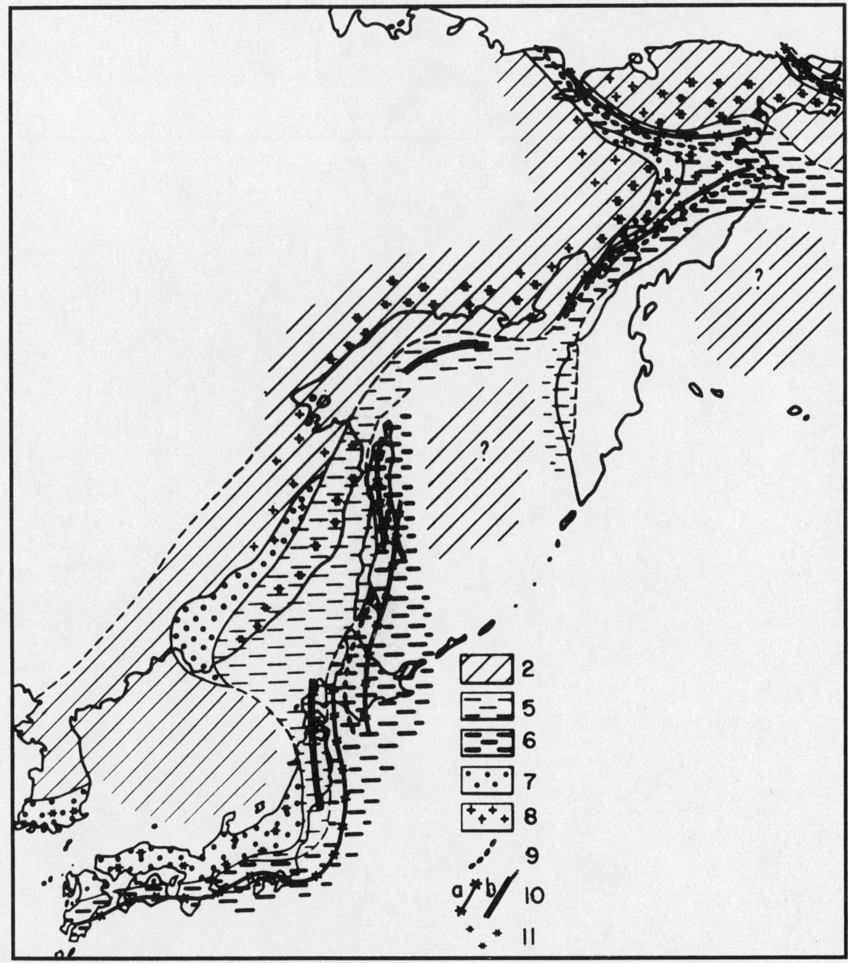

Fig. 6 Palaeotectonic scheme of the early Alpine stage (for legend, see Fig. 2)

along its interior edge, which built up the Okhotsk-Chukotka volcanic belt. An offshoot of the latter, gradually dying out, is traced to the south-west from the South-Aniuy trough. The wide scope of volcanic activity and its simultaneous manifestations in various regions of the Pacific ring (Aptian-Albian—Late Cretaceous) once more confirm a planetary character of the crucial processes at this stage.

After commencement of the orogenic period of the early Alpine troughs, a zone of most intense geosynclinal subsidence shifted east, into the south-eastern Koriak Upland, eastern Kamchatka, the Kuril Archipelago, eastern Hokkaido, and into the most exterior zone of south-western Japan—regions which earlier belonged to oceanic crust. In the Palaeogene these regions were subject to a new and noticeably reduced stage of geosynclinal evolution, the *Pacific* (Kamchatka) stage proper (Fig. 7), with orogenesis beginning as early as Middle-Upper Miocene. The areas of the Komandorskie Ostrova and the Kurils lagged behind in this respect, undergoing only the pre-orogenic stage of development together with their adjacent deep-sea trenches.

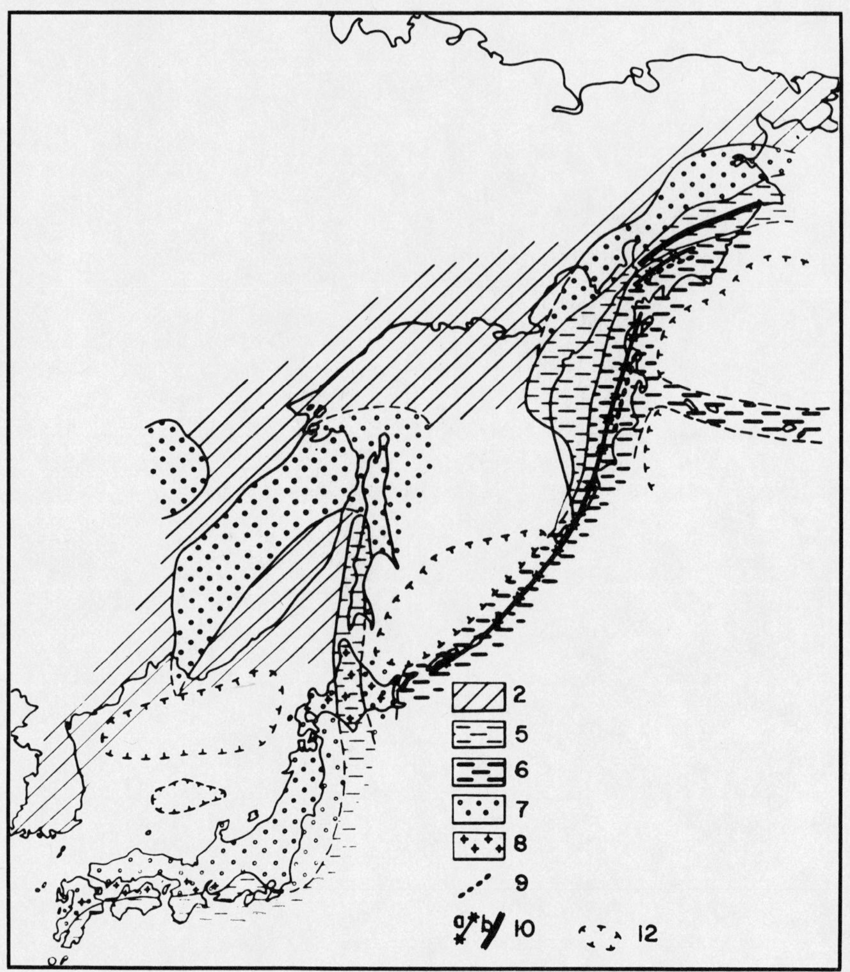

Fig. 7 Palaeotectonic scheme of the late Alpine stage (for legend, see Fig. 2)

MARGINAL SEAS AND ISLAND ARCS

At the same time as peri-Pacific geosynclines of the last generation were being formed, that is, from the end of the Cretaceous, the formation of marginal seas began with deep-sea basins devoid of a granitic layer, that is, with a crust similar to oceanic (the Aleutian, Komandorskie Ostrova Trenches, the north and south Japan Trench).

This process was apparently connected with uplifting of island arcs and their movement upon deep-sea trenches along the so-called Benioff zones (or, on the contrary, underthrusting of the trenches).

It is an important observation that the seas of Okhotsk and of Japan originated on the site of ancient median masses, as is also true of the Bering Sea deep basin. One may suppose that the formation of new oceanic crust regions is to a certain extent, but not altogether, due to rifting as distinct from the moving apart of whole blocks of median masses which experienced uplift along weakened axial zones. As well, the crust of the median masses was 'ready for oceanization' as a result of a prolonged, polyphase process of metamorphic differentiation, during which silica and alkali was transported into the upper horizons of the crust and subsequently 'washed out', the basic content in the lower horizons being increased (Khain 1969).

As to the island arcs, these may be subdivided into at least two types, which are also recognized by other geologists (e.g. Beloussov & Ruditch 1960). The first type, *mature arcs* (the Kamchatka and Japan Arcs), had already undergone several stages of geosynclinal development beginning with the Baikalian. Formerly they were a part of the continent (like the Sikhote-Alin Arc), but then they were separated once more because of the formation of marginal-sea depressions in their rear. The second type, *juvenile arcs* (the Aleutian, Komandorskie Ostrova, Kuril, and Izu-Bonin Arcs) originated in the Late Cretaceous. They are partly on the site of the continuations of faults which once gave rise to the arcs of the first type, e.g. the Izu-Bonin Arc is on the continuation of the Sakhalin-Hokkaido fault zone. The formation of the triad: marginal sea—island arc—deep-sea trench, was certainly a single process. In the case of mature arcs, like the Japan Arc, a folded system formed earlier and lying on the edge of the trench was apparently separated from the median mass behind, composed of older consolidated rocks, and began to move upon the oceanic trench, crushing down its margin and assuming the shape of an arc. This process might be initiated by creation of an area of reduced density of the upper mantle ('mantle diapir' of Karig 1971) above the Benioff zone due to high heat flow, connected with movement of oceanic lithosphere from a mid-oceanic ridge.

This explanation does not seem to be valid for young island arcs of the Kuril type. These were probably formed, not on the edge of the continent, but within an area of oceanic crust along a deep-seated fault zone, at first vertical and later transformed into a dipping Benioff zone, the arc curvature increasing and the troughs widening to the rear. If these differences in mechanisms of formation of mature and juvenile arcs were as suggested, then the oceanic crust in the rear of the first should be younger than the crust of the neighbouring ocean, while the crust in the rear of the second should be contemporaneous with it or even older.

CRUST AND MANTLE

It was established by seismic survey that the region under review is an area transitional from typical continental crust in the west to typical oceanic in the east, the transition being complicated by intermediate types of crust. The age and composition of individual layers vary considerably too.

The *sedimentary layer* in the extreme west includes a wide range of deposits beginning with the Upper Proterozoic. In areas of marginal seas and island arcs it comprises sediments beginning with the Upper Cretaceous only, and locally (the Central-Okhotsk rise) beginning with the Neogene. The maximum thickness of this layer in the sea areas is 5-8 km, locally reduced to 1-2 km. In the extreme east the sedimentary layer thickness in the ocean is even less, and its basement age is not older than early Mesozoic.

The *granitic layer* in the western periphery of the segment is represented by Early Precambrian formations; to the east it falls into two layers, the lower of which, apparently, corresponds to the granitic-metamorphic Baikalian complex, and the upper is Hercynian and/or Cimmerian. In juvenile island arcs equivalents of the upper layer comprise deposits as old as Cretaceous inclusive, while in the central part of the Kuril Arc and in the ocean it dies out completely.

The *basaltic layer* of the cratonic-continental framing should have been formed as early as the Archaean. To the east it is apparently of Early Precambrian age, and in the island arcs area, of Late Precambrian or Palaeozoic. In the ocean it is, most probably, mainly late Palaeozoic or early Mesozoic, while in the marginal seas is of late Mesozoic or, locally, even early Cenozoic age (by analogy with the Philippine Sea, where the age of the layer top was established by drilling).

The *upper mantle* is characteristically of lower density under juvenile island arcs, the origin of volcanic centres being connected with this phenomenon (see articles by G. Gorshkov and S. Fedotov in this volume). In other regions boundary velocities of longitudinal waves (8·0-8·1 km/s) indicate its more normal state. At the boundaries of separate structural elements deep-seated faults are recorded by seismic sounding. In the Holocene and at present, ultra-deep overthrusts or underthrusts at the boundary between island arcs and deep-sea trenches are most important and active. Ultrabasic belts permit the location of similar 'Benioff zones' in the late Mesozoic, or, with less certainty, in older epochs.

CONCLUSIONS

Finally, we shall attempt some conclusions:

1. By the end of Early Precambrian the region apparently belonged to a primary continental craton, and the Pacific Ocean did not yet exist.

2. In Late Precambrian (Late Proterozoic) this craton began to split and geosynclines originated. In the east the proto-Pacific might have appeared. In the transitional zone between the continent and the ocean a geosynclinal belt was formed, its first stage of development finishing at the beginning of the Phanerozoic by continental crust regeneration throughout a vast area (Fig. 8).

3. During the early Palaeozoic, tectonic and magmatic activity of the region was relatively weak. Geosynclines were of predominant para- and miogeosynclinal character and were developing on continental crust. Only south of the Kolyma and Omolon massifs may more intense development be presumed, with volcanic manifestations.

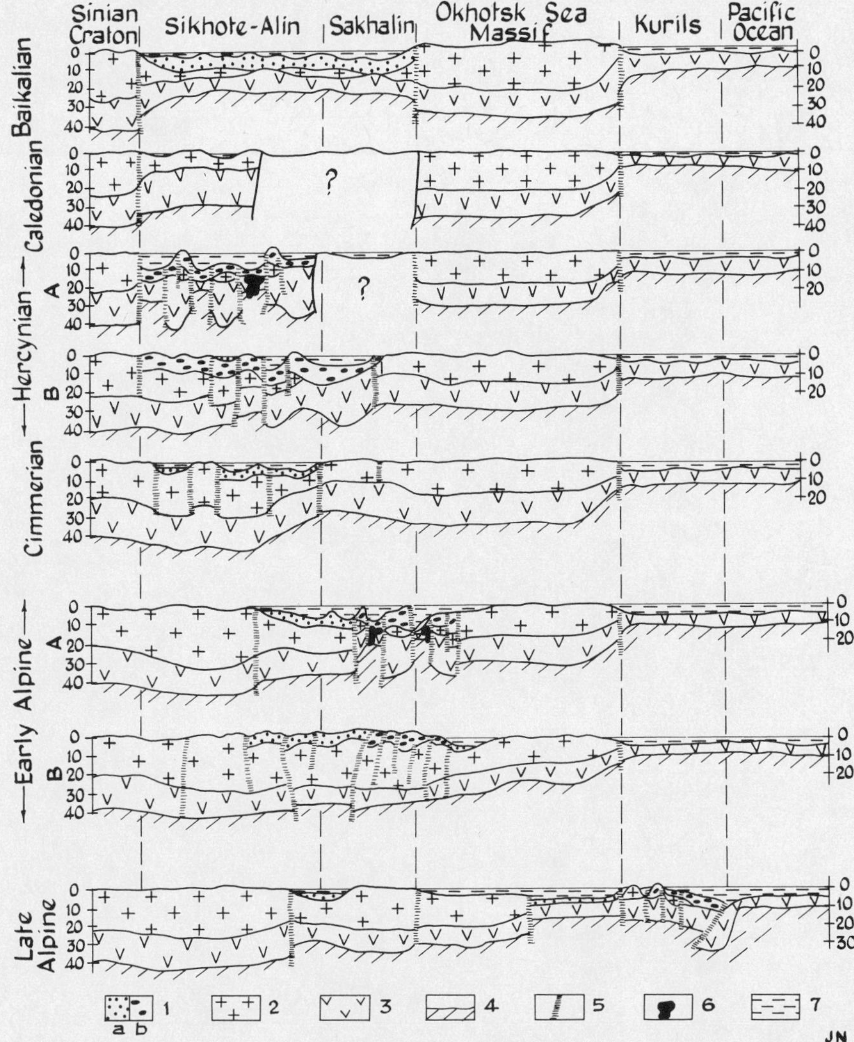

Fig. 8 Suggested evolution of the crust of the north-western segment of the Pacific belt. 1, sedimentary-volcanic piles of miogeosynclinal, marginal and intermontane troughs (a) and of eugeosynclinal troughs (b) in the stage of formation; 2, granitic-gneissic layer and sedimentary-metamorphic complex of previous cycles of development; 3, basaltic layer; 4, upper mantle; 5, deep faults; 6, ultrabasic belts; 7, marine basins.

4. In the middle and late Palaeozoic subsidence rapidly increased, though troughs were still formed on the continental crust nearly everywhere. Accumulation of miogeosynclinal sequences reached its peak in the beginning of the Mesozoic, while in the Jurassic, uplifting predominated in the western part of the segment and by the end of Jurassic/beginning of Cretaceous, geosynclinal development was finished.

5. The early Mesozoic (Cimmerian) stage had a decisive influence upon the formation of the Verkhoyansk, Chukotka and Mongol-Okhotsk folded systems. In southern areas of the segment it is less pronounced, being an echo of late Palaeozoic movements on the one hand, a precursor of late Mesozoic movements on the other.

6. A sudden change took place in Late Jurassic, new formation of oceanic crust taking place in linear troughs (rifts?) along the whole of the segment, accompanied by extremely intense submarine ensimatic volcanism and formation of volcanic belts. The north-eastern Koriak-Kamchatka area was at the same time essentially rebuilt, the directions of tectonic elements being changed from north-west to north-east; at the same time the Pacific Ocean's sphere of influence 'intruded upon' the area which was earlier connected genetically with the Arctic geosynclinal belt but the development of which was finished. Such reshaping of the structural plan might have been connected somehow with phenomena occurring in the north-western Pacific Ocean, as reflected in a complicated pattern of linear magnetic anomalies.

In the second half of the Cretaceous, the geosynclinal systems of Hokkaido, Sakhalin, Taigonos, western Kamchatka, Koriak and western Chukotka enter into an orogenic period of their evolution, the zone of maximum intensity of geosynclinal subsidence shifting east into eastern Kamchatka, Kurils and so on. At the same time the formation of marginal seas of sub-oceanic depth began. In the Miocene, zones of maximum subsidence shift again, into the region of present deep-sea trenches, the marginal seas assuming their present outline.

7. As the foregoing indicates, the complex history of the region cannot be confined to simplified schemes of accretion of the continental crust at the expense of the oceanic from the outset of geologic history, or absorption of continental crust by the oceanic from the end of the Palaeozoic. The north-western segment of the Pacific belt was a battlefield of these two tendencies, the main accretion of the continental crust taking place in the Early Precambrian, its partial destruction at the outset of subsequent tectonic cycles, and its rebuilding at the end of these cycles. The activating and rejuvenating stages outlined in the history of the geosynclinal systems were probably the same as those leading to the formation of the Pacific Ocean basin.

REFERENCES AND SELECTED BIBLIOGRAPHY

Akramovsky, I. I. 1970. Tectonic scheme of the Anadyr River basin (North-eastern end of the Asiatic branch of the Pacific mobile belt). *Geol. i Geofiz.* **10** (in Russian).

Beloussov, V. V. & Ruditch, E. M. 1960. The place of island arcs in the development of the Earth's structures. *Sov. Geol.* **10** (in Russian).

Belyi, V. F. & Tillman, S. M. 1966. Tectonics and history of development of the Okhotsk-Chukotka volcanic belt. *Geotektonika*, **2** (in Russian).

Bersenev, I. I. 1970. History of the geologic development of the Primorie region and Sea of Japan in Mesozoic and Cenozoic. *Summary of doctoral theses*, Moscow (in Russian).

Bogdanov, N. A. 1969. Thalassogeosynclines of the Pacific ring. *Geotektonika*, **3** (in Russian).

Chikov, B. M. 1970. Tectonics of the Okhotsk median mass. *Trudy Inst. Geol. Geofiz. SO AN SSSR, Fasc.* **86,** Nauka Publ., Moscow (in Russian).

Gainanov, A. G., Kosminskaya, I. P. & Stroev, P. A. 1968. Geophysical investigations of deep structure of the Bering Sea. *Fizika Zemli*, **8** (in Russian).
Gnibidenko, H. S. 1969. Metamorphic complexes in the structures of north-western sector of the Pacific Belt. Nauka Publ., Moscow (in Russian).
Karig, D. E. 1971. Origin and development of marginal basins in the Western Pacific. *J. geophys. Res.* **76** (11).
Khain, V. E. 1969. Metamorphic regeneration of areas of recurrent orogenesis and the problem of neo-formation of oceanic basins. *Geotektonika*, **3** (in Russian).
Kosminskaya, I. P., Zverev, S. M., Tulina, Yu. V. & Krakshina, R. M. 1963. Main structural features of the crust of the Sea of Okhotsk and the Kurile-Kamchatka zone of the Pacific Ocean according to deep seismic sounding. *Izv. AN SSSR, Ser. Geol.* **1** (in Russian).
Krasny, L. I. (Ed.) 1966. *Geologic structure of the North-western Pacific mobile belt*. Nedra Publ., Moscow (in Russian).
Markov, M. S., Averianova, V. N., Kartanov, I. P., Solovieva, I. A. & Shuvaev, A. S. 1967. Meso-Cenozoic history and structure of the earth crust in the Okhotsk region. *Trudy geol. Inst., Fasc.* **168,** Moscow (in Russian).
Matsumoto, T., Yamaguchi, M., Yanagi, T. *et al.* 1968. The Precambrian problem in younger orogenic zones: an example from Japan. *Can. J. Earth Sci.* **5.**
Merzlyakov, V. M. 1971. *Stratigraphy and tectonics of the Omulev uplift, North-East Siberia*. Nauka Publ., Moscow (in Russian).
Milashin, A. P., Siplatov, V. A., Yunov, A. O. *et al.* 1970. Seismic data on the structure of the sedimentary layer in the southern part of the Tatarsky Strait. *Geotektonika*, **1** (in Russian).
Minato, M., Gorai, M. & Hunahashi, M. (Eds) 1965. *The geologic development of the Japanese Islands*. Tasihiji Shokan, Tokyo.
Murauchi, S., Den, N., Asano, S., Hotta, H., Asanuma, T., Yosii, T., Hagiwara, K., Ichikawa, K., Iizuka, S., Sato, T. & Yasui, T. 1967. Crustal structure of the Japan Sea derived from the deep seismic observations. *J. Phys. Earth*, **72** (6).
Pushcharovsky, Yu. M. 1968. The Pacific tectonic belt of the earth's crust. In *Tectonics of the Soviet Far East and adjacent aquatic areas*. Nauka Publ., Moscow (in Russian).
——— 1969. Resonance-tectonic structures. *Geotektonika*, **1** (in Russian).
Rodnikov, A. G. & Khain, V. E. 1971. Tendencies in the crust development in the north-western Pacific mobile belt (in the light of data on deep structure). *Geotektonika*, **3** (in Russian).
Sereda, L. I. 1971. Alpides of Central and South-East Chukotka. *Summary of candidate's theses, MGU* (in Russian).
Seslavinsky, K. B. 1970. Structure and history of development of South-Aniuy suture trough (Western Chukotka). *Geotektonika*, **5** (in Russian).
Shishkin, V. A. Study of the Early Palaeozoic gold-bearing metamorphic complex in the Shamanikha-Stolby region, Cis-Kolyma. *Summary of candidate's theses, Kaz. GU* (in Russian).
Shor, G. G., Jr. 1964. Structure of the Bering Sea and Aleutian Ridge. *Marine Geology*, **1.**
Smirnov, A. M. On the structural position and age of the metamorphic Kamchatka and Sakhalin strata. In *Materials on Tectonics and Petrology of the Pacific Ore Belt* (Eds N. P., Vassilkovsky & A. A. Marakushev). Nauka Publ., Moscow (in Russian).
Tillman, S. M. 1962. Tectonics and history of development of the north-eastern Cis-Kolyma region. *Trudy SVKPIG* **1,** Magadan (in Russian).
Vlasov, G. M. 1969. Foredeeps and volcanism. In *Volcanic facies of Kamchatka*. Nauka Publ., Moscow (in Russian).
Yegiazarov, B. Kh. 1969. *Geologic structure of Alaska and Aleutian Islands*. Nedra Publ.,

Leningrad (in Russian).

Zverev, S. M., Tulina, Yu. V., Livshits, M. K. & Treskov, Yu. A. 1969. New data on the crust structure in the Sakhalin-Hokkaido-Primorie zone. In *Structure and development of crust in the Soviet Far East*. Nauka Publ., Moscow (in Russian).

Palaeomagnetism and Plate Tectonics of Eastern Asia

M. W. McElhinny

Department of Geophysics and Geochemistry
Australian National University, G.P.O. Box 4, Canberra, A.C.T. 2601
Australia

ABSTRACT

Palaeomagnetic data from the far north-east regions of the U.S.S.R. suggest that the Verkhoyansk and Sikhote-Alin Mountains represent collision zones between lithospheric plates; the eastern plates were welded on to Asia (by Early Cretaceous time) as a result of this collision.

INTRODUCTION

A considerable amount of palaeomagnetic data, covering almost all areas of the Soviet Union, has been acquired by Russian workers over the past decade. These represent almost a third of the palaeomagnetic information for the earth's surface. In terms of the theory of plate tectonics the existence of mountain belts in the centre of continents is explained as representing the sites of collision zones between regions formerly separated from one another (Dewey & Bird 1970). There are a number of such regions in eastern Asia, and one of the most obvious ways of testing these ideas is through palaeomagnetism.

In order to establish the existence of a collision zone, the procedure is to compare the apparent polar-wander paths for the adjacent regions. For the period of time up to the present during which the two regions have been welded together, the apparent polar-wander paths should coincide. The time at which they start to diverge (going back in time) then dates the time of their collision, the diverging paths demonstrating that the two regions were separate plates prior to that time. Hamilton (1970) has already discussed the geological history of the Urals, suggesting that this mountain belt represents the site of a collision zone during the late Palaeozoic. Hamilton cites Soviet palaeomagnetic data to support this contention.

Mesozoic mobile belts occupy large areas of the eastern U.S.S.R. and China. The Verkhoyansk Mountains separate the Siberian platform in the west from the Kolyma platform to the east. This mobile belt was formed in Lower Cretaceous times from a geosyncline of late Palaeozoic and Mesozoic sediments. In addition there is a Mesozoic mobile belt to the south of the Aldan massif of eastern Transbaikalia and Amur and closely connected with it is the Mesozoic mobile belt of Sikhote-Alin (see Fig. 2 below). Hamilton (1970) regards these various orogenic belts of the structural chaos of Asia, south and east of the Siberian platform, as having formed as small continental plates that were swept against each other and into Asia. The orogenic belts thus represent, if Hamilton's interpretation is correct, the sites of collision zones in terms of plate tectonic theory. If the North Atlantic opened along the region of the Mid-Atlantic Ridge and separated Europe from North America, then one might expect this tensional feature to be compensated by a compression zone on the other side of the globe. Indeed Wilson (1965) proposed that the Mid-Atlantic Ridge transformed into the Verkhoyansk Mountains. The data at present available from the far east make it possible to test these ideas.

PALAEOMAGNETIC DATA

Khramov and Ye Sholpo (1970) have recently summarized all available palaeomagnetic data for the Soviet Union up to 1967. Since that date an important paper summarizing a vast amount of information for the far north-east region of the U.S.S.R. (the Verkhoyansk region, east of the Verkhoyansk Mountains) has been published by Pecherskiy (1970). In this region there are both tectonic and metamorphic complications. Late Palaeozoic results from the Umkuveyem depression need to be treated with some caution, because according to Pecherskiy (1970) this depression was formed as a result of block movements within the Yablonskiy massif, and he suggests that some rotation has occurred. Pecherskiy attempts to allow for any metamorphic effects by making corrections to his results on the basis of observations of the preferred directions of the long axes of grains within his samples. This is an unusual procedure for which there seems little justification. The results from this region are therefore analysed according to standard palaeomagnetic procedures. The cleaned directions of magnetization are always taken, and where reversals are present, these are averaged. The results from the Siberian platform and the Verkhoyansk region are summarized in Tables 1 and 2 respectively.

Table 1

SUMMARY OF PALAEOMAGNETIC DATA FROM SIBERIA, PERMIAN TO CRETACEOUS

Period	*N*	*K*	A_{95}	*North Pole*	*Ref. No.*
Permian	3	53	17	37 N, 150 E	R/120, 145-6
Triassic	16	31	7	47 N, 151 E	R/93-103, 115-119
Cretaceous	5	1,235	2	65 N, 176 E	R/73-4, *[1]

Reference numbers following the letter R refer to entries in the tables of Khramov and Ye Sholpo (1970). N, number of poles averaged; K, precision parameter; A_{95}, radius of circle of 95 per cent confidence about mean pole.

[1] Pospelova *et al.* (1968).

Table 2

SUMMARY OF PALAEOMAGNETIC DATA FOR THE VERKHOYANSK REGION (KOLYMA BLOCK), PERMIAN TO CRETACEOUS

Period	*N*	*K*	A_{95}	*North Pole*	*Ref. No.*
Permian	1	—	—	52 N, 279 E	12/108
Triassic	5	35	13	63 N, 237 E	12/97-99, 103-4
Jurassic	7	15	16	72 N, 144 E	12/81, 85-8, 91-2
Cretaceous	6	43	10	60 N, 166 E	12/66, 68-70, 76-7

Reference numbers refer to the lists published by McElhinny (1968-72). N, number of poles averaged; K, precision parameter; A_{95}, radius of circle of 95 per cent confidence about mean pole.

Vlassov and Popova (1963) have produced some measurements from the Soviet Far Eastern Maritime Province to the east of the Sikhote-Alin Mountains in the Vladivostok region. However, very little palaeomagnetic work has been carried out in China. Gurariy *et al.* (1966) have investigated Cambrian and Cretaceous sediments from North Korea, whilst Lee *et al.* (1963) and Chen Zhiqiang *et al.* (1965) have studied Mesozoic and Tertiary red beds from China. Although none of the Chinese work involved cleaning procedures, now a standard technique in the subject, there is remarkably good agreement between results from widely-separated localities in China. The consistency suggests these results are reasonable estimates of the palaeomagnetic field in China during the Jurassic and Cretaceous. The information for Sikhote-Alin and China is summarized in Tables 3 and 4, respectively.

For the four regions of the east only the Permian to Cretaceous information has been presented. The four apparent polar-wander paths are illustrated in Fig. 1. Although there are only Jurassic and Cretaceous results from China, they are very similar to the Siberian results of the same age, suggesting that the Chinese and Siberian platforms were already part of the same plate in Jurassic times. How-

Table 3

PALAEOMAGNETIC DATA FROM THE SIKHOTE ALIN REGION, PERMIAN TO THE CRETACEOUS

Period	*N*	*K*	A_{95}	*North Pole*	*Ref. No.*
Permian	2	—	—	18 N, 198 E	R/138-9
Triassic	1	—	—	54 N, 186 E	R/90
Cretaceous	1	—	—	58 N, 146 E	R/77

Reference numbers following the letter R refer to entries in the tables of Khramov and Ye Sholpo (1970). N, number of poles averaged; K, precision parameter; A_{95}, radius of circle of 95 per cent confidence about mean pole.

Table 4

PALAEOMAGNETIC DATA FROM CHINA, PERMIAN TO CRETACEOUS

Period	*N*	*K*	A_{95}	*North Pole*	*Ref. No.*
Jurassic	5	64	8	55 N, 149 E	10/72-6
Cretaceous	7	60	7	61 N, 161 E	10/51-2, 57-61

Reference numbers refer to the lists published by McElhinny (1968-72). N, number of poles averaged; K, precision parameter; A_{95}, radius of circle of 95 per cent confidence about mean pole.

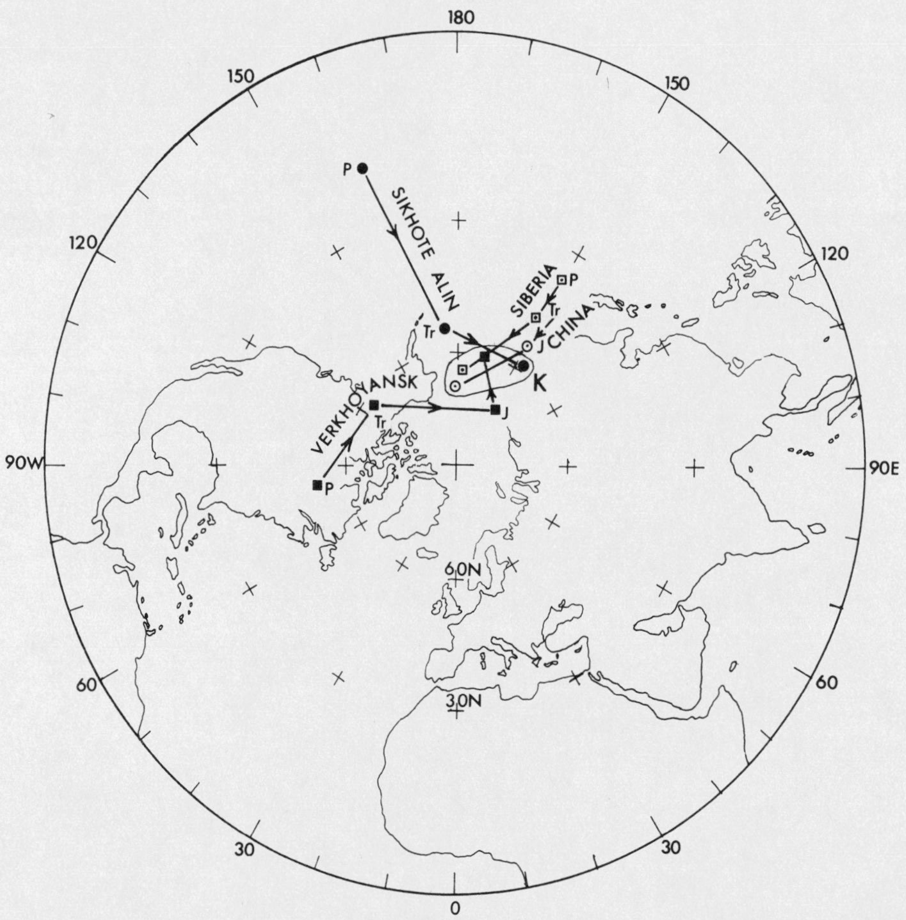

Fig. 1 Comparison of the apparent polar-wander paths for the various regions of the Far East, U.S.S.R., from the Permian to the Cretaceous. The Cretaceous poles are circled and indicate the time when the paths converge. Polar stereographic projection.

ever, the paths for the Verkhoyansk and Sikhote-Alin regions differ widely from one another and from the Siberian path during the Permian. The three paths approach one another during the Triassic, and converge during the Jurassic, becoming tightly grouped during the Cretaceous. This feature provides strong support for the collision theory and suggests that both the Verkhoyansk and Sikhote-Alin Mountains represent the sites of collision zones at which these regions became welded on to Asia by the Early Cretaceous.

CRETACEOUS AND TERTIARY DATA FOR THE FAR EAST

The Cenozoic mobile belts of the far east occupy the extreme north-eastern part of Asia including the Kamchatka peninsula and the island arcs of the Kurils, Japan and Sakhalin. Kawai *et al.* (1961) proposed a Cretaceous-Tertiary geotectonic movement on the basis of palaeomagnetic results, which showed that the main island of Japan had been bent to form the present bow-shaped structure. The deformation of the Japanese Arc had previously been postulated by Carey (1958). Kawai *et al.* (1969) have summarized the most recent information from Japan (especially the north-east part) including K-Ar ages. Table 5 summarizes the Cretaceous results for the far east, including Japan, Sakhalin, Kamchatka and Korea.

Cenozoic volcanic rocks from the Northeast and Southwest parts of Japan give palaeomagnetic results which are in general agreement during the Tertiary (see summary in Irving 1964). On the other hand, Cretaceous results from the various regions differ. Those from Southwest Japan and Kamchatka have easterly declina-

Table 5

CRETACEOUS PALAEOMAGNETIC DATA FROM KOREA, JAPAN, SAKHALIN, AND KAMCHATKA

Region	*Age*	D_m, I_m	*North Pole*	*Ref. No.*
North Korea	Ku	26, +67	69 N, 182 E	10/55
South Korea	K	20, +53	73 N, 220 E	8/49
SW Japan	K	30, +47	63 N, 230 E	5/13
SW Japan	K-T	239, −61	44 N, 194 E	8/35
NE Japan	Kl (120 m.y.)	321, +55	59 N, 62 E	*[1]
NE Japan	Ku (90 m.y.)	51, +53	49 N, 219 E	*[1]
Kamchatka	Kl-u	61, +75	61 N, 225 E	12/65
Sakhalin	Ku	338, +68	75 N, 78 E	12/53

Reference numbers refer to the lists published by McElhinny (1968-72). D_m, I_m are the declination east of true north and the inclination (positive downwards), respectively.

[1] Kawai *et al.* (1969).

tions, whereas those from Northeast Japan and Sakhalin show westerly declinations. Results from North and South Korea are in general agreement, and have declinations similar to Southwest Japan. These declinations are indicated in Fig. 2 for each of these regions, and they show that differences in declination of about 70° are involved. The present angle between the arms of the main island of Japan is about 60°, so the palaeomagnetic results are in general agreement with the bending hypothesis, at least within the limits of accuracy. They therefore suggest that both Northeast Japan

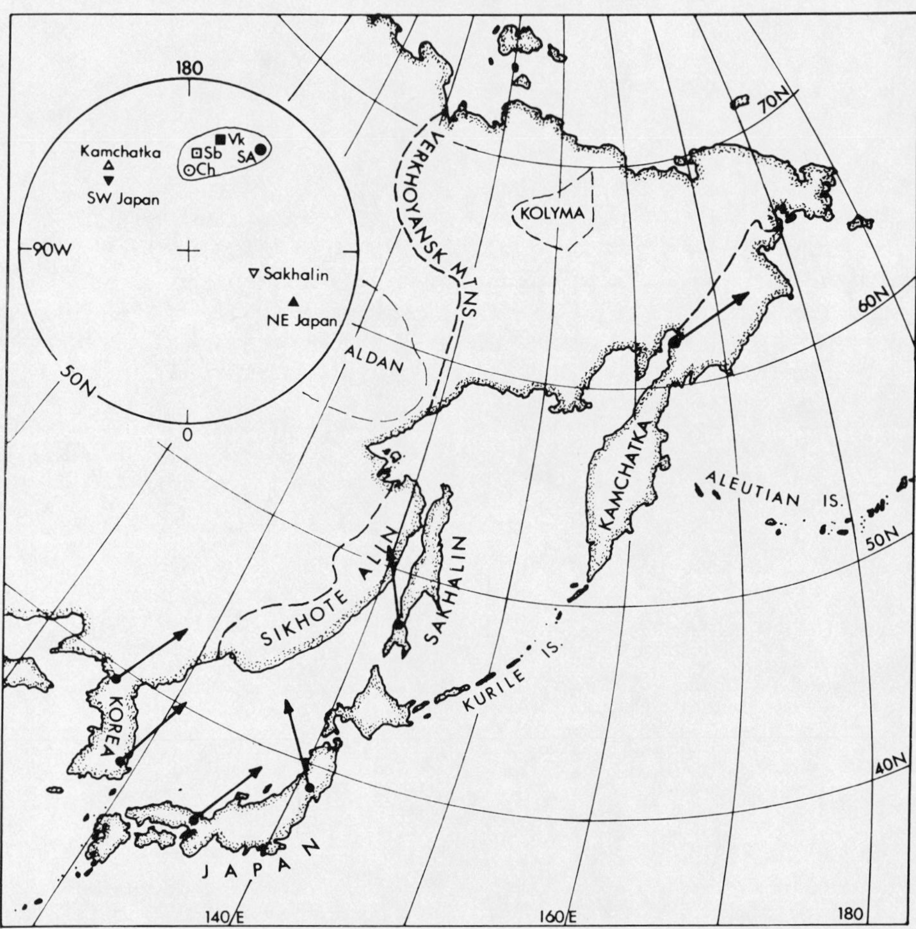

Fig. 2 Cretaceous palaeomagnetic data for the Far East, U.S.S.R. The palaeomagnetic directions (declinations) are indicated for the various sampling regions in Korea, Japan, Sakhalin and Kamchatka and show that Northeast Japan and Sakhalin have rotated with respect to Southwest Japan and Kamchatka. The inset shows the Cretaceous palaeomagnetic poles plotted on a stereographic projection from 50 N. The ringed poles correspond to those in Fig. 1 for the four regions of the Asian mainland.

and Sakhalin have been rotated with respect to Southwest Japan and Kamchatka. On the basis of K-Ar ages, Kawai *et al.* (1969) suggested the main bending took place between 120 and 90 m.y. ago, since these are the ages associated with Lower and Upper Cretaceous rocks from Northeast Japan tabulated in Table 5.

The Cretaceous results from the Cenozoic mobile belt of Japan-Sakhalin-Kamchatka can be compared with those from the other regions of Asia (Siberia, China, Verkhoyansk and Sikhote Alin). The inset of Fig. 2 compares the Cretaceous palaeomagnetic poles for the various regions. The Southwest Japan and Kamchatka poles agree well, but deviate from the group of four for the various regions of Asia. The latter also differ from the poles for the bent regions of Northeast Japan and Sakhalin, as might be expected. These differences provide evidence that Kamchatka and Southwest Japan have moved relative to the eastern part of Asia since the Cretaceous. The interpretation of this movement depends largely on the origin of the basins west of the Japan and Kuril-Kamchatka island arcs. Beloussov and Ruditch (1961) take a somewhat classical view that their origin is essentially due to crustal subsidence, but Karig (1970) ascribes their origin to crustal extension on a plate tectonic model. On this model the 'interarc basins' of the Western Pacific were formed by extensional rifting within an older 'frontal arc'. As a result, the trench-frontal arc complexes migrate away from the Asian continent with creation of new basins with oceanic crust on the convex side of the frontal arcs. The palaeomagnetic data support this model rather than the classical one since relative motion is involved.

REFERENCES

Beloussov, V. V. & Ruditch, E. M. 1961. Island arcs in the development of the earth's structure. *J. Geol.* **69,** 647-58.

Carey, S. W. 1958. The tectonic approach to continental drift. In *Continental Drift—A Symposium.* (Univ. of Tasmania, Hobart), pp. 177-355 (Eds. S. W. Carey).

Chen Zhiqiang, Wang Cenghang & Deng Xinghui. 1965. Some results of paleomagnetic research in China. In *The present and past of the geomagnetic field.* Nauka Publ., Moscow, pp. 309-11 (translated by E. R. Hope, Directorate of Scientific Information Services, DRB, Canada T462R, 1966).

Dewey, J. F. & Bird, J. M. 1970. Mountain belts and the new global tectonics. *J. geophys. Res.* **75,** 2625-47.

Gurariy, G. Z., Kropotkin, P. N., Pevzner, M. A., Ro Vu Son & Trubikhin, V. M. 1966. Laboratory evaluation of the usefulness of North Korean sedimentary rocks for palaeomagnetic studies. *Izv. Akad. Nauk. SSSR, Earth Phys. Ser.* 128-36.

Hamilton, W. 1970. The Uralides and the motion of the Russian and Siberian platforms. *Bull. geol. Soc. Am.* **81,** 2553-76.

Irving, E. 1964. *Paleomagnetism and its application to geological and geophysical problems.* Wiley and Sons, New York.

Karig, D. E. 1970. Ridges and basins of the Tonga-Kermadec island arc system. *J. geophys. Res.* **75,** 239-55.

Kawai, N., Ito, H. and Kume, S. 1961. Deformation of the Japanese islands as inferred from rock magnetism. *Geophys. J. R. astr. Soc.* **6,** 124-9.

Kawai, N., Hirooka, K. & Nakajima, T. 1969. Palaeomagnetic and Potassium-Argon age information supporting Cretaceous-Tertiary hypothetic bending of the main island of Japan. *Palaeogeog. Palaeoclim. Palaeoecol.* **6,** 277-82.

Khramov, A. N. & Sholpo, L. Ye. 1967. Synoptic tables of U.S.S.R. paleomagnetic data. Appendix I of *Paleomagnetism* (Nedra Publ., Leningrad) pp. 213-33 (translated by E. R. Hope, Directorate of Scientific Information Services, DRB Canada T510R, 1970).

Lee, C., Lee, H., Liu, H., Liu, C. & Yeh, S. 1963. Preliminary study of paleomagnetism of some Mesozoic and Cainozoic red beds of South China. *Acta Geologica Sinica*, **43,** 241-6 (translated by E. R. Hope, Directorate of Scientific Information Services, DRB Canada T7C, 1966).

McElhinny, M. W. 1968-72. Palaeomagnetic directions and pole positions VIII, X, XII. *Geophys. J. R. astr. Soc.* **15,** 409-30 (1968); **19,** 305-27 (1969) (In press, 1972.)

Pecherskiy, D. M. 1970. Paleomagnetic studies of Mesozoic deposits of the north-east of the U.S.S.R. *Izv. Akad. Nauk. SSSR, Earth Phys. Ser.* 69-83.

Pospelova, G. A., Larionova, G. Ya & Anuchin, A. V. 1968. Paleomagnetic investigations of Jurassic and lower Cretaceous sedimentary rocks of Siberia. *Int. Geol. Rev.* **10,** 1108-18.

Vlassov, A. Ya & Popova, A. V. 1963. Position of the pole in the Permian, Triassic and Cretaceous periods according to the findings of paleomagnetic studies of sedimentary rocks in the Soviet Far Eastern Maritime Province. In *Rock Magnetism and Paleomagnetism.* (Siberian Acad Sci., Krasnoyarsk), pp. 333-9 (Ed. A. Ya Vlassov). (Translated by E. R. Hope, Directorate of Scientific Information Servies, DRB Canada T428R, 1965).

Wilson, J. T. 1965. A new class of faults and their bearing on continental drift. *Nature*, **207,** 343-7.

Structure and Origin of the Japan Sea

THOMAS W. C. HILDE[1] AND JOHN M. WAGEMAN[2]

[1] *Visiting Scientist and Advisor*
Institute of Oceanography, National Taiwan University, Taipei, Taiwan, China.
[2] *Pacific Oceanographic Laboratories,*
NOAA, Seattle, Washington, U.S.A.

ABSTRACT

The Sea of Japan is a marginal sea with two major structural provinces, separated approximately by 40° 30′ N latitude. North of this latitude the Sea of Japan Basin, 3,500 m in depth, contains an average of 2 km of primarily undeformed flat-lying sediments deposited on a smooth oceanic or basaltic layer (6·7 km/s seismic velocity). Although the sediments are thickest along the western margin of the basin, where they fill narrow linear basement depressions which parallel the continental contour, there is a regional increase in sediment thickness to the east and south-east. Greatest sediment thicknesses are 2·2 km and 2·6 km along the east and west margins of the basin respectively (assumed sediment velocity, 2·0 km/s). Folding and faulting has been confined to the extreme east margin of the basin and the continental slope of Japan. South of 40° 30′ N the Sea of Japan consists of linear ridges and basins striking approximately NE-SW. The ridges are capped by similar sections of folded and faulted sediments overlying igneous rock which is exposed in places. These sediments predate most or all of the sediments in the basins between the ridges. The linear southern basins contain between 1 and 2 km of sediment overlying an uneven basement of apparent volcanic origin. Folding and volcanic intrusion is evident, especially in the lower part of the sediment section of these southern basins. The major ridge structures, the Korea Continental Borderland and Yamato Rise, have foundations of granitic rock similar in composition and age (Mesozoic) to granitic rocks in Korea and Japan. Rifting of these blocks away from the Asian continent, accompanied by intrusion and extrusion of volcanics in the south and extensive volcanic intrusion in the north, is suggested as the primary activity forming the Sea of Japan. The mechanism may be similar to mid-ocean ridge spreading resulting from ascending magma produced by frictional heat along the Benioff zone. The sediment distribution, geologic structure, heat flow, and geomagnetism of the Sea of Japan are consistent with formation by this process. Spreading was probably initiated as early as Late Cretaceous time.

INTRODUCTION

The Sea of Japan is one of several marginal seas comprising the Asia-Pacific Ocean boundary. As in the case of the other marginal seas, it is separated from the Pacific by an island arc-trench system, the Japanese Islands and the Japan and Southwest Japan Trenches, where subduction of oceanic lithosphere is occurring along the Pacific side.

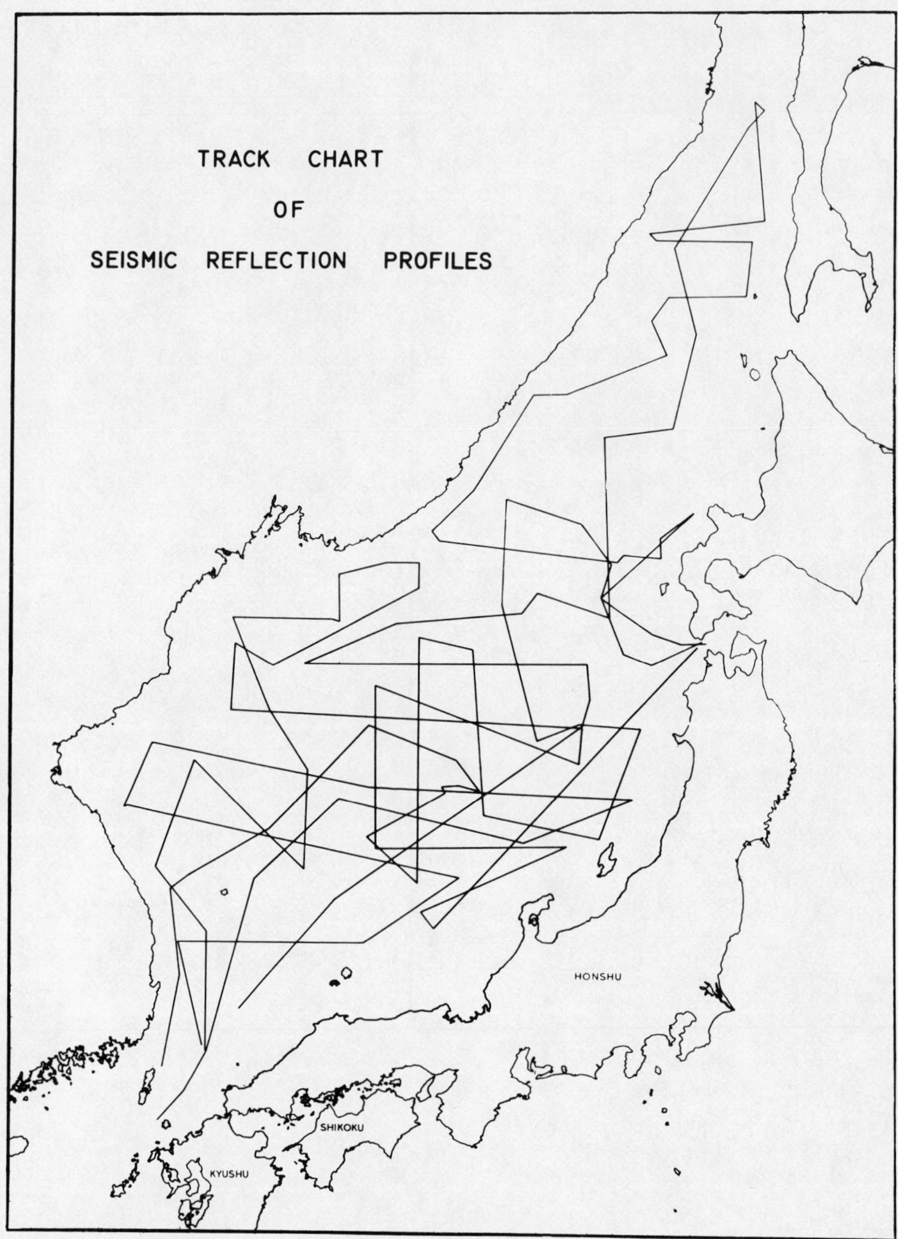

Fig. 1 Tracks of R/V *Hunt* Japan Sea cruises along which seismic reflection data were collected

Characteristic evidence of subduction includes a trench, the Benioff seismic zone dipping beneath the island arc, volcanism in the island arc and folded sediments in the trench. Subduction of the Pacific Ocean lithosphere is apparently the result of sea-floor spreading; however, it is not the end-product. Karig (1971) has demonstrated that there is evidence of spreading on the concave side of (or behind) island arcs and that this spreading may be the tectonic process which has formed the marginal seas. Matsuda and Uyeda (1970) have suggested that the formation of marginal seas of the Western Pacific is directly related to the subduction of Pacific Ocean crust beneath the island arcs and therefore related to the oceanic sea-floor spreading process. According to these ideas subduction then results in island arc and marginal sea development. In the case of the Philippine Sea, marginal sea formation (spreading according to Karig, 1971), has associated with it further subduction of the marginal sea lithosphere in trenches along its western margin; the Southwest Japan Trench or Nankai Trough, the Ryukyu Trench and the Philippine Trench.

The Sea of Japan has been examined for evidence within its structure which would indicate how it was formed. Seismic reflection profiles totalling 9,245 miles (Fig. 1) and 18,845 miles of bathymetric records, collected by the U.S. Naval Oceanographic Office, are the primary data used in this study (Hilde *et al.* 1969, Hammond *et al.* in press). Geophysical and geological data from other studies of the Sea of Japan and surrounding regions, both published and unpublished, were referred to in making the interpretation.

The 9,245 miles of seismic reflection profiling records were analysed and the depth to basement (the deepest distinct reflector) was read wherever possible. Profiles of the structural interpretations were constructed (Fig. 3). Sediment thicknesses were measured and compiled, using an assumed standard sediment velocity of 2 km/s, and contoured to produce an isopach map of the total sediment thickness above the acoustic basement (Fig. 5).

BATHYMETRY AND GEOLOGY

The major division of topographic features (Fig. 2) in the Sea of Japan lies along 40° 30′ N. North of this latitude is the large Sea of Japan Basin and Abyssal Plain. The Tartary Trough, several seamounts, including Bogorov Seamount, and the ridges and troughs along the continental slope off Honshu and Hokkaido Islands are other prominent features north of 40° 30′ N. Ridge and trough topography, predominant south of 40° 30′ N, includes the Yamato Rise, or Ridge, Korea Continental Borderland (Korea Plateau), Tsushima Basin, Yamato Basin, and the ridges and troughs along the continental slope of Honshu.

The ridges and troughs which characterize the eastern continental slope trend roughly north-south. South of 40° N, however, many scarps bordering these features strike NE-SW, the dominant structural trend in the southern Sea of Japan. In the region of Sado Ridge, scarps with the same strike, oblique to the main north-south direction of the ridges, have produced an *en échelon* structural pattern. Steep straight slopes (over 30°) which bound the ridges and the flat trough floors suggest fault origin

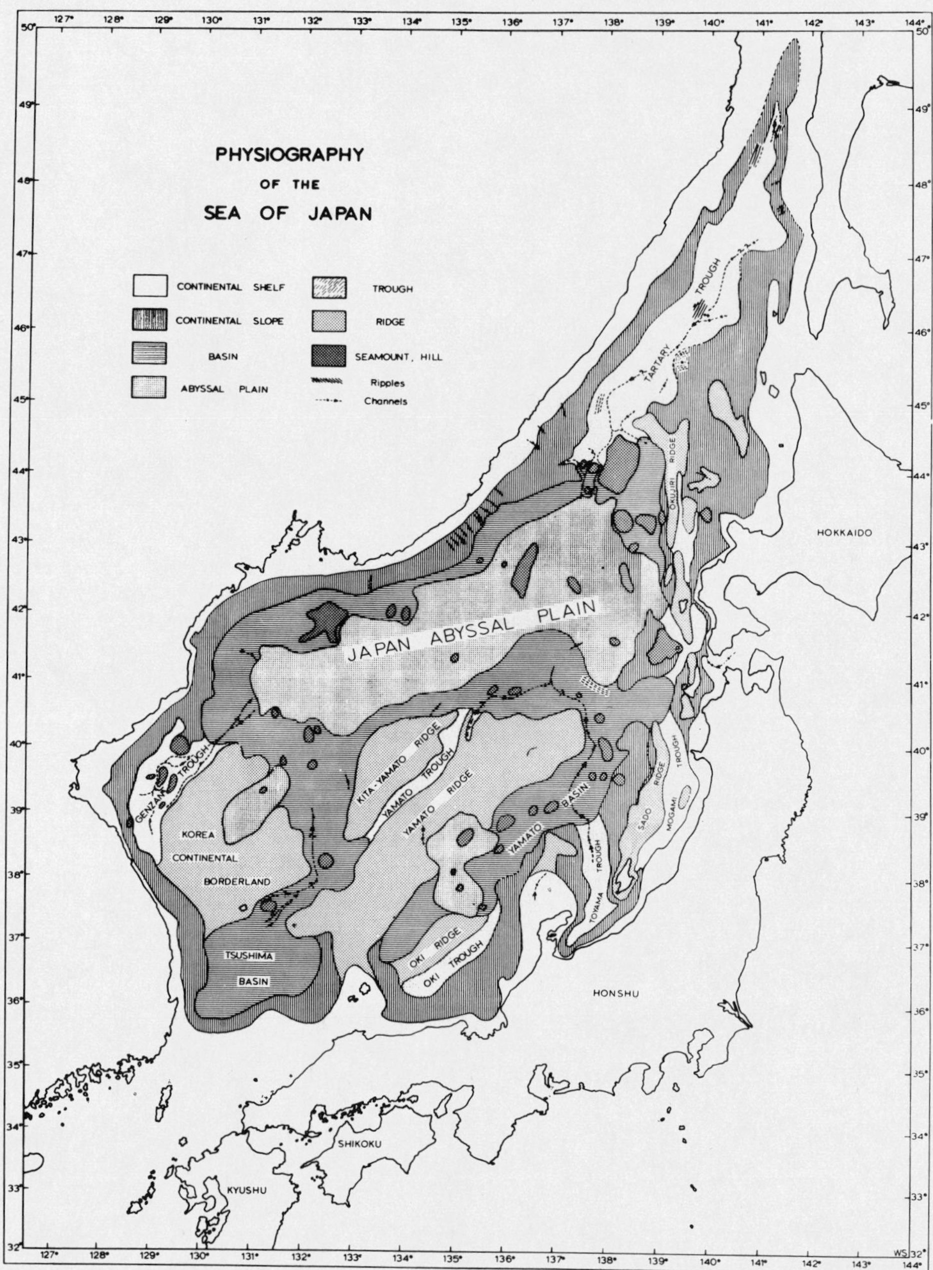

Fig. 2 Major physiographic features of the Japan Sea

with subsequent sediment accumulation in the troughs. The narrow width and great length of this zone indicate that the ridges and troughs are part of a major tectonic zone. A fault origin was suggested for these features by Yabe and Tayama (1934) who identified several scarps from charts issued by the Hydrographical Department of the Imperial Navy of Japan. More recent work by Mogi and Sato (1958) shows that flat surfaces atop Mogami Bank (part of Sado Ridge) dip to the west due to recent movements. Seismic reflection work by Hotta (1967) indicates folded and faulted sediments on Sado Ridge with thick accumulations of younger sediment in the Mogami Trough and Yamato Basin. This is also shown in Figs 3 and 4. Oki Ridge is at 270-550 m depth and is tilted to the west similar to the Sado Ridge; it is topped by Tertiary and pre-Tertiary gravels (Niino 1948). Elsewhere in this zone, farther north at the south-east end of Tartary Trough, large fault scarps bordering the ridges offset and truncate older sediments. This entire continental slope is characterized by folded sediments and normal faults, as illustrated in Fig. 4, and can be considered a boundary between the Japan Sea and the Japanese Islands. The geologic structures of this region indicate that it is a zone of convergence.

Many of the troughs along the eastern continental slope, such as the Toyama Trough (Fig. 2), are presently the site of transport and erosional channels or canyons through which sediment is carried to the deeper basins. The channel emanating from Toyama Trough (Toyama Channel) has levees along the convex side of bends which are large enough to be expressed in 100 fathom contours. In some cases these channels extend hundreds of kilometres along the basin floor, ultimately contributing sediment to the Japan Abyssal Plain as evidenced by the existence of a depositional fan at the north edge of Yamato Ridge (Fig. 2). Sediment cores reveal a predominance of silts and clays in the basins and the Japan Abyssal Plain, although abundant layers of coarser material suggests that turbidity currents have contributed significant amounts of sediment to the basins (Hammond *et al.* in press, Kaseno & Omura 1969).

Although few crossings of the eastern continental slope and shelf were made during this survey, submarine terraces were noted in several places. Nine terraces surrounding the Japanese Islands were identified by Yabe and Tayama (1934); five on the continental shelf and others to depths of 700-800 m (380-440 fathoms). Drowned valley terraces and rounded gravels found at these depths are attributed to a time of lower sea-level by Mogi and Sato (1958), and Niino (1948, 1952). Although the world-wide occurrence of terraces at about 2,000 m depth and the abundant local occurrence around Japan may be evidence for a former low stand of sea-level (Hoshino 1967), seismic reflection data from the Japan Sea indicate that most of the deeper terraces there are structural rather than erosional features. The deeper terraces are probably simple fault blocks or sediment-filled structural troughs similar to some of the deeper terraces on the Pacific side of the Japanese Islands (Hilde *et al.* 1969, Tayama 1950, 1952).

The continental slope on the west side of the Sea of Japan lacks the ridge and trough topography but is steep (greater than 10° slopes) with many canyons and channels. Based on the small amount of seismic data collected for this feature, it appears to be a sediment-draped fault structure. Some of the greatest thicknesses of sediment in the Sea of Japan exist in linear basement depressions which are parallel

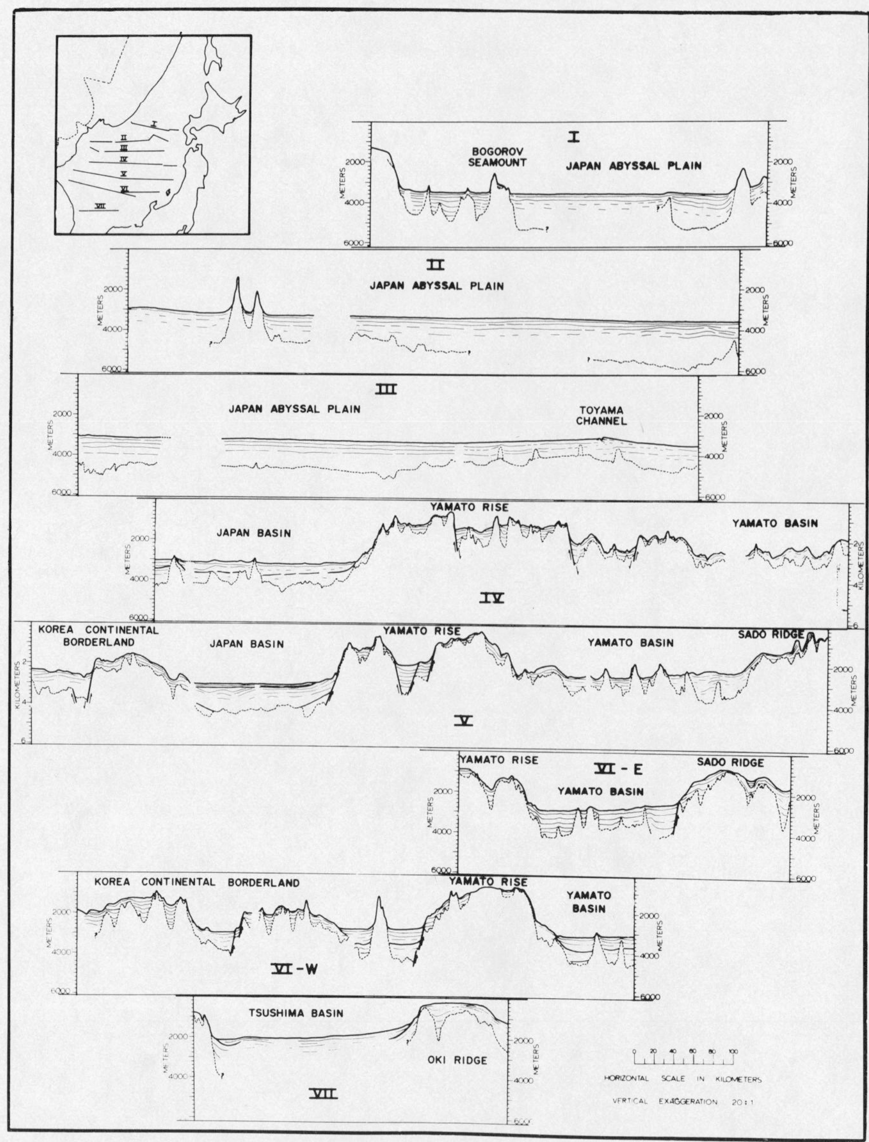

Fig. 3 Interpretations of east-west seismic reflection profiles. Locations are given in the index at the upper left. Basement is indicated by the dashed lines, with sediment-section structutal features represented above. Faults, unconformities and particularly strong reflectors are shown as heavy solid lines. Depth calculations are based on a velocity of 2 km/s for the sediment sections.

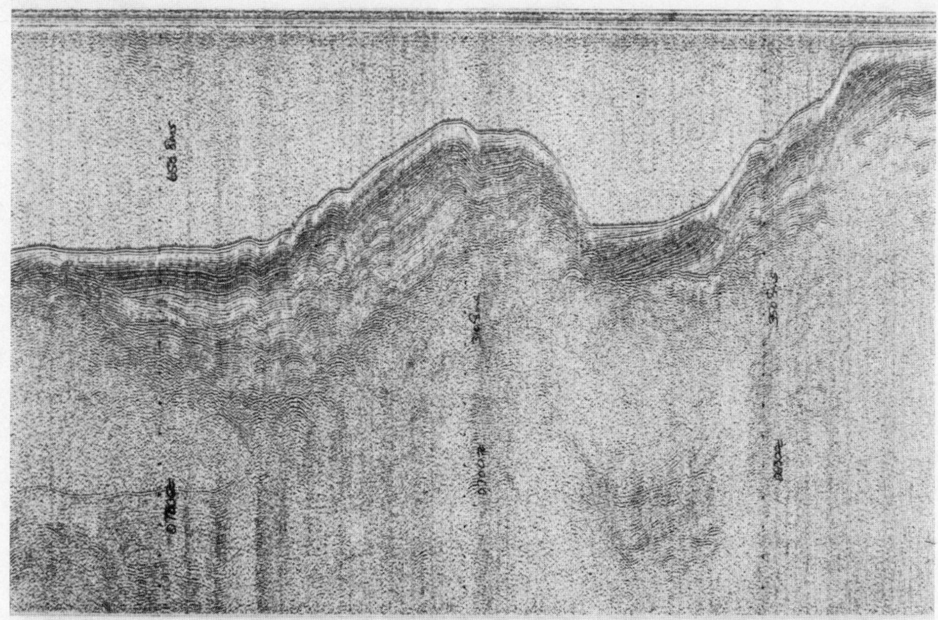

Fig. 4 Seismic reflection records showing folded and faulted sedimentary layers making up the continental slope off Honshu. Truncated beds are apparent on Sado Ridge at the right. The vertical scale is 4 s and the horizontal distance is approximately 25 km

to and at the base of this continental slope (Fig. 3, profiles II and III, and Fig. 5).

The most prominent individual topographic feature in the Sea of Japan is the Yamato Rise, which is divided into the Kita-Yamato Ridge and Yamato Ridge by the Yamato Trough (Fig. 2). The overall strike of this linear rise is NE-SW, a recurrent trend throughout the sea and notably the same as the trend of the Korea Continental Borderland, which is also similar in size and depth. Steep slopes, some greater than 20°, are present on all sides except to the south. Smooth areas and rounded Tertiary and older gravels found atop the Yamato Rise (Niino 1952) indicate former sea-level erosion. Because the shoal depth of the bank is less than Pleistocene sea-level changes, the gravel could have been rounded during a former low stand of sea-level. The presence of pre-Tertiary rock (Niino 1931) suggests that the Yamato Rise must have been formed by tectonic processes during or prior to the early history of the Sea of Japan. Steep fault scarps, however, truncate a folded sedimentary unit on the rise, and if the Tertiary gravel is from this unit, then the rise has undergone tectonism since that time. In several places, what appears to be igneous basement is exposed (Fig. 3). Igneous rocks sampled from the Yamato Rise, Kita-Oki Bank, Oki Bank and Hakusan-se have been studied by Hoshino and Homma (1966). They have correlated meta-diorites from the Yamato Rise with Mesozoic rocks from the Hida metamorphic group of the Inner Zone of Southwest Japan. Rocks of this group are also exposed

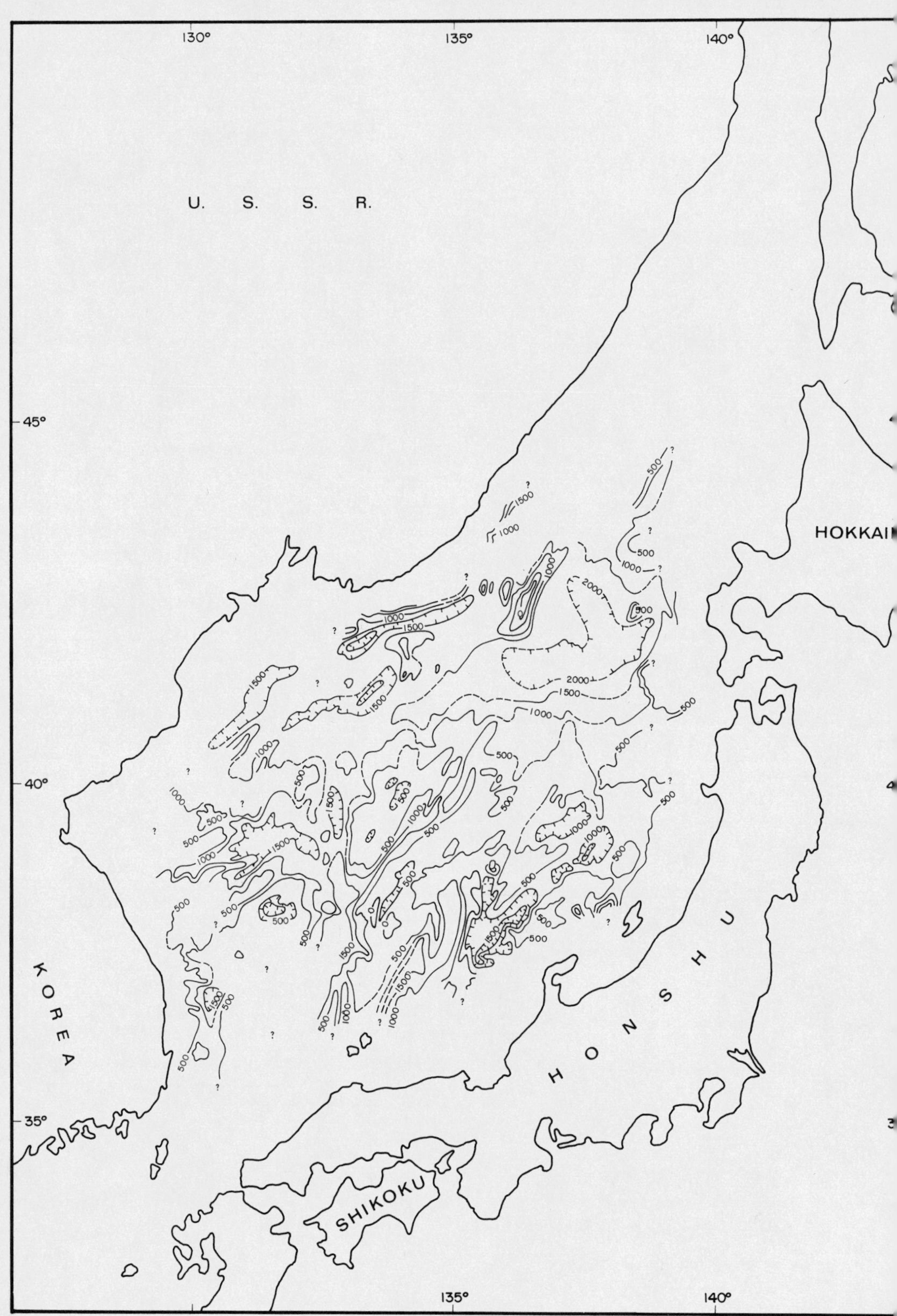
130°
135°
140°
U. S. S. R.
45°
40°
35°
HOKKAI
KOREA
HONSHU
SHIKOKU
2000
1500
1000
500
135°
140°

in the Noto Peninsula and the Oki Islands (Imai 1963). Basalt and andesite dredged from the Yamato Rise have been dated at 18-22 m.y. and andesites from shoal areas on the continental slope just east of the Yamato Basin have been dated at 4-8 m.y. by K-Ar methods (Uneo *et al.* unpubl. manuscript). These dates are consistent with periods of volcanism recognized in the Japanese Islands (Kaneoka & Ozima 1970). Even more important for establishing relationships of major structural blocks in the Sea of Japan is a 220-225 m.y. radiometric age for a granodiorite sample collected from the Yamato Rise (M. Ozima 1971, pers. comm.). The petrologic similarities of earlier Yamato Rise samples with the granitic rocks of the Hida region, along with this dated sample, are evidence that the Yamato Rise has a granitic basement and is a tectonically separated fragment of the Hida region continental rocks.

The Yamato Trough, which separates the Kita-Yamato and Yamato Ridges, is probably a graben and contains over 1,000 m of sediments. A narrow terrace extends along the south-east side of the trough at approximately 1,830 m (1,000 fathoms). The Yamato Ridge is connected to the continental shelf near Oki Islands beneath two saddles, less than 1,460 m (800 fathoms) deep, at approximately 37° 30′ N-133° 30′ E and 38° 30′ N-133° 30′ E.

The Korea Continental Borderland is a large complex shoal region off the north-east coast of Korea. This borderland is comprised of several terraces, ridges and peaks. One peak at 38° 16′ N-130° 15′ E rises to a depth of 22 m (12 fathoms). The depth of the borderland is between 1,100 and 1,460 m (600-800 fathoms) where it abuts the continental slope. Yabe and Tayama (1934) defined this continental slope as a fault scarp. Its strike is one of the major directions of faulting (NW-SE) on the Korea peninsula. From the 1,100-1,460 m (600-800 fathoms) depth, steep slopes descend to the Japan Basin. The basement of the Korea Continental Borderland is most likely the granitic rock of the Kyonggi and Yongnam Massifs and Okchon Orogenic Zone of Korea (Anon. 1956). These zones, composed of Mesozoic rocks, project directly into the offshore continental borderland.

Tsushima Basin is a large bowl-shaped depression (Fig. 2) approximately 2,000 m (1,100 fathoms) deep that is connected to the Japan Basin by a narrow deep separating the Korea Continental Borderland and Yamato Rise. The floor of this basin is smoothed by sedimentation but turbidity channels probably carry some sediment north into the Japan Basin. Sediment thickness in the Tsushima Basin was undeterminable with the seismic system used, but exceeds a thickness of at least 2,000 m. Shell Oil Company has recently drilled a well on the continental shelf, just south of Tsushima Basin, to a depth of 4,000 m without encountering older than Tertiary sediments (Hoshino 1971, pers. comm.). Tsushima Island, located mid-way between Korea and Japan in Tsushima Straits, is also composed of Tertiary sediments, while thick sections of Cretaceous and older non-marine sediments are exposed on each side of Tsushima Straits in Korea and Japan (Anon. 1956, Anon. 1960, Matsumoto 1963, Asano 1963).

Fig. 5 Isopach map of sediment thickness above the acoustic basement. A velocity of 2 km/s was assumed. The contour interval is 500 m.

Between the Yamato Rise and Honshu Island is the narrow Yamato Basin. This basin, at a depth of approximately 2,960 m (1,620 fathoms), is separated from the deeper Japan Basin by a 2,470 m (1,350 fathoms) sill at 39° 30′ N-137° 15′ E. Sediments from the Yamato Rise and Honshu Island, passing through the Oki Trough and off the continental slope, must be trapped in this enclosed deep. However, most sediments shed from Honshu through the Toyama Trough are probably carried north through Toyama Channel to the Japan Abyssal Plain. The distribution of the sediments and relief of the Yamato Basin are primarily due to rough, apparently volcanic, basement which protrudes in several places as seamounts (Fig. 5).

The Japan Abyssal Plain varies in depth from 3,100 m (1,700 fathoms) near the coast of Siberia to 3,650 m (1,990 fathoms) at the base of the continental slope off south-western Hokkaido. Large areas of this sea floor are nearly horizontal. Projecting through the sediment of the abyssal plain is Bogorov Seamount, a narrow north-south, 75 km (40 mile) long structure that is only 18·5 km (10 miles) wide. 'Andesitobasalts' dredged from Bogorov Seamount during the 42nd cruise of R.V. *Vityaz* (Mamayeva 1968), and its shape (Fig. 2) indicate that Bogorov is an extinct acidic volcano. Large ripple or wave-like structures with internal cross-bedding are associated with channels extending to the abyssal plain out of the Genzan Trough, on the fan north of Yamato Rise, and out of Tartary Trough. The associated waves are probably related to periods of especially high density flow. Along the east side of the abyssal plain, great amounts of sediment from Hokkaido and regions to the north have probably been trapped in the structural troughs to form the present flat trough floors and some of the abundant terraces.

The Tartary Trough extends from the continental shelf near 49° N, between Sakhalin Island and Siberia, south to 44° N, where it is terminated by a 900 m (500 fathom) drop to the Japan Basin. The large, flat-topped seamount at 44° N-138° 15′ E and other small peaks appear to be part of a structural dam holding back a thick accumulation of sediment to the north.

Remnants of continental crust, volcanic peaks and flows, and folded and faulted structures make up the ridges and basins that comprise the Sea of Japan. Subsequent sediment deposition has variously masked the morphology of these features while filling the basins. Different basin depths are probably in large part due to the amounts of sediment they contain. A fairly rapid rate of sedimentation could be expected in the Sea of Japan which receives run-off from vast land areas. However, the reported rate of 1·5 cm/1,000 yr. (Yasui *et al.* 1968) for the Japan Basin is much lower than rates for most other marginal seas (Menard 1967). If the 1·5 cm/1,000 yr figure can be assumed a constant rate for the deposition of the 2 km of sediment in the Japan Basin, then sediment would have first started to accumulate during late Mesozoic time.

STRUCTURE

Three major stratigraphic units were recognizable from the seismic reflection records: (1) basement, which is assumed in most cases to be igneous rock because of the similarity to reflections from other regions of known igneous rock, and because in some cases this reflector can be traced to outcrops of known igneous rock; (2) a folded, faulted and discontinuous sediment unit overlying basement, particularly evident in the southern Sea of Japan and on the Yamato Rise; (3) the uppermost sediments, flat-lying, forming the present sea floor in the basins and troughs. This latter unit makes up a major portion of the total sediment thickness in the Japan Basin and is observed to overlie unconformably unit 2 in the southern Sea of Japan.

Sediment beneath the Japan Abyssal Plain is generally thicker than 1·5 km, and for a large area it is over 2 km thick (Fig. 5). The greatest recorded thickness is over 2·6 km at 41° 20′ N-133° 30′ E. No major unconformities were observed in the sediment section beneath the abyssal plain, and numerous internal parallel reflectors suggest that the sediments contain abundant turbidite and/or volcanic-ash layers. Fewer reflectors are evident in the lower part of the section. This could either be a result of attenuation of the signal due to depth, or indicate a significant change in sediment character. The basement deepens from west to east beneath the abyssal plain (Fig. 3, profile II) and on the west rises to crop out on the surface of Bogorov and other seamounts. Compared to the basement further south, such as in profile IV, the basement is relatively smooth beneath the abyssal plain. However, a linear zone of rough basement peaks and troughs parallels the Asian continental slope beneath the western part of the Japan Basin (Fig. 5). Several small features of the sea floor are due to buried basement relief, as along the western edge of profile I of Fig. 3. At the east side of the Japan Basin the sediments are gently folded at the base of the continental slope (profiles I and II), and more intensely folded on the continental slope.

North of the Japan Abyssal Plain, in the Tartary Trough, the basement was either too deep to be detected or the sediment character prevented a basement reflection. Separating the Tartary Trough and the Japan Basin is the structural dam mentioned in the previous discussion. This structure, most likely volcanic, is responsible for the thick accumulation of sediment in the Tartary Trough and, in part, the Tartary Trough's shallower depth. By observing the linear distribution of the other volcanic peaks along the west side of the Sea of Japan it can be seen that this dam-like structure is in line with these features. Step-like changes in depth along the axis of the Tartary Trough further north may reflect faulting or basement relief.

On an east-west crossing (Fig. 3, profile III), just north of Yamato Rise, the basement is much shallower than beneath the central Japan Abyssal Plain, which indicates that the basement rock is that of the Yamato Rise. The large fan, just north of Yamato Rise, was crossed on this section and showed the turbidite channel with its levees and an internal structure of complex interbeds. The channel's migratory history and the significance of turbidite sedimentation are obvious in the profile records. Several narrow vertical structures were found which may be diapirs. Such structures are commonly found in deltaic or fan deposits (Shepard *et al.* 1968).

Where the basement is very deep, it is difficult to determine the rock character with confidence. Murauchi and Yasui (1968) report a velocity structure of three layers (2·1, 3·0, and 4·8 km/s) about 3·5 km thick, overlying a basaltic layer (6·7 km/s) 5 km thick beneath the Japan Basin, north-west of the Yamato Rise. Beneath the Mohorovicic discontinuity, they found an 8·1 km/s velocity. Russian scientists

(Kovylin & Neprochnov 1965, Kovylin 1966) presented data from seismic refraction and reflection studies along a profile in the central Japan Basin and along a profile in the western basin. They found two main layers, a 2·0-2·8 km/s sediment layer varying between 0·7 and 2·2 km thick, and a basaltic layer beneath with an average velocity of 6·6 km/s. Andreyeva and Udintsev (1958) obtained similar values in an earlier study in the western part of the basin. The difference between the Russian and Japanese results is most likely due to the difference in station locations. The more complex structure reported by the Japanese is probably typical of the southern Sea of Japan. Beneath Yamato Rise they found layers with velocities typical of both basalt and granite, overlain by 4·9 and 3·6 km/s layers. The 3·6 km/s velocity is probably from the folded and faulted Tertiary sedimentary rock, which dips beneath the basin floor (Fig. 3, profiles IV and VI-W, and Fig. 6) and is exposed on the west side of the Yamato Rise. The Russian results more likely typify the structure beneath the Japan Basin and Abyssal Plain. If their velocities are used for the sediment unit, it is apparent that the basement mapped as indicated in Figs 3 and 5, is the top of the 6·6-6·7 km/s or 'basaltic' layer.

In the southern Sea of Japan, the basement is probably the units represented by velocities of 4·8 km/s (west of Yamato Rise), 4·9 km/s (Yamato Rise), 5·5 km/s (Yamato Basin), and 4·2 km/s (north end of Yamato Basin) (Murauchi & Yasui 1968,

Fig. 6 Seismic reflection records from the west edge of Yamato Rise showing the folded and faulted sediment unit overlying the basement on Yamato Rise. Younger sediments in the basin to the left unconformably overlap this unit. The vertical scale is 4 s and the horizontal distance approximately 25 km.

Yasui *et al.* 1968). Velocities of this range can be attributed to a wide variety of rock types (Raitt 1963); however, most basement reflections from the southern sea are typical of igneous rocks and in several places crop out as apparent volcanic structure (Fig. 3, profiles IV through VI). Probably the basement relief shown in Fig. 3 is nearly all an igneous surface.

Sediment distribution in Yamato Basin is complex, with the greatest thicknesses in narrow zones along either margin of the basin (Fig. 5). A shallow basement with thin sediment cover lies beneath the axis of the basin, and a basement ridge extends diagonally beneath the southern part of the Yamato Basin between Oki Ridge and the Yamato Rise. Although some of these structures protrude, the topographic floor of the Yamato Basin is generally smooth, due to sedimentation (Fig. 3).

Another thick section of sediment, over 1,500 m thick and accumulated in a narrow north-south zone, exists between 132° E and 133 ° E along the west margin of the Yamato Rise. This section connects at the south with a section of undetermined thickness beneath the Tsushima Basin. The Yamato Rise and the Korea Continental Borderland, similar in size, depth and trend, are separated by this elongate basin.

Beneath the Yamato Rise there is rock which displays granitic seismic velocities (Murauchi & Yasui 1968). A seismic reflection survey on the continental shelf adjacent to the Korea Continental Borderland (Huntec Limited 1968) was interpreted as revealing Cretaceous igneous rock and Tertiary sediments, unconformably overlain by a thin layer of Recent sediments in some places, and exposed in others. As discussed in the previous section, a Mesozoic granitic basement is likely for both features. Seismic reflection records from the Korea Continental Borderland and the Yamato Rise reveal that both shoal areas have a shallow igneous basement overlain by similar thicknesses of folded and faulted sediment (Figs 3 and 5). The similarity in structures and ages of rock units for these two features are indicative of their common geologic history.

Sediments in the basins of the southern Sea of Japan are divided in many cases by an unconformity, but only minor folding is evident in the lower unit. The folded sediments of the ridges, where not truncated by faults, appear to dip beneath the more recent sediment of the basin and may be continuous with the deeper sediments. Because the sediments in the basins display only minor folding, the major tectonic activity in the Sea of Japan appears to have acted differently on the ridges as distinct from the basins. This is consistent with extension occurring in the basins and the ridges being subject to compression as a result of the basin extension.

DISCUSSION

That large fragments of Mesozoic continental crust exist in the Japanese Islands, and as isolated and semi-isolated blocks in the Sea of Japan seems well established. In the Japanese Islands the Neogene tectonic zones have been developed discordant to the zonation of these rocks (Kimura 1967, Gorai 1968, Kimura & Tokuyama 1970). The crust surrounding the continental blocks in the Sea of Japan is oceanic—as we have seen in the previous section of this paper—in terms of seismic velocity and layer thickness. Therefore the Mesozoic continental fragments furthest from the Asian continent have been incorporated in the more recent structures forming the Japanese Islands, while others have been scattered behind during the evolution of the Sea of Japan. This discussion is intended to show that the structure of the sea supports this idea, is consistent with origin by sea-floor spreading in a somewhat similar manner to the recent ideas of Karig (1971, and this volume), Matsuda and Uyeda (1970), and Murauchi (1971), and allows us to understand better other related geological and geophysical data.

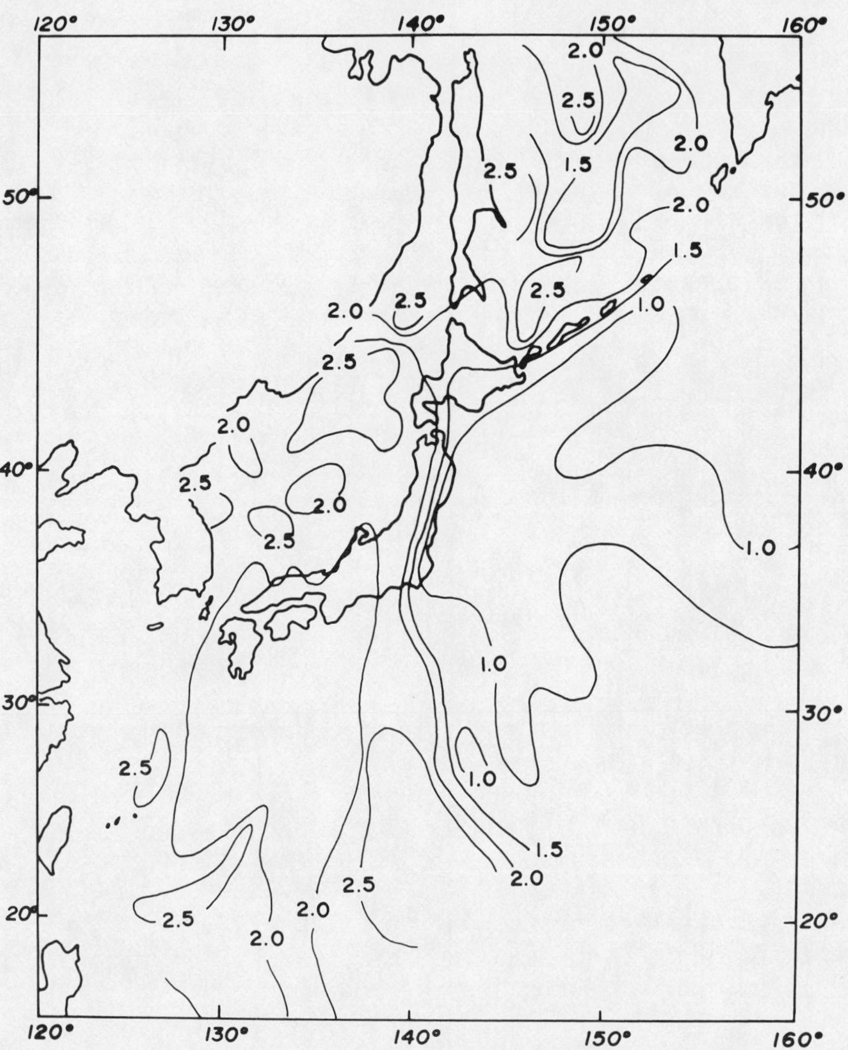

Fig. 7 Heat flow in the Japan Sea and Western Pacific after Yasui *et al.* (1968). Contours are in μ cal/cm^2 s.

Heat-flow measurements in the Sea of Japan (Yasui *et al.* 1968), reveal higher than normal values. Contours of these values show that the Japan Basin and Tsushima Basin have a heat flow of greater than 2·5 μcal/cm^{2}s, while the values for the Yamato Rise are less than 2·0 μcal/cm^2 s (Fig. 7). The contours in this figure do not show the generally high heat flow in the Yamato Basin. The higher than normal heat flow for the Sea of Japan is explained in terms of a 500° C temperature excess and 4 per cent partial melting in the mantle beneath the sea as determined from seismic wave studies by Abe and Kanamori (1970). Hasebe *et al.* (1970) have demonstrated by mathematical studies that, given an oceanic lithosphere descending beneath the continental side of trenches along the earthquake zone at rates consistent with those determined by sea-floor spreading studies, heat generation and convection with upward mass transfer of magma can be expected. Rifting of the overlying crust in response to heat convection and emplacement of ascending magma is a likely consequence.

Rifting and spreading behind island arcs, if similar to mid-ocean ridge spreading, should produce alternately normal and reversed parallel strips of magnetized crust. Magnetic surveys in the Sea of Japan (Yasui *et al.* 1967) have established that NE-SW magnetic lineations do exist. These lineations have recently been mapped in greater detail in the Sea of Japan Basin (Isezaki, *et al.* 1971). They were found to be half or less the wave length and amplitude (10-20 miles and 200 gammas) of Pacific anomalies and not obviously related to a spreading centre. Isezaki *et al.* (1971) point out this lack of symmetry and the possibility that more than one spreading centre may explain the lack of correlation with dated anomalies from the Pacific. However, our data suggest that spreading occurred at the far west side of the basin in essentially a one-sided manner towards the east, with a very slow rate of spreading westward. Symmetry would not be expected in this case for magnetic anomalies mapped in the central part of the basin. This would also explain the eastward displacement of the Mesozoic blocks of granitic crust.

Ascent of magma throughout the Sea of Japan is proposed by Matsuda and Uyeda (1970). They believe that this hypothesis is supported by the magnetic data. Uniformly high heat flow in the basins could also be an argument for this. However, identification of individual magnetic anomalies from one profile to another (Isezaki *et al.* 1971) and the uniform NE-SW strike of the anomalies seem stronger evidence for a more systematic process such as spreading from a centre as proposed by Vine and Matthews (1963).

The Benioff zone beneath the sea steepens sharply beneath the west-central part of the Japan Basin (Fig. 8). Assuming that the deeper part of the zone is older and represents its slope and location prior to the origin of the Japan Sea, one may readily imagine that the more gently sloping shallower portion of the Benioff zone resulted from an eastward shifting of the Japanese Islands and trench. This change of slope in the Benioff zone could be the point above which rifting was initiated to form the sea.

A break and petrological change in volcanic activity in the Japanese Islands occurred during Early Tertiary (Matsushita 1963). If volcanism in the islands is directly related to the magmatic injection and spreading in the Sea of Japan, then it would seem that its formation either began in mid-Tertiary time or, if earlier, that the process of formation has been episodic. In fact, Dott, Jr (1969) suggests that the episodic nature of

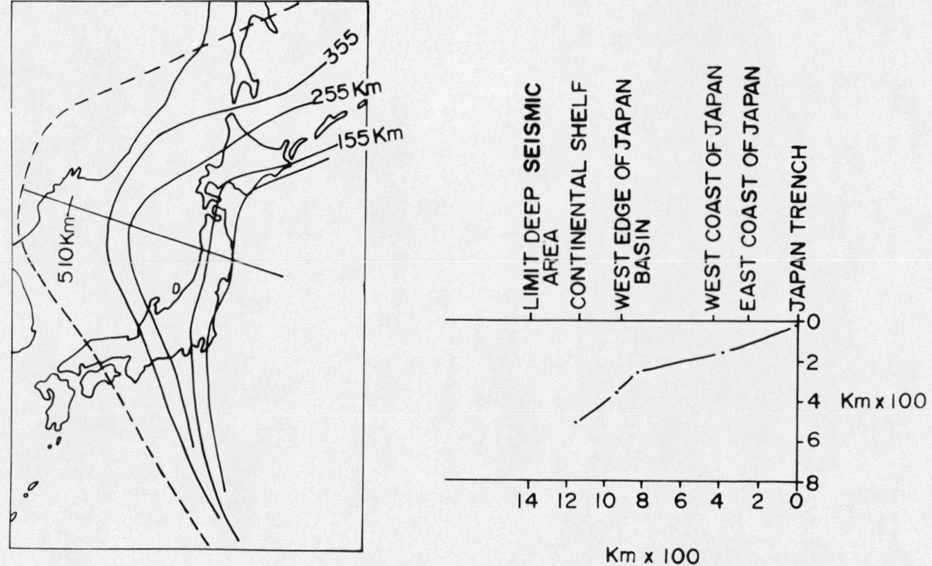

Fig. 8 Isobaths of mean epicentral positions for earthquakes along the seismic zone beneath the Japan Sea and surrounding area (after Sugimura 1960). The dashed contour indicates the limit of deep seismic activity. At the right is a profile based on these isobaths along the section indicated on the map, extending from the Japan Trench to 510 km depth.

circum-Pacific orogeny supports evidence that sea-floor spreading in the oceans is also episodic. Tectonic activity in the oceans, continental margins, and marginal seas appears increasingly to be related to a common process. Matsuda and Uyeda (1970) point out that large changes in orogenic trends in the metamorphic belts of Hokkaido, which are in a reverse arrangement to those of south-western Japan, can possibly be explained by the formation of the Sea of Japan; this began during late Mesozoic time with Japan Sea crust underthrusting eastward.

The separation of similar sections of Cretaceous sediment exposed in Korea and Japan by 4,000 m of Tertiary sediment in the Tsushima Straits is suggestive of rifting in Late Cretaceous or Early Tertiary. More complete information is needed on the age and character of these Tertiary sediments to test this suggestion.

It seems that the answer to the question of the age of the Sea of Japan must come ultimately from the sea itself rather than from geologic events recorded in the Japanese Islands. More extensive sampling and dating of the Sea of Japan volcanic rocks and a matching of the Japan Basin magnetic anomalies with those of the Pacific could provide the answer. The seismic reflection profiles reveal a thickening of the sediment section from west to east in the Japan Basin, which suggests spreading from west to east. Therefore the oldest volcanic rocks injected into the sea should be found at the eastern margin of the Japan Basin. It can be hoped that some of these rocks are exposed along the lower continental slope as a result of faulting. Furthermore, volcanic rocks of greatly different ages would be located in close proximity along the west margin of the basin if spreading were predominantly from west to east.

Seismic reflection data from the sea reveal primarily undisturbed sediments in the basins with folding confined to the basin margins. We interpret this to be the result

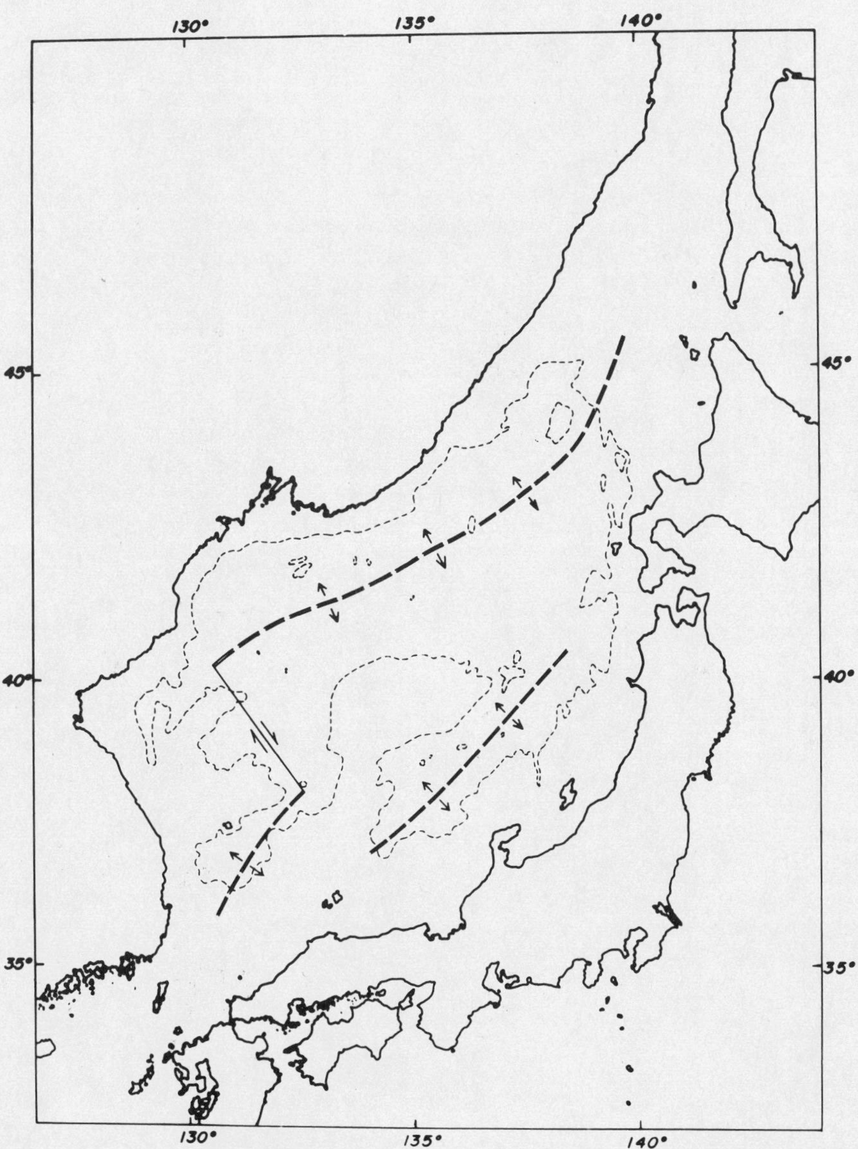

Fig. 9 Spreading centres along which (1) initial rifting of the continental margin occurred and subsequent Japan Sea crust originated in the Japan Basin and Tsushima Basin, and (2) later spreading occurred in the Yamato Basin.

of extension in the basins and convergence at the margins. A thickening of the Japan Basin sediment section from the west (where there is a rough, uneven basement of volcanic rock) towards the east is believed to be due to sea-floor spreading from this rough basement zone. Location of this spreading centre is indicated in Fig. 9. It is along this line that the original breaking up of the continental margin most likely occurred. A second and more recent spreading centre in the Yamato Basin (Fig. 9), where there is an axial basement high with the thickest sediments at the margins, has since probably generated more oceanic crust and resulted in the separation of Honshu and the Yamato Rise. The 22 m.y. age of volcanic rocks from the western margin of the Yamato Basin (Uneo *et al.* unpubl. manuscript) is believed to represent the time at which movement started for this second spreading centre.

The idea that the Sea of Japan originated by rifting of the continental margin with subsequent sea-floor spreading from the proposed spreading centres is supported by the observed geologic structures, sediment distribution, the magnetic anomalies and heat-flow features. Earthquake data and theoretical studies can be also interpreted to support this conclusion. Geologic studies provide time constraints which suggest initiation of rifting during the late Mesozoic or Early Tertiary.

REFERENCES

Abe, K. & Kanamori, H. 1970. Mantle structure beneath the Japan Sea as revealed by surface waves. *Bull. Earthq. Res. Inst. Tokyo Univ.* **48,** 1011-21.

Andreyeva, I. B. & Udintsev, G. B. 1958. Bottom structure of the Sea of Japan, from the *Vityaz* expedition data. *Int. Geol. Rev.* **10,** 1-15.

Anonymous, 1956. *An outline of the geology of Korea.* Geol. Surv. Korea.

——— 1960. *An outline of the geology of Japan.* Geol. Surv. Japan.

Asano, K. 1963. The Palaeogene. In *Geology of Japan* (Eds F. Takai, T. Matsumoto & R. Toriyama). Univ. Tokyo Press, Tokyo.

Dott, Jr, R. H. 1969. Circum-Pacific late Cenozoic structural rejuvenation: Implications for sea floor spreading. *Science*, **166** (3907), 874-6.

Gorai, M. 1968. Some geological problems in the development of Japan and the neighboring island arcs. In *The Crust and Upper Mantle of the Pacific Area.* (Eds L. Knopoff, C. L. Drake & P. J. Hart). *Am. Geophys. Un., Geophys. Monogr.* **12,** 481-5.

Hammond, W. T., Hilde, T. W. C., Hulseman, J., Jarvela, L. E., Little, L., Osterhagen, J. H., Searcy, III, W. P. & Wageman, J. M. (In press.) Sea of Japan, oceanography and geophysics. *U.S. Naval Oceanographic Office, spec. publ.* 133-18-1.

Hasebe, K., Fujii, N. & Uyeda, S. 1970. Thermal processes under island arcs. *Tectonophysics,* **10,** 335-55.

Hilde, T. W. C., Wageman, J. M. & Hammond, W. T. 1969. The structure of Tosa Terrace and Nankai Trough off south eastern Japan. *Deep Sea Res.* **16,** 67-75.

——— 1969. Sea of Japan structure from seismic reflection data. *EOS Trans. Am. Geophys. Un.* (1969 meeting—abst.) **50** (4), 208.

Hoshino, M. 1967. Deep-sea terraces. *Fac. Oceanography Publ., Tokai Univ.* **2,** 57-84.

Hoshino, M. & Hotta, H. 1966. Geology of submarine banks in the Japan Sea. *Earth Science,* **82** (in Japanese).

Hotta, H. 1967. The structure of sedimentary layer in the Japan Sea. *Geophys. Bull., Hokkaido Univ.* **18,** 111-31 (in Japanese).

Huntec Limited, Toronto, Canada. 1968. Report of the offshore geophysical survey in the Pohang area, Republic of Korea. *Econ. Comm. Asia the Far East* (ECAFE), CCOP, Tech. Bull. **1,** 1-12.

Imai, H. 1963. Pre-Tertiary igneous activity, metamorphism and metallogenesis. In *Geology of Japan* (Eds F. Takai, T. Matsumoto & R. Toriyama). Univ. Tokyo Press, Tokyo.

Isezaki, N., Hata, K. & Uyeda, S. 1971. Magnetic survey of the Japan Sea (Part 1). *Bull. Earthq. Res. Inst. Tokyo Univ.* **49,** 77-83.

Kaneoka, I. & Ozima, M. 1970. On the radiometric ages of volcanic rocks from Japan. *Volcano,* **2** (15), 10-21 (in Japanese).

Karig, D. E. 1971*a*. Structural history of the Mariana island arc system. *Bull. geol. Soc. Am.* **82,** 323-44.

——— 1971*b*. Origin and development of marginal basins in the Western Pacific. *J. geophys. Res.* **76** (11), 2542-61.

Kaseno, Y. & Omura, A. 1969. On the core samples collected by M.R.V. *Seifu Maru* from the Japan Sea floor in 1966 and 1967. *Bull. Japan Sea Res. Inst., Kanazawa Univ.* **1,** 35-8. (in Japanese).

Kimura, T. 1967. Structural division of Japan and the Honshu arc. *Jap. J. Geol. Geogr.* **38** (2-4), 117-31.

Kimura, T. & Tokuyama, A. 1971. Geosynclinal prisms and tectonics in Japan. *Mem. geol. Soc. Japan,* **6,** 9-20.

Kovylin, V. M. 1966. Results of seismic studies in the southwest of the Sea of Japan abyssal basin. *Oceanology,* **6** (2), 238-49 (in Russian).

Kovylin, V. M. & Neprochnov, Y. P. 1965. Crustal structure and sedimentary layer in the central part of the Japan Sea derived from seismic data. *Izv. Akad. Nauk SSSR* (*geol.*) **4,** 10-26 (in Russian).

Mamayeva, R. B. 1968. Oceanographic investigations of the Pacific Ocean carried out by Soviet expeditions in 1967. *Int. Mar. Sci.* **6** (2), 11-13.

Matsuda, T., Nakamura, K. & Sugimura, A. 1967. Late Cenozoic orogeny in Japan. *Tectonophysics,* **4** (4-6), 349-66.

Matsuda, T. & Uyeda, S. 1971. On the Pacific-type orogeny and its model—extension of the paired belts concept and possible origin of marginal seas. *Tectonophysics,* **11,** 5-27.

Matsumoto, T. 1963. The Cretaceous. In *Geology of Japan* (Eds F. Takai, T. Matsumoto & R. Toriyama). Univ. Tokyo Press, Tokyo.

Matsushita, S. 1963. Outline of geology. In *Geology of Japan* (Eds F. Takai, T. Matsumoto & R. Toriyama), 2-5. Univ. Tokyo Press, Tokyo.

Menard, H. W. 1967. Transitional types of crust under small ocean basins. *J. geophys. Res.* **72** (12), 3061-73.

Mogi, A. & Sato, T. 1958. On the bottom configuration and sediments in the adjacent sea of Mogami Bank, Japan Sea. *Bull. hydrogr. Office Japan,* **55,** 37-53 (in Japanese).

Murauchi, S. 1971. The renewal of island arcs and the tectonics of marginal seas. In *Island Arc and Marginal Sea.* Tokai Univ. Press, Tokyo (in Japanese).

Murauchi, S. & Yasui, M. 1968. Geophysical studies of the ocean floors in the seas adjacent to Japan. *Kagaku* (*Science*), **34** (4), 192-200 (in Japanese).

Niino, H. 1931. On the bottom deposits of Yamato Tai in the Sea of Japan. *J. geol. Soc. Japan,* **40** (472), 86-100.

——— 1948. Sediments of Oki Bank in the Japanese Sea. *J. sedim. Petrol.* **18** (2), 79-85.

——— 1952. The bottom character of the banks and submarine valleys on and around the continental shelf of Japanese Islands. *J. Tokyo Univ. Fish.* **38** (3) 391-410.

Raitt, R. W. 1963. The crustal rocks. In *The Sea* (Ed. M. N. Hill). Interscience, New York.

Shepard, F. P., Dill, R. F. & Heezen, B. C. 1968. Diapiric intrusions in foreset slope sediments off Magdalena Delta, Columbia. *Bull. Am. Ass. Petrol. Geol.* **52** (11), 2197-207.

Sugimura, A. 1960. Zonal arrangement of some geophysical and petrological features in Japan and its environs. *J. Fac. Sci. Tokyo Univ.* (2), **12,** 133-53.

Tayama, R. 1950. The submarine configuration off Shikoku, especially the continental slope. *Bull. hydrogr. Dep., Japan*, spec. publ. **7,** 54-82 (in Japanese).

——— 1952. On the depth curve chart of the adjacent seas of Japan (description of J.H.D. Chart 6901). *Bull. hydrogr. Dep., Japan*, **32,** 160-7 (in Japanese).

Ueno, N., Kaneoka, I., Ozima, M., Zashi, S., Sato, T. & Iwabuchi, Y. (unpubl. manuscript). K-Ar ages, ratio of Sr isotopes and ratio of K-Rb of igneous rock in the Japan Sea (in Japanese).

Vine, F. J. & Matthews, D. H. 1963. Magnetic anomalies over oceanic ridges. *Nature*, **199** (4897), 947-9.

Yabe, H. & Tayama, R. 1934. Bottom relief of the seas bordering the Japanese Islands and Korean Peninsula. *Bull. Earthq. Res. Inst. Tokyo Univ.* **12** (3), 562-5.

Yasui, M., Hashimoto, Y. & Uyeda, S. 1967. Geomagnetic studies of the Japanese Sea, (1)—anomaly pattern in the Japan Sea. *Oceanogrl Mag.* **19** (2), 221-31.

Yasui, M., Kishii, T., Watanabe, T. & Uyeda, S. 1968. Heat flow in the Sea of Japan. In *The Crust and Upper Mantle of the Pacific Area* (Eds L. Knopoff, C. L. Drake & P. J. Hart), *Am. Geophys. Un., Geophys. Monogr.* **12,** 3-16.

Yasui, M., Uyeda, S., Murauchi, S. & Den, N. 1969. Current aspects of geophysical studies in the Kuroshio and its adjacent seas. *Proc. CSK Symp.*, Apr. 29-May 4, East-West Center, Honolulu, Hawaii, 21 pp.

Crustal Structure and Evolution in the North-western Part of the Pacific Belt*

H. S. GNIBIDENKO

Sakhalin Complex Scientific Research Institute,
Far East Science Centre, Academy of Sciences of the U.S.S.R.,
Novoalexandrovsk, Sakhalin, U.S.S.R.

ABSTRACT

Analysis of geological and geophysical information on the north-western part of the Pacific belt (comprising folded systems, marginal seas and island arcs, located between the Pacific Ocean and the Siberian and Sinian Precambrian cratons) reveals that this is a region of alternation of crustal areas of different stages of tectonic development: from a thalassocraton in the northern Pacific and recent geosyncline systems of island arcs, to areas with folding completed, 'early-consolidation' massifs and 'middle' massifs.

Tectonic differences between areas of this region are supported by geophysical data that testify to variation in types and thickness of crust, and also to differences in thermodynamic conditions in the crust and upper mantle for areas of different stages of geological development.

The crust in the areas of high tectonic activity in the Asia-to-Pacific transition zone show isostatic disturbance caused by lateral inhomogeneities in density of the upper mantle. These inhomogeneities are associated with processes of physico-chemical differentiation of the subcrustal material.

The available data on the structure and history of geological development of the north-western part of the Pacific belt conform with a model of crust formation resulting from an irreversible geosynclinal process that started in the Precambrian and is proceeding in recent times within island arcs. Geosyncline systems (including recent island arcs) were emplaced on a thalassocraton as ensimatic geosynclines.

INTRODUCTION

There are two opposing viewpoints about the emplacement of geosyncline systems that have formed folded areas in the north-western part of the Pacific belt:

1. The systems are geosynclines regenerated on sialic basements; generation of these results in degradation of the sialic portion of the crust, leading to its complete disappearance ('basification' after V. V. Beloussov 1968). Marginal seas and troughs

* Editor's footnote: I am informed by the Soviet National Pacific Committee that Dr Gnibidenko's paper was submitted independently of the Committee, and that the original contribution to the Congress Proceedings was not sponsored by it. The Committee has asked me to make this known.

(distinct from arc trenches) characterized by oceanic-type crust are considered to represent new formations that resulted from a geosynclinal regime of regeneration and from degradation of the granitic-metamorphic layer of the crust. Metamorphic rock complexes now exposed in different parts of this sector are regarded as relics of the degraded sialic basement (Minato *et al.* 1965, Krasny 1966*a*, Smirnov 1968).

2. The geosyncline systems are ensimatic geosynclines (Wells 1949) whose development into folded belts is a process of transformation of oceanic-type crust into continental crust (Drake & Nafe 1968, Gnibidenko & Shashkin 1970). In this case, the metamorphic rock complexes are considered in relation to development of geanticlinal uplifts (Gilluly 1957). Intensive metamorphism and granitization within these uplifts results in metamorphic zones of different age that, in the aggregate, form the granitic-metamorphic layer, which may appear at the surface in particular areas. Marginal seas and their deeps in this development model represent oceanic crust relics which are not yet involved in the intensive geosyncline process; they act as trough-traps for the sedimentary-volcanogenic material that comes from the continent and island arcs.

An alternative way of expressing these viewpoints is related to an understanding of the character of subcrustal processes. In the former it is sialic crust degradation; it testifies that a great amount of heat may accumulate sporadically in the upper mantle which leads to melting and absorption of the sialic part of the crust and is accompanied by powerful convective movement of the material. Models of the mode of elimination (basification) of light sialic material and the sources of heat required (Beloussov 1966, 1968) seem to be quite complicated, and the assumption of reversibility of physico-chemical processes in the upper mantle as an indispensable premise seems unwarranted (Vassilkovsky 1962, Koch 1967).

From the second viewpoint the process involves generation of sialic crust; this concept follows logically from the recognition of subcrustal differentiation (Vinogradov 1962). The upper mantle undergoes a prolonged process which results in an inhomogeneous but horizontally-layered structure with gradual displacement of light (sialic) elements into the crust. Reduction in density of the upper horizons of the mantle results from the concentration of light and easily melted components of the subcrustal material. As well, the same process is the cause for general uplift and leads to penetration of a portion of differentiation products into the crust and on to its surface. There is consequent increase in crustal thickness and a change of type. Thus it can be noted that anomalous physico-chemical properties of the upper mantle corresponded, or correspond now, to the tectonically most active areas.

TECTONICS OF THE NORTH-WESTERN PART OF THE PACIFIC BELT

The north-western part of the Pacific belt can be subdivided into the continental part and the transition zone, the boundary between which is the Chukotka-Cathaysian volcanogenic belt.

The continental part of the belt is represented by Mesozoic folded systems with outcrops of basement of varying age (Yanshin 1966), and is bounded to the west by Precambrian cratons and the Palaeozoic folded system of the Mongol-Okhotsk belt.

The Asia-to-Pacific transition zone is located between the Chukotka-Cathaysian volcanogenic belt and the edge of the oceanic slope. It includes marginal seas—the Bering, Okhotsk, Japan and East China Seas—and also island arcs with deep trenches—the Ryukyu, Japan, Sakhalin-Hokkaido, Kuril and western Aleutian. The Kamchatka Peninsula and the Koryak Upland are included here. All of this zone is an area of Cenozoic folding.

Within the limits of this sector of the Pacific belt, the total amplitude of relief reaches 13-15 km. A number of morphostructural elements (Gerasimov & Meshcheryakov 1967) are distinguished which occupy the lowest place in the hierarchy: mountain systems composed of folded and magmatic complexes of different ages; low-lying plains and shelves made up of weakly deformed Cenozoic strata on a basement varying in age; and island arcs and deep trenches.

The continental part

The central place among morphostructural elements of north-eastern U.S.S.R. is occupied by the Kolyma-Omolon middle massif (Korzhuyev 1969) which is bounded with Mesozoic folded systems in the east and in the west, and in the south the part of the volcanogenic belt near Okhotsk (Drabkin 1970).

The basement of the massif is composed of Precambrian and early Palaeozoic metamorphic complexes, overlain by post-Silurian terrigenous-carbonaceous and volcanogenic deposits (Simakov 1967, Gelman & Terekhov 1968, Gerasimova *et al.* 1969, Furdui 1969, Shpetny 1969, Shpetny & Pepeliayev 1969, Shishkin 1969).

The Yano-Kolyma Mesozoic folded system, located west of the Kolyma-Omolon middle massif, is composed of miogeosynclinal and eugeosynclinal formations. The latter are exposed only along the periphery of the massif in the Chersky mountain system, represented by Ordovician and, possibly, pre-Ordovician deposits in axial parts of anticlinoria that are intensely metamorphosed in a number of cases (Proshchenko 1962, Merzlyakov 1967, Rusakov & Vinogradov 1969, Shevchenko 1969, Gorbov & Zagruzina 1970, Dubovikov 1970).

The Chukotka Mesozoic folded system east of the massif is also composed of miogeosynclinal and eugeosynclinal formations. Palaeozoic and possibly older deposits now exposed in the North Anyuisky Ridge and in the Chukotka Peninsula have undergone metamorphism here (Gnibidenko 1969, Drabkin 1970).

Crustal thickness within the north-east U.S.S.R. is about 36-39 km and reaches 45 km beneath the lower part of the Chersky mountain system, decreasing towards the Arctic and the Pacific Oceans, a characteristic feature being increased thickness of the basalt layer (20-25 km) in the area of the newest uplift of the Chersky system ridges. Formation of the earth's crust and its layers is associated with material differentiation processes in the upper mantle (Fotiadi *et al.* 1968).

The Mongol-Okhotsk and the Laoelinsk Palaeozoic folded systems located between the eastern parts of the Siberian and the Chinese cratons are represented by miogeosynclinal and eugeosynclinal formations. Metamorphic complexes previously regarded as relics of degraded sialic basement (Smirnov 1963, 1964) have been formed, so recent data suggest, as part of the continuing process of the irreversible development of a geosyncline upon these folded systems (Shashkin 1967, 1968, 1970). Here the maximum crustal thickness of about 40 km (Lishnevsky 1969) is attributed to the Palaeozoic frame of the Bureinsky massif (Krasny 1966*b*) of early consolidation. Crustal thickness decreases to 25 km towards the Okhotsk Sea.

Within the limits of Sikhote-Alin, between the Precambrian Khankaisky massif of early consolidation (Gnibidenko 1964) and the Sikhote-Alin portion of the volcanogenic belt, there is located a folded system of Palaeozoic and Mesozoic ages (Bersenev 1969), which was emplaced as an ensimatic geosyncline (Mishin 1968, 1970). Here, crustal thickness is about 27-36 km (Argentov *et al.* 1970, Treskova *et al.* 1970).

Between the Chinese craton and the Cathaysian part of the volcanogenic belt, there are Palaeozoic and Mesozoic folded systems, both miogeosynclinal and eugeosynclinal (Kobayashi 1959, Tupitsyn 1962, Mikunov 1963, Masaitis 1964) whose metamorphic complexes are again metamorphosed geosynclinal deposits, but not relics of a degraded sialic craton (Gnibidenko 1969).

The zone of transition from the continent to the ocean-marginal seas and adjacent land areas

In accordance with the tectonic zoning by age of the main folding, the Asia-to-Pacific transition zone belongs to the area of Cenozoic tectogenesis with outcrops of basement of varying age (Yanshin 1966) and with basement plates of the Bering, Okhotsk, and East China Seas, to judge from a complex of geological and geophysical data (Ewing *et al.* 1965, Hoshino & Hotta 1966, Markov *et al.* 1967, Gainanov *et al.* 1968, Milashin *et al.* 1968, Scholl *et al.* 1968, Stone 1968, Zhuravlyov *et al.* 1968, Beresnev & Kovylin 1969, Hopkins *et al.* 1969, Scholl & Hopkins 1969, Vashchilov *et al.* 1969, Beresnev & Kovylin 1970*a* and *b*, Beresnev *et al.* 1970, Chikov *et al.* 1970, Gainanov *et al.* 1970, Kovylin *et al.* 1971, Kummer & Creager 1971).

Systems of anticlinoria, synclinoria, inherited and superposed basins in the Koryak Upland, in Kamchatka, Sakhalin, Sikhote-Alin and in the Korean Peninsula are second-order structural elements, which in a number of cases are characterized by distinct geomorphological expression. The strike of these structural elements is clearly observed within the shelves of the Bering Sea, the Okhotsk Sea and the East China Sea plates, where they are related to such elements as uplifts, arches, troughs and basins of a Mesozoic, Palaeozoic and more ancient basement overlain with a corner of Cenozoic deposits. The available data on the structure of the Bering Sea and the East China Sea shelves (Scholl *et al.* 1968, Scholl *et al.* 1970, Wageman *et al.* 1970, Kummer & Craeger 1971) testify to the existence of buried Mesozoic-Palaeogene uplifts along the shelf edges, which played the role of a barrier to sediments that came from the continent in Cenozoic time; the sediment filled the 'trough-trap' in front of this dam. A portion of the sediments represents erosion of these uplifts. Such a Mesozoic uplift-barrier will probably also be revealed along the Okhotsk Sea shelf edge.

Metamorphic complexes that are now exposed and that were regarded as relics of a degraded Precambrian sialic basement (Stille 1964, Smirnov 1963, 1964, Parfyonov 1970) cannot now be regarded as evidence of disintegration and basification (oceanization) of a Precambrian platform in this region. Metamorphic rocks forming these complexes are heterochronous formations which constitute the basal portions of regional stratigraphic sections. They constitute different structural forms: from an early-stage consolidation massif and an anticlinorium core to a contact-metamorphism zone (Matsumoto *et al.* 1968, Gnibidenko 1969*a* and 1970*a*).

Island arcs are recent geosyncline systems at different development stages (Gnibidenko & Shashkin 1970) conjugate with deep trenches and troughs. On the ocean side, the trenches are bounded by weakly expressed oceanic swells. A part of the island arc zone (Taiwan, Sakhalin-Japan and the eastern portion of the Aleutian Arc) is composed of folded systems at the orogenic development stage, whereas the Ryukyu and the Kuril Arcs, the central Aleutian Arc, the Shirshov and the Bauers uplifts in the Bering Sea and the Yamato Rise in the Japan Sea are geanticlinal uplifts of recent geosynclinal systems (Vlasov 1964, Konishi 1965, Ho 1967, Minato *et al.* 1965, Gnibidenko 1969*b*, Bark 1970, Vereshchagin 1970, Shor 1970, Scholl *et al.* 1970).

Palaeogeographic analysis (Vassilkovsky 1967, 1968) testifies to the fact that first and second order structural elements were emplaced on an oceanic crust, that is, as geosyncline systems of ensimatic type, and that island arcs (Aleutian, Kuril, Sakhalin-Japan and Ryukyu) are crustal portions that register consecutive stages of geosynclinal development of the crust.

Marginal seas and their deep troughs

The granitic-metamorphic layer wedges out on the slopes of the marginal sea troughs and the horizontally bedded complex of sedimentary deposits overlies a simatic basement that is convergent to the basaltic layer of the ocean in both composition and structure.

The upper part of the sedimentary section of deep troughs in the Bering, the Okhotsk and the Japan Seas show the first kilometre or more characterized by distinct layering, while the lower part of the section is relatively homogeneous because it contains an insignificant number of reflecting boundaries constituting an acoustically transparent layer (Ewing *et al.* 1965, Kovylin & Neprochnov 1965, Kovylin *et al.* 1966, Milashin *et al.* 1968, Scholl *et al.* 1968, Beresnev & Kovylin 1970*a* and *b*, Snegovskoy 1971, Snegovskoy & Alexandrov, in press; Kovylin *et al.* 1971). It is probable that the upper stratified sediments resulted from turbidity relayering and volcanic activity (Horn *et al.* 1969), while the lower homogeneous pile accumulated under conditions far removed from sources of detrital sediment. The thickness of the sedimentary pile reaches 3-4 km.

Although the homogeneous pile accumulated in a basin separated from the open ocean, the time of its accumulation was characterized by relatively low tectonic activity in the source areas, as compared to that of the upper, layered strata. The age of these sediments is not likely to be older than Cenozoic (Snegovskoy & Alexandrov, in press; Scholl *et al.* 1968), though its thickness is almost three times that of open-ocean sediments. This may have been caused by increase in the rate of sedimentation in Cenozoic time, after the marginal seas and troughs in the upper Mesozoic were separated from the ocean by barriers of island arcs, potential suppliers of sediment.

All the available data on the structure of deep trenches and on the emplacement conditions (which should be regarded as ensimatic) of geosynclinal systems on the land areas adjacent to marginal sea troughs are in agreement with the concept of the 'relict' nature of troughs (Menard 1967); they are portions of an oceanic crust within the geosyncline system but not yet involved in intensive geosynclinal processes.

GEOPHYSICAL DATA AS RELATED TO THE STRUCTURE AND PROCESSES IN THE EARTH'S CRUST AND UPPER MANTLE

Geophysical data and crustal structure

Geological differences in crustal structure in the north-western sector of the Pacific belt are supported by geophysical data that testify to the existence of different types and variations of crustal thickness in this region. Crustal thickness of from 40-45 to 20-25 km is characteristic for the continental part, shelves and island arcs, decreasing to 5-10 km with transition to the Pacific Ocean. These variations are related to first order morphostructural elements: the crust is of continental type (with a developed granitic-metamorphic layer) under mountain systems and plains of the continental part and under shelves of the marginal seas, and is of the oceanic type under deep troughs and edge swells (Galperin & Kosminskaya 1964, Rikitake *et al.* 1968, Shilo & Nikolayevsky 1968, Fotiadi *et al.* 1969*a* and *b*, Argentov *et al.* 1970).

Thicknesses of the basaltic and the granitic-metamorphic layers vary within wide ranges. The granitic-metamorphic layer thickness reaches approximately half the total crustal thickness with transition from island arcs to shelves and land. The basaltic layer, however, is thicker than the granitic-metamorphic one in (*a*) Yano-Kolyma and Chukotka Mesozoic folded systems; (*b*) in the eastern part of the Kamchatka Cenozoic folded system; (*c*) in the eastern part of the Palaeozoic system in the Mongol-Okhotsk belt; and (*d*) the Sikhote-Alin Mesozoic folded system. This is probably connected with insufficiently developed granitization processes in these areas (Fotiadi *et al.* 1968).

The character of magnetic anomalies changes according to the structural plan of the crust, second order structural elements (anticlinoria, synclinoria, uplifts and troughs) being reflected most distinctly in anomalous fields. Magnetic anomalies in tectonically active areas, those in island arcs in particular, are relatively more differentiated and intensive. The same regularity is manifested as regards the majority of submarine rises, whereas deep troughs are characterized by relatively weakly expressed anomalies. It should be noted that with transition from the ocean to the continent, linear magnetic anomalies peculiar to the oceanic crust become more diffuse in the transition zone, so that for the continent only the oval and 'amoeba-like' anomaly types are characteristic, and linearity is manifested very weakly. From the oceanic to continental crust magnetoactive bodies of the subcrustal type change in the transition zone to mixed-type bodies whose upper surface is located in the crust and the lower one in the upper mantle. Further on to the continent magneto-active bodies are observed only within the crust (Tuyezov *et al.* 1967). In view of this the oceanic plan of the magnetic field must have been diffused in the process of development of the continental crust (Kochergin *et al.* 1970).

Bouguer gravity anomalies vary from negative or slightly positive over the continent to intense positive ones over the North-western Pacific. The areas of positive anomaly correspond to second-order positive structural elements (anticlinoria and uplifts). Anomalous gravity fields corresponding to first order structural elements (deep troughs, islands, shelves) persist to depths which testify that these structural elements are caused by upper mantle inhomogeneities (Pavlov *et al.* 1970, Stroev 1971, Gainanov *et al.* in press).

Structure and processes in the upper mantle

Observations of propagation velocities of longitudinal and transverse waves from earthquakes, and also gravity data, show that the upper mantle in the Asia-to-Pacific transition zone has inhomogeneous physical properties, both in vertical and horizontal directions (Tuyezov *et al.* 1967, Tarakanov & Leviy 1968, Fedotov & Slavina 1968, Vashchilov *et al.* 1969, Tarakanov 1969, Kanamori 1970, Abe & Kanamori 1970), which may be caused by differentiation of the subcrustal material.

The upper mantle under the transition zone has been shown to be differentiated with respect to density, with reduction to 0·05-0·1 g/cm beneath island arcs and submarine rises (Vashchilov *et al.* 1969, Gainanov *et al.* in press). Presence of isostatic anomalies within these regions appears to be related to upper mantle processes. It is a peculiar fact that positive structural elements of the transition zone (island arcs and submarine rises and edge portions of the shelves are undercompensated isostatically, which fact, along with seismicity and volcanism, testifies to continuing differentiation of mantle material within these regions; this results in density-reduction areas caused by additional flow of sialic material and this in turn causes uplift of a crustal portion against isostatic submergence forces (Sychev 1969).

Activity of mantle material differentiation processes is supported by analysis of temperature and pressure distribution at the Mohorovicic discontinuity for marginal seas, deep troughs, island arcs and trenches (Uyeda & Horai 1964, Takeuchi & Uyeda 1965, Tikhomirov 1970, Hasebe *et al.* 1970). Thermodynamic conditions differ appreciably for these, in morphostructural elements and so there exist different facies of recent metamorphism at comparable depths. Anomalous heat distribution at the base of the crust for different morphostructural elements of the transition zone can be satisfactorily explained as due to unequal amounts of heat coming from the upper mantle, indicative of processes of continuing differentiation of mantle material.

DISCUSSION: EVOLUTION OF THE EARTH'S CRUST

The above data from the North-western Pacific belt are in agreement with the model in which crust formation results from an irreversible geosynclinal process (that forms the granitic-metamorphic portion of the crust) caused by upper mantle differentiation, probably in accord with the scheme suggested by Ringwood and Green (1968). For this belt, crustal development models that provide for degradation of the sialic portion of the crust as a result of basification (Beloussov 1968) need not be involved.

Evidence of disintegration and degradation of the sialic mass (craton) for this portion of the belt, as mentioned in the Introduction, can be reduced to two statements:

1. Metamorphic complexes are sialic relics of a disintegrated craton whose granitic-metamorphic layer was annihilated by basification.

2. Deep troughs are newly formed portions of the oceanic crust at places within the continental one as a result of the same basification process.

At present both statements, however, have to be taken as poorly grounded. The first of the two must be rejected because it has become evident that metamorphic complexes are not relics of a degraded Precambrian (or later) craton (Gnibidenko 1970*b*), but are heterochronous metamorphized geosynclinal formations that enter into the composition of Mesozoic and Cenozoic fold systems of the North-western Pacific belt.

After analyzing the crustal structure of deep troughs in the marginal seas, along with available data on geology of the adjacent land areas and island arcs, it is also possible to reject the hypothesis of their being newly formed from the continental crust: the available data testify rather to the fact that the troughs are relict portions of the oceanic crust (Menard 1967) separated from the ocean by barriers of island arcs during the process of geosynclinal development in Mesozoic time.

The history of continental crust formation in the North-western Pacific belt can be viewed as the continuing, irreversible development of the granitic-metamorphic layer as a result of the geosynclinal process (Gnibidenko & Shashkin 1970, Gnibidenko 1970*a*). This geosynclinal process started within the continental portion of the belt as long ago as the Precambrian and spread over the whole territory of the transition zone, including the island arcs, during the Palaeozoic and Mesozoic.

It should be noted that crustal development of long duration in this part of the belt assumes a similar long existence of the system of vertical and lateral upper mantle inhomogeneities. This disagrees with development models that attach their main significance to major horizontal displacements of crustal blocks (Dewey & Horsfield 1970, Matsuda & Uyeda 1971, Packham & Falvey 1971), or to disintegration and degradation of continental masses (Minato & Hanahasi 1970). This system would not be preserved in these models, but would be destroyed by convective displacements in the upper mantle.

I do not deal further with mobilistic models of crustal development, recently analyzed by Fourmarier (1971), because I adhere to a position of moderate crustal movement admitting only relatively small horizontal displacement of crustal blocks along fractures.

CONCLUSION

Crustal structure of the North-western Pacific belt exemplifies an irreversible geocynclinal process that has resulted in transformation of oceanic-type crust into continental in this region. Precambrian and Phanerozoic geosyncline systems were emplaced here as ensimatic geosynclines.

Deep troughs in the Bering, the Okhotsk and the Japan marginal seas are relics of oceanic type crust which are not yet involved in intensive geosynclinal process.

At present the process proceeds intensively within island arcs and adjacent portions of the deep troughs and within arc-trenches. Upper mantle differentiation leads to irreversible changes in upper mantle composition and to gradual damping of geosynclinal activity as the geosyncline develops and transforms into a folded system.

ACKNOWLEDGEMENTS.

It is my pleasant duty to state my gratitude to Dr P. M. Sychev and Dr R. Z. Tarakanov for their helpful discussion of the ideas dealt with in this paper. Many thanks are due to Mr M. S. Fedorishin who took the trouble of translating this paper into English, and to Mrs T. G. Bykova for her devotedly sincere help in preparing the material for publication.

SELECT BIBLIOGRAPHY AND REFERENCES

Abe, K. & Kanamori, H. 1970. Mantle structure beneath the Japan Sea as revealed by surface waves. *Bull. Earthq. Res. Inst. Tokyo Univ.* **48** (6A), 1011-21.

Argentov, V. V., Ospanov, A. B. & Popov, A. A. 1970. Crustal structure of the south-west Primorie. In *Geology and Geophysics of the Pacific Belt* (Ed. H. S. Gnibidenko). *Trans. Sakhalin Complex Sci. Res. Inst. Novoalexandrovsk*, **25,** 71-8 (in Russian).

Bark, K. 1970. The Aleutian Island Arc and Alaskan continental margin. In *Continental Margins and Island Arcs* (Ed. U. H. Poole). Mir, Moscow (in Russian).

Beloussov, V. V. 1966. *The earth's crust and upper mantle of the continents.* Nauka Publ., Moscow (in Russian).

——— 1968. The earth's crust and upper mantle of the oceans. Ibid. (in Russian).

Beresnev, A. F., Gainanov, A. G., Kovylin, V. M. & Stroev, P. A. 1970. Crustal and upper mantle structure of the Japan Sea and the adjacent Pacific zone. In *Problems of Structure of the Earth's Crust and Upper Mantle. Upper Mantle Rept*, 7 (Eds V. A. Magnitsky, N. A. Belyaevsky & I. S. Vol'vovsky). Nauka Publ., Moscow (in Russian).

Beresnev, A. F. & Kovylin, V. M. 1969. Some peculiarities of deep crustal structure of the southern Japan Sea. *Izv. Akad. Nauk SSSR* (*geol.*), **5,** 17-22 (in Russian).

——— 1970*a*. Crustal structure of the Japan Sea in the vicinity of the continental slope of the southern Primorie and north-eastern Korea. *Trans. Oceanol. Inst. Akad. Nauk SSSR*, **87,** 168-73 (in Russian).

——— 1970*b*. Basement relief and thicknesses of bottom sediments in the central part of the Japan Sea. *Okeanologiya*, **10** (1), 113-16 (in Russian).

Bersenev, I. I. (Ed.) 1969. Primorie Territory. I—Geologic Description. In *Geology of the USSSR*, **32.** Nedra Publ., Moscow (in Russian).

Chikov, B. M., Yunov, A. Yu & Belyaev, I. V. 1970. The Okhotsk Sea structure and its correlation to coastal folded complexes. *Geol. i Geofiz.* **1,** 57-68 (in Russian).

Dewey, J. F. & Horsfield, B. 1970. Plate tectonics, orogeny and continental growth. *Nature*, **225** (5232), 521-5.

Drabkin, I. E. (Ed.) 1970. North-east of the USSR. II—Geologic Description. In *Geology of the USSR*, **30.** Nedra Publ., Moscow (in Russian).

Drake, C. L. & Nafe, J. E. 1968. The transition from ocean to continent from seismic refraction data. In *The Crust and Upper Mantle of the Pacific Area* (Eds L. Knopoff, C. L. Drake & J. Hart) *Am. Geophys. Un., Geophys. Monogr.* **12,** 174-86.

Dubovikov, L. K. 1970. On the question of the age of metamorphic strata of the Tas-Khayakhtakhsky anticlinorium (Yakutskaya ASSR). In *Materials on Geology and Mineral Resources of the Yakutskaya ASSR* (*North-eastern Yakutiya*) (Ed. I. D. Vorona), **16,** 33-4. Yakutsk (in Russian).

Ewing, M., Ludwig, W. J. & Ewing, J. 1965. Oceanic structural history of the Bering Sea. *J. geophys. Res.* **70** (18), 4593-600.

Fedotov, S. A. & Slavina, L. B. 1968. Estimation of longitudinal wave velocities in the upper mantle beneath north-western part of the Pacific and Kamchatka. *Izv. Akad. Nauk SSSR, Fizika Zemli,* **2,** 8-31 (in Russian).

Fotiadi, E. E., Berezin, M. A., Volkov, A. N., Livshits, M. Kh., Smirnov, L. M., Sychev, P. M., Tarakanov, R. Z., Tuyezov, I. K. & Shteinberg, G. S. 1969*a*. Geophysical study of the inner zone deep structure of the Pacific mobile Belt in the east of the USSR. In *Structure and Development of the Earth's Crust in the Soviet Far East* (Eds E. E. Fotiadi & I. K. Tuyezov). Nauka Publ., Moscow (in Russian).

Fotiadi, E. E., Karataev, G. I. & Moiseenko, F. S. 1968. Some regularities in crustal structure and development from geophysical data by way of example in Siberia and the Far East. In *Earth's Crust and Upper Mantle* (Ed. V. V. Beloussov). Nauka Publ., Moscow (in Russian).

Fotiadi, E. E., Nikolaevsky, A. A., Kravchenko, Yu. V., Ryabov, A. V. & Shapochka, I. I. 1969*b*. Geophysical study of tectonic structure and deep crustal structure of the outer Pacific mobile belt in the east of the USSR. In *Structure and Development of the Earth's Crust in the Soviet Far East* (Eds E. E. Fotiadi & I. K. Tuyezov). Nauka Publ., Moscow (in Russian).

Fourmarier, P. 1971. *Problems of continental drift*. Mir, Moscow (in Russian).

Furdui, R. S. 1969. About Riphean deposits of the Omolonsky massif. *Dokl. Akad. Nauk SSSR,* **188** (1), 197-3 (in Russian).

Gainanov, A. G., Isayev, E. N., Stroev, P. A. & Ushakov, S. A. 1970. Isostasy and lithosphere structure of the Bering Sea and the Aleutian Arc. In *Marine Gravimetric Investigations* (Ed. V. V. Fedynsky), Izdatelstvo MGU, Moscow, **5,** 32-40 (in Russian).

Gainanov, A. G., Kosminskaya, I. P. & Stroev, P. A. 1968. Geophysical investigation of deep structure of the Bering Sea. *Izv. Akad. Nauk SSSR, Fizika Zemli,* **8,** 3-11 (in Russian).

Gainanov, A. G., Pavlov, Yu. A., Stroev, P. A. & Tuyezov, I. K. 1972. *Anomalous gravity fields of the Far East marginal seas and the adjacent Pacific*. Nauka Publ., Novosibirsk (in Russian).

Galperin, E. I. & Kosminskaya, I. P. (Eds) 1964. *Crustal Structure in the Asia-to-Pacific Transition Zone*. Nauka Publ., Moscow (in Russian).

Gelman, M. L. & Terekhov, M. I. 1968. New data on Precambrian crystalline complex of the Omolonsky massif. In *Problems of Geology, Petrology and Metallogeny of the Metamorphic Complexes of East of the USSR* (Ed. A. M. Smirnov), pp. 30-1. Vladivostok (in Russian).

Gerasimov, I. P. & Mescheryakov, Yu. A. (Eds) 1967. *Relief of the Earth* (*Morphostructure and Morphosculpture*). Nauka Publ., Moscow (in Russian).

Gerasimova, I. A., Gusarov, B. M., Dylevsky, E. F., Kovalchuk, I. A. & Simakov, K. V. 1969. The Omolonsky block regional tectonics. In *Mesozoic Tectogenesis. Theses of reports of Scientific Council 7th Session on tectonics of Siberia and the Far East* (Eds N. F. Sokolovskaya & T. V. Umnova). Magadan (in Russian).

Gilluly, J. 1957. Geologic contrasts between continents and oceanic basins. In *Crust of the Earth* (Ed. A. Poldervaart). Inostrannaya Literatura, Moscow (in Russian transl.).

Gnibidenko, H. S. 1964. On tectonics of the Khankaisky Middle massif. In *Materials on Tectonics and Petrology of the Pacific Ore Belt* (Eds N. P. Vassilkovsky & A. A. Marakushev). Nauka Publ., Moscow (in Russian).

Gnibidenko, H. S. 1969*a*. *Metamorphic complexes in the structures of northwestern sector of the Pacific Belt*. Nauka Publ., Moscow (in Russian).

——— (Ed.) 1969*b*. Metamorphic Complexes of Sakhalin Island. *Trans. Sakhalin Complex Sci. Res. Inst. Yuzhno-Sakhalinsk,* **22** (in Russian).

——— 1970*a*. Metamorphism role in geosynclinal process. In *Geology and Geophysics of the Pacific Belt* (Ed. H. S. Gnibidenko). *Trans. Sakhalin Complex Sci. Res. Inst. Novo-alexandrovsk,* **25,** 12-17 (in Russian).

——— 1970*b*. On the basement of the north-west sector of the Pacific Belt. *Tectonophysics,* **9** (6), 513-23.

Gnibidenko, H. S. & Shashkin, K. S. 1970. Basic principles of the geosynclinal theory. *Tectonophysics,* **9** (1), 5-13.

Gorbov, V. V. & Zagruzina, I. A. 1970. Absolute age of metamorphic rocks of the Uyandinsky horst. *Kolyma,* **10,** 34-5. Magadan (in Russian).

Hasebe, K., Fujii, N. & Uyeda, S. 1970. Thermal processes under island arcs. In *Geothermal, Problems* (Eds S. Uyeda & A. M. Jessop). *Tectonophysics,* **10** (1-3), 335-55.

Ho, C. S. 1967. Structural evolution of Taiwan. *Tectonophysics,* **4** (4-6), 367-78.

Hopkins, D. W., Scholl, D. W., Addicott, W. O., Pierce, R. L., Smith, R. B., Wolfe, J. A., Gershanovich, D., Kotenev, B., Lohman, K. E., Lipps, J. H. & Obradovich, J. 1969. Cretaceous, Tertiary, and Early Pleistocene rocks from the continental margin in the Bering Sea. *Bull. geol. Soc. Am.* **80** (8), 1471-80.

Horn, D. R., Delach, M. N. & Horn, B. M. 1969. Distribution of volcanic ash layers and turbidites in the North Pacific. *Bull. geol. Soc. Am.* **80** (9), 1715-23.

Hoshino, M. & Hotta, H. 1966. Geology of submarine banks in the Japan Sea. *Earth Science* (*J. Assoc. Geol. Collaboration in Japan*), **82,** 10-16 (in Japanese).

Kanamori, H. 1970. Mantle beneath the Japanese arc. *Phys. Earth Planet. Inter.* **3,** 475-83.

Kobayashi, T. 1959. Geology of Korea and the adjacent China territory. Inostrannaya Literatura, Moscow (in Russian transl.).

Koch, R. A. 1967. Zum Wesen des Grundpostulats der Geologie. *Philos. natur.* **10** (1), 102-6.

Kochergin, E. V. Krasny, M. L., Sychev, P. M. & Tuyezov, I. K. 1970. Anomalous geomagnetic field of north-western part of the Pacific mobile belt and its relation to the tectonic structure. *Geol. i Geofiz.* **12,** 77-9 (in Russian).

Konishi, K. 1965. Geotectonic framework of the Ryukyu Islands (Nansei Shoto). *J. geol. Soc. Japan,* **71,** 437-57.

Korzhuyev, S. S. 1969. The role of the Kolymsky middle massif in the formation of North-East Asia morphostructure. In *Geography and Geomorphology of Asia* (Eds Yu. A. Meshcher-yakov & S. S. Korzhuyev). Nauka Publ., Moscow (in Russian).

Kovylin, V. M., Karp, B. Ya. & Shayakhmentov, R. B. 1966. The structure of earth's crust and sedimentary strata of the Japan Sea from seismic data. *Dokl. Akad. Nauk SSSR,* **168** (5), 1048-51 (in Russian).

Kovylin, V. M. & Neprochnov, Y. P. 1965. Crustal structure and sedimentary layer in the central part of the Japan Sea derived from seismic data. *Izv. Akad. Nauk SSSR* (*geol.*), **4,** 10-26 (in Russian).

Kovylin, V. M., Shayakhmentov, R. B. & Mouravova, E. A. 1971. The sedimentary strata and underlying basement structure in the vicinity of conjugation of Korea continental crust and the oceanic Japanese basin crust. *Izv. Akad. Nauk SSSR (geol.),* **5,** 125-8 (in Russian).

Krasny, L. I. (Ed.) 1966*a*. *Geologic structure of the North-western Pacific mobile belt*. Nedra Publ., Moscow (in Russian).

——— (Ed.) 1966*b*. Khabarovsky and Amurskaya regions. I—Geologic Description. In

Geology of the USSR, **19,** Nedra Publ., Moscow (in Russian).
Kummer, J. T. & Creager, J. S. 1971. Marine geology and Cenozoic history of the Gulf of Anadyr. *Marine Geology* **10** (4), 257-80.
Lishnevsky, E. N. 1969. The main features of tectonics and deep structure of continental part of the USSR Far East from gravimetric data. In *Structure and Development of Earth's Crust in the Soviet Far East* (Eds E. E. Fotiadi & I. K. Tuyezov). Nauka Publ., Moscow (in Russian).
Markov, M. S., Averianova, V. N., Kartashov, I. P., Solovieva, I. A. & Shuvaev, A. S. 1967. Meso-Cenozoic history and structure of the earth crust in the Okhotsk region. *Trudy Geol. Inst. Fasc.* **168,** Moscow (in Russian).
Masaitis, V. L. (Ed.) 1964. *Geology of Korea*. Nedra Publ., Moscow (in Russian).
Matsuda, T. & Uyeda, S. 1971. On the Pacific-type orogeny and its model—extension of the paired belts concept and possible origin of marginal seas. *Tectonophysics*, **11** (1), 5-27.
Matsumoto, T. 1967. Fundamental problems in the circum-Pacific orogenesis. *Tectonophysics*, **4** (4-6), 595-613.
Matsumoto, T., Yamaguchi, M., Yanagi, T., Matsushita, S., Hayase, I., Ishizaka, K., Kawano, Yo. & Ueda, Yo. 1968. The Precambrian problem in younger orogenic zones: an example from Japan. *Can. J. Earth Sci.* **5** (3), Pt. 2, 643-8.
Menard, H. W. 1967. Transitional types of crust under small ocean basins. *J. geophys. Res.* **72** (12), 3061-73.
Merzlyakov, V. M. 1967. A new type of the Ordovician cross-section on the Kolymsky massif. *Kolyma,* **7,** 44-6. Magadan (in Russian).
Mikunov, V. F. 1963. New works on the tectonics of China. *Izv. Akad. Nauk SSSR (geol.)*, **2,** 50-9 (in Russian).
Milashin, A. P., Snegovskoy, S. S. & Tuyezov, I. K. 1968. Structure of sedimentary strata of the Japan Sea from continuous reflection profiling data. *Dokl. Akad. Nauk SSSR,* **183** (5), 1060-3 (in Russian).
Minato, M., Gorai, M. & Hunahashi, M. (Eds) 1965. *The geologic development of the Japanese Islands*. Tsikiji Shokan, Tokyo.
Minato, M. & Hunahashi, M. 1970. Origin of the earth's crust and its evolution. *J. Fac. Sci. Hokkaido Univ.* **4** (Geol. & Miner.) **24** (4), 515-61.
Mishin, V. P. 1968. Formation-tectonic division into districts of the Southern Primorie and the adjacent China and Korea territories for Late Palaeozoic. In *Geology of the Asia-to-Pacific Transition Zone* (Ed. N. P. Vassilkovsky). Nauka Publ., Moscow (in Russian).
——— 1970. On Middle Palaeozoic geosyncline structure of the Southern Sikhote-Alin. In *Problems of Geology, Geochemistry and Metallogeny of the North-western sector of the Pacific Belt* (Ed. I. N. Govorov). Vladivostok (in Russian).
Packham, G. H. & Falvey, D. A. 1971. An hypothesis for the formation of marginal seas in the western Pacific. *Tectonophysics*, **11** (2), 79-109.
Parfyonov, L. M. 1970. Precambrian structure of East Asia. In *Tectonic Problems of Precambrian of Continents* (Ed. Yu. A. Kosygin). *Trans. Inst. Geol. Geophys., Siberian Branch, Acad. Sci. USSR*, **129,** 131-54. Nauka Publ., Moscow (in Russian).
Pavlov, Yu. A., Tuyezov, I. K., Yeryomina, G. F., Lyutaya, L. M., Pavlova, I. S. & Andreev, A. A. 1970. The gravity field of the Asia-to-Pacific transition zone, transformed into the upper semispace. In *Geophysical Investigations of Structure of Earth's Crust and Upper Mantle of the Asia-to-Pacific Transition Zone* (Ed. I. K. Tuyezov). *Trans. Sakhalin Complex Sci. Res. Inst., Yuzhno-Sakhalinsk,* **24,** 43-67 (in Russian).
Proshchenko, E. G. 1962. On the question about age of metamorphic rocks of the Selennyakhsky Mountain Ridge (Yakutskaya ASSR). *Geol. i Geofiz.* **3,** 41-8 (in Russian).

Pushcharovsky, Yu. M. 1967. The Pacific tectonic segment of the earth's crust. *Geotektonika*, **5**, 90-102 (in Russian).

——— 1968. The Pacific tectonic belt of the earth's crust. In *Tectonics of the Soviet Far East and the adjacent aquatic areas* (Ed. Yu. A. Kosygin). Nauka Publ., Moscow (in Russian).

Rikitake, T., Miyamura, S., Tsubokawa, I., Murauchi, S., Uyeda, S., Kuno, H. & Gorai, M. 1968. Geophysical and geological data in and around the Japan Arc. *Can. J. Earth Sci.* **5** (4), Pt 2, 1101-18.

Ringwood, A. E. & Green, D. H. 1968. Experimental investigation of gabbro passing into eclogite and some geophysical conclusions. In *The Upper Mantle Petrology* (Ed. Ryabchikov). Mir, Moscow (in Russian).

Rusakov, I. M. & Vinogradov, V. A. 1969. Eugeosynclinal and miogeosynclinal regions of the North-East of the USSR. In *Scientific Notes—Regional Geology. Trans. Sci. Res. Inst. Geol. Arctic, Leningrad,* **15,** 5-27 (in Russian).

Scholl, D. W., Buffington, E. C. & Hopkins, D. M. 1968. Geologic history of the continental margin of North America in the Bering Sea. *Marine Geology*, **6** (4), 297-330.

Scholl, D. W., Buffington, E. C., Hopkins, D. M. & Alpha, T. R. 1970. The structure and origin of the large submarine canyons of the Bering Sea. *Marine Geology*, **8** (3-4), 187-210.

Scholl, D. W., Greene, H. G. & Marlow, M. S. 1970. Eocene age of the Adak 'Paleozoic (?)' rocks, Aleutian Islands, Alaska. *Bull. geol. Soc. Am.* **81** (12), 3583-92.

Scholl, D. W. & Hopkins, D. M. 1969. Newly discovered Cenozoic basins, Bering Sea shelf, Alaska. *Bull. Am. Ass. Petrol. Geol.* **53** (10), 2067-78.

Shashkin, K. S. 1967. On Early Paleozoic eugeosyncline system of the Mongolian-Okhotsky folded belt. In *Tectonics of Eastern Siberia and the Far East of the USSR. Theses of reports on Fifth Session of Scientific Council on tectonics of Siberia and the Far East* (Ed. Yu. A. Kosygin). Novosibirsk (in Russian).

——— 1968. On the metamorphic complex nature of the north-east framing of the Zeisko-Bureinsky massif. In *Problems of Geology, Petrology and Metallogeny of Metamorphic Complexes of East of the USSR* (Ed. A. M. Smirnov). Vladivostok (in Russian).

——— 1970. Structure-formational zones of the Mongolian-Okhotsky belt and some peculiarities of their development. In *Problems of Geology, Geochemistry and Metallogeny of northwestern sector of the Pacific Belt* (Ed. I. N. Govorov). Vladivostok (in Russian).

Shevchenko, V. V. 1969. Paleozoic deposits of the middle current basin of the Indigirka River. In *Transactions of Interdepartment Conference on the Development of the Unified Stratigraphic Scheme of the Yakutskaya ASSR, 1961. I—Precambrian and Paleozoic: Materials on Geology and Mineral Resources of the Yakutskaya ASSR* (Ed. I. S. Bredikhin). Rept 13, Yakutsk (in Russian).

Shilo, N. A. & Nikolayevsky, A. A. 1968. The structure of the earth's crust and upper mantle of northwestern part of the Pacific mobile Belt. In *Earth's Crust and Upper Mantle* (Ed. V. V. Beloussov). Nauka Publ., Moscow (in Russian).

Shishkin, V. A. 1969. On the crystalline basement exposures on the Shamanikho-Stolbovsky territory, Prikolymie. In *Mesozoic Tectogenesis. Theses of reports of Scientific Council 7th Session on tectonics of Siberia and the Far East* (Eds N. F. Sokolovskaya & T. V. Umnova). Magadan (in Russian).

Shor, G. G. 1970. Island arcs and continental margins of the western part of North America. In *Continental Margins and Island Arcs* (Ed. U. H. Poole). Mir, Moscow (in Russian).

Shpetny, A. P. 1969. The Omolonsky massif is the structure of Caledonian consolidation. In *Mesozoic Tectogenesis. Theses of reports of Scientific Council 7th Session on tectonics of Siberia and the Far East* (Eds N. F. Sokolovskaya & T. V. Umnova). Magadan (in Russian).

Shpetny, A. P. & Pepeliayev, B. V. 1969. The main tectonic features and the history of the

Prikolymskoye Uplift development. In *Mesozoic Tectogenesis* . . . (in Russian).

Simakov, K. V. 1967. Pre-Permian deposits of the Omolonsky Block. *Geol. i Geofiz.* **12,** 57-66 (in Russian).

Smirnov, A. M. 1963. The conjugation of the Chinese platform with the Pacific folded belt. *Izdatelstvo Akad. Nauk SSSR.* Moscow-Leningrad (in Russian).

——— 1964. On the structural position and age of the metamorphic Kamchatka and Sakhalin strata. In *Materials on Tectonics and Petrology of the Pacific Ore Belt* (Eds N. P. Vassilkovsky & A. A. Marakushev). Nauka Publ., Moscow (in Russian).

——— 1968. Role of the Precambrian basement in structural evolution of the Pacific mobile belt (particularly its northwestern section). *Pacific Geol.* **1,** 145-65.

Snegovskoy, S. S. 1971. On sedimentary deposits of the South-Okhotskaya abyssal basin. *Dokl. Akad. Nauk SSSR,* **196** (1), 87-90 (in Russian).

Snegovskoy, S. S. & Alexandrov, S. M. 1972. On tectonics of the western edge of the Kuril basin. *Geotektonika,* in press (in Russian).

Stille, G. 1964. *Circum-Pacific folding in space and time—Selective Publications.* Mir, Moscow (in Russian transl.).

Stone, D. B. 1968. Geophysics in the Bering Sea and surrounding areas: A review. *Tectonophysics,* **6** (6), 433-60.

Stroev, P. A. 1971. Gravity anomalies in the Japan Sea. *Dokl. Akad. Nauk SSSR,* **198** (4), 818-21 (in Russian).

Sychev, P. M. 1969. Gravity anomalies and causes of crustal vertical motion in the Asia-to-Pacific transition zone. *Geotektonika,* **1,** 13-25 (in Russian).

Takeuchi, H. & Uyeda, S. 1965. A possiblity of present-day regional metamorphism. *Tectonophysics,* **2** (2), 59-68.

Tarakanov, R. Z. 1969. Velocity mosaic in the upper mantle and possibilities of area travel-time curve plotting. In *Geophysical Investigations of Structure of Earth's Crust and of Upper Mantle of the Asia-to-Pacific Transition Zone* (Ed. I. K. Tuyezov). *Trans. Sakhalin Complex Sci. Res. Inst. Yuzhno-Sakhalinsk,* **20,** 133-53 (in Russian).

Tarakanov, R. Z. & Leviy, N. V. 1968. A model for the upper mantle with several channels of low velocity and strength. In *The Crust and Upper Mantle of the Pacific Area* (Eds L. Knopoff, C. L. Drake, & J. Hart). *Am. Geophys. Un., Geophys. Monogr.* **12,** 43-50.

Tikhomirov, V. M. 1970. Thermodynamic conditions in the earth's crust and upper mantle of the Okhotsk Sea, Kuril Islands, and the Near Kuril Pacific. In *Geology and Geophysics of the Pacific Belt* (Ed. H. S. Gnibidenko). *Trans. Sakhalin Complex Sci. Res. Inst. Novoalexandrovsk,* **25,** 23-33 (in Russian).

Treskova, Yu. A., Kiselyova, L. G. & Gnibidenko, H. S. 1970. About the crustal structure of the Southern Sikhote-Alin (from deep seismic sounding reconnaissance survey profile of Spassk-Tadushi). In *Geology and Geophysics* . . . **25,** 66-70 (in Russian).

Tupitsyn, N. V. (Ed.) 1962. *Principles of tectonics of China.* Gosgeoltekhizdat, Moscow (in Russian).

Tuyezov, I. K., Krasny, M. L., Pavlov, Yu. A. & Solov'iev, O. N. 1967. Magneto-active body distribution in earth's crust and upper mantle of the Far East sector of the Asia-to-Pacific transition zone. *Geotektonika,* **4,** 95-101 (in Russian).

Tuyezov, I. K., Sychev, P. M., Pavlov, Yu. A. & Gimpelson, M. S. 1967. Density substance inhomogeneities of the earth's upper mantle in the southern Soviet sector of the Asia-to-Pacific transition zone. In *Regional Geophysical Investigations in Siberia* (Eds V. N. Gaisky, G. I. Karataev, A. A. Kaufman, F. S. Moiseenko, N. N. Puzyryov & V. S. Surkov). Nauka Publ., Novosibirsk (in Russian).

Uyeda, S. & Horai, K. 1964. Terrestrial heat flow in Japan. *J. geophys. Res.* **69** (10), 2121-41.

Vashchilov, Yu. Ya., Gainanov, A. G. & Stroev, P. A. 1969. Layer-blocked structure of earth's crust and upper mantle in the Japan, Okhotsk, and Bering Seas from gravimetric data. In *Marine Gravimetric Investigations* (Ed. V. V. Fedynsky). Izdatelstvo MGU, Moscow, **4,** 80-91 (in Russian).

Vassilkovsky, N. P. 1962. On the geologic process direction in the earth's history. *Geol. i Geofiz.* 1962-**11,** 41-51 (in Russian).

——— 1967. On the geological nature of the Pacific Mobile Belt. *Tectonophysics,* **4** (4-6), 583-93.

——— 1968. Structure peculiarities and geologic history of the north-Asiatic part of the Pacific Belt. In *Geology of the Asia-to-Pacific Transition Zone* (Ed. N. P. Vassilkovsky). Nauka Publ., Moscow (in Russian).

Vereshchagin, V. I. (Ed.) 1970. Sakhalin Island. Geologic Description. In *Geology of the USSR,* **33,** Nedra Publ., Moscow (in Russian).

Vinogradov, A. P. 1962. The earth mantle origin. *Izv. Akad. Nauk SSSR (geol.),* 1962-**11,** 3-17 (in Russian).

Vlasov, G. M. (Ed.) 1964. Kamchatka, the Kurile and Komandorskiye Islands. I—Geologic Description. In *Geology of the USSR,* **31.** Nedra Publ., Moscow (in Russian).

Wageman, J. M., Hilde, T. W. C. & Emery, K. O. 1970. Structural framework of East China Sea and Yellow Sea. *Bull. Am. Ass. Petrol. Geol.* **54** (9), 1611-43.

Wells, F. G. 1949. Ensimatic and ensialic geosynclines. *Bull. geol. Soc. Am.* **60,** 1927.

Yunov, A. Yu. 1970. A new variant of the deep geologic structure of the Okhotsk Sea bottom. *Dokl. Akad. Nauk SSSR* (*geol.*), **191** (4), 893 (in Russian).

Zhuravlyov; A. V., Sevost'yanov, K. M. & Taboyakov, A. Ya. 1968. Some problems of the geologic development history of the Okhotsk Sea. *Geol. i Geofiz.* **8,** 27-35 (in Russian).

PETROLOGY AND GEOCHEMISTRY OF ISLAND ARCS IN RELATION TO TECTONIC ENVIRONMENT

Introduction

IAN MCDOUGALL
Department of Geophysics and Geochemistry
Australian National University, P.O. Box 4, Canberra, A.C.T. 2601
Australia

This symposium was initiated when it became clear that geochemically oriented papers would not conveniently find a place in the symposia already suggested for Section D. Geochemical studies on the rocks of which island arcs are built provide important information on the genesis of the rocks and therefore of the island arcs themselves. It seemed very opportune and desirable to provide a forum for the discussion of these aspects in the context of the overall theme of Section D, particularly in view of the remarkable synthesis of data from diverse fields that is presently taking place through the concepts of sea-floor spreading and plate tectonics. The general aims of the symposium were given in brief in a statement that was sent to possible contributors and I think that it is appropriate to reproduce it here:

> It is widely recognized that the development of island arcs genetically is related to the underlying structure of the regions in which they occur and to the tectonic evolution of the ocean basins. The aim of this symposium is to give a synthesis of the evidence from the petrology (including experimental petrology) and geochemistry (including isotopic studies) of the igneous rocks in island arcs of the Pacific Ocean region in relation to the tectonic environment, including the dipping seismic zones. Attention will be directed toward the broader aspects of variation of composition, type and location of igneous activity in space and time in the island arcs, together with the inferences that can be drawn as to the nature of the processes occurring beneath and within the island arcs.

In my view the papers given in the symposium provided a very good coverage of the present knowledge and understanding of petrogenesis and the development of island arcs. I believe that the papers and abstracts that follow speak eloquently for themselves in this respect, and call for no additional comment from myself.

Magmatic Consequences of Plate Tectonics[1]

D. H. Green

Department of Geophysics and Geochemistry, Australian National University, P.O. Box 4, Canberra City, A.C.T. 2601, Australia

EXPANDED ABSTRACT

Experimental studies of the mineralogy of pyrolite and the melting relations of various basaltic magmas under high-pressure conditions have been integrated to produce an internally consistent model of source composition, derived liquid compositions and residual mantle compositions. The presence of the low-velocity zone in the upper mantle is attributed to a small (<5 per cent) degree of melting of pyrolite containing approximately 0·1 per cent water. The small liquid fraction present in the low-velocity zone is highly undersaturated olivine nephelinite or olivine melilite nephelinite. Other magma types of direct upper-mantle derivation may be assigned to a petrogenetic grid expressing the depth (pressure) of magma segregation, degree of partial melting of the pyrolite source, water content and approximate temperature of the magma. The high-Al_2O_3 olivine tholeiites which are well developed at oceanic ridges are products of high degrees of melting (~20 per cent) and magma segregation at shallow (20-40 km) depths. Quartz tholeiite magmas are derivative magmas produced from parental olivine tholeiites by low pressure crystallization and extraction of olivine. Rarely, such magmas may be primary if magma segregation from a peridotite source occurs at depths <10 km.

Volcanic activity of explosive, highly-undersaturated magma type occurs when tectonic processes directly tap the low-velocity zone. Magmas of alkali basalt and olivine tholeiite type are produced by higher degrees of melting and at shallower depths of magma segregation. These magmas result from large-scale diapiric upwelling of pyrolite from the low-velocity zone and this process is characteristic of regions of convective movements within the upper mantle. The magmatic characteristics and evolution of continental and oceanic rift systems and of the Hawaiian volcanic province can be interpreted in relation to the depths and conditions of magma genesis. If this interpretation is correct, then magma characteristics may be used to infer information on the dynamics of the mantle beneath volcanic provinces.

The petrogenetic aspects of basaltic volcanism can be understood within the plate-tectonic models for rift systems and island chains, e.g. Hawaii. Within *island arc regions* the development of tensional features in the lithosphere immediately behind the arcs may provide opportunity for basaltic volcanism from upwelling of peridotite within the low-velocity zone. If the oceanic crust is converted to eclogite and sinks deep into the upper mantle, then this material provides a source for calc-alkali andesitic magmas by partial melting of eclogite and garnet amphibolite mineral assemblages. The release of water by dehydration of greenschists

[1] This is an expanded abstract for the paper given at the Twelfth Pacific Science Congress, as this paper was essentially the same as that prepared for the Upper-Mantle Symposium at the I.U.G.G. Meeting in Moscow (Aug. 1971). The latter paper has been published with the title Magmatic Activity as the Major Process in Chemical Evolution of the Earth's Crust and Mantle, *Tectonophysics*, **13,** 47-71, 1972.

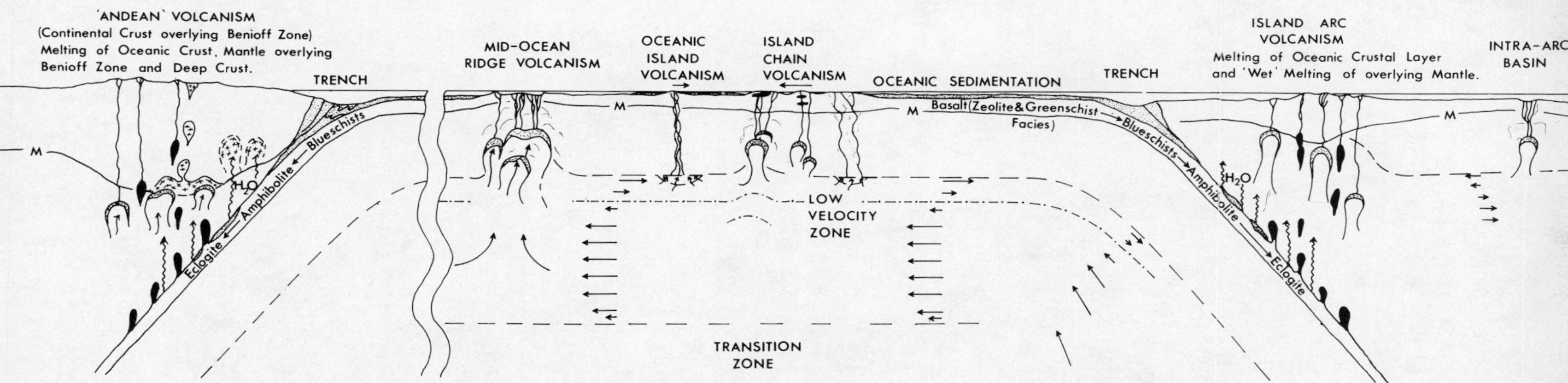

Fig. 1 Schematic diagram illustrating the petrogenetic processes of significance in the plate-tectonics hypothesis. The initial formation and later local modification by volcanism and sedimentation of the basaltic oceanic crust is shown. Two examples of downgoing lithospheric slabs, one in the island arc situation, one at a continent/ocean boundary are also illustrated, and the complexity of magma genesis beneath such regions is emphasized. Patterned areas capping peridotite diapirs indicate segregation of basaltic magmas, black areas rising from the Benioff zone indicate andesitic or dacitic magmas of the calcalkaline suite, and areas with patterns of crosses indicate deep crustal melting and rhyolitic or granitic (*s.l.*) intrusions. Stippling indicates sediment or metamorphosed sedimentary cover.

and amphibolites in the downgoing slab may produce migmatization in near-surface rocks of the 'hanging-wall' to the sinking lithospheric plate, if such rocks are of crustal type (i.e. Andean-type crustal thicknesses). Dehydration at deeper levels (amphibolite→eclogite) and migration of water into overlying peridotite in regions of thin continental crust may cause melting in the peridotite leading to development of hydrous tholeiitic magmas and their emplacement in essentially synchronous and close spatial relationship with calc-alkali andesites. There will be a strong tendency for such hydrous tholeiite magmas to partially crystallize and fractionate as they approach the surface, leading to derivative magmas (? island arc tholeiite series). The island arc regions are thus characterized by complexity in magma genesis with the likelihood that magmas may originally derive from three contrasted source rocks: (1) peridotite of the lithosphere overlying the downgoing slab; (2) crustal rocks in regions of thick crust overlying a downgoing slab; and (3) basaltic volcanics and intermixed oceanic sediments forming the upper part of the downgoing slab. Further complexity is added by opportunity for crystal fractionation, magma mixing, or contamination by passage through thick continental crust.

A diagrammatic summary of the main types of magmatic activity and their dynamic relation to the concepts of plate tectonics is given in Fig. 1.

Petrochemistry of Volcanic Rocks in the Kuril Island Arc with some Generalizations on Volcanism

G. S. Gorshkov

Institute for Earth Physics, Academy of Sciences of the U.S.S.R., B. Gzuzinskaya 10, Moscow D-242, U.S.S.R.

ABSTRACT

Using the Kuril Arc as a leading example, it can be shown that the petrochemistry of the volcanic rocks of that island chain appears to be independent of crustal character. From this, the idea of mantle-feeding of volcanoes is further stressed. The nature of volcanic products, it seems, is dependent on subcrustal processes, including composition and temperature as well as depth of the upper mantle. This accords with the general notion of the generation of primary basalts in mid-oceanic ridges and the creation of calcalkaline magmas from submerging slabs of eclogitic crust in the areas of island arcs. Volcanism is the source of both oceanic and continental crust.

The Kuril Arc has been studied quite thoroughly in both its volcanological and geophysical aspects. Some of the regularities detected here may have a significance for other island arcs also.

The Kuril chain belongs to the system of island arcs that borders the continent of Asia on the east; it extends from the south of Kamchatka to the island of Hokkaido, separating the marginal Sea of Okhotsk from the Pacific Ocean.

The islands of the Kuril Arc are divided into two chains, the Lesser Kurils and the Greater Kurils. The non-volcanic Lesser Kuril chain extends north-eastward of Hokkaido for 105 km and then becomes the submarine Vitiaz Ridge; its islands are composed of volcanic and sedimentary rocks of Upper Cretaceous age. The Greater Kuril chain is volcanic and extends for 1,150 km; its basement is composed of Tertiary volcanic-sedimentary rocks (the oldest are late Oligocene-early Miocene). According to details of the topography and petrochemistry, it is possible to separate a main volcanic zone, with most of the islands and sub-aerial volcanoes, from a western zone, with seven small islands and most of the submarine volcanoes. In the Kurils there are at least eighty-five separate Quaternary volcanoes and volcanic groups, of which sixty have erupted during the Holocene and thirty-seven since the eighteenth century. There are more than 100 undersea volcanoes, but only two submarine eruptions are known.

South-east of the Kuril chain lies the Kuril-Kamchatka Trench, with its deepest point of 10,542 m. The distance between the axis of the trench and the volcanic arc varies from 180 km in the middle part of the chain, to 200-20 km near the northern islands.

The Kuril region is one of the most seismic regions of the U.S.S.R. The earthquake foci form a clearly-defined focal zone dipping beneath the islands. Beneath the volcanoes the focal zone extends to a depth of 150-180 km. The motions at the earthquake foci indicate movements of the upthrust type, in which the continental part moves up over the oceanic part (or the oceanic moves under the continental); the area of deep-sea trench is subjected to subsidence.

The structure of the crust along the strike is not homogeneous: in the north Kurils the crust is of a continental type; 'suboceanic', amounting to oceanic crust, is typical for the central Kurils; at the south Kurils the crust is 'subcontinental' (*The Structure of the Earth's Crust* . . ., 1964).

The upper mantle structure essentially differs from both typical oceanic and continental regions: from the base of the crust to a depth of 70-80 km, longitudinal wave velocity remains constant at 7·7 km/s (instead of the 'normal' 8·1 km/s). It is as if the low-velocity layer in the mantle has 'floated' from depth to the crust boundary. At the same time, at depths of 60-110 km, and especially clearly at 80-90 km, absorption of transverse seismic wave energy strongly increases. The specific character of the upper parts of the mantle remains along the whole of the arc, irrespective of the difference in the crust structure above.

Judging by gravity anomalies, the density of the mantle beneath the Kurils is decreased by 0·11 g/cm^3; an increase in mantle density coincides with the earthquake focal zone and amounts to 0·06 g/cm^3 (Livshits 1965).

The heat flow at the Kurils themselves was not measured, but to the east of the islands it is only 1·0 HFU, and to the west—in the Sea of Okhotsk—it is up to 2·5 HFU.

PETROCHEMICAL DATA

The lavas of the volcanoes of the Kuril islands are rather varied in their petrographic relationship: all varieties from basic basalts to acid liparites can be found there. Pyroxene andesites are the most widespread; basalts and basaltic-andesites are also common. Dacites and acid andesites are found more rarely as lavas, but vast deposits of pumice are often composed of these rock types. Liparites are very rare and are found only as pumice deposits.

Petrochemical analysis was made according to A. N. Zavaritsky's method (1955) on the basis of 209 selected analyses from all the islands of the Kuril chain.

It was found that the rocks from the north and central Kuril islands actually belong to the same type; the lavas from south Kuril differ slightly. A very clear lateral inhomogeneity is detected, and lavas of the western zone have a more alkaline character, though they belong still to the calcalkaline type.

An extremely important factor is that the petrochemistry of the volcanic rocks does not depend on thickness and even on the type of the crust. Thus, moving from north to south from the Kronotsky region in the north of Kamchatka to Simushir island on the Kuril islands we shall pass over from purely continental crust, through subcontinental, to an actually oceanic zone. In petrochemical respects, however, along the whole distance of 1,200 km, volcanic rocks of the continental crust in Kamchatka do not differ from those of the oceanic crust of Simushir island (Fig. 1).

If we move eastward by a dozen kilometres and analyse the lavas of volcanoes stretching along 1,500 km from the central Kamchatka depression to the Kuril island of Broughton, we observe that in comparison with the eastern zone, the rocks become somewhat more alkaline, but remain similar, over the whole distance of 1,500 km. Thus, even a small displacement across the strike of the arc reveals a noticeable variation of rock chemistry within one and the same type of the crust. While moving along the strike the petrochemistry of the rocks does not vary essentially even over different types of the crust.

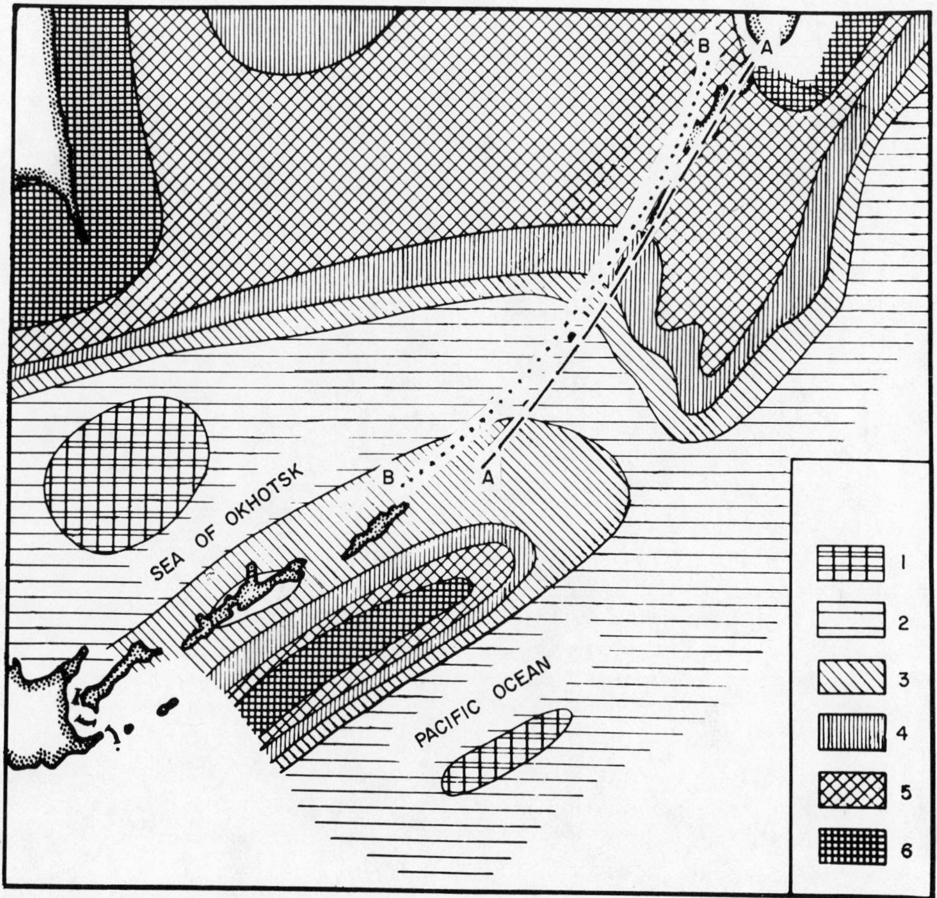

Fig. 1 Thickness of consolidated crust in the area of the Kuril Islands and different alkalinity of volcanic rocks. 1, 5 km; 2, 5-10 km; 3, 10-15 km; 4, 15-20 km; 5, 20-25 km; 6, 25-30 km; A-A, calcalkaline rocks; B-B, more alkaline rocks.

SOME GENERAL CONSIDERATIONS

An analysis of volcanic rock petrochemistry shows that volcanism is associated with sub-crustal areas of the earth and that, as a rule, the crust does not essentially affect lava composition.

The idea of mantle-feeding of volcanoes was expressed 15 years ago (Gorshkov 1956) on the basis of seismic observations in Kamchatka. Since then the idea has developed on the basis of comparison of geophysical and petrochemical data (Gorshkov 1958 to 1970). Even in the earlier papers, the main ideas were advanced: (1) magmatic chambers (those of calcalkaline volcanism included) are within the limits of the upper mantle; the low-velocity layer in the mantle is considered to be the most favourable for melting; (2) the composition and structure of the upper mantle under oceans, continents, island arcs and mid-oceanic ridges are different; these differences are displayed in the existence of two main classes of rocks—continental and oceanic; (3) volcanism is a 'through-crust' process, the role of crustal substance assimilation being very limited; and (4) volcanism is a reflection of processes in the upper mantle and therefore can be considered as an indicator of composition and state of the upper mantle.

For the time being, the hypothesis of mantle-feeding volcanoes is generally accepted.

The author has examined all the available geophysical data and chemical analysis of lavas from the most volcanic areas of the Pacific Ocean and its environs (Gorshkov 1967, 1970). As a result, a conclusion can be drawn that the specific relations of volcanicity to geophysical fields established in the Kuril islands, are common for all the island arcs of the Pacific volcanic rim.

It has been stated that there are two classes of volcanic rocks, distinguished by the slopes of their variational curves relative to the co-ordinate axes in the Zavaritsky system (Fig. 2). The rocks of mid-oceanic ridges, island arcs and intra-continental volcanoes belong to the continental class; lavas of intraoceanic volcanoes to the oceanic class. The slope of the oceanic variation curves indicates a more rapid rate of increase in alkalinity during differentiation in comparison with the rocks of the continental class. Initial magmas of continental and oceanic classes, similar in their chemical composition, reveal very different series of differentiation. For continental tholeiite basalt the following rocks will be derivative: basaltic andesite—andesite—dacite—rhyolite; while for oceanic tholeiite basalt they are as follows: olivine basalt—hawaiite—trachyte. In their turn, similar alkaline rocks of the continental and oceanic classes are the products of quite various series of differentiation. Thus, trachy-basalt magma will be initial for the continental trachyte, while normal olivine basalt magma will be initial for oceanic trachyte. I think these differences are of fundamental value, though they are underestimated by most researchers.

During recent years (with particular relevance to the experiments of Ringwood and D. Green), a tendency has grown to consider the whole diversity of magmas as a function of their generation depth (pressure) only. The existence of two classes of volcanic rocks with extremely various differentiation trends suggests that the composition of parent rocks plays an essential role, along with the depth of magma formation and that of fractionation. It is believed that under oceans and continents the mantle composition differs and this gives rise to a systematic difference of melted magmas. This difference is distinctly displayed later during surface crystal fractionation.

The results of deep-sea drilling in the Atlantic (Maxwell *et al.* 1970) and in the

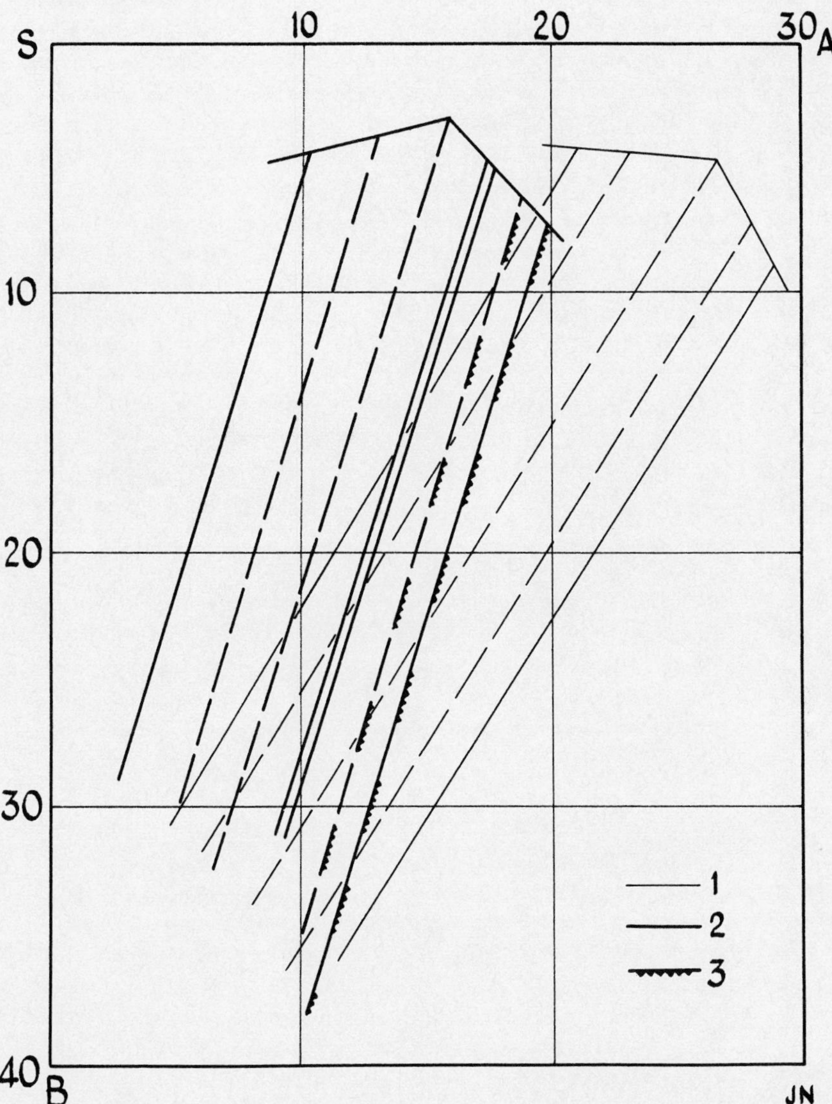

Fig. 2 Sketch showing disposition of the variation curves for the oceanic and continental classes of rocks in the Zavaritsky system: 1, oceanic class of rocks; 2, calcalkaline rocks of the continental class; 3, alkaline rocks of the continental class.

Pacific Oceans (Fisher *et al.* 1971) tend to confirm the sea-floor spreading hypothesis. Some essential details have not yet been explained, for instance: the system of parallel Mariana and Philippine Arcs, reverse focal-plane dip in certain arcs of the South-west Pacific, the meeting of some arcs at right angles and so on. But on the global scale, this hypothesis solves the problems of volcanism quite sufficiently, including the Kuril islands.

The reason of lateral alkalinity variation in island arcs is still not quite clear. Green and Ringwood (1969) believe that partial melting of basalt and amphibolite and, on the lower level, of eclogite, in the descending slab of the oceanic crust gives magma of different alkalinity at different levels of generation.

In connection with this hypothesis it should be pointed out that volcanoes appear only at a considerable distance from the deep-sea trench (that is, from the beginning of submergence). The depth of the focal surface under volcanoes reaches 150-200 km, while the width of volcanic chains is not great (a dozen or so kilometres). Thus, melting must take place only in a narrow interval of depths in the eclogite zone. Experiments for such depth intervals have not been made as yet and it is still uncertain if a small pressure change can lead to noticeable change in alkalinity of melted silicate liquid. Probably, the separation proper of magmas takes place essentially higher—in the depth interval which is estimated for magmatic chambers by seismic methods of location (40-80 km). It is quite possible that melting of magmas or their fractionation is limited to a certain geo-isotherm (or interval of isotherms) which merges smoothly from the ocean toward the continent. At the same time high heat flow over the rear part of island arcs indicates some kind of active deep process besides the passive submerging of the oceanic crust.

Taking into consideration the sum of these statements, the hypothesis of generation of primary basalts in mid-oceanic ridges and subsequent partial melting of calc-alkaline magmas in island arcs of a submerging slab of eclogitic crust is quite acceptable.

One can depict in the following generalizations the essential regularity of development of volcanism (Fig. 3).

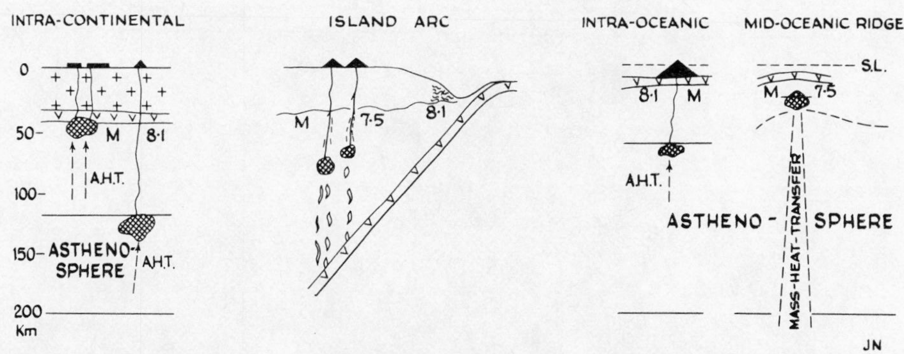

Fig. 3 Sketch of volcanism for different global conditions. M, Moho discontinuity; A.H.T., additional heat transfer. See text for details.

1. An intensive heat supply flows in the mid-oceanic ridges and, in all probability, is marked by the emergence of substance from deeper parts of the mantle (obviously from near the contact with the core). Magma is generated at very high levels (of the order of 15-20 km), and high-alumina tholeiites and even quartz tholeiites (Iceland) are formed. It is here that oceanic crust is created.

2. Generation of calcalkaline magmas of island arcs from eclogites in the submerging slab of the oceanic crust formed in mid-oceanic ridges is quite possible. This correlates well with the fact that mid-oceanic ridge and island-arc rocks belong to the continental class. But it is in the zone of island arcs that processes of continental crust formation take place.

It is quite probable that besides the passive submergence and melting of oceanic crust some other active processes occur in the upper mantle of areas of the Pacific rim.

3. The source of volcanism in the tectonically quiet areas of oceanic platforms is the low-velocity layer where material is in a state close to melting or is even already partially melted. In regions of local, yet relatively inconsiderable, heating in the upper parts of the low-velocity layer (60-70 km for the ocean) conditions occur suitable for magma fusion and separation. Under these conditions, olivine tholeiites are formed and, by the end of the volcanic cycle (evidently, with some increase of the depth of generation or fractionation), also alkaline olivine magmas (probably with geo-isotherm decrease). On some islands (Tahiti, Cook) strongly alkaline basalts are known, whereas tholeiites are absent or covered by later alkaline lavas. In this case, we may suppose that in the layer of oceanic asthenosphere, the levels of magma generation are deeper.

In many cases, evidently, magmatic chambers of intraoceanic volcanoes are located in that layer of the asthenosphere which moves together with lithosphere.

4. Regions of intracontinental volcanism are the most varied but have been studied least of all. In relatively quiet tectonically regions (outside the rift zones), with a small increase of heat supply, magma generation occurs, as in the field of oceanic platforms, near the roof of the low-velocity layer (120-140 km for continental regions). Greater depths are responsible for magma generation of higher alkalinity.

In the Baikal rift zone, the thickness of the crust is decreased, the heat flow increased and the low-velocity layer is on a higher level. Evidently magma generation occurs at higher levels but still at the depths responsible for melting of alkaline basalts, i.e. within the depth interval from 35-70 km.

Traps are of tholeiite or weakly-alkaline lavas with chemical character of the continental class. Perhaps traps are formed in the highest horizons of the mantle, or lower horizons of the crust, at the expense of eclogites under conditions of a considerable regional increase of heat flow.

5. Heat and mass transfer in the upper mantle is the reason for volcanic activity. Primary heat sources may be very deep and may be connected, in particular, with gravitational differentiation on the core-mantle interface (Artyushkov 1970). The zones of mass-heat transfer have, as a rule, a linear character which causes linear orientation of the greatest part of volcanic zones.

The upper mantle composition under oceans and continents differ, respectively, and it is this which gives rise to the existence of two classes of volcanic rocks. This difference is caused by the advective uplift of substance from deeper parts of the mantle in the region of mid-oceanic ridges. Here oceanic crust is formed, although, paradoxically, 'oceanic crust', from the petrochemical standpoint, refers to the continental class of rocks. The oceanic class of volcanic rocks is limited only to intra-oceanic islands. Transformation of the oceanic crust into continental crust occurs in the area of island arcs.

Volcanism is the source of both oceanic and continental crust.

REFERENCES

Artyushkov, E. A. 1970. Density differentiation on the core-mantle interface and gravity convection. *Phys. Earth Planet. Interiors*, **2,** 318-25.

Fedotov, S. A. 1965. Upper mantle properties of the southern part of Kurile Island arc according to detailed seismological data. *Tectonophysics*, **2** (2-3), 219-25.

Fischer, A. G. *et al.* 1971. Initial reports of the Deep Sea Drilling Program. *U.S. Government Printing Office*, **6,** 1329 pp. Washington.

Gorshkov, G. S. 1956. On the depth of magmatic hearth of Klyuchevskoy Volcano. *Dokl. Akad. Nauk SSSR*, **106** (4), 703-5 (in Russian).

——— 1958. On some theoretical problems of volcanology. *Bull. volcan.* (ser. 2), **19,** 103-13.

——— 1960. Quaternary volcanism and petrochemistry of recent lavas in the Kurile Island. In *Petrographic Provinces, Igneous and Metamorphic Rocks, Intern. Geol. Congr., XXI Session, Reports of Soviet Geologists, Problem 13*, 334-40; *Acad. Sci. U.S.S.R., Moscow* (in Russian with English summary).

——— 1962. Petrochemical features of volcanism in relation to the types of the Earth's crust. In *Crust of the Pacific Basin* (Eds G. A. Macdonald and H. Kuno), *Am. Geophys. Un., Geophys. Monogr.* **6,** 110-15.

——— 1963. Global characteristics of the petrochemistry of volcanic rocks and the main structures of the Earth. In *Petrochemical Characteristics of Young Volcanism*, 5-16 (in Russian).

——— 1965. On the relation of volcanism and the upper mantle. *Bull. volcan.* **28,** 159-67.

——— 1967. *Volcanism of the Kurile Island Arc.* Nauka Publ., Moscow, 287 pp. (in Russian).

——— 1969*a*. Geophysics and petrochemistry of andesite volcanism of the Circum-Pacific belt. In *Proceedings of the Andesite Conference* (Ed. A. R. McBirney), *Bull. Ore. St. Dep. Geol. miner. Ind.* **65,** 91-8.

——— 1969*b*. Intraoceanic islands, East Pacific Ridge, and island arcs: volcanism and upper mantle. *Tectonophysics*, **8,** 213-21.

——— 1969*c*. Two types of alkaline rocks—two types of upper mantle. *Bull. volcan.* **33** (4), 1186-98.

——— 1970. *Volcanism and the Upper Mantle, Investigations in the Kurile Island Arc.* XV, 385 pp. Plenum Press, N.Y.

——— 1972. Progress and problems in volcanology. *Tectonophysics*, **13** (1-4), 123-40.

Green, D. H. 1970. A review of experimental evidence on the origin of basaltic and nephelinitic magmas. *Phys. Earth Planet. Interiors*, **3,** 221-35.

Green, D. H. & Ringwood, A. E. 1967. The genesis of basaltic magmas. *Contr. Mineral. Petrol.* **15** (2), 103-90.

Green, T. H. & Ringwood, A. E. 1969. High pressure experimental studies on the origin of andesites. In *Proceedings of the Andesite Conference* (Ed. A. R. McBirney), *Bull. Ore. St. Dep. Geol. miner. Ind.* **65,** 21-32.

Livshits, M. Kh. 1965. On the problem of the physical make-up of the deep-seated material of the Earth's crust and upper mantle in the Kurile zone of the Pacific ring. *Geol. i Geofiz.* **1.**

Maxwell, A. E. *et al.* 1970. Deep sea drilling in the South Atlantic. *Science,* **168** (3935), 1047-59.

Structure of the Earth's Crust in the Transition Region from the Asiatic Continent to the Pacific Ocean. Nauka Publ., Moscow, 308 pp. (in Russian) 1964.

Zavaritsky, A. N. 1955. *Igneous Rocks.* Nauka Publ., Moscow (in Russian).

Tertiary Orogenesis and High-Pressure Metamorphism in New Caledonia

R. N. Brothers

Geology Department, Auckland University, Auckland, New Zealand

ABSTRACT

As judged from stratigraphic evidence, Tertiary orogenesis in New Caledonia may have commenced as early as late Eocene, but tectonic activity reached a climax in the late Oligocene and Lower Miocene strata characteristically are not deformed or metamorphosed. A series of major Tertiary thrust plates, involving ultramafic rocks, can be divided distinctly into two groups. *In the south* of the island a large ultramafic sheet has been thrust at a low angle from east to west over Eocene sediments without any attendant high-pressure metamorphism. *In the north,* peridotites and basalts occupy a well-defined tectonic line (the sillon) along the west coast and appear to have steep contacts with adjacent Permian-Eocene strata. High-pressure metamorphism in this northern sector has been K/Ar dated at 21-38 m.y. and the westward limit of the metamorphic belt has been defined by the first appearance of lawsonite. This 'lawsonite line' forms a westward-facing arc which transects Eocene, Cretaceous and Mesozoic strata; in the latter basement rocks the Tertiary high-pressure mineralogy is superposed on low-grade greenschist assemblages which belong to a Late Jurassic metamorphic event. The lawsonite line has no genetic relationship to the large ultramafic massifs of the west coast sillon, but its position is marked by a series of thin intrusive serpentinites which appear to define schuppen with inferred west-to-east sense of overthrusting.

Multiple Correlation Between Composition of Volcanic Rocks and Depth of Earthquake Foci

Arata Sugimura

Geological Institute, Faculty of Science, University of Tokyo, Hongo, Tokyo 113, Japan

ABSTRACT

The correlation between the chemical composition of lavas and depths to the seismic zone has been studied quantitatively for the East Japan volcanic belt. The correlation between the normative composition and the depth is as follows: (1) The correlation coefficient increases with the number of combined minerals used, but when more than four minerals are considered the increase is small. (2) In the case of four normative minerals, the maximum coefficient is 0·714 for the whole group of volcanic rocks, 0·862 for basaltic rocks, 0·684 for andesitic rocks, and 0·574 for dacites and rhyolites. The basaltic rocks thus show the highest correlation with depths of earthquake foci. (3) The combinations of minerals that give the maximum coefficients for basaltic rocks are *fa* in the case of one mineral; *fa* and *ab* in the case of two; *fa*, *ab*, and *wo* in the case of three; *fa*, *ab*, *wo*, and *fs* in the case of four; and *fa*, *fs*, *Q*, *C*, and *an* in the case of five minerals. It seems that the presence and amount of olivine contribute much to the correlation with depths.

As to the origin of island-arc volcanic rocks, two important differences from current opinion are featured. One is that andesites may be crystallization differentiates from primary basaltic magmas. A primary magma is defined as an initial liquid of a closed system which ascends from above the upper limit of the partially molten zone under an island arc. The other point is that this partially molten zone may extend well above the upper surface of the downgoing slab of oceanic lithosphere. No large part of the slab need be molten. This means that the ultimate origin of island-arc volcanic rocks would be in the asthenosphere under the continental lithosphere but above the greater part of the downgoing slab.

INTRODUCTION

The relationship between island-arc volcanism and intermediate-depth earthquakes is one of the most important features of island arc tectonics. Almost all the active volcanic belts are underlain by mantle earthquake zones, the foci commonly defining a plane that dips away from the trenches. The plane may be called the seismic plane.

The silica content of parent magmas, from which the volcanoes in Japan are derived, decreases in a regular way with increasing depth of the seismic plane beneath the volcanoes, and the alkali content increases in the same way (Kuno 1956, 1959; Sugimura 1958, 1960; Katsui 1959, 1961).

This paper consists of two parts: one gives the results of calculations on the correlation between chemistry of volcanoes and depths of earthquake foci based on data from the Japanese Islands, and the other discusses the depth of generation of parent magmas.

CORRELATION

The Quaternary basaltic rocks in Japan and its environs show a tendency to increase in SiO_2 content and decrease in the contents of Na_2O and K_2O from the continent toward the island arcs. The maximum values of SiO_2 and the minimum values of Na_2O and K_2O are distributed along the volcanic fronts. The averages of Na_2O and K_2O of mafic volcanic rocks ($SiO_2 \leq 52{\cdot}5\%$) for every volcano are tabulated in terms of four petrographic provinces by Sugimura (1961: Table 1). The depths of deep and intermediate earthquakes under these four provinces differ from each other regularly, the averages being approximately 150 km, 200 km, 300 km and 500 km from trench-side to continent-side, respectively. On the basis of the table referred to above, Fig. 1 was prepared, which is the first diagram to correlate chemical composition with depth in the mantle. Correlation coefficients between K_2O and the depth were obtained by Hatherton & Dickinson (1969).

Fig. 2 illustrates a simple case to explain the multiple correlation coefficient

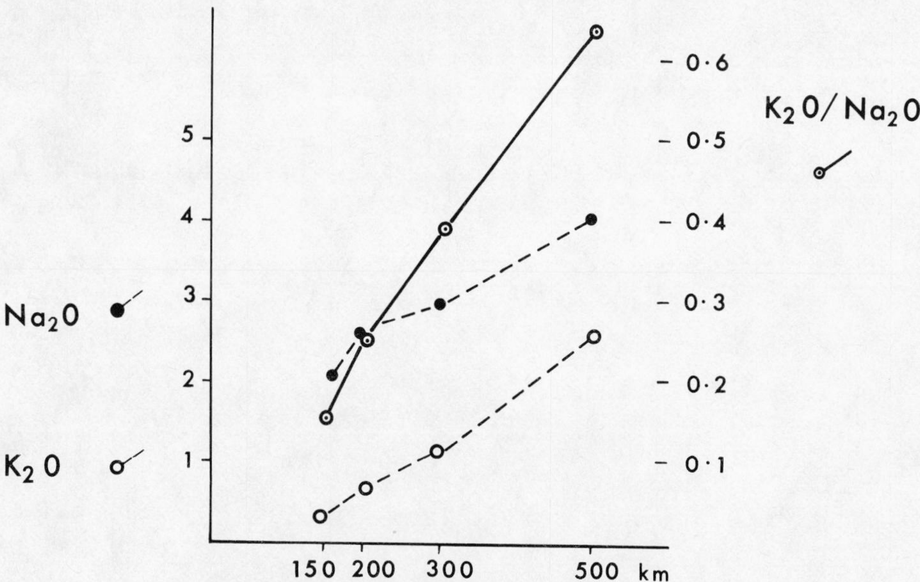

Fig. 1 Alkaline compositions of basalt from volcanoes in Japan and its environs; relationship between weight percentage and depths in km of earthquake foci under the volcanoes. After Sugimura (1961).

described in this paper. The letters z, a and b are independent variables in this figure. If there is a complete linear regression between z and combination of a and b, data points are on the plane drawn on the diagram at the right of Fig. 2. But, if we ignore the b component, the correlation between z and a becomes incomplete, as illustrated in the left-hand diagram of the figure. In general, correlation with one variable z should be better for two variables a and b than for one variable a. This is also the reason why Sugimura (1961) and Dickinson & Hatherton (1967) limited the data of Na_2O and K_2O within some particular range of SiO_2. The idea of increasing the number of variables can be extended to the thirteen major chemical components of rocks; a fourteen-dimensions diagram may be imagined for the extreme case.

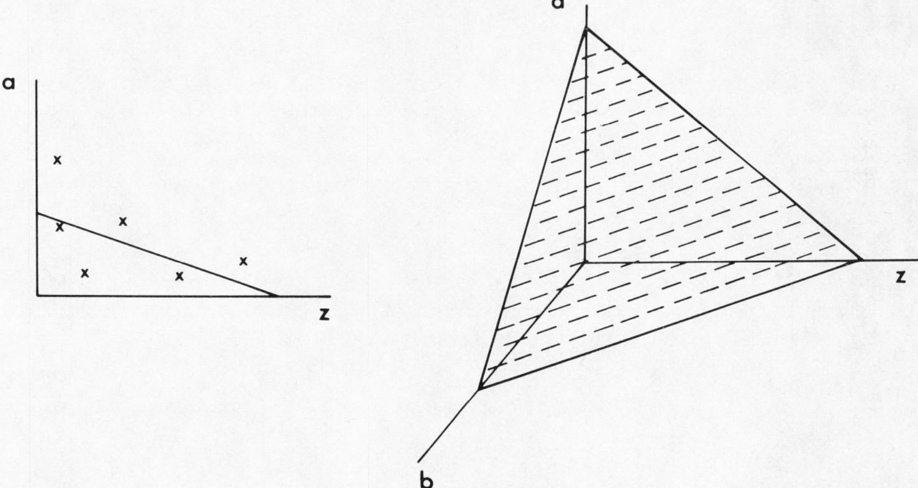

Fig. 2 Multiple correlation is better than single correlation. The crosses are the projected points, from scattered points on the shaded plane, to the a-z plane. The two diagrams show that even when z is completely correlated with a and b (the right diagram, $\rho=1{\cdot}0$), the correlation between a and z is not always complete (the left diagram, $\rho\leq 1{\cdot}0$).

In all cases in the following calculations, we assume a linear regression for simplicity. Correlation coefficient between x and y is

$$\rho_{xy}=\mu_{xy}/\sigma_x\,.\,\sigma_y,$$

where μ is covariance and σ^2 is variance. Multiple correlation coefficient between 1 and others (2, 3, ..., n) is

$$\rho_1=\sqrt{1-R/R_1},$$

where

$$R=\begin{vmatrix} \rho_{11}, \rho_{12}, \ldots, \rho_{1n} \\ \rho_{21}, \rho_{22}, \ldots, \rho_{2n} \\ \vdots \\ \rho_{n1}, \rho_{n2}, \ldots, \rho_{nn} \end{vmatrix}$$

and

$$R_1=\begin{vmatrix} \rho_{22}, \rho_{23}, \ldots, \rho_{2n} \\ \rho_{32}, \rho_{33}, \ldots, \rho_{3n} \\ \vdots \\ \rho_{n2}, \rho_{n3}, \ldots, \rho_{nn} \end{vmatrix}.$$

The data comes from 239 analyses of volcanic rocks in the East Japan volcanic belt—exclusive of the rocks from the Asian continent—selected from the table

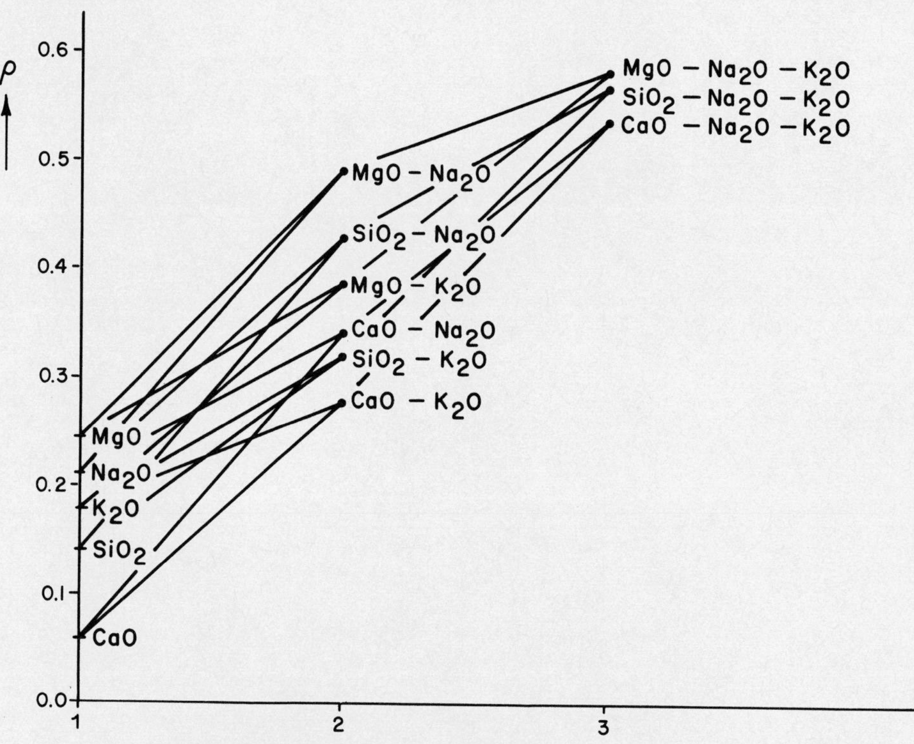

Fig. 3 Correlation coefficient ρ of oxides-composition with depth of earthquake foci. The horizontal axis indicates the number N of combination of oxides. Note that the correlation for some combinations of three oxides is fairly good compared with the one for single oxides. MgO for N=1, MgO and Na_2O for N=2, and MgO, Na_2O, and K_2O for N=3 give the maximum coefficients for each number N of combinations.

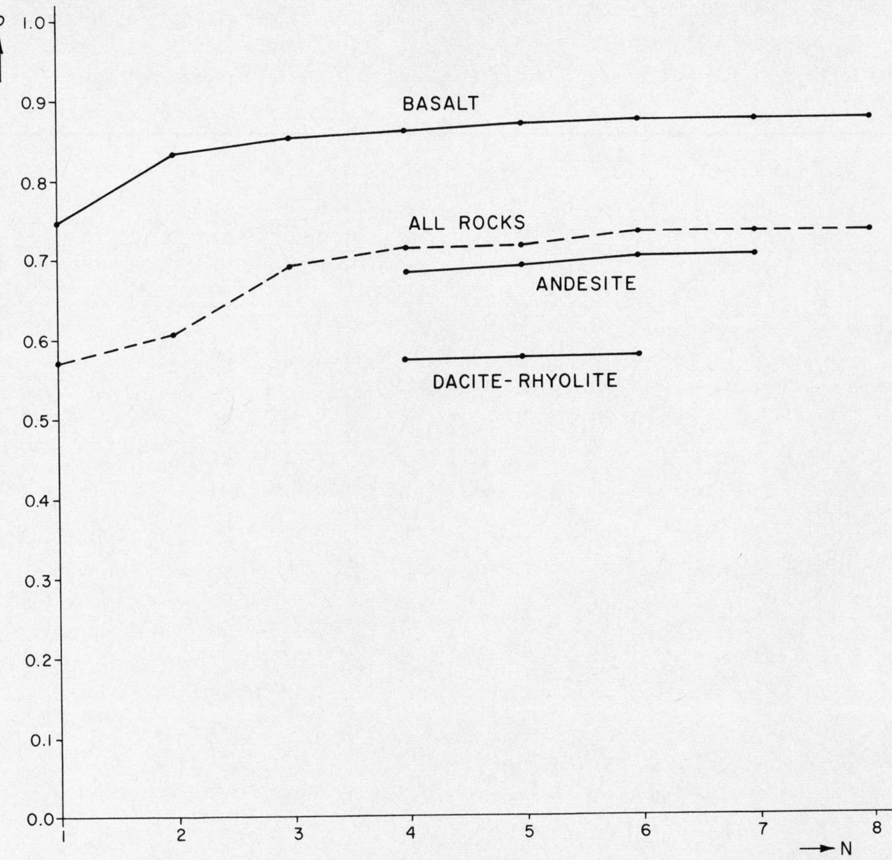

Fig. 4 Correlation coefficient ρ of normative composition with depth of earthquake foci. N is the number of combinations of normative minerals, the names of which are shown by symbols in Table 2 for all rocks, Table 3 for andesitic rocks, and Table 4 for basaltic rocks. Only the maximum coefficients are indicated for each number N of combinations. Basaltic rocks show better correlation with depth of earthquake foci than more acidic rocks.

published by the Geological Survey of Japan (Ono 1962). The depths under the volcanoes to the seismic plane, which connects the centres of distribution of earthquake foci, are from Sugimura (1960). The computer OKITAC 5090 at the University of Tokyo was used for the calculation. The results are shown in Tables 1, 2, 3, and 4 and Figs 3 and 4. Fig. 3 shows only some of the simpler cases and indicates that the coefficient increases with the number N of combination of variables. All combinations up to $N=8$ were dealt with and the maximum coefficients for $N=1$ to 8 are given in Table 1. The combinations of oxides indicating the maximum coefficients are also shown in this table. We can notice that H_2O (+), H_2O (—), TiO_2 and P_2O_5 do not appear here and seem not to relate with the depth z to the seismic zone. The maximum coefficient increases rapidly to $N=3$ and then the increase slows down. The author paid special attention to the combination for $N=3$, that is MgO, Na_2O, and K_2O and obtained a formula for the regression with the depth z (Sugimura 1968).

The second step of this work is to apply this method to the combinations of normative minerals instead of those of oxides. In this case, an eighteen-dimension diagram may be imagined since there are seventeen usual normative minerals. The results are as follows: (1) The maximum coefficient of three components is 0·692 for *fa* (Fe_2SiO_4), *fs* ($FeSiO_3$) and *Q* (SiO_2); (2) the maximum coefficient of four components is 0·714 for *fa*, *fs*, *Q*, and *ab* ($NaAlSi_3O_8$); and so on as tabulated in Table 2. This shows that the amounts of olivine, pyroxene, silica and albite have good correlation with the tectonic depths. The coefficients for the combinations of normative minerals are higher than those for oxides.

Table 1

CORRELATION COEFFICIENTS WITH DEPTH OF EARTHQUAKE FOCI AND COMBINATIONS OF OXIDE COMPONENTS OF ALL VOLCANIC ROCKS

0·246	MgO							
0·490	MgO	Na_2O						
0·583	MgO	Na_2O	K_2O					
0·617	MgO	Na_2O	K_2O	CaO				
0·631	MgO	Na_2O	K_2O	CaO	FeO			
0·635	MgO	Na_2O	K_2O	FeO	SiO_2	Al_2O_3		
0·640	MgO	Na_2O	K_2O	CaO	Al_2O_3	MnO	Fe_2O_3	
0·646	MgO	Na_2O	K_2O	CaO	FeO	SiO_2	MnO	Fe_2O_3

Table 2

CORRELATION COEFFICIENTS WITH DEPTH OF EARTHQUAKE FOCI AND COMBINATIONS OF NORMATIVE COMPONENTS OF ALL VOLCANIC ROCKS

0·572	*fa*							
0·607	*fa*	*fs*						
0·692	*fa*	*fs*	*Q*					
0·714	*fa*	*fs*	*Q*	*ab*				
0·716	*fa*	*fs*	*Q*	*ab*	*C*			
0·732	*fa*	*fs*	*Q*	*ab*	*C*	*or*		
0·732	*fa*	*fs*	*Q*	*ab*	*C*	*or*	*fo*	
0·733	*fa*	*fs*	*Q*	*ab*	*C*	*or*	*fo*	*wo*

Table 3

CORRELATION COEFFICIENTS WITH DEPTH OF EARTHQUAKE FOCI AND COMBINATIONS OF NORMATIVE COMPONENTS OF ANDESITIC ROCKS

0·684	*fo*	*C*	*or*	*ab*				
0·691	*fa*	*C*	*or*	*Q*	*fs*			
0·703	*fa*	*C*	*or*	*Q*	*fs*	*fo*		
0·704	*fa*	*C*	*or*	*Q*	*fs*	*fo*	*wo*	
0·704	*fa*	*C*	*or*	*Q*	*fs*	*ab*	*wo*	*mt*

Table 4

CORRELATION COEFFICIENTS WITH DEPTH OF EARTHQUAKE FOCI AND COMBINATIONS OF NORMATIVE COMPONENTS OF BASALTIC ROCKS

0·746	*fa*							
0·832	*fo*	*ab*						
0·852	*fa*	*ab*	*wo*					
0·862	*fa*	*ab*	*wo*	*fs*				
0·868	*fa*	*fs*	*Q*	*C*	*an*			
0·873	*fa*	*fs*	*Q*	*C*	*an*	*en*		
0·874	*fa*	*fs*	*Q*	*C*	*an*	*en*	*wo*	
0·874	*fa*	*fs*	*Q*	*C*	*an*	*en*	*wo*	*fo*

If the data are confined to andesitic rocks ($53{\cdot}0\% < SiO_2 \leq 63{\cdot}0\%$), we obtain the result given in Table 3. The results for basaltic rocks ($SiO_2 \leq 53{\cdot}0\%$) are given in Table 4. Olivine, pyroxene, plagioclase, and silica in basaltic rocks are more sensitive to the change of depth to the seismic plane. For example, the value is 0·852 for *fa*, *ab*, and *wo* ($CaSiO_3$). Fig. 4 shows the comparison of the maximum correlation coefficients for all rocks, basaltic rocks, andesitic rocks, and dacitic and rhyolitic rocks. There is better correlation of basalts with depth to the seismic plane than is so for the more felsic rocks. This is one of the important results of this work.

DISCUSSION

The high correlation coefficient seems to support the traditional view that the parent magma of the volcanic suite is of basaltic composition. Presumably, andesite and other felsic rocks, as well as the vapour necessary to form andesite magma, may be produced by differentiation and contamination of the parent basaltic magma.

Recent detailed studies of geodetic and petrologic features of Kilauea Volcano in Hawaii show that only some of the new magma is erupted at the surface; almost the same quantity as the erupted lava must remain underground and contribute towards the uplifting of the volcano.

We calculated the volumes of Japanese volcanoes, using a model of double cones, in which the lower cone is the basement of the volcano (Sugimura *et al.* 1963). The elevation difference of the tops of the upper and lower cones, which we called the thickness *T* in calculation, is almost one-half of the elevation of the volcano above its foot. It would imply that only one-half of the ascending magma was erupted at the surface if the lower cone was formed by the uplift of the basement, as envisaged in the Hawaiian study.

A large amount of andesite produced by differentiation of basaltic magma requires that almost the same amount of ultramafic differentiates remains under the surface.

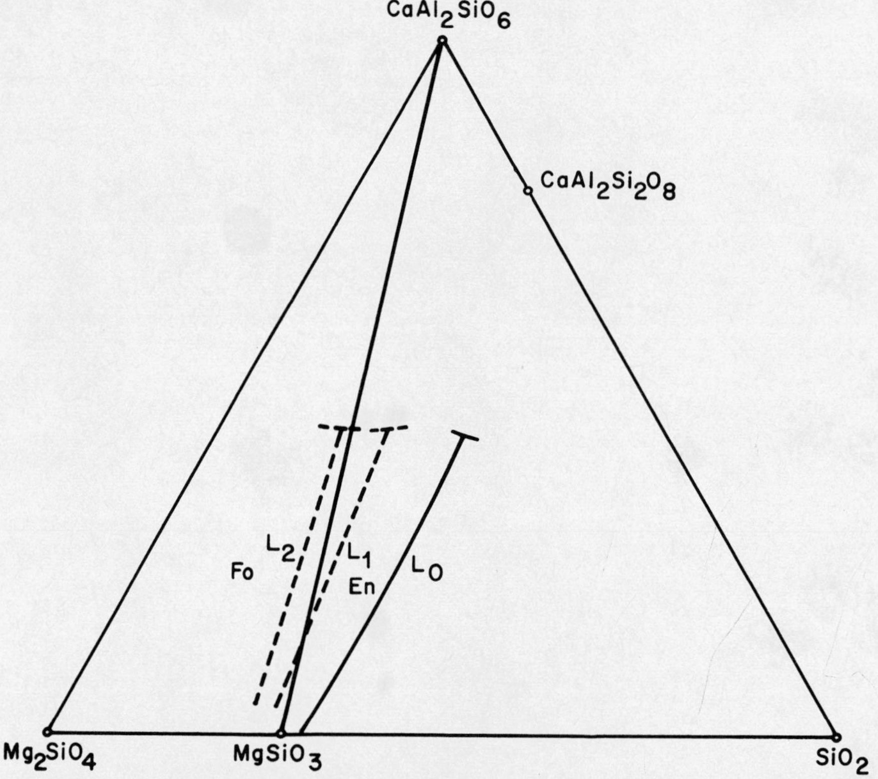

Fig. 5 Forsterite (Fo) and enstatite (En) liquidus boundary at different pressures in the system Mg_2SiO_4—$CaAl_2SiO_6$—SiO_2. Solid curve L_0 is at 1 atm. Dashed curves L_1 and L_2 are at pressures near 20 kb and 30 kb respectively. The initial melt tends to be rich in Si (corresponding to *Q* molecule) at lower pressure and rich in Mg (corresponding to *fo* molecule) at higher pressure. After Kushiro (1965).

The andesite as the product of fractional differentiation seems to be quantitatively reasonable.

The combination of normative minerals highly correlated with the depth to the seismic zone seems to be consistent with the result of Kushiro's (1965) dry experiment (Fig. 5). The initial melt may shift with pressure towards a composition with less silica and more forsterite.

The multiple correlation results given, as well as the experiment, shows that tholeiitic magma would be a partial melt at a shallower level and the alkaline basaltic or shoshonitic magma would be from a deeper level. But it is only qualitatively established, because these pressure values are about one-third of those at the respective depths to the seismic plane.

This suggests that the composition of the melt would be settled at the level of one-third of the depth to the seismic plane. The author calls this level the critical depth; it increases towards the continent or the side away from the trench.

The critical depth (Fig. 6) would be on the upper surface of the partially molten zone under an island arc, which can be detected as a low *Q* (high absorption) and low *V* zone by absorption of seismic waves (Utsu 1966, 1971) and also can be inferred to exist by geothermal calculations (for example those of Hasebe *et al.* 1970). The view of

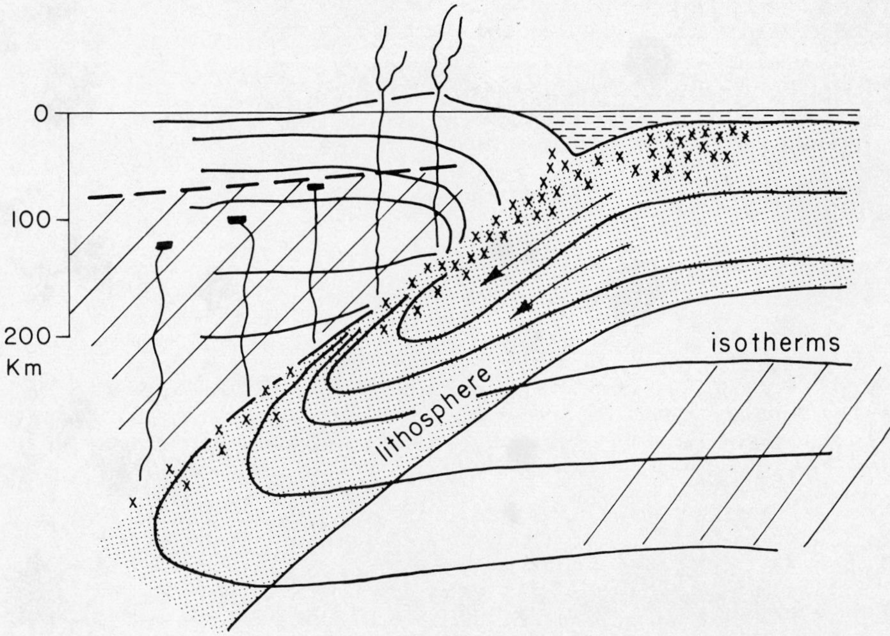

Fig. 6 Proprosed thermal structure under active island arcs. Oblique lines indicate a probable partially-molten zone. A dashed line indicates the critical depth for ascending magma, where its chemical composition would be settled. After Uyeda and Sugimura (1968).

Utsu (1971) is that the lower surface of the low Q zone should be above the seismic plane with a respectable gap to high Q and high V. This point is of importance in the following opinion of the author on the ascent of magma.

In Fig. 7, *d* indicates depth; *T* identifies temperature. This figure shows the change of temperature of rock and magma with depth under the volcanic front. Slab means the downgoing oceanic lithosphere. The curve for rock is based on the calculation of Hasebe *et al.* (1970, Fig. 8). The part where the curve for rock coincides with the one for magma represents the partially molten zone. *C* is the critical depth on the upper surface of the partially molten zone. Above the critical depth, magma would ascend

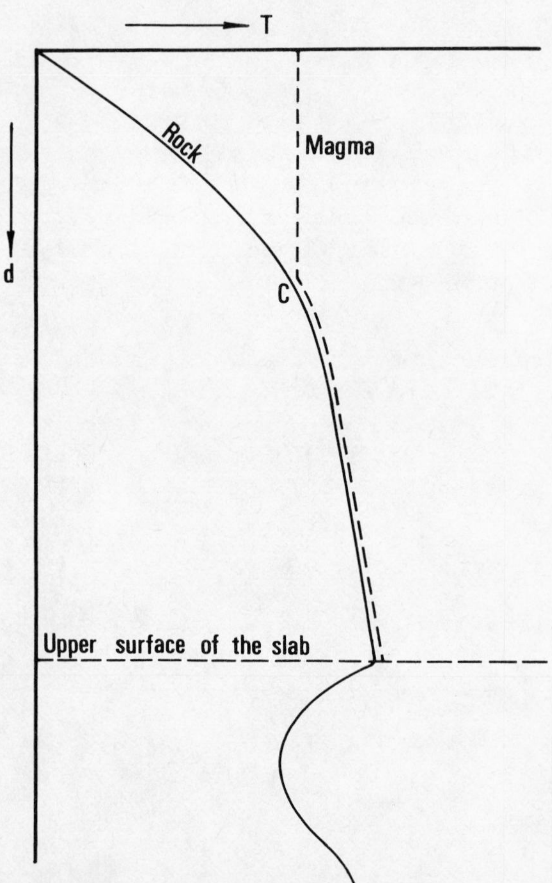

Fig. 7 Proposed change of temperature with depth under the volcanic arc. The slab means the underthrusting oceanic lithosphere, in which the temperature is low and no magma is generated. The range where the temperature of rock is almost the same as that of magma is the partially-molten zone. Within this zone, the magma would be a chemically-open system to the rock. The top of the zone indicates the critical depth, where the chemical composition of parent magma is fixed.

along conduits or fissures and cause some earthquakes, the lower limit of which should be 30 km-50 km for tholeiitic magma and about 100 km for alkaline basaltic magma. This does not contradict the seismological observations. Magma above the critical depth may be regarded as chemically almost closed to the wall rocks. Beneath the critical depth, the difference of temperature between magma and rock would be very small and there may occur zone melting as well as penetrative viscous convection. Earthquakes should be unlikely to occur within this partially molten zone, a view supported by the fact that no focus has been found in this zone (Wadati & Takahashi 1965). If partial zone melting takes place, the magma there is not chemically closed but is an open system to the upper mantle (Kushiro 1968).

Thus, the critical depth would determine the composition of the last state of equilibrium of the liquid. This depth may be about one-third of the distance to the upper surface of the slab. The author would like to define a parent magma as an initial liquid operating as a closed system against the wall rocks. The liquid beneath the critical depth changes in composition under the strong influence of the wall rocks and the composition would be near the invariant point of the phase diagram for the corresponding pressure. The liquid above the critical depth, however, changes in composition mainly by fractional crystallization. This view would be consistent quantitatively with the dry experiment, seismic and thermal studies and chemical variation of volcanic rocks across island arcs.

ACKNOWLEDGEMENTS

This work was begun at the suggestion of S. Banno and A. Poldervaart in 1964. A part of it has been published in a paper by the author in 1968, the manuscript of which was written in 1964 and revised in 1965. The first half ('Correlation') of this present paper was presented before the annual meeting of the Geological Society of Japan held in Nagoya in October of 1967 and before the spring meeting of the Volcanological Society of Japan held in Tokyo in May of 1968, but at both meetings was given orally in Japanese without pre-print or post-print.

The Twelfth Pacific Science Congress was the occasion of the first English presentation. Dr I. McDougall, the Convener of Symposium D5 ('Petrology and Geochemistry of Island Arcs in Relation to Tectonic Environment'), asked the author to say something on the origin of lavas, and so the latter half of this paper was added. The author is now inclined to emphasize this part, following the symposium, because many contributors to the symposium seemed over-ready to accept some novel ideas. The author is much indebted to staff of the Department of Geology, Australian National University, and to Dr McDougall and to Professor A. J. R. White for help in preparing the manuscript.

REFERENCES

Dickinson, W. R. & Hatherton, T. 1967. Andesitic volcanism and seismicity around the Pacific. *Science*, **157,** 801-3.

Hasebe, K., Fujii, N. & Uyeda, S. 1970. Thermal processes under island arcs. *Tectonophysics*, **10,** 335-55.

Hatherton, T. & Dickinson, W. R. 1969. The relationship between andesitic volcanism and seismicity in Indonesia, the Lesser Antilles, and other island arcs. *J. geophys. Res.* **74,** 5301-10.

Katsui, Y. 1959. Chemical compositions of the lavas from Quaternary volcanoes of Hokkaido. *Bull. geol. Comm. Hokkaido,* **38,** 27-47 (in Japanese).

——— 1961. Petrochemistry of the Quaternary volcanic rocks of Hokkaido and surrounding areas. *J. Fac. Sci. Hokkaido Univ.* (Ser. 4) **11,** 1-58.

Kuno, H. 1956. Genetical system of igneous rocks and its relation to crustal and subcrustal structures in Japan. *Science, Tokyo,* **26,** 19-22 (in Japanese).

——— 1959. Origin of Cenozoic petrographic provinces of Japan and surrounding areas. *Bull. volcan.* **20,** 37-76.

Kushiro, I. 1965. The liquidus relations in the systems forsterite-$CaAl_2SiO_6$-silica and forsterite-nepheline-silica at high pressures. *Carnegie Inst., Ann. Rept. Director, geophys. Lab. (1964-65),* 103-9.

——— 1968. Compositions of magmas formed by partial zone melting of the earth's upper mantle. *J. geophys. Res.* **73,** 619-34.

Ono, K. 1962. Chemical Composition of Volcanic Rocks in Japan. *Geol. Surv. Japan (Kawasaki),* 441 pp.

Sugimura, A. 1958. Marianen-Japan-Kamtschatka Orogen in Tätigkeit. *Earth Sci. Tokyo,* **37,** 34-9 (in Japanese with German abstract on p. 39).

——— 1960. Zonal arrangement of some geophysical and petrological features in Japan and its environs. *J. Fac. Sci. Tokyo Univ.* (Sec. 2), **12,** 133-53.

——— 1961. Regional variation of the K_2O/Na_2O ratios of volcanic rocks in Japan and environs. *J. geol. Soc. Japan* **67,** 292-300 (in Japanese with English abstract on p. 292).

——— 1968. Spatial relations of basaltic magmas in island arcs. In *Basalts,* 2. (Eds H. H. Hess & A. Poldervaart). Interscience Publishers, New York-London, pp. 537-71.

Sugimura, A., Matsuda, T., Chinzei, K. & Nakamura, K. 1963. Quantitative distribution of late Cenozoic volcanic materials in Japan. *Bull. volcan.* **26,** 125-40.

Utsu, T. 1966. Regional differences in absorption of seismic waves in the upper mantle as inferred from abnormal distributions of seismic intensities. *J. Fac. Sci. Hokkaido Univ.* (Ser. 7), **2,** 359-74.

——— 1971. Seismological evidence for anomalous structure of island arcs with special reference to the Japanese region. *Rev. Geophys. Space Phys.* **9,** 839-90.

Uyeda, S. & Sugimura, A. 1968. Island arcs. *Science, Tokyo,* **38,** 91-7, 138-45, 269-77, 322-31, 382-90, 443-7, 499-504 (in Japanese).

Wadati, K. & Takahashi, M. 1965. Seismic activity under the volcanic area. *Proc. Japan Acad.* **41,** 938-42.

Strontium Isotopes in Island Arc Volcanic Rocks

J. GILL AND W. COMPSTON

Department of Geophysics and Geochemistry
Australian National University, P.O. Box 4, Canberra, A.C.T. 2601
Australia

ABSTRACT

The 87Sr/86Sr ratios of island arc volcanic rocks rule out both old sialic crust and unmodified ocean-floor basalts as principal source materials for island arc volcanism.

There is a positive correlation between Rb/Sr and 87Sr/86Sr ratios in some island arc tholeiitic suites and a decrease of 87Sr/86Sr ratios with increasing distance from the trench in some island arcs. Although alteration and/or metamorphism of ocean-floor basalts could produce the requisite Sr isotope ratios prior to subduction, the non-randomness of ratio variations in island arcs may discount this possibility. Instead, these variations suggest either that sediments contribute to magmas formed during subduction and that this contribution decreases with depth, or that the cold downgoing slab is isotopically unequilibrated before fusion but that equilibration increases as depth and temperatures increase.

Because decreasing 87Sr/86Sr ratios accompany increasing K, Rb, and Sr contents and Rb/Sr ratios in some island arc volcanic rocks, these variations in alkali contents and ratios cannot be explained by inferring additional crustal contamination or mantle wall-rock reaction as depth to the Benioff zone increases.

INTRODUCTION

The isotope ratio 87Sr/86Sr can be used to identify Sr which has resided in the sialic crust. This is possible because most of the earth's Rb lies in the crust whereas most of its Sr is in the mantle (Hedge & Walthall 1963). Because the isotope 87Rb changes to 87Sr by radioactive decay, the amount of radiogenic Sr and the ratio of radiogenic to stable Sr (i.e. 87Sr/86Sr) will increase more quickly in the crust than mantle.

A typical Rb-Sr inventory of the earth is given in Table 2 of Armstrong (1968). The 87Sr/86Sr ratio of the earth at the time of its formation was probably close to 0·6990 (a value obtained from studies of meteoritic and lunar samples; cf. Papanastassiou & Wasserburg 1969). Changes of this ratio in the sialic crust and mantle with time will depend on when and how they separated from one another. If the separation was gradual but largely accomplished within the first 1,000 m.y. of earth history, the development will be as is sketched in Fig. 1. There we use the bulk Rb/Sr ratio given for the earth by Armstrong and refer to this starting material as 'undepleted mantle', capable of being fractionated to yield a 'crustal component' and residual 'depleted mantle'. Modern Sr from the sialic crust will have an 87/86 ratio of about 0·715-0·72; Sr from undepleted mantle will have an 87/86 ratio of about 0·706; and Sr from mantle having lost some portion of its crustal component will have an 87/86 ratio between 0·701 and 0·706.

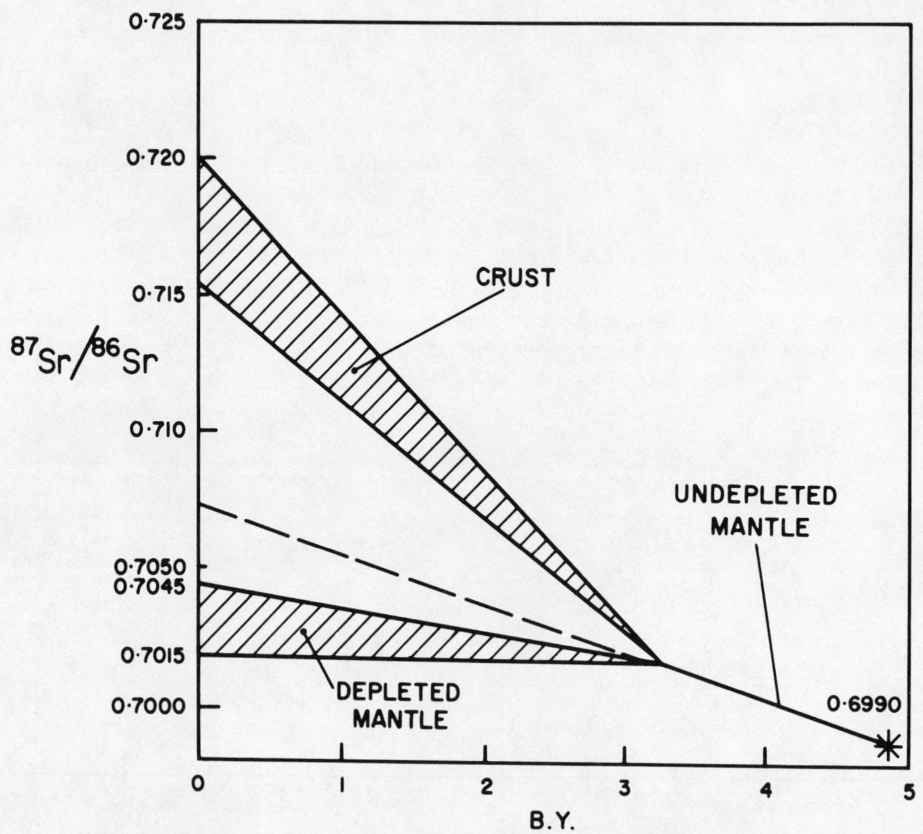

Fig. 1 Evolution of 87Sr/86Sr in various enviroments during earth history.

Details of such Sr isotopic evolution are much debated (Armstrong 1968, Hurley & Rand 1969, Hart & Brooks 1970) but it is undisputed that Sr from the sialic crust has been clearly labelled during earth history.

Modern Sr isotope analyses usually have a precision of about $\pm$0·0001-5. All analytical data presented or discussed in this paper have been normalized so that the measured 87Sr/86Sr ratio for Eimer and Amend $SrCO_3$ would be 0·7080 in any laboratory from which data have been used.

Sr FROM THE MODERN MANTLE

Recent intra-oceanic volcanism is most likely to sample the 87Sr/86Sr ratio of the modern mantle. Such volcanism produces rocks having ratios between 0·701 and 0·706 (Gast 1967, Peterman & Hedge 1971). Fresh ridge tholeiites from the Atlantic, Pacific, and Indian Oceans have a mean ratio of 0·7025; the range is from 0·7020-0·7030 except for one sample at 0·7012 (Hedge & Peterman 1970, Hart 1971). In contrast, tholeiitic and alkali basalts of oceanic islands have ratios of 0·703-0·706. Rb/Sr ratios likewise differ, usually being $\sim$0·008 in ridge tholeiites but $>$0·02 in island basalts.

These different populations are illustrated in Fig. 2, where it is apparent, as Tatsumoto *et al.* noted in 1965, that most ridge and some Hawaiian basalts have Rb/Sr ratios too low to produce the isotopic composition of their Sr even given the age of the earth in which to do so. At the degree of partial melting thought necessary to produce tholeiitic basalt from a peridotitic source, Rb/Sr ratios of the melt will approximate those of the source (Griffin & Murthy 1969). Thus basalts whose analyses lie above the single-stage evolution line in Fig. 2 (see caption for explanation) must have come from a source region which once had a higher Rb/Sr ratio than it did at the time of magma genesis (Gast 1967, 1968). This is thought to indicate widespread extraction of Rb (and K, Ba, La and Th) from the mantle at some time after the earth's formation, probably associated with crustal development, leaving behind a mantle with heterogeneous Rb and Sr distributions. Peterman and Hedge (1971) take the ratio $K_2O/(Na_2O+K_2O)$ as a primary feature of magma compositions, little affected by fractionation. They note a positive correlation between 87Sr/86Sr and $K_2O/(Na_2O+K_2O)$ ratios in oceanic basalts and suggest that this indicates varying degrees of previous Rb and K extraction.

If these variations are due to random mantle heterogeneities, it is not clear why rocks with low ratios are limited to ocean ridges. Green (1971) suggests that alkali and large cation enrichment (and therefore higher Rb/Sr) occurs at the top of the low-velocity zone (LVZ), and that ocean ridge volcanism taps mantle from the base of the LVZ which is depleted in these elements. However, if the Rb/Sr ratios of Hawaiian and ridge tholeiites reflect those of the upper and lower LVZ, respectively, those differences must have existed for 1,500 m.y. to increase 87Sr/86Sr ratios from 0·7025 -0·7040.

If mantle phases do not achieve isotopic equilibrium on the grain-to-grain scale, as is discussed for the anhydrous moon by Compston and Gray (1972) and for alpine peridotites by Kuroda *et al.* (1971) and Graham and Ringwood (1971), one might attribute the high 87Sr/86Sr ratios of alkali basalts to small degrees of partial melting involving phlogopite. Using the data of Griffin and Murthy (1969, Table 5), the 87/86 ratio of Sr in phlogopite would increase by 0·0015 in 2·6 m.y: However, isotopic disequilibrium on this scale is both difficult to imagine in a hydrous, high-temperature environment, and does not explain the differences in isotopic composition of Sr between Hawaiian and ridge tholeiites.

Whatever the reason, Sr produced directly from the mantle can have 87/86 ratios between 0·701 and 0·706.

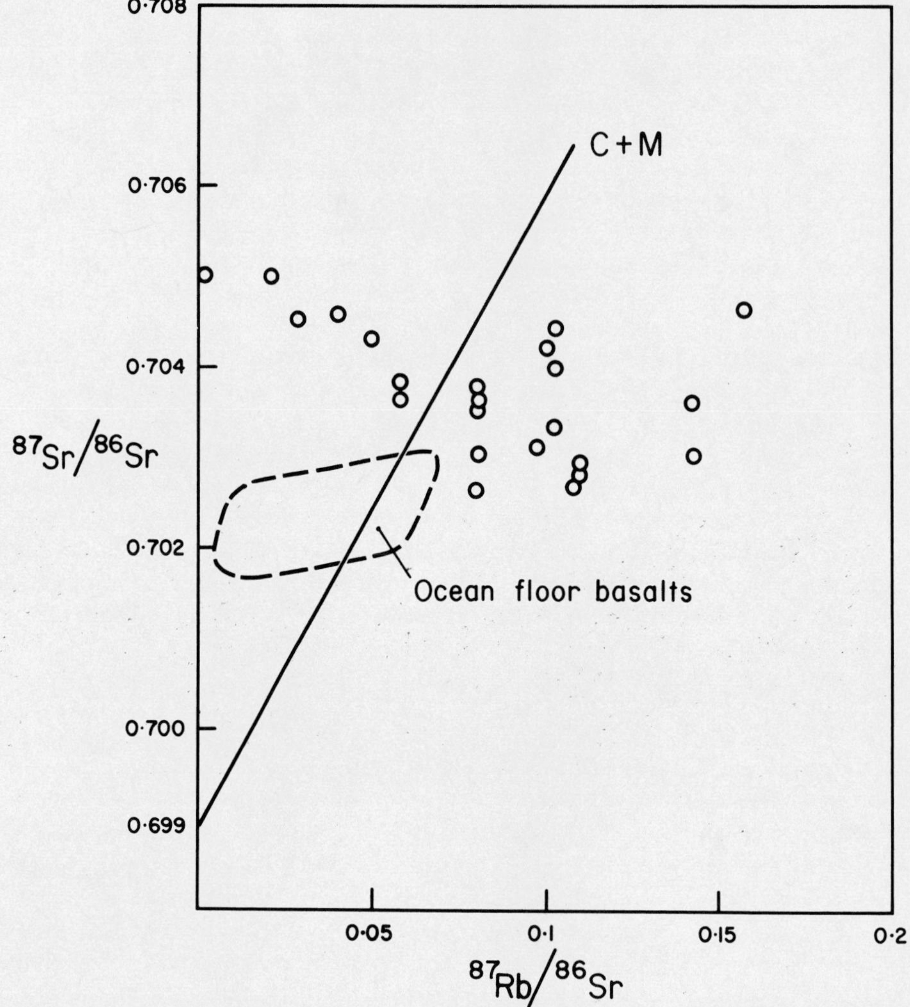

Fig. 2 Variation of 87Sr/86Sr with Rb/Sr ratios in oceanic basalts for which this information is available. Data is from Bence (1966), Tatsumoto *et al.* (1965), and Hart (1971) for ocean floor basalts. Open circles represent data on Hawaiian basalts taken from Powell and DeLong (1966). The line terminating at 'C +M' is a single stage evolution line which defines the 87Sr/86Sr ratio of all environments whose Rb/Sr ratios have remained constant throughout 4,600 m.y. of earth history. All points above this line represent basalts from source regions whose Rb/Sr ratios were too low at the time of partial fusion to have generated sufficient 87Sr from 87Rb during that time to explain the observed 87Sr/86Sr ratios of those basalts. Crystal fractionation usually leads to higher Rb/Sr ratios but should not affect 87Sr/86Sr ratios.

Sr IN WESTERN PACIFIC ISLAND ARCS

Hedge (1966), Pushkar (1968), Kurasawa (1970), Hedge and Knight (1969), Ewart and Stipp (1968), Peterman *et al.* (1970) and Gill (1970) have published data on the isotopic composition of Sr from Western Pacific island arcs. New data for samples from New Georgia (Solomon Islands), the New Hebrides, and Fiji are given in Table 1 and Fig. 3; data for Tonga, also presented in Fig. 3, will be published separately. Table 2 summarizes the data available for the South-western Pacific.

Fig. 3 and Table 2 illustrate the consistency of island arc 87Sr/86Sr ratios, which range from 0·703-0·705. Note the positive correlation between Rb/Sr and 87Sr/86Sr in volcanics from Tonga and some of those from Fiji.

Many geochemical aspects of island arc magmas change as the distance from their associated trench and Benioff zone increases (Sugimura 1968 and this volume, Gill & Gorton this volume, Jakeš & Gill 1970, Dickinson & Hatherton 1967). Volcanics erupted closest to the trench are usually members of an island arc tholeiitic series, those further away belong to a calcalkaline series, and those still further away represent a high-K variety of the calcalkaline series, or a shoshonite association (Jakěs & Gill 1970, Gill & Gorton, this volume, Fig. 1). Hedge and Knight (1969) report that 87Sr/86Sr ratios in volcanics from northern Honshu, Japan, decrease from 0·7041-0·7043 closest to the trench to 0·7026-0·7031 furthest from it. Data are not sufficient to assess variations with Rb/Sr within suites. Note that Kurasawa (1970) reports the opposite trend in south-west Honshu, but this is due to high ratios in the alkali basalts of Southwest Japan. These basalts differ in such distinctive features as K/Na ratios and TiO_2 contents from other island arc alkalic rocks and may only indirectly reflect the subduction process.

The 87Sr/86Sr ratios of late Miocene volcanic rocks from Fiji (Fig. 3*b*) also decrease as distance from the inferred trench position increases. Rb/Sr ratios are more variable within than between suites over this distance. Gill and Gorton (this volume) argue on independent geochemical and geological grounds that Vanua Levu represents the late Miocene volcanic front in Fiji, that the calcalkaline andesites of south-east Viti Levu were erupted behind that front, and the high-K andesites of Kandavu still further behind it. If these arguments are sound and volcanics of these three islands were contemporaneous and related to the same subduction configuration, then we have documented a second case in which 87Sr/86Sr ratios decrease as the K, Rb, and Sr contents of the magmas increase.

Page (pers. comm. 1971) has found no change in 87Sr/86Sr ratios between the north-coast volcanics of New Britain and those of Talasea studied by him and Peterman *et al.* (1970). Stipp (1968) found a westward decrease in 87/86 ratios of basalt Sr in New Zealand.

IMPLICATIONS FOR MAGMA GENESIS IN ISLAND ARCS

Island arc magmas have too little 87Sr to involve reworked sialic crust. Thus old, fractionated (high Rb/Sr) crust can be neither the source nor a major contaminant of island arc volcanism.

Table 1

NEW Sr ISOTOPE DATA FROM MELANESIA[1]

	Sample No.	Rb ppm	Sr ppm	87Sr/86Sr
A. FIJI (late Miocene)				
1. Vanua Levu	798	8·8	202	0·7041
	806	14	415	0·7041
	810	6·2	169	0·7040
	814	9·1	737	0·7041
	818	16	393	0·7035
	820	6·1	432	0·7037
	821	16	347	0·7037
	M96	6·1	95	0·7041
	B535	12	92	0·7043
2. Viti Levu (Namosi Andesite)	66	16	481	0·7040
	873	35	536	0·7036
	874	28	652	0·7035
	876	17	536	0·7037
3. Kandavu	390	51	1,330	0·7032
B. FIJI (late Eocene to early Miocene; also see Gill (1970)				
	60	2·1	128	0·7037
	387	3·1	90	0·7045
	903	31	256	0·7034
	904	8·8	353	0·7032
	915	3·3	160	0·7041
	920	5·1	279	0·7032
C. NEW HEBRIDES (Aoba)				
	576	17	643	0·7039

[1] For chemical composition and description of samples analysed see Hindle and Gill (in prep.) for Vanua Levu; Gill (1970 and in prep.) for other Fiji samples; and Stanton and Bell (1969) for New Georgia. All isotope ratios have been normalized to 8·37520 for 88Sr/86Sr and 0·7080 for E & A $SrCO_3$ 87Sr/86Sr. Replicate analyses of E & A $SrCO_3$ and rock samples consistently have a precision of $\pm$0·0001-2. Rb and Sr contents were determined by XRF with a precision of $\pm$5 per cent for the lowest Rb concentrations and $\pm$2 per cent of Sr for Fiji samples. New Georgia Rb and Sr contents were determined by a less precise XRF method and are approximate only. Their Rb/Sr ratios should be correct within $\pm$10 per cent.

Table 1 (cont.)

	Sample No.	Rb ppm	Sr ppm	87Sr/86Sr
D. SOLOMONS (New Georgia)				
	364	3·9	90	0·7040
	414	2·8	110	0·7035
	372	6·1	80	0·7039
	450	10	200	0·7040
	443	13	140	0·7030
	413	13	140	0·7033
	412	75	470	0·7036
	536	18	250	0·7043
	377	22	210	0·7040
	428	23	200	0·7037
	230	22	290	0·7038
	325	24	300	0·7035
	349	21	170	0·7038

Yet island arc magmas have too much 87Sr to be simple partial melts of oceanic basalts, having 87Sr/86Sr ratios of 0·7025 and thrust beneath island arcs along Benioff zones, even if these basalts are 100 m.y. old. Nevertheless, the number of alternative hypotheses consistent with the island arc data is great.

Table 2

SUMMARY OF Sr ISOTOPE COMPOSITIONS IN SOUTH-WEST PACIFIC VOLCANIC ROCKS

Area	87Sr/86Sr[1]		*Source*
	Mean	*Range*	
1. Talasea, New Britain	0·7035	0·7034-0·7038	Peterman *et al.* (1970)
2. New Georgia, Solomon Islands	0·7037	0·7030-0·7042	This paper
3. Aoba, New Hebrides	0·7039		This paper
4. Vanua Levu, Fiji	0·7040	0·7036-0·7043	This paper
5. Viti Levu, Fiji	0·7038	0·7032-0·7048	This paper and Gill (unpubl.)
6. Kandavu, Fiji	0·7032		This paper
7. Lau, Fiji	0·7032	0·7030-0·7033	Gill (unpubl.)
8. Tonga	0·7040	0·7038-0·7043	This paper
9. Taupo, New Zealand	0·7054	0·7040-0·7066	Ewart and Stipp (1968)

[1] All ratios normalized to 0·7080 for E & A $SrCO_3$.

The observed ratios are well within the range of mantle-derived volcanics and could therefore represent either various partial melts of hydrous peridotite (Kushiro *et al.* 1968) or fractionated derivatives of mantle-derived basalts. Neither, however, explain the instances of positive correlation between 87Sr/86Sr and Rb/Sr ratios.

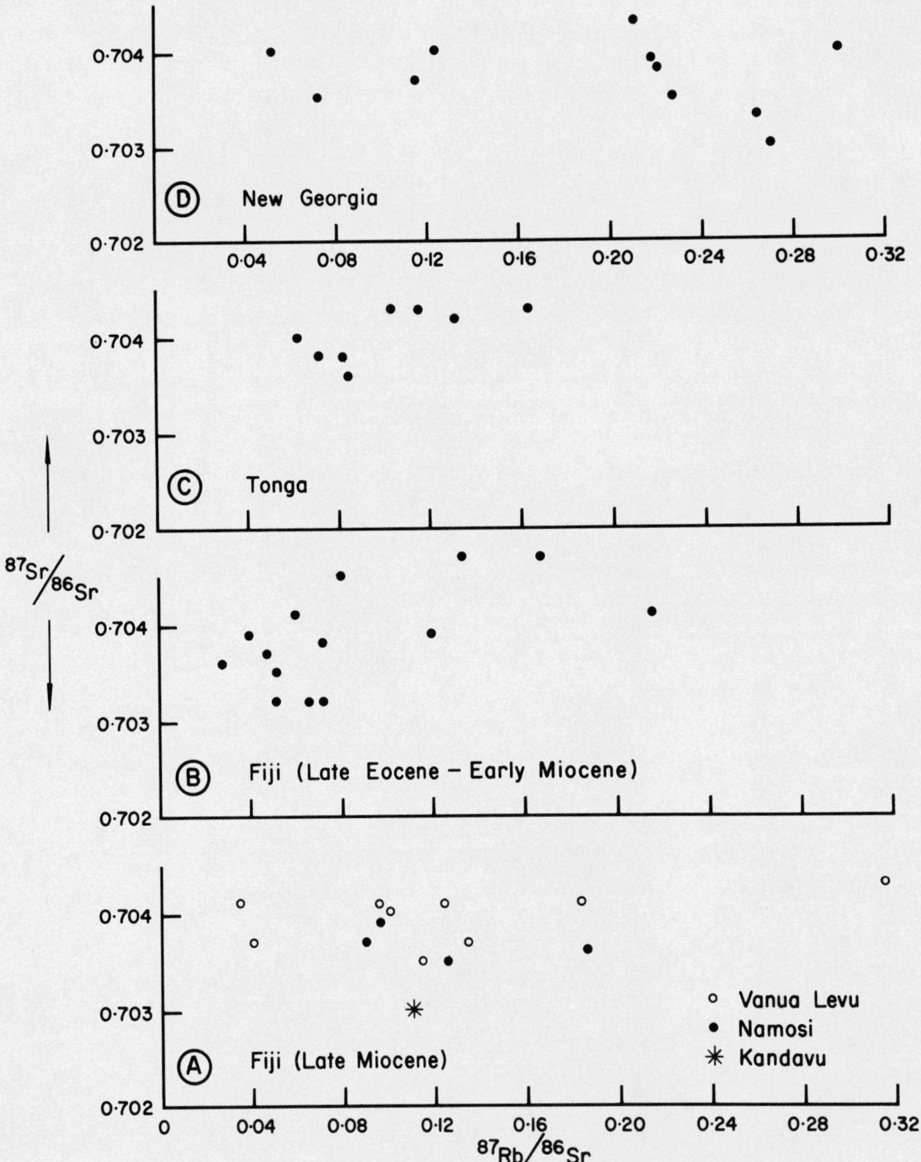

Fig. 3 Variation of 87Sr/86Sr with Rb/Sr ratios in Melanesian volcanic rocks. Data is from Table 1 and Gill (1970, and unpubl.).

Alternatively, underthrust basalts could be the source of island arc volcanism if their ratios were 0·703-0·705. This could be accomplished in at least two ways: partial equilibration of ocean-floor basalt Sr with sea-water Sr (87/86=0·709) during or after eruption, or isotopic disequilibrium with the downgoing slab. Hart and Nalwalk (1970) attribute ratios of 0·705-0·706 in dredged oceanic basalts to partial equilibration with sea-water. Indirect equilibration might also occur during burial metamorphism. Gill (1970) reported high 87Sr/86Sr ratios in some of his first period volcanics which had experienced burial metamorphism. In one case (sample 68-60) we have found the 87Sr to reside in an HCl-soluble phase so that Sr in the insoluble residue had an 87/86 ratio lower by 0·0011. An alternative or complementary suggestion is for the Rb/Sr ratio of ocean-floor basalt to increase by alteration, leading eventually to increased 87Sr/86Sr ratios. Hart (1971, Fig. 1) shows that Rb/Sr ratios can increase 2-7 times as a result of alteration, thus reducing the time necessary for development of 87Sr by an equivalent amount. Fusion of such altered and/or metamorphosed basalt could yield island arc volcanics with their observed 87Sr/86Sr ratios but the consistency of ratios in various island arcs requires remarkable uniformity for these alteration effects. Moreover, if isotopic equilibrium is attained within the oceanic crust, varying degrees of partial fusion would not produce the Rb/Sr-87Sr/86Sr correlation or the regular spatial variations in 87Sr/86Sr ratios discussed above.

A third alternative involving some kind of mixing process must be invoked to explain these variations. Authigenic oceanic sediments will have the 87Sr/86Sr ratios of sea-water; detrital sediments will have ratios very similar to those of their provenence (Dasch 1969, Biscaye & Dasch 1971). Involvement of either during magma genesis would increase both 87Sr/86Sr and Rb/Sr ratios of the melt by an amount proportional to its weight fraction.

Many authors have appealed to sediment contamination as a way to produce the concentrations of alkali elements and radiogenic Sr and Pb in island arc volcanics (Armstrong 1968, 1971; Tatsumoto 1969, Jakeš & Gill 1970, Hart *et al.* 1970). Armstrong calculates that over 90 per cent of the lead in arc magmas is from oceanic sediments. That this is unlikely for Sr can be illustrated by referring to sample 68-66 in Table 1.

This andesite has been studied experimentally by Green (1972, and this volume) who suggests it represents a partial melt derived from eclogite. Fig. 4 illustrates the Sr contents to be expected from melting an eclogite of oceanic tholeiite composition containing 110 ppm Sr and with a clinopyroxene + garnet + rutile residuum. We have used the equations of Shaw (1970) and taken $K_{Sr}^{liq/cpx} = 6{\cdot}7$, $K_{Sr}^{cpx/gar} = 20{\cdot}0$, and $K_{Sr}^{liq/rut} = \infty$ (Gast 1968, Philpotts & Schnetzler 1970). As discussed by Gill (in prep.) a 19 per cent partial melt of oceanic tholeiite best approximates the major element composition of sample 68-66, using Green's data for the composition of liquidus clinopyroxene and garnet at experimental conditions of 36 kb, 1,100° C, and 10 per cent H_2O. From Fig. 4 this should yield Sr concentrations between 430-530 ppm in the melt depending on whether or not the liquid and residuum have maintained equilibrium during melting. Sample 68-66 has 481 ppm Sr and an 87Sr/86Sr ratio of 0·7040 (Gill 1970).

The amount of sediment Sr needed to increase the 87-86 ratio of a melt depends on

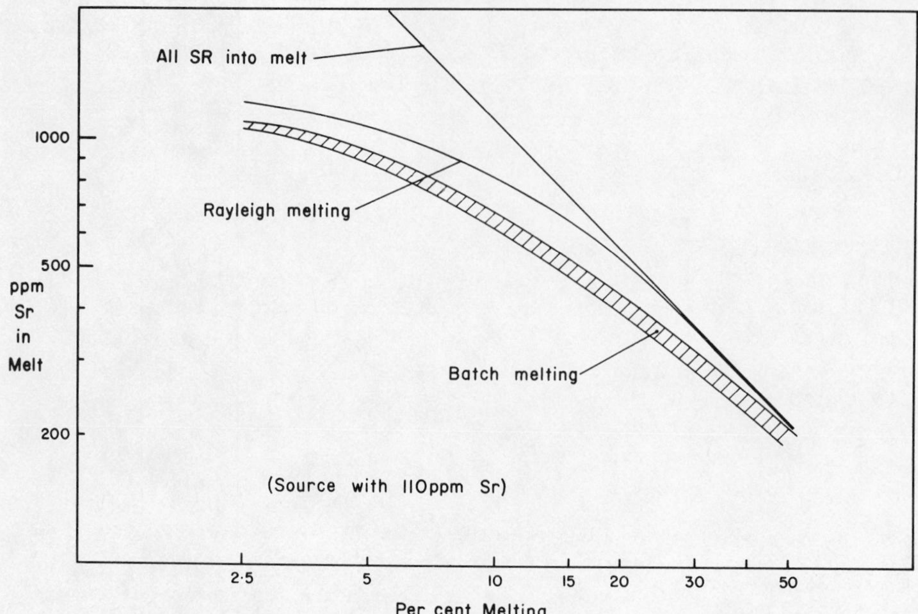

Fig. 4 Predicted concentration of Sr in partial melts of eclogite.

the 87Sr/86Sr ratio of the sediment. The maximum ratio to be expected would be 0·72. A more realistic estimate for Western Pacific sediments undergoing subduction would lie between the ratio for sea-water (0·709) and that of volcaniclastic greywacke (e.g. 0·7066; Ewart & Stipp 1968). To increase the 87Sr/86Sr ratio from 0·7025 (ocean-floor basalt) to·7040 (sample 68-66) requires assimilation of 41 ppm Sr if its 87/86 ratio is 0·72, 124 ppm Sr if its 87/86 ratio is 0·709, and 198 ppm Sr if its 87/86 ratio is 0·7066. The agreement between the Sr content of sample 68-66 and that predicted from melting eclogite alone is sufficiently close that sediment assimilation is unlikely to provide the sole or even major explanation for its 87/86 ratio. Deep-sea sediments are more likely to be clays than carbonates, and such clays will have approximately 180 ppm Sr (Turekian & Wedepohl 1961). Appeal to the incorporation of sediments in order to explain the 87/86 ratio of Sr in sample 68-66 requires melting more sediment than basalt during magma genesis, a possibility excluded by many other geochemical parameters (Gill, in prep.).

A different kind of mixing process could occur if isotopic equilibration is impeded by the low temperatures within the slab. If so, phases with high Rb/Sr and therefore eventually high 87Sr contents might persist until melting. In a hydrous environment, initial melts from basalt will be quartz-rich and will presumably extract elements like Rb (Green 1972, and this volume). In Tonga and Fiji, rhyodacites (SiO_2=63-80 per cent) of the island arc tholeiitic series have higher Rb/Sr and 87Sr/86Sr ratios than do associated andesites and basalts, and may reflect such a situation.

It may be significant that this correlation is most pronounced in rocks of the island arc tholeiitic series which are associated with the shallowest earthquake foci and therefore below which the slab is most likely to remain hydrous and cold, and its basalts to exist in amphibolite facies assemblages. The rhyodacites from Fiji with higher Rb/Sr and 87Sr/86Sr ratios contain no more Sr than do oceanic tholeiites themselves, and this requires $K_{Sr}^{liq/xl} \sim 1{\cdot}0$ during magma genesis. Such a bulk distribution coefficient is possible in an amphibolite facies residuum composed of amphibole, clinopyroxene and plagioclase, but not in an eclogite facies mixture of clinopyroxene and garnet, using the data of Gast (1968), Philpotts and Schnetzler (1970) and Korringa and Noble (1970).

In situations where 87Sr/86Sr ratios of volcanic rocks decrease as distance between these rocks and the trench or Benioff zone increases, simple melting of any isotopically homogeneous source is ruled out. If the downgoing slab is that source, the amount of 87Sr from it which enters the melt must decrease with depth. If the 87Sr comes from sediments, the amount of sediment contaminating any magmas produced must also decrease with depth. The opposite conclusion was reached by Donnelly *et al.* (1971) who used relative alkali element abundances. Higher concentrations of these elements more likely indicate smaller degrees of melting than additional sediment contamination. Alternatively, if the 87Sr comes from a high Rb/Sr phase whose Sr remains isotopically unequilibrated with its surrounding, either that phase must disappear during dehydration or isotopic equilibrium must be approached as depth and temperatures increase. If overlying mantle rather than the slab is the source region for island arc volcanism, Rb/Sr ratios of that mantle are regularly zoned either with depth or distance from the trench. Either or both could be consistent with earlier fractionation of Rb from Sr during crustal growth.

Unlike variations in K and other alkali contents (Dickinson & Hatherton 1967, Gill & Gorton, this volume) a decrease in 87Sr/86Sr ratios with distance from the trench cannot be explained by increased crustal contamination or mantle 'wall-rock reaction' as depth to the Benioff zone increases. It must be a primary magma feature but does not discriminate between melts from the mantle or underthrust lithosphere.

CONCLUSION

The average 87Sr/86Sr ratio in island arc volcanic rocks rules out both sialic crust and unmodified oceanic tholeiite as their principal source material. There are, nevertheless, so many alternatives by which to explain this average ratio that routine Sr isotope measurements are unlikely to make further positive contributions to the study of island arc magma genesis. Narrowing the list of alternatives requires a realistic assessment of Sr contents to be expected in partial melts, accurate identification of small ($<0{\cdot}001$) variations in 87Sr/86Sr ratios within island arcs, and faith that nature is uniform on that scale.

POSTSCRIPT

During the year since preparation of this manuscript we have continued to evaluate the role of eclogite in the genesis of sample 68-66. This has changed the details but not the conclusion of the argument given above. Using more likely experimental conditions, the 'best' approximation involves a partial melt of about 30 per cent containing 300-370 ppm Sr (Fig. 4). To obtain a 30 per cent melt with the Sr and Ba concentrations of sample 68-66 would require fusing a mixture of 4·5 per cent oceanic clay + 3 per cent carbonate + 92·5 per cent fresh ocean-floor basalt. This will have an 87Sr/86Sr ratio of 0·7040 only if that of the clay is >0·72. These conditions are very unlikely in a Western Pacific island arc.

REFERENCES

Armstrong, R. L. 1968. A model for the evolution of strontium and lead isotopes in a dynamic Earth. *Rev. Geophys.* **6,** 175-99.

——— 1971. Isotopic and chemical constraints on models of magma genesis in volcanic arcs. *Earth Planet. Sci. Letters,* **12,** 137-42.

Bence, A. E. 1966. The differentiation history of the earth by rubidium-strontium isotopic relationships. In *Variations in isotopic abundances of strontium, calcium, and argon and related topics* (Ed. P. M. Hurley), M.I.T. 1381-414, 14th Ann. Prog. Rept, pp. 35-78.

Biscaye, P. E. & Dasch, E. J. 1971. The rubidium, strontium, strontium-isotope system in deep-sea sediments: Argentine Basin. *J. geophys. Res.* **76,** 5087-96.

Compston, W. & Gray, C. M. 1972. Lunar model Rb-Sr ages and magma genesis. *Earth Planet. Sci. Letters,* **15.**

Dasch, E. J. 1969. Strontium isotopes in weathering profiles, deep-sea sediments, and sedimentary rocks. *Geochim. cosmochim. Acta,* **33,** 1521-52.

Dickinson, W. R. & Hatherton, T. 1967. Andesitic volcanism and seismicity around the Pacific. *Science,* **157,** 801-3.

Donnelly, T. W., Rogers, J. J. W., Pushkar, P. & Armstrong, R. L. 1971. Chemical evolution of the igneous rocks of the eastern West Indies: an investigation of thorium, uranium, and potassium distributions, and lead and strontium isotopic ratios. *Mem. geol. Soc. Am.* **130.**

Ewart, A. & Stipp, J. J. 1968. Petrogenesis of the volcanic rocks of the Central North Island, New Zealand, as indicated by a study of Sr 87/86 ratios, and Sr, Rb, K, U, and Th abundances. *Geochim. cosmochim. Acta,* **32,** 699-736.

Gast, P. W. 1967. Isotope geochemistry of volcanic rocks. In *Basalts: I* (Eds H. Hess and A. Poldevaart), 325-58.

——— 1968. Trace element fractionation and the origin of tholeiitic and alkaline magma types. *Geochim. cosmochim. Acta,* **32,** 1057-86.

Gill, J. B. 1970. Geochemistry of Viti Levu, Fiji, and its evolution as an island arc. *Contr. Mineral. Petrol.* **27,** 179-203.

Gill, J. & Gorton, M. (This volume.) A proposed geological and geochemical history of eastern Melanesia.

Graham, A. L. & Ringwood, A. E. 1971. Lunar-basalt genesis: the origin of the europium anomaly. *Earth Planet. Sci. Letters,* **12** (4), 105-15.

Green, D. H. 1971. Composition of basaltic magmas as indicators of conditions of origin: application to oceanic volcanism. *Phil. Trans. R. Soc. London* (A), **268,** 707-25.

Green, T. 1972. Crystallization of calc-alkaline andesite under controlled high-pressure hydrous conditions. *Contr. Mineral. Petrol.* **34,** 150-66.

Griffin, W. L. & Murthy, V. R. 1969. Distribution of K, Rb, Sr and Ba in some minerals relevant to basalt genesis. *Geochim. cosmochim. Acta,* **33,** 1389-414.

Hart, S. R. 1971. K, Rb, Cs, Sr, and Ba contents and Sr isotope ratios of ocean floor basalts. *Phil. Trans. R. Soc. London* (A), **268,** 573-87.

Hart, S. R. & Brooks, C. 1970. Rb-Sr mantle evolution models. *Carnegie Inst. Year Book*, **69,** 426-9.

Hart, S. R., Brooks, C., Krogh, T. E., Davis, G. L. & Nava, D. 1970. Ancient and modern volcanic rocks: a trace element model. *Earth Planet. Sci. Letters*, **10,** 17-28.

Hart, S. R. & Nalwalk, A. J. 1970. K, Rb, Cs and Sr relationships in submarine basalts from the Puerto Rico trench. *Geochim. cosmochim. Acta*, **34,** 145-56.

Hedge, C. & Walthall, F. 1963. Radiogenic Sr^{87} as an index of geologic processes. *Science*, **140,** 1214-17.

Hedge, C. E. 1966. Variations in radiogenic strontium found in volcanic rocks. *J. geophys. Res.* **71,** 6119-20.

Hedge, C. E. & Knight, R. J. 1969. Lead and strontium isotopes in volcanic rocks from northern Honshu, Japan. *Geochem. J.* **3,** 15-24.

Hedge, C. E. & Peterman, Z. E. 1970. The strontium isotopic composition of basalts from the Gordon and Juan de Iuca Rises, Northeastern Pacific Ocean. *Contr. Mineral. Petrol.* **27,** 114-20.

Hurley, P. M. & Rand, R. J. 1969. Pre-drift continental nucleii. *Science,* **164,** 1229-42.

Jakeš, P. & Gill, J. 1970. Rare earth elements and the island arc tholeiitic series. *Earth Planet. Sci. Letters,* **9,** 17-28.

Korringa, M. K. & Noble, D. C. 1970. Feldspar-liquid partition coefficients for Sr and Ba based on a Rayleigh fractionation model. *Geol. Soc. Am. Ann. Meeting,* p. 598 (Abst.).

Kurasawa, H. 1970. Strontium and lead isotopes of volcanic rocks in Japan. In *Recent Developments in Mass Spectroscopy* (Eds K. Ogata and T. Hayakawa), pp. 666-70. *Proc. Int. Conf. Mass Spectroscopy*, Kyoto, Japan. Univ. Park Press, Baltimore.

Kuroda, V., Iizumi, S. & Tazaki, K. 1971. On some problems in origin of the Alpina type ultramafic rocks (Abst.). *Int. Geochem. Congr.* (Moscow), **1,** 65-6.

Kushiro, I., Yoder, H. S. & Nishikawa, M. 1968. Effect of water on the melting of enstatite. *Bull. geol. Soc. Am.* **79,** 1685-92.

Papanastassiou, D. A. & Wasserburg, G. J. 1969. Initial strontium isotopic abundances and the resolution of small time differences in the formation of planetary objects. *Earth Planet. Sci. Letters,* **5,** 361-76.

Peterman, Z. E. & Hedge, C. E. 1971. Related strontium isotopic and chemical variations in oceanic basalts. *Bull. geol. Soc. Am.* **82,** 493-500.

Peterman, Z. E., Lowder, G. G. & Carmichael, I. S. E. 1970. Sr87/Sr86 ratios of the Talasea series, New Britain, Territory of New Guinea. *Bull. geol. Soc. Am.* **81,** 39-40.

Philpotts, J. A. & Schnetzler, C. C. 1970. Phenocryst-matrix partition coefficients for K, Rb, Sr and Ba, with applications to anorthosite and basalt genesis. *Geochim. cosmochim. Acta.* **34,** 307-22.

Powell, J. L. & DeLong, S. E. 1966. Isotopic composition of strontium in volcanic rocks from Oahu. *Science*, **153,** 1239-42.

Pushkar, P. 1968. Strontium isotope ratios in volcanic rocks of three island arc areas. *J. geophys. Res.* **73,** 2701-13.

Shaw, D. M. 1970. Trace element fractionation during anatexis. *Geochim. cosmochim. Acta*, **34,** 237-42.

Stanton, R. L. & Bell, J. D. 1969. Volcanic and associated rocks of the New Georgia Group, British Solomon Islands Protectorate. *Overseas Geol. Miner. Resour.* **10,** 113-45.

Stipp, J. J. 1968. The geochronology and petrogenesis of the Cenozoic volcanics of North Island, New Zealand. Ph.D. thesis, Aust. Nat. Univ., Canberra.

Sugimura, A. 1968. Spatial relations of basaltic magmas in island arcs. In *Basalts, 2.* (Eds H. H. Hess and A. Poldevaart), 537-71.

Tatsumoto, M. 1969. Lead isotopes in volcanic rocks and possible ocean-floor thrusting beneath island arcs. *Earth Planet. Sci. Letters,* **6,** 369-76.

Tatsumoto, M., Hedge, C. E. & Engel, A. E. J. 1965. Potassium, rubidium, strontium, thorium, uranium and the ratio of Sr-87 to Sr-86 in oceanic tholeiitic basalt. *Science,* **150,** 886-8.

Turekian, K. K. & Wedepohl, K. H. 1961. Distribution of the elements in some major units of the Earth's crust. *Bull. geol. Soc. Am.* **72,** 175-92.

High-pressure, Hydrous Crystallization of an Island Arc Calcalkaline Andesite

TREVOR H. GREEN

School of Earth Sciences, Macquarie University
North Ryde, N.S.W. 2113, Australia

EXPANDED ABSTRACT

A series of experimental runs has been conducted in a piston-cylinder high-pressure apparatus on a glass prepared from a natural island arc calcalkaline andesite from Fiji (composition given in Table 1). The crystallization sequence was determined for the pressure interval 9-36 kb under anhydrous conditions and with 2, 5 and 10 per cent by weight of water carefully added.

Under anhydrous conditions plagioclase is the liquidus phase to 13·5 kb, joined by clinopyroxene at lower temperatures. At 18-36 kb clinopyroxene is the liquidus phase, joined at lower temperatures by plagioclase at 18 kb, and by garnet and then quartz (or coesite) at 27-36 kb.

With the addition of water the liquidus is depressed by 80° C for 2 per cent H_2O, 130° C for 5 per cent H_2O and 210°C for 10 per cent H_2O added, and also the sequence of crystallization shows marked changes (see Fig. 1). At low pressures clinopyroxene is the liquidus phase and the appearance of plagioclase is restricted to temperatures well below the liquidus. Amphibole becomes a major phase, particularly at temperatures $<950°$ C, but it does not appear on the liquidus. The upper-pressure limit of stability of amphibole is about 25 kb. The appearance of quartz is suppressed to near-solidus temperatures in hydrous runs. This results in a very large field of crystallization of garnet-clinopyroxene (Fig. 1). Garnet is the liquidus phase at 27-36 kb with >5 per cent H_2O present.

Electron microprobe analyses of critical phases allows calculation of controls on crystal fractionation trends. Thus measured garnet compositions have a high Fe/Mg ratio (compared with co-existing clinopyroxene and/or amphibole) and a significant grossular content, increasing with increasing water content and pressure, and with decreasing temperature. Clinopyroxenes contain significant jadeite increasing with increasing pressure and decreasing temperature. Tschermark's molecule in solid solution in the pyroxene is at a maximum at 9-18 kb for runs with low water content. Amphiboles do not show regular trends in composition with P, T or water content. They plot in the field of magnesio-hornblende towards the ferro-tschermakitic corner (Leake 1968).

The determined fractionation trends for hydrous conditions fall into three categories: (*a*) 5-15 kb—amphibole-clinopyroxene dominate fractionation and a moderate increase in Fe/Mg and a slight increase in K/Na occur; (*b*) 15-25 kb-garnet joins amphibole and clinopyroxene and there is a moderate increase in Fe/Mg and K/Na; (*c*) >25 kb—garnet-clinopyroxene control the fractionation and there is only a slight increase in Fe/Mg but a significant increase in K/Na and a pronounced silica enrichment.

This 'garnet-clinopyroxene' control is effective for both anhydrous and hydrous conditions, but as Fig. 1 clearly illustrates, it becomes more marked with water present. Also the ratio of

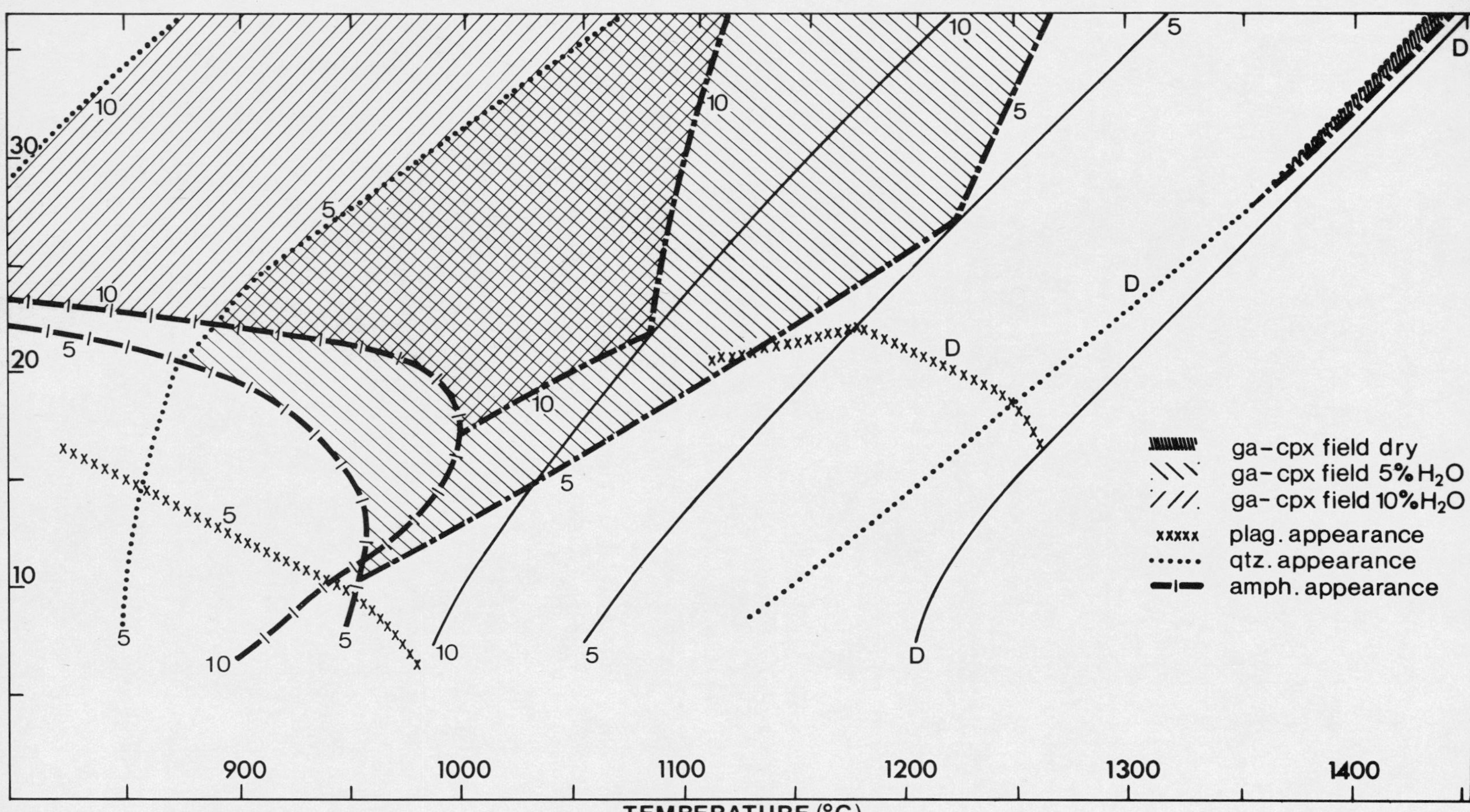

Fig. 1 Combined P T plot for anhydrous and hydrous experiments showing the effect of water on (*a*) enlargement of the garnet-clinopyroxene crystallization field; (*b*) suppression of quartz, plagioclase appearance; (*c*) stability of amphibole.

garnet to pyroxene increases with increasing water content, and this influences the detailed fractionation trends, producing residual liquidus with a lower Fe/Mg ratio, but with little change in K/Na or SiO_2, since the clinopyroxene becomes more sodic as the garnet-clinopyroxene ratio increases.

In recent years the concept of the new global tectonics has focused attention on orogenic belts and island arc areas as zones of collision and consumption of the lithosphere. These zones are the sites of extensive magmatic activity involving addition of large volumes of material to the crust. In particular the calcalkaline igneous rock series and the newly defined island arc tholeiitic series constitute the bulk of this activity (Jakeš & Gill 1970, Gill 1970). Jakeš and Gill (1970) indicated that the silica mode for the first eruptive cycle in island arcs (the island arc tholeiitic series) was about 53 per cent, while the silica mode for rocks of the second cycle of activity (the true calcalkaline igneous rock series) was 59 per cent.

The results on the crystallization of andesite in the present series of experiments are directly

Table 1

COMPOSITION OF ANDESITE GLASS USED IN THE EXPERIMENTAL WORK, AND COMPARISON OF THE COMPOSITION OF DACITES AND BASALTIC ANDESITE FROM THE SECOND PERIOD OF ERUPTION ON FIJI (GILL 1970 AND PERS. COMM.) WITH CALCULATED DERIVATIVES OF HIGH-PRESSURE FRACTIONATION OF THE ANDESITE

	1*a*	1*b*	2*a*	2*b*	3*a*	3*b*
SiO_2	59·39	60·24	65·45	65·0	55·43	57·6
TiO_2	0·68	0·69	0·52	0·56	0·82	0·7
Al_2O_3	16·73	16·98	16·59	17·0	18·05	17·4
Fe_2O_3	3·66	0·88	—	—	—	—
FeO	2·61	5·35	3·86[1]	3·4[1]	8·03[1]	7·5[1]
MnO	0·13	0·13	0·09	0·08	0·13	0·2
MgO	3·08	3·14	1·59	1·7	4·26	4·1
CaO	7·12	7·22	5·17	5·2	8·36	8·1
Na_2O	3·97	3·91	4·60	4·5	3·42	3·4
K_2O	1·27	1·26	1·45	1·7	1·28	1·0
P_2O_5	0·20	0·20				
Loss	0·55					

[1] Total Fe expressed as FeO.

1*a*=andesite 68-66 (Gill 1970); 1*b*=andesite glass; 2*a*=dacite 874 (Gill, pers. comm.); 2*b*=andesite 68-66 less 15% garnet and 12% clinopyroxene; 3*a*=basaltic andesite 876 (Gill, pers. comm.); 3*b*=andesite 68-66 plus 15% garnet and 5% clinopyroxene.

Garnet and clinopyroxene analyses obtained from runs on the andesite glass at 36 kb, 1,000-1,100° C, 10% H_2O.

Note. Such calculations can only be approximate, particularly in the case of addition of crystals—this modifies the bulk composition so that the compositions of crystals in equilibrium with this new parent liquid will differ from those in equilibrium with the andesite near its liquidus. Nevertheless, these calculations demonstrate the adequacy of the garnet-clinopyroxene model for governing the observed fractionation trends in the second period of eruption.

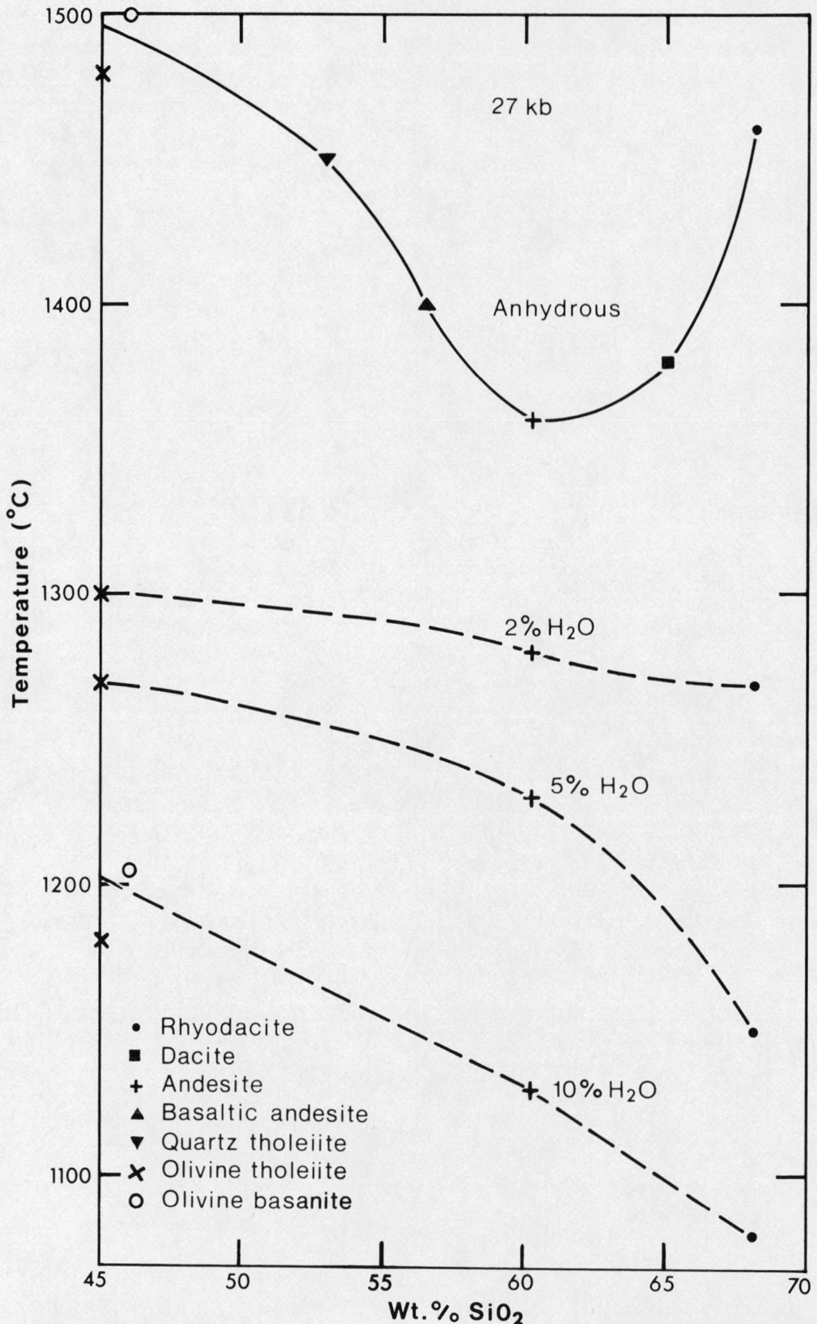

Fig. 2 Liquidus temperatures at 27 kb for a range of compositions, mainly of calcalkaline nature, except for the lower silica examples of olivine tholeiite and olivine basanite (these compositions were used because no other data on basic

applicable to a consideration of the origin of the rocks of the second eruptive cycle on Fiji. In terms of major-element chemistry, the derivation of the Fijian dacites from this igneous cycle may be satisfactorily explained by the fractionation of hydrous andesite at pressures >25 kb (see Table 1). Alternatively the dacites may result from lower degrees of melting of the downgoing hydrous lithosphere. Similarly, the more basic members of this eruptive period may be derived according to a model of eclogite-controlled fractional melting or crystallization (Table 1). Models involving amphibole fractionation at lower pressures are less satisfactory for explaining compositions in the Fijian second period of eruption, but in other environments models which include amphibole controlled fractionation may form part of a continuum of melting processes in subduction zones.

One of the most important features of the present experimental work is the verification of previous results (Green & Ringwood 1968), namely that the anhydrous andesite liquidus falls in a low-temperature trough between the liquidi for more acid and basic compositions at high pressures. The presence of water exerts a critical control on this feature, shifting the minimum liquidus temperature to more silicic compositions with increasing water content (Fig. 2). This result is consistent with andesite being more abundant than either basaltic andesite or dacite in the calcalkaline period of eruption on Fiji (with a silica mode of 59 per cent). Thus if *anhydrous* melting of the mafic oceanic crust in the subduction zone took place at $\gtrsim$80 km depth then the first melt formed would correspond to andesite.

However, it is likely that the oceanic crust, in its early stages at least, is hydrous, carrying water from the hydrosphere into the mantle. Hence to obtain dominant andesite, rather than more siliceous compositions from partial melting, it is necessary to dehydrate the oceanic crust before it reaches the depths from where calcalkaline volcanism may originate. If the sinking hydrous lithosphere dehydrates and possibly undergoes minor partial melting at the same time (likely maximum depths would correspond to the final breakdown of amphibole at 70-80 km), then highly siliceous, hydrous magmas result (Green & Ringwood, in press). These may subsequently rise into the overlying peridotitic wedge and instigate melting of the peridotite (addition of water to the peridotite significantly lowers the solidus—D. H. Green 1970). At the same time the composition of the partial melt from the peridotite is modified through the addition of a highly siliceous melt, and also through hydrous fractional crystallization. Such derivative magmas would be the first to erupt from the subduction zones beneath island arc areas, and may correspond to the island arc tholeiitic series. The major contribution would be from the mantle, but it would not be a magma in equilibrium with peridotite, because of the significant hydrous siliceous portion added. This could produce an igneous rock series with a silica mode of 53 per cent and detailed geochemical features satisfying the properties outlined by Jakeš and Gill (1970) for the island arc tholeiitic series. Jakeš and Gill pointed out that the Ni and Cr content of this rock series indicated that it could not have been in equilibrium with an olivine-rich peridotitic upper mantle.

Subsequently, as the now dehydrated oceanic crust descends to deeper levels, further melting may occur, producing the island arc calcalkaline series with a silica mode approximating to andesite. This model effectively limits large-scale development of andesitic rocks to depths

---

compositions with controlled amounts of water present are available at present). Olivine tholeiite data are from J. Nicholls (pers. comm.) and olivine basanite data from D.H. Green (1970 & pers. comm.). The diagram shows the andesite liquidus lying in a marked thermal valley for anhydrous conditions, but with the addition of water the minimum liquidus temperatures are displaced towards more silicic compositions.

below where dehydration has occurred (i.e. depths $\gtrsim$80 km) since it is only under these conditions that andesite will be a lower melting composition.

POSTSCRIPT

From available data it is worth noting that true calcalkaline andesitic volcanoes lie > 80 km above the Benioff seismic zone, the zone from which the magmas possibly arise (Dickinson & Hatherton 1967; Dickinson, pers. comm. 1971).

ACKNOWLEDGEMENTS

Prof. A. E. Ringwood and Dr D. H. Green kindly made available facilities at the Australian National University, and Messrs Ware and Kiss gave analytical assistance. Mr J. B. Gill provided the sample of andesite and allowed access to unpublished analyses. Dr R. H. Vernon critically read the manuscript.

Financial support has been provided by the Australian Research Grants Committee (C70/17358) and by Macquarie University.

REFERENCES

Dickinson, W. R. & Hatherton, T. 1967. Andesitic volcanism and seismicity around the Pacific. *Science*, **157,** 801.

Gill, J. B. 1970. Geochemistry of Viti Levu, Fiji, and its evolution as an island arc. *Contr. Mineral. Petrol.* **27,** 179.

Green, D. H. 1970. The origin of basaltic and nephelinitic magmas. *Trans. Leicester lit. phil. Soc.* **64,** 28.

Green, T. H. & Ringwood, A. E. 1968. Genesis of the calc-alkaline igneous rock suite. *Contr. Mineral. Petrol.* **18,** 105.

——— (In prep.) Crystallization of garnet-bearing rhyodacite under high pressure hydrous conditions.

Jakeš, P. & Gill, J. 1970. Rare earth elements and the island arc tholeiitic series. *Earth Planet. Sci. Letters,* **9,** 17.

Leake, B. E. 1968. A catalog of analysed calciferous and subcalciferous amphiboles together with their nomenclature and associated minerals. *Spec. Pap. geol. Soc. Am.* **98,** 1.

The Petrology and Geochemistry of the Tongan Islands

A. EWART[1] AND W. B. BRYAN[2]

[1] *Department of Geology and Mineralogy, University of Queensland, St Lucia, Brisbane 4067, Australia.*

[2] *Woods Hole Oceanographic Institution, Woods Hole, Massachusetts, 02543, U.S.A.*

ABSTRACT

Tonga comprises a double chain of approximately N-S trending islands. The western line of islands comprise the active volcanoes. The eastern island chain is limestone covered, although on Eua, the southernmost island, a pre-Upper Eocene volcanic suite is exposed.

The active volcanic islands, each distinct morphologically, are dominated by basaltic andesite, except for Fonualei (predominantly dacite), and the unique Metis Shoal which produced rhyolite in the 1967-8 eruption. Acid andesites are subordinate in volume. The lavas contain phenocrystic bytownite, augite, hypersthene, and occasionally pigeonite. Magnetite microphenocrysts occur only in the more acidic lavas. Hydrous phases are completely absent. Pigeonite occurs in the groundmass of the more basic lavas. Chemically, these lavas are characterized by low alkalis, Ba, Pb, Zr, TiO_2, and P_2O_5, and moderately low MgO. The suite shows moderately high Fe enrichment. V/Ni and K/Rb ratios are high. REE abundances average 5-10 times chondritic values and show no fractionation relative to the chondritic pattern.

Using detailed element balance calculations, it is possible to explain the acidic lavas of the suite by a single stage crystal fractionation of basaltic andesite, although some problems are raised by Sr isotopic data. The origin of the basaltic andesites is problematic and one aspect considered is based on theoretical trace element partition during fractional melting of lithosphere, assumed to be ocean ridge basalt. Results tentatively suggest that the andesites may not be derived by simple melting of such a source rock.

The ?Lower Tertiary Eua volcanic suite, consisting of basalts, andesites, and very rare dacites, is geochemically even more 'primitive' than the active volcanoes. It is suggested that it represents the topmost exposure of an underlying ophiolite complex.

GEOLOGICAL SETTING

The islands of the Kingdom of Tonga lie at the northern end of an almost linear island arc system that extends NNE-SSW from northern New Zealand, through the Kermadecs, to near Samoa. The Tongan Islands comprise two separate island chains (Fig. 1), each distinct geologically. The western chain comprises the line of active volcanoes, lying some 160 km west of the Tonga Trench axis. The volcanoes mark the western edge of the Tonga Ridge, and are erupting lavas of basaltic andesite to dacite compo-

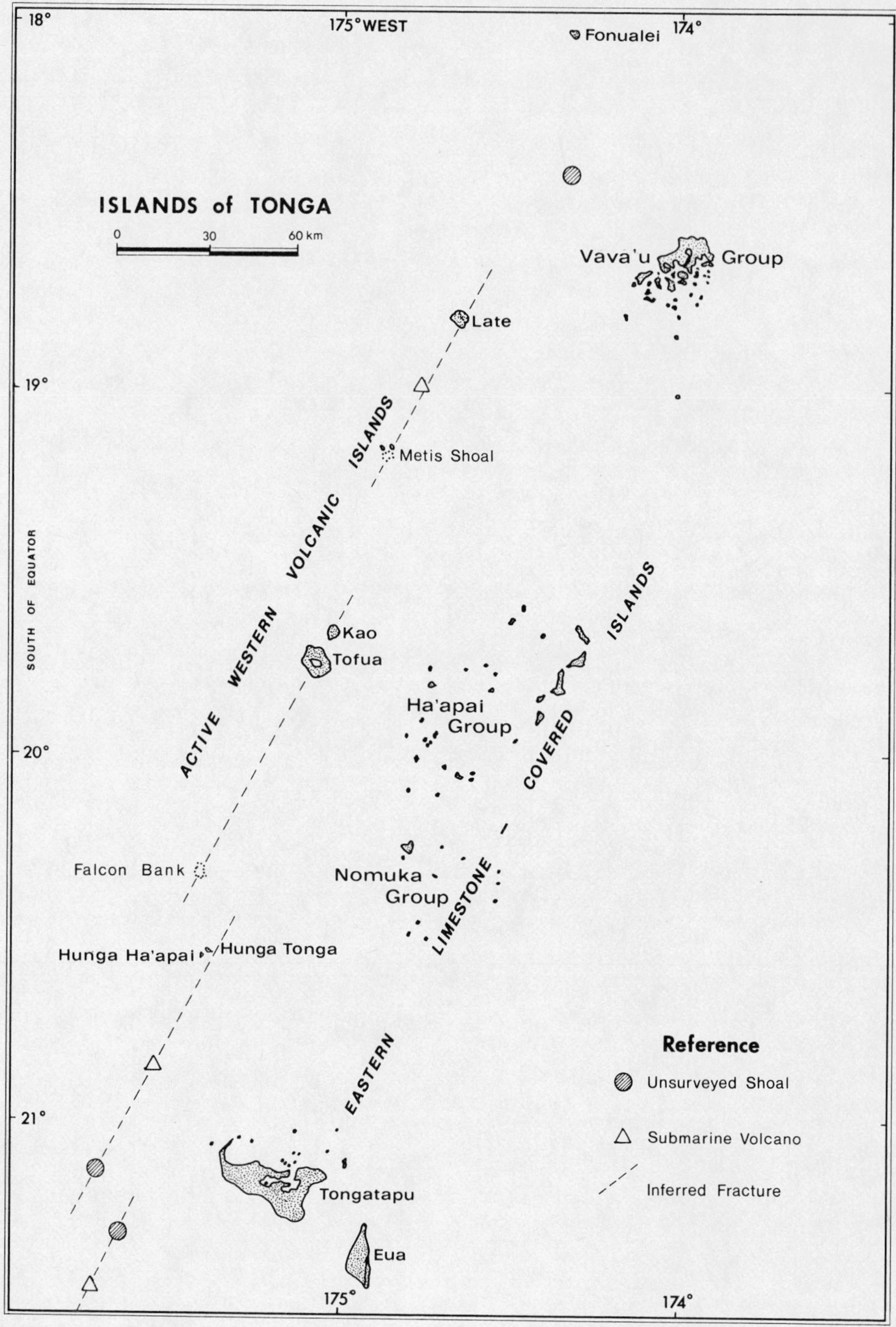

ISLANDS of TONGA
0 30 60 km
18°
175°WEST
174°
Fonualei
Vava'u Group
Late
19°
Metis Shoal
ACTIVE WESTERN VOLCANIC ISLANDS
SOUTH OF EQUATOR
Kao
Tofua
Ha'apai Group
EASTERN LIMESTONE - COVERED ISLANDS
20°
Falcon Bank
Nomuka Group
Hunga Ha'apai
Hunga Tonga
21°
Tongatapu
Eua
175°
174°
Reference
Unsurveyed Shoal
Submarine Volcano
Inferred Fracture

sitions. The eastern island chain lies some 95-130 km west of the trench and comprise limestone-covered islands, except for Eua at the southern end, where a lower Tertiary volcanic sequence is exposed beneath the limestone.

Tonga forms part of a typical island arc system with an offshore trench, a typical island arc gravity anomaly (Talwani *et al.* 1961, Hatherton 1969), and a westward dipping zone of intense seismic activity (Sykes 1966, Isacks *et al.* 1969, Mitronovas *et al.* 1969). This zone lies at a depth of about 100 km below the active volcanoes. Karig (1970, and this volume) has suggested that the Lau-Havre Trough, lying immediately west of the Tonga Ridge, is a young (< 10 m.y.) dilatational basin which has resulted in the eastward movement of the Tonga Ridge and presumably also the trench.

Petrologically, the special interest in Tonga lies in its apparent geological youth, representing an early stage of island arc (and continental?) growth. It is of some interest to compare the lavas with those from the Taupo Volcanic Zone, New Zealand, which are apparently more 'mature', and erupted in a continental environment.

THE VOLCANIC SUCCESSION OF EUA

The particular interest in Eua lies in the exposure, beneath the limestone, of a series of slightly metamorphosed basic-intermediate lavas, gabbros, and tuffs of pre-Upper Eocene age. This sequence does not outcrop elsewhere in Tonga, but is presumed to underlie the other eastern limestone-covered islands. This older volcanic sequence could thus date from the inception of the Tongan Arc, although if Karig's (1970) interpretations are correct, they were emplaced well west of their present geographic location.

The following is the inferred geological history of Eua, based on the interpretations of Hoffmeister (1932) and Stearns (1971). (*a*) Basaltic and andesitic volcanism, now evident from lavas, agglomerates, conglomerates, and tuffs, cut by frequent dykes; boulders of quartz gabbro occur, but not found *in situ*. This is the older volcanic series of Hoffmeister. Age: pre-Upper Eocene. (*b*) Deposition of a hard, pure foraminiferal and algal limestone (of Upper Eocene age), followed by a period of uplift. (*c*) Deposition of tuffaceous marlstone series, dated as late Eocene; depth of deposition 200-600 ft (Todd 1970, Cole 1970, Ladd 1970). (*d*) Deposition of tuffs and tuffaceous limestones of Miocene age—this is the younger volcanic series of Hoffmeister. (*e*) Uplift and block faulting. (*f*) Complex sequence of submergence and emergence during Plio-Pleistocene accompanied by growth of a coral limestone cover.

Petrology

Analysed volcanic rocks include one olivine basalt, high alumina tholeiites, basaltic andesites, andesites, one dacite tuff, and a quartz gabbro boulder. Mineralo-

---

Fig. 1 Location map of the principal Tongan Islands, showing the double island chain and the possible *en échelon* arrangement of the western volcanic islands.

gically, the basalts and andesites are characterized by phenocrysts of plagioclase (bytownite-anorthite in the most basic lavas, labradorite in the acidic andesites) and augite; microphenocrysts of titanomagnetite occur sporadically, and olivine pseudomorphs occur in the olivine basalt. Secondly, all rocks examined are altered, with development of uralite (actinolite plus chlorite), chlorite (ripidolite), epidote, calcite, and pyrite. Orthopyroxene has not been found, but may be uralitized as the augites are invariably quite fresh.

Chemistry

This volcanic suite is characterized by extremely low K, high Na/K ratios, low TiO_2 abundances and normative diopside, and does not show the same tendency for strong iron enrichment that is seen in the Recent Tongan lavas (Table 1). The Eua suite is also chemically more variable. Trace elements are also noteworthy for very low Rb and Ba, low Sr, Rb/Sr and Ni/Co ratios, and high K/Rb and V/Ni ratios. No correlation is found between K/Rb and either K or SiO_2. Initial Sr isotopic ratios (J. G. Gill, pers. comm.) give 0·7036 (high alumina tholeiite) and 0·7040 (acid andesite). Rare earth element (REE) data for these same two samples show total REE of 12·5 and 47·4 ppm respectively, with the tholeiite exhibiting a marked light REE depletion. The andesite REE pattern is subparallel to the chondritic pattern. The chemical characteristics are interpreted to be primary magmatic, and not modified by metamorphism.

Origin of the Eua igneous suite

One important geochemical aspect of many of the trace and minor element abundances within the Eua suite is that these abundances appear to bridge the gap between ocean ridge basalts and the Recent Tongan basaltic andesites.

It is suggested (Ewart *et al.* in prep.) that the Eua igneous rocks may represent the uppermost exposed portion of an underlying ophiolite complex. This suggestion is critically linked with the dredged occurrence of fresh to granulated and serpentinized peridotite and dunite from the near-shore flank of the Tonga Trench, near the axis (Fisher & Engel 1969). This interpretation implies that the Tonga Ridge is the positive topographic expression of an elongate ophiolite mass. Although speculative, the geological setting and the mineralogical and chemical features of the Eua rocks are certainly consistent with those recognized in described ophiolite complexes (e.g. Pantazis 1967, Davies 1968, Moores & Vine 1971, Reinhardt 1969).

THE YOUNGER VOLCANIC ISLANDS OF TONGA

Data presented are based on visits to the islands of Hunga Ha'apai, Late, and Fonualei, plus samples of Metis Shoal provided by W. G. Melson. Studies on the islands of Koa and Tofua are currently being completed elsewhere (P. G. Harris, pers. comm.).

The islands of Hunga, Late, Kao, and Tofua are dominated by basaltic andesites (Table 1), whose compositions lie within a very restricted range. Fonualei is dominated by chemically remarkably uniform dacites. Acid andesites are evidently quite

Table 1

AVERAGE ANALYTICAL DATA FOR THE TERTIARY AND RECENT TONGAN VOLCANIC LAVAS COMPARED TO THE AVERAGE OF NEW ZEALAND ANDESITES

	Eua		Late	Fonualei		Metis	New Zealand
	(1)	(2)	(3)	(4)	(5)	(6)	(7)
SiO_2	51·98	59·31	53·67	60·31	65·11	73·60	57·89
TiO_2	0·86	0·63	0·56	0·66	0·58	0·52	0·70
Al_2O_3	17·53	17·11	16·62	14·60	14·13	12·29	15·52
FeO	5·56	3·65	7·49	7·09	6·13	2·71	5·43
Fe_2O_3	4·96	3·03	2·91	3·07	1·87	1·31	1·89
MnO	0·24	0·13	0·18	0·21	0·18	0·06	0·14
MgO	5·03	3·06	4·87	2·59	1·52	1·07	5·96
CaO	9·50	5·99	11·01	7·42	5·87	3·61	7·92
Na_2O	2·43	3·78	1·77	2·69	2·97	3·17	2·59
K_2O	0·19	0·38	0·46	0·79	1·11	1·47	1·25
P_2O_5	0·09	0·11	0·08	0·17	0·19	0·07	0·12
H_2O	1·47	2·34	0·24	0·45	0·23	0·13	0·77
Total	100·16	100·01	99·86	100·05	99·89	100·25	100·18
Na_2O/K_2O	12·8	9·95	3·85	3·41	2·68	2·16	2·07
$Mg/Mg+\Sigma Fe$ (atomic %)	47·2	46·1	46·2	31·9	25·8	32·9	59·9
Trace elements (ppm):							
Rb	1·3	2·4	6	11	16	21	50
Ba	38	68	105	205	280	610	215
Pb	<2	<2	2·3	2·9	4·0	5·0	7
Sr	115	140	225	300	300	130	243
Zr	43	110	26	39	47	68	98
Cu	92	55	135	35	27	120	72
Ni	27	5	22	<2	<2	4	49
Co	28	14	31	28	14	10	37
V	290	125	310	185	93	130	167
Cr	52	15	41	6	4	7	210
K/Rb	1,215	1,315	635	595	575	580	281
Rb/Sr	0·011	0·017	0·027	0·037	0·053	0·16	0·21

1. Average of 4 tholeiites and basaltic andesites from the pre-Upper Eocene volcanic suite of Eua. Total includes 0·10 per cent CO_2 and 0·22 per cent S.
2. Averages of 2 andesites, occurring in conspicuous E-W dykes, from the Eua pre-Upper Eocene volcanic suite. Total includes 0·29 per cent CO_2 and 0·20 per cent S.
3. Average of 8 basaltic andesites from the active volcano of Late.
4. Average of 2 andesites from the pre-tuff sequence of the active volcano of Fonualei.
5. Average of 11 dacites from the active volcano of Fonualei.
6. Analysis of the residual glass from the 1967-8 eruption of Metis Shoal.
7. Average andesite analyses from the Taupo Volcanic Zone, New Zealand. Major element data from Steiner (1958) and Taylor and White (1966). Trace elements after Taylor and White (1966) and Ewart and Stipp (1968, Rb, Sr, and K/Rb).

subordinate in volume, although they have been found on Fonualei, Late and also Tofua (Bauer 1970).

Mineralogy

Phenocryst mineralogy of the active volcanoes is quite uniform: plagioclase, clinopyroxene, orthopyroxene, and in the acidic andesites and dacites also titanomagnetite. Pigeonite phenocrysts have been found in two basaltic andesites from Late. Plagioclase compositions range from An_{80-88}, the dacite plagioclases lying in the lower part of this range. Clinopyroxenes range from approximately $Mg_{50}Fe_{10}Ca_{40}$ in the basaltic andesites to $Mg_{36}Fe_{27}Ca_{37}$ in the dacites. Orthopyroxenes range from $Mg_{75}Fe_{20}Ca_5$ in the basaltic andesites to $Mg_{50}Fe_{45}Ca_5$ in the dacites. Pyroxene compositions from the acidic andesites are intermediate between these limits. Data on the distributions of Mg, Mn, Ti, V, Sc, and Ni between coexisting pyroxenes reveal well-defined linear correlations, indicative of equilibrium distributions.

Groundmass mineralogy comprises intermediate plagioclase, pigeonite in basaltic andesites, hypersthene in acidic andesites and dacites, iron oxides, rare apatite, and frequent glass. Fine-grained potash feldspar and quartz are identifiable in the more coarsely crystalline dacites.

In summary, two outstanding mineralogical features can be emphasized: (1) the absence, or lack of evidence of the former existence, of any hydrous mineral phase; (2) the absence of phenocrystic magnetite in the basic andesites, and its restriction to the more acidic rocks.

The 1967-8 Metis Shoal eruption (Melson *et al.* 1970)

The erupted lava consists of vesicular rhyolitic glass (Table 1) containing 'phenocrysts' of augite ($Mg_{41}Fe_{21}Ca_{39}$), orthopyroxene of at least two distinct compositions ($Mg_{63}Fe_{33}Ca_3$ and $Mg_{79}Fe_{18}Ca_4$), bytownite, titanomagnetite, and corroded olivine (Fo_{93}) with orthopyroxene rims and chrome spinel inclusions. Clearly, this lava contains a non-equilibrium mineralogy, and so far appears to be unique in Tonga.

Chemistry of the volcanoes

The active Tongan volcanic suite is noteworthy for its relatively high CaO and total Fe contents, high Fe^{2+}/Fe^{3+} ratios, and the low alkalis, especially K_2O. The Tongan rocks clearly belong to one of the Pacific 'low-potash' suites. Fig. 2 illustrates data from Hunga, Late, Fonualei and Metis plotted in the conventional AFM triangle and compared to the lavas from the Kermadecs and the Taupo Volcanic Zone, New Zealand. The Tongan data lie on a well defined trend (except Metis) and contrast strongly with the New Zealand data, both in terms of the scatter of data and the degree of Fe enrichment. The differences between the two suites are especially exemplified by the dacitic compositions ($SiO_2=63-69$ per cent).

Data for Rb, Sr, Pb, and Ba (Table 1) also emphasize the 'depleted' geochemistry of the Tongan lavas; the high K/Rb and low Rb/Sr ratios are noteworthy and contrast with the New Zealand andesites. The K/Rb ratios show a complete overlap between the various lava compositions, although the average values decrease with increasing SiO_2 (Table 1). The Tongan lavas are typically 'orogenic' with respect to

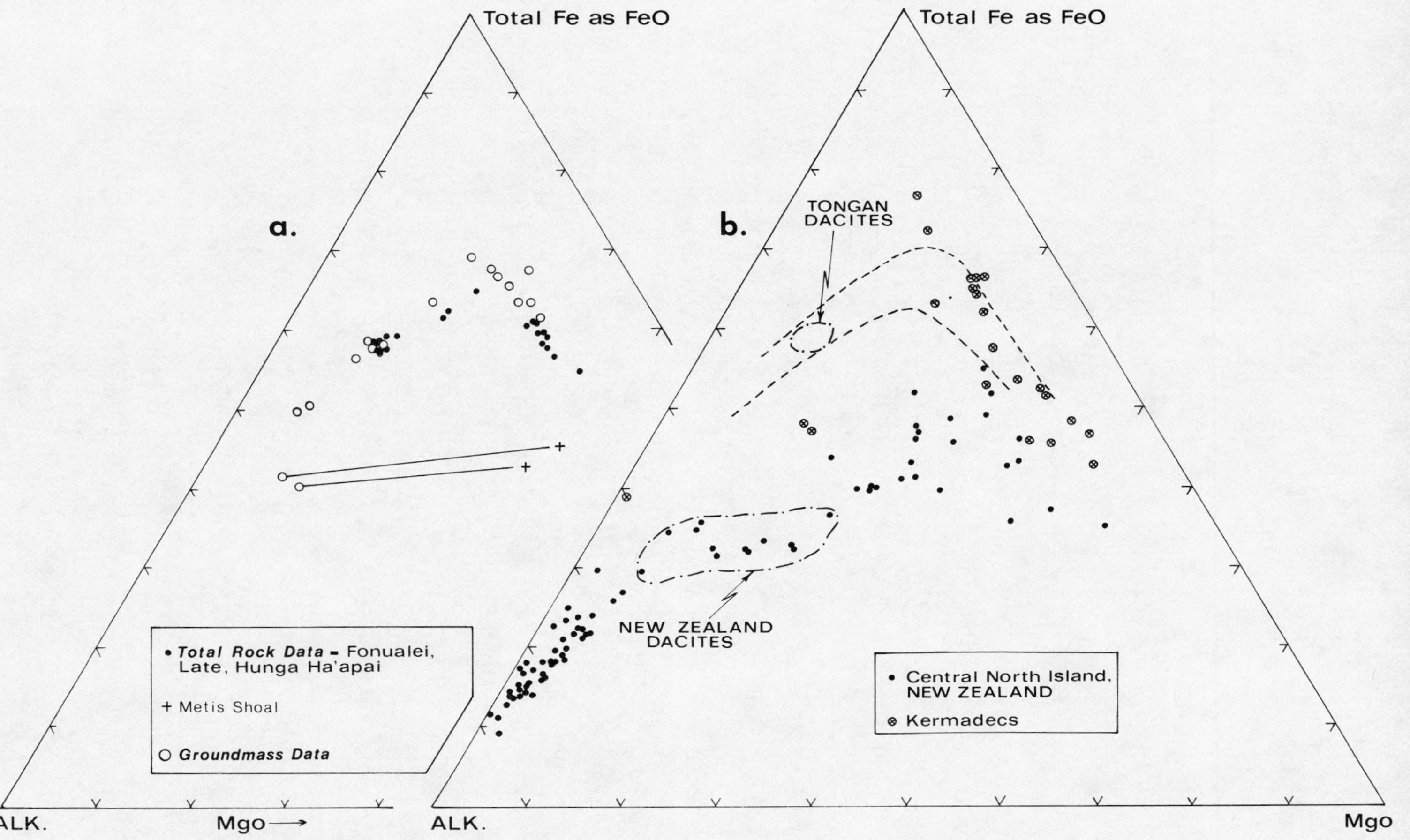

Fig. 2 AFM diagrams comparing the Recent Tongan basaltic andesite-dacite suite (and their co-existing groundmass components) with the basalt-andesite-rhyolite suite from the Taupo region, New Zealand (after Steiner 1958, Lewis 1968, Ewart 1969), and data for the Kermadecs (Brothers & Martin 1970, Brothers & Searle 1970). The dotted zone in Fig. (b) represents the trend of the Tongan data from Fig. (a).

the ferromagnesian element abundances (i.e. Ni, Co, V, Ti, and Cr), showing low Ni/Co and high V/Ni ratios. TiO_2 contents are 'circum-Pacific'. Zr is also noteworthy for its low abundance.

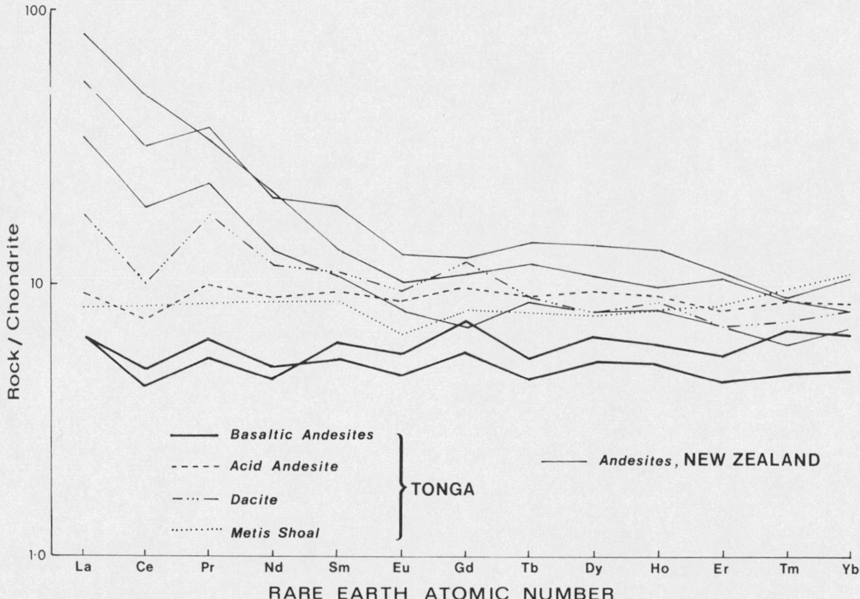

Fig. 3 REE abundances of samples of the Recent Tongan volcanic lavas, compared to three REE determinations from New Zealand andesites (after Ewart, Taylor & Capp 1968). New Tongan REE data determined by A. L. Graham. Metis Shoal data from Melson, Jarosewich and Lundquist (1970).

REE determinations (A. L. Graham, pers. comm.) are presented in Fig. 3. The basaltic andesite patterns show no fractionation relative to chondritic abundances, although enriched by a factor of some 5-6 times (total REE: 17-18 ppm). This compares with an enrichment of 15-25 times in ocean ridge basalts. The REE contents show a progressive increase in the acid andesite and dacites. All the REE patterns exhibit some evidence of slight Eu depletion. The Tongan REE patterns and abundances are clearly distinct from the New Zealand data (Fig. 3), the latter showing higher abundances and light REE enrichment.

The Tonga data show a well defined and regular increase in the abundances of Rb, Sr, Pb, Ba, REE, Zr, and decrease in the abundances of Ni, Co, V, Cr, Sc, and Cu in the sequence basaltic andesite to acid andesite to dacite. The Metis lava does not show a continuation of all of these trends.

In summary, attention is drawn to the marked geochemical differences between the Tongan and New Zealand andesites (Table 1), especially the alkalis and highly charged cations. The Tongan lavas belong to the 'island arc tholeiite series' of Jakeš and Gill (1970), while the New Zealand andesites show the more classical 'calc-alkaline' characteristics.

PETROGENETIC ASPECTS OF THE ACTIVE TONGAN VOLCANIC SUITE

The active volcanic suite presents at least two distinct petrogenetic problems both worth considering: (1) the origin of the basaltic andesites which evidently represent the most primitive of the magma types; (2) the development of the acidic andesites, dacites, and Metis Shoal rhyolite.

Contemporary researchers (e.g. McBirney 1969, Raleigh & Lee 1969, Taylor *et al.* 1969) relate andesite magma generation with melting in the topmost portion of the downthrust lithosphere (Isacks *et al.* 1968) beneath island arcs. The basaltic lithosphere is presumed to be transformed to amphibolitic and/or eclogitic mineralogy. The experimental results of Green and Ringwood (1968) suggest that melting of such material is capable of producing calcalkaline magmas.

Trace element fractionation and the basaltic andesites

One aspect of the above model will be considered here, namely the theoretical ability of the lithosphere, taken to be ocean ridge basalt, to produce the trace element abundances in the Tongan basaltic andesites. The REE are specifically considered. The approach followed is the use of the anatectic partition equations developed by Shaw (1970). The equations used are for both modal and non-modal melting, and may be solved to give either C^1/C_0 (ratio of concentration of element in liquid momentarily in equilibrium with residual solid to initial concentration of element in the solid) or C^{-1}/C_0, where C^{-1} is the element concentration in the aggregate liquid fractions described by C^1. Equations used were nos. 8, 10, 13, and 14 of Shaw's, p. 239-41. It is necessary to know distribution coefficients of each element considered for whichever combination of mineral phases are assumed to undergo melting, for given degrees of fractional melting.

Average REE data for ocean ridge basalts, taken here as the potential starting compositions (C_0), were taken from Kay *et al.* 1970 (excepting their sample V2140), while most of the other data used were from Engel, Engel, and Havens (1965). REE partition coefficients used were as adopted by Schilling (1971), and for garnet after Schnetzler and Philpotts (1970). In view of the variability and uncertainty of these coefficients, the calculations can provide no more than approximations. The results (Figs 4 and 5) are normalized to chondritic patterns (Frey *et al.* 1968) so as to facilitate comparison with analytical data.

In the first set of calculations (Fig. 4) it was simply assumed that the melted lithosphere was monomineralic as far as trace distributions were concerned; it was hoped to see the effects of various minerals on gross REE patterns of derived liquids. From Fig. 4, it is clear that REE fractionation in the aggregate fractional melts from the pyroxenes and amphibole depends on the degree of melting: those liquids produced by high degrees of melting show patterns subparallel to the chondritic

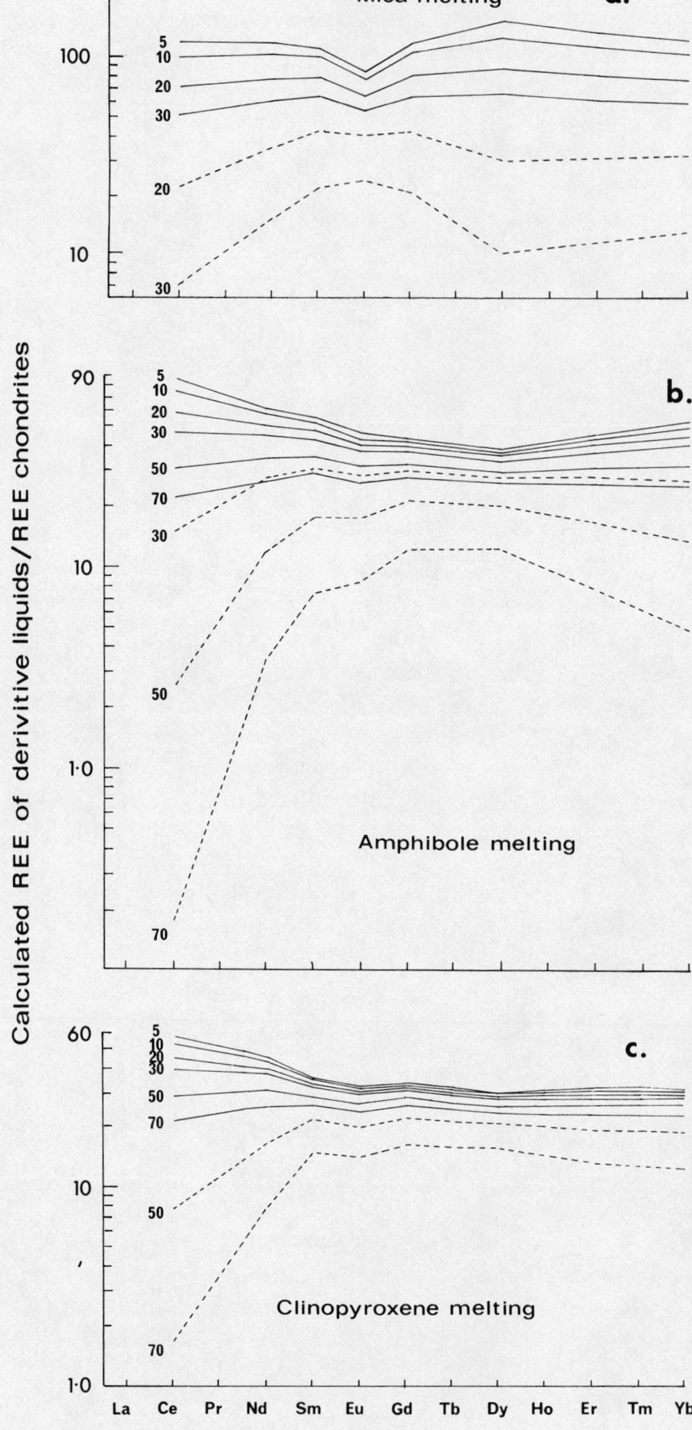

Calculated REE of derivitive liquids/REE chondrites
Mica melting
a.
100
10
5
10
20
30
20
30
b.
90
10
1·0
5
10
20
30
50
70
30
50
70
Amphibole melting
c.
60
10
1·0
5
10
20
30
50
70
50
70
Clinopyroxene melting
La
Ce
Pr
Nd
Sm
Eu
Gd
Tb
Dy
Ho
Er
Tm
Yb

patterns. The mica patterns exhibit little change. Eu anomalies are also evident. Furthermore, the REE concentrations in the aggregate liquids are all greater than in the starting compositions (=ocean-ridge basalts), which is contrary to the finding for the Tongan basaltic andesites (Fig. 3). Continous liquid separation results in extreme REE fractionation, and at high degrees of melting the total REE abundances are greatly reduced. Such extreme fractionation patterns, however, are not currently observed in island arc lavas. The clinopyroxene continuous separation REE patterns seem to show the closest approach to those observed in the Tongan basaltic andesites (and similar island arc tholeiitic lavas—Jakeš and Gill 1970).

In the second set of calculations shown (Fig. 5), the results of some combinations of non-modal melting from various 'amphibolitic' and 'eclogitic' mineral mixtures are reproduced. For the garnet-free assemblages, the general results are somewhat similar to the monomineralic calculations. In the case of amphibole melting from 'amphibolite', the calculation was repeated (Fig. 5*c*), but amphibole partition coefficients ten times higher, and so closer to the values suggested by Gast (1968), were used. The results still indicate higher REE abundances in the derived fractional melts than observed in the Tongan basaltic andesites. The models in which liquids are

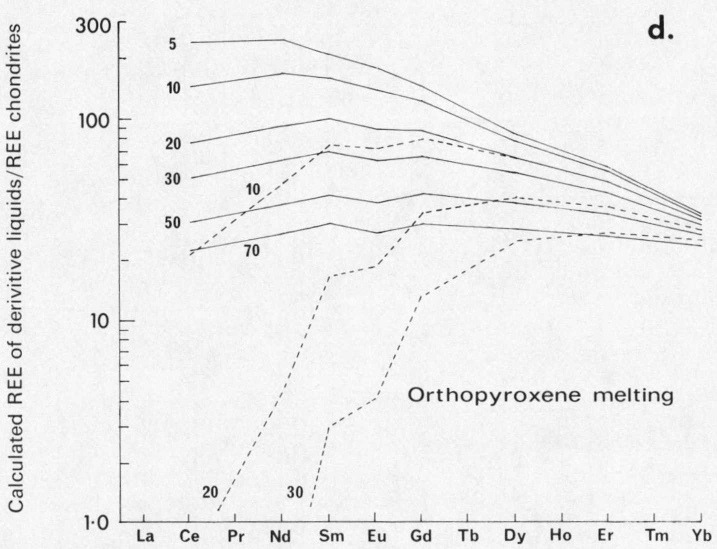

Fig. 4 Calculated REE abundances (normalized to chondrites) of liquids derived by fractional melting of a hypothetical monomineralic parent having the 'average' REE abundances of ocean ridge basalts. Interrupted lines represent liquid compositions, for given degrees of fractional melting, where the liquid is assumed to be momentarily in equilibrium with the residual solid. Solid lines are the liquid compositions, for given degrees of fractional melting, of the aggregate liquid fractions. Numbers beside each line represent the percentage fractional melting. Partition equations after Shaw (1970). Distribution coeffcients after Schilling (1971). Further details given in text.

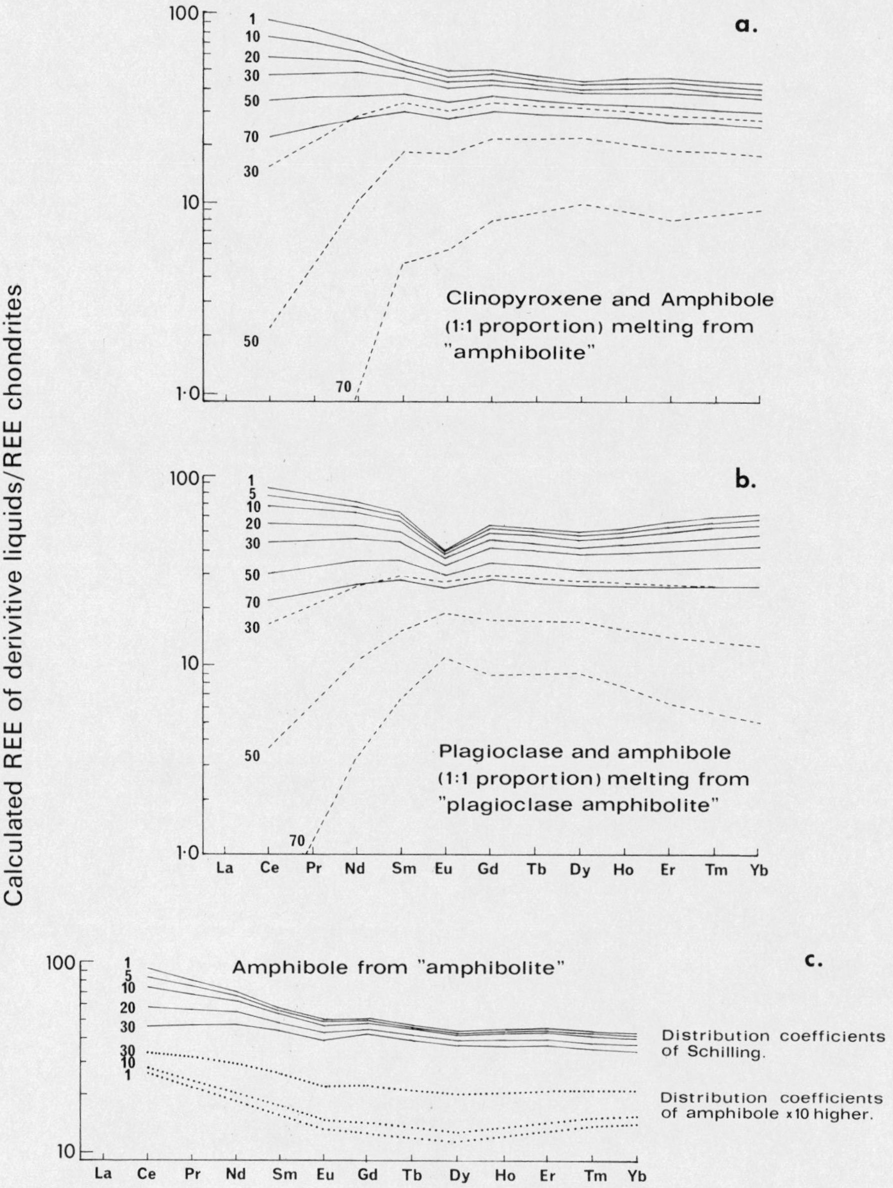

produced from garnet-bearing assemblages (garnet assumed to be residual) show the expected very strong lighter REE fractionation, except at high degrees of continuous liquid separation. On the basis of the garnet partition coefficients used, it would seem that the proportion of garnet permissible in source rock, which may give rise to the island arc andesitic magmas, is severely limited. If, however, the garnet partition coefficients for the heavier REE are in reality somewhat lower, as seems likely, then

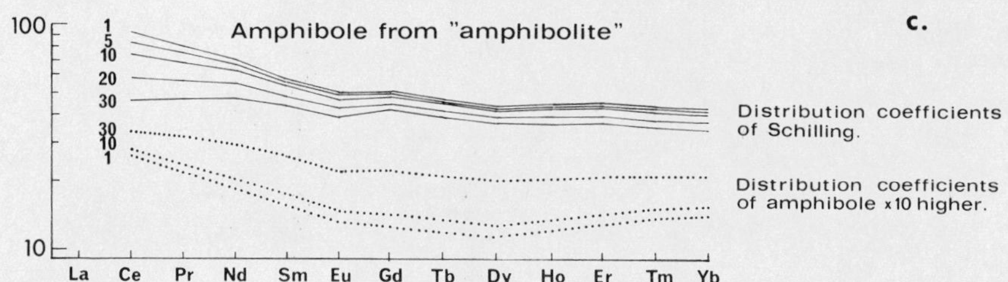

melting of garnet-bearing source rocks provides a feasible mechanism for producing the more highly fractionated lighter REE patterns found in the typical 'calcalkaline' andesites (e.g. New Zealand, Fig. 3) as compared to the 'island arc tholeiitic' andesites, such as found in Tonga.

In summary, there appears to be no problem in producing island arc magmas having

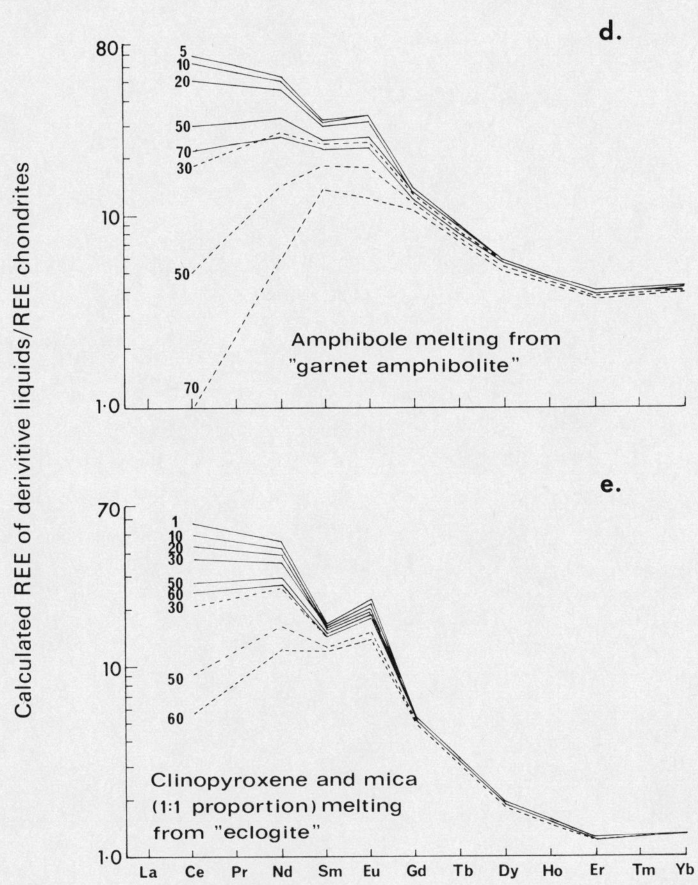

Fig. 5 Calculated REE abundances (normalized to chondrites) of liquids derived by non-modal fractional melting from various hypothetical mineralogical mixtures, the bulk REE abundances of which correspond to 'average' ocean ridge basalts. Symbols as in Fig. 4. The following are the assumed mineralogical compositions of the various hypothetical mixtures: 'amphibolite' = 30 per cent amphibole, 40 per cent clinopyroxene, 20 per cent orthopyroxene, 10 per cent phlogopite; 'plagioclase amphibolite' = 40 per cent amphibole, 30 per cent plagioclase, 30 per cent clinopyroxene; 'garnet amphibolite' = 70 per cent amphibole, 20 per cent clinopyroxene, 10 per cent garnet; 'eclogite' = 55 per cent clinopyroxene, 35 per cent garnet, 10 per cent phlogopite.

REE patterns subparallel to chondritic patterns. However, the REE abundances would seem to be decidedly higher than observed in the Tongan basaltic andesites and similar lava types (Jakeš & Gill 1970), indicating that these lavas were not produced by a simple process of fractional melting from such starting compositions. Alternative possibilities require either (*a*) melting of a source material with an even more depleted REE distribution than ocean ridge basalts; (*b*) interaction of a magma produced from lithospheric melting with overlying pyrolitic mantle; or (*c*) derivation of the basaltic andesites of Tonga by crystal fractionation of a geochemically highly depleted basaltic precursor. The second possibility seems to be precluded by the calculations of Nicholls and Carmichael (in press), and by the low Ni and Cr contents of the Tongan lavas, unless subsequently modified by crystal fractionation.

Although the above discussion has been only concerned with the REE, numerous similar calculations have been carried out with the elements Rb, Sr, Ba, Cr, Ni, Co, Sc, and V. Although detailed results cannot be documented here, it is of interest to note that the 'best fits' between calculated and observed data for the Tongan basaltic andesites, using the above models, are obtained in those models in which relatively high degrees (> 30 per cent) of fractional melting of pyroxene are involved.

Table 2

A. LEAST-SQUARES APPROXIMATION, BASED ON MAJOR ELEMENT ANALYSES ONLY, TO LATE ISLAND BASALTIC ANDESITE (SAMPLE 111547-5[1]) CALCULATED AS A LINEAR COMBINATION OF LATE ACID ANDESITE (SAMPLE 111547-13), PLUS ANALYSED AUGITE, HYPERSTHENE, AND PLAGIOCLASE PHENOCRYSTS FROM BASALTIC ANDESITE (111547-5) AND MAGNETITE FROM ACID ANDESITE (111547-13)

	Observed	*Calculated*	*Variable*	*Weight fraction*
SiO_2	54·11	54·10	Andesite (111547-13)	0·5999
Al_2O_3	17·03	17·03	Augite	0·0964
FeO	9·65	9·65	Hypersthene	0·0399
MgO	4·87	4·88	Plagioclase	0·2531
CaO	11·28	11·28	Magnetite	0·0108
Na_2O	1·75	1·88		
K_2O	0·49	0·43	Sum of squares of residuals	= 0·0292
TiO_2	0·58	0·61		
Results of trace element data substituted into above variables[2]:				
Rb	6	5·4		
Ba	125	104		
Sr	230	226		
Zr	24	23		
Cu	145	139		
Ni	25	21		
Co	29	32		
V	320	401		
Cr	55	61		

Table 2 (cont.)

B. LEAST-SQUARES APPROXIMATION, BASED ON MAJOR ELEMENT ANALYSES, TO LATE BASALTIC ANDESITE (111547-5) CALCULATED AS A LINEAR COMBINATION OF DACITE (111458-20), PLUS AUGITE, HYPERSTHENE, AND PLAGIOCLASE PHENOCRYSTS FROM LATE BASALTIC ANDESITE (111547-5), PLUS MAGNETITE FROM DACITE (111548-4)

	Observed	*Calculated*	*Variable*	*Weight fraction*
SiO_2	54·11	54·11	Dacite (111548-20)	0·4259
Al_2O_3	17·03	17·03	Augite	0·1737
FeO	9·65	9·64	Hypersthene	0·0378
MgO	4·87	4·88	Plagioclase	0·3166
CaO	11·28	11·28	Magnetite	0·0477
Na_2O	1·75	1·82		
K_2O	0·49	0·49	Sum of squares of residuals	=0·0234·
TiO_2	0·58	0·71		
Results of trace element data substituted into above variables[2]:				
Rb	6	6		
Ba	125	121		
Sr	230	245		
Zr	24	20		
Cu	145	26-32[3]		
Ni	25	23-30[3]		
Co	29	27-31[3]		
V	320	249-600[3]		
Cr	55	93-104[3]		

[1] Numbers refer to rock collection in the United States National Museum, Washington.

[2] Trace element data taken from a different, but closely similar plagioclase and pyroxene phenocrysts from which major element calculations made.

[3] The range of values arise from taking trace element values in different analysed magnetites.

Development of the recent acid lavas of Tonga

A characteristic feature of the Tongan suite is the well defined and regular variation of major and trace element chemistry through the rock series, with the possible exception of the Metis Shoal rhyolite. This is suggestive of crystal fractionation, and to test this possibility, a series of least squares linear mixing calculations (Bryan *et al.* 1969) have been (and still are) made for various combinations of lava bulk compositions and analysed phenocryst compositions. Major element compositions are recalculated water-free, with total Fe as FeO. Results of two such calculations are presented in Table 2. In order to test these calculations further, trace-element data for the rocks and minerals have been inserted into the final least squares combinations —based on the major element data— and these results are also shown.

From Table 2, it is clear that the major element data are consistent with a simple crystal fractionation model interrelating the lava compositions. This conclusion is reinforced by most of the trace-element data, although problems are raised by Sr isotopic results, noted below. The mineral proportions required by the calculations are entirely consistent with modal data. It is noteworthy that: (*a*) magnetite is required for satisfactory solutions to all the calculations so far made; and (*b*) Ba, Cu, V, and Cr are the trace elements showing greatest deviation between the calculated and observed abundances. These discrepancies are reduced when calculations involve mixing lava compositions from the same island. In the case of V and Cr, the discrepancies are readily explained in terms of the observed variability of magnetite (V) and augite (Cr) with respect to these elements. The 'inter-island' Cu discrepancy is problematical and perhaps suggests the possible separation of a Cu-bearing phase during dacite fractionation.

Preliminary calculations are also consistent with the crystal fractionation derivation of the Metis Shoal rhyolite glass from basaltic andesite, but interestingly, not directly from the dacites.

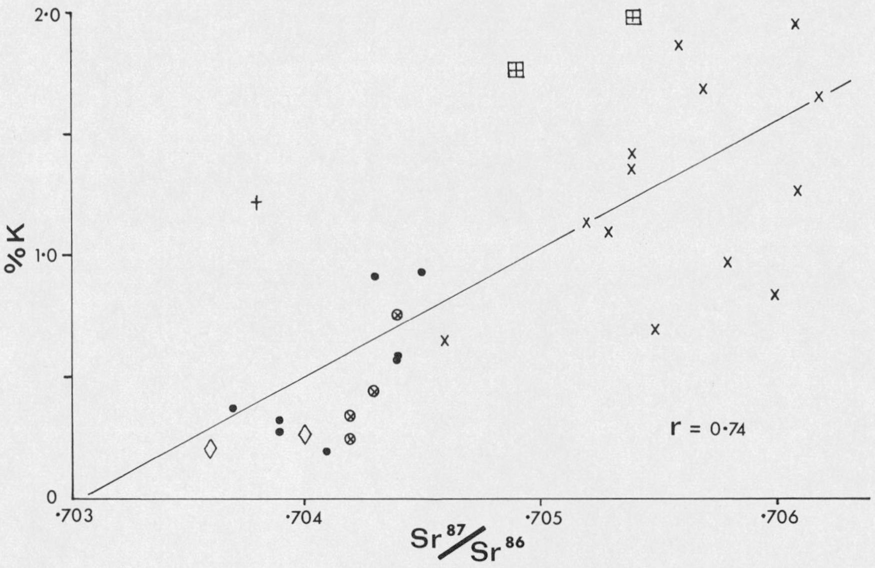

Fig. 6 Initial Sr 87/86 versus %K for the Tongan Volcanic Suite compared to the basalt-andesite-rhyolite suite of the Taupo region, New Zealand. Data from J.B. Gill (unpubl.) and Ewart and Stipp (1968).

Sr isotopes

Initial Sr isotopic ratios of the Recent Tongan suite range from 0·7037-0·7045 (J. B. Gill, pers. comm.). The most significant fact is a marked positive correlation of Sr^{87}/Sr^{86} with Rb/Sr, except for the Metis Shoal rhyolite. This suggests the possibility of either Sr isotopic fractionation during crystal fractionation, or contamination. The latter could imply that contamination was required to initiate crystal fractionation. These possibilities prompted a plot (Fig. 6) of Sr^{87}/Sr^{86} versus %K for the Tongan lavas and the basalt-andesite-dacite lavas from the Taupo Volcanic Zone, New Zealand (Ewart & Stipp 1968). It must be emphasized that two sets of rocks are being compared, which are separated by some hundreds of kilometres, although belonging to extreme ends of the same island arc system. Furthermore Stipp (1968) has demonstrated significant Sr isotopic zoning in northern New Zealand, but the lavas from west of the Taupo Volcanic Zone are generally older and do not appear to have any direct present day continuity with the Tongan Arc. The significant aspect raised by Fig. 6 is the positive correlation between K and the Sr isotopes. It is certainly suggestive of young crustal contamination.

ACKNOWLEDGEMENTS

Field work was sponsored by the Smithsonian Institution and was supported by research grants from the National Geographic Society and the University of Queensland. A research grant (A.R.G.C.—B67/16723) to one author (A.E.) enabled purchase of x-ray equipment on which the analytical work was largely undertaken. A. S. Bagley wrote the computer programme for the partition equations.

POSTSCRIPT

SOME THOUGHTS ON ANDESITE PETROGENESIS

A. Ewart

1. The correlation of K_2O with depth to the Benioff zone is now well established (e.g. Dickinson 1968). I would suggest, however, that this is not a direct or first order genetic correlation. For example, in Tonga there is an eastward decrease in K_2O from the Recent to the Eua Tertiary lavas, which can be correlated with decreasing depth to the seismic zone. According to Karig (1970), however, the older Eua volcanic sequence was emplaced well west of its present geographic location, and has subsequently moved eastwards. The Recent volcanic suite in contrast is developing *in situ*. Thus, the correlation of K_2O with the present day seismicity must be considered coincidental.

A much more important fact appears to be the restriction, as far as I can ascertain, of the high potash andesites and shoshonites to areas in which a crust of continental thickness is developed. This suggests that the potash contents of these lavas may well be controlled by processes other than melting along the Benioff zone.

2. If the circum-Pacific andesites are produced from melting of downthrust oceanic crust, and assuming the spreading centre to be the East Pacific Rise, then it might be expected that andesites in the Western Pacific should be more radiogenic than those of the Eastern Pacific. There is certainly no clear cut evidence of this type, although the highest Sr^{87}/Sr^{86} ratios in

andesites so far seem to come from the Western Pacific (e.g. New Zealand). Calculations, however, show that the time required to increase the Sr^{87}/Sr^{86} ratios of fresh oceanic ridge basalts (0·7025) to 'average' andesitic ratios (0·7035), with Rb/Sr ratios of 0·01, is in excess of 2,500 m.y., which is much older than the age of the Pacific crust. This raises the alternative question of why andesites do have significantly higher Sr isotopic ratios than oceanic ridge basalts. One explanation could lie in the known increase of Sr^{87}/Sr^{86} with sea-water alteration (Hart & Nalwalk 1970), which might also be expected to be greater in the Western Pacific crust by virtue of its longer exposure to sea-water. Alternatively, the more radiogenic Sr may be the result of admixture of oceanic sediment to the downthrust lithosphere, and their subsequent composite melting.

3. A very real problem is now arising in regard to the nomenclature and real distinction of oceanic and circum-Pacific volcanic suites. What in fact are the critical chemical and mineralogical distinctions? The situation is aggravated by several recent developments: for example, the recognition of an 'island arc tholeiitic series' by Jakeš and Gill (1970), which show many trace-element features similar to the ocean-floor basalts; and the occurrence of ophiolites in island arc environments, which are frequently interpreted as upthrust slices of oceanic crust and mantle. Further complications are the occurrence of young, and apparently typical ocean-floor basalts in marginal basins opening behind the Western Pacific island arcs, and the reported analyses of isolated andesitic compositions in dredges from the East Pacific Rise by Kay *et al.* (1970) and Hart (1971).

It is obvious that the older idea of a clear distinction between circum-oceanic and ocean-basin volcanic suites is clearly grossly over-simplified, and in fact contrary to the implications of plate tectonics. It is also of interest to note that Karig (1970), in order to account for the origin of his marginal basins, appeals to diapiric uprise of material from the Benioff zone, essentially similar to the process commonly advocated for andesite genesis within the arcs themselves. With regard to critical mineralogical differences between ocean-floor basalts and island arc andesites and basaltic andesites, perhaps one difference that offers the possibility of being critical is the invariable absence of phenocrystic Ca-poor pyroxenes (especially hypersthene) in the oceanic-floor basalts and the invariable presence of Ca-poor pyroxenes (usually hypersthene) as phenocrysts in the island arc lavas.

4. The occurrence of relatively magnesian-rich olivines has been recorded frequently in basic and basaltic andesites. In Tonga, compositions of Fo_{90}-Fo_{93} are recorded (Bauer 1970; Melson, Jarosewich & Lundquist 1970), while Clark (1960) records optical compositions of Fo_{60} to 'nearly pure forsterite'. Compositions of up to Fo_{84-85} are recorded by Coats (1952) Lowder (1970) and Wilcox (1954). According to the olivine data of Roeder and Emslie (1970), compositions more Mg-rich than Fo_{84} would be in equilibrium with liquids with Fe^{2+}/Mg ratios (mol.) of 0·63, which correspond to basaltic magmas. The composition Fo_{93} recorded in the Tongan Metis Shoal lava (Melson *et al.* 1970) would seem originally to have crystallized from a picritic magma, although now occurring as xenocrysts in a rhyolitic glass! The main point is, however, that the occurrence of Mg-rich olivines indicates a basaltic, or in extreme cases, picritic parentage of these olivines, and presumably also the andesitic lavas in which these olivines occur.

REFERENCES

Bauer, G. R. 1970. The geology of Tofua Island, Tonga. *Pacif. Sci.* **24,** 333.

Brothers, R. N. & Martin, K. R. 1970. The geology of Macauley Island, Kermadec Group, South-west Pacific. *Bull. volcan.* **34,** 330.

Brothers, R. N. & Searle, E. J. 1970. The geology of Raoul Island, Kermadec Group, Southwest Pacific. *Bull. volcan.* **34,** 7.

Bryan, W. B., Finger, L. W. & Chayes, F. 1969. Estimating proportions in petrographic mixing equations by least-squares approximation. *Science,* **163,** 926.

Clark, R. H. 1960. Petrology of the volcanic rocks of Tongariro subdivision. In *The geology of Tongariro subdivision* (Ed. D. R. Gregg) *Bull. geol. Surv. N.Z.* n.s. **40,** 107.

Coats, R. R. 1952. Magmatic differentiation in Tertiary and Quaternary volcanic rocks from Adak and Kananga Islands, Aleutian Islands, Alaska. *Bull. geol. Soc. Am.* **63,** 485.

Cole, W. S. 1970. Larger foraminifera of late Eocene age from Eua, Tonga. *U.S. geol. Surv. Prof. Pap.* 640-B, 15 pp.

Davies, H. L. 1968. Papuan ultramafic belt. *23rd Intern. Geol. Congr. Prague,* **1,** 209.

Dickinson, W. R. 1968. Circum-Pacific andesite types. *J. geophys. Res.* **73,** 2261.

Engel, A. E. J., Engel, C. G. & Havens, R. G. 1965. Chemical characteristics of oceanic basalts and the upper mantle. *Bull. geol. Soc. Am.* **76,** 719.

Ewart, A. 1969. Petrochemistry and feldspar crystallization in the silicic volcanic rocks, central North Island, New Zealand. *Lithos* **2,** 371.

Ewart, A. & Bryan, W. B. (In press.) The petrology and geochemistry of the igneous rocks from Eua, Tonga—an early Tertiary ophiolite complex? *Bull. geol. Soc. Am.*

Ewart, A. & Stipp, J. J. 1968. Petrogenesis of the volcanic rocks of the Central North Island, New Zealand, as indicated by a study of Sr^{87}/Sr^{86} ratios, and Sr, Rb, K, U, and Th abundances. *Geochim. cosmochim. Acta,* **32,** 699.

Ewart, A., Taylor, S. R. & Capp, A. C. 1968. Trace and minor element geochemistry of the rhyolitic volcanic rocks, Central North Island, New Zealand. Total rock and residual liquid data. *Contr. Mineral. Petrol.* **18,** 76.

Fisher, R. L. & Engel, C. G. 1969. Ultramafic and basaltic rocks dredged from the nearshore flank of the Tonga Trench. *Bull. geol. Soc. Am.* **80,** 1373.

Frey, F. A., Haskin, M. A., Poetz, J. A. & Haskin, L. A. 1968. Rare earth abundances in some basic rocks. *J. geophys. Res.* **73,** 6085.

Gast, P. W. 1968. Trace element fractionation and the origin of tholeiitic and alkaline magma types. *Geochim. cosmochim. Acta,* **32,** 1057.

Green, T. H. & Ringwood, A. E. 1968. Genesis of the calc-alkaline igneous rock suite. *Contr. Mineral. Petrol.* **18,** 105.

Hart, S. R. 1971. K, Rb, Cs, Sr, and Ba contents and Sr isotope ratios of ocean floor basalts. *Phil. Trans. R. Soc. London. A.* **268,** 573.

Hart, S. R. & Nalwalk, A. J. 1970. K, Rb, Cs, and Sr relationships in submarine basalts from the Puerto Rico trench. *Geochim. cosmochim. Acta,* **34,** 145.

Hatherton, T. 1969. Similarity of gravity anomaly patterns in asymmetric active regions. *Nature,* **224,** 357.

Hoffmeister, J. E. 1932. Geology of Eua, Tonga. *Bull. Bernice P. Bishop Mus.* **96,** 93 pp.

Isacks, B., Oliver, J. & Sykes, L. R. 1968. Seismology and the new global tectonics. *J. geophys. Res.* **73,** 5855.

Isacks, B., Sykes, L. R. & Oliver, J. 1969. Focal mechanisms of deep and shallow earthquakes in the Tonga-Kermadec region and the tectonics of island arcs. *Bull. geol. Soc. Am.* **80,** 1443.

Jakeš, P. &. Gill, J. 1970. Rare earth elements and the island arc tholeiitic series. *Earth Planet. Sci. Letters,* **9,** 17.

Karig, D. E. 1970. Ridges and basins of the Tonga-Kermadec island arc system. *J. geophys. Res.* **75,** 239.

Kay, R., Hubbard, N. J. & Gast, P. W. 1970. Chemical characteristics and origin of ocean ridge volcanic rocks. *J. geophys. Res.* **75,** 1585.

Ladd, H. S. 1970. Eocene mollusks from Eua, Tonga. *U.S. geol. Surv. Prof. Pap.* **640**-C, 12 pp.

Lewis, J. F. 1968. Tauhara volcano, Taupo zone. Part II—Mineralogy and petrology. *N.Z. Jl Geol. Geophys.* **11,** 651.

Lowder, G. G. 1970. The volcanoes and caldera of Talasea, New Britain: Mineralogy. *Contr. Mineral. Petrol.* **26,** 324.

McBirney, A. R. 1969. Compositional variations in Cenozoic calc-alkaline suites of Central America. *Proc. Andesite Conference* (Ed. A. R. McBirney) *Bull. Ore. St. Dep. Geol. miner. Ind.* **65,** 185.

Melson, W. G., Jarosewich, E. & Lundquist, C. A. 1970. Volcanic eruption at Metis Shoal, Tonga, 1967-8: description and petrology. *Smithsonian Contributions to the Earth Sciences,* **4,** 18 pp.

Mitronovas, W., Isacks, B. & Seeber, L. 1969. Earthquake locations and seismic wave propagation in the upper 250 km of the Tonga Island arc. *Bull. seism. Soc. Am.* **59,** 1115.

Moores, E. M. & Vine, F. J. 1971. The Troodos massif, Cyprus and other ophiolites as oceanic crust: evaluation and implications. *Phil. Trans. R. Soc. London, A.* **268,** 443.

Nicholls, J. & Carmichael, I. S. E. (In press.) The equilibration temperature and pressure (P_{total}) of various lava types with spinel- and garnet- peridotite. *Am. Miner.*

Pantazis, T. M. 1967. The geology and mineral resources of the Pharmakas-Kalavasos area. *Mem. geol. Surv. Cyprus,* **8,** 190 pp.

Raleigh, C. B. & Lee, W. H. K. 1969. Sea-floor spreading and island-arc tectonics. *Proc. Andesite Conference* (Ed. A. R. McBirney), *Bull. Ore. St. Dep. Geol. miner. Ind.* **65,** 99.

Reinhardt, B. M. 1969. On the genesis and emplacement of ophiolites in the Oman Mountains geosyncline. *Schweiz. miner. petrogr. Mitt.* **49,** 1.

Roeder, P. L. & Emslie, R. F. 1970. Olivine-liquid equilibrium. *Contr. Mineral. Petrol.* **29,** 275.

Schilling, J. G. 1971. Sea-floor evolution: rare-earth evidence. *Phil. Trans. R. Soc. London, A.* **268,** 663.

Schnetzler, C. C. & Philpotts, J. A. 1970. Partition coefficients of rare-earth elements between igneous matrix material and rock-forming mineral phenocrysts—II. *Geochim. cosmochim. Acta,* **34,** 331.

Shaw, D. M. 1970. Trace element fractionation during anatexis. *Geochim. cosmochim. Acta,* **34,** 237.

Stearns, H. T. 1971. Geological setting of an Eocene fossil deposit on Eua Island, Tonga. *Bull. geol. Soc. Am.* **82,** 2541.

Steiner, A. 1958. Petrogenetic implications of the 1954 Ngauruhoe lava and its xenoliths. *N.Z. Jl Geol. Geophys.* **1,** 325.

Stipp, J. J. 1968. The geochronology and petrogenesis of the Cenozoic volcanics of North Island, New Zealand. Ph.D. thesis, Aust. Nat. Univ., Canberra.

Sykes, L. R. 1966. The seismicity and deep structure of island arcs. *J. geophys. Res.* **71,** 2981.

Talwani, M., Worzel, J. L. & Ewing, M. 1961. Gravity anomalies and crustal section across the Tonga trench. *J. geophys. Res.* **66,** 1265.

Taylor, S. R., Capp, A. C., Graham, A. L. & Blake, D. H. 1969. Trace element abundances in andesites, II. Saipan, Bougainville and Fiji. *Contr. Mineral. Petrol.* **23,** 1.

Taylor, S. R. & White, A. J. R. 1966. Trace element abundances in andesites. *Bull. volcan.* **29,** 177.

Todd, R. 1970. Smaller foraminifera of late Eocene age from Eua, Tonga. *U.S. geol. Surv. Prof. Pap.* **640**-A, 23 pp.

Wilcox, R. E. 1954. Petrology of Paricutin volcano, Mexico. *Bull. U.S. geol. Surv.* **965**-C.

Distribution and Petrology of Late Cenozoic Volcanoes in Papua New Guinea[1]

R. W. JOHNSON, D. E. MACKENZIE, I. E. SMITH[2],
AND G. A. M. TAYLOR
Bureau of Mineral Resources, P.O. Box 378,
Canberra City, A.C.T. 2601, Australia

ABSTRACT

Four areas of late Cenozoic volcanoes are recognized in Papua New Guinea. These are: (1) the Mainland volcanoes, clustered in two groups, one in the Highlands, the other in eastern Papua; (2) the Bismarck volcanic arc, which extends along the north coasts of New Guinea and New Britain; (3) an Outer volcanic arc, consisting of the islands north and east of New Ireland, possibly the St Matthias Group, and the Admiralty Islands; (4) Bougainville Island, at the north-western end of the Solomon Islands chain. The Highlands and east Papuan volcanoes are made up of calcalkaline and shoshonitic rocks. Lavas in the Bismarck volcanic arc range from tholeiitic basalt to andesite, dacite, and rhyolite. The andesites show slight to moderate iron-enrichment characteristic of calcalkaline rocks, but alkali contents are variable for any given silica content, and many lavas have low values typical of tholeiitic rocks. A northward increase in K_2O content of lavas in the New Britain part of the arc correlates with depth to an underlying, northward-dipping Benioff zone. The islands north and east of New Ireland in the Outer volcanic arc are composed of basic undersaturated lavas of shoshonitic affinities. Volcanoes on Bougainville Island have produced andesitic and dacitic rocks characteristic of many circum-Pacific calcalkaline associations. While some aspects of the petrology and distribution of the late Cenozoic volcanoes of Papua New Guinea can be explained by partial melting of a down-going slab of oceanic lithosphere, the apparent absence of Benioff zones beneath some of the volcanic areas suggests that the possibility of generating magmas of island-arc type in different tectonic environments should also be considered. Moreover, although it is possible that tholeiitic and calcalkaline rocks are generated by partial melting of a downgoing lithospheric slab, the high potassium content and basaltic compositions of the shoshonitic rocks infer that processes other than partial melting of tholeiitic oceanic crust may be involved in their generation.

INTRODUCTION

Papua New Guinea is part of a tectonically active and complex region between the Pacific and Indo-Australian plates. During the late Cenozoic, and concurrently

[1] This paper is published with the permission of the Director, Bureau of Mineral Resources, Canberra.
[2] Present address: Department of Geology, Australian National University, P.O. Box 4, Canberra City, A.C.T. 2601, Australia.

with tectonic activity, volcanism took place in widely separated areas, producing clusters of volcanoes in regions such as the Highlands, and narrow arc-like chains of volcanoes in areas such as New Britain and Bougainville Island (Fig. 1).

Several accounts have been produced on the petrology and geology of different volcanic areas in Papua New Guinea, e.g. Taylor 1958, Ruxton 1966, Morgan 1966, Taylor *et al.* 1969, Jakeš and White 1969, Lowder and Carmichael 1970, Jakeš and Smith 1970, but it is only since 1969 that systematic sampling on a regional basis has been undertaken (cf. Johnson, Mackenzie & Smith, 1971). This paper summarizes petrographic and major element chemical data obtained during the past three years, much of which was previously unpublished. It is an interim report compiled from work which is still in progress in four different areas of Papua New Guinea.

There are four zones of late Cenozoic volcanism in Papua New Guinea (Fig. 1):

1. The Mainland volcanoes, clustered in two groups, one in the Highlands, and the other in eastern Papua (including the D'Entrecasteaux Islands).

2. The Bismarck volcanic arc. This name refers to the belt of volcanoes on the southern margin of the Bismarck Sea. The arc extends from Rabaul, in the east, along the north coast of New Britain, and west to the islands off the north coast of New Guinea.

3. An Outer volcanic arc, consisting of the islands north and east of New Ireland, possibly the St Matthias Group, and the Admiralty Islands.

4. Bougainville Island, which is at the north-western end of the Solomon Islands chain.

In this paper, author responsibility for the above areas is as follows: Mainland volcanoes—Mackenzie (Highlands) and Smith (eastern Papua); Bismarck volcanic arc—Johnson; Outer volcanic arc—Taylor (islands north and east of New Ireland). Additional data used in this paper has been taken from both published and unpublished sources.

VOLCANIC AND SEISMIC ACTIVITY

The Bismarck volcanic arc is the most volcanically active of the four areas; it contains several volcanoes which have erupted during this century (Fisher 1957). On the other hand, the Highlands volcanoes are all extinct, except for Doma Peaks in the southern Highlands and Mount Yelia in the eastern Highlands, both of which show some solfataric activity. In eastern Papua there have been eruptions from three centres during the past 100 years (Baker 1946, Taylor 1958, Smith 1969); other centres, particularly those of the D'Entrecasteaux Islands, have probably been active within the past 500 to 1,000 years.

With the exception of Tuluman volcano, which erupted between 1953 and 1957 (Reynolds & Best 1957, Reynolds 1958), the volcanoes of the Outer volcanic arc are extinct, or show solfataric activity. Similarly, the volcanoes of Bougainville Island are also either extinct or in solfataric stage, except for Mount Bagana which has erupted several times this century (Smith 1969).

Seismicity in Papua New Guinea was described by Denham (1969), and its

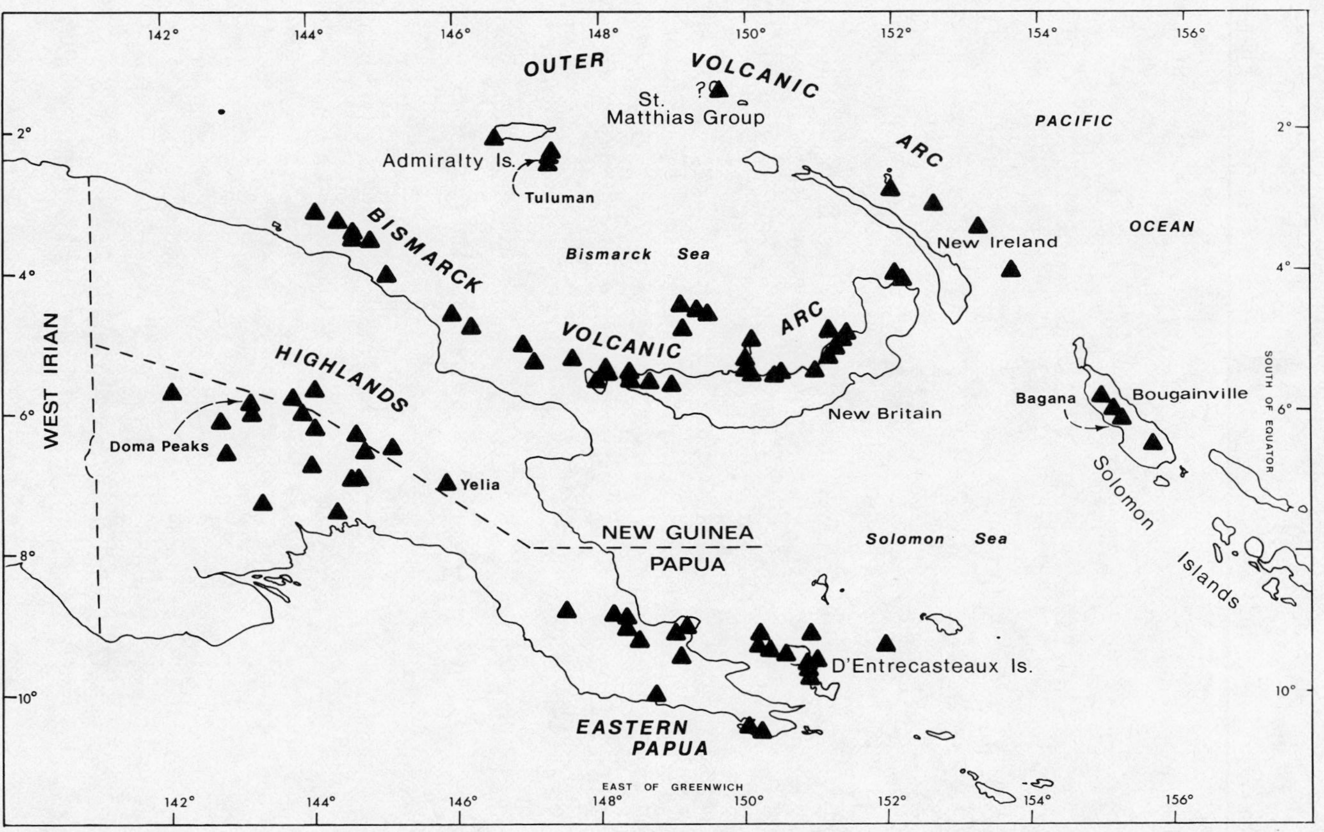

Fig. 1 Distribution of late Cenozoic volcanoes in Papua New Guinea. The principal volcanoes are shown as solid triangles.

relationship to the distribution and chemistry of the late Cenozoic volcanoes was discussed by Johnson, Mackenzie, and Smith (1971). The Bismarck volcanic arc and Bougainville Island coincide with belts of intense seismic activity. A vertical Benioff zone underlies Bougainville Island, and a Benioff zone dips 70° northwards beneath New Britain. Beneath the western part of the Bismarck volcanic arc there is a concentration of intermediate depth (70-150 km) earthquake foci, but these do not appear to define a Benioff zone.

Over the past ten years, high magnitude earthquakes (greater than about magnitude 4·5) in the Highlands and eastern Papua have been rare compared to those in the Bismarck volcanic arc and Bougainville Island. Similarly, seismicity in the Outer volcanic arc has not been intense, and only a very weak seismic belt is present along the convex side of the volcanic arc.

PETROLOGY

The Mainland volcanoes

The large stratovolcanoes of the Papua New Guinea Highlands are made up of lava flows, pyroclastic deposits, and lahars of shoshonitic and calcalkaline compositions. There is no clear petrographic separation between lavas of each association. All the lavas are strongly porphyritic, and contain phenocrysts of plagioclase and clinopyroxene. The more basic lavas contain olivine phenocrysts, and in many of them alkali feldspar is present as mantles on plagioclase phenocrysts and as interstitial patches in the groundmass. With increasing silica content, the amount of modal alkali feldspar decreases and orthopyroxene phenocrysts are present instead of olivine phenocrysts. In some specimens, orthopyroxene is accompanied by phenocrysts of hornblende and, more rarely, of biotite.

Eight analyses from the Highlands volcanoes have been published (Jakeš & White 1969); in the following account these are used with thirty-four new analyses (Mackenzie & Chappell, in press). The main chemical features of the Highlands lavas are high but variable Al_2O_3, low MgO and CaO, and high alkalies, especially K_2O. Most of the lavas with over 53 wt per cent SiO_2 contain normative quartz; most of those with less than 53 wt per cent SiO_2 contain normative olivine. On an FMA diagram (Fig. 2*c*), the calcalkaline rocks plot within the range of Kuno's (1950, 1968) 'hypersthenic series' (calcalkaline), and the shoshonites show a trend of moderate iron-enrichment that intersects the calcalkaline field. On a K_2O versus SiO_2 diagram (Fig. 3) all the Highlands lavas plot in a broad field, showing a gradual overall increase in K_2O with increasing SiO_2. The increased K_2O is presumably accommodated in plagioclase feldspar. With the exception of K_2O, which is highest in the shoshonites, there is no clear chemical separation between shoshonitic and calcalkaline rocks; both groups appear to be gradational into one another.

In eastern Papua, the late Cenozoic volcanic rocks form large stratovolcanoes, numerous small ash and lava cones and, in some areas, flat-lying piles of lava and agglomerate. Chemically, the lavas are shoshonitic and calcalkaline (Ruxton 1966, Jakeš & Smith 1970), and are similar to the Highlands lavas. Preliminary results from the D'Entrecasteaux Islands (Fig. 1) suggest that there are also alkali basalts

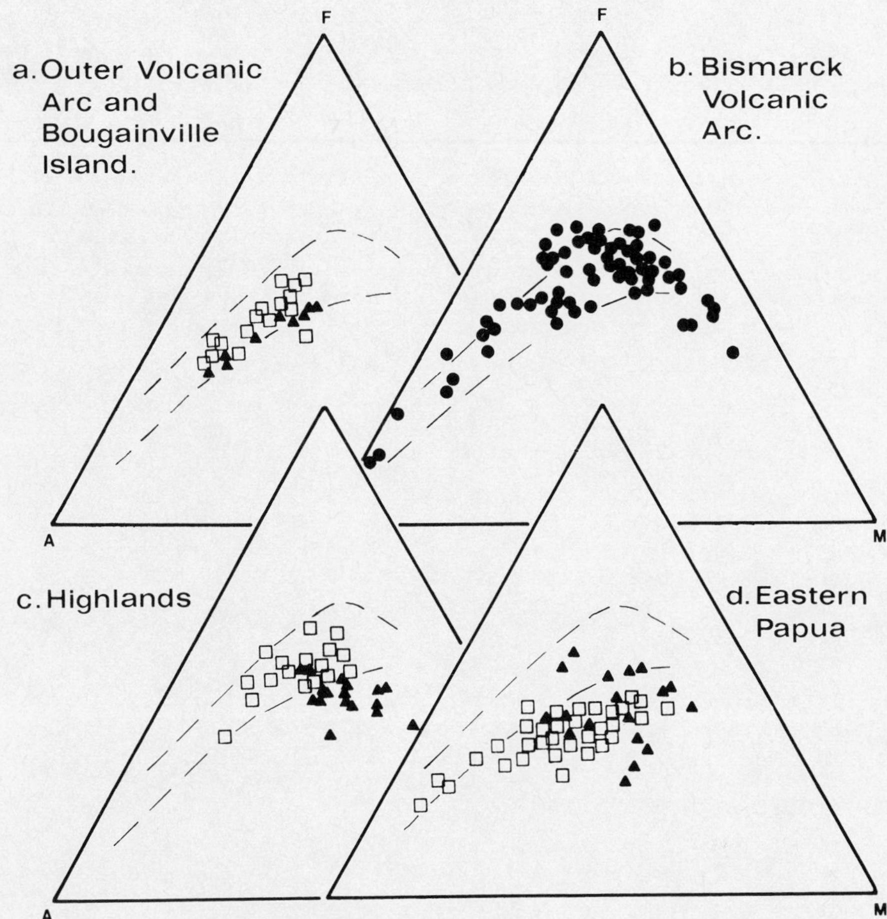

Fig. 2 FMA (total iron as FeO) plot of late Cenozoic volcanic rocks from Papua New Guinea. Calcalkaline lavas are shown as open squares, shoshonitic lavas as solid triangles, and all lavas of the Bismarck volcanic arc as large dots. In (a), all the Bougainville Island lavas are calcalkaline, and all the Outer volcanic arc lavas are shoshonitic. The limits of Kuno's (1950, 1968) 'hypersthenic series' (calcalkaline) are shown by the broken lines.

associated with peralkaline rhyolites. The calcalkaline rocks range from high-alumina basalt to dacite, but hornblende andesite predominates. The shoshonitic lavas are mainly basaltic; they contain phenocrysts of clinopyroxene, in some rocks accompanied by olivine or plagioclase phenocrysts, or both, and less commonly by biotite phenocrysts. The shoshonites are characterized by biotite and potash feldspar in the groundmass.

Chemical features common to both shoshonitic and calcalkaline associations in eastern Papua are variable Al_2O_3 contents together with the absence of any trend towards iron-enrichment (Fig. 2*d*). As in the case of the Highlands volcanoes, the shoshonitic rocks have higher K_2O contents and higher K_2O/Na_2O ratios than do the calcalkaline rocks with the same silica content, but many shoshonites from eastern Papua contain more K_2O than those from the Highlands (Fig. 3).

In contrast to the Highlands volcanoes which show no obvious spatial zonation, the shoshonitic and calcalkaline volcanoes in eastern Papua are spatially distinct: calcalkaline volcanoes are present along the north coast, and shoshonitic volcanoes

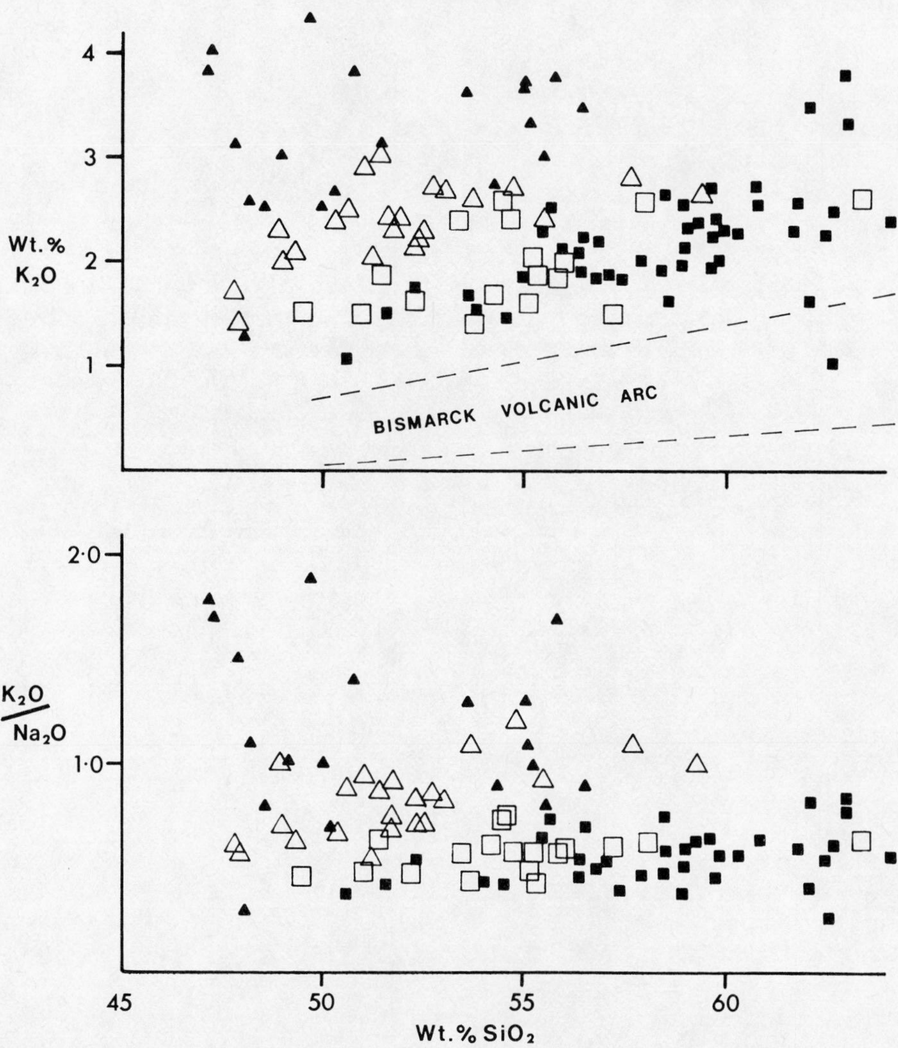

Fig. 3 K_2O *vs* SiO_2 and K_2O/Na_2O *vs* SiO_2 plots for lavas from the Highlands (open symbols) and eastern Papua (solid symbols). Shoshonitic lavas are shown as triangles and calcalkaline lavas as squares.

are found to the south. It also appears that shoshonitic lavas were erupted first (during the Pliocene) and that both shoshonitic and calcalkaline lavas have been erupted throughout the Quaternary.

The Bismarck Volcanic Arc

The volcanoes of the Bismarck volcanic arc consist of a series of hypersthene-normative lavas ranging from olivine-bearing basalt to andesite, dacite, and rhyolite. Andesite is the most abundant lava type, basalt and dacite are less common, and rhyolite is comparatively rare. The lavas are highly porphyritic and contain, in order of decreasing abundance, phenocrysts of oscillatory-zoned plagioclase, augite, pleochroic orthopyroxene, olivine, and iron-titanium oxide. Many of the plagioclase-rich lavas have high Al_2O_3 contents. In the basaltic rocks olivine phenocrysts are commonly rimmed by calcium-poor pyroxenes, indicating tholeiitic compositions. In New Britain amphibole phenocrysts are found only in lavas with more than about 70 wt per cent silica, but they are present in some andesites from the islands west of New Britain.

Lavas from different parts of the arc show different total-alkali and K_2O contents. These range from low values (considered by Jakeš and Gill (1970) to be typical of the 'island arc tholeiitic series') in lavas along the north coast of New Britain, to higher K_2O and total-alkali contents (typical of many calcalkaline associations) in lavas off the north coast of New Guinea (Fig. 4). In the New Britain volcanoes there is a progressive increase northwards in K_2O content of rocks with the same silica content (Fig. 4). This increase can be correlated with depth to the underlying Benioff zone (cf. Dickinson 1968). All the lavas of the Bismarck volcanic arc show slight or moderate iron-enrichment similar to many circum-Pacific lavas, for example, the 'hypersthenic series' of Kuno (1950, 1968) and other associations generally termed 'calcalkaline' (Fig. 2*b*).

In terms of iron-enrichment and alkali content, the lavas show the chemical features of both calcalkaline and tholeiitic rocks. Rather than distinguish two petrological associations—calcalkaline and tholeiitic—in this volcanic arc, it is preferred to recognize a single association showing slight or moderate iron-enrichment, within which marked and regular variations in alkali content characterize different parts of the arc.

The Outer Volcanic Arc

Preliminary work on samples from the islands north and east of New Ireland (Fig. 1) indicates that most of the lavas are undersaturated basaltic rocks with shoshonitic affinities. The lavas are strongly porphyritic: plagioclase and clinopyroxene are the dominant phenocrysts, and they are accompanied by phenocrysts of one or more of the following: olivine, hornblende, biotite, leucite, hauyne, analcite, zeolites, iron-titanium oxide, and apatite. These are set in a crypto-crystalline groundmass. Plagioclase compositions range from bytownite to oligoclase, but are most commonly labradorite. In some specimens the feldspar phenocrysts are anorthoclase.

Chemical analysis of eleven specimens reveals compositions comparable to undersaturated basic members of the shoshonite association (Joplin 1968). Silica values

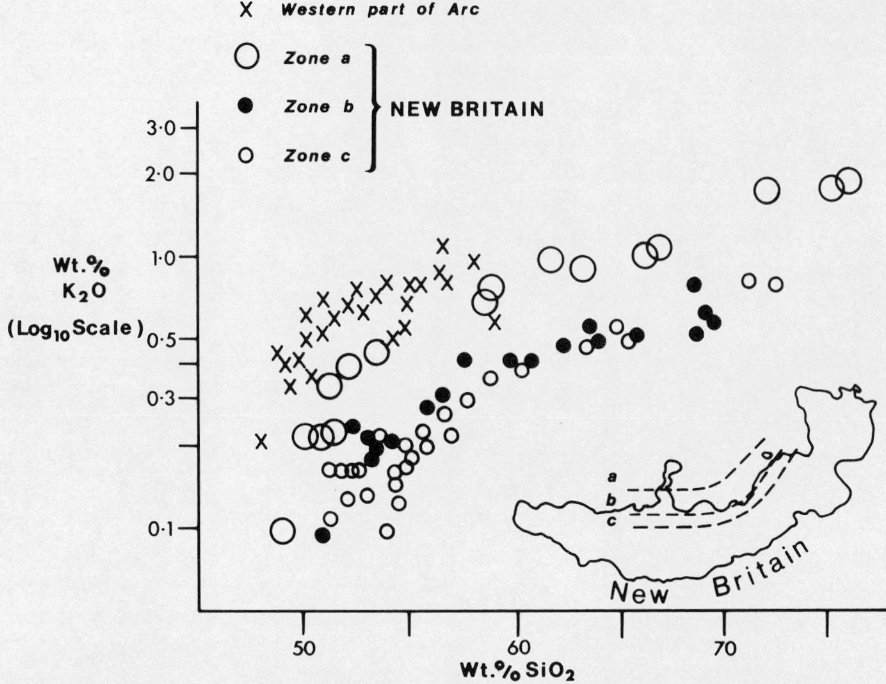

Fig. 4 K_2O *vs* SiO_2 plot for lavas of the Bismarck volcanic arc, illustrating the increase in K_2O northwards across the New Britain part of the arc. Lavas of zone *a* have the highest, and those of zone *c* the lowest, K_2O contents; the lavas of zone *b* have intermediate K_2O values. Most lavas from the western part of the arc are higher in K_2O than those from New Britain.

range between 47·2 and 54·0 wt per cent. Within this range Al_2O_3 is variable, CaO, Na_2O and K_2O are high, and TiO_2 is low. The values for K_2O are comparable with values in other shoshonitic rocks, but because of the high Na_2O contents the ratio K_2O/Na_2O is in most cases less than 1·0, and is lower than in most shoshonites (Fig. 5). On an FMA diagram most of the rocks plot within the field of calcalkaline lavas (Fig. 2*a*).

Samples from Tuluman volcano, and from other Quaternary volcanic islands in St Andrew Strait, were collected by Johnson in July 1971, but at the time of writing these have not been examined in thin section or chemically analysed. However, many of the islands are known to be composed of acidic rocks (flow-banded obsidian lavas, and pumice), and two analyses of rocks from the Tuluman Islands given by Reynolds (1958) show high total-alkali contents and peralkalinity indices of 0·98 and 1·04.

Bougainville Island

The late Cenozoic volcanoes of Bougainville Island are made up of calcalkaline andesites and dacites (Blake & Miezitis 1967, Taylor *et al.* 1969). Some of the andesites

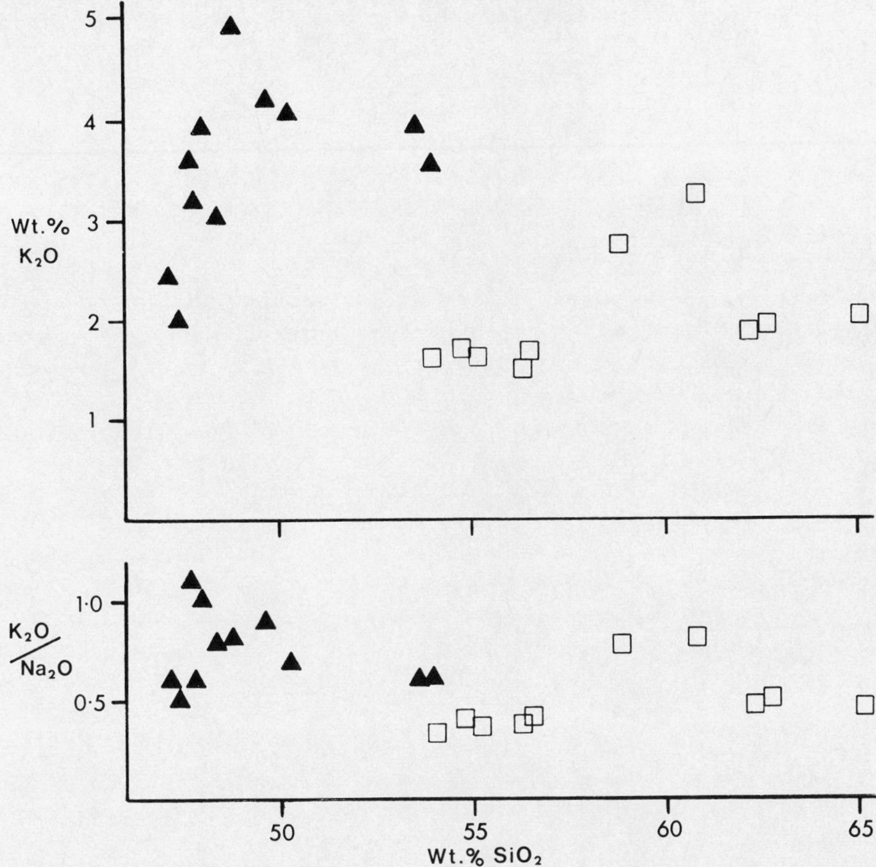

Fig. 5 K_2O *vs* SiO_2 and K_2O/Na_2O *vs* SiO_2 plots for calcalkaline lavas from Bougainville Island (□) and shoshonitic lavas from the Outer volcanic arc (▲).

are low-Si types (basaltic-andesites); others are high-K andesites (containing more than 2·5 wt per cent K_2O; Fig. 5). The andesites contain phenocrysts of plagioclase and either, or both, of pyroxene and hornblende.

DISCUSSION

Recent work on several areas of the South-west Pacific has shown that calcalkaline andesite is not necessarily the most common rock-type within what has popularly been called the 'Andesite Line'. Island-arc environments are now known to include lavas of tholeiitic, alkaline, and shoshonitic associations, in addition to those of calcalkaline compositions (for example, Kuno 1959, Jakeš & Gill 1970). As shown in the foregoing, all these lavas associations are also found in Papua New Guinea (see also Jakeš & White 1969).

Zonation of lava types across island-arcs has been described in several circum-Pacific areas; it has been shown that tholeiitic, calcalkaline, and alkaline or shoshonitic volcanoes occupy belts successively distant from the submarine trench, and overlying successively deeper parts of the Benioff zone (e.g. in Japan; Kuno 1959). Current explanations for this zonation involve various degrees of partial melting at different depths in the upper part of a downgoing slab of oceanic lithosphere (whose upper surface is defined by the Benioff zone), or in the upper mantle immediately above the Benioff zone.

Our work in Papua New Guinea suggests that this 'subduction' model may be an over-simplification, and that mantle (and possibly crustal) processes, unrelated to a downgoing slab of lithosphere, may be involved in the generation of magmas of island-arc type. For example, the variation in K_2O northwards across New Britain is consistent with the subduction model, but the Bismarck volcanic arc continues westwards to the islands off the north coast of New Guinea, where there appears to be no Benioff zone.

The suggestion that the genesis of shoshonites is caused by melting in the down-going slab (Jakeš & White 1969) is also difficult to reconcile with the apparent absence of Benioff zones beneath any of the three areas of shoshonitic volcanism (Highlands, eastern Papua, and islands north and east of New Ireland) in Papua New Guinea at the present day. However, we cannot exclude the possibility that magmas formed in a downgoing slab during the earlier part of the late Cenozoic have been erupted in the comparatively recent geological past, after the subduction system had ceased to exist.

Another difficulty with the subduction model lies in accounting for the composition of shoshonites by partial melting of downgoing lithosphere which has an olivine tholeiite composition. The high potassium contents and the apparent predominance of basaltic rocks in the shoshonite associations of Papua New Guinea are difficult to reconcile with the results of partial melting experiments on tholeiitic compositions at mantle temperatures and pressures (e.g. Green & Ringwood 1967). The behaviour of potassium-bearing phases (amphibole, mica) at high pressures, however, has not yet been studied in detail, and it is possible these minerals have a major influence on the chemistry of shoshonitic magmas (Jakeš & White 1970).

REFERENCES

Baker, G. 1946. Preliminary note on volcanic eruptions in the Goropu Mountains, south-eastern Papua during the period December 1943 to August 1944. *J. Geol.* **54,** 19.

Blake, D. H. & Miezitis, Y. 1967. Geology of Bougainville and Buka, New Guinea. *Bull. Bur. Miner. Resour. Aust.* **93.**

Denham, D. 1969. Distribution of earthquakes in the New Guinea-Solomon Islands region. *J. geophys. Res.* **74,** 4290.

Dickinson, W. R. 1968. Circum-Pacific andesite types. *J. geophys. Res.* **73,** 2261.

Fisher, N. H. 1957. *Catalogue of the active volcanoes of the world.* Part V. Catalogue of the active volcanoes and solfatara fields of Melanesia. *Int. volc. Assoc. Naples.*

Green, D. H. & Ringwood, A. E. 1967. The genesis of basaltic magmas. *Contr. Mineral. Petrol.* **15,** 103.

Jakeš, P. & Gill, J. B. 1970. Rare earth elements and the island arc tholeiitic series. *Earth Planet. Sci. Letters,* **9,** 17.

Jakeš, P. & Smith, I. E. 1970. High-K calc-alkaline rocks from Cape Nelson, eastern Papua. *Contr. Mineral. Petrol.* **28,** 259.

Jakeš, P. & White, A. J. R. 1969. Structure of the Melanesian arcs and correlation with distribution of magma types. *Tectonophysics,* **8,** 223.

——— 1970. K/Rb ratios of rocks from islands arcs. *Geochim. cosmochim. Acta* **34,** 849.

Johnson, R. W., Mackenzie, D. E. & Smith, I. E. 1971. Seismicity and late Cainozoic volcanism in parts of Papua-New Guinea. *Tectonophysics,* **12,** 15.

Joplin, G. A. 1968. The shoshonite association: A review. *J. geol. Soc. Aust.* **15,** 275.

Kuno, H. 1950. Petrology of Hakone volcano and the adjacent areas, Japan. *Bull. geol. Soc. Am.* **61,** 957.

——— 1959. Origin of Cenozoic petrographic provinces of Japan and surrounding areas. *Bull volcan.* **20,** 37.

——— 1968. Differentiation of basalt magmas. In *Basalts. The Poldervaart treatise on rocks of basaltic composition* (Eds H. H. Hess and A. Poldervaart). **2,** 623. Wiley and Sons, New York.

Lowder, G. G. & Carmichael, I. S. E. 1970. The volcanoes and caldera of Talasea, New Britain: geology and petrology. *Bull. geol. Soc. Am.* **81,** 17.

Mackenzie, D. E. & Chappell, B. W. (In press.) Shoshonitic and calc-alkaline lavas from the New Guinea Highlands. *Contr. Mineral. Petrol.*

Morgan, W. R. 1966. A note on the petrology of some lava types from east New Guinea. *J. geol. Soc. Aust.* **13,** 583.

Reynolds, M. A. 1958. Activity of Tuluman volcano, St Andrew Strait, Admiralty Islands, September 1955-March 1957. *Bur. Miner. Resour. Aust. Rec.* 1958/14 (unpubl.).

Reynolds, M. A. & Best, J. G. 1957. The Tuluman volcano, St Andrew Strait, Admiralty Islands. *Rep. Bur. Miner. Resour. Aust.* **33.**

Ruxton, B. P. 1966. A late Pleistocene to Recent rhyodacite-trachybasalt-basaltic latite volcanic association in northeast Papua. *Bull. volcan.* **29,** 347.

Smith, I. E. 1969. Notes on the volcanoes Mount Bagana and Mount Victory, Territory of Papua New Guinea. *Bur. Miner. Resour. Aust. Rec.* 1969/12 (unpubl.).

Taylor, G. A. M. 1958. The 1951 eruption of Mount Lamington, Papua. *Bull. Bur. Miner. Resour. Aust.* **38.**

Taylor, S. R., Capp, A. C., Graham, A. L. & Blake, D. H. 1969. Trace element abundances in andesites. II. Saipan, Bougainville and Fiji. *Contr. Mineral. Petrol.* **23,** 1.

Geology of Macquarie Island in Relation to Tectonic Environment

R. VARNE AND M. J. RUBENACH

Department of Geology, University of Tasmania
G.P.O. Box 252C, Hobart, Tasmania 7001

ABSTRACT

Macquarie Island is an exposed part of the crest of the Macquarie Ridge. The rocks of the island may have formed at a slow-spreading mid-oceanic ridge. The rock association resembles an ophiolite complex. Although the ridge may be a nascent island arc, the rocks that form the island differ in Cr and Ni abundances and Ni/Co ratios from island arc volcanics and could have been generated before the ridge was formed.

INTRODUCTION

Macquarie Island lies on the Macquarie Ridge about 1,100 km south-south-west of the southern tip of New Zealand, the nearest major continental landmass. The island is elongated north-north-west along the ridge axis and is about 39 km long and up to 3 km wide. Rocks similar to those that occur on the island have been recovered from both north and south in dredge hauls from the crest of the Macquarie Ridge (Summerhayes 1969, Watkins & Gunn 1971). Bathymetric data (Cullen 1969) also suggest that morphologically the island is part of the ridge crest that breaks sea-level.

It has recently been proposed that Macquarie Island is formed of uplifted oceanic crust originally generated as a spreading plate boundary in a mid-oceanic ridge environment (Varne *et al.* 1969), but Summerhayes (1969) has argued that the Macquarie Ridge is a Tertiary-Quaternary island arc and that the rocks of Macquarie Island are compositionally dissimilar to ocean-floor basalts. In this article we summarize the results of recent geological work on the island (Varne & Rubenach, 1972), then discuss the implications of the abundances of Co, Cr and Ni in some basalts and dolerites from the island, and finally use the framework of plate tectonics theory to speculate about the origin of the island and its rocks. Although the summary of the geology is a shortened form of the congress address, all that follows this is essentially postscript. Co, Cr and Ni abundances were determined on the advice of S. R. Taylor, who pointed out in discussion their relevance as geochemical indicators of magmatic affinities, and the brief discussion of the origin of the island has been inserted at the suggestion of P. J. Coleman.

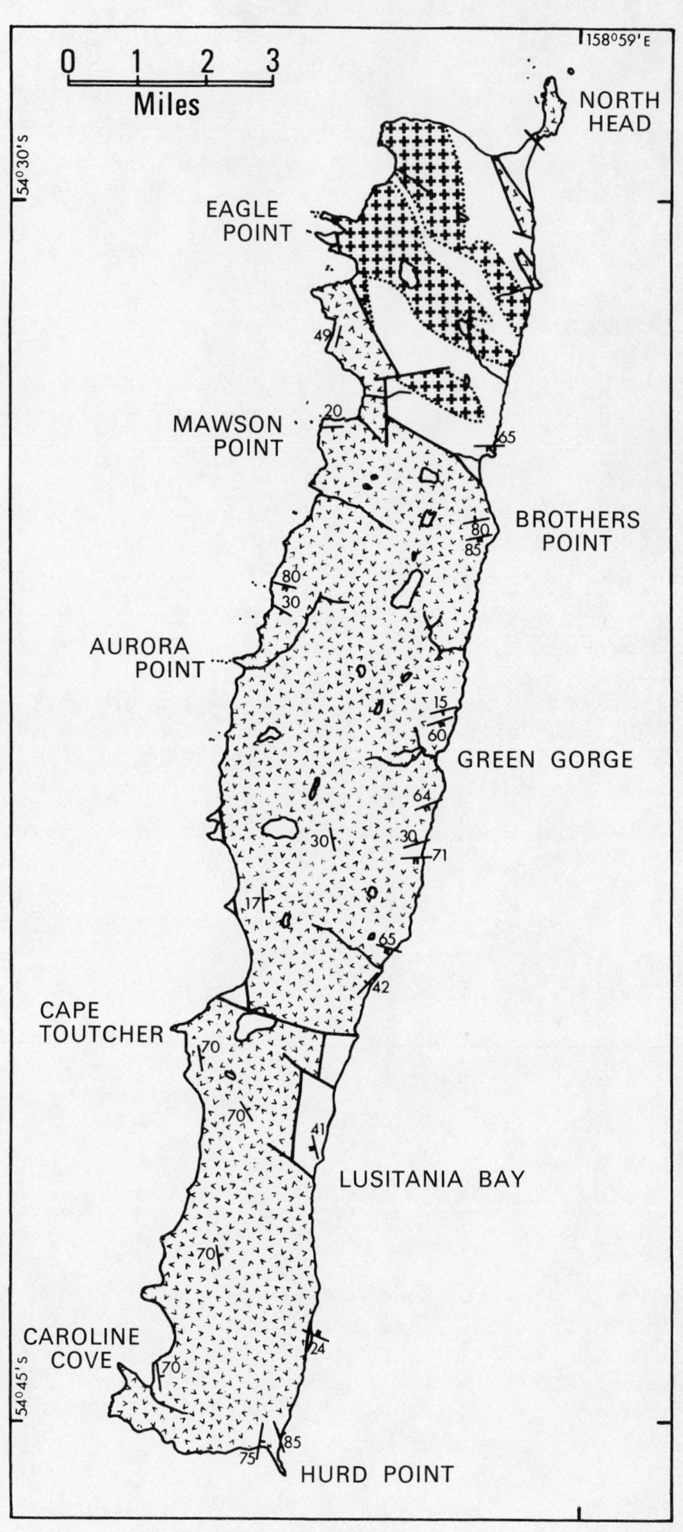

0
1
2
3
Miles
158°59'E
54°30'S
54°45'S
NORTH HEAD
EAGLE POINT
MAWSON POINT
BROTHERS POINT
AURORA POINT
GREEN GORGE
CAPE TOUCHER
LUSITANIA BAY
CAROLINE COVE
HURD POINT

A SUMMARY OF THE GEOLOGY OF MACQUARIE ISLAND

The island is formed almost entirely of basalts and dolerites and their metamorphosed derivates, gabbros and serpentinized harzburgites. The northern part of the island is formed mainly of intrusive rocks whereas the southern part is formed mainly of extrusive rocks (Fig. 1). A notable feature among the rock units exposed on the island are the dolerite dyke swarms, composed of series of narrow dykes lying parallel or sub-parallel to one another. Over large areas, no screens of country rock are identifiable within these swarms. In the northern part of the island, the dolerites of the dyke swarms have been metamorphosed to amphibolite facies assemblages without textural modification or the development of schistosity. Where exposed, the contacts between the dyke swarms and the volcanic rocks are faulted, as are contacts between the volcanic rocks and the gabbro and serpentinized harzburgite masses.

The volcanic rocks are mainly basaltic pillow lavas accompanied by volcanic breccias and more massive lavas. They are also cut by series of parallel dykes, but nowhere are these dykes as numerous as within the dyke swarms. The volcanic rocks are little altered and where they have been metamorphosed, the metamorphism is of lower grade than within the dyke swarms. *Globigerina*-ooze, although widely distributed as interstitial material in the pillow lavas, is abundant in only few localities. At North Head, the ooze contains poorly preserved coccoliths, mostly of Lower or Middle Miocene age although a few reworked Cretaceous forms may also be present (J. A. Wilcoxon & P. G. J. Quilty, pers. comm. 1971). In the central part of the island thin turbidites, composed of detritus derived from fine-grained basaltic rocks, are interbedded with volcanic lavas and breccias.

The island can be considered as made up of a number of fault-bounded blocks, with the northern part of the island apparently derived from deeper crustal levels than the southern part. A vertical section through the island, undisturbed by faulting, might well show an upper layer of little-metamorphosed basaltic rocks and sediments intruded by many dykes, and a lower layer of metamorphosed dolerite dyke swarms, and gabbro and serpentinized peridotite masses.

Ni, Co AND Cr ABUNDANCES IN SOME MACQUARIE ISLAND BASALTS AND DOLERITES

Rocks similar to those exposed on the island are commonly recovered in dredge hauls

---

Fig. 1 Generalized geological map of Macquarie Island with superficial deposits omitted. Serpentinized peridotite and gabbro masses are marked with crosses; extrusive igneous rocks are marked with Vs; dyke swarms are blank. Strikes on lavas are shown with a single tick and strikes on dykes with a double tick. Faulted contacts are drawn as heavy lines and gradational or uncertain contacts as dotted lines.

from the ocean floors, particularly from fracture zones or regions of irregular topography. Varne *et al.* (1969) pointed out that basalts and dolerites from the island resemble ocean-floor basalts in their major element compositions. Trace-element data support this suggestion. Macquarie Island basalts and dolerites possess similar Ti, Zr and Y abundances to ocean-floor basalts (Varne & Rubenach 1972).

Ocean-floor basalts also differ from island arc basalts and andesites in their Co, Cr and Ni abundances, and by Ni/Co ratios. Thirty-one lavas and dykes from Macquarie Island, selected as petrographically representative, have been analysed for these elements, and the results summarized (Fig. 2) for comparison with those of Taylor *et al.* (1969). The Co, Cr, and Ni contents of rocks analysed from Macquarie Island are clearly similar to the basalts and different from the andesites. Jakeš and Gill (1970) have argued that some island arc volcanic series are predominantly tholeiitic in character, include ophiolites as an integral part and differ little from the basaltic rocks of the ocean floors. Therefore it was suggested that it is unnecessary to assume that the ophiolites of the Macquarie Ridge were derived from a mid-ocean ridge or pre-island arc environment. However, island arc tholeiites are reported to contain 0-30 ppm of Ni and 0-50 ppm of Cr and the ocean-floor basalts to contain 30-200 ppm of Ni and 200-400 ppm of Cr (Jakeš & Gill 1970). Clearly, the Ni and Cr abundances of the Macquarie Island rocks are similar to those stated to characterize ocean-floor basalts (Fig. 2), and not those characterizing island arc tholeiites.

SPECULATIONS ON THE ORIGIN OF MACQUARIE ISLAND

If on geochemical grounds, Macquarie Island is part of the oceanic crust, the emplacement of the dyke swarms of the island presumably required 100 per cent crustal extension and a mode of formation amounting to sea-floor spreading (Moores & Vine 1971). The hypothetical vertical section through the island echoes recent ideas of oceanic-crust structure and petrology—particularly Cann's (1970) plate tectonics interpretation—and also the stratigraphic sequences of ophiolite complexes such as the Troodos complex of Cyprus (Gass 1968) and the South Oman complex of Arabia (Reinhardt 1969), where intense dyke swarms also occur.

To plate tectonic theorists, ophiolite complexes are slices of oceanic crust, emplaced at consuming plate margins, that mark the locations of ancient island arcs and orogenic belts. Macquarie Island may then represent an intermediate stage between ophiolite complexes interpreted as ancient oceanic crust, and oceanic crust now in the process of formation at actively-spreading mid-oceanic ridges.

Plate tectonics theory requires large-scale horizontal movements involving both crust and uppermost mantle. Ophiolitic rocks such as those of Macquarie Island may have moved great distances from their site of generation at a spreading mid-oceanic ridge or within a spreading marginal basin. Differences in spreading rates, the proximity of the spreading zone to continental margins and the relation of the spreading to island arc formation could all lead to differences in the structure and petrology of the developing oceanic crust (Dewey & Bird 1971, Moores & Vine 1971). A slow rate of spreading could favour, for example, the emplacement of dyke swarms,

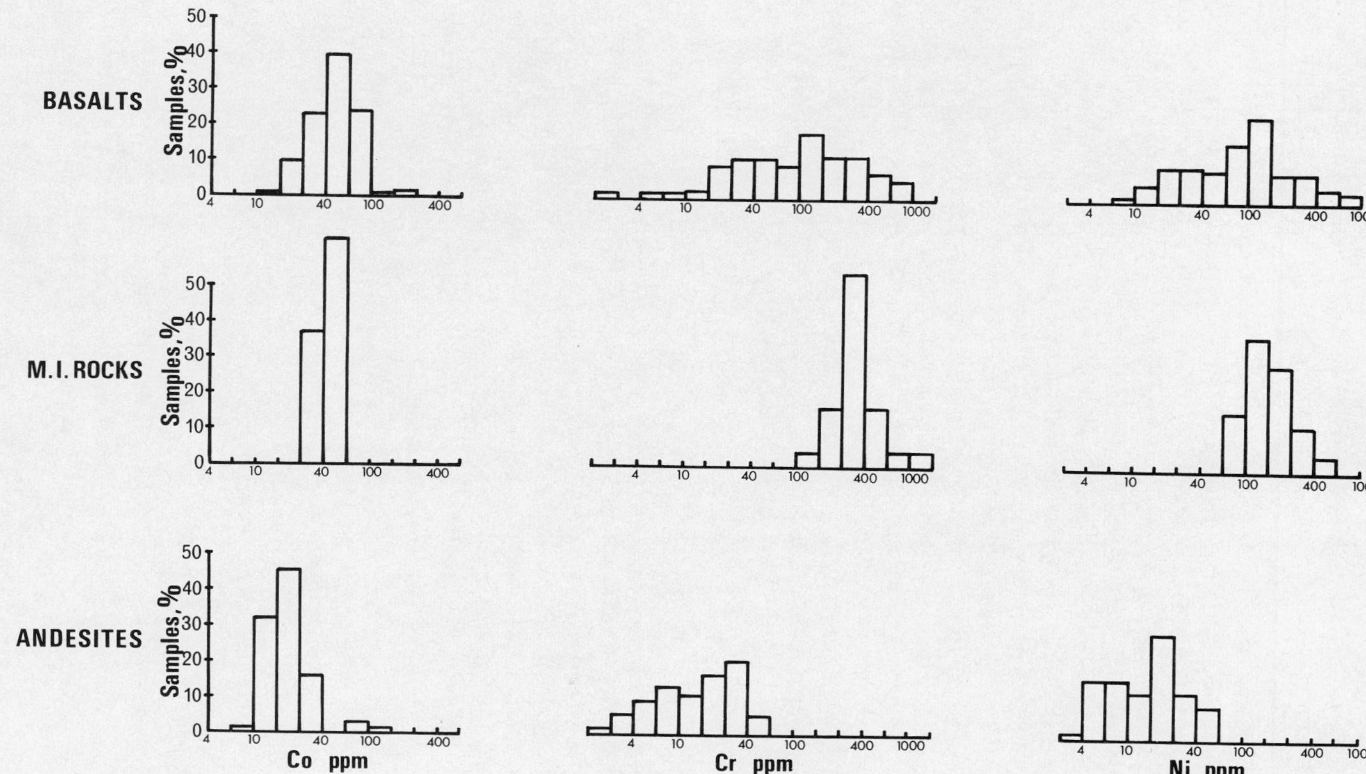

Fig. 2 Frequency diagrams of Co, Cr and Ni abundances in a group of basalts, a group of Macquarie Island rocks and a group of andesites. Data for the groups of basalts and andesites from Taylor *et al.* (1969).

the appearance of well-developed cumulate layering in gabbros, well-developed regional metamorphism and a structurally complex oceanic crust, whereas fast spreading may lead to a simple-layered crust lacking dyke swarms and regional metamorphism. Fast spreading could allow the eruption of large volumes of relatively undifferentiated basaltic magmas, whereas greater differentiation and the eruption of derivative magmas might occur during slow spreading. Basaltic andesites and andesites may be present within the volcanic pile developed in a marginal basin environment. The sediments intercalated with the volcanics may also vary greatly, depending on their source area, history of transport and environment of deposition.

The presence on Macquarie Island of dyke swarms, layered gabbros, minor unconformities and metamorphism apparently of regional type could then be suggestive of generation at a slow-spreading zone. A part (and possibly all) of the volcanic rocks and sediments were deposited on the ocean floor at considerable depths. Although no sediments characteristic of continental shelf deposition or continental derivation have been found, the association of rocks on the island could be considered broadly to represent a trench or 'eugeosynclinal' association, but volcanic rocks typical of an island arc environment appear to be absent. It is suggested that the rocks of the island formed at a slowly-spreading mid-oceanic ridge.

Although Macquarie Island forms part of the crest of the Macquarie Ridge, the rocks of the island were not necessarily formed by a process related to the tectonic evolution of the ridge. In plate tectonics theory the ridge marks the boundary between the Indo-Australian and Pacific plates, and has been interpreted to have arisen as a result of interaction between these plates. Marine magnetic profiling data imply that the present plate geometry in the region may have become established only after spreading ceased in the Tasman Sea about 10 m.y. ago (Griffiths & Varne 1972). Some of the freshest volcanic rocks on the island are associated with sediments that appear to be of Middle or Lower Miocene age, and it appears possible that the rocks forming the island were generated before the tectonic evolution of the ridge began.

The theme of Symposium D5 of the Twelfth Pacific Science Congress was 'Petrology and geochemistry of island arcs in relation to tectonic environment'. Although the Macquarie Ridge may represent a nascent island arc, it appears that the rocks that form part of the ridge bear more geochemical resemblance to oceanic crust than they do to island arc volcanics. If island arc or andesitic volcanic rocks are erupted along the ridge in the future, then presumably they will develop over a basement of oceanic crust.

REFERENCES

Cann, J. R. 1970. New model for the structure of the oceanic crust. *Nature,* **226,** 928-30.

Cullen, D. J. 1969. Macquarie Island, provisional bathymetry, scale 1:200,000, Island Series. N.Z. Oceanogr. Inst., Wellington.

Dewey, J. F. & Bird, J. M. 1971. Origin and emplacement of the ophiolite suite: Appalachian ophiolites in Newfoundland. *J. geophys. Res.* **76,** 3179-206.

Gass, I. G. 1968. Is the Troodos massif of Cyprus a fragment of Mesozoic ocean floor? *Nature,* **220,** 39-42.

Griffiths, J. R. & Varne, R. 1972. Evolution of the Tasman Sea, Macquarie Ridge and Alpine fault. *Nature* (*Phys. Sci.*), **235,** 83-6.

Jakeš, P. & Gill, J. 1970. Rare earth elements and the island arc tholeiite series. *Earth Planet. Sci. Letters*, **9,** 17-28.

Moores, E. M. & Vine, F. J. 1971. The Troodos massif, Cyprus and other ophiolites as oceanic crust: evaluation and implications. *Phil. Trans. R. Soc. London, Ser. A.* **268,** 443-66.

Reinhardt, B. M. 1969. On the genesis and emplacement of ophiolites in the Oman Mountains Geosyncline. *Schweiz. miner. petrogr. Mitt.* **49,** 1-30.

Summerhayes, C. P. 1969. Marine geology of the New Zealand sub-Antarctic sea floor, *Bull. N.Z. Dep. scient. ind. Res.* **190,** 94 pp.

Taylor, S. R., Kaye, M., White, A. J. R. & Ewart, A. 1969. Genetic significance of Co, Cr, Ni, Sc and V content of andesites. *Geochim. cosmochim. Acta*, **33,** 275-86.

Varne, R., Gee, R. D. & Quilty, P. G. J. 1969. Macquarie Island and the cause of oceanic linear magnetic anomalies. *Science*, **166,** 230-3.

Varne, R. & Rubenach, M. J. 1972. Geology of Macquarie Island and its relationship to oceanic crust. In *Antarctic Oceanology II: The Australian-New Zealand Sector*, *Antarctic Res. Ser.* (Ed. D. E. Hayes). *Am. Geophys. Un.*, *Geophys. Monogr.* **19.**

Watkins, N. D. & Gunn, B. M. 1971. Petrology, geochemistry and magnetic properties of some rocks dredged from the Macquarie Ridge. *N.Z. Jl Geol. Geophys.* **14,** 153-68.

A Proposed Geological and Geochemical History of Eastern Melanesia

J. Gill and M. Gorton

Department of Geophysics and Geochemistry
Australian National University, P.O. Box 4, Canberra, A.C.T. 2601, Australia

ABSTRACT

There are spatial variations in the geochemistry of island arc volcanism, which can be used to infer the subduction polarity of synchronous volcanic rocks. By summarizing and using these variations we demonstrate that the Fiji and Lau Islands faced subduction from the north-east during the Upper Miocene. This polarity is also inferred for the New Hebrides during the Lower Miocene. We propose the continuity of an ancestral New Hebrides-Fiji-Tonga Ridge which developed during the Eocene between a marginal sea (South Fiji Basin) and the Australia-Pacific plate boundary. The ridge remained continuous until the Lower Miocene. Fiji and Tonga have separated from one another during the last 5·5 m.y., whereas the Fiji-New Hebrides separation may be older. Fragmentation resulted in a transition to almost entirely basaltic or shoshonitic volcanism in Fiji in which K_2O and K/Na seem to have decreased as rifting proceeded. The New Hebrides Ridge itself is currently being split in two in a similar fashion and with similar petrological results.

INTRODUCTION

The eastern boundary of the modern Australian plate is a discontinuous series of trenches and volcanic ridges on which lie the New Hebrides, Fiji, Lau, Tonga, and Kermadec islands. This paper proposes a tentative history for that area during the Tertiary, based largely on its exposed geology and on the variation in chemical composition of its volcanic rocks.

Throughout the twentieth century it has been supposed that these ridges were in some way a Tertiary continuation of the progressive eastward accretionary growth of the Australian continent (Suess 1904, Glaessner 1950, Coleman 1967). Each mode of geological thought has sought to explain this migration of orogenic focus in terms of the reigning paradigms of its day, and we shall do the same by arguing in terms of plate tectonics, the migration of trenches, and the development of inter-arc basins. By 'subduction' we shall mean the thrusting of one plate beneath another; by 'subduction zone' we shall mean the interface or fault surface between such plates, including its expression at the earth's surface in submarine trenches; and by 'polarity' we shall mean the direction of dip of this fault and therefore the assymetric spatial distribution of associated features.

Our attention has focused largely on Fiji because it occupies the central portion of the area and comprises its largest land surface, yet has traditionally been considered its most enigmatic portion. It has also been mapped and studied quite thoroughly by the Fiji Geological Survey Department. Fiji today is not an active island arc although its lithologies, facies relationships, geochemistry, and geographic position all suggest that it was one throughout much of its history (Dickinson 1967, Rodda 1967, Gill 1970). The art of inferring the geological history of Fiji is therefore an exercise in palaeo-plate tectonics and must rely on the principal tools of that trade, such as recognition of: linear volcanic ridges and sedimentary basins; Franciscan-like melanges; ophiolites and alpine ultramafics; glaucophane schists and paired metamorphic belts; and spatial variations in the composition of volcanic rocks. Of these, only the first and last are known in Fiji although the third may be present in Tonga (Ewart *et al.,* in press) and the New Hebrides (Mitchell & Warden 1971). Thus our reconstruction is based mainly on the spatial and temporal variations in geochemistry of volcanic rocks exposed on bathymetrically defined linear ridges.

GEOCHEMICAL VARIATIONS IN ISLAND ARCS AND PALAEO-PLATE TECTONICS

Most modern island arcs are characterized by large quantities of intermediate and acidic (>53 per cent SiO_2) volcanics as well as basalts. The converse is also true: voluminous intermediate and acidic volcanism is usually associated with a subduction environment. We shall, therefore, regard this situation as 'typical' of island arcs without speculating on its genetic reason.

Although most modern island arc volcanoes are concentrated in narrow and remarkably straight bands parallel to their associated trenches, there are many places where some volcanoes occur behind this main volcanic front (e.g. south-west and north-east Honshu, Japan, eastern Aleutians, northern Scotia islands, New Britain, Indonesia, northern Izu islands). The number of volcanoes and the amount of material extruded decreases with distance from the trench (cf. Sugimura 1968, Fig. 10). The chemical characteristics of volcanism likewise vary with distance from the trench (Kuno 1959, 1966; Sugimura 1968, Jakeš & White 1970, Jakeš & Gill 1970). A qualitative summary of observed trends taken from the above sources and from our own unpublished data is given in Fig. 1 (this model will be developed further elsewhere and an attempt made to quantify it). These variations are thought to be independent of the age and thickness of crust upon which volcanism occurs. It is not our purpose here to assign a genetic significance to these variations, but simply to assert them as a description of the present actualistic situation, and thereby to provide a more complete geochemical approach to palaeo-subduction than is possible with only the K-h approach of Dickinson (1970, pp. 829-36). Care should be exercised when applying this model. Only suites of rocks that are close enough in age to have been produced during the same subduction configuration and for which there is no evidence of structural dislocation or significant chemical alteration, should be used.

In addition to these spatial zonations, many authors have described analogous

(⟶ indicates direction of increase)

⟵ Na/K, Y, heavy REE

⟵ K/Rb, Fe (max), SiO_2 range

⟶ Th/U, Rb/Sr, La/Yb

⟶ K, Rb, Ba, Cs, P, Pb, Th, U, light REE

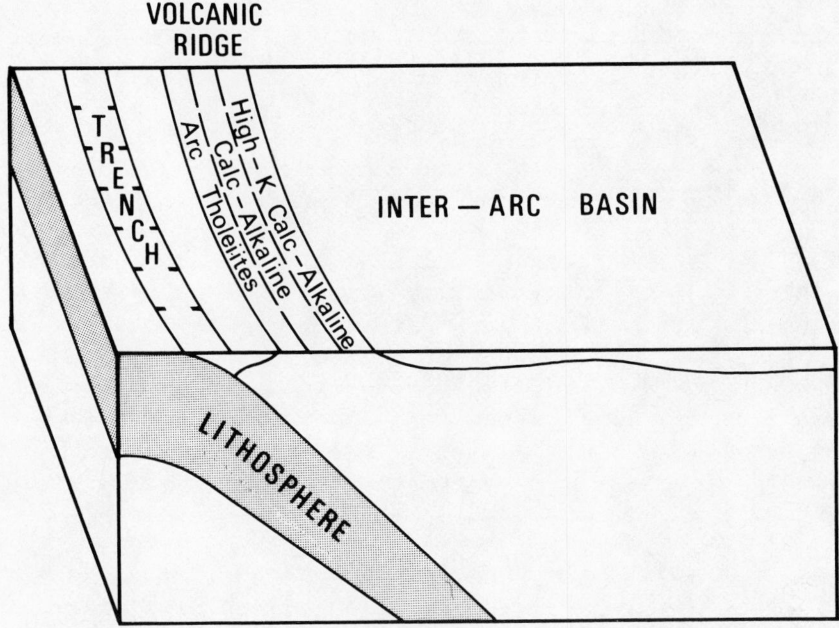

Fig. 1 Geochemical variations in island arcs (see discussion in text). 87Sr/86Sr ratios decrease also with distance from the trench (cf. Gill & Compston, this volume).

temporal variations in the geochemistry of island arc volcanism in which erosional unconformities often separate volcanics of differing compositional affinities (Baker 1968, Jakeš & White 1970, Gill 1970, Donnelly *et al.* 1971). These temporal variations, in which successively younger rocks would appear to have been extruded further from a trench axis by reference to Fig. 1, may be due to an ocean-ward migration of subduction sites and volcanic fronts with time. As this migration occurs, an area of initial tholeiitic volcanism can become further and further removed from the trench and the character of successive volcanic products at that point can change in the sense illustrated in Fig. 1. Failure to recognize this led Gill (1970), for example, to false conclusions about the tectonic evolution of Fiji.

Because Fiji is the central and most enigmatic portion of this area, and because only the products of its volcanism remain as tectonically significant evidence, it is important to stress that those volcanics are not featureless piles of indistinguishable andesite. Instead they exhibit regular geochemical variations some of which are precisely those found in modern, normal island arcs.

If island arc volcanism is characterized by certain spatial variations in magma composition, then these variations may be of use tectonically. When one finds, as in Fiji, roughly contemporaneous volcanic rocks in the geologic record which exhibit these same spatial variations and between which there is no evidence of structural dislocation, the simplest explanation is that they are the result of magmatism associated with a subduction zone having the polarity implied by Fig. 1. This is not a unique interpretation, but it is the simplest.

STATUS OF GEOCHEMICAL STUDIES

Good geochemical control for eastern Melanesia has become available during the last three years. There are now over 250 analyses of igneous rocks from Fiji of which three-fourths also contain data for fifteen to forty trace elements. Some of these analyses have been published by Rodda (1969) and Gill (1970), but the rest will be published elsewhere and are only summarized here. Over 200 analyses, some of which are of poorer quality, are available for the New Hebrides, although very few include well-determined trace-element data. We have drawn on data summarized by Mallick (this volume), Colley and Warden (in prep.), and our own unpublished material. Data for Tonga is taken from Richard (1962), Ewart *et al.* (in press and this volume), Melson *et al.* (1970), and Bauer (1970); and for the Kermadec islands from Brothers (1970).

FIRST PERIOD VOLCANISM: EOCENE TO LOWER MIOCENE

The oldest fauna known from eastern Melanesia is Upper Eocene or Tertiary *b* in age [Cretaceous fossils have been dredged from the western wall of the Tonga Trench (J. Hawkins, pers. comm.) but these could have been underplated during subduction]. Upper Eocene shallow-water fossils but not volcanics have been recognized both in conglomerate clasts (Coleman 1969) and in dredge hauls (D. Karig, pers. comm.) from the New Hebrides Ridge. Identical fauna and lithology is found in the basement of Viti Levu, Fiji (Cole 1960) and Eua, Tonga (Cole 1970). Volcanics are associated with the latter two sites and their composition has been described by Gill (1970) and Ewart *et al.* (in press), respectively.

Volcanism apparently continued until the Lower Miocene in the New Hebrides and Fiji but not in Tonga. Late Oligocene and Lower Miocene or Tertiary *e* to f_{1-2} fauna lie interbedded with volcaniclastics and rare flows on the western islands of the New Hebrides Ridge; the composition of these volcanics has been described by Mitchell (1966), Robinson (1969) and Mallick (this volume). Volcanics of this age are also known from Viti Levu, Fiji (Rodda 1967). The absence of identified Oligocene fauna makes it difficult to know whether volcanism was continuous from Eocene to

Lower Miocene or sporadic. There were no apparent changes in magma composition during this period in Fiji (Gill 1970, and unpubl.).

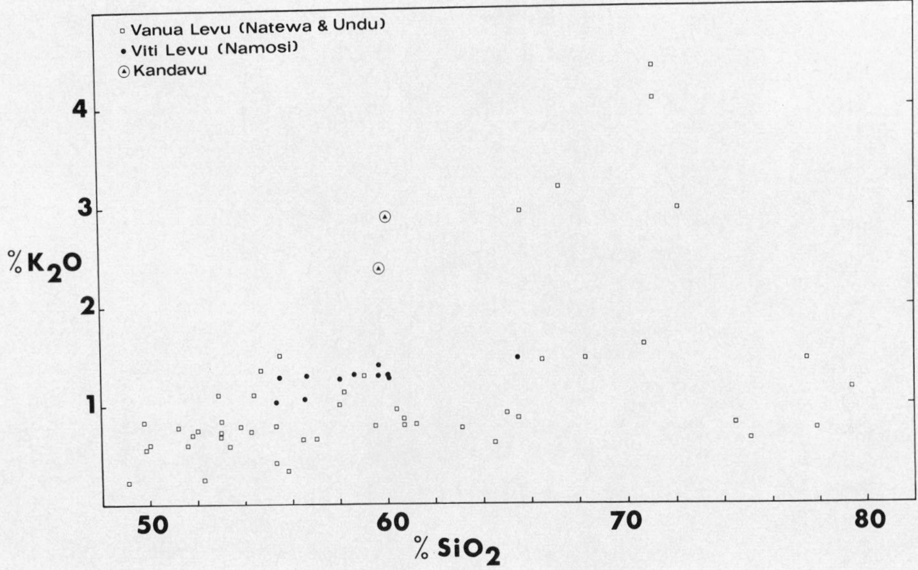

Fig. 2 Fiji (late Miocene) K_2O-SiO_2 variations. Data are from Rodda (1967), Hindle and Gill (in prep.) for Vanua Levu, and Gill (in prep.) for Namosi and Kandavu.

Some aspects of the composition of these first period volcanics are summarized in Table 1. The Eua, Tonga, material is least fractionated relative to chondritic abundances of many elements, and Ewart argues that they form the uppermost portion of an alpine ultramafic assemblage. It is important to note, as Ewart does, that such an interpretation is in conflict with most recent speculation about alpine ultramafics insofar as he does *not* consider those of Tonga to be oceanic crust formed at a mid-ocean ridge and tectonically emplaced during subduction. The tectonic emplacement interpretation would be in conflict with their youthfulness and the low Ti and Zr and higher Sr 87/86 ratios of the Eua basalts relative to those of modern mid-ocean tholeiites. Thus the Tongan material could be products of volcanism behind but near a trench and early in the evolution of the Tonga Ridge, in a fashion suggested by Jakeš and Gill (1970) for members of the island arc tholeiitic series.

Data for the Eocene-Lower Miocene volcanics of Fiji are based on about twice the number of samples reported by Gill (1970) but differ little from his general summary. These volcanics are more enriched in most large cations than those from Eua. It is not known, however, whether a less-enriched assemblage lies unexposed beneath Vanua Levu, Fiji, which has a crustal thickness equivalent to that of Viti Levu (J. Worthington, pers. comm.) or whether a more enriched assemblage occupies a similar position beneath Tonga Tapu or the Ha'apai Group, Tonga.

Table 1

REPRESENTATIVE ANALYSES OF FIRST PERIOD VOLCANIC ROCKS

	Tonga		*Fiji*			*New Hebrides*		
	Eua-7[1] *a*	Eua-11[1] *b*	69-920 *c*	68-60[2] *d*	68-50 *e*	18[3] *f*	19[3] *g*	36[3] *h*
SiO_2	50·11	61·35	49·72	59·22	73·31	52·58	62·59	68·26
TiO_2	0·43	0·77	1·07	1·08	0·51	0·91	0·53	0·79
Al_2O_3	21·00	17·41	18·37	15·13	13·13	18·35	16·28	16·01
Fe_2O_3	2·98	3·36	11·59*	8·47	1·59	4·26	4·38	1·59
FeO	5·74	3·46	—	2·54	2·09	5·10	2·26	2·06
MnO	0·18	0·10	0·19	0·15	0·12	0·19	0·10	0·04
MgO	6·04	2·94	4·64	3·50	0·78	3·76	1·40	0·57
CaO	11·39	6·06	11·50	6·17	2·65	9·93	7·07	4·86
Na_2O	1·23	4·09	2·31	3·32	4·78	3·53	3·65	4·15
K_2O	0·24	0·32	0·44	0·30	0·91	0·97	1·27	1·51
P_2O_5	0·04	0·14	0·16	0·13	0·12	0·30	0·33	0·16
Rb	1·2	2·3	5·1	2·1	6·8	—	—	—
Sr	115	145	280	130	116	—	—	—
Ba	14	50	56	70	218	—	—	—
Pb	1	1	1	2	1	—	—	—
Th	—	—	0·3	<0·3	<0·3	—	—	—
U	—	—	0·2	0·1	0·2	—	—	—

Zr	20	120	55	68	71	—	—	—
Hf	—	—	—	1·5	4·5	—	—	—
La	0·8	—	—	2·4	2·7	—	—	—
Yb	1·2	—	—	2·5	6	—	—	—
Y	12	34	17	34	43	—	—	—
Ni	25	2	10	nd	nd	—	—	—
Co	30	14	32	27	nd	—	—	—
Cr	75	7	50	2	nd	—	—	—
Sc	34	18	34	35	16	—	—	—
V	230	120	266	190	9	—	—	—
Cu	25	67	98	77	nd	—	—	—
Sr 87/86	0·7034	0·7039	0·7032	0·7037	0·7048	—	—	—

[1] Ewart *et al.* (in press).
[2] Gill (1970).
[3] Mitchell (1966).

All analyses in this and following tables are re-calculated to anhydrous equivalents. Fe_2O_3* = total iron as Fe_2O_3. Sr 87/86 ratios are normalized to 0·7080 for E and A standard Sr. 'nd' means not detected; other omissions mean not determined. Data are from our unpublished studies except where referenced.

If Mitchell and Warden (1971) are correct in suggesting contemporaneity between Lower Miocene volcanism of the western New Hebrides and the ultrabasics and metamorphic basement of the eastern islands, then a polarity can be inferred in which the subduction zone would lie east of the New Hebrides Ridge. The composition of these Lower Miocene volcanics is erratic but generally richer in alkalis than those of Fiji or Tonga.

Broadly contemporaneous island arc volcanism thus took place in Fiji, Tonga, and the New Hebrides during the Eocene to Lower Miocene. It seems likely that these areas formed a continuous volcanic ridge on the Australian side of a west-dipping subduction zone which marked the boundary between the Pacific and Australian plates at this time. This configuration commenced at about the time when Australia separated from Antarctica (Le Pichon & Heirtzler 1968) and the time of westward overthrusting of possible oceanic or inter-arc basin crust on to a once-continuous New Caledonia-New Guinea Ridge (Davies & Smith 1971, Lillie & Brothers 1970, Avias, this volume). We therefore suggest that the Australia-Pacific plate boundary and its associated west-dipping subduction complex migrated towards the Pacific during the early Eocene resulting in the development of an ancestral New Hebrides-Fiji-Tonga Ridge. The apparently synchronous overthrusting along the New Caledonia-New Guinea Ridge suggests that this trench migration accompanied the opening of an inter-arc basin which is now the South Fiji Basin. For a time, there may have existed in eastern Melanesia either a situation like that of the modern Philippines Sea with two active subduction zones facing the Pacific, or one with westward subduction beneath the New Hebrides-Fiji-Tonga Ridge and westward obduction on to the New Caledonia-New Guinea Ridge. There is, however, no evidence that part of New Caledonia migrated eastward together with the trench to form a basement for the new island arc system, as is the presumed case during evolution of inter-arc basins (Karig 1971).

SECOND PERIOD VOLCANISM: LATE MIOCENE

Faunas of late Miocene or Tertiary f_3 to *g* or N.17-18 age are associated with basement volcanic rocks on Vanua Levu, Fiji (Rickard 1966, Blow 1967). The composition of these volcanics is described by Hindle and Gill (in prep.). Similar faunas are found within marls associated with the Namosi andesites of Viti Levu (Rodda 1967, Blow 1967) the compositions of which have been delineated by Taylor *et al.* (1969) and Gill (1970). The rocks of unmapped and undated Kandavu may also be of late Miocene age (Phillips 1965). Limited analytical data for them is available from Rodda (1969) and Gill (unpublished).

The composition of these volcanics is summarized in Table 2*a-e*. This provides an effective north-south geochemical section across roughly synchronous volcanic rocks of Fiji (Section A-A′ on Fig. 6). Figs 2, 3 and 4 further illustrate geochemical differences between these areas. Despite considerable diversity of Vanua Levu rocks, a marked trend is nevertheless apparent and, when compared with the model given in Fig. 1, strongly suggests that these islands faced a subduction zone to their north during the late Miocene. The concentrations of K, Rb, Ba, Cs, P, Pb, Th, U, and La and the ratios Rb/Sr, Th/U, and La/Yb increase north to south whereas the maximum SiO_2 range and total iron and Y contents and the average Na/K and K/Rb ratios increase south to north.

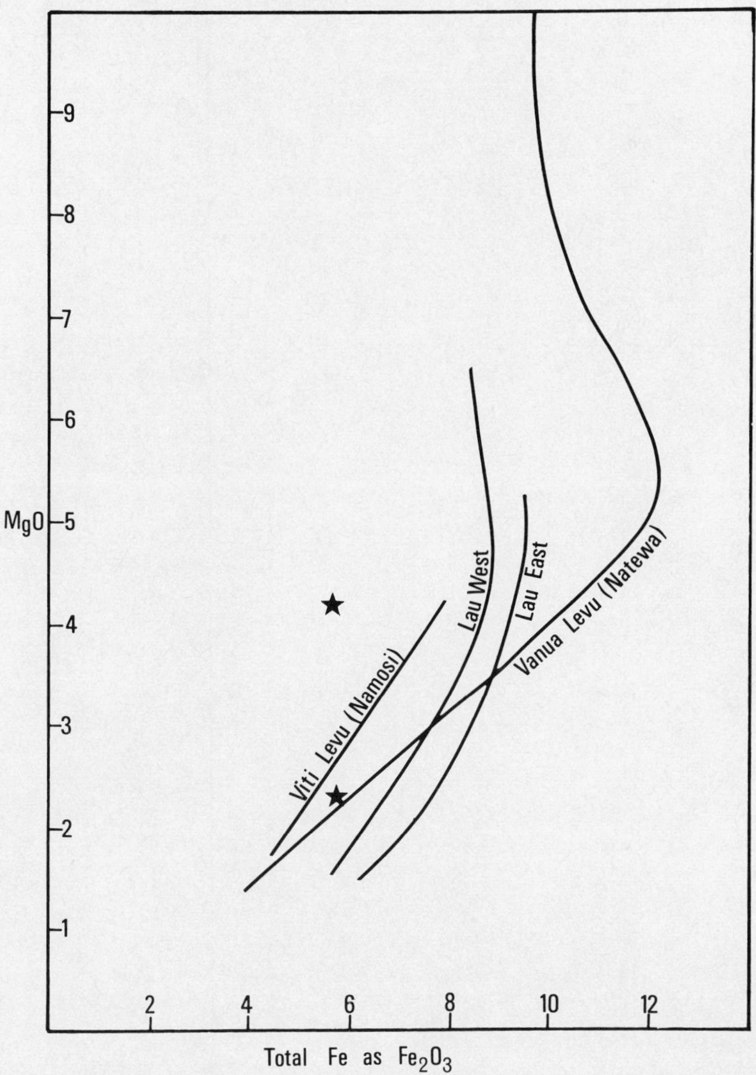

Fig. 3 Fiji (late Miocene) Mg-Fe variation curves. Data are summarized from the sources listed beneath Fig. 2 and Gill (unpubl.) for Lau. Stars indicate the widely differing analyses for two Kandavu samples (the upper point represents a 1918 analysis). Vanua Levu data is more scattered than this curve indicates.

Table 2

REPRESENTATIVE ANALYSES OF SECOND PERIOD VOLCANIC ROCKS

	Fiji					Lau		New Hebrides		
	Vanua Levu			Viti Levu	Kandavu	West	East			
	69-818	69-810	M96	X96[1]	71-390	71-374	71-385	610	626	593
	a	*b*	*c*	*d*	*e*	*f*	*g*	*h*	*i*	*j*
SiO_2	50·04	56·95	79·37	58·60	60·64	55·34	56·64	52·39	52·25	61·69
TiO_2	0·74	0·85	0·20	0·66	0·62	0·96	0·93	0·85	0·76	0·72
Al_2O_3	15·53	16·75	10·42	18·07	17·08	17·33	16·86	16·95	17·54	14·71
Fe_2O_3	11·65*	8·86*	2·49*	3·27	5·92*	8·90*	8·75*	5·26	4·91	3·70
FeO	—	—	—	3·37	—	—	—	4·64	5·01	3·13
MnO	0·19	0·15	0·05	—	0·11	0·17	0·16	0·20	0·17	0·09
MgO	6·73	4·15	0·28	3·52	2·18	4·63	4·24	5·61	4·78	2·80
CaO	12·25	8·49	1·76	7·55	5·74	8·63	8·16	9·46	9·59	6·74
Na_2O	2·12	3·02	4·08	3·47	4·47	2·83	3·27	3·34	3·07	3·25
K_2O	0·59	0·65	1·17	1·28	2·89	1·00	0·79	1·12	1·67	2·85
P_2O_5	0·15	0·13	0·18	0·21	0·34	0·21	0·20	0·19	0·25	0·31
Rb	16	6	6	22	51	15	9	14	26	70
Sr	390	170	95	454	1330	266	304	372	514	340
Ba	285	80	119	337	768	135	125	214	224	437
Pb	2	1	3	2	8	2	2	2	3	5

Th	<0·3	0·3	0·4	1·4	4·2	0·6	0·6	0·3		
U	0·2	0·2	0·5	0·5	1·7	0·6	0·45	0·4	—	—
Zr	56	95	134	97	145	100	64	64	58	81
Hf	0·6	1·4	2	1·3	2·3	1·5	1·5	1·3	—	—
La	3	7	6·6	11·1	27·5	7	9·8	4·1	—	—
Yb	1·3	2·4	2·8	1·4	1·4	2·4	4·3	1·7	—	—
Y	21	31	33	18	17	29	59	24·1	20	24
Ni	45	8	nd	8	6	17	14	34	28	16
Co	46	23	nd	16	18	25	23	27	26	18
Cr	148	10	3	37	8	31	20	74	25	108
Sc	46	27	9	18	12	27	36	32	23	23
V	300	208	nd	163	166	214	220	319	325	223
Cu	140	36	6	31	59	50	40	350	215	338
Sr 87/86	0·7036	0·7041	0·7042	0·7036	0·7032	0·7031	0·7033	—	—	—

[1] Taylor *et al*. (1969).

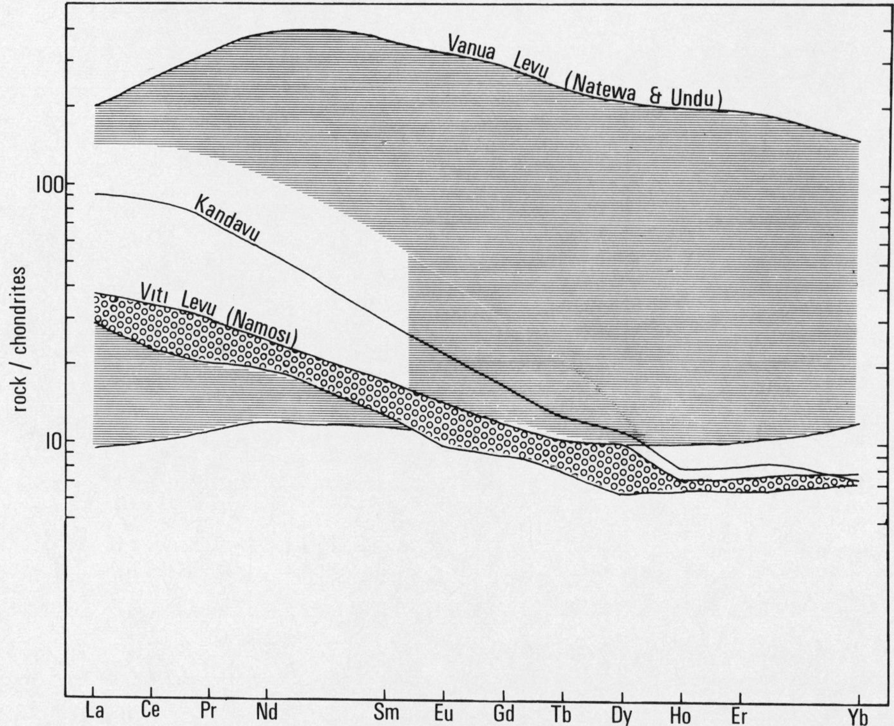

Fig. 4 Fiji (late Miocene) REE patterns. Data are from Taylor *et al.* (1969), Hindle and Gill (in prep.), and Gill (in prep., and unpubl.). Shaded fields represent the range of five Vanua Levu and four Namosi samples, respectively.

The basement volcanics of the Lau Ridge are known as the Lau Volcanics (Ladd & Hoffmeister 1945). Their age is disputed. The molluscs and larger foraminifera of the overlying Futuna Limestones have been assigned a Middle Miocene or Tertiary *f* age and correlated with the Suva Marl of Viti Levu (Ladd & Hoffmeister 1945, H. Ladd and C. Adams, pers. comm. 1971). The latter formation also contains planktonic foraminifera described by Blow (1967) as N.17-18 or late Miocene and is generally considered to be of that age (Rodda 1967). K-Ar measurements by Gill and McDougall for five samples of the Lau Volcanics from Vanua Balavu, Katafaga, and Cicia all indicate ages within the range 7·5-9·0 m.y. or late Miocene (these are part of a larger age-determination project the results of which will be published later). If these radiometric ages and the Futuna Limestone-Suva Marl correlation are correct, the older fossils within the Futuna Limestone must have been reworked. Thus the volcanics which form the visible basement of the Lau Ridge seem to be as young as those which dominate Vanua Levu, south-east Viti Levu, and possibly Kandavu. By inference, they would overlie a Middle Miocene or older sub-basement.

A similar though less well-defined sense of tectonic polarity can also be inferred from the geochemistry of these rocks. Table 2*f*-*g* summarizes their composition. We have grouped Cikobia-i-Lau, Munia, and Katafaga together as 'eastern islands' and Vanua Balavu and Cicia as 'western islands'. An east-to-west increase in K, Rb, Ba, U, La/Yb and Rb/Sr can be seen, and a decrease in Na/K, K/Rb, and maximum Fe and Y, suggesting that the subduction zone lay to the east.

Thus there is strong geochemical evidence that the late Miocene (5·5-9 m.y. ago) was a period of active island arc volcanism in Fiji and that its associated subduction zone lay to the north and east of the Lau Ridge. Any suggestion that Fiji evolved suigenerically during this period or in isolation from traditional island arc environments having the polarity described (Malahoff, preprint; Chase, 1971) must be rejected or modified as they cannot account for these spatial geochemical variations.

Similar arguments cannot be advanced for the New Hebrides or Tonga. Volcanics associated with a late Miocene fauna are known only from the eastern New Hebrides islands. The only possible Miocene volcanism recorded in Tonga is the 'Younger Volcanic Series' of Eua (Hoffmeister 1932, Ewart *et al.*, in press), a weathered tuffaceous horizon overlying Upper Eocene limestone. Its mineralogy differs from that of late Miocene volcanics of the Lau Ridge in that there is hornblende present but very little hypersthene. Nevertheless its correlation with the Lau Volcanics is the only apparent link between the observable geology of Tonga and Lau.

Fig. 5 is a tentative proposal for the configuration of the Pacific-Australian plate boundary during the late Miocene. A similar diagram could be drawn for the first period of volcanism (Eocene-early Miocene), although its trench and volcanic front might be slightly closer to Australia. This proposal is consistent with the subduction polarity inferred for the Fijian profiles A-A′ and B-B′ of Fig. 6 and also with that inferred for the New Hebrides in the early Miocene (Mitchell & Warden 1971). It suggests that the Vitiaz Trench and Cape Johnson Trough may be remnant subduction sites. At least the Fiji-Lau-Tonga portion of the diagram is likely to be valid for this period. Whether the New Hebrides was then where we suggest it was is less certain, and is a point discussed towards the end of this paper.

THIRD PERIOD VOLCANISM: PLIOCENE TO RECENT

The character of volcanism in the New Hebrides and Fiji changed dramatically during the Pliocene and, especially in Fiji, ceased to be that of a typical island arc.

Volcanism of this period in Fiji is almost exclusively basaltic; geochemical features are summarized in Table 3. The province includes shoshonites in northern Viti Levu, analyses of which are given by Dickinson *et al.* (1968), Rodda (1969, pp. 9-13), and Gill (1970). It also includes quartz-, hypersthene-, and nepheline-normative olivine basalts (some of which carry lherzolite nodules) and differentiates from north-east and south-east Viti Levu, the Lomaiviti islands, south-west Vanua Levu, Taveuni, and the northern Lau islands. At least four centres (Bua, Taveuni, Koro, and Korobasaqa) have yielded basalts with the Ti and Zr contents of mid-ocean varieties. The tholeiites of the Lau Basin (Sclater *et al.* 1972) could be included in this province.

One of the shoshonite centres has been firmly dated at 4·8-5·3 m.y. old (McDougall 1963), the other yielding erratic K-Ar ages between 4·8-9·0 m.y. (Rodda *et al.* 1967).

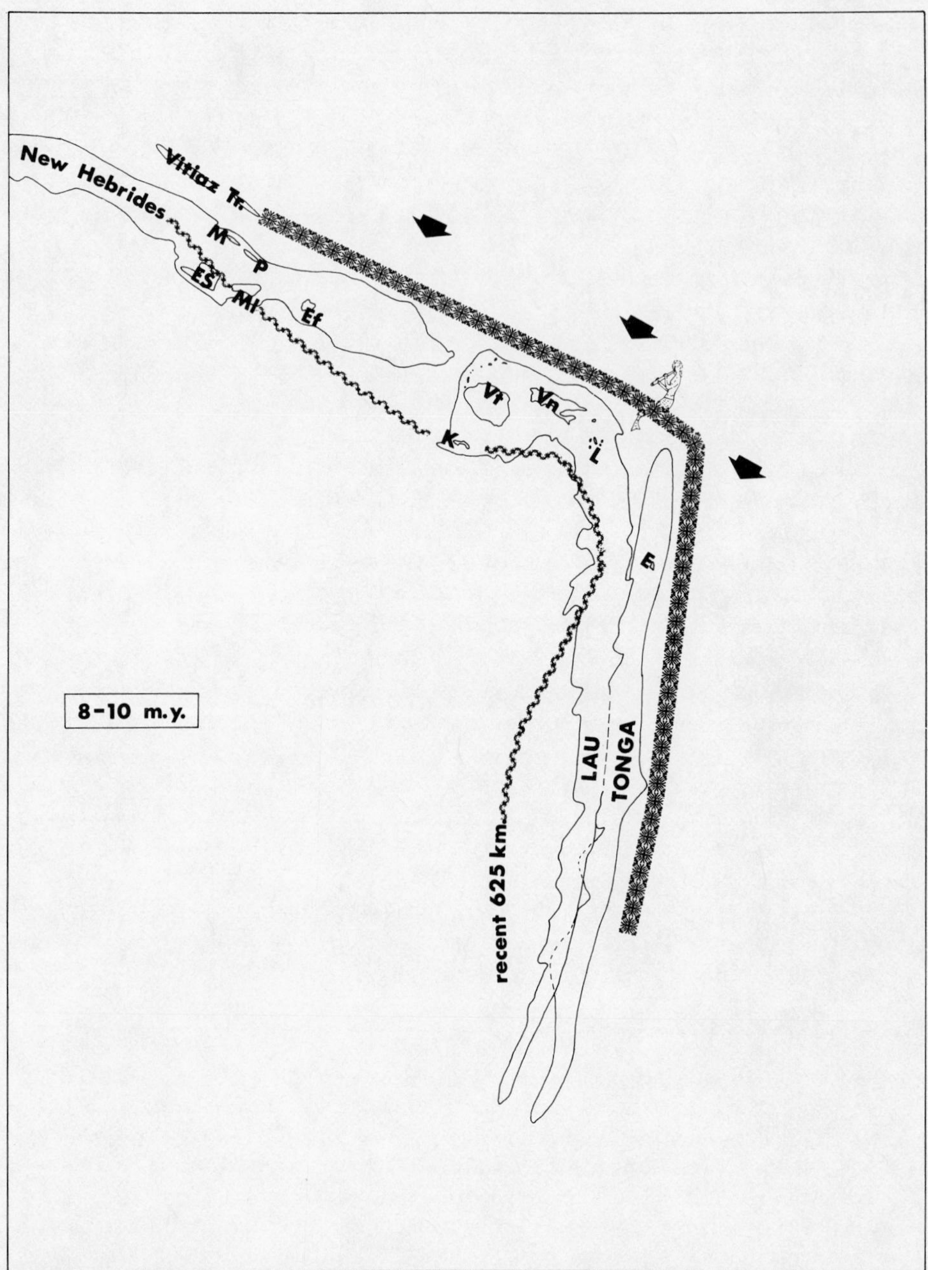

Fig. 5 A proposed configuration of the New Hebrides-Fiji-Tonga Ridge before fracturing. Ridge outlines represent their modern 2-km isobaths although the Tonga portion is our estimate of its pre-Pliocene shape, i.e. the modern 'non-volcanic ridge'. The New Hebrides Ridge should be similarly modified; see Fig. 7. The southern Lau Ridge and the Vitiaz Trench have been fixed in their present position for reference

Lacking rigorously consistent data for volcanism older than 5 m.y. ago at Tavua or other basaltic centres of this province, we take that figure as the approximate time of initiation of the third period of volcanic activity. It continued until almost 3 m.y. ago in the northern Lau islands (Gill & McDougall, unpubl.), until about 2,000 years ago in Taveuni (E. Frost, pers. comm.), and to as recently as 1948 at Niua'fou in the Lau Basin (Richard 1962). The geomorphology of Viti Levu has been interpreted as indicating over 800 m of regional uplift since the Pliocene (Dickinson, unpubl. MS.), or within the last 5·5 m.y.

Volcanism of this period in the New Hebrides can be divided into two groups. During the early Pliocene high-K rocks were erupted on a ridge extending from Epi south to Efate and possibly Tanna. They include little-known plutonics from the basement of Tanna, high-K calcalkaline andesites from western Epi in which $K_2O/Na_2O \sim 1$, and the trachytes-to-dacites of Efate with similar alkali ratios (Ash 1970, Colley & Warden, in prep.).

In sharp contrast, basalts and minor andesites characterize the Pleistocene to Recent volcanism, which extends the length of the group in a well-defined line lying above 200 km earthquake hypocentres. Tanna, which is associated with deeper earthquakes, is exceptional in producing strongly alkali-enriched basaltic andesites. Elsewhere rocks range from tholeiites to alkali basalts and associated andesites.

Because the Pliocene to Recent volcanism of Fiji and the New Hebrides is so unlike that which preceded it and what is normal in island arcs, we interpret this later volcanism and the simultaneous regional uplift as being related to fragmentation of the New Hebrides-Fiji-Tonga Ridge, rather than to simple subduction. This is also a non-unique interpretation as similar low-Ti basaltic volcanism dominates the present-day New Hebrides and New Georgia (in the Solomons) which are spatially conjoined with subduction. Not until the genesis of island arc magmas is better understood can one be certain of the relationship between subduction and the third-period volcanics of Fiji or the New Hebrides.

The overall change in character from oldest shoshonites to youngest low-K tholeiites is similar to the change in volcanic character which apparently accompanies rupturing of continents preceding and during drift (cf. Green 1971, pp. 718-20).

---

in this reconstruction; the Tonga Ridge has been rotated counter-clockwise (although opening of the Lau Basin and Havre Trough cannot be explained by simple rotation about a point in the Taupo region of New Zealand); the Fiji islands rotated clockwise; and the New Hebrides Ridge rotated counter-clockwise about a point amidst the Santa Cruz islands. The patterned area forming a continuation of the Vitiaz Trench is the inferred site of crustal subduction at this time. The 625 km contour of modern earthquake foci is taken from Karig (1971, Fig. 4) and is quite speculative west of Fiji. The apparent geometric fit, inferred subduction polarity, the youth of ocean basins (which are predicted by this model to be less than 8 m.y. old) and fortuitous alignment of the Vitiaz Trench and some modern deep earthquakes, support this reconstruction. Geographic abbreviations are: M, Maewo; P, Pentecost; ES, Espíritu Santo; Ml, Malekula; Ef, Efate; Vt, Viti Levu; K, Kandavu; Vn, Vanua Levu; L, northern Lau islands; and E, Eua.

Table 3

REPRESENTATIVE ANALYSES OF THIRD PERIOD VOLCANIC ROCKS

	Tonga-Kermadec			*Fiji*			*New Hebrides*			
	10415[1]	1[2]	39[2]	68-64[3]	71-829	69-841	680	516	538	698
	a	*b*	*c*	*d*	*e*	*f*	*g*	*h*	*i*	*j*
SiO_2	49	53·68	66·77	51·78	47·80	53·30	61·06	50·73	49·86	51·02
TiO_2	1·2	0·57	0·61	0·63	1·83	0·76	0·87	0·89	0·89	0·71
Al_2O_3	18·3	17·74	14·43	20·27	16·89	19·42	15·25	16·37	16·57	14·00
Fe_2O_3	1·9	2·65	1·08	3·68	9·57*	9·38*	2·23	4·37	4·59	3·62
FeO	6·6	7·56	6·91	3·72	—	—	5·40	6·41	6·45	6·80
MnO	0·2	0·19	0·19	0·15	0·16	0·20	0·16	0·21	0·20	0·19
MgO	7·8	4·25	1·57	3·77	8·86	3·77	2·36	5·92	5·74	8·52
CaO	12·4	11·06	3·95	9·24	10·16	8·90	5·12	10·69	10·93	12·02
Na_2O	1·8	1·80	3·13	2·96	3·33	3·06	3·39	3·02	2·99	2·06
K_2O	0·4	0·40	1·15	3·34	0·95	0·74	3·65	1·16	1·80	0·86
P_1O_5	0·15	0·08	0·19	0·45	0·43	0·47	0·49	0·22	0·34	0·20
Rb	—	6	17	56	21	18	81	20	28	14
Sr	—	235	300	1230	465	512	442	532	930	399
Ba	—	100	190	677	275	360	1032	471	543	215
Pb	—	4	17	8	2·5	3	12	5	6	4

Th	—	—	—	1·3	2·7	1·7	4·6	—	1·9	—
U	—	—	—	0·56	0·67	0·46	1·6	—	0·76	—
Zr	—	28	49	46	146	124	140	66	65	50
Hf	—	—	—	1·1	—	—	3	—	1·2	—
La	—	2·1	5·9	8·5	—	—	28	—	14	—
Yb	—	0·95	1·6	1·5	—	—	2·7	—	1·5	—
Y	—	17	24	12	28	26	36	27	22	18
Ni	—	13	nd	13	170	11	6	32	34	59
Co	—	28	13	21	43	24	15	31	30	39
Cr	—	15	4	40	402	5	27	96	20	323
Sc	—	35	25	14	30	11	15	30	22	41
V	—	310	95	220	189	130	180	410	388	305
Cu	—	145	26	200	57	35	53	137	150	140
Sr 87/86	—	0·7038	0·7043	0·7036	0·7035	0·7034	—	—	—	—

[1] Brothers and Martin (1970).
[2] Ewart *et al.* (in prep.).
[3] Gill (1970).

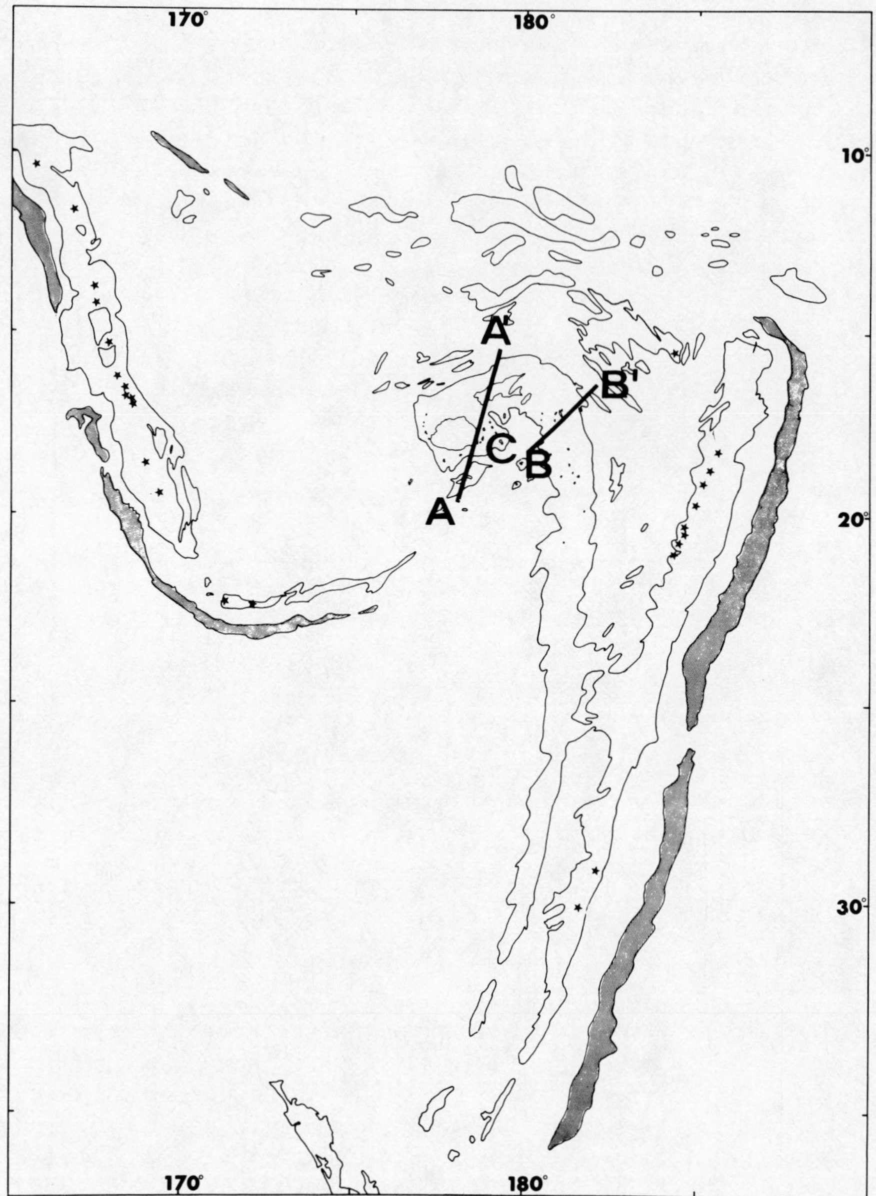

Fig. 6 Location of cross-sections discussed in the text. Area C is meant to include the Lomaiviti islands and eastern Viti Levu.

Volcanism in Fiji began on the ridge itself and was later concentrated in area C of Fig. 6—that area most likely to be affected by counter-clockwise rotation of the northern Lau Ridge.

If this interpretation is correct, normal subduction volcanism (i.e. that in which intermediate and acidic material figures prominently) ended in Fiji approximately 6 m.y. ago, and disruption of the volcanic ridge formed thereby had begun by 5 m.y. ago. Second, it implies that the locus of basaltic volcanism moved during this period in the direction of the modern trenches to the east and west of Fiji as there is neither historically-active volcanism in modern Fiji, nor seismic attenuation beneath it, whereas both appear to be present in and beneath the Lau Basin and Fiji Plateau (Barazangi & Isacks 1971, Sclater *et al.* 1972, Chase 1971). Third, it suggests an explanation for the K_2O variations within the modern New Hebrides (Mallick, this volume) that has no significance for arc polarity. The variations in composition of third-period volcanics from Fiji (Table 3) are thought to reflect variations in source material and degree of fusion, rather than depth to an associated Benioff zone.

Third-period volcanism of Tonga and Kermadec is dominantly basaltic-andesite to dacite and typical of the island arc tholeiitic series (Ewart *et al.,* in prep., Bauer 1970, Richard 1962, Brothers 1970). Its tectonic environment is almost archetypal for a normal intra-oceanic island arc.

DATE OF FRAGMENTATION OF THE NEW HEBRIDES-FIJI-TONGA RIDGE

We have proposed a former continuity of the presently fragmented volcanic ridges on the eastern boundary of the Australian plate, which persisted through at least the Lower Miocene. Our reconstruction (Fig. 5) requires a reversal of tectonic polarity and about 45° clockwise rotation of the New Hebrides Ridge, creation of new crust forming the Fiji Plateau, and simultaneous subduction of an ancestral North Fiji Basin beneath the migrating New Hebrides trench and arc. The idea of continuity has been suggested in various forms by several people (Hess & Maxwell 1953, Carey 1963, Coleman 1967, Karig & Mammerickx 1972); the principal remaining question is when the disruption began. There are two options: Middle Miocene or Pliocene to Recent.

An early Middle Miocene or Tertiary f_3 (9-12·5 m.y.; Page & McDougall 1970) separation of the New Hebrides from Fiji appears more consistent with New Hebridean geology as it is the time of greatest preserved deformation and faulting there. Robinson (1969) reports evidence that strong east-west compressional stress affected Santo and Malekula during this period and Rodda (1967) suggests it was also a time of uplift and deformation in Fiji. This may also have been the time when New Guinea, as the leading edge of Australia, over-ran a westward extension of the New Britain Trench (Page 1971) and when the Ontong Java Plateau of the Pacific plate impinged upon the Solomon Islands Ridge (Moberly 1971).

If instead, separation and polarity reversal commenced in the Pliocene, or less than 5·5 m.y. ago, it would coincide with the change in volcanism noted above for Fiji and the New Hebrides. Moreover, if this event was a passive response to some major re-adjustment of Pacific-Australian plate relationships, it is unlikely that fragmentation would have commenced sooner in the area west of Fiji than east of it. This implies comparable ages for the Fiji Plateau and Lau Basin. The Lau Basin must postdate the age of volcanics forming the basement of the Lau Ridge. If the late Miocene K-Ar dates mentioned above for these volcanics are correct, the Lau Basin and by inference the Fiji Plateau are no older than Pliocene in age. Such youthfulness for the Fiji Plateau encourages speculation that its anomalous deep earthquake foci, which shoal

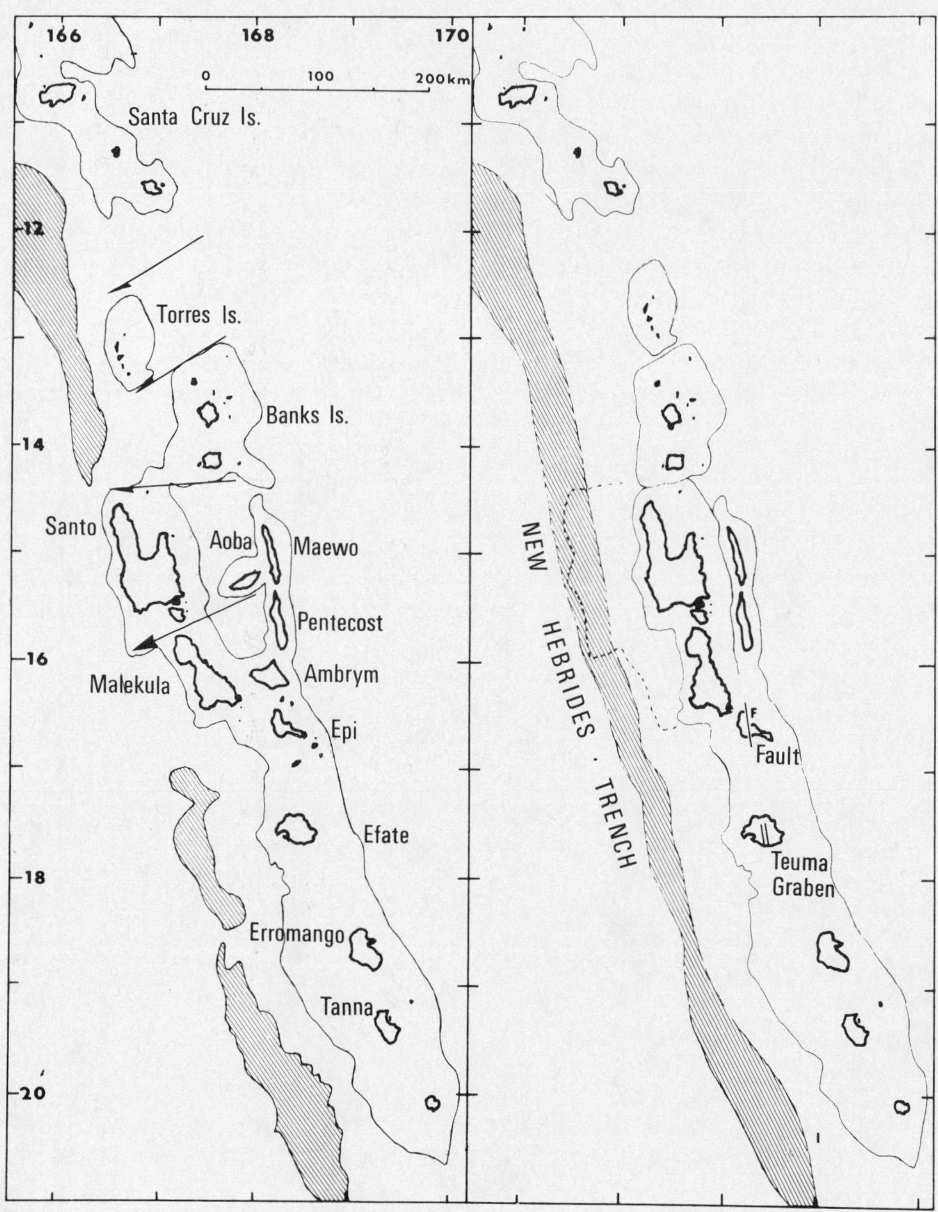

to the east (Santo 1970), may originate within detached, foundering lithosphere dating from the earlier subduction configuration of opposite polarity. Likewise the 250-300 km depths attained by foci near the New Hebrides Trench may represent the depth to which lithosphere has been downthrust so far, during the current configuration. If so, lithosphere is discontinuous and deep-focus *S* waves should be attenuated even at seismic stations near the New Hebrides Trench.

The limitation of recognized late Miocene volcanism to the eastern New Hebrides could indicate either that reversal of subduction polarity had already occurred by then or that minor eastward trench migration had taken place, as was inferred for Fiji.

Karig (1971, 1972) has proposed that the central *Y*-shaped part of the New Hebrides has resulted from rifting apart of the two arms of the *Y*. When these two sections are joined by matching bathymetric contours (Fig. 7), the suture thereby defined coincides with a major fault cutting Epi and with the Teuma Graben of Efate. Pliocene volcanics have been uplifted 700-900 m to the west of the former (Warden 1967) and considerable post-Pliocene uplift is also apparent in the latter (Williams & Warden 1964). This was also a time of general uplift in the central New Hebrides.

The volcanoes of Aoba and Ambrym, which lie within this proposed rift, produce rocks which are almost exclusively transitional between alkali and tholeiite basalt. These may be more related to the extensional environment than to normal island arc processes although they have TiO_2 contents typical of island arcs. The K_2O variation described from the Banks Islands (Mallick, this volume) may reflect the rifting (as we discussed earlier) rather than differential depth to the Benioff zone.

In migrating westward, Santo and Malekula may have overridden the central New Hebrides Trench, thus accounting for its disappearance in this region despite the continuity of volcanism and seismicity. East of Santo earthquakes having focal depths of about 150 km extend for some distance normal to the arc, indicating a flattening of the Benioff zone.

CONCLUSIONS

Detailed knowledge of the geochemistry of island arc volcanic rocks can be a useful tool in palaeo-plate tectonic studies, especially in areas such as eastern Melanesia where other criteria by which to establish the site and polarity of former subduction

---

Fig. 7 Left: the present-day New Hebrides including 1,500 m and 5,000 m (shaded) contours. Arrows indicate inferred break-up. Right: reconstruction of New Hebrides before rifting. The New Hebrides Trench has been restored and the present positions of Santo and Malekula are dotted. Note alignment of the west coasts of Maewo and Pentecost with the central fault on Epi and the Teuma Graben on Efate. A preliminary K-Ar date of about 0·6 m.y. has been obtained by one of us (MG) on a fresh but glassy sample from a formation on west Epi, which is cut by the central fault and which therefore predates rifting.

zones are absent. This is strictly true, however, only if a model such as that of Fig. 1 represents all modern examples, if uniformitarianism applies, and if the model is independent of crustal thickness and age and grossly variable fractionation processes.

We have distinguished three periods of igneous activity in eastern Melanesia. The first, covering the Eocene to Lower Miocene, was predominantly submarine and witnessed the gradual formation of the New Hebrides-Fiji-Tonga Ridge east of an early Tertiary marginal sea (South Fiji Basin) and behind the newly established boundary between the Australian and Pacific plates. In Tonga and Fiji the volcanics of this period belong to the island arc tholeiitic series. The second period, separated from the first by an erosional unconformity in Fiji and the New Hebrides and confined to the late Miocene (5·5-9 m.y. ago), is best developed in Fiji. There a polarity can be inferred from the geochemical systematics of volcanic rocks, suggesting south-westward subduction of the Pacific plate. Volcanism of this period is recorded in the eastern New Hebrides and possibly on Eua, Tonga, but polarity cannot be inferred for these areas.

We suggest that the eastern boundary of the Australian plate involved west-dipping subduction and a normal, continuous island arc during the first and possibly both of these periods. It may have looked something like what is proposed in Fig. 5. We attribute the present distribution of islands to fracturing of this island arc during the Middle Miocene and/or Pliocene to Recent, caused or at least accompanied by a different resolution of stresses between Pacific and Australian plates. This fracturing resulted in shoshonitic and basaltic volcanism in Fiji. The newly established configuration includes normal subduction volcanism of the island arc tholeiitic series in the Tonga and Kermadec chains, and tholeiitic basalt volcanism in the Lau Basin and probably Fiji Plateau. Continued rifting is splitting the New Hebrides Ridge itself, resulting in dominantly basaltic volcanism of diverse kinds.

REFERENCES

Ash, R. P. 1970. Efate. In *New Hebrides Geol. Surv. Ann. Rept* (1968) (Ed. D. I. J. Mallick), 9-14.

Avias, J. (this volume). Major features of the New Guinea-Louisiade-New Caledonian-Norfolk Arc system.

Baker, P. E. 1968. Comparative volcanology and petrology of the Atlantic island-arcs. *Bull. volcan.* **32,** 189-206.

Barazangi, M. & Isacks, B. 1971. Lateral variations of seismic wave attenuation in the upper mantle above the inclined earthquake zone of the Tonga Island Arc: Deep anomaly in the upper mantle. *J. geophys. Res.* **76,** 8493-516.

Bauer, G. R. 1970. The geology of Tofua Island, Tonga. *Pacif. Sci.* **24,** 333-50.

Blow, W. H. 1967. *Proc. First Int. Conf. Geneva: Planktonic microfossils*, **1,** p. 305 (Eds P. Bronniman & H. H. Renz). E. J. Brill, Leiden.

Brothers, R. N. 1970. Petrochemical affinities of volcanic rocks from the Tonga-Kermadec Island arc, Southwest Pacific. *Bull. volcan.* **34,** 308-29.

Brothers, R. N. & Martin, K. R. 1970. The geology of Macauley Island, Kermadec Group, South-west Pacific. *Bull. volcan.* **34,** 330-46.

Carey, S. W. 1963. The assymetry of the Earth. *Aust. J. Sci.* **25,** 369-82 and 479-88.

Chase, C. G. 1971. Tectonic history of the Fiji Plateau. *Bull. geol. Soc. Am.* **82,** 3087-110.

Cole, W. S. 1960. Upper Eocene and Oligocene larger foraminifera from Viti Levu, Fiji. *U.S. geol. Surv. Prof. Pap.* 374-A.

——— 1970. Larger foraminifera of late Eocene age from Eua, Tonga. *U.S. geol. Surv. Prof. Pap.* **640**-B.

Coleman, P. J. 1967. A possible resolution of the Melanesian Re-entrant. *Upper Mantle Project: Second Aust. Progress Rept.* 192-4 (Ed. A. E. Ringwood). Aust. Acad. Sci. Canberra.

——— 1969. Derived Eocene larger foraminifera on Maewo, eastern New Hebrides, and their South-west Pacific implications. *New Hebrides Geol. Surv. Rept.* 1967, 36-7 (Ed. D. I. J. Mallick).

Colley, H. & Warden, A. J. (In prep.). The petrology of the New Hebrides.

Davies, H. L. & Smith, I. E. 1971. Geology of Eastern Papua: a synthesis. *Bull. geol. Soc. Am.* **82,** 3299-312.

Dickinson, W. R. 1967. Tectonic Development of Fiji. *Tectonophysics* **4,** 543-53.

——— 1970. Relations of andesites, granites, and derivative sandstones to arc-trench tectonics. *Rev. Geophys. Space Phys.* **8,** 813-60.

——— (unpublished manuscript). Dissected erosion surfaces in Northwest Viti Levu, Fiji. On file with Fiji Geological Survey Dept.

Dickinson, W. R., Rickard, M. J., Coulson, F. I. E., Smith, J. G. & Lawrence, R. L. 1968. Late Cenozoic shoshonitic lavas in north-western Viti Levu, Fiji. *Nature,* **219,** 148.

Donnelly, T. W., Rogers, J. J. W., Pushkar, P. & Armstrong, R. L. 1971. Chemical evolution of the igneous rocks of the eastern West Indies: an investigation of thorium, uranium, and potassium distributions, and lead and strontium isotopic ratios. *Mem. geol. Soc. Am.* **130.**

Ewart, A., Bryan, W. B. & Graham, A. L. (In press.) The petrology and geochemistry of the igneous rocks from Eua, Tonga—an early Tertiary ophiolite complex? *Bull. geol. Soc. Am.* See also Ewart & Bryan, this volume.

Gill, J. 1970. Geochemistry of Viti Levu, Fiji, and its evolution as an island arc. *Contr. Mineral. Petrol.* **27,** 179-203.

Glaessner, M. F. 1950. Geotectonic position of New Guinea. *Bull. Am. Ass. Petrol. Geol.* **34,** 856-81.

Green, D. H. 1971. Composition of basaltic magmas as indicators of conditions of origin: application to oceanic volcanism. *Phil. Trans. R. Soc. London.* (A) **268,** 707-25.

Hess, H. H. & Maxwell, J. C. 1953. Major structural features of the South-west Pacific: a preliminary interpretation of H.O. 5484 bathymetry chart, New Guinea to New Zealand. *Proc. Pacific Sci. Congr.*, New Zealand, **2,** 14-17.

Hoffmeister, J. E. 1932. Geology of Eua, Tonga. *Bull. Bernice P. Bishop Mus.* **96.**

Jakeš, P. & Gill, J. 1970. Rare earth elements and the island arc tholeiitic series. *Earth Planet. Sci. Letters,* **9,** 17-28.

Jakeš, P. & White, A. J. R. 1969. Structure of the Melanesian arcs and correlation with distribution of magma types. *Tectonophysics,* **8,** 223-36.

——— 1970. K/Rb ratios of rocks from island arcs. *Geochim. cosmochim. Acta,* **34,** 849-56.

Karig, D. E. 1971. Origin and development of marginal basins in the Western Pacific. *J. geophys. Res.* **76,** 2542-61.

Karig, D. E. & Mammerickx, J. 1972. Tectonic framework of the New Hebrides Island arc. *Marine Geology,* **12,** 187-205.

Kuno, H. 1959. Origin of Cenozoic petrographic provinces of Japan and surrounding areas. *Bull. volcan.* **20,** 37-76.

——— 1966. Lateral variation of basalt magma type across continental margins and island arcs. *Bull. volcan.* **29,** 195-222.

Ladd, H. S. & Hoffmeister, J. E. 1945. Geology of Lau, Fiji. *Bull. Bernice P. Bishop Mus.* **181.**

Le Pichon, X. & Heirtzler, J. R. 1968. Magnetic anomalies in the Indian Ocean and sea-floor spreading. *J. geophys. Res.* **73,** 2101-17.

Lillie, A. R. & Brothers, R. N. 1970. The geology of New Caledonia. *N.Z. Jl Geol. Geophys.* **13,** 145-83.

McDougall, I. 1963. K-Ar Ages of Some Rocks from Viti Levu, Fiji. *Nature*, **198,** 677.

Malahoff, A. (In prep.) The Fiji plateau, an active spiralling tectonic system.

Mallick, D. I. J. 1972. Some petrological and structural variations in the New Hebrides. This volume.

Melson, W. G., Jarosewich, E. & Lundquist, C. A. 1970. Volcanic eruption at Metis Shoal, Tonga, 1967-8: description and petrology. *Smithsonian Contributions to the Earth Sciences* **4.**

Mitchell, A. H. G. 1966. Geology of South Malekula. *New Hebrides geol. Surv. Rept* **3.**

Mitchell, A. H. G. & Reading, H. G. 1971. Evolution of island arcs. *J. Geol.* **79,** 253-84.

Mitchell, A. H. G. & Warden, A. J. 1971. Geological evolution of the New Hebrides island arc. *J. geol. Soc. London*, **127,** 501-29.

Moberly, R. 1971. Youthful oceanic lithosphere of marginal seas, western Pacific (Abst.). *Proc. Twelfth Pacif. Sci. Congr.* (*Abstracts*), Canberra, **1,** 393.

Page, R. W. 1971. The geochronology of igneous rocks in the New Guinea region. Ph.D. thesis, Aust. Nat. Univ., Canberra.

Page, R. W. & McDougall, I. 1970. Potassium-argon dating of the Tertiary f_{1-2} stage in New Guinea and its bearing on the geological time-scale. *Am. J. Sci.* **269,** 321-42.

Phillips, K. A. 1965. A provisional Geological Map of Fiji. *Ann. Rep. geol. Surv. Fiji* (1964), 4-6.

Richard, J. J. 1962. Catalogue of the active volcanoes of the world. Part 13, Kermadec, Tonga and Samoa. *Int. volc. Assoc.* Naples.

Rickard, M. J. 1966. Reconnaissance Geology of Vanua Levu. *Mem. geol. Surv. Fiji*, **2.**

Robinson, G. P. 1969. Geology of North Santo. *New Hebrides geol. Surv. Rept.*

Rodda, P. 1967. Outline of the geology of Viti Levu. *N.Z. Jl Geol. Geophys.* **10,** 1260-73.

——— 1969. Analyses of rocks from Fiji. *Geol. Surv. Dept*, Fiji.

Rodda, P., Snelling, N. J. & Rex, D. C. 1967. Radiometric age data on rocks from Viti Levu, Fiji. *N.Z. Jl Geol. Geophys.* **10,** 1248-59.

Santo, T. 1970. Regional study of the characteristic seismicity of the world. Part III: New Hebrides region. *Bull. Earthq. Res. Inst. Tokyo Univ.* **48,** 1-18.

Sclater, J. G., Hawkins, J. W. & Mammerickx, J. 1972. Crustal extension between the Tonga and Lau Ridges: petrologic and geophysical evidence. *Bull. geol. Soc. Am.* **83,** 505-18.

Suess, E. 1904. *The Face of the Earth*, **4.** Clarendon Press, Oxford.

Sugimura, A. 1968. Spatial relations of basaltic magmas in island arcs. In *Basalts, 2.* (Eds H. H. Hess & A. Poldervaart), 537-71. Interscience, N.Y.

Taylor, S. R., Capp, A. C., Graham, A. L. & Blake, D. H. 1969. Trace element abundances in andesites. II. Saipan, Bougainville and Fiji. *Contr. Mineral. Petrol.* **23,** 1-26.

Tomita, T. 1935. On the chemical composition of the Cenozoic alkaline suite of the circum-Japan-Sea region. *J. Shanghai Sci. Inst.* **1,** 227-306.

Warden, A. J. 1967. The geology of the Central Islands. *New Hebrides geol. Surv. Rept* 5.

Williams, C. E. F. & Warden, A. J. 1964. *New Hebrides geol. Surv. Prog. Rept*, 1959-62.

Phase Transformations and Mantle Dynamics

A. E. Ringwood

Department of Geophysics and Geochemistry,
Australian National University, P.O. Box 4, Canberra City, A.C.T. 2601, Australia

ABSTRACT

Major phase transitions occur in the normal mantle at depths near 400 and 650 km accompanied by density changes of 8-10 per cent. Their temperature gradients are probably positive and in the vicinity of 20-30 bars/° C. These phase transitions influence the mantle engine which transports lithosphere plates. They inhibit the occurrence of 'Vening-Meinesz'-type mantle convection, postulated to occur in the presence of very small superadiabatic temperature gradients. It does not appear likely therefore, that lithosphere plates behave as passive objects, transported on the backs of mantle-wide convection currents of this kind.

On the other hand, the sinking of a slab of lithosphere beneath an oceanic trench occurs under highly superadiabatic conditions. The levels at which major phase transitions occur in the sinking slabs are displaced upwards by 30-100 km, compared to the depths at which they occur in normal mantle. This causes a marked increase in the average density of the slab, which sinks into the mantle because of the effect of gravitational body forces arising from this excess density. Phase transformations are thus shown to play the major role in driving the lithosphere slab into the mantle at depths greater than 300 km, and also control the stress distribution within the slab.

The hypothesis that deep earthquakes are caused by phase transformations may now be reconsidered. In a dynamic mantle, the difficulties faced earlier by this hypothesis are greatly weakened. It now appears quite likely that deep earthquakes may be caused by failure under stresses generated directly or indirectly by phase transformations. Additional possible effects of phase transformations in a dynamic mantle include epeirogenic crustal movements, early arrival of seismic waves at island-arc stations and generation of the characteristic positive gravity anomalies over island arcs.

Reconstruction of Past Arc-Trench Systems from Petrotectonic Assemblages in the Island Arcs of the Western Pacific

WILLIAM R. DICKINSON

Geology Department, Stanford University, Stanford, California, 94305 U.S.A.

ABSTRACT

Associations of specific rock assemblages and structural styles of deformation can be interpreted so as to identify the tectonic elements of ancient arcs and related trenches. Arc assemblages are characterized by dominantly volcanic and volcaniclastic sequences—generally of andesitic composition but including a range of petrologic types from basalt lavas to ignimbrites—laid down in a range of environments including terrestrial, narrow shelf, and local basin; these are later metamorphosed under greenschist to amphibolite conditions, and intruded by granitic to dioritic plutons. Where transverse variations in the potassicity or total alkalinity of the extrusives or intrusives can be established, the polarity of the arc can be inferred. Marginal arcs along the edges of continental masses include largely terrestrial andesitic or more felsic volcanics, and commonly harbour large granitic batholiths in their roots. Intra-oceanic arcs by contrast include large volumes of marine volcaniclastics surrounding andesitic to basaltic volcanic piles intruded by smaller and more dioritic plutons. Trench assemblages are characterized by cherty pelagites, terrigenous turbidites, and basaltic pillow lavas that were deposited in deep water on oceanic crust. These strata were dislocated and intermingled to melange condition by complex undersea sliding and multiple thrusting in subduction zones, then metamorphosed under greenschist to blueschist conditions. Shreds of ophiolitic complexes are included in the melanges. Interposed between arc and trench assemblages are moderately deformed terrigenous clastic sequences. These are deposited in analogues of the shelf, slope, and trough settings found in modern arc-trench systems between arcs and outer acoustic basement barriers. The sequences are later metamorphosed under subgreenschist conditions, and typically separated from trench assemblages by semicontinuous ophiolite belts.

Relations of these kinds of petrotectonic assemblages in time and space for complex arcs of the Western Pacific reveal different patterns of tectonic evolution. The principal palaeogeographic styles of arc behaviour include: (*a*) congruent development in place by either prograde or retrograde migration of the locus of arc activity with respect to underlying crust during unchanged polarity; (*b*) bodily drift of the arc structure away from a hinterland, with the formation of new sea floor in the wake by arc-rear spreading in a pattern different from spreading along intra-oceanic rises; (*c*) reversal of polarity of intra-oceanic arcs by transfer of the associated trench from one side to the other; (*d*) collision of intra-oceanic arc structures with continental margins, in which case accretion of the arc may be followed by flipping of the subduction zone and consequent reversal of polarity prior to resumed arc activity; and (*e*) collision of marginal arcs with other arcs or continents which are accreted or welded to the

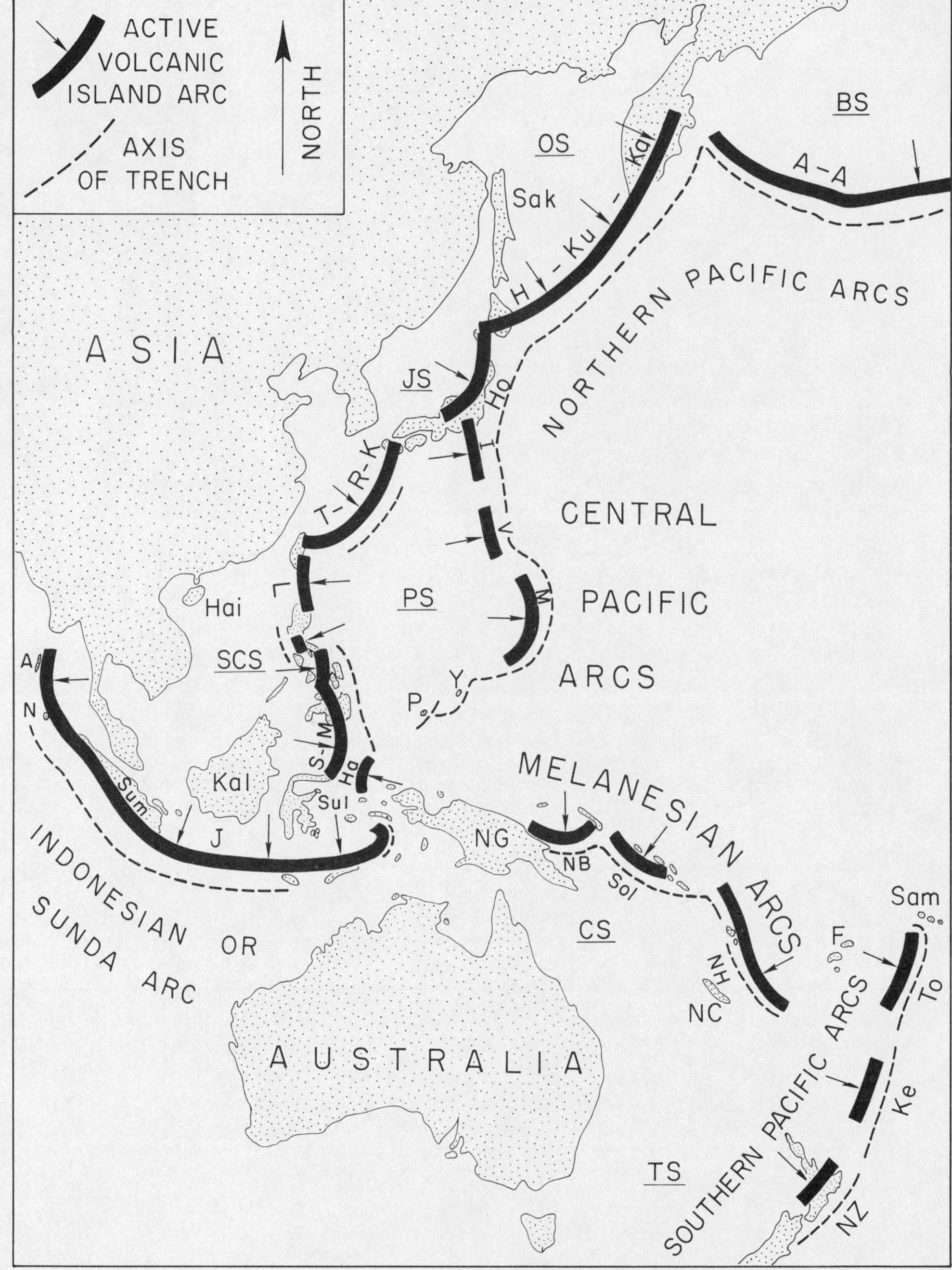

Fig. 1 Diagrammatic map showing active arc-trench systems of the Western Pacific region. Dark curving lines are active volcanic island arc chains. Arrows behind arcs

continental margin as subduction along the arc-trench system is either choked or stepped outward.

The tectonic history of the Western Pacific arcs since the Palaeozoic can be reconstructed in outline by adopting four major hypotheses:

(1) The lands and submerged ridges lying east and south of the Moluccan region just west of New Guinea were associated together with Australia and Antarctica in a cluster that lay far from Asia before spreading events and arc construction during the Tertiary.

(2) The Indonesian and Philippine (?) islands are remnants and fragments of a once coherent Sunda peninsular projection of Asia; a post-Palaeozoic marginal arc-trench system along the southern flank of the Sunda peninsula and adjacent southern Asia is still active east of India, but was terminated in the Himalayan region by a continental collision during the Tertiary.

(3) Ancestral members of the offshore fringing arc system extending from China to Kamchatka were linked segments of a mid-Cretaceous and younger marginal arc-trench system along the eastern edge of Asia prior to arc migration and arc construction during the Tertiary; tectonic relations across the South China Sea between this marginal arc and the Sunda peninsular region are uncertain.

(4) The configurations of the present margins of the adjacent Asian continent are the final product of a series of continental collisions that welded continental fragments together along suture belts that are now intracontinental; the Ural suture between the Russian and Siberian blocks records a Palaeozoic collision, but the welding of the Kolyma block to the Siberian block in the Verkhoyansk region, and the joint juxtaposition of the previously (?) connected Sino-Japanese and 'Sunda' blocks to Siberia and central Asia were apparently Mesozoic events.

INTRODUCTION

In the plate model of global tectonics, arc-trench systems with inclined seismic zones are interpreted as indicators of plate junctures, where vectors of relative motion have a strong component of convergence (Isacks, Oliver & Sykes 1968). Trench regions are thought to be the main loci of crustal subduction, where plates of lithosphere being consumed begin their descent into the asthenosphere along courses marked by the inclined seismic zones. The magmatism in the associated arcs is apparently related in some regular way to the positions of the inclined seismic zones that dip beneath the arcs. The magmatic arcs occupy either island chains or continental margins that

---

show known or inferred polarity. Dashed lines indicate axes of subparallel trenches. Arcs shown include: A-A, western end of Alaskan-Aleutian; H-Ku-Ka, Hokkaido-Kuril-Kamchatka; Ho, Honshu; T-R-K, Taiwan-Ryukyu-Kyushu; I-Izu; V, Volcano; M, Mariana; L, Luzon; S-M, Sangi-Mindanao; Ha, Halmahera; NB, New Britain; Sol, Solomons; NH, New Hebrides; To, Tonga; Ke, Kermadec; NZ, New Zealand. Prominent marginal seas (in underlined letters) include: BS, Bering Sea; OS, Sea of Okhotsk; JS, Sea of Japan; SCS, South China Sea; PS, Philippine Sea; CS, Coral Sea; TS, Tasman Sea. Other islands indicated include: Sak, Sakhalin; Hai, Hainan; A, Andaman Island; N, Nicobar Island; Sum, Sumatra; J, Java; Kal, Kalimantan; Sul, Sulawesi; P, Palau; Y, Yap; NG, New Guinea; NC, New Caledonia; F, Fiji; Sam, Samoa.

stand roughly parallel to the trenches near the edges of the consuming, or over-riding, plate margins.

Fully active arc-trench systems display chains of explosive volcanoes, bathymetric deeps, and an array of geophysical parameters which include seismic events, gravity anomalies, and characteristic heat-flow provinces. Less active or dormant systems of late Cenozoic age are still marked by inactive or quiescent volcanic chains, and by filled troughs in the place of open trenches, even though geophysical indicators are absent or equivocal. Older arc-trench systems commonly lack prominent geographic features as well, but can be recognized on the basis of certain rock assemblages whose origins can be related to processes that operate only in specific parts of arc-trench systems. This paper discusses the general nature and chief variants of these *petrotectonic assemblages* formed in arc-trench systems; then shows how the concepts developed can be used to help interpret the past behaviour of salient arc-trench systems and related tectonic elements in the Western Pacific region.

WESTERN PACIFIC TECTONIC FRAMEWORK

The concept of moving plates of lithosphere diverging from spreading rises on an earth of constant volume has an implicit corollary for the history of arc-trench systems around the circum-Pacific periphery. The post-Palaeozoic breakup of the major continents has formed most of the present ocean basins other than the Pacific during Mesozoic and Cenozoic time. The margins of the other ocean basins have been mostly inactive, with the notable exception of the Alpine-Himalayan belt, where the Tethyan Sea was presumably consumed. It follows that arc-trench systems of the Pacific region must have consumed a large proportion of the lithosphere, whose destruction is required to balance the lithosphere created by accretion to receding plate margins along intra-oceanic rise systems during the last 100-250 m.y. By analogy with the current situation, I presume that these required arc-trench systems were mainly around the circum-Pacific periphery. It thus seems likely that the history of consuming plate margins among arc-trench systems of the Western Pacific has a significant time-depth on the order of at least 100-250 m.y. The rock record of early phases of that history should be partly exposed locally in the more eroded parts of the modern arc structures.

The present arc-trench systems of the Western Pacific region are arranged in three complex curvilinear arrays that radiate from common ground in eastern Indonesia (Fig. 1). The northern arm includes the bifurcated arcs of the central Pacific and the simpler chains of the northern Pacific. The western arm is formed by the arcs that face the Indian Ocean, and the eastern arm extends through the Melanesian chains to the arcs of the southern Pacific. This unique pattern of branching arcs reflects a regional triple junction of trench-trench-trench type (McKenzie & Morgan, 1969) between three of the six major plates of lithosphere on the present globe (Fig. 2). Along all significant segments of the mutual junctures between the Pacific, Eurasian, and Indo-Australian plates, calculated vectors of relative motion include a significant component of convergence (Le Pichon 1968). In detail, the juncture is severely compli-

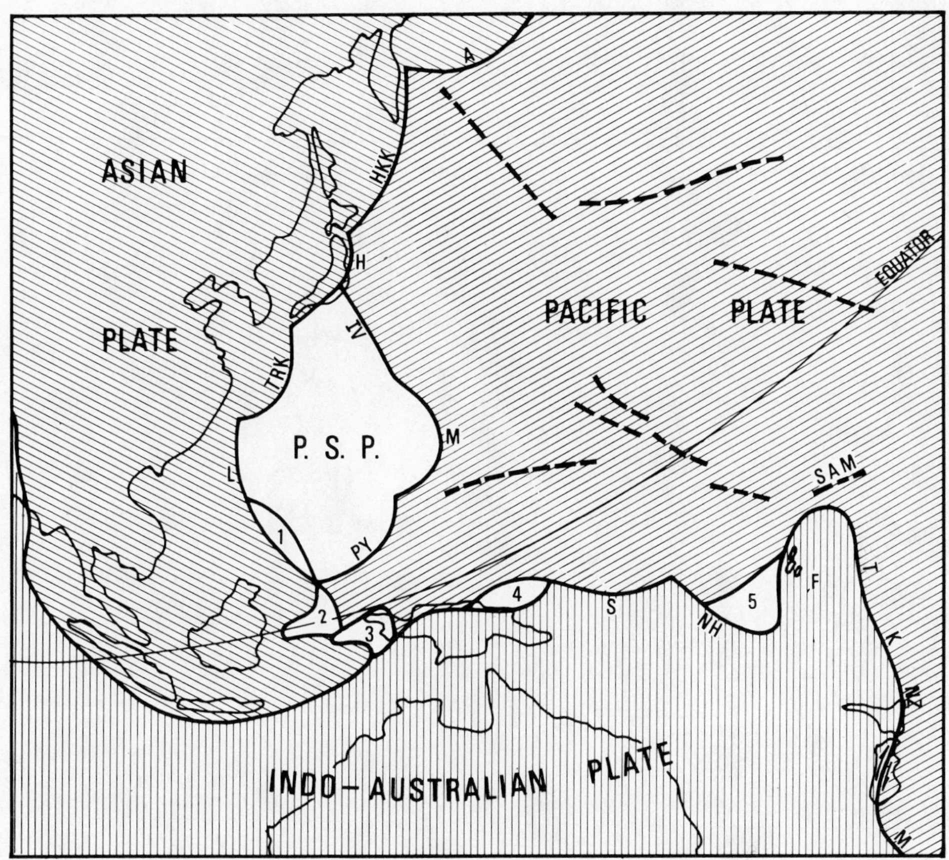

Fig. 2 Sketch map showing boundaries of lithosphere plates in the Western Pacific region as delineated by belts of shallow seismicity. Shorelines of continents and major islands shown on Asian and Indian plates. Dashed lines in Pacific plate indicate trends of major island and seamount chains ('SAM' denotes Samoa to aid comparison with Fig. 1). Configurations of unpatterned small plates are speculative and generalized. Simple juncture between Asian and Pacific plates includes Aleutian (A), Hokkaido-Kuril-Kamchatka (HKK), and Honshu (H) arcs. Philippine Sea plate (P.S.P.) is bounded (*a*) on west by Taiwan-Ryukyu-Kyushu arc (TRK), Luzon reversed arc (L), and complex region in Philippines shown as small plate 1; and (*b*) on east by linked Izu-Volcano (IV) and Marianas (M) active arcs, and by Palau-Yap (PY) trend of inactive arcs. Small plates 2 and 3 shown schematically west of New Guinea lie within Moluccan region of triple juncture east of Sulawesi (Celebes). Small plate 4 off north-east New Guinea encloses Bismarck Sea north of New Britain arc. Small plate 5 west of Fiji (F) is schematic to denote complex region on Fiji Plateau. Junctures between Pacific and Indian plates include reversed Solomons (S) and New Hebrides (NH) Arcs, Tonga (T)/Kermadec (K)/New Zealand (NZ) arc systems, Alpine transform (half-arrows), and reversed Macquarie (M) Arc. Juncture between Asian and Indian plates is Indonesian Arc of Sumatra and Java with continuation east along Lesser Sunda chain and west along Andaman-Nicobar chain.

cated by the presence of several small plates, and a determination of the vectors of relative motion between all the plates involved is inherently difficult. Summations of angular velocity vectors must be carried across two or more rise systems to derive a vector of relative motion for each of the three major junctures involved. The possibly erratic behaviour of the intervening small plates adds to the potential for error in detail. Careful evaluation of slip vectors obtained from first-motion solutions for earthquakes within the region can resolve much of the ambiguity for current motions, but results cannot be extrapolated far into the past when patterns of small plates may have been different.

These peculiarities of the Western Pacific tectonic framework mean that the histories of the local arc-trench systems, and of the local plate configurations that have sustained them, must be established from local data almost independently of global reasoning. Valid interpretations of the original positions of various tectonic elements related to

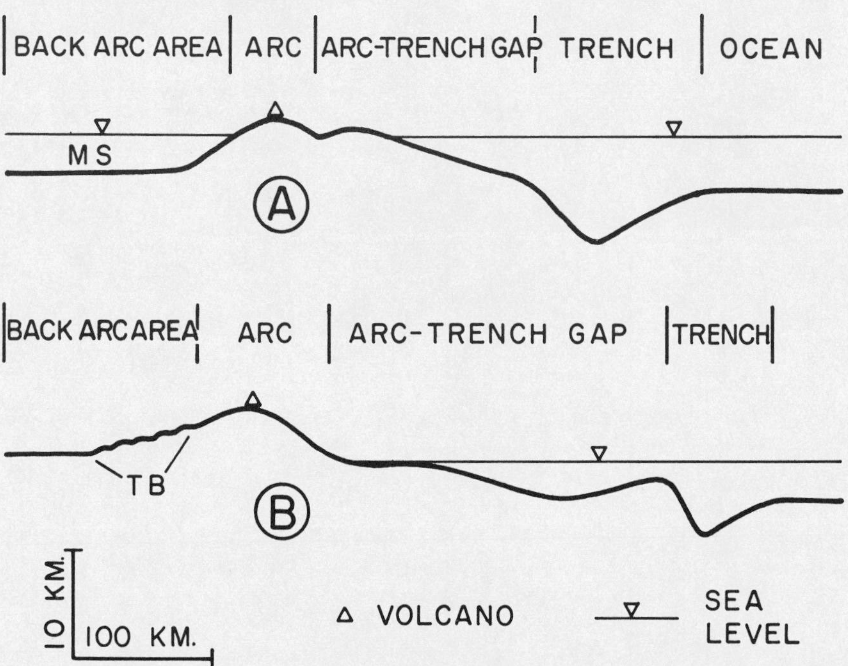

Fig. 3 Sketch of transverse topography and bathymetry of two idealized arc-trench systems. Upper profile (A) is island arc with marginal sea (MS) behind arc; arc-trench gap includes uplifted belt near arc and deep slope offshore. Lower profile (B) is marginal arc with continental interior behind it beyond thrust belt (TB—see text for explanation); arc-trench gap includes fringing shelf and deep trough offshore, separated from trench by outer basement barrier at crest of slope break above inner wall of trench. Features shown behind arcs are typical for settings depicted. Features shown in arc-trench gaps are illustrative of main types only; both kinds of settings display a variety of arc-trench gaps.

past arc-trench systems can stem only from identifying specific types of rock assemblages known to form in particular parts of arc-trench systems.

ARC-TRENCH SYSTEMS

The correlation of rock assemblages and geologic processes with geophysical observations and tectonic features in Japan has been summarized by Miyashiro (1967),

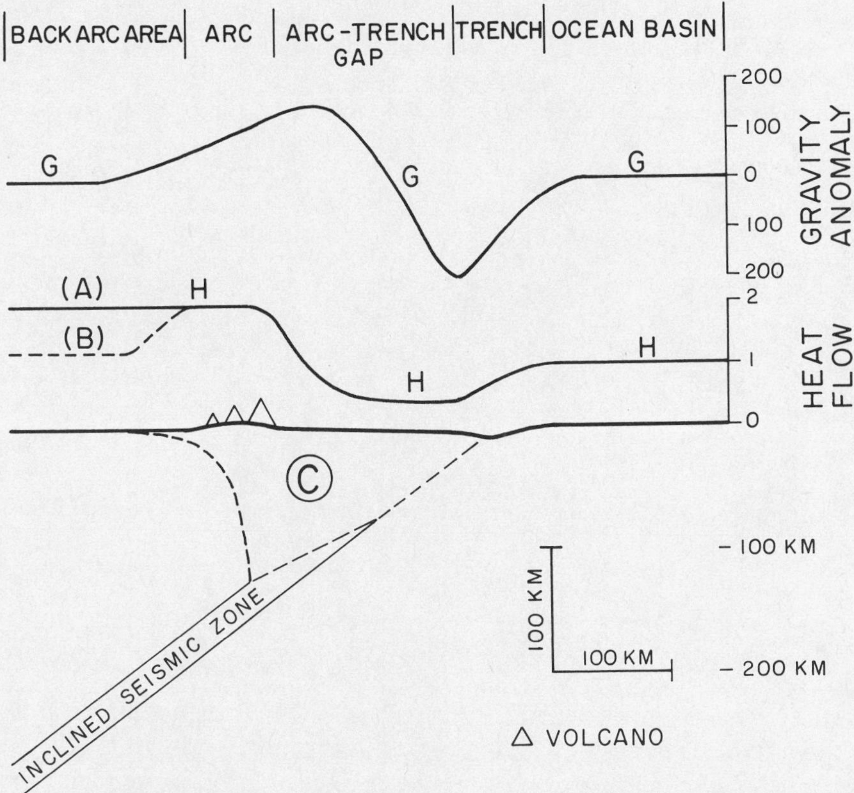

Fig. 4 Generalized sketch showing characteristic geophysical features of arc-trench systems in profile. Heavy line is topographic-bathymetric surface. Line G is gravity anomaly profile, where distance between crest and trough is about 115 km (Hatherton 1969*a*, 1969*b*). Line H is heat-flow profile, where segments in back-arc area indicate: (A) observed pattern for marginal seas behind island arcs, and (B) inferred pattern for thrust belts and continental interiors behind marginal arcs. Triangular space (C) bounded by dashed lines is region of diffuse shallow seismicity beneath arc and arc-trench gap. Inclined seismic zones vary in dip from 15°-75°, with 30°-60° dips most common, and may be curviplanar rather than planar. Vertical distance, *h*, from arc volcanoes to earthquake foci of intermediate depth in seismic zone beneath is 75-275 km, with 100-175 km most common (see Fig. 6).

and by Matsuda and Uyeda (1971). Valuable extrapolations of their insights to other regions, and significant additions to the catalogue of arc-related processes, have been presented by Hamilton (1969*a*, 1969*b*, 1970), Karig (1970, 1971*a*, 1971*b*), and others. I have elsewhere summarized petrologic relations in arc-trench systems (Dickinson 1970).

Figs 3, 4, and 5 depict, respectively, the most significant bathymetric-topographic, geophysical, and geologic features of arc-trench systems in section. The bathymetric and topographic variants shown are idealizations selected from voluminous data. The geophysical model is a composite from numerous compilations. The geologic sketches are frankly interpretive but are generally consistent with previous reconstructions. Spatial correlation of the three figures is given by the indicated positions of the four main transverse tectonic elements of arc-trench systems; namely, trench, arc-trench gap, arc, and backarc area. Each element has persistent longitudinal continuity. The polarity of such a system can be expressed by stating that it faces toward the side with the trench.

Trenches

The trench regions are characteristically asymmetric deeps with steep inner walls and gentle outer slopes. The projections of the inclined seismic zones in the mantle beneath the arcs would intersect the surface somewhere in the vicinity of the steep inner walls. Normal faults observed from continuous seismic profiling of some outer slopes, and extensional first-motion solutions from similar settings, suggest that the trenches occur where oceanic plates of lithosphere bend downward to begin descent into the asthenosphere. The materials swept into the trenches from the sea floors by this process of consumption are the rocks of the mafic oceanic crust together with its blanket of oceanic sediments, its local capping of seamounts, and its underpinning of depleted mantle. This suite is the petrotectonic assemblage called an ophiolite sequence, a pseudostratigraphic succession of: (*a*) peridotite or serpentinite; (*b*) layered gabbroic and metagabbroic rocks with minor associated trondhjemitic diorites; (*c*) doleritic or diabasic sheets or screens; (*d*) basaltic and spilitic pillow lavas with minor keratophyric associates; and (*e*) varied marine sedimentary strata with prominent cherts and argillites (Coleman 1971, Dewey & Bird 1971). Comparative rates of plate consumption and sediment supply to the trenches presumably govern to a large extent trench depths and configurations of trench floors, as well as thicknesses of turbidites accumulated along the trenches and stacked in the upper horizons of ophiolite sequences. Heat flow is low in trench regions, in harmony with the hypothesis that cold surficial materials are depressed to unusual depths.

The boundary between the trench and the arc-trench gap is taken as the prominent slope break that occurs at the top of the inner wall of the trench. On continuous seismic profiler records, this position commonly coincides with the crest of an acoustic basement ridge or barrier, either exposed or buried at shallow depth as a subsurface lip. The internal composition of these barriers and their lateral extensions beneath the thin pockets of layered sediment along the nearly bare inner walls of the trenches is not known with any certainty. The negative gravity anomalies with peaks just inboard of the trench axes suggest that considerable volumes of light sediments that

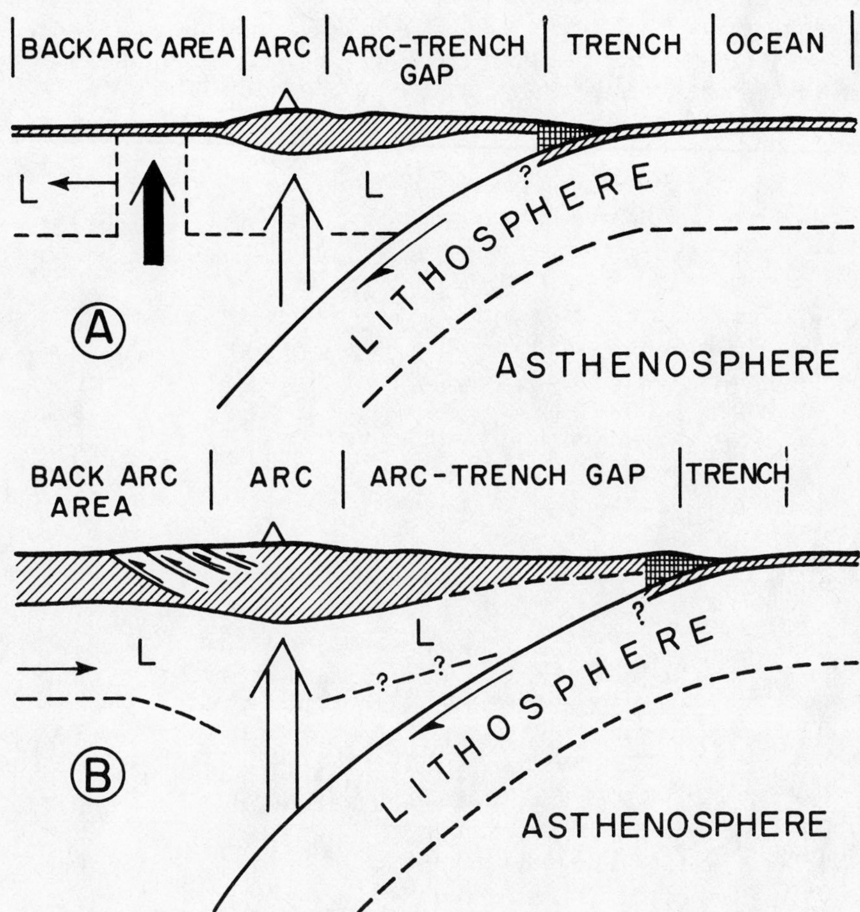

Fig. 5 Hypothetical geologic interpretations of arc-trench profiles (A, B) of Fig. 3 to true vertical scale. Shaded areas are crust. Cross-hatched areas are melanges and associated rocks of subduction zones beneath outer basement barriers and inner walls of trenches. Open arrows are paths of arc magmas toward surface. Crustal plutons are emplaced between arrowheads and volcanoes. Thickness of lithosphere (L) is shown arbitrarily as 75 km in oceanic regions and 100 km in continental regions. Solid arrow in profile A denotes schematically the diapiric rise of mantle and magmas to build new lithosphere and crust in backarc area as existing lithosphere and crust recede from arc-trench system (e.g. small arrow). Thrust symbols behind arc in profile B indicate belt of folds and thrusts in response to crowding of lithosphere against rear of arc-trench system (e.g. small arrow). Half-arrows denote descent of oceanic lithosphere beneath arc-trench system in both cases.

ride into the trenches do not descend into the mantle with the rest of the lithosphere, but instead are scraped off beneath the inner walls of the trenches. If so, the elevated barriers of acoustic basement may stand high as an isostatic response to the tectonic stacking of subducted materials beneath the inner walls of the trenches. The tops of the barriers may be rocks that rode over the subduction zone, or they may themselves be composed entirely of subducted and deformed oceanic materials lifted as on an elevator by continued subduction.

The materials carried into the subduction zones are now widely regarded as those that form the substance of the blueschist and greenschist terranes in the low *T/P* members of paired metamorphic belts (e.g. Ernst 1970). Mineral facies vary slightly from belt to belt, and the structural condition of the rocks ranges from schistose tectonites to bedded sediments, but melanges dislocated by pervasive shearing are common or dominant. Protoliths are mainly greywackes and shreds or slabs torn from ophiolitic sequences.

Arc-trench gaps

The arc-trench gaps (Dickinson 1971*c*) are heterogeneous belts of variable width between arcs and trenches. Uplifted blocks undergoing erosion are present in many arc-trench gaps, but most include as well elongate tracts of subsidence in which essentially undisturbed sediments accumulate. The sediment traps include terrestrial basins, unstable shelves, transverse slopes with sediment pockets, and deep marine troughs. The sedimentary sequences are subject to neither the subduction and intense deformation of the trench regions, nor to the magmatism and high heat flow of the arc regions. Heat flow remains low across nearly the full width of modern arc-trench gaps, and old sedimentary sequences ascribed here to this setting display burial metamorphism of zeolitic or slightly higher grade facies without severe penetrative deformation. Arc-trench gap sequences include terrestrial, shelf, and turbidite strata that grade laterally into or unconformably onlap the igneous rocks and related strata of the arcs, and are thrust over or unconformably overlap the materials of the subduction zone near the trench. They commonly mask an underlying transition from semi-continental to semi-oceanic crust. Between several pairs of inferred Mesozoic trench and arc-trench gap assemblages around the circum-Pacific periphery, the faulted zones of contact between the two are marked by semi-continuous ophiolite belts representing oceanic crust depositionally beneath the outer flanks of the arc-trench gap sequences (Dickinson 1971*c*).

The width of an arc-trench gap is a function of the dip of the inclined seismic zone and the vertical depth from the arc volcanoes to that zone. Arc-trench gaps of different width and character thus probably reflect fundamental dynamic relations. The integrity of an arc-trench system across the arc-trench gap is emphasized by the diffuse shallow seismicity that is observed typically throughout a region with triangular cross-section beneath the gap. The positive gravity anomalies with peaks just outboard of the arcs may reflect the presence of dense slabs of lithosphere descending at depth beneath the arc-trench gaps (Oliver 1970).

Arcs

The boundary between the arc and the arc-trench gap is a sharply defined magmatic front, where the first or only row of volcanoes stands. This position coincides roughly with a sharp increase in heat flow to the abnormally high levels characteristic of the arcs. The elevated heat flow is widely attributed to the advective transfer of heat to crustal levels by the ascent of magmas from the mantle below. The generally andesitic volcanism in the arcs is taken to be but the surface expression of complex magmatic provinces that include granitic plutons at depth. The metamorphic terranes of greenschist and amphibolite facies in the high T/P members of paired metamorphic belts are interpreted as the roots of arcs in which the plutons are emplaced. Arc magmatism thus constructs volcano-plutonic orogens in which cogenetic extrusive and intrusive igneous rocks are both integral components.

The ultimate sources of the magmas in the arcs remain speculative. Potential sources include the subjacent crust, the mantle beneath, and parts of the lithosphere descending along or beneath the inclined seismic zone at still deeper levels. Correlation of petrologic variations in young lavas with vertical depths to inclined seismic zones below directs attention to materials in their vicinity. The K/Si ratio is especially useful, as demonstrated when a suitable K index (*after* Bateman & Dodge 1970, p. 415) is plotted against depth, h, to the seismic zone for currently active arcs of the circum-Pacific region (Fig. 6). Near the seismic zones, there are two attractive sources for partial melts: (*a*) eclogitic materials formed in the uppermost layers of the descending slabs of lithosphere from the inversion of oceanic crust; and (*b*) peridotitic materials in the low-velocity zone near the top of the asthenosphere in the over-riding block. The fact that the chains of arc volcanoes stand consistently above regions where the inclined seismic zones are at intermediate focal depths suggests that the linearity of the chains is controlled in some fundamental way by intersections of the inclined seismic zones and the low-velocity zone (Dickinson & Hatherton 1967). The linkage between tectonic setting and petrologic variations detected by the *K-h* correlation could still be less direct than implied by the simple model of partial melting at or near the seismic zone, and induced diapiric motions in the mantle above the seismic zone can be invoked as an auxiliary mechanism to achieve partial melting. In any case, the empirical *K-h* correlation allows crude palaeotectonic reconstructions of past arc-trench systems by plotting palaeoseismic zones wherever adequate petrochemical data on transverse variations in the composition of suitable volcanic or plutonic rocks are available.

The *K-h* correlation for arc magmas is entirely relative to silica content, and carries no explicit information about changing bulk compositions of the suites as proportions of basalt, andesite, and dacite vary. Generalizations about bulk variations are difficult to support with adequate data, but most would agree that basalts and basaltic andesites loom large in simple intra-oceanic arcs, that andesitic and dacitic rocks are characteristic of complex arcs, and that voluminous rhyodacitic and rhyolitic ignimbrites in arc settings are restricted to arc segments with continental foundations. Presumably, comagmatic plutonic associates can be fitted to the same inference, with large granitic batholiths mainly confined to arcs along continental margins and more dioritic plutons common in detached arcs. These statements imply that the generation of continental crust by arc magmatism proceeds by evolutionary stages. The situation may mean that magmas in the continental arcs include partial melts of deep crustal rocks heated by the passage and injection of hot magmas from the mantle. The apparent consistency of the *K-h* correlation through regions with greatly contrasting crustal structure argues against this interpretation. The significant effect of a thick crust of low density may be simply to block the buoyant rise of magmas emerging from the mantle, and thus to promote differentiation of mafic magmas to more felsic derivatives.

Palaeogeographic contrasts between oceanic and continental arcs are also important. Intra-oceanic arcs evolve as great elongate piles of mainly submarine volcanic and

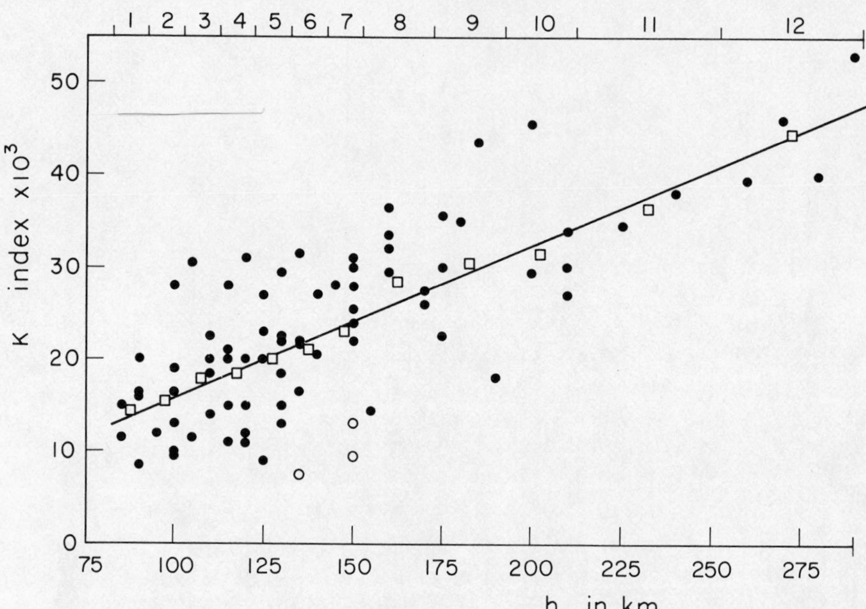

Fig. 6 Graph showing correlation between levels of potash content in Quaternary lava suites of active circum-Pacific arcs (ordinate) and vertical depths, *h* in kilometres, from eruption sites to estimated mean positions of inclined seismic zones in mantle beneath arcs (abscissa). 'K index' is the ratio K_2O/SiO_2 at 57·5 per cent SiO_2 as determined from simple Harker K_2O-SiO_2 variation diagrams using percentages of oxides from chemical analyses recalculated volatile-free. Each point plotted represents a volcano or volcano cluster for which adequate petrologic and seismic data are available. Open squares depict average values of *K* index for all points falling within respective depth intervals (1-12) denoted across top of graph (intervals are 10 km increments for *h* of 80-150 km, 20 km increments for *h* of 150-210 km, and 40 km increments for *h* of 210-290 km). Sloping line is drawn by inspection through these average values. Arcs represented by numbers of solid-circle points indicated by parentheses include: Alaskan-Aleutian (2), Kamchatka-Kuril-Hokkaido (18), Honshu (10), Kyushu-Ryukyu-Taiwan (10), Indonesia (12), Papua-Solomons (7), Tonga-Kermadec-NZ (4), Western Americas (8), Lesser Antilles (5). Three open-circle points consistently below the prevailing scatter are for the Izu Arc. Data from references for Dickinson (1970, Fig. 3) and selected recent publications (Bauer 1970, Bryan *et al.*, in press; Brothers & Martin 1970, Brothers & Searle 1970, James, in press; Johnson *et al.* 1970, Wang 1970).

volcaniclastic strata that may be interpreted as trough fillings in the geologic record. Local subaerial facies and relatively minor plutons in the roots of the main volcanic edifices can also be expected. Marginal arcs probably shed detritus rapidly from mainly subaerial volcanic fields overlying thick crustal foundations, and harbour large batholiths at depth. Complex detached arcs may display intermediate behaviour.

Backarc areas

Areas behind arcs include two main kinds of tectonic elements of contrasting style. The back of one kind of arc is marked by an abrupt band of normal faulting or a sharp hinge zone of major subsidence, and beyond is a marginal sea or small ocean basin (Karig 1971*b*). The back of the other kind of arc is marked by a belt of thrust or reverse faults inclined beneath the rear of the arc, and beyond is a foreland basin with a sialic floor sloping toward the arc from a cratonic mass on the other side of the basin (Hamilton 1969*a*). The extensional aspect of the first setting leads to detachment of the arc from continental margins or arc fragments behind it, and to the development of oceanic crust of ophiolitic character in the intervening ground. The contractional aspect of the second setting leads to welding of the arc to the adjacent continent, and probably to the development of a metamorphic infrastructure related to the thrust belt behind the arc, which becomes a two-sided orogen (Burchfiel & Davis 1968). Ocean basins behind various Western Pacific arcs generally show the high heat flows expected for complex spreading centres. No abnormal heat flows have been reported to my knowledge from thrust belts or foreland basins behind arcs.

The fundamental reasons for the contrasting tectonics in backarc areas is not definitely known, but different gross relative motions between lithosphere and asthenosphere are probably involved. Arc-trench systems with thrust belts in their rears may have descending lithosphere slabs that exhibit what Elsasser (1971, Fig. 3) has called retrograde motions. He shows that reduction of the total size of an ocean basin like the Pacific cannot be achieved simply by the spreading of lithosphere from intrabasinal rises and its descent at marginal arc-trench systems. For shrinkage of the net area of the basin, the bounding continental masses must approach one another. If this is to occur, the lines of flexure in descending slabs of lithosphere associated with some or all of the marginal arc-trench systems must migrate inward with respect to the overall shape of the ocean basin. This requirement probably implies a jamming together of lithosphere segments across the associated arc-trench systems. The inherent crowding may well inhibit spreading and foster contractional thrusting in backarc areas.

STYLES OF ARC EVOLUTION

The contrast between extensional and contractional backarc areas calls attention to the evolution of arc-trench systems, which are unlikely to maintain static configurations. The history of an arc during consistent polarity of subduction and magmatism can be termed *congruent development*. In this simplest case, evolution can occur while the arc remains in place with respect to the original backarc area, or while the arc migrates as a marginal sea opens in its wake. Intra-oceanic arcs can also reverse polarity with a shift of the subduction zone from one side of the arc structure to the other. Finally, arc-trench systems can collide with continental margins or with other arcs by consuming the lithosphere lying between (Dewey & Bird 1970, Dickinson 1971*a*). Collisions involving intra-oceanic arcs can cause reversal of polarity. Collisions involving arcs on continental margins are the principal means of welding continental fragments together along suture belts (Hamilton 1970).

Congruent development in Japan

Japan affords a type example for the congruent development of arc-trench systems (Fig. 7). Appropriate petrotectonic assemblages with the same polarity include

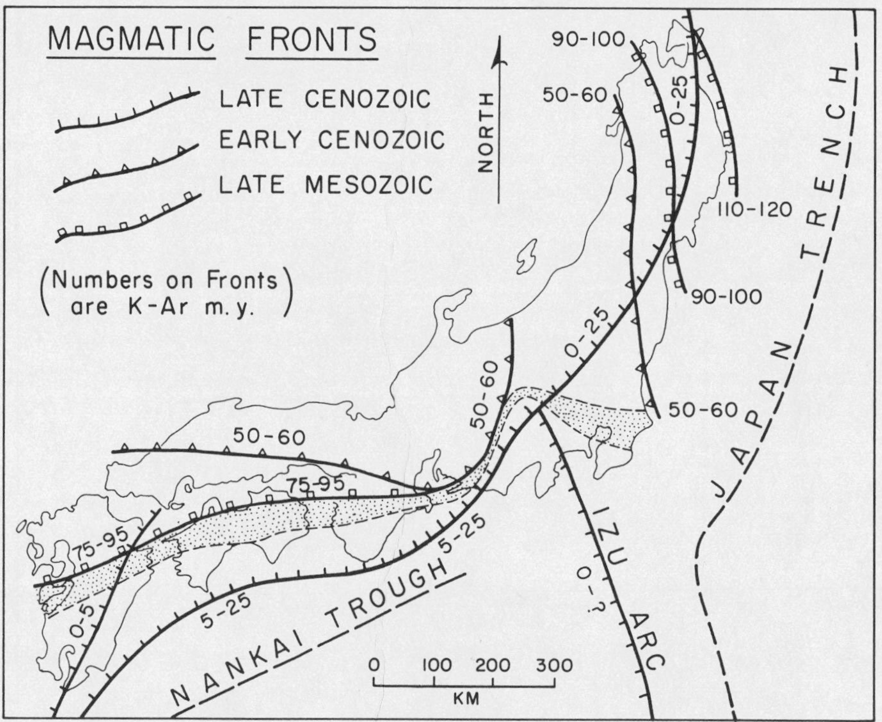

Fig. 7 Map of Honshu and adjacent islands to show petrologic features related to arc-trench systems in Japan. Shaded belt includes metamorphic and sedimentary terranes in old arc-trench gap of late Mesozoic and early Cenozoic age (see text); exposures to south are old trench assemblages of Shimanto belt on south coast and exposures to north are Ryoke metamorphic belt with associated granitic plutons and cogenetic volcanics of old arc assemblages. Successive positions of magmatic fronts reflect evolution of arc-trench systems through time. Modified after Miyashiro (1967, Figs 7, 15), Kawano and Ueda (1967, Fig. 1), and Matsuda and Uyeda (1971, Figs 3, 5, 7, 8).

volcanics and sediments of still active late Cenozoic systems, as well as plutonics and metamorphics of deeply eroded, ancestral late Mesozoic and early Cenozoic systems (Matsuda & Uyeda 1971). Attention is directed here to relations on Honshu and nearby offshore islands, between the northern end of the Ryukyu arc-trench system in Kyushu to the south and the southern end of the Kuril arc-trench system in Hokkaido to the north. The northern end of the Izu-Marianas chain of arc-trench systems standing between the Philippine Sea and the main Pacific Ocean meets Honshu at the Fossa Magna, which separates north-east Honshu from south-west Honshu and Shikoku. Each of the two regions displays a coherent Cretaceous and Cenozoic succession of tectonic elements, but the similar arrays differ somewhat in the two regions, and tectonic trends are not continuous from one to the other (Fig. 7). The inherent instability of a trench-trench-trench triple junction may account partly for the contrast.

The spine of north-east Honshu is a chain of stratovolcanoes representing the active arc related to the sediment-poor Japan Trench offshore. Within the arc-trench gap is an inner belt of late Cenozoic uplifts including the Abukuma and Kitakami massifs near the coast (Matsuda *et al.* 1967), and an outer zone of sedimentation on a deep slope beyond a narrow coastal shelf (Ludwig *et al.* 1966). The active volcanoes cap a generally concordant pile of upper Cenozoic volcanogenic rocks that include marine and terrestrial sediments accumulated in blocky basins indicative of local foundering within the arc, and also coeval granitic intrusions exposed in intervening upwarped areas (Matsuda *et al.* 1967). At the base of this volcanic pile are Lower Miocene beds that rest unconformably on older granitic and metamorphic rocks, also exposed in the massifs of the nearby uplift belt within the arc-trench gap. Upper Cretaceous and Lower Tertiary granitic rocks that yield different radiometric ages in belts trending at an angle to the present volcanic chain presumably mark the successive magmatic fronts of an ancestral arc-trench system slightly discordant to the present one (Fig. 7). The mid-Cenozoic tectonic discontinuity is also reflected by the wholesale subsidence of the western flank of north-east Honshu since the Miocene, but no subduction zone has been recognized anywhere on land along the eastern flank of the present arc.

South-west Honshu lacks active volcanoes, and the Nankai Trough offshore is probably an inactive trench largely filled with sediments (Murauchi *et al.* 1968). Upper Tertiary granitic rocks exposed on southern peninsular projections of Honshu and Shikoku (Kawano & Ueda 1967) are interpreted here as the roots of the now dormant arc related to the filled trench. These small granitic bodies intrude the Shimanto belt of highly deformed Upper Cretaceous and Lower Tertiary strata metamorphosed in the greenschist and prehnite-pumpellyite metagreywacke facies. The rocks of the Shimanto belt are greywacke, shale, chert, submarine basaltic volcanics, and ultramafic rocks interpreted as the trench assemblage of an ancestral arc-trench system (Matsuda & Uyeda 1971). Shimanto rocks are overlain by less deformed strata along an intra-Miocene unconformity that again emphasizes a mid-Cenozoic transition in tectonic history within Japan. The arc assemblage associated with the old Shimanto Trench is the volcano-plutonic complex built on the mainland of south-west Honshu by cogenetic granitic plutonism and andesitic-rhyolitic volcanism in the Cretaceous and early Tertiary (Ichikawa *et al.* 1968). Again, successive magmatic fronts can be identified (Fig. 7). Between the old arc and trench assemblages are two kinds of terranes that apparently occupied the old arc-trench gap. The greater part of this ground is underlain by rocks that were probably exposed to erosion in a slowly rising uplift belt (Matsuda & Uyeda 1971, p. 12), perhaps the counterpart of the outer acoustic basement barrier in modern arc-trench systems (Karig 1970, 1971*b*). The rocks involved are upper Palaeozoic strata of the Chichibu belt along the southern side of the arc-trench gap and metamorphic rocks of the Sambagawa belt, with mainly upper Palaeozoic but locally lower Mesozoic protoliths, along the northern side. Contacts between the two terranes are locally gradational, and together they represent the low T/P metamorphic belt paired with the high T/P Ryoke metamorphic belt to the north into which the plutons of the old arc were injected (Miyashiro 1967). On the north side of this barrier (?) terrane, and also locally along its southern flank, are thick exposures of bedded Cretaceous strata, largely clastic marine sediments, that evidently accumulated in elongate basins within the arc-trench gap (Dickinson 1971*c*). Geologic evidence for late Cenozoic strike-slip displacement along the median tectonic line between the paired Sambagawa and Ryoke metamorphic belts (Kaneko 1966) suggests that the trend of the old arc-trench system may now be the site of a complex trench-trench transform between the north end of the Ryukyu Arc in Kyushu and a triple junction near the Fossa Magna.

Accretionary model of congruent evolution

The successive accretion of subducted oceanic materials against the trench flank of an arc structure (e.g. Hamilton 1969*b*) might be expected to induce a prograde migration of the magmatic front outward with respect to crustal rocks within a growing arc structure (e.g. Hamilton 1970). Subducted materials originally within the low T/P metamorphic belt just inboard of the trench would be transferred in sequence across the migrating magmatic front, and into the high T/P metamorphic belt to become wall rocks for granitic plutons of the arc roots (Matsuda & Uyeda 1971, Fig. 15). When intra-oceanic arcs or microcontinental scraps of sialic crust are swept into subduction zones and lodge there (e.g. Hamilton 1969*b*), the outward migration of magmatic fronts may occur as discrete jumps. When Middle Jurassic arc rocks of the present Sierra Nevada foothills lodged in the subduction zone along the continental margin of California, the magmatic front in the adjacent Sierra Nevada batholith locally jumped westward about 100 km between Early Jurassic and Late Jurassic time (e.g. Dickinson 1970, Fig. 6).

The model for accretionary migration of arc-trench tectonic elements applies well to the Kamchatka and Sunda orogens. Hamilton (in press) discusses the latter in detail. On Java, Cenozoic arc volcanics overlie Mesozoic (?) trench melanges, and Mesozoic granitic rocks occupy a belt partly north of the present volcanic chain. Subduction complexes of Early Tertiary age are exposed off Sumatra in the Mentawai Islands along the crest of an emergent ridge between the subduction zone of the present trench and a deep sedimentary trough in the arc-trench gap. For Kamchatka, Avdeiko (1971) has summarized the history of a succession of paired arcs and trenches that were active as the magmatic front migrated from the Okhotsk belt north-west of Kamchatka near the beginning of the Cretaceous to its present position near the south-east coast. The mean rate of migration has been on the order of 3 km/m.y., but apparently not at a steady or continuous rate. Instead, a succession of four volcano-plutonic orogens are present as elongate highlands separated by three intervening elongate depressions underlain by thick sequences of clastic sedimentary strata. To simplify a progression that was more complex in detail, the magmatic fronts and the trenches shifted jointly eastward in three discrete steps of about 125 km each spaced at intervals of roughly 40-50 m.y. Published diagrams (Avdeiko 1971, Fig. 3) permit the speculative interpretation that the lowlands between the parallel volcano-plutonic orogens of the completed system may be the sites of sedimentary troughs that developed in a succession of arc-trench gaps as the evolving arc-trench system stepped outward. This interpretation is suggested by the fact that the sedimentary rocks preserved in the basin below each lowland are largely coeval with volcanic and plutonic rocks exposed in the adjacent highland to the west. The principal fillings of the three elongate basins are turbidites of Cretaceous, Palaeogene, and Neogene age, respectively from west to east. If the interpretation is valid, each shift of the magmatic front took place by changing the site of magmatism from the pre-existing volcanic arc to the acoustic basement barrier between trench and arc-trench gap. The inference finds some support in the fact that the pre-granitic wall rocks and underpinnings of the three volcano-plutonic highlands are mainly metamorphosed spilitic volcanics and siliceous sediments of oceanic aspect. Such complexes could well represent crumpled prisms of subducted materials bunched in wads to form successive acoustic basement barriers, each later and in turn the root of an arc.

Migration of magmatic fronts

The prograde, or progressive outward, migration of magmatic fronts associated with accretionary development of complex arc structures does not apply to all cases of congruent development. For Honshu, distinct retrograde migration of magmatic fronts is indicated for the late Mesozoic and Early Tertiary (Fig. 7). Several other regions display similar behaviour. Plutons in the Andean batholith, whose origin is related to ancestral stages of the Andean arc (James, 1971), become younger eastward, going away from the trench, from mid-Mesozoic to mid-Cenozoic times (Farrar *et al.* 1970, Giletti & Day 1968). The young volcanics along the Andean crest lie still farther east. For the Coast Range batholith of British Columbia, radiometric dates also occupy successive belts that young eastward during the Late Cretaceous and Early Tertiary (Hutchison 1970, Fig. 13). In the Sierra Nevada of California from Late Jurassic to Late Cretaceous, three prominent belts of granitic plutons grouped into several intrusive sequences (Bateman & Dodge 1970) belonging to three intrusive epochs (Evernden & Kistler 1970) form bands lying side by side, with the oldest on the west and the youngest on the east.

The retrograde migrations of magmatic fronts in these instances took place at mean rates on the order of 1 km/m.y., comparable to the rate of prograde migration for Sumatra-Java (Hamilton, in press) and a significant fraction of the prograde rate for Kamchatka (see above). James (1971) has suggested that retrograde migration may reflect progressive depression of isotherms near the upper margin of the descending slab of lithosphere beneath the arc, or progressive depletion of fusibles in the overlying mantle to greater and greater depths. In any case, both prograde and retrograde migrations of magmatic fronts appear equally real, and the likelihood that arcs with long histories may exhibit both is strong.

Migration of arc-trench systems

Apart from the migration of magmatic fronts with respect to crustal rocks within an arc-trench system, the systems themselves can migrate intact with respect to external features behind arcs (Karig 1970, 1971*a*, 1971*b*). Again, Japan illustrates this style of behaviour well. The Sea of Japan has opened since the Mesozoic, probably since the intra-Miocene tectonic discontinuity, and the granitic terranes of the ancestral arc roots were once continuous with similar terranes in Korea and maritime Siberia as part of a marginal arc along the fringe of the Asian mainland (e.g. Matsuda & Uyeda 1971). Marginal seas of oceanic depth and with oceanic crustal structure may commonly form by spreading of lithosphere in the wake of migrating island arcs that began their history as fringing arcs (e.g. Packham & Falvey 1971). The rock assemblages of the marginal basin floors are truly oceanic and presumably ophiolitic suites, even though irregular patterns of magnetic anomalies in the marginal seas suggest that the manner of spreading is more diffuse than that along intra-oceanic rises with regular axi-symmetric anomaly patterns. Stranded within the oceanic basins behind migrating arcs are microcontinental fragments like the Yamato Bank in the Sea of Japan and elongate shreds of semicontinental crust that represent detached slivers of the rear flanks of arc structures.

The most striking evidence for the bulk migration of arc-trench systems with respect to tectonic elements in their rears are the young troughs that Karig has termed inter-arc basins. These include the Lau Basin (Sclater *et al.* 1971) and Havre Trough behind the Tonga-Kermadec Arc, and the Mariana Trough behind the Marianas Arc. These basins, grossly lunate in plan, lie immediately behind the main, active arc structures, from which they are separated by steep scarps marking rifted edges. They are nearly free of sediment except for clastic wedges of variable size just behind the active arcs. Behind the inter-arc basins are submerged ridges, termed 'third arcs' by Karig and interpreted by him to represent segments of the main or 'frontal' arcs rifted away by the spreading that formed the inter-arc basins. The Lau-Colville Ridge with Miocene volcanics of arc aspect at each end is an example. The flanks of the third arcs facing the inter-arc basins are also steep, rifted edges but the other flanks are mantled by wedges of clastic sediment thought to have been derived from an ancestral, combined arc structure prior to separation of the third arc from the main arc.

The entire Philippine Sea may have been formed by successive episodes of arc-rear spreading in a pattern that was asymmetric overall (Fig. 8). The lack of filled trenches along the forward sides of the submerged ridges lying between the constituent basins argues against migration by jumping (or leap-frogging) open ocean, to initiate a series of nascent arc-trench systems. Moreover, Lower Tertiary volcanics occur in the present frontal arcs of the Marianas and Palau. On the other hand, the geometry of successive inter-arc basins and third arcs with their flanking sediment prisms also precludes a model of steady progressive migration. What emerges instead is an hypothesis of

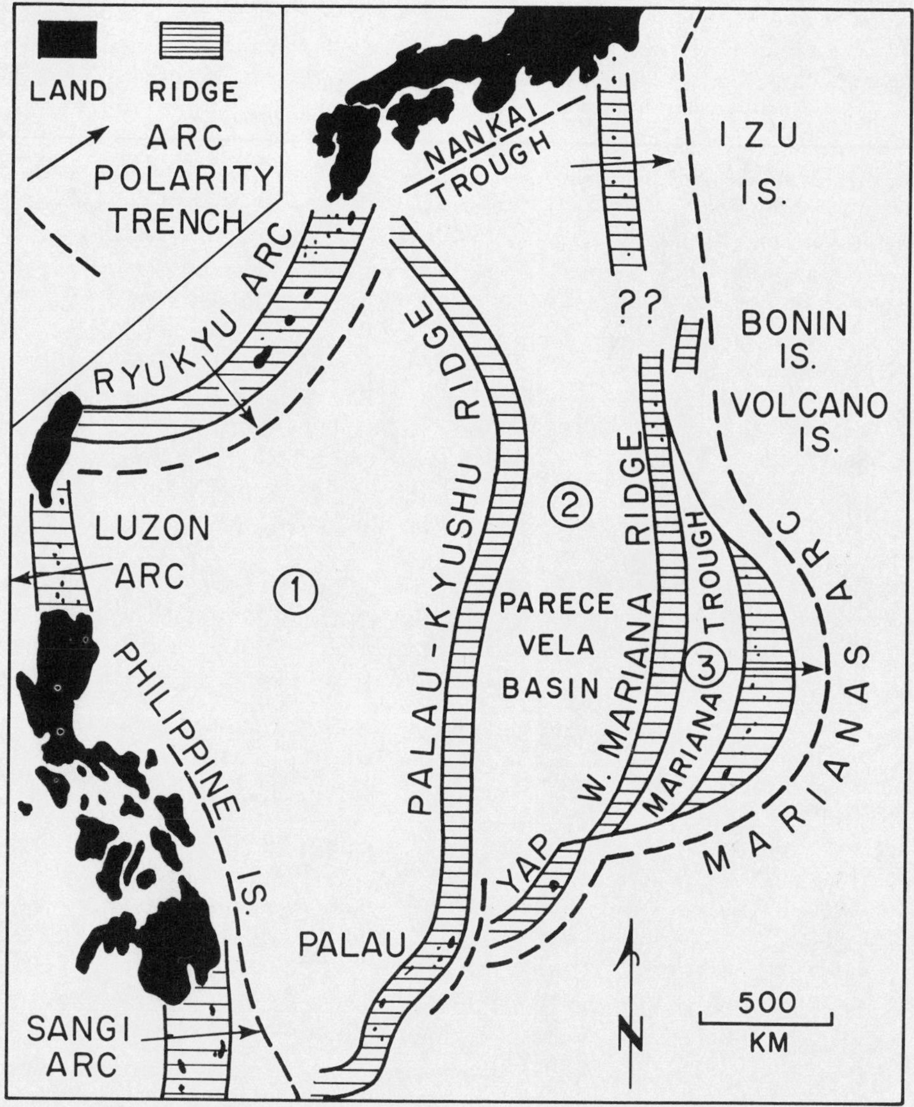

Fig. 8 Map of the Philippine Sea and bordering islands to illustrate Karig's (1971*a*) hypothesis that the sea grew as a succession of inter-arc basins (1-3) formed by arc-rear spreading during episodes of arc migration. The current inter-arc basin (3), Mariana Trough, formed in Pliocene-Recent times between West Mariana Ridge, a third arc, and the active Marianas frontal arc. By inference, the Parece-Vela Basin (2) and analogues to the north-west of the Izu-Bonin Arc formed in a similar fashion during Oligocene-Miocene times. The basins (1) west of the Palau-Kyushu Ridge, the presumed Oligocene-Miocene third arc, may have formed by even earlier Eocene (?) arc migration. Plate consumption by trenches on the western flank of the sea has destroyed or modified evidence of previous history.

discontinuous migration by spasmodic arc-rear spreading during a succession of semi-discrete tectonic pulses. The hypothesis applies mainly to the part of the Philippine Sea from the Palau-Kyushu Ridge to the east. To the west, a complete picture must include: (*a*) the active Ryukyu arc-trench system, which is consuming the edge of the basin and has antecedents back into the Tertiary (Konishi 1965); (*b*) the reversed arc facing China between Luzon and Taiwan (Katsumata & Sykes 1969); and (*c*) the main bulk of the complex Philippine Arc facing the Philippine Sea and bordered by the Mindanao Trench. The indicated mean rate of postulated arc-rear spreading in the Philippine Sea is in excess of 2·5 cm/yr, and about 5 cm/yr at the peak of migration pulses like the recent one that formed the Mariana Trough.

Reversal of arc polarity

Geologic relations in the Melanesian region (Coleman 1970) suggest that intra-oceanic arc-trench systems can be modified by reversal of polarity as well as by migration. In both the Solomons and the northern New Hebrides, western island chains nearest the present trenches and eastern island chains behind the present lines of volcanoes expose Tertiary sequences of contrasting character. These older petro-tectonic assemblages suggest that the polarity of the two arc-trench systems was previously opposite to the present one. They then faced toward the Pacific, presumably as northern extensions of the ancestral Tonga-Kermadec-Lau system reaching north from New Zealand. The present misalignment in the vicinity of Fiji is presumably related to subsequent spreading on the Fiji Plateau behind the New Hebrides (Chase, 1971). The Lower Tertiary Wainimala-Tholo volcano-plutonic orogen of Fiji (Dickinson 1967) was presumably part of the old arc-trench system, although the orientation of its tectonic trends are now askew as a result of subsequent rotation and deformation during oroclinal flexure.

In the Solomons (Coleman 1966), the active volcanoes of Bougainville and New Georgia in the 'volcanic province' are built upon and beside a Lower and Middle Tertiary arc assemblage of volcanics and associated volcanogenic sediments in the 'central province'. These rest upon a greenschist amphibolitic Cretaceous basement of uncertain character (but see Hackman, this volume). Gabbroic and granitoid dioritic plutons also occur in the central province. On the north-east, the side away from the present trench, the central province is bounded by a sigmoidal fracture system that is the locus of elongate serpentinite bodies, some of them clearly thrust sheets. Beyond is the 'Pacific province' of basaltic lavas, thought to be oceanic crust, overlain by organogenic oceanic sediments of Late Cretaceous and Early Tertiary age. In the speculative interpretation offered here, the central province is held to be an Early Tertiary arc terrane while the Pacific province is a related terrane of oceanic materials accreted against a subduction zone marked roughly by the serpentinite belt.

In the northern New Hebrides, the active volcanoes occupy a central chain of islands roughly midway between two other chains of islands which expose older rocks (Géze 1963). In the western chain are Lower and Middle Tertiary volcanic and volcani-clastic strata that represent a variety of arc facies (e.g. Mitchell 1970). Cogenetic dioritic intrusions occur locally. In the eastern chain, perhaps analogous tectonically to the 'Pacific province' of the Solomons, are Tertiary basaltic volcanics with associated turbidites and organogenic sediments. Serpentinites are exposed locally on one island. Although any interpretation is tentative until more data are available (e.g. Mitchell & Warden 1971—not available at the time of writing), the active volcanoes may stand on the ruins of a Tertiary arc-trench system whose polarity was reversed to create the presently active system.

Overall tectonic relations in the region south of Melanesia between Australia and New Zealand are immensely complex (e.g. Wright 1966, Cullen 1967, 1970). The Lord Howe Rise and Norfolk Ridge apparently extend as thick crustal fingers across a region whose basins are truly oceanic (e.g., Shor *et al.* 1971). Although no coherent synthesis is offered here (Fig. 9), plate tectonic analysis of the region's history must take into account arc-rear spreading and arc reversal as well as more conventional ideas of spreading and drift. The complex relations of tectonic elements in the Indonesian-Philippine region (Fig. 1), with its curling and locally opposed arcs, its small ocean basins of curious shape, and its juxtaposed terranes of anomalous rock masses also probably reflect both styles of behaviour in abundance.

Origins of intra-oceanic arcs

It remains unclear whether all segments of intra-oceanic arcs have migrated from marginal positions fringing continents. There is no apparent necessity to make this assumption, and nothing in the known geology of the Izu-Bonin-Mariana-Yap-Palau or the Solomons-New Hebrides-Fiji-Tonga-Kermadec chains of arcs requires it. Such an assumption would imply that the initial configurations of all intra-oceanic arcs conformed to the shapes of continental margins inherited from previous episodes of rifting, sedimentation, and accretion. Intuitively, this is difficult to accept as a generality. Nascent arc-trench systems, even if partly marginal to continents, might break locally across oceanic embayments lying in concave re-entrants of continental margins, and might extend themselves as long wings into ocean basins off major convex angles in continental margins.

For deeply eroded arcs, the nature of the basement beneath the magmatic arc assemblages may serve to indicate whether the intruded underpinnings are detached continental slivers or uplifted oceanic crust. Unfortunately, this would not resolve the question fully. The rocks that actually compose present arc structures may have been formed entirely during intra-oceanic migration of the systems even though they started as marginal, fringing arcs. The successive calving of third arcs from the rear flanks of migrating arcs, coupled with accretionary outward growth of the front flanks in each successive position, could allow for continuous evolution during migration without any of the original substance of the arc completing the full migration path.

Where collisions occur between intra-oceanic arcs and continental margins, as discussed next, arcs may be either: (*a*) entirely foreign entities born within or beyond the ocean basin off the continent in question; or (*b*) formerly marginal arcs that migrated offshore, perhaps later to reverse polarity and subsequently to return by consuming the lithosphere of the intervening marginal sea. The two cases may be impossible to distinguish unless there prove to be differences in the ophiolitic scraps caught in the resulting suture zones. These might reflect any differences that may

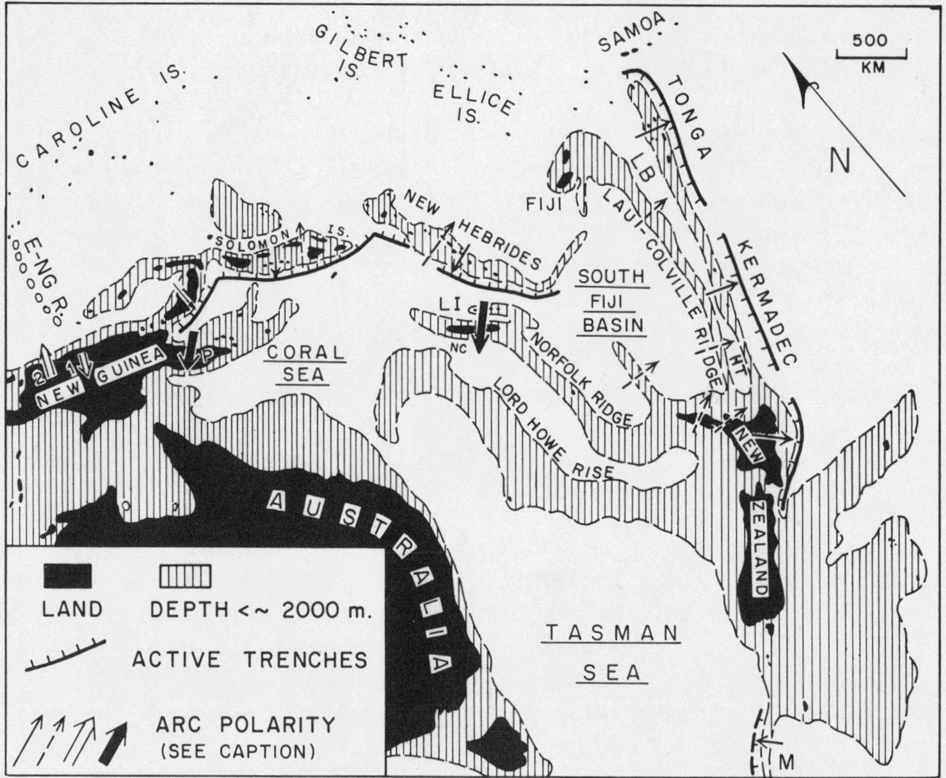

Fig. 9 Map of Melanesian-New Zealand region north-east of Australia, showing the main ridges and basins. Dashed line is approximate 2,000 m depth contour, generalized to emphasize continuity of submerged ridges. Position of trenches and simple arrows show polarity of active arcs, including incipient(?) Macquarie Arc (M) south of New Zealand. Behind Tonga-Kermadec Arc, Lau Basin (LB) and Havre Trough (HT) are inter-arc basins and Lau-Colville Ridge is 'third arc' structure. Dashed arrows denote inferred Tertiary polarity of migrating and reversed arc-trench systems. Large open arrows in New Guinea denote sequential (1 to 2) polarity inferred for collided (1) and flipped (2) arc-trench systems along north coast during Tertiary (see text). Large solid arrows in Papua (P) and New Caledonia (NC) denote inferred polarity of collided arcs, one possibly represented by Loyalty Islands (LI), responsible for mid-Tertiary overthrust ('obduction') of ophiolite complexes. Line of circles north of New Guinea denotes Eauripik-New Guinea ridge with crest at about 3,000 m depth.

exist between the nature of the oceanic crust or sediments in marginal seas formed by arc-rear spreading as opposed to open ocean basins formed by the 'normal' spreading concentrated at rise systems. As the thickness of the oceanic crust in the two settings appears comparable (e.g. Karig 1970, Fig. 10; Packham & Falvey, Fig. 5), significant differences in the magmatic rocks of ophiolite complexes from the two settings appear unlikely. Attention is thus directed toward the underlying refractory peridotites, and especially to the overlying sedimentary associates, among which remnants of the volcaniclastic wedges built behind arcs may be distinctive.

Arc collisions and continental assembly

The consumption of oceanic lithosphere by arc-trench systems has the potential to bring exotic continental margins, or other arc structures, against the subduction zones associated with the trenches. As the thorough consumption of lithosphere capped by thick sialic crust is gravimetrically unlikely, such a juxtaposition probably chokes the subduction zone. The process can logically be termed the collision of crustal masses (e.g. Dickinson 1971*a*). Where marginal arcs are involved, collisions can weld separate continental masses together along suture belts of ophiolitic and other oceanic materials (Hamilton 1970). In the Western Pacific region, collisions of Cretaceous or younger age were uncommon, and mainly involved arc segments and microcontinental scraps in the Indonesian and Philippine regions (Hamilton, in press).

The tectonic results of arc collisions with an inactive continental margin are displayed along the northern coast of New Guinea. Southern New Guinea is an extension of Australia, which separated from Antarctica early in the Tertiary. As discussed by Dewey and Bird (1970) to illustrate one type of crustal collision, Papua Australia encountered, during the Tertiary, a south-facing arc-trench system, or systems. The encounter lodged the arc structures against the continental margin, which was crumpled by thrusting during the collision. This accretion of the arc structure was followed closely by flipping of the subduction zone, which also stepped over to the far side of the accreted belt. By this means, the previously inactive continental margin was converted to a complex marginal arc facing north beyond the accreted belt.

The most spectacular geologic result of the collision events was the thrusting of ophiolitic oceanic crust over sialic rocks along the edge of the continent (Davies 1968). This process has been given the special name 'obduction' (Coleman 1971), but is treated here as simply the partial subduction of a continental margin. A similar and roughly contemporary thrust sheet of peridotite and associated oceanic rocks in New Caledonia (Avias 1967) may record the partial subduction of the northern end of the Norfolk Ridge in front of an arc structure represented by the underpinnings of the Loyalty Islands. These Tertiary collision events in the general region of the Caroline Basin, the Bismarck Sea, and the Coral Sea (see Fig. 9) must be related to Tertiary episodes of local spreading, arc migration, and arc reversal in the same area. The pattern of small plates that exists now may have undergone various modifications in the past, and a full synthesis of the Tertiary history will doubtless be complex.

MID-CRETACEOUS MARGIN OF ASIA

Despite uncertainties about the history of nearly all the arc-trench systems of the Western Pacific, a general reconstruction of the margins of Asia in mid-Cretaceous times (Fig. 10) can be made by removing from the board (Fig. 1) the effects of younger

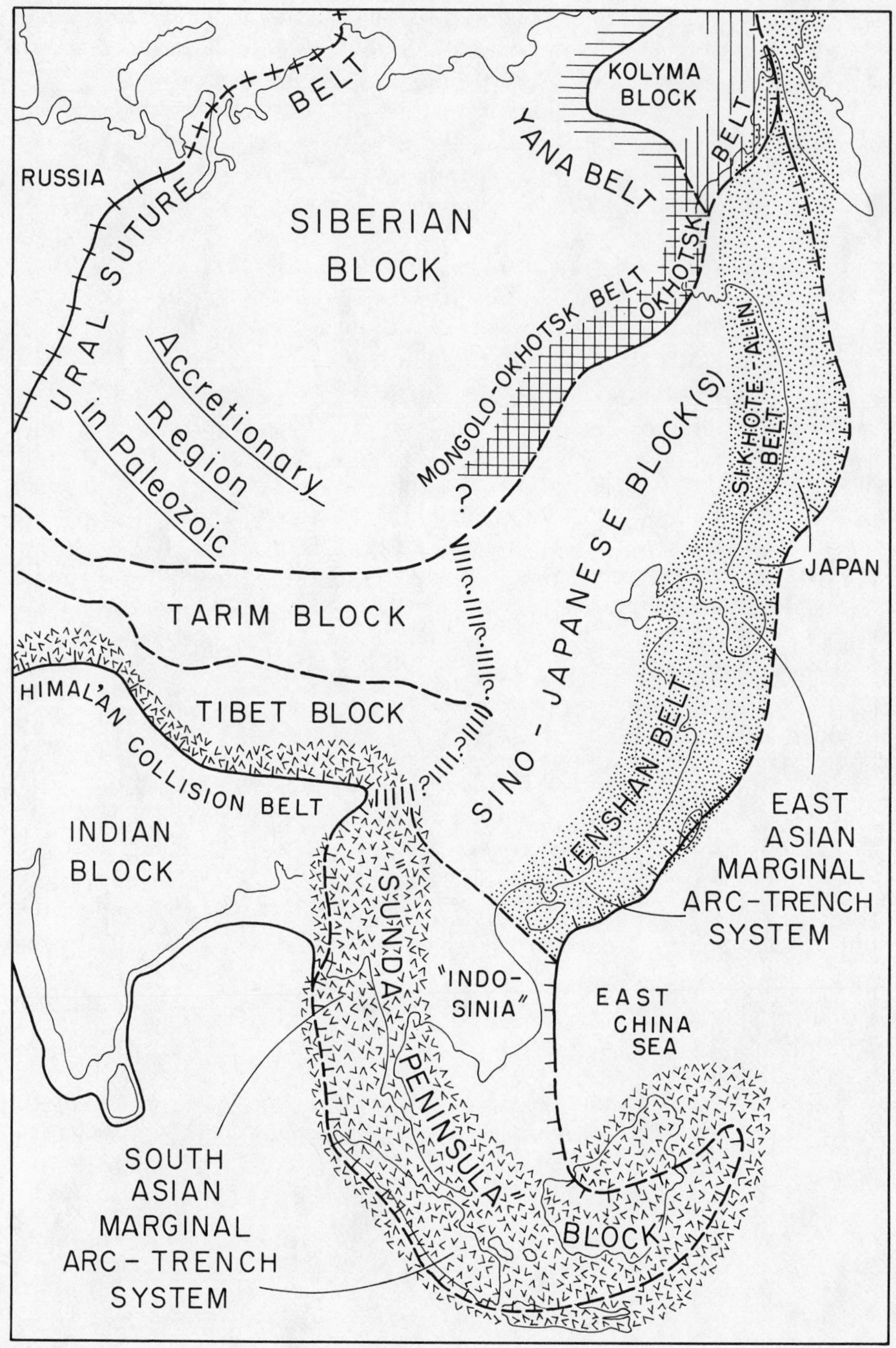
KOLYMA BLOCK
BELT
RUSSIA
URAL SUTURE
YANA BELT
SIBERIAN BLOCK
OKHOTSK
BELT
MONGOLO-OKHOTSK BELT
Accretionary Region in Paleozoic
SIKHOTE-ALIN BELT
SINO-JAPANESE BLOCK(S)
JAPAN
TARIM BLOCK
TIBET BLOCK
HIMAL'AN COLLISION BELT
YENSHAN BELT
EAST ASIAN MARGINAL ARC-TRENCH SYSTEM
INDIAN BLOCK
"SUNDA PENINSULA" BLOCK
"INDO-SINIA"
EAST CHINA SEA
SOUTH ASIAN MARGINAL ARC-TRENCH SYSTEM

events. The main operations involved are the grouping of all the lands south-east of the Moluccan region (Fig. 9) into a loosely associated foreign realm, and the clustering of the remaining marginal arcs against the fringe of the Asian mainland.

Australia and most of New Guinea then retreat well away from Asia to attach as a single unit to Antarctica (Dietz & Sproll 1969). With less rigour, New Zealand, the drowned plateaux to the south-east, and the submerged crustal spurs of the Lord Howe and Norfolk Ridges can be associated also with a combined Australia-Antarctica. In the process, the intervening oceanic basins of apparently young age are closed. The Melanesian arcs from New Britain to Fiji, and the Tonga-Lau-Kermadec complex of arcs are removed arbitrarily. This operation assumes that these systems were either an intra-oceanic chain not built until near the time that separation of Australia and Antarctica occurred, or else a marginal chain of similar age flanking some part of the lands I have loosely associated with an ancestral Australia-Antarctica. In either case, the chain was anchored at one end in what is now New Zealand, where the clockwise sweep of a fan-like array of successive Tertiary arc trends can be traced across the North Island (Hatherton 1969*c*, Fig. 13). The youngest trend in the central volcanic region is aligned with the Tonga-Kermadec Arc, and the oldest volcanic trend extends along the north-western peninsular tip of New Zealand. A pre-Cretaceous arc-trench system delineated by distinctive facies of greywackes was probably continuous along a trend similar to the latter from New Zealand to New Caledonia (Dickinson 1971*b*).

West of the Moluccan region, the Sunda shelf and its surrounding islands form a peninsular extension of continental Asia. The Lesser Sunda islands are a Tertiary arc, either built across oceanic crust from a western anchor along the south side of the Sunda peninsula, or moved into an intra-oceanic position by arc migration off the tip of the Sunda peninsula. Farther west, the Andaman-Nicobar chain was also detached slightly from the western side of the Sunda peninsula during the Tertiary (e.g. Rodolfo 1969). The correct pre-Tertiary positions of the older rock masses in the Philippines are uncertain but I assume they were located at one or more extremities of the reconstructed Sunda peninsula, with the Sulu and Celebes basins probably closed. This treatment is based upon the inference that the Early and Middle Tertiary history of the marginal geosyncline of north-west Borneo (Haile 1963) indicates that the deep basin of the South China Sea north of the Sunda peninsula was already in existence during the Cretaceous.

North of the Philippines, all the offshore islands can be removed or collapsed against Asia for a mid-Cretaceous reconstruction. For Taiwan, structural relations (Ho 1967) suggest a late Cenozoic collision between a reversed intra-oceanic island

---

Fig. 10 Sketch map of eastern Eurasia depicting salient pre-Tertiary relations discussed in text. Hachured line is inferred mid-Cretaceous continental margin but correct configuration is uncertain near east end of 'Sunda Peninsula'. Pattern of pre-Tertiary arcs and/or transforms required in region of South China Sea is unknown, hence not shown. Other heavy lines are inferred suture belts between continental blocks welded together during the assembly of Eurasia.

arc offshore and the continental margin, which was probably inactive earlier in the mid-Cenozoic (see also Meng, this volume). Exposures of deformed sediments and ophiolitic scraps mixed in a melange terrane lie east of the central range, and andesitic rocks crop out near the east coast as well as on islands offshore. The Cenozoic migration of arc-trench systems across the Philippine Sea to the east was discussed earlier, as was the migration of Japan during the opening of the Sea of Japan. The Okinawa Trough behind the Ryukyu Arc may also be an old inter-arc basin. North of Japan, the Kuril Arc is essentially an intra-oceanic volcanogenic pile built since mid-Cretaceous time (Markhinin 1968) as a southern extension of the accretionary arc structures of Kamchatka.

Asian marginal arc systems

From mid-Cretaceous to mid-Tertiary time, abundant plutonic and volcanic associations of arc aspect in the Sikhote-Alin belt and its correlatives (Ustiev 1965) indicate that the eastern edge of Asia was active as a marginal arc-trench system from Kamchatka to China (Fig. 10). Evidence includes the successive volcano-plutonic orogens of Kamchatka (Avdeiko 1971), the magmatic belts discussed for Japan and the continent behind it, and extensions of similar magmatism to the south in the Taiho belt of Korea and the Yenshan belt of coastal China (Ichikawa *et al.* 1968). Correlative paired metamorphic belts in Taiwan (Yen 1967) similar to those farther north support the inference of a southern continuation of the marginal system. Plutons related to this marginal arc apparently do not extend south-west of Hainan (e.g. Bederke & Wunderlich 1968, p. 43).

A complex transform system extending across or along the western side of an ancestral South China Sea basin may have connected the southern end of the Cretaceous-Tertiary arc-trench system along the eastern margin of Asia to the eastern end of a similar ancestral marginal arc-trench system along the southern flank of the Sunda peninsula (Fig. 10). Radiometrically dated Cretaceous and Tertiary granitic rocks in peninsular Thailand (Burton & Bignell 1969), the Malay peninsula (Hutchison 1968), and Sumatra (Katili 1962) afford evidence for the presence of an arc. Paired metamorphic belts of Mesozoic and Cenozoic age in Sulawesi (Miyashiro 1961, p. 299) probably represent an eastern segment of the system near the tip of the Sunda peninsula. Older antecedents may be represented by radiometrically dated Jurassic and Triassic granitic rocks in Thailand (Klompé 1962), Malaya (Alexander 1962, Hutchison 1968), and the islands north-east of Sumatra (Katili 1967). Andesitic volcanic rocks in the same region possibly suggest prior arc activity as old as Permian (Alexander 1962, Katili 1969).

A western extension of the marginal arc along the southern side of the Sunda peninsula probably lay along the southern edge of the Tibetan block, where it connected with the Mesozoic and Tertiary granitic plutons of the Karakoram Range and Hindu Kush north of the Indus River (Desio *et al.* 1964). The youngest plutons there are Miocene. Termination of arc activity in the Himalayan region can be attributed to collision with the Indian subcontinent (Gansser 1966). Intensely deformed rocks of the Himalayas on the edge of the Indian crustal mass lodged against exotic melanges of a subduction zone along the Indus suture belt south of

Tibet. The collision ultimately choked subduction as far east as the Arakan Yoma region of Burma, where an uplifted belt of deformed sedimentary rocks cut by serpentinites (Rodolfo 1969) lies east of the Tertiary basinal strata of Assam (Evans 1964). A nascent arc-trench system destined to balance the global pattern of motions by replacing the system eliminated along the belt of collision and suture may be forming now along a zone of anomalous seismicity that extends partly across the Bay of Bengal from Ceylon toward Sumatra (Sykes 1970).

Asian continental collisions

Farther north, other tectonic belts within Eurasia probably represent older suture belts related to an irregular sequence of collisions that assembled various continental fragments into the present landmass (e.g. Hamilton 1970). The marginal arc-trench system along the eastern edge of Asia could not have been a coherent entity until the assembly was complete. This judgment does not preclude the existence of fragments of older arc-trench systems along the edges of any of the constituent blocks prior to final assembly. In Japan, the upper Palaeozoic metamorphic rocks in the Hida-Sangun paired metamorphic belts (Miyashiro 1961, 1967), and scattered granitic rocks of middle Palaeozoic age (Kawano & Ueda 1967), may be relics of such ancient systems.

The welding together of the Russian and Siberian platforms or cratons along the ophiolitic suture belt of the Urals formed the nucleus of the present Eurasian landmass (Fig. 10). The continental collision was completed in the late Palaeozoic following extensive Palaeozoic arc activity along the edges of the approaching continents and within the ocean between (Hamilton 1970). In the late Palaeozoic and early Mesozoic, the eastern flanks of the Siberian craton were subsequently the sites of thick miogeoclinal prisms of clastic sedimentary strata in the Verkhoyansk and Baikal-Amur regions (e.g. Shatsky & Bogdanov 1959). By inference, these sequences accumulated along stable continental margins facing ocean basins since closed by collisions.

The welding of additional continental masses to Siberia followed mid-Mesozoic activation of these margins. Evidence for activation includes Middle Jurassic granitic plutons in the Yana belt on the eastern side of the Verkhoyansk region (Shatsky & Bogdanov 1959), and Jurassic volcano-plutonic complexes of arc aspect in the Mongolo-Okhotsk belt, which extends for 1,000 km from the Sea of Okhotsk into the Transbaikal region (Ustiev 1965). The Yana and Mongolo-Okhotsk belts together formed a linked marginal arc system of mid-Mesozoic age along the edges of the Siberian craton (Fig. 10). Through the accretion of continental fragments to those edges, and a consequent stepping outward of arc activity, this system evolved by stages into the Cretaceous-Tertiary marginal arc system along the eastern edge of Asia.

Termination of the Yana marginal arc and strong folding of the sedimentary sequence to the west occurred in the Late Jurassic when the Kolyma block of north-eastern Siberia lodged against the eastern (Verkhoyansk) margin of the Siberian block. It was at this time that the locus of arc magmatism in eastern Siberia stepped abruptly outward from the Yana belt, now in an intracontinental setting, to the Okhotsk belt along the coast (Ustiev 1965). Volcano-plutonic complexes of Late Jurassic and

Cretaceous age in the Okhotsk belt (Fig. 10) are the oldest members of the accretionary suite of arc structures in the northern (Kuril-Kamchatka) segment of the Cretaceous-Tertiary marginal arc system along the eastern edge of Asia.

Arc magmatism in the Okhotsk belt has counterparts along strike in the now intra-continental Mongolo-Okhotsk belt, where the mid-Mesozoic volcano-plutonic activity continued into mid-Cretaceous times. By implication, the Sino-Japanese block or blocks did not lodge finally against the south-eastern (Baikal-Amur) margin of Siberia until some time in the mid-Cretaceous. The main locus of arc magmatism then stepped outward to complete the construction of the marginal arc system along the eastern edge of Asia by linking the southern (Sino-Japanese) segment to the northern segment flanking the Kolyma block. Jurassic magmatism in eastern China, and locally in Japan, indicates that the Sino-Japanese arc segment was already active prior to the mid-Cretaceous when activity along the Mongolo-Okhotsk belt was terminated by inferred collision. From a regional view, the two apparently formed a double arc system for a time.

From data available to me now, nothing definite can be said about the time of assembly of the Tarim, Tibet, and Sunda peninsula blocks west and south of the Sino-Japanese block, which is itself heterogeneous internally. The prevalence of Palaeozoic terranes in the Tarim-Tibet region may indicate that these blocks were welded to the southern edge of Siberia prior to the Mesozoic. The suture belt predicted along the western side of the Sino-Japanese block(s) is not apparent from published maps. Relations between China and the Indosinian nucleus (Klompé 1962) of the Sunda peninsula to the south suggest that the Sino-Japanese and Sunda blocks had been joined together as a coherent mid-Mesozoic entity prior to their assembly with Siberia.

SUMMARY

The broad outlines of Cenozoic and Mesozoic episodes in the tectonic history of the Western Pacific island arcs and adjacent parts of Eurasia have been reconstructed here using two related concepts to organize the available data: (1) the plate tectonic model for major crustal movements modified to include the idea of spreading behind arcs; and (2) the relation between petrologic associations and tectonic elements in arc-trench systems as expressed by the idea of petrotectonic assemblages. Used in conjunction, the two arguments lead to unique interpretations for some areas or events, and to a finite array of alternate interpretations in other instances. In all cases, the conclusions reached embody inherent predictions that can be tested by seeking specific data. If our future reasoning about tectonic relations is guided by the principles adopted here, or by improved versions of them, there is the promise that we can proceed by a series of finite steps in thinking and knowledge toward better understanding of tectonic history. The value of this paper may well lie less in the absolute accuracy of my conclusions than in the extent to which I have illustrated the power of the approach used. I have deliberately avoided most traditional geosynclinal terminology, not to denigrate its immense value in the past, but to show that we can accept tacitly the insights it offers, and yet forge beyond them.

POSTSCRIPT

Although not the exclusive concern of my paper, I would like simply to emphasize two broad points that seem to me to be of salient importance to the topic of petrochemistry in relation to tectonic environment in island arcs.

The first point has to do with the interpretation of results from experimental petrology in a tectonic context. In the light of experimental results, both D. H. Green and T. H. Green have discussed in this symposium two models for the derivation of andesitic magmas by partial melting of oceanic crust of basaltic composition. According to plate tectonic theory, this type of source material is present in the upper levels of slabs of lithosphere descending beneath island arcs along sub-crustal courses marked roughly by the inclined seismic zones.

Attention is drawn to the vicinity of the seismic zones by data (reviewed by Gill in this volume) showing that levels of potash and other trace elements contained in the lavas of active island arcs vary systematically transverse to the arc trends. At least for potash, the variation within the volcanic suites of all the active arcs can be correlated successfully with respective vertical depths from the volcanoes to the inclined seismic zones beneath (see Fig. 6 and its relevant text above). Some have argued that the andesitic melts might be derived from partial fusion of hydrous mantle just above the seismic zones, but D. H. Green (this volume) presented experimental data apparently indicating that melts of appropriate composition cannot be derived in this fashion. Others have argued that the andesitic melts which reach the surface may be partial differentiates, or other derivatives, of more primitive basaltic magmas from the mantle above the seismic zones. This possibility still seems open to me, but I will assume here that the andesitic melts are essentially primary partial melts as the two models to be discussed require.

In any case, as Gill and Compston (this volume) argue, observed strontium isotopic ratios in andesitic and associated rocks of the arc suites are so low as to exclude apparently the incorporation of all but quantitatively insignificant amounts of the following materials into the magmas: (*a*) old sialic crust; (*b*) terrigenous oceanic sediments derived from old sialic crust; or (*c*) calcareous oceanic sediments. The only other source materials readily conceivable are: (*a*) mantle beneath arcs; (*b*) basaltic oceanic crust descending along the inclined seismic zones; or (*c*) juvenile crust of the arcs or sediments derived from such juvenile crustal rocks.

The two possible models for partial melting of descending oceanic crust of basaltic composition to yield andesitic magmas directly are: (*a*) melting of high-pressure eclogitic phases at pressures in excess of 25 kb ($\sim$75 km depth); and (*b*) melting of partly hydrous amphibolitic phases at lower pressures. T. H. Green (this volume) presented experimental data apparently indicating that only the first model, of melting at high pressures, will yield melts of truly appropriate composition, and that it will do so over a wide range of water pressures.

The tectonic point to be made is that the geometry of arc-trench systems also favours the alternative of melting at high pressures. In active arcs the volcanic front, which is the first and typically most prominent line of volcanoes, stands generally within the range of 100-150 km above the inclined seismic zone beneath. Data are inherently imprecise, but it is possible to state without uncertainty that no arc volcanoes stand less than 75 km above the seismic zone, and some stand as much as 275 km above the seismic zone. If a direct spatial relationship between the generation of arc magmas and the position of inclined seismic zones is accepted, any petrogenetic model to be applied to actual arc lavas must be compatible with pressures at the source on the order of 25-100 kb, probably typically 30-60 kb. In the framework of existing models, this constraint is as strong as any experimental constraint. It is gratifying, in this case, that both tectonic and experimental constraints lead to the same choice of model, provided the restriction to the two alternatives is truly valid.

The second point has to do with the disposal of lithosphere that moves down into the mantle. On general petrologic and thermodynamic grounds, little or none of the lithosphere that represents asthenosphere depleted of its fusibles to build oceanic crust can remain at or return to shallow levels in the mantle without spoiling the capacity of the upper mantle to feed the continuing volcanism that builds oceanic crust at spreading centres (Ringwood, this volume). The construction of oceanic crust at spreading centres along divergent plate junctures is, apparently, but an initial step in the emergence of crustal materials from the mantle in an irreversible, evolutionary pattern. A second step is the construction of continental crust in arc-trench systems, in part by the tectonic stacking of oceanic sediments and ophiolitic slabs, but mainly through arc magmatism, both volcanic and plutonic. This crustal evolution, so significant for surficial geology, is but one face of a set of processes that involve the mantle as well. Volumetrically, the material that descends forever as the lithosphere sinks, is at least one order of magnitude, and perhaps two orders of magnitude, greater than the total amount of material that is either crammed into melange belts on the flanks of magmatic arcs, or added as igneous increments to the arc structures themselves.

It follows that the most fundamental petrologic questions posed by plate tectonic theory do not concern the origins of rise and arc magmas, but the composition and ultimate fate of the slabs of lithosphere that disappear into the deeper mantle. Implicit in the plate tectonic concept, as applied to petrology, is the idea that irreversible geochemical evolution of the mantle is linked inherently to plate tectonic processes, hence is underway at present on a grand scale. Elsewhere, with W. C. Luth, I have suggested that the whole inner mantle, tentatively identified as the mesosphere, may be essentially a 'depositional' accumulation of lithosphere that has sunk through the asthenosphere. In this model, an accretionary mesosphere has enlarged gradually outward during geologic time from the core boundary to the present boundary between inner and outer mantle at about 650 km depth. Of necessity in this model, the asthenosphere has been progressively shrinking during the same time span. Whether or not this speculative model for the evolution of prominent mantle layers in parallel with an overall geochemical evolution proves satisfactory, the major point made is still valid. Some model for the disposal of lithosphere, the depleted material, within the mantle is a necessary accompaniment to the plate tectonic model for the evolution of crust, the emergent material.

REFERENCES

Alexander, J. B. 1962. A short outline of the geology of Malaya with special reference to Mesozoic orogeny. In *Crust of the Pacific basin. Am. Geophys. Un., Geophys. Monogr.* **6,** 81-6. Washington D.C.

Avdeiko, G. P. 1971. Evolution of geosynclines on Kamchatka. *Pacific Geol.* **3,** 1-14.

Avias, J. 1967. Overthrust structure of the main ultrabasic New Caledonian massifs. *Tectonophysics*, **4,** 531-42.

Bateman, P. C. & Dodge, F. W. 1970. Variations of major chemical constituents across the central Sierra Nevada batholith. *Bull. geol. Soc. Am.* **81,** 409-20.

Bauer, G. R. 1970. The geology of Tofua Island, Tonga. *Pacif. Sci.* **24,** 333-50.

Bederke, E. & Wunderlich, H. G. 1968. 'Atlas zur Geologie'. Bibliograph. Inst., Mannheim, Germany, 75 pp.

Brothers, R. N. & Martin, K. R. 1970. The geology of Macauley Island, Kermadec Group, South-west Pacific. *Bull. volcan.* **34,** 330-46.

Brothers, R. N. & Searle, E. J. 1970. The geology of Raoul Island, Kermadec Group, South-west Pacific. *Bull. volcan.* **34,** 7-37.

Bryan, W. B., Stice, G. D. & Ewart, A. 1972. Geology, petrography, and geochemistry of the volcanic islands of Tonga. *J. geophys. Res.* **77,** 1566-85.

Burchfiel, B. C. & Davis, G. A. 1968. Two-sided nature of the Cordilleran orogen and its tectonic implications. *23rd Intern. Geol. Congr. Rpt*, Sect. 3, 175-84.

Burton, C. K. & Bignell, J. D. 1969. Cretaceous-Tertiary events in Southeast Asia: *Bull. geol. Soc. Am.* **80,** 681-8.

Chase, C. G. 1971. Tectonic history of the Fiji Plateau. *Bull. geol. Soc. Am.* **82,** 3087-110.

Coleman, P. J. 1966. The Solomon Islands as an island arc. *Nature*, **211,** 1249-51.

——— 1970. Geology of the Solomon and New Hebrides Islands as part of the Melanesian Re-entrant, South-west Pacific. *Pacif. Sci.* **24,** 289-314.

Coleman, R. G. 1971. Plate tectonic emplacement of upper mantle peridotites along continental edges. *J. geophys. Res.* **76,** 1212-22.

Cullen, D. J. 1967. Island arc development in the southwest Pacific. *Tectonophysics*, **4,** 163-72.

——— 1970. A tectonic analysis of the southwest Pacific. *N.Z. Jl Geol. Geophys.* **13,** 7-20.

Davies, H. L. 1968. Papuan ultramafic belt. *23rd Intern. Geol. Congr. Rpt*, **1,** 209-20.

Desio, A., Tongiorgi, F. & Ferrara, G. 1964. On the geological age of some granites of the Karakoram, Hindu Kush, and Badakhshan. *21st Intern. Geol. Congr. Rpt*, pt 11, p. 479-96.

Dewey, J. F. & Bird, J. M. 1970. Mountain belts and the new global tectonics. *J. geophys. Res.* **75,** 2625-47.

——— 1971. Origin and emplacement of the ophiolite suite. *J. geophys. Res.* **76,** 3179-206.

Dickinson, W. R. 1967. Tectonic development of Fiji. *Tectonophysics*, **4,** 543-54.

——— 1970. Relations of andesites, granites, and derivative sandstones to arc-trench tectonics. *Rev. Geophys. Space Phys.* **8,** 813-60.

——— 1971*a*. Plate tectonic models of geosynclines. *Earth Planet. Sci. Letters*, **10,** 165-74.

——— 1971*b*. Detrital modes of New Zealand greywackes. *Sediment. Geol.* **5,** 37-56.

——— 1971*c*. Clastic sedimentary sequences deposited in shelf, slope, and trough settings between magmatic arcs and associated trenches. *Pacific Geol.* **3,** 15-30.

Dickinson, W. R. & Hatherton, T. 1967. Andesitic volcanism and seismicity around the Pacific. *Science*, **157,** 801-3.

Dietz, R. S. & Sproll, W. P. 1969. Morphological continental drift fit of Australia and Antarctica. *Nature*, **222,** 345-8.

Elsasser, W. M. 1971. Sea-floor spreading as thermal convection. *J. geophys. Res.* **76,** 1101-12.

Ernst, W. G. 1970. Tectonic contract between the Franciscan mélange and the Great Valley Sequence, crustal expression of a late Mesozoic Benioff zone. *J. geophys. Res.* **75,** 886-902.

Evans, P. 1964. The tectonic framework of Assam. *J. geol. Soc. India*, **5,** 80-96.

Evernden, J. F. & Kistler, R. W. 1970. Chronology of emplacement of Mesozoic batholithic complexes in California and western Nevada. *U.S. geol. Surv. Prof. Pap.* **623,** 42 p.

Farrar, E., Clark, A. H., Haynes, S. J. & Quirt, G. S. 1970. K-Ar evidence for the post-Paleozoic migration of granitic intrusion foci in the Andes of northern Chile. *Earth Planet. Sci. Letters*, **10,** 60-5.

Gansser, A. 1966. The Indian Ocean and the Himalayas. *Eclog. geol. Helv.* **59,** 831-48.

Géze, B. 1963. Observations tectonique dans le Pacifique. *Bull. Soc. géol. Fr.* 7e. Ser. **5,** 154-64.

Giletti, B. J. & Day, H. W. 1968. Potassium-argon ages of igneous intrusive rocks of Peru. *Nature*, **220,** 570-2.

Haile, N. S. 1963. The Cretaceous-Cenozoic northwest Borneo geosyncline. *Bull. geol. Surv. Br. Borneo*, **4,** 1-18.

Hamilton, W. 1969*a*. The volcanic central Andes, a modern model for the Cretaceous batholiths and tectonics of western North America. *Bull. Ore. St. Dep. Geol. miner. Ind.* **65,** 175-84.

Hamilton, W. 1969*b*. Mesozoic California and the underflow of Pacific mantle. *Bull. geol. Soc. Am.* **80,** 2409-30.

——— 1970. The Uralides and the motion of the Russian and Siberian platforms. *Bull. geol. Soc. Am.* **81,** 2553-76.

Hatherton, T. 1969*a*. Gravity and seismicity of asymmetric active regions. *Nature,* **221,** 353-5.

——— 1969*b*. Similarity of gravity anomaly patterns in asymmetric active regions. *Nature,* **224,** 357-8.

——— 1969*c*. The geophysical significance of calc-alkaline andesites in New Zealand. *N.Z. Jl Geol. Geophys.* **12,** 436-59.

Ho, C. S. 1967. Structural evolution of Taiwan. *Tectonophysics,* **4,** 367-78.

Hutchison, C. S. 1968. Dating tectonism in the Indosinian-Thai-Malayan orogen by thermoluminescence. *Bull. geol. Soc. Am.* **79,** 375-86.

Hutchison, W. W. 1970. Metamorphic framework and plutonic styles in the Prince Rupert region of the central Coast Mountains, British Columbia. *Can. J. Earth Sci.* **7,** 376-405.

Ichikawa, K., Murakami, N., Hase, A. & Wadatsumi, K. 1968. Late Mesozoic igneous activity in the inner side of southwest Japan. *Pacific Geol.* **1,** 97-118.

Isacks, B., Oliver, J. & Sykes, L. R. 1968. Seismology and the new global tectonics. *J. geophys. Res.* **73,** 5855-99.

James, D. E. 1971. Plate tectonic model for the evolution of the central Andes. *Bull. geol. Soc. Am.* **82,** 3325-46.

Johnson, R. W., Mackenzie, D. E. & Smith, I. E. 1970. Short papers on Quaternary volcanic areas in Papua-New Guinea. *Rec. Bur. Miner. Resour. Geol. Geophys. Aust.* 1970/72, 17 p.

Kaneko, S. 1966. Transcurrent displacement along the median line of south-western Japan. *N.Z. Jl Geol. Geophys.* **9,** 45-59.

Karig, D. E. 1970. Ridges and basins of the Tonga-Kermadec island arc system. *J. geophys. Res.* **75,** 239-54.

——— 1971*a*. Structural history of the Mariana island arc system. *Bull. geol. Soc. Am.* **82,** 323-44.

——— 1971*b*. Origin and development of marginal basins in the Western Pacific. *J. geophys. Res.* **76,** 2542-61.

Katili, J. A. 1962. On the age of the granitic rocks in relation to the structural features of Sumatra. In *Crust of the Pacific Basin, Am. Geophys. Un., Geophys. Monogr.* **6,** 116-21. Washington, D.C.

——— 1967. Structure and age of the Indonesian tin belt with special reference to Bangka. *Tectonophysics,* **4,** 403-18.

Katsumata, M. & Sykes, L. R. 1969. Seismicity and tectonics of the western Pacific-Izu-Mariana-Caroline and Ryukyu-Taiwan regions. *J. geophys. Res.* **74,** 5923-48.

Kawano, Y. & Ueda, Y. 1967. Periods of igneous activities of granitic rocks in Japan by K-A dating method. *Tectonophysics,* **4,** 523-30.

Klompe, Th. H. F. 1962. Igneous and structural features of Thailand. In *Crust of the Pacific basin. Am. Geophys. Un., Geophys. Monogr.* **6,** 122-134. Washington, D.C.

Konishi, K. 1965. Geotectonic framework of the Ryukyu Islands (Nansei-Shoto). *J. geol. Soc. Japan,* **71,** 437-57.

Le Pichon, X. 1968. Sea-floor spreading and continental drift. *J. geophys. Res.* **73,** 3661-97.

Ludwig, W. J. *et al.* 1966. Sediments and structure of the Japan Trench. *J. geophys. Res.* **71,** 2121-37.

McKenzie, D. P. & Morgan, W. J. 1969. Evolution of triple junctions. *Nature,* **224,** 125-33.

Markhinin, E. K. 1968. Volcanism as an agent of formation of the earth's crust. In *The Crust and Upper Mantle of the Pacific Area. Am. Geophys. Un., Geophys. Monogr.* **12,** 412-23.

Washington, D.C.

Matsuda, T., Nakamura, K. & Sugimura, A. 1967. Late Cenozoic orogeny in Japan. *Tectonophysics*, **4,** 349-66.

Matsuda, T. & Uyeda, S. 1971. On the Pacific-type orogeny and its model—extension of the paired belts concept and possible origin of marginal seas. *Tectonophysics*, **11,** 5-27.

Mitchell, A. H. G. 1970. Facies of an Early Miocene volcanic arc, Malekula Island, New Hebrides. *Sedimentology*, **14,** 201-44.

Mitchell, A. H. G. & Warden, A. J. 1971. Geological evolution of the New Hebrides island arc. *J. geol. Soc. London*, **127,** 501-29.

Miyashiro, A. 1961. Evolution of metamorphic belts. *J. Petrology*, **2,** 277-311.

——— 1967. Orogeny, regional metamorphism, and magmatism in the Japanese Islands. *Meddr. dansk geol. Foren.* **17,** 390-446.

Murauchi, S. *et al.* 1968. Crustal structure of the Philippine Sea. *J. geophys. Res.* **73,** 3143-72.

Oliver, J. 1970. Structure and evolution of the mobile seismic belts. *Phys. Earth Planet. Interiors*, **2,** 350-62.

Packham, G. H. & Falvey, D. A. 1971. An hypothesis for the formation of marginal seas in the western Pacific. *Tectonophysics*, **11,** 79-109.

Rodolfo, K. S. 1969. Bathymetry and marine geology of the Andaman Basin, and tectonic implications for South-east Asia. *Bull. geol. Soc. Am.* **80,** 1203-30.

Sclater, J. G., Hawkins, J. W., Mammerickx, J. & Chase, C. G. 1972. Crustal extension between the Tonga and Lau ridges. Petrologic and geophysical evidence. *Bull. geol. Soc. Am.* **83,** 505-18.

Shatsky, N. S. & Bogdanov, A. A. 1959. Explanatory notes on the tectonic map of the USSR and adjoining countries. *Int. Geol. Rev.* **1,** 1-59.

Shor, G. G., Kirk, H. K. & Menard, H. W. 1971. Crustal structure of the Melanesian area. *J. geophys. Res.* **76,** 2562-86.

Sykes, L. R. 1970. Seismicity of the Indian Ocean and a possible nascent island arc between Ceylon and Australia. *J. geophys. Res.* **75,** 5041-55.

Ustiev, Y. K. 1965. Problems of volcanism and plutonism and volcano-plutonic formations. *Int. Geol. Rev.* **7,** 1994-2016.

Wang, Y. 1970. Variation of potash content in the Pleistocene andesites from Taiwan. *Proc. geol. Soc. China*, **13,** 41-50.

Wright, J. B. 1966. Convection and continental drift in the south-west Pacific. *Tectonophysics*, **3,** 69-81.

Yen, T. P. 1967. Structural analysis of the Tananao Schist of Taiwan. *Bull. geol. Surv. Taiwan*, **18,** 110.

Collected References

Abe, K. & Kanamori, H. 1970. Mantle structure beneath the Japan Sea as revealed by surface waves. *Bull. Earthq. Res. Inst. Tokyo Univ.* **48,** (6A), 1011-21.

Akramovsky, I. I. 1970. Tectonic scheme of the Anadyr River basin (North-eastern end of the Asiatic branch of the Pacific mobile belt). *Geol. i Geofiz.* **10** (in Russian).

Aktiebolag Elektrisk Malmletning. 1967. Report on an airborne geophysical survey in the British Solomon Islands (Stockholm), 1965-6 (2 vols).

Alexander, J. B. 1962. A short outline of the geology of Malaya with special reference to Mesozoic orogeny. In *Crust of the Pacific basin. Am. Geophys. Un., Geophys. Mongr.* **6,** 81-6. Washington, D.C.

Allen, C. R. 1962. Circum-Pacific faulting in the Philippines-Taiwan region. *J. geophys. Res.* **67,** 4795-812 *Philipp. Geol.* **16,** 122-45.

——— 1965. Transcurrent faults in continental areas. In *A symposium on continental drift. Phil. Trans. R. Soc.* **258,** 82-9.

Amato, F. L. 1965. Stratigraphic paleontology in the Philippines. *Philipp. Geol.* **19,** 1-24.

Andal, D. R., Esquerra, J. S., Hashimoto, W., Reyes, B. P. & Sato, T. 1968. The Jurassic Mansalay formation, southern Mindoro, Philippines. *Geology and Palaeontology of Southeast Asia*, **4,** 179-97 (Eds T. Kobayashi & R. Toriyama). Univ. Tokyo Press, Tokyo.

Andal, P. P. 1966. A report on the discovery of Fusilinids in the Philippines. *Philipp. Geol.* **20,** 14-22.

Andrews, J. E., Burns, R. E., Churkin, M., Davies, T. A., Dumitrika, P., Edwards, A. R., Galehouse, J. S., Kennett, J. P., Packham, G. H. & Lingen, G. J. van der. 1972. Deep sea drilling project: leg 21, Tasman Sea-Coral Sea, preliminary results. *Int. Symp. on Oceanography of the South Pacific*, Wellington, N.Z.

Andreyeva, I. B. & Udintsev, G. B. 1958. Bottom structure of the Sea of Japan, from the *Vityaz* expedition data. *Int. Geol. Rev.* **10,** 1-15.

Anonymous. 1956. *An outline of the geology of Korea.* Geol. Surv. Korea.

——— 1960. *An outline of the geology of Japan.* Geol. Surv. Japan.

——— 1969. Ancient seafloor spreading. *Nature,* **224,** 1056.

Aprelkov, S. E. 1971. Tectonics and history of volcanism of Southern Kamchatka. *Geotektonika,* **2** (in Russian).

Argentov, V. V., Ospanov, A. B. & Popov, A. A. 1970. Crustal structure of the south-west Primorie. In *Geology and Geophysics of the Pacific Belt* (Ed. H. S. Gnibidenko). *Trans. Sakhalin Complex Sci. Res. Inst. Novoalexandrovsk*, **25,** 71-8 (in Russian).

Armstrong, R. L. 1968. A model for the evolution of strontium and lead isotopes in a dynamic Earth. *Rev. Geophys.* **6,** 175-99.
——— 1971. Isotopic and chemical constraints on models of magma genesis in volcanic arcs. *Earth Planets. Sci. Letters*, **12,** 137-42.

Artyushkov, E. A. 1970. Density differentiation on the core-mantle interface and gravity convection. *Phys. Earth Planet. Interiors*, **2,** 318-25.

Asano, K. 1963. The Palaeogene. In *Geology of Japan* (Eds F. Takai, T. Matsumoto & R. Toriyama). Univ. Tokyo Press, Tokyo.

Ash, R. P. 1970. Efate. In *New Hebrides Geol. Surv. Ann. Rept* (1968) (Ed. D. I. J. Mallick), 9-14.
——— (In prep.) Geology of Efate. *New Hebrides geol. Surv., Regional Rept.*

Atwater, Tanya. 1970. Implications of plate tectonics for the Cenozoic tectonic evolution of western North America. *Bull geol. Soc. Am.* **81,** 3513.
——— 1971. Evidence from plate tectonics for the age of initiation of deformation on the San Andreas-Gulf of California system. *Geol. Soc. Am. Cordilleran Sect. 67th Annual Meeting, Abstracts with programs*, **3** (2), 134 (Abstract).

Atwater, Tanya & Menard, H. W. 1970. Magnetic lineations in the northeast Pacific. *Earth Planet. Sci. Letters*, **7,** 445.

Atwater, Tanya & Mudie, J. D. 1968. Block faulting on the Gorda Rise. *Science*, **159,** (3816), 729-31.
——— 1971. Lineation, symmetry, and small features on the Gorda Rise (Abstr.). *EOS Trans. Am. geophys. Un.* **52** (4), 237.

Australasian Petroleum Company. 1961. Geological results of petroleum exploration in Western Papua, 1937-61. *J. geol. Soc. Aust.* **8** (1), 133 pp.

Avdeiko, G. P. 1971. Evolution of geosynclines on Kamchatka. *Pacific Geol.* **3,** 1-14.

Avias, J. 1949. Note préliminaire sur quelques phénomènes actuels ou subactuels de pétrogenèse et autres dans les marais côtiers de Moindou et Canala, *C. R. Som. Soc. Géol. Fr.* **277,** 280.
——— 1953. Contribution à l'étude stratigraphique et paléontologique des formations antécrétacées de la Nouvelle-Calédonie centrale. *Sci. de la Terre*, **1** & **2,** 1-276, Nancy.
——— 1959. Les récifs coralliens de la Nouvelle-Calédonie et quelques-uns de leurs problèmes. *Bull. Soc. géol. Fr., 7th series*, **1,** 424-30.
——— 1961. On some new points of view adopted concerning the stratigraphic and correlative knowledge of the sedimentary structures of New Caledonia. *Proc. Ninth Pacif. Sci. Congr.* (1962), **12,** 325-7.
——— 1967. Overthrust structure of the main ultrabasic New Caledonian massifs. *Tectonophysics*, **4,** 531-42.

——— 1969. Coral reefs and New Caledonia neotectonic history. *VIIème Congrès INQUA, Paris 1969—Résumés des Communications*, p. 61.

——— 1971. Sur la signification et sur la génese des grandes ceintures de roches ultrabasiques et roches de leur cortège dans les chaines orogéniques eugéosynclinales. *C.R. Acad. Sci. Paris*, **273,** 667-70.

Avias, J. & Routhier, P. 1962. Carte géologique au 1/100.000eme de la Nouvelle-Calédonie (avec notice explicative). Feuille No. 5: Ponérihouen-Poya, *ORSTOM*, Paris.

Baikov, A. I. & Marchenko, A. F. 1969. *On the role of metamorphism and metasomatosis processes in mineralization.* Naukova Dumka, Kiev (in Russian).

Bailey, E. H., Blake, M. C. & Jones, D. L. 1970. On-land Mesozoic oceanic crust in California Coast ranges. *U.S. geol. Surv. Prof. Pap.* **700**-C, 70-81.

Bain, J. H. C., Davies, H. L. & Ryburn, R. J. 1971. Regional geology of Papua-New Guinea: some new concepts (abstract). *12th Pacific Sci. Congr. Rec. Proc.* (Abstracts), **1,** 450. See also Bain, this volume.

Bain, J. H. C., Mackenzie, D. E. & Ryburn, R. J. 1970. Geology of the Kubor Anticline Central Highlands of New Guinea. Rec. Bur. Miner. Resour. Aust. 1970/79 (unpubl.).

Baker, G. 1946. Preliminary note on volcanic eruptions in the Goropu Mountains, south-eastern Papua during the period December 1943 to August 1944. *J. Geol.* **54,** 19.

Baker, P. E. 1968. Comparative volcanology and petrology of the Atlantic island-arcs. *Bull. volcan.* **32,** 189-206.

Baltzer, F. 1970. Datation absolue de la transgression holocène sur la côte ouest de la Nouvelle-Calédonie sur des échantillons de tourbe à palétuviers. Interprétation néotectonique. *C.R. Acad. Sci. Paris*, **271,** 2251-4.

Baltzer, F., Guillon, J. H., Launay, J. C. & Trescases, J. J. 1967. Geological and geophysical publications on New Caledonia. *N.Z. Jl Geol. Geophys.* **10,** 1275-9.

Baltzer, F. & Trescases, J. J. 1971. Erosion, transport et sédimentation liées aux cyclones tropicaux dans les massifs d'ultrabasites de Nouvelle Calédonie. Première approche du bilan général de l'alteration, de l'érosion et de la sédimentation sur péridotites en zone tropicale. *Cahiers ORSTOM*, (*Géol.*) **3** (2).

Band, R. B. 1968. The geology of Southern Viti Levu and Mbengga. *Bull. geol. Surv. Fiji*, **15**, 49 pp.

Banghar, A. R. & Sykes, L. R. 1968. Focal mechanisms of earthquakes in the Indian Ocean and adjacent regions. *J. geophys. Res.* **74,** 632.

Barazangi, M. & Dorman, J. 1969. World seismicity maps compiled from ESSA, Coast and Geodetic Survey, epicentre data, 1961-7. *Bull. seisml. Soc. Am.* **59,** 369-80.

Barazangi, M. & Isacks, B. L. 1971. Lateral variations of seismic wave attenuation in the upper mantle above the inclined earthquake zone of the Tonga Island Arc: Deep anomaly in the upper mantle. *J. geophys. Res.* **76** (35), 8493-516.

Bark, K. 1970. The Aleutian Island Arc and Alaskan continental margin. In *Continental Margins and Island Arcs* (Ed. U. H. Poole). Mir, Moscow (in Russian).

Bartholomew, R. W. 1959. Geology of Savusavu Bay West—Vanua Levu. *Bull. geol. Surv. Fiji*, **5,** 28 pp.
——— 1960. Geology of the Nandi Area—Western Viti Levu. *Bull. geol. Surv. Fiji*, **7,** 27 pp.

Bateman, P. C. & Dodge, F. W. 1970. Variations of major chemical constituents across the central Sierra Nevada batholith. *Bul. geol. Soc. Am.* **81,** 409-20.

Bauer, G. R. 1970. The geology of Tofua Isalnd, Tonga. *Pacif. Sci.* **24,** 333-50.

Bederke, E. & Wunderlich, H. G. 1968. 'Atlas zur Geologie'. Bibliograph. Inst., Mannheim, Germany, 75 pp.

Beloussov, V. V. 1960. Tectonic map of the earth. *Geol. Rundsch.* **50,** 316-24.
——— 1961. Developmert of the earth and tectogenesis. *Philipp. Geol.* **15,** 27-58.
——— 1966. *The earth's crust and upper mantle of the continents.* Nauka Publ., Moscow (in Russian).
——— 1968. The earth's crust and upper mantle of the oceans. Ibid. (in Russian).

Beloussov, V. V. & Ruditch, E. M. 1960. The place of island arcs in the development of the Earth's structures. *Sov. Geol.* **10** (in Russian).
——— 1961. Island arcs in the development of the earth's structure. *J. Geol.* **69,** 647-58.

Belyi, V. F. & Tillman, S. M. 1966. Tectonics and history of development of the Okhotsk-Chukotka volcanic belt. *Geotektonika*, **2** (in Russian).

Bence, A. E. 1966. The differentiation history of the earth by rubidium-strontium isotopic relationships. In *Variations in isotopic abundances of strontium, calcium, and argon and related topics* (Ed. P. M. Hurley), M.I.T. 1381-1414, 14th Ann. Prog. Rept, pp. 35-78.

Benoit, M. & Dubois, J. 1971. The earthquake swarm in the New Hebrides Archipelago, August 1965. *Recent Crustal Movements.* Bull. R. Soc. N. Z. **9,** 141-8.

Benson, W. N. 1924. The structural features of the margin of Australasia. *Trans. N.Z. Inst.* **55,** 99-137.

Beresnev, A. F., Gainanov, A. G., Kovylin, V. M. & Stroev, P. A. 1970. Crustal and upper mantle structure of the Japan Sea and the adjacent Pacific zone. In *Problems of Structure of the Earth's Crust and Upper Mantle. Upper Mantle Rept*, 7 (Eds V. A. Magnitsky, N. A. Belyaevsky & I. S. Vol'vovsky). Nauka Publ., Moscow (in Russian).

Beresnev, A. F. & Kovylin, V. M. 1969. Some peculiarities of deep crustal structure of the southern Japan Sea. *Izv. Akad. Nauk SSSR* (*geol.*), **5,** 17-22 (in Russian).

——— 1970. Crustal structure of the Japan Sea in the vicinity of the continental slope of the southern Primorie and north-eastern Korea. *Trans. Oceanol. Inst. Akad. Nauk SSSR*, **87,** 168-73 (in Russian).

——— 1970. Basement relief and thickness of bottom sediments in the central part of the Japan Sea. *Okeanologiya*, **10** (1), 113-16 (in Russian).

Bersenev, I. I. (Ed.) 1969. Primorie Territory. I—Geologic Description. In *Geology of the USSR*, **32.** Nedra Publ., Moscow (in Russian).

——— 1970. History of the geologic development of the Primorie region and Sea of Japan in Mesozoic and Cenozoic. *Summary of doctoral theses*. Moscow (in Russian).

Birch, F. 1961. The velocity of compressional waves in rock to 10K bars (pt 2), *J. geophys. Res.* **66,** 2199-224.

Biscaye, P. E. & Dasch, E. J. 1971. The rubidium, strontium, strontium-isotope system in deep-sea sediments: Argentine Basin. *J. geophys. Res.* **76,** 5087-96.

Blake, D. H. & Miezitis, Y. 1967. Geology of Bougainville and Buka, New Guinea. *Bull. Bur. Miner. Resour. Aust.* **93.**

Blake Jr, M. C. & Landis, C. A. 1971. The Dun Mountain Melange—a proposed western margin of the Torlesse terrane in northeast Nelson (abstract). *Symp. on Torlesse Supergroup, Vict. Univ. Wellington*, **29.**

Blow, W. H. 1967. *Proc. First Int. Conf. Geneva: Planktonic microfossils*, **1,** p. 305 (Eds P. Bronniman & H. H. Renz). E. J. Brill, Leiden.

Bogdanov, N. A. 1967. The Palaeozoic of eastern Australia and Melanesia. *Trans. Geol. Inst. Akad. Nauk SSSR*, **181** (in Russian).

——— 1967. Paleozoic geosynclines of the western part of the Circum-Pacific belt. *Tectonophysics*, **4** (4-6), 581 (Abstract).

——— 1969. Thalassogeosynclines of the Circum-Pacific belt. *Geotektonika*, **3** (in Russian). (Eng. trans. *Geotectonics*, **3,** 141-7.)

——— 1969. Thalassogeosynclines of the Pacific ring. *Geotektonika*, **3** (in Russian).

——— 1970. Some aspects of tectonics of eastern Koryak Mountains. *Dokl. Akad. Nauk SSSR*, **192** (3) (in Russian).

Böse, E. 1906. La fauna de moluscos del Senoniano de Cardena, San Luis Potosi. *Boln. Inst. Geol. Méx.* **24,** 1-95.

Bosum, W. *et al.* 1970. Aero-magnetic survey of offshore Taiwan. *Econ. Comm. Asia & Far East (ECAFE), CCOP, Tech. Bull.* **3,** 1-34. Bangkok.

Bott, M. H. P. 1971. The Interior of the Earth, 63-70, 268, Edward Arnold, London.

Bowin, C. 1966. Gravity over trenches and rifts. In *Continental margins and island arcs. Geol. Surv. Pap. Can.* 66-15, 430-9.

Brady, H. B. 1888. Note on the so-called 'Soapstone' of Fiji. *Q. Jl geol. Soc. Lond.* **44,** 1-10.

Branagan, D. F. 1969. Palaeovolcanology in New South Wales: a stratigraphic summary. *Spec. Publ. geol. Soc. Aust.* **2,** 155.

Brooks, J. A. (Ed.). 1971. Investigations of crustal structure in the New Britain-New Ireland region. Part I: Geophysical and Geological Data. *Rec. Bur. Miner. Resour. Aust.* In press.

Brooks, J. A., Connelly, J. B., Finlayson, D. M. & Wiebenga, W.A. 1971. St George's Channel-Bismarck Sea Trough. *Natrue* **229,** 205-7.

Brothers, R. N. 1970. Lawsonite-albite schists from northernmost New Caledonia. *Contr. Mineral. Petrol.* **25,** 185-202.

——— 1970. Petrochemical affinities of volcanic rocks from the Tonga-Kermadec Island arc, Southwest Pacific. *Bull. volcan.* **34,** 308-29.

Brothers, R. N. & Martin, K. R. 1970. The geology of Macauley Island, Kermadec Group, Southwest Pacific. *Bull. volcan.* **34,** 330-46.

Brothers, R. N. & Searle, E. J. 1970. The geology of Raoul Island, Kermadec Group, Southwest Pacific. *Bull. volcan.* **34,** 7-37.

Brouwer, H. A. 1925. *The Geology of the East Indies.* MacMillan, New York, 160 pp.

Brown, D. A., Campbell, K. S. W. & Crook, K. A. W. 1968. *The geological evolution of Australia and New Zealand.* Pergamon Press.

Brown, R. J., Borg, H. & Bath, M. 1971. Strike and dip of crustal boundaries—a method and its application. *Geofis. pura appl.* **88,** 60-74.

Bryan, W. B., Finger, L. W. & Chayes, F. 1969. Estimating proportions in petrographic mixing equations by least-squares approximation. *Science*, **163,** 926.

Bryan, W. B., Stice, G. D. & Ewart, A. 1972. Geology, petrography, and geochemistry of the volcanic islands of Tonga. *J. geophys. Res.* **77,** 1566-85.

Bune, V. I. *et al.* 1969. Methods of detailed studies of seismicity. *Trudy Inst. Fiz. Zemli AN SSSR*, **9** (176), 1969 (in Russian).

Burchfiel, B. C. & Davis, G. A. 1968. Two-sided nature of the Cordilleran orogen and its tectonic implications. *23rd Intern. Geol. Congr. Rpt*, Sect. **3,** 175-84.

Burton, C. K. & Bignell, J. D. 1969. Cretaceous-Tertiary events in Southeast Asia. *Bull. geol. Soc. Am.* **80,** 681-8.

Cann, J. R. 1970. New model for the structure of the oceanic crust. *Nature*, **226,** 928-30.

Carey, S. W. 1958. The tectonic approach to continental drift. In *Continental Drift—A Symposium* (Univ. of Tasmania, Hobart), pp. 177-355 (Ed. S. W. Carey).

——— 1963. The assymetry of the Earth. *Aust. J. Sci.* **25,** 369-82 and 479-88.

——— 1970. Australia, New Guinea and Melanesia in the current revolution in concepts of the evolution of the earth. *Search*, **1** (5), 178-88.

Challis, G. A. & Guillon, J. H. 1971. Etude comparative à la microsonde électronique du clinopyroxène des basaltes et roches ultramafiques de Nouvelle Calédonie. Possibilité d'une origine commune de ces roches. *Bull. Bur. Rech. Géol. Min.* **4** (2).

Chase, C. G. 1971. Tectonic history of the Fiji Plateau. *Bull. geol. Soc. Am.* **82,** 3087-110.

Chase, R. L. & Bunce, E. T. 1969. Under-thrusting of the eastern margin of the Antilles by the floor of the western North Atlantic Ocean, and origin of the Barbados ridge. *J. geophys. Res.* **74,** 1413-20.

Chayes, F. 1964. A petrographic distinction between Cenozoic volcanics in and around the open oceans. *J. geophys. Res.* **69,** 1573-88.

Chen Zhiqiang, Wang Cenghang & Deng Xinghui. 1965. Some results of paleomagnetic research in China. In *The present and past of the geomagnetic field.* Nauka Publ., Moscow, pp. 309-11 (translated by E. R. Hope, Directorate of Scientific Information Services, DRB, Canada T462R, 1966).

Chevalier, J. P. 1968. Géomorphologie de l'île de Mare. In *Expédition francaise sur les récifs coralliens de la Nouvelle-Calédonie*, vol. 3. Editions de la fondation Singer-Polignac, Paris. 155 pp.

Chikov, B. M. 1970. Tectonics of the Okhotsk median mass. *Trudy Inst. Geol. Geofiz., SO AN SSSR, Fasc.* **86,** Nauka Publ., Moscow (in Russian).

Chikov, B. M., Yunov, A. Yu. & Belyaev, I. V. 1970. The Okhotsk Sea structure and its correlation to coastal folded complexes. *Geol. i Geofiz.* **1,** 57-68 (in Russian).

Chou, J. T. 1969. A petrographic study of the Mesozoic and Cenozoic rock formations in the Tungliang well TL-1 of the Penghu Island, Taiwan, China. *Econ. Comm. Asia & Far East (ECAFE), CCOP, Tech. Bull.* **2,** 97-115. Bangkok.

Christian, L. B. 1964. Post-Oligocene tectonic history of the Cagayan basin, Philippines. *Philipp. Geol.* **18,** 114-47.

Christoffel, D. A. 1971. Motion of the New Zealand Alpine Fault deduced from the pattern of sea-floor spreading. Recent Crustal Movements. *Bull. R. Soc. N.Z.* **9,** 25-30.

Christoffel, D. A. & Ross, D. I. 1970. A fracture zone in the southwest Pacific Basin south of New Zealand and its implications for sea-floor spreading. *Earth Planet. Sci. Letters*, **8,** 125.

Cifali, G., D'Addario, G. W., Polak, E. J. & Wiebenga, W. A. 1969. Rabaul preliminary crustal seismic test, New Britain, 1966. *Rec. Bur. Miner. Resour. Aust.* 1969/125 (unpubl.).

Clark, R. H. 1960. Petrology of the volcanic rocks of Tongariro subdivision. In *The geology of Tongariro subdivision* (Ed. D. R. Gregg). *Bull. geol. Surv. N.Z.* n.s. **40,** 107.

Clark, R. H. & Wellman, H. W. 1959. The Alpine Fault from Lake McKerrow to Milford Sound. *N.Z. Jl Geol. Geophys.* **2,** 590-601.

Clark, S. P. Jr. (Ed.) 1966. Handbook of physical constants, *Mem. geol. Soc. Am.* **97**.

Coats, R. R. 1952. Magmatic differentiation in Tertiary and Quaternary volcanic rocks from Adak and Kananga Islands, Aleutian Islands, Alaska. *Bull. geol. Soc. Am.* **63,** 485.

Cole, W. S. 1960. Upper Eocene and Oligocene larger foraminifera from Viti Levu, Fiji. *U.S. geol. Surv. Prof. Pap.* 374-A.

——— 1970. Larger foraminifera of late Eocene age from Eua, Tonga. *U.S. geol. Surv. Prof. Pap.* 640-B, 15 pp.

Coleman, P. J. 1962. An outline of the geology of Choiseul, Solomon Islands. *J. geol. Soc. Aust.* **8,** 135-58.

——— 1965. Stratigraphical and structural notes on the British Solomon Islands with reference to the First Geological Map, 1962. *Geol. Rec. Br. Solomon Isl.* **2** (1959-62), 17-31.

——— 1966. Upper Cretaceous (Senonian) bathyal pelagic sediments with *Globotruncana* from the Solomon Islands. *J. geol. Soc. Aust.* **13,** 439-47.

——— 1966. The Solomon Islands as an island arc. *Nature*, **211,** 1249-51.

——— 1967. A possible resolution of the Melanesian Re-entrant. *Upper Mantle Project: Second Aust. Progress Rept*, 192-4 (Ed. A. E. Ringwood). Aust. Acad. Sci., Canberra.

——— 1969. Derived Eocene larger foraminifera on Maewo, eastern New Hebrides, and their South-west Pacific implications. *New Hebrides Geol. Surv. Rept.* 1967, 36-7 (Ed. D. I. J. Mallick).

——— 1970. Geology of the Solomon and New Hebrides Islands, as part of the Melanesian Re-entrant, South-west Pacific. *Pacif. Sci.* **24,** 289-314.

Coleman, P. J., Grover, J. C. & Stanton, R. L. 1965. A First Geological Map of the British Solomon Islands. *Rec. geol. Surv. Br. Solomon Isl.* **2** (1951-62), 16-17.

Coleman, P. J. & Veevers, J. J. 1971. Microfossils from Philip Island indicate a minimum Age of Lower Miocene for the Norfolk Ridge, South-west Pacific. *Search*, **2** (8), 289.

Coleman, R. G. 1967. Glaucophane schists from California and New Caledonia. *Tectonophysics*, **4** (4-6), 479-98.

——— 1971. Plate tectonic emplacement of upper mantle peridotites along continental edges. *J. geophys. Res.* **76,** 1212-22.

Colley, H. 1969. Andesitic volcanism in the New Hebrides. *Proc. geol. Soc. London*, **1662,** 46-51.

Colley, H. & Ash, R. P. 1971. Geology of Erromango. *New Hebrides geol. Surv., Regional Rept.*

Colley, H. & Warden, A. J. (In prep.). The petrology of the New Hebrides.

Compston, W. & Gray, C. M. 1972. Lunar model Rb-Sr ages and magma genesis. *Earth Planet. Sci Letters*, **15.**

Coombs, D. S. 1963. Trends and affinities of basaltic magmas and pyroxenes as illustrated on the diopside-olivine-silica diagram. *Miner. Soc. Am., Spec. Paper*, **1,** 227-50.

Corby, G. W. *et al.* 1951. Geology and oil possibilities of the Philippines. *Dept. Agric. & Nat. Resources Tech. Bull.* **21.** Manila.

Coudray, J. 1969. Observations nouvelles sur les formations miocènes et post-miocènes de la région de Nepoui (Nouvelle-Caledonie): précisions lithologiques et preuves d'une tectonique "recente" sur la côte Sud-Ouest de ce territoire. *C.R. Acad. Sci. Paris*, **269,** 1599-602.

——— 1971. Nouvelles données sur la nature et l'origine du complexe récifal côtier de la Nouvelle-Calédonie: études sédimentologiques et paléoécologiques préliminaires d'un forage réalisé dans le récif barrière de la côte sud-ouest. *Quatern Res.* **1** (2), 236-46.

Coudray, J. & Gonord, H. 1966. Découverte d'une microfaune paléocène dans les formations volcano-sédimentaires de la Nouvelle-Calédonie. *C.R. Acad. Sci. Paris*, **263,** 716.

Coulson, F. I. E. 1971. The Geology of western Vanua Levu. *Bull. geol. Surv. Fiji*, **17,** 49 pp.

Cox, A. 1962. Analysis of present geomagnetic field for comparison with paleomagnetic results. *J. Geomagn. Geoelect.* **13,** 101-12.

——— 1968. Lengths of geomagnetic polarity intervals. *J. geophys. Res.* **73,** 3247-60.

Cox, A. & Doell, R. R. 1962. Magnetic properties of the basalt in hole EM7, Mohole project. *J. geophys. Res.* **67,** 3997-4004.

Craig, P. (In press.) The Geology of Santa Cruz. *Br. Solomon Isl. Geol. Surv.*

Crenn, Y. 1953. Anomalies gravimétriques magnétiques liées aux roches basiques de la Nouvelle Calédonie. *Annls. Géophys.* **9** (4), 291-9.

Cullen, D. J. 1967. Island arc development in the southwest Pacific. *Tectonophysics*, **4,** 163-72.

——— 1967. A note on the regional structure of the southwest Pacific. *N.Z. Jl Sci.* **10,** 813-15.

——— 1967. Mantle convection and sea-floor spreading in the South-west Pacific. *Nature*, **216,** 356-7.

——— 1967. The Antipodes fracture zone, a major structure of the south-west Pacific. *N.Z. Jl Mar. Freshwater Res.* **1,** 16-25.

——— 1969. Macquarie Island, provisional bathymetry, scale 1:200,000, Island Series. N.Z. Oceanogr. Inst., Wellington.

——— 1970. Tectonic map of the south-west Pacific (1/10,000,000). *New Zealand Inst. Cart., Misc. series* **20.**

——— 1970. 'Two-way stretch' of sialic crust and plate tectonics in the South-west Pacific. *Nature*, **226,** 741-2.

——— 1970. A tectonic analysis of the southwest Pacific. *N.Z. Jl Geol. Geophys.* **13,** 7-20.

Daly, R. A. 1933. *Igneous rocks and the depths of the earth.* McGraw-Hill, New York and Lond. 598 pp.

Dasch, E. J. 1969. Strontium isotopes in weathering profiles, deep-sea sediments, and sedimentary rocks. *Geochim. cosmochim. Acta*, **33,** 1521-52.

Davies, D. & MacKenzie, D. P. 1969. Seismic travel time residuals and plates. *Geophys. J. R. astr. Soc.* **18,** 51-63.

Davies, H. L. 1968. Papuan ultramafic belt. *23rd Intern. Geol. Congr. Prague.* **1,** 209-20.
——— 1971. Peridotite-gabbro-basalt complex in eastern Papua: an overthrust plate of oceanic mantle and crust. *Bull. Bur. Miner. Resour. Aust.* **128.**

Davies, H. L. & Smith, I. E. 1971. Geology of Eastern Papua. *Bull. geol. Soc. Am.* **82,** 3299-312.

Davis, W. M. 1925. Les côtes et les récifs coralliens de la Nouvelle Calédonie. *Annls Géogr.* **34,** 244-69, 332-59, 424-41, 521-58.

Dehlinger, P., Couch, R. W. & Gemperle, M. 1967. Gravity and structure of the eastern part of the Mendocino escarpment. *J. geophys. Res.* **72,** 1233-47.

Denham, D. 1968. Thickness of the Earth's crust in Papua, New Guinea and the British Solomon Islands. *Aust. J. Sci.* **30,** 277.
——— 1969. Distribution of earthquakes in the New Guinea-Solomon Islands region. *J. geophys. Res.* **74,** 4290-9.

Dergunov, A. B., Zaitsev, N. S., Mossakovsky, A. A. & Perfil'yev, A. S. 1971. Hercynides of Mongolia and the Palaeotethys problem. In *Problems of theoretical and regional tectonics.* Nauka Publ., Moscow (in Russian).

Desio, A., Tongiorgi, F. & Ferrara, G. 1964. On the geological age of some granites of the Karakoram, Hindu Kush, and Badakhshan. *21st Intern. Geol. Congr. Rpt*, pt 11, p. 479-96.

Dewey, J. F. & Bird, J. M. 1970. Mountain belts and the new global tectonics. *J. geophys. Res.* **75,** 2625-47.
——— 1971. Origin and emplacement of the ophiolite suite: Appalachian ophiolites in Newfoundland. *J. geophys. Res.* **76,** 3179-206.

Dewey, J. F. & Horsfield, B. 1970. Plate tectonics, orogeny and continental growth. *Nature*, **225,** (5232), 521-5.

Dickinson, W. R. 1962. Petrogenetic significance of geosynclinal andesitic volcanism along the Pacific margin of North America. *Bull. geol. Soc. Am.* **73,** 1241-56.
——— 1967. Tectonic Development of Fiji. *Tectonophysics* **4,** 543-53.
——— 1968. Circum-Pacific andesite types. *J. geophys. Res.* **73,** 2261.
——— 1970. Relations of andesites, granites, and derivative sandstones to arc-trench tectonics. *Rev. Geophys! Space Phys.* **8,** 813-60.
——— (unpublished manuscript). Dissected erosion surfaces in Northwest Viti Levu, Fiji. On file with Fiji Geological Survey Dept.
——— 1971. Plate tectonics in geologic history. *Science*, **174** (4005), 107-13.
——— 1971. Plate tectonic models of geosynclines. *Earth Planet. Sci. Letters*, **10,** 165-74.

——— 1971. Detrital modes of New Zealand greywackes. *Sediment. Geol.* **5,** 37-56.
——— 1971. Clastic sedimentary sequences deposited in shelf, slope, and trough settings between magmatic arcs and associated trenches. *Pacific Geol.* **3,** 15-30.

Dickinson, W. R. & Hatherton, T. 1967. Andesitic volcanism and seismicity around the Pacific. *Science*, **157,** 801-3.

Dickinson, W. R., Rickard, M. J., Coulson, F. I. E., Smith, J. G. & Lawrence, R. L. 1968. Late Cenozoic shoshonitic lavas in north-western Viti Levu, Fiji. *Nature*, **219,** 148.

Dietz, R. S. 1961. Continent and ocean basin evolution by spreading of the sea-floor. *Nature* **190,** 854.
——— 1963. Collapsing continental rise—an actualistic concept of geosynclines and mountain building. *J. Geol.* **71,** 314-44.

Dietz, R. S. & Holden, J. C. 1970. The break-up of Pangaea. *Scient. Am.* **223,** 30-41.

Dietz, R. S. & Sproll, W. P. 1969. Morphological continental drift fit of Australia and Antarctica. *Nature*, **222,** 345-8.

Dolmatov, B. K. & Khotin, M. Yu. 1969. Formation of pre-Palaeogene intrusive complexes on Kamchatka Cape peninsula (Eastern Kamchatka). *Sov. Geol.* **5** (in Russian).

Donnelly, T. W., Rogers, J. J. W., Pushkar, P. & Armstrong, R. L. 1971. Chemical evolution of the igneous rocks of the eastern West Indies: an investigation of thorium, uranium, and potassium distributions, and lead and strontium isotopic ratios. *Mem. geol. Soc. Am.* **130.**

Dott, Jr, R. H. 1969. Circum-Pacific late Cenozoic structural rejuvenation: Implications for sea-floor spreading. *Science*, **166** (3907), 874-6.

Dow, D. B. & Dekker, F. E. 1964. The geology of the Bismarck Mountains, New Guinea. *Rept Bur. Miner. Resour. Geol. Geophys. Aust.* **76.**

Dow, D. B., Smit, J. A. J., Bain, J. H. C. & Ryburn, R. J. (In press.) Geology of the South Sepik Region. *Bull. Bur. Miner. Resour. Aust.* **133.**

Drabkin, I. E. (Ed.) 1970. North-east of the USSR. II—Geologic Description. In *Geology of the USSR*, **30.** Nedra Publ., Moscow (in Russian).

Drake, C. L., & Nafe, J. E. 1968. The transition from ocean to continent from seismic refraction data. In *The Crust and Upper Mantle of the Pacific Area* (Eds. L. Knopoff, C. L. Drake & J. Hart). *Am. Geophys. Un., Geophys. Monogr.* **12,** 174-86.

Dubois, J. 1966. Temps de propagation des ondes *P* à des distances épicentrales de 30 à 90 degrés. Région Sud Ouest Pacifique. *Annls Geophys.* **22** (4), 642-5.
——— 1968. Etude de la dispersion des ondes de Rayleigh dans la région du Sud-Ouest Pacifique. *Annls Geophys.* **24** (1), 359-68.
——— 1969. Contribution a l'étude structurale du Sud-Ouest Pacifique d'après les ondes

sismiques observées en Nouvelle-Calédonie et aux Nouvelles-Hébrides. *Annls Geophys.* **24** (4), 923-72.

——— 1970. Etude de la propagation des ondes *S* dans la région Nouvelle-Calédonie, Nouvelles-Hébrides. *Rapp. ORSTOM* (à diffusion restreinte), Paris.

——— 1971. Propagation of *P* waves and Rayleigh waves in Melanesia: structural implications. *J. geophys. Res.* **76** (29), 7217-40.

Dubois, J., Larue, B., Pascal, G. & Reichenfeld, C. 1971. Seismology and structure of the New Hebrides. This volume.

Dubois, J., Launay, J. & Recy, J. 1971. Un bourrelet de la plaque australienne avant son plongement sous la plaque oceanique serait à l'origine des mouvements tectoniques Quaternaires observés dans la region Nouvelle-Calédonie/Iles Loyautés. *Rapp. ORSTOM*, Paris.

Dubois, J. & Reichenfeld, C. 1971. Sur la vitesse de phase des ondes de Rayleigh aux Nouvelles-Hébrides. Rapp. ORSTOM, Paris (unpubl.).

Dubourdieu, G. 1968. Sur les forces géologiques en action autour du Pacifique. 62 pp., *Bibl.. Collège de France*, Paris.

——— 1970. A propos du mécanisme terrestre. 70 pp., *Bibl. Lab. de Géol.*, *Collège de France*, Paris.

Dubovikov, L. K. 1970. On the question of the age of metamorphic strata of the Tas-Khayakhtakhsky anticlinorium (Yakutskaya ASSR). In *Materials on Geology and Mineral Resources of the Yakutskaya ASSR* (*North-eastern Yakutiya*) (Ed. I. D. Vorona), **16,** 33-4. Yakutsk (in Russian).

Edwards, A. B. 1950. The petrology of the Miocene sediments of the Aure Trough, Papua. *Proc. R. Soc. Vict.* **60,** 123-48.

Edwards, A. B. & Glaessner, M. F. 1953. Mesozoic and Tertiary sediments from the Waghi Valley, New Guinea. *Proc. R. Soc. Vict.* **64** (2).

Efimov, A. A. & Efimova, L. P. 1967. *Kytlym platinum-bearing massif.* Nedra Publ., Moscow.

Elsasser, W. M. 1971. Sea-floor spreading as thermal convection. *J. geophys. Res.* **76,** 1101-12.

Engel, A. E. J., Engel, C. G. & Havens, R. G. 1965. Chemical characteristics of oceanic basalts and the upper mantle. *Bull. geol. Soc. Am.* **76,** 719.

Erlikh, E. N., Shantzer, A. E. & Kutiev, F. Sh. 1971. Meimechites of Eastern Kamchatka. *Izv. Acad. Sci. USSR geol. Ser.* **2** (in Russian).

Ernst, W. G. 1970. Tectonic contact between the Franciscan mélange and the Great Valley Sequence, crustal expression of a late Mesozoic Benioff zone. *J. geophys. Res.* **75,** 886-902.

Espirat, J. J. 1963. Etude géologique de la région de la Nouvelle-Calédonie septentrionale. (Thesis, Clermont University Library.)

Espiritu, E. A. *et al.* 1968. Biostratigraphy of Bondoc Peninsula, Quezon. *Philipp. Geol.* **22**, 63-90.

Evans, P. 1964. The tectonic framework of Assam. *J. geol. Soc. India*, **5,** 80-96.

Evernden, J. F. & Kistler, R. W. 1970. Chronology of emplacement of Mesozoic batholithic complexes in California and western Nevada. *U.S. geol. Surv. Prof. Pap.* **623,** 42 p.

Ewart, A. 1969. Petrochemistry and feldspar crystallization in the silicic volcanic rocks, central North Island, New Zealand. *Lithos* **2,** 371.

Ewart, A. & Bryan, W. B. 1971. Geology, petrography and geochemistry of the volcanic islands of Tonga (abstract). *12th Pacific Sci. Congr. Rec. Proc.* (Abstracts), **1,** 454. See also this volume.

——— (In press.) The petrology and geochemistry of the igneous rocks from Eua, Tonga—an early Tertiary ophiolite complex? *Bull. geol. Soc. Am.* See also Ewart & Bryan, this volume.

Ewart, A. & Stipp, J. J. 1968. Petrogenesis of the volcanic rocks of the Central North Island, New Zealand, as indicated by a study of Sr^{87}/Sr^{86} ratios, and Sr, Rb, K, U, and Th abundances. *Geochim. cosmochim. Acta*, **32,** 699-736.

Ewart, A., Taylor, S. R. & Capp, A. C. 1968. Trace and minor element geochemistry of the rhyolitic volcanic rocks, Central North Island, New Zealand. Total rock and residual liquid data. *Contr. Mineral. Petrol.* **18,** 76.

Ewing, J. I., Houtz, R. E. & Ludwig, W. J. 1970. Sediment distribution in the Coral Sea. *J. geophys. Res.* **75,** 1963-72.

Ewing, M., Hawkins, L. V. & Ludwig, W. J. 1970. Crustal structure of the Coral Sea. *J. geophys. Res.* **75,** 1953-62.

Ewing, M., Ludwig, W. J. & Ewing, J. 1965. Oceanic structural history of the Bering Sea. *J. geophys. Res.* **70** (18), 4593-600.

Fairbridge, R. W. 1961. Basis for submarine nomenclature in the South-west Pacific Ocean. *Dt. hydrogr. Z.* **15,** 1-15.

Falvey, D. A. & Talwani, M. 1969. Gravity map and tectonic fabric of the Coral Sea (abstr.). *Geol. Soc. Am. 1969 Meeting, Abstracts*, **7,** 62.

Farrar, E., Clark, A. H., Haynes, S. J. & Quirt, G. S. 1970. K-Ar evidence for the post-Paleozoic migration of granitic intrusion foci in the Andes of northern Chile. *Earth Planet. Sci. Letters*, **10,** 60-5.

Faure, H. & Elouard, P. 1967. Schéma des variations du niveau de l'océan Atlantique sur la côte de l'Ouest de l'Afrique depuis 40,000 ans. *C.R. Acad. Sci. Paris*, **265,** 784-7.

Fedotov, S. A. 1965. Upper mantle properties of the southern part of Kurile Island arc according to detailed seismological data. *Tectonophysics*, **2** (2-3), 219-25.

——— 1968. On deep structure, properties of the upper mantle and volcanism of the Kuril-Kamchatka island Arc according to seismic data. In *The crust and upper mantle of the Pacific area* (Eds. L. Knopoff, C. L. Drake & P. J. Hart). *Am. Geophys. Un., Geophys. Monogr.* **12,** 131-9.

Fedotov, S. A. & Farberov, A. I. 1966. On screening of transversal seismic waves and on the magmatic chamber in the upper mantle in the region of the Avachinskaya group of volcanoes. In *Vulkanism i glubinnoye stroyeniye Zemli.* Nauka Publ., Moscow (in Russian).

Fedotov, S. A. & Slavina, L. B. 1968. Estimation of longitudinal wave velocities in the upper mantle beneath north-western part of the Pacific and Kamchatka. *Izv. Akad. Nauk SSSR, Fizika Zemli,* **2,** 8-31 (in Russian).

Fernandez, J. C. & Pulanco, D. H. 1970. Reconnaissance geology of north-western Luzon. *Min. Eng. Mag.* **21,** 14-28. Manila.

Fernandez, N. S. 1960. Notes on the geology and chromite deposits of the Zambales range. *Philipp. Geol.* **14,** 1-8.

Fischer, A. G. & Heezen, B. C. 1969. Deep sea drilling project: Leg 6. *Geotimes,* **14,** 13.

Fischer, A. G., Heezen, B. C., Boyce, R. E., Bukry, D., Douglas, R. G., Garrison, R. E., Kling, S. A., Krasheninnikov, V., Lisitzin, A. P. & Pimm, A. C. 1970. Geological history of the Western North Pacific. *Science,* **168** (3936), 1210-14.

Fischer, A. G., Heezen, B. C., Lisitzin, A. P., Pimm, A. C., Garrison, R. E., Boyce, R. E., Kling, S. A., Bukry, D., Krasheninnikov, V. & Douglas, R. G. 1971. Initial reports of the Deep Sea Drilling Program. *U.S. Government Printing Office,* **6,** 1329 pp. Washington.

Fisher, N. H. 1957. *Catalogue of the Active Volcanoes of the World.* Part V. Catalogue of the active volcanoes and solfatara fields of Melanesia. *Int. volc. Assoc. Naples.*

Fisher, R. L. & Engel, C. G. 1969. Ultramafic and basaltic rocks dredged from the nearshore flanks of the Tonga Trench. *Bull geol. Soc. Am.* **80,** 1373-8.

Fitch, F. H. 1963. Geological relationship between the Philippines and Borneo. *Philipp. Geol.* **17,** 41-7.

Fitch, T. J. 1970. Earthquake mechanisms in the Himalayan, Burmese, and Andaman regions and continental tectonics in central Asia, *J. geophys. Res.* **75,** 2699.

Fitch, T. J. 1970. Earthquake mechanisms and island arc tectonics in the Indonesian-Philippine region. *Bull. seism. Soc. Am.* **60,** 565-91.

Fitch, T. J. & Molnar, P. 1970. Focal mechanisms along inclined earthquake zones in the Indonesian-Philippine region. *J. geophys. Res.* **75,** 1431-44.

Fleming, C. A. 1967. Biogeographic change related to Mesozoic orogenic history in the S.W. Pacific. *Tectonophysics,* **4** (4-6), 419-27.

——— 1970. The Mesozoic of New Zealand: Chapters in the history of the Circum-Pacific Mobile Belt. *J. geol. Soc. London*, **125,** 125.

Forbes, R. B. 1969. Dredged trachyte and basalt from Kodiak Seamount and the adjacent Aleutian Trench, Alaska. *Science*, **166,** 502-4.

Fotiadi, E. E., Berezin, M. A., Volkov, A. N., Livshits, M. Kh., Smirnov, L. M., Sychev, P. M., Tarakanov, R. Z., Tuyezov, I. K. & Shteinberg, G. S. 1969. Geophysical study of the inner zone deep structure of the Pacific mobile Belt in the east of the USSR. In *Structure and Development of the Earth's Crust in the Soviet Far East* (Eds E. E. Fotiadi & I. K. Tuyezov). Nauka Publ., Moscow (in Russian).

Fotiadi, E. E., Karataev, G. I. & Moiseenko, F. S. 1968. Some regularities in crustal structure and development from geophysical data by way of example in Siberia and the Far East. In *Earth's Crust and Upper Mantle* (Ed. V. V. Beloussov). Nauka Publ., Moscow (in Russian).

Fotiadi, E. E., Nikolaevsky, A. A., Kravchenko, Yu. V., Ryabov, A. V. & Shapochka, I. I. 1969. Geophysical study of tectonic structure and deep crustal structure of the outer Pacific mobile belt in the east of the USSR. In *Structure and Development of the Earth's Crust in the Soviet Far East* (Eds. E. E. Fotiadi & I. K. Tuyezov. Nauka Publ., Moscow (in Russian).

Fourmarier, P. 1971. *Problems of continental drift.* Mir, Moscow (in Russian).

Francheteau, J., Harrison, C. G. A., Sclater, J. G. & Richards, M. L. 1970. Magnetization of Pacific seamounts: a preliminary polar curve for the North-eastern Pacific. *J. geophys. Res.* **75,** 2035-61.

Frey, F. A., Haskin, M. A., Poetz, J. A. & Haskin, L. A. 1968. Rare earth abundances in some basic rocks. *J. geophys. Res.* **73,** 6085.

Fromager, D. 1968. Nouvelles données pétrographiques et structurales sur les massifs d'ultrabasites et leur contact avec les terrains sédimentaires entre la baie de Canala et la rivière Camboui (Nouvelle-Calédonie). *C.R. somm. Soc. Géol. Fr.* (1968), 83-4.

Fukada, A. 1953. A new species of Nerinea from central Hokkaido. *J. Fac. Sci. Hokkaido Univ.*, Ser. 4, **8,** 211-16.

Furdui, R. S. 1969. About Riphean deposits of the Omolonsky massif. *Dokl. Akad. Nauk SSSR*, **188** (1), 197-3 (in Russian).

Furumoto, A. S., Hussong, D. M., Campbell, J. F., Sutton, G. H., Malahoff, A., Ross, J. C. & Woollard, G. P. 1970. Crustal and upper mantle structure of the Solomon Islands as revealed by seismic refraction survey of November-December 1966. *Pacif. Sci.* **24,** 315-32.

Furumoto, A. S., Wiebenga, W. A., Webb, J. P. & Sutton, G. H. 1972. Crustal structure of the Hawaiian Archipelago, Northern Melanesia, and Central Pacific Basin by seismic refraction method. *Tectonophysics*. In press.

Gainanov, A. G., Isayev, E. N., Stroev, P. A. & Ushakov, S. A. 1970. Isostasy and lithosphere structure of the Bering Sea and the Aleutian Arc. In *Marine Gravimetric Investigations* (Ed. V. V. Fedynsky), Izdatelstvo MGU, Moscow, **5**, 32-40 (in Russian).

Gainanov, A. G., Kosminskaya, I. P. & Stroev, P.A. 1968. Geophysical investigation of deep structure of the Bering Sea. *Izv. Akad. Nauk SSSR, Fizika Zemli*, **8**, 3-11 (in Russian).

Gainanov, A. G., Pavlov, Yu. A., Stroev, P. A. & Tuyezov, I. K. 1972. *Anomalous gravity fields of the Far East marginal seas and the adjacent Pacific*. Nauka Publ., Novosibirsk (in Russian).

Gainanov, A. G., Zverev, S. M., Kosminskaya, I. P., Tulina, Yu. V., Livshitz, M. Kh., Sichev, P. M., Tuyezov, I. K., Fotiadi, E. E., Milashin, A. P., Soloviev, O. N. & Stroev, P. A. 1968. The crust and upper mantle in the transition zone from the Pacific Ocean to the Asiatic continent. In *The Crust and Upper Mantle of the Pacific Area* (Eds. L. Knopoff, C. L. Drake & P. J. Hart). *Am. Geophys. Un., Monogr.* **12,** 367-78.

Galperin, E. I. & Kosminskaya, I. P. (Eds.) 1964. *Crustal Structure in the Asia-to-Pacific Transition Zone*. Nauka Publ., Moscow (in Russian).

Gansser, A. 1966. The Indian Ocean and the Himalayas. *Eclog. geol. Helv.* **59,** 831-48.

Gardner, J. 1970. Submarine geology of the western Coral Sea. *Bull. geol. Soc. Am.* **81,** 2599-614.

Gass, I. G. 1968. Is the Troodos massif of Cyprus a fragment of Mesozoic ocean floor? *Nature*, **220,** 39-42.

Gast, P. W. 1967. Isotope geochemistry of volcanic rocks. In *Basalts: I* (Eds. H. Hess and A. Poldevaart), 325-58.
——— 1968. Trace element fractionation and the origin of tholeiitic and alkaline magma types. *Geochim. cosmochim. Acta*, **32,** 1057-86.

Gelman, M. L. & Terekhov, M. I. 1968. New data on Precambrian crystalline complex of the Omolonsky massif. In *Problems of Geology, Petrology and Metallogeny of the Metamorphic Complexes of East of the USSR* (Ed. A. M. Smirnov), pp. 30-1. Vladivostok (in Russian).

Gerasimov, I. P. & Mescheryakov, Yu. A. (Eds) 1967. *Relief of the Earth* (*Morphostructure and Morphosculpture*). Nauka Publ., Moscow (in Russian).

Gerasimova, I. A., Gusarov, B. M., Dylevsky, E. F., Kovalchuk, I. A. & Simakov, K. V. 1969. The Omolonsky block regional tectonics. In *Mesozoic Tectogenesis. Theses of reports of Scientific Council 7th Session on tectonics of Siberia and the Far East* (Eds N. F. Sokolovskaya & T. V. Umnova). Magadan (in Russian).

Gervasio, F. C. 1964. A study of the tectonics of the Philippine Archipelago. *22nd Intern. Geol. Congr., New Delhi, 1964, Proc.* **4,** 582-607.
——— 1967. Age and nature of orogenesis of the Philippines. *Tectonophysics*, **4,** 379-402.

Géze, B. 1963. Observations tectonique dans le Pacifique. (Hawaii, Tahiti, Nouvelles Hébrides). *Bull. Soc. geol. Fr.* 7e. Ser. **5,** 154-64.

Giletti, B. J. & Day, H. W. 1968. Potassium-argon ages of igneous intrusive rocks of Peru *Nature,* **220,** 570-2.

Gill, J. B. 1970. Geochemistry of Viti Levu, Fiji, and its evolution as an island arc. *Contr. Mineral. Petrol.* **27,** 179-203.

Gill, J. & Gorton, M. (This volume.) A proposed geological and geochemical history of eastern Melanesia.

Gilluly, J. 1957. Geologic contrasts between continents and oceanic basins. In *Crust of the Earth* (Ed. A. Poldervaart). Inostrannaya Literatura, Moscow (in Russian transl.).

Glaessner, M. F. 1950. Geotectonic position of New Guinea. *Bull. Am. Ass. Petrol. Geol.* **34** (5), 856-81.

——— 1952. Geology of Port Moresby, Papua. In *The Sir Douglas Mawson Anniversary Volume,* Univ. Adelaide.

Glasser, E. 1904. Rapport à M. le Ministre des Colonies sur les richesses minérales de la Nouvelle-Calédonie. *Annls Mines Carbur., Paris,* **5,** 503-620, 623-93.

Gnibidenko, H. S. 1964. On tectonics of the Khankaisky Middle massif. In *Materials on Tectonics and Petrology of the Pacific Ore Belt* (Eds N. P. Vassilkovsky & A. A. Marakushev). Nauka Publ., Moscow (in Russian).

——— 1969. *Metamorphic complexes in the structures of northwestern sector of the Pacific Belt.* Nauka Publ., Moscow (in Russian).

——— (Ed.) 1969. Metamorphic complexes of Sakhalin Island. *Trans. Sakhalin Complex Sci. Res. Inst. Yuzhno-Sakhalinsk,* **22** (in Russian).

——— 1970. Metamorphism role in geosynclinal process. In *Geology and Geophysics of the Pacific Belt* (Ed. H. S. Gnibidenko). *Trans. Sakhalin Complex Sci. Res. Inst. Novoalexandrovsk,* **25,** 12-17 (in Russian).

——— 1970. On the basement of the north-west sector of the Pacific Belt. *Tectonophysics,* **9** (6), 513-23.

Gnibidenko, H. S. & Shashkin, K. S. 1970. Basic principles of the geosynclinal theory. *Tectonophysics,* **9** (1), 5-13.

Gonord, H. 1967. Note sur quelques observations nouvelles précisant âge et mode de formation du flysch volcanique sur la côte sud-occidentale de la Nouvelle-Calédonie. *C.R. somm. Soc. Géol. Fr.* (1967), 287-9.

——— 1970. Découverte de formations sédimentaires d'âge éocène C (Eocène moyen à superieur) dans la châine centrale de la Nouvelle-Calédonie. *C.R. Acad. Sci. Paris,* **271,** 1953-5.

Gonord, H. & Bard, J. P. 1971. Découverte d'associations antésénoniennes à lawsonite, pumpellyite et glaucophane dans les 'masses cristallophyliennes' paléozoiques du centre de la Nouvelle-Calédonie. *C.R. Acad. Sci. Paris,* **273,** 280-3.

Gorai, M. 1968. Some geological problems in the development of Japan and the neighboring island arcs. In *The Crust and Upper Mantle of the Pacific Area* (Eds L. Knopoff, C. L. Drake & P. J. Hart). *Am. Geophys. Un., Geophys. Monogr.* **12,** 481-5.

Gorbov, V. V. & Zagruzina, I. A. 1970. Absolute age of metamorphic rocks of the Uyandinsky horst. *Kolyma*, **10,** 34-5. Magadan (in Russian).

Gorshkov, G. S. 1956. On the depth of magmatic hearth of Klyuchevskoy Volcano. *Dokl. Akad. Nauk SSSR*, **106** (4), 703-5 (in Russian).

——— 1958. On some theoretical problems of volcanology. *Bull. volcan.* (ser. 2), **19,** 103-13.

——— 1960. Quaternary volcanism and petrochemistry of recent lavas in the Kurile Island. In *Petrographic Provinces, Igneous and Metamorphic Rocks, Intern. Geol. Congr., XXI Session, Reports of Soviet Geologists, Problem 13*, 334-40; *Acad. Sci. USSR, Moscow* (in Russian with English summary).

——— 1962. Petrochemical features of volcanism in relation to the types of the Earth's crust. In *Crust of the Pacific Basin* (Eds G. A. Macdonald and H. Kuno), *Am. Geophys. Un., Geophys. Monogr.* **6,** 110-15.

——— 1963. Global characteristics of the petrochemistry of volcanic rocks and the main structure of the Earth. In *Petrochemical Characteristics of Young Volcanism*, 5-16 (in Russian).

——— 1965. On the relation of volcanism and the upper mantle. *Bull. volcan.* **28,** 159-67.

——— 1967. *Volcanism of the Kurile Island Arc*. Nauka Publ., Moscow, 287 pp. (in Russian).

——— 1969. Geophysics and petrochemistry of andesite volcanism of the Circum-Pacific belt. In *Proceedings of the Andesite Conference* (Ed. A. R. McBirney), *Bull. Ore. St. Dep. Geol. miner. Ind.* **65,** 91-8.

——— 1969. Intraoceanic islands, east Pacific Ridge, and island arcs: volcanism and upper mantle. *Tectonophysics*, **8,** 213-21.

——— 1969. Two types of alkaline rocks—two types of upper mantle. *Bull. volcan.* **33** (4), 1186-98.

——— 1970. *Volcanism and the Upper Mantle, Investigations in the Kurile Island Arc*. XV, 385 pp. Plenum Press, N.Y.

——— 1972. Progress and problems in volcanology. *Tectonophysics*, **13** (1-4), 123-40.

Graham, A. L. & Ringwood, A. E. 1971. Lunar-basalt genesis: the origin of the europium anomaly. *Earth Planet. Sci. Letters*, **12** (4), 105-15.

Grange, L. I. 1932. Taupo earthquakes, 1922. Rents and faults formed during earthquakes of 1922 in Taupo District. *N.Z. Jl Sci. Technol.* **19,** 65-144.

Grant, F. S. & West, C. F. 1965. *Interpretation theory in applied geophysics*. McGraw-Hill, New York.

Green, D. H. 1961. Ultramafic breccias from the Musa Valley, eastern Papua. *Geol. Mag.* **98** (1), 1-26.

——— 1970. The origin of basaltic and nephelinitic magmas. *Trans. Leicester lit. phil. Soc.* **64,** 28.

——— 1970. A review of experimental evidence on the origin of basaltic and nephelinitic magmas. *Phys. Earth Planet. Interiors*, **3,** 221-35.

——— 1971. Composition of basaltic magmas as indicators of conditions of origin: application to oceanic volcanism. *Phil. Trans. R. Soc. London* (A) **268,** 707-25.

Green, D. H. & Ringwood, A. E. 1967. The genesis of basaltic magmas. *Contr. Mineral Petrol.* **15** (2), 103-90.

Green, R. & Pitt, R. P. B. 1967. Suggested rotation of New Guinea. *J. Geomagn. Geoelect.* **19,** 317-21.

Green, T. 1972. Crystallization of calc-alkaline andesite under controlled high-pressure hydrous conditions. *Contr. Mineral. Petrol.* **34,** 150-66.

Green, T. H., Green, D. H. & Ringwood, A. E. 1967. The origin of high alumina basalts and their relationships to quartz tholeiites and alkali basalts. *Earth Planet. Sci. Letters,* **2,** 41-51.

Green. T. H. & Ringwood, A. E. 1968. Genesis of the calc-alkaline igneous rock suite. *Contr. Mineral. Petrol.* **18,** 105.

——— 1969. High pressure experimental studies on the origin of andesites. In *Proceedings of the Andesite Conference* (Ed. A. R. McBirney), *Bull. Ore. St. Dep. Geol. miner. Ind.* **65,** 21-32.

——— (In prep.) Crystallization of garnet-bearing rhyodacite under high pressure hydrous conditions.

Grey, R. R. 1967. Time-stratigraphic correlation of Tertiary rocks in the Philippines. *Philipp. Geol.* **21,** 1-21.

Griffin, W. L. & Murthy, V. R. 1969. Distribution of K, Rb, Sr and Ba in some minerals relevant to basalt genesis. *Geochim. cosmochim. Acta,* **33,** 1389-414.

Griffiths, J. R. & Varne, R. 1972. Evolution of the Tasman Sea, Macquarie Ridge and Alpine fault. *Nature.* (*Phys. Sci.*) **235,** 83-6.

Grossling, B. F. 1967. The internal magnetization of seamounts and its computer calculation. *U.S. geol. Surv. Prof. Pap. 554-F.*

Grover, J. C. 1968. The British Solomon Islands: some geological implications of the gravity data, 1966. In *The Crust and Upper Mantle of the Pacific area. Am. Geophys. Un., Geophys. Monogr.* **12,** 296-306.

Grow, J. A. & Atwater, Tanya. 1970. Mid-Tertiary tectonic transition in the Aleutian Arc. *Bull. geol. Soc. Am.* **81,** 3715.

Grow, J. A., Spiess, F. N. & Mudie, J. D. 1971. Near-bottom geophysical measurements from Aleutian Trench near 173° W (Abstract). *EOS Trans. Am. geophys. Un.* **52** (4), 246.

Guillon, J. H. 1969. Données nouvelles sur la composition et la structure du grand massif péridotitique du Sud de la Nouvelle-Calédonie. *Cah. Géol. ORSTOM,* **1** (1), 7-25, Paris.

——— (In press.) Geology of New Caledonia and Loyalty islands. In *Data for Orogenic Studies,* Geol. Soc. London.

Guillon, J. H. & Routhier, P. 1971. Les stades d'évolution et de mise en place des massifs ultramafiques de Nouvelle-Calédonie. *Bull. Bur. Rech. Geol. Min.* **4** (2).

Gurariy, G. Z., Kropotkin, P. N., Pevzner, M. A., Ro Vu Son & Trubikhin, V. M. 1966. Laboratory evaluation of the usefulness of North Korean sedimentary rocks for palaeomagnetic studies. *Izv. Akad. Nauk. SSSR, Earth Phys. Ser.* 128-36.

Gutenberg, B. & Richter, C. F. 1954. *Seismicity of the Earth and Associated Phenomena.* Princeton University Press, Princeton, New York. 310 pp.

Hackman, B. D. 1968. The geology of east and central Guadalcanal: a preliminary statement, 1966. *Geol. Rec. Br. Solomon Isl.* **3,** 16-25.

——— 1971. The regional geology of Guadalcanal: a contribution to the geology of fractured island arcs. Ph.D. thesis, Univ. W. Australia.

——— 1971. The Solomon Islands fractured arc. *12th Pacific Sci. Congr. Rec. Proc.* (Abstracts), **1,** 366. See also this volume.

Haile, N. S. 1963. The Cretaceous-Cenozoic northwest Borneo geosyncline. *Bull. geol. Surv. Br. Borneo.* **4,** 1-18.

——— 1970. Notes on the geology of the Tambelan Anambas and Bunguran (Natuna) Islands, Sunda Shelf, Indonesia, including radiometric age determinations. *Econ. Comm. Asia & Far East* (*ECAFE*) *CCOP, Tech. Bull.* **3,** 55-90.

——— 1971. Confirmation of Late Cretaceous age for granite from the Bunguran and Anambas islands, Sunda Shelf, Indonesia. *Geol. Soc. Malaysia, Newsletter*, No. 30, 6-8.

Hamilton, W. 1969. The volcanic central Andes, a modern model for the Cretaceous batholiths and tectonics of western North America. *Bull. Ore. St. Dep. Geol. miner. Ind.* **65,** 175-84.

——— 1969. Mesozoic California and the underflow of Pacific mantle. *Bull. geol. Soc. Am.* **80,** 2409-30.

——— 1970. The Uralides and the motion of the Russian and Siberian platforms. *Bull. geol. Soc. Am.* **81,** 2553-76.

——— 1970. Tectonic Map of Indonesia, a progress report. *U.S. Geol. Surv.* Denver, Colorado, 29 pp.

Hammond, W. T., Hilde, T. W. C., Hulseman, J., Jarvela, L. E., Little, L., Osterhagen, J. H., Searcy, III, W. P. & Wageman, J. M. (In press.) Sea of Japan, oceanography and geophysics. *U.S. Naval Oceanographic Office, spec. publ.* 133-18-1.

Harland, W. B. 1967. Geosynclines. *Geol. Mag.* **104,** 182-8.

Harloff, C. E. A. 1929. Voorlopige mededeling over de geologie van het Pratertiair van Loh Oelo in Midden Java. *De Mijningenieur*, **10** (8), 172-7.

Harrington, H. J. 1965. Geology and morphology of Antarctica. *Monographiae Biologicae*, **15,** 1.

Harrison, J. 1969. Review of the sedimentary history of the island of New Guinea. *J. Aust. Petrol. Expl. Ass.* **9,** 41-8.

Hart, S. R. 1971. K, Rb, Cs, Sr, and Ba contents and Sr isotope ratios of ocean-floor basalts. *Phil Trans. R. Soc. London* (A), **268,** 573-87.

Hart, S. R. & Brooks, C. 1970. Rb-Sr mantle evolution models. *Carnegie Inst. Year Book*, **69,** 426-9.

Hart, S. R., Brooks, C., Krogh, T. E., Davis, G. L. & Nava, D. 1970. Ancient and modern volcanic rocks: a trace element model. *Earth Planet. Sci. Letters*, **10,** 17-28.

Hart, S., Glassley, E. E. & Karig, D. E. (In press.) Basalts and sea-floor spreading behind the Marianas island arc. *Earth Planet. Sci. Letters.*

Hart, S. R. & Nalwalk, A. J. 1970 K, Rb, Cs and Sr relationships in submarine basalts from the Puerto Rico trench. *Geochim. cosmochim. Acta*, **34,** 145-56.

Hasebe, K., Fujii, N. & Uyeda, S. 1970. Thermal processes under island arcs. In *Geothermal Problems* (Eds S. Uyeda & A. M. Jessop). *Tectonophysics*, **10** (1-3), 335-55.

Hashimoto, I. 1961. Stratigraphic sequence and geologic structure in the neighbourhood of Nobeoka city, Miyazaki Prefecture. *Rept Earth Sci., Dept. General Educ., Kyushu Univ.* **7,** 37-57 (in Japanese).

Hashimoto, W. 1951. Submarine morphology of the Philippine Archipelago and its geological significance. *Philipp. J. Sci.* **80,** 55-88.

——— 1969. Paleontology of the Philippines. *Geology and Palaeontology of Southeast Asia*, **6.** 293-329 (Eds T. Kobayashi & R. Toriyama). Univ. Tokyo Press, Tokyo.

Hashimoto, W. & Sato, T. 1968. Contribution to the geology of Mindoro and neighbouring islands, the Philippines. In *Geology and Palaeontology of Southeast Asia*, **5,** 192-210 (Eds T. Kobayashi & R. Toriyama). Univ. Tokyo Press, Tokyo.

Haskell, N. A. 1953. The dispersion of surface waves in multi-layered media. *Bull. seism. Soc. Am.* **43,** 17-34.

Hatherton, T. 1969. Gravity and seismicity of asymmetric active regions. *Nature*, **221,** 353-5.

——— 1969. Similarity of gravity anomaly patterns in asymmetric active regions. *Nature*, **224,** 357-8.

——— 1969. The geophysical significance of calc-alkaline andesites in New Zealand. *N.Z. Jl Geol. Geophys.* **12,** 436-59.

Hatherton, T. & Dickinson, W. R. 1969. The relationship between andesitic volcanism and seismicity in Indonesia, The Lesser Antilles, and other island arcs. *J. geophys. Res.* **74,** 5301-10.

Haug, E. 1900. Les géosynclinaux et les aires continentales contribution a l'etude des transgressions et des regressions marines. *Bull. Soc. géol. Fr.* ser 3, **28,** 617-710.

Hayes, D. E. & Pitman, W. C. 1970. Magnetic lineations in the north Pacific. *Mem. geol. Soc. Am.* **126,** 291.

Hayes, D. E. & Pitman III, W. C. 1970. A review of marine geophysical observations in the Southern Ocean. *Proc. SCAR* (*Scient. Comm. Antarctic Res.*), *Oslo*.

Hayes, D. E. & Ringis, J. 1972. The early opening of the central Tasman Sea (abstract) *Int. Symposium on Oceanography of the South Pacific*, Wellington, N.Z.

Hayes, E. E., Talwani, M. & Christoffel, D. A. 1970. The Macquarie Ridge complex. *Proc. SCAR* (*Scient. Comm. Antarctic Res.*), *Oslo*.

Hedge, C. & Walthall, F. 1963. Radiogenic Sr^{87} as an index of geologic processes. *Science*, **140,** 1214-17.

Hedge, C. E. 1966. Variations in radiogenic strontium found in volcanic rocks. *J. geophys. Res.* **71,** 6119-20.

Hedge, C. E. & Knight, R. J. 1969. Lead and strontium isotopes in volcanic rocks from northern Honshu, Japan. *Geochem. J.* **3,** 15-24.

Hedge, C. E. & Peterman, Z. E. 1970. The strontium isotopic composition of basalts from the Gordo and Juan de Iuca Rises, northeastern Pacific Ocean. *Contr. Mineral. Petrol.* **27,** 114-20.

Heirtzler, J. R., Dickson, G. O., Herron, E. M., Pitman, III, W. C. & Le Pichon, X. 1968. Marine magnetic anomalies, geomagnetic field reversals, and motions of the ocean floor and continents. *J. geophys. Res.* **73,** 2119-36.

Henderson, J. 1932. Earthquakes in New Zealand. *N.Z. Jl Sci. Technol.* **14,** 129-39.
——— 1933. The geological aspects of the Hawke's Bay earthquakes. *N.Z. Jl Sci. Technol.* **15,** 38-75.
——— 1937. The West Nelson earthquakes of 1929. *N.Z. Jl Sci. Technol.* **15,** 38-75.

Herron, E. M. 1971. Crustal plates and sea-floor spreading in the southeastern Pacific. *Antarct. Res. Ser.* **15,** 229.

Hess, H. H. 1962. History of the ocean basins. In *Petrologic Studies*, *Buddington Volume*, 599-620, Geol. Soc. Am., New York.

Hess, H. H. & Maxwell, J. C. 1953. Major structural features of the South-west Pacific—a preliminary interpretation of H.O. 5484 bathymetry chart, New Guinea to New Zealand. *Proc. Pacif. Sci. Congr.*, *Wellington*, *New Zealand*, **2,** 14-17.

Hilde, T. W. C., Wageman, J. M. & Hammond, W. T. 1969. Sea of Japan structure from seismic reflection data. *EOS Trans. Am. Geophys. Un.* (1969 meeting—abstract). **50** (4), 208.
——— 1969. The structure of Tosa Terrace and Nankai Trough off south eastern Japan. *Deep Sea Res.* **16,** 67-75.

Hill, D. & Denmead, A. K. 1960. The geology of Queensland. *J. geol. Soc. Aust.* **7.**

Hindle, W. (In prep.). The Geology of west-central Vanua Levu. *Bull. geol. Surv. Fiji*, **19.**

Hirst, J. A. 1965. Geology of East and North-East Viti Levu. *Bull. geol. Surv. Fiji*, **12,** 51 pp.

Ho, C. S. 1967. Structural evolution of Taiwan. *Tectonophysics*, **4** (4-6), 367-78.

Hochstein, M. P. 1967. Interpretation of magnetic anomalies across Norfolk Ridge. *N.Z. Jl Geol. Geophys.* **10,** 1302-8.
——— 1967. Seismic measurements in the Cook Islands, South-west Pacific Ocean. *N.Z. Jl Geol. Geophys.* **10,** 1499-526.

Hoffmeister, J. E. 1932. Geology of Eua, Tonga. *Bull. Bernice P. Bishop Mus.* **96,** 93 pp.

Hohnen, P. D. 1970. Geology of New Ireland. Rec. Bur. Miner. Resour. Aust. 1970/49 (unpubl.).

Hopkins, D. W., Scholl, D. W., Addicott, W. O., Pierce, R. L., Smith, R. B., Wolfe, J. A., Gershanovich, D., Kotenev, B., Lohman, K. E., Lipps, J. H. & Obradovich, J. 1969. Cretaceous, Tertiary, and Early Pleistocene rocks from the continental margin in the Bering Sea. *Bull. geol. Soc. Am.* **80** (8), 1471-80.

Horn, D. R., Delach, M. N. & Horn, B. M. 1969. Distribution of volcanic ash layers and turbidites in the north Pacific. *Bull. geol. Soc. Am.* **80** (9), 1715-23.

Hoshino, M. 1967. Deep-sea terraces. *Fac. Oceanography Publ., Tokai Univ.* **2,** 57-84.

Hoshino, M. & Hotta, H. 1966. Geology of submarine banks in the Japan Sea. *Earth Science (J. Assoc. Geol. Collaboration in Japan)*, **82,** 10-16 (in Japanese).

Hotta, H. 1967. The structure of sedimentary layer in the Japan Sea. *Geophys. Bull., Hokkaido Univ.* **18,** 111-31 (in Japanese).

Houtz, R. E. 1959. Regional Geology of Lomawai-Momi-Nandroga, Viti-Levu. *Bull. geol. Surv. Fiji*, **3,** 20 pp.
——— 1960. Geology of Singatoka Area—Viti Levu. *Bull. geol. Surv. Fiji*, **6,** 19 pp.
——— 1963. Regional Geology—Keiyasi Area. *Bull. geol. Surv. Fiji*, **10,** 13 pp.

Houtz, R., Ewing, J., Ewing, M. & Lonardi, A. G. 1967. Seismic reflection profiles of the New Zealand plateau. *J. geophys. Res.* **72,** 4713-29.

Huntec Limited, Toronto, Canada. 1968. Report of the offshore geophysical survey in the Pohang area, Republic of Korea. *Econ. Comm. Asia & Far East* (ECAFE), CCOP, *Tech. Bull.* **1,** 1-12.

Hurley, P. M. & Rand, R. J. 1969. Pre-drift continental nucleii. *Science*, **164,** 1229-42.

Hutchison, C. S. 1968. Dating tectonism in the Indosinian-Thai-Malayan orogen by thermo-luminescence. *Bull. geol. Soc. Am.* **79,** 375-86.

Hutchinson, W. W. 1970. Metamorphic framework and plutonic styles in the Prince Rupert region of the central Coast Mountains, British Columbia. *Can. J. Earth Sci.* **7,** 376-405.

Ibbotson, P. 1969. The Geology of East-central Vanua Levu. *Bull. geol. Surv. Fiji*, **16,** 44 pp.

Ichikawa, K., Murakami, N., Hase, A. & Wadatsumi, K. 1968. Late Mesozoic igneous activity in the inner side of southwest Japan. *Pacific Geol.* **1,** 97-118.

Igo, H. 1961. On the disconformity and aluminaceous shales of the Carboniferous Ichinotani formation, Hida massif. *J. geol. Soc. Japan*, **67,** 261-73 (in Japanese).

Imai, H. 1963. Pre-Tertiary igneous activity, metamorphism and metallogenesis. In *Geology of Japan* (Eds F. Takai, T. Matsumoto & R. Toriyama). Univ. Tokyo Press, Tokyo.

Irving, E. 1964. *Paleomagnetism and its application to geological and geophysical problems.* Wiley and Sons, New York.

Irving, E. M. 1952. Geological history and petroleum possibilities of the Philippines. *Bull. Am. Ass. Petrol. Geol.* **36** (3), 437-76.

Isacks, B. & Molnar, P. 1971. Distribution of stresses in the descending lithosphere from a global survey of focal-mechanism solutions of mantle earthquakes. *Rev. Geophys. Space Phys.* **9,** 103.

Isacks, B., Oliver, J. & Sykes, L. R. 1968. Seismology and the new global tectonics. *J. geophys. Res.* **73,** 5855-99.

Isacks. B., Sykes, L. R. & Oliver, J. 1969. Focal mechanisms of deep and shallow earthquakes in the Tonga-Kermadec region and the tectonics of island arcs. *Bull. geol. Soc. Am.* **80,** 1443-70.

Isezaki, N., Hata, K. & Uyeda, S. 1971. Magnetic survey of the Japan Sea (Part 1). *Bull. Earthq. Res. Inst. Tokyo Univ.* **49,** 77-83.

Jacobs, K. H. 1970. Three-dimensional seismic ray tracing in a laterally heterogeneous spherical earth. *J. geophys. Res.* **75** (32), 6675-89.

Jakeš, P. & Gill, J. 1970. Rare earth elements and the island arc tholeiitic series. *Earth Planet. Sci. Letters*, **9,** 17-28.

Jakeš, P. & Smith, I. E. 1970. High-K calc-alkaline rocks from Cape Nelson, eastern Papua. *Contr. Mineral. Petrol.* **28,** 259.

Jakeš, P. & White, A. J. R. 1969. Structure of the Melanesian arcs and correlation with distribution of magma types. *Tectonophysics*, **8,** 223-36.
——— 1970. K/Rb ratios of rocks from island arcs. *Geochim. cosmochim. Acta*, **34,** 849-56.

James, D. E. 1971. A plate tectonic model for the evolution of the central Andes. *Bull. geol. Soc. Am.* **82,** 3325-46.

Jenkins, D. A. L. & Martin, A. J. 1969. Recent investigations into the geology of the Southern Highlands, Papua. *Econ. Comm. Asia & Far East* (*ECAFE*). 4th Symposium on the development of petroleum resources of Asia and the Far East, Canberra, Australia.

John, V. P. St. 1970. The gravity field and structure of Papua and New Guinea. *J. Aust. Petrol. Expl. Assoc.* **10,** 41-54.

Johnson, D. A. 1971. Studies of deep-sea erosion using deep-towed instrumentation. Thesis, Univ. Calif., San Diego, Marine Physical Lab. Scripps Instit. Oceanography, San Diego, California 92152 (SIO Reference 71-21, 1 September 1971).
——— (In prep.) Ocean floor erosion in the equatorial Pacific.

Johnson, R. W., Mackenzie, D. E. & Smith, I. E. 1970. Short papers on Quaternary volcanic areas in Papua-New Guinea. *Rec. Bur. Miner. Resour. Geol. Geophys. Aust.* 1970/72, 17 p.
——— 1971. Seismicity and late Cainozoic volcanism in parts of Papua-New Guinea. *Tectonophysics*, **12,** 15.

Johnson, R. W., Mackenzie, D. E., Smith, I. E. & Taylor, G. A. M. 1972. Distribution and petrology of Late Cenozoic volcanoes in Papua New Guinea. This volume.

Johnson, T. & Molnar, P. 1972. Focal mechanisms and tectonics of the New Guinea, New Britain, Solomons, New Hebrides, and Tonga-Kermadec areas, New Zealand and the Macquarie ridge. (In prep.).

Joplin, G. A. 1968. The shoshonite association: A review. *J. geol. Soc. Aust.* **15,** 275.

Kanamori, H. 1970. Mantle beneath the Japanese arc. *Phys. Earth Planet. Inter.* **3,** 475-83.

Kaneko, S. 1966. Transcurrent displacement along the median line of south-western Japan. *N.Z. Jl Geol. Geophys.* **9,** 45-59.

Kaneoka, I. & Ozima, M. 1970. On the radiometric ages of volcanic rocks from Japan. *Volcano*, **2** (15), 10-21 (in Japanese).

Kanmera, K. 1971. Palaeozoic and early Mesozoic geosynclinal volcanicity in Japan. *Mem. geol. Soc. Japan*, **6,** 97-110 (in Japanese).

Kanmera, K. & Nakazawa, K. 1968. Review of the history and present status of studies on the Mesozoic and Palaeozoic systems, and some problems of geosynclines in Japan. *Geological Sciences in Japan—Past, Present and Future*, 33-57 (in Japanese). Geol. Soc. Japan (75th Anniv. vol.).

Karig, D. E. 1970. Ridges and basins of the Tonga-Kermadec island arc system. *J. geophys. Res.* **75,** 239-55.
——— 1971. Structural History of the Mariana island arc system. *Bull. geol. Soc. Am.* **82,** 323-44.
——— 1971. Origin and development of marginal basins in the Western Pacific. *J. geophys. Res.* **76,** 2542-61.
——— 1972. Remnant Arcs. *Bull. geol. Soc. Am.* **83,** 1057-68.

Karig, D. E. & Mammerickx, J. 1972. Tectonic framework of the New Hebrides Island arc. *Marine Geology*. **12,** 187-205.

Kaseno, Y. & Omura, A. 1969. On the core samples collected by M. R. V. *Seifu Maru* from the Japan Sea floor in 1966 and 1967. *Bull. Japan Sea Res. Inst., Kanazawa Univ.* **1,** 35-8 (in Japanese).

Katili, J. A. 1962. On the age of the granitic rocks in relation to the structural features of Sumatra. In *Crust of the Pacific basin. Monogr. Am. Geophys. Un., Geophys. Monogr.* **6,** 116-21. Washington, D.C.

——— 1967. Structure and age of the Indonesian tin belt with special reference to Bangka. *Tectonophysics*, **4,** 403-18.

——— 1969. Permian volcanism and its relation to the tectonic development of Sumatra. *Bull, volcan.* **33** (2), 530-40.

——— 1970. Large transcurrent faults in South-east Asia with special reference to Indonesia. *Geol. Rundsch.* **59** (2), 581-600.

——— 1971. A review of geotectonic theories and tectonic maps of Indonesia. *Earth Sci. Rev.* **7,** 143-63.

——— 1971. Additional evidence of transcurrent faulting in Sumatra and Sulawesi. *Bull. Nat. Inst. Geol. Mining.* **3** (3), 15-28. Bandung.

Katili, J. A. & Hehuwat, F. 1967. On the occurence of large transcurrent faults in Sumatra, Indonesia. *J. Geosci. Osaka City Univ.* **10,** 5-17.

Katili, J. A., Kartaadiputra, L. & Surjo. 1960. Magma type and tectonic position of the Una-Una island, Indonesia. *Bull. volcan.* **26,** 431-54.

Katili, J. A. & Soetadi, R. 1971. Neotectonics and seismic zones of Indonesia. *Bull. Proc. R. Soc. N.Z.* **9,** 39-45.

Katili, J. A. & Tjia, H. D. 1969. Outline of Quaternary tectonics of Indonesia. *Bull. Nat. Inst. Geol. Mining*, **2** (1), 1-10. Bandung.

Katsui, Y. 1959. Chemical compositions of the lavas from Quaternary volcanoes of Hokkaido. *Bull. geol. Comm. Hokkaido* **38,** 27-47 (in Japanese).

——— 1961. Petrochemistry of the Quaternary volcanic rocks of Hokkaido and surrounding areas. *J. Fac. Sci. Hokkaido Univ.* (Ser. 4) **11,** 1-58.

Katsumata, M. & Sykes, L. R. 1969. Seismicity and tectonics of the western Pacific-Izu-Mariana-Caroline and Ryukyu-Taiwan regions. *J. geophys. Res.* **74,** 5923-48.

Kawai, N., Hirooka, K. & Nakajima, T. 1969. Palaeomagnetic and Potassium-Argon age information supporting Cretaceous-Tertiary hypothetic bending of the main island of Japan. *Palaeogeog. Palaeoclim. Palaeoecol.* **6,** 277-82.

Kawai, N., Ito, H. and Kume, S. 1961. Deformation of the Japanese islands as inferred from rock magnetism. *Geophys. J. R. astr. Soc.* **6,** 124-9.

Kawano, Y. & Ueda, Y. 1967. Periods of igneous activities of granitic rocks in Japan by K-A dating method. *Tectonophysics*, **4,** 523-30.

Kay, R., Hubbard, N. J. & Gast, P. W. 1970. Chemical characteristics and origin of ocean ridge volcanic rocks. *J. geophys. Res.* **75,** 1585.

Khain, V. E. 1969. Metamorphic regeneration of areas of recurrent orogenesis and the problem of neo-formation of oceanic basins. *Geotektonika,* **3** (in Russian).

Kheraskov, N. P. 1963. Some generalizations on formation and development of the structure of the earth crust. *Trans. Geol. Inst. Akad. Nauk SSSR,* **91** (in Russian).

Khramov, A. N. & Sholpo, L. Ye. 1967. Synoptic tables of U.S.S.R. paleomagnetic data. Appendix I of *Paleomagnetism* (Nedra Publ., Leningrad) pp. 213-33 (translated by E. R. Hope, Directorate of Scientific Information Services, DRB Canada T510R, 1970).

Kienle, Jurgen. 1971. Gravity and magnetic measurements over Bowers Ridge and Shirshov Ridge, Bering Sea. *J. geophys. Res.* **76,** 7138-80.

Kimura, T. 1960. On the geologic structure of the Palaeozoic group in Chugoku, West Japan. *Sci. Papers Coll. General Educ., Univ. Tokyo,* **10,** 109-24.

——— 1961. The Akaishi tectonic line, in the eastern part of Southwest Japan. *Jap. J. Geol. Geogr.* **32,** 119-36.

——— 1961. The lateral faulting and geologic structure of the eastern part of Southwest Japan. *Jap. J. Geol. Geogr.* **32,** 317-30.

——— 1967. Structural division of Japan and the Honshu arc. *Jap. J. Geol. Geogr.* **38,** 117-31.

——— 1968. Some folded structures and their distribution in Japan. *Jap. J. Geol. Geogr.* **39,** 1-26.

——— 1969. The phases and cycles of the orogenic movements. *J. Geogr., Tokyo,* **78,** 299-340 (in Japanese).

Kimura, T. & Tokuyama, A. 1971. Geosynclinal prisms and tectonics in Japan. *Mem. geol. Soc. Japan,* **6,** 9-20.

Kimura, T., Tokuyama, A., Gonzales, B. A. & Andal, D. R. 1968. Geologic structures in the Tayabas Isthmus district, Philippines. *Geology and Palaeontology of Southeast Asia.* **4,** 156-78. Univ. Tokyo Press, Tokyo.

Kitano, K. 1970. Alkaline basalts from the Erimo seamount. *J. geol. Soc. Japan,* **76,** 399-404 (in Japanese).

Klompe, Th. H. F. 1957. Pacific and Variscian Orogeny in Indonesia, a structural synthesis. *Proc. 9th Pacif. Sci. Congr.* **12,** 76-115.

——— 1962. Igneous and structural features of Thailand. In *Crust of the Pacific basin. Am. Geophys. Un., Geophys. Monogr.* **6,** 122-134, Washington, D.C.

Klompe, Th. H. F., Katili, J., Johannas & Soekendar, 1957. Late Paleozoic-Early Mesozoic volcanic activity in the Sunda Land area. *Proc. 9th Pacif. Sci. Congr.* **12,** 204-17.

Knipper, A. L. 1971. Gabbroic rocks of the ophiolitic 'formation' in the geological record of the oceanic crust. *Geotektonika,* **2** (in Russian).

——— 1971. History and evolution of the serpentinite melange of Lesser Caucasus. *Geotectonika,* **6** (in Russian).

Kobayashi, T. 1941. The Sakawa orogenic cycles and its bearing on the origin of the Japanese Islands. *J. Fac. Sci., Tokyo Univ.* **5,** 219-578.

——— 1956. A contribution to the geo-tectonics of North Korea and South Manchuria. *J. Fac. Sci., Tokyo Univ.* **10,** 133-311.

——— 1956. The shifting of the chert bearing facies caused by the migration of geosyncline. *Konikl. Nederland. Geol. Mijinb. Genoot. Verh.* **16,** 1-11.

——— 1959. Geology of Korea and the adjacent China territory. Inostrannaya Literatura, Moscow (in Russian transl.).

Kobayashi, T., Hujita, A. & Kimura, T. 1945. On the geology of the central part of southern Shikoku. *Jap. J. Geol. Geogr.* **20,** 19-45.

Koch, R. A. 1967. Zum Wesen des Grundpostulats der Geologie. *Philos. natur.* **10** (1), 102-6.

Kochergin, E. V., Krasny, M. L., Sychev, P. M. & Tuyezov, I. K. 1970. Anomalous geomagnetic field of north-western part of the Pacific mobile belt and its relation to the tectonic structure. *Geol. i Geofiz.* **12,** 77-9 (in Russian).

Koesoemadinata, R. P. 1969. Outline of the geologic occurence of oil in Tertiary basins of West Indonesian. *Bull. Am. Ass. Petrol. Geol.* **53** (11), 2368-76.

Koike, K., Watanabe, K. & Igo, H. 1970. Triassic conodont biostratigraphy in Japan. *J. geol. Soc. Japan*, **76,** 261-9 (in Japanese).

Konishi, K. 1965. Geotectonic framework of the Ryukyu Islands (Nansei-Shoto). *J. geol. Soc. Japan*, **71,** 437-57.

Korringa, M. K. & Noble, D. C. 1970. Feldspar-liquid partition coefficients for Sr and Ba based on a Rayleigh fractionation model. *Geol. Soc. Am. Ann. Meeting*, p. 598 (Abstract).

Korzhuyev, S. S. 1969. The role of the Kolymsky middle massif in the formation of North-East Asia morphostructure. In *Geography and Geomorphology of Asia* (Eds Yu. A. Meshcheryakov & S. S. Korzhuyev). Nauka Publ., Moscow (in Russian).

Kosminskaya, I. P., Zverev, S. M., Tulina, Yu. V. & Krakshina, R. M. 1963. Main structural features of the crust of the Sea of Okhotsk and the Kurile-Kamchatka zone of the Pacific Ocean according to deep seismic sounding. *Izv. AN SSSR, Ser. Geol.* **1** (in Russian).

Kovylin, V. M. 1966. Results of seismic studies in the southwest of the Sea of Japan abyssal basin. *Oceanology*, **6** (2), 238-49 (in Russian).

Kovylin, V. M., Karp, B. Ya. & Shayakhmentov, R. B. 1966. The structure of earth's crust and sedimentary strata of the Japan Sea from seismic data. *Dokl. Akad. Nauk SSSR*, **168** (5), 1048-51 (in Russian).

Kovylin, V. M. & Neprochnov, Y. P. 1965. Crustal structure and sedimentary layer in the central part of the Japan Sea derived from seismic data. *Izv. Akad. Nauk SSSR (geol.)* **4,** 10-26 (in Russian).

Kovylin, V. M., Shayakhmentov, R. B. & Mouravova, E. A. 1971. The sedimentary strata and underlying basement structure in the vicinity of conjugation of Korea continental crust and the oceanic Japanese basin crust. *Izv. Akad. Nauk SSSR* (*geol.*), **5,** 125-8 (in Russian).

Krasny, L. I. (Ed.) 1966. *Geologic structure of the North-western Pacific mobile belt.* Nedra Publ., Moscow (in Russian).

——— (Ed.) 1966. Khabarovsky and Amurskaya regions. I—Geologic Description. In *Geology of the USSR,* **19,** Nedra Publ., Moscow (in Russian).

Kraus, E. 1951. *Vergleichende Baugeschichte der Gebirge.* Akad.-Verlag, Berlin, 588 pp.

Krause, D. C. 1967. Bathymetry and geologic structure of the north-western Tasman Sea—Coral Sea-south Solomon Sea area of the south-western Pacific Ocean. *Mem. N.Z. oceanogr. Inst.* **41,** 48 pp.

Krummenacher, D. & Noetzlin, J. 1966. Ages isotopique K/A de roches prélevées dans les possessions françaises du Pacifique. *Bull. Soc. géol. Fr.* (Sér. 7), **8,** 173-5.

Kuenen, Ph. H. 1935. Geological interpretation of the bathymetrical results. Sci. Results Snellius Expedition Eastern Pt (East Indian Archipelago), 1929-30, **5** (1), 124 pp.

Kummer, J. T. & Creager, J. S. 1971. Marine geology and Cenozoic history of the Gulf of Anadyr. *Marine Geology,* **10** (4), 257-80.

Kuno, H. 1950. Petrology of Hakone volcano and the adjacent areas, Japan. *Bull. geol. Soc. Am.* **61,** 957.

——— 1956. Genetical system of igneous rocks and its relation to crustal and subcrustal structures in Japan. *Science, Tokyo,* **26,** 19-22 (in Japanese).

——— 1959. Origin of Cenozoic petrographic provinces of Japan and surrounding areas. *Bull. volcan.* **20,** 37-76.

——— 1966. Lateral variation of basalt magma type across continental margins and island arcs. *Bull. volcan.* **29,** 195-222.

——— 1968. Differentiation of basalt magmas. In *Basalts. The Poldervaart treatise on rocks of basaltic composition* (Eds. H. H. Hess and A. Poldervaart). **2,** 623. Wiley and Sons, New York.

Kurasawa, H. 1970. Strontium and lead isotopes of volcanic rocks in Japan. In *Recent Developments in Mass Spectroscopy* (Eds K. Ogata and T. Hayakawa), pp. 666-70. Proc. Int. Conf. Mass Spectroscopy, Kyoto, Japan. Univ. Park Press, Baltimore.

Kuroda, V., Iizumi, S. & Tazaki, K. 1971. On some problems in origin of the Alpine type ultramafic rocks (Abstract) *Int. Geochem. Congr.* (Moscow), **1,** 65-6.

Kushiro, I. 1965. The liquidus relations in the systems forsterite-$CaAl_2SiO_6$-silica and forsterite-nepheline-silica at high pressures. *Carnegie Inst., Ann. Rept. Director, geophys. Lab.* (*1964-65*), 103-9.

——— 1968. Compositions of magmas formed by partial zone melting of the earth's upper mantle. *J. geophys. Res.* **73,** 619-34.

Kushiro, I., Yoder, H. S. & Nishikawa, M. 1968. Effect of water on the melting of enstatite. *Bull. geol. Soc. Am.* **79,** 1685-92.

Lacroix, A. 1941. Composition minéralogique et chimique des laves des volcans des îles de l'Océan Pacifique situées entre l'equateur et le tropique de Capricorne, le 175° de longitude ouest et le 165° de longitude est. *Mém. Acad. Sci. Paris,* **63,** 97 pp.

——— 1942. Les péridotides de la Nouvelle-Calédonie, leurs serpentines et leurs gites de nickel et de cobalt. Les gabbros qui les accompagnent. *Mém. Acad. Sci.* (2nd sér.) **66,** 1-14.

Ladd, H. S. 1970. Eocene mollusks from Eua, Tonga. *U.S. geol. Surv. Prof. Pap.* **640**-C, 12 pp.

Ladd, H. S. & Hoffmeister, J. E. 1945. Geology of Lau, Fiji. *Bull. Bernice P. Bishop Mus.* **181.**

Larson, R. L. 1970. Near-bottom studies of the east Pacific Rice Crest and tectonics of the Gulf of California. Thesis, Univ. Calif., San Diego, Marine Physical Lab. Scripps Instit. Oceanography, San Diego, California 92152 (SIO Reference 70-22, 1 July 1970).

——— 1971. Near-bottom geologic studies of the East Pacific Rise Crest. *Bull. geol. Soc. Am.* **82,** 823-41.

Larson, R. L. & Spiess, F. N. 1970. Slope distributions of the East Pacific Rise Crest. Univ. Calif., San Diego, Marine Physical Lab. Scripps Instit. Oceanography, San Diego, California 92152 (SIO Reference 70-8, 10 March 1970).

Larue, B. 1970. Séismicité aux Nouvelles-Hébrides, rapport préliminaire. *Rapp. ORSTOM,* Paris.

Laudon, T. S. 1968. Land gravity survey of the Solomon and Bismarck Islands. In *The Crust and Upper Mantle of the Pacific area. Am. Geophys. Un., Geophys. Monogr.* **12,** 279-95.

Launay, J. & Recy, J. 1970. Nouvelles données sur une variation relative récente du niveau de la mer dans toute la région Nouvelle-Calédonie, Iles Loyautés. *C.R. Acad. Sci. Paris,* **270,** 2159-61.

——— 1971. Variations relatives du niveau de la mer et néotectonique en Nouvelle-Calédonie au Pléistocène supérieur et à l'Holocène. *Rapp. ORSTOM,* Paris.

Leake, B. E. 1968. A catalog of analysed calciferous and subcalciferous amphiboles together with their nomenclature and associated minerals. *Spec. Pap. geol. Soc. Am.* **98,** 1.

Lee, C., Lee, H., Liu, H., Liu, C. & Yeh, S. 1963. Preliminary study of paleomagnetism of some Mesozoic and Cainozoic red beds of South China. *Acta Geologica Sinica,* **43,** 241-6 (translated by E. R. Hope, Directorate of Scientific Information Services, DRB Canada T7C, 1966).

Lee, P. J. 1962. Mesozoic and Cenozoic rocks of the Paochung well, Yunlin, Taiwan. *Petrol. Geol. Taiwan,* **1,** 75-86.

Lee, W. H. K., Uyeda, S. & Taylor, P. T. 1966. Geothermal studies of continental margins and island arcs. In *Continental margins and island arcs. Geol. Surv. Pap. Can.* 66-15, 398-414.

Lensen, G. J. 1970. Elastic and non-elastic surface deformation in New Zealand. *Bull. N.Z. Soc. Earthquake Eng.* **3,** 131-42.

Lensen, G. J. & Otway, P. M. 1971. Earthshift and post-earthshift deformation associated with the May, 1968, Inanqahua earthquake, New Zealand. Recent Crustal Movements. *Bull. R. Soc. N.Z.* **9.**

Le Pichon, X. 1968. Sea-floor spreading and continental drift. *J. geophys. Res.* **73** (12), 3661-97.

Le Pichon, X. & Heirtzler, J. R. 1968. Magnetic anomalies in the Indian Ocean and sea-floor spreading. *J. geophys. Res.* **73,** 2101-17.

Lewis, J. F. 1968. Tauhara volcano, Taupo zone. Part II—Mineralogy and petrology. *N.Z. Jl Geol. Geophys.* **11,** 651.

Liggett, K. (In prep.) Geology of Maewo. *New Hebrides geol. Surv. Regional Rept* [see also *New Hebrides geol. Surv., Rept (1965)*, 8-12].

Lillie, A. R. & Brothers, R. N. 1970. The geology of New Caledonia. *N.Z. Jl Geol. Geophys.* **13,** 145-83.

Linden, W. J. M. van der. 1967. Structural relationships in the Tasman Sea and South-West Pacific Ocean. *N.Z. Jl Geol. Geophys.* **10,** 1280-301.

——— 1969. Extinct mid-ocean ridges in the Tasman Sea and in the Western Pacific. *Earth Planet. Sci. Letters*, **6,** 483-90.

——— 1969. Rotation of the Melanesian Complex and of West Antarctica—a key to the configuration of Gondwana? *Palaeogeogr. Palaeoclim. Palaeoecol.* **6** (1), 37-44.

Lishnevsky, E. N. 1969. The main features of tectonics and deep structure of continental part of the USSR Far East from gravimetric data. In *Structure and Development of Earth's Crust in the Soviet Far East* (Eds E. E. Fotiadi & I. K. Tuyezov). Nauka Publ., Moscow (in Russian).

Livshits, M. Kh. 1965. On the problem of the physical make-up of the deep-seated material of the Earth's crust and upper mantle in the Kurile zone of the Pacific ring. *Geol. i Geofiz.* **1.**

Lliboutry, L. 1969. Sea-floor spreading, continental drift and lithosphere sinking with an asthenosphere at melting point. *J. geophys. Res.* **74** (27), 6525-44.

Loth, J. E. & Zwierzycki, J. 1926. De Kristallyne schisten op Java ouder dan Kryt. *De Mijningenieur*, **2** (2), 22-5.

Lowder, G. G. 1970. The volcanoes and caldera of Talasea, New Britain: Mineralogy. *Contr. Mineral. Petrol.* **26,** 324.

Lowder, G. G. & Carmichael, I. S. E. 1970. The volcanoes and caldera of Talasea, New Britain: geology and petrology. *Bull. geol. Soc. Am.* **81,** 17.

Ludwig, W. J. 1970. The Manila Trench and West Luzon Trough—III. Seismic refraction measurement. *Deep Sea Res.* **17,** 553-71.

Ludwig, W. J., Ewing, J. I., Murauchi, S., Den, N., Asano, S., Hotta, H., Hayakawa, M., Asanuma, T., Ichikawa, K. & Nagurchi, I. 1966. Sediments and structure of the Japan Trench. *J. geophys. Res.* **71,** 2121-37.

Lumb, J. T. 1970. Magnetic properties of rocks from the Cook Islands, south-west Pacific Ocean. Appendix to Woodward and Hochstein (1970). *N.Z. Jl Geol. Geophys.* **13,** 220-4.

Lumb, J. T. & Carrington, L. 1971. Magnetic surveys in the South-west Pacific and rock sampling for magnetic studies in the Cook Islands. *Bull. R. Soc. N.Z.* **8,** 81-9.

Lumb, J. T., Hochstein, M. P. & Woodward, D. J. 1972. Interpretation of magnetic measurements in the Cook Islands, South-west Pacific Ocean. This volume.

Luyendyk, B. P. 1969. Origin of short-wavelength magnetic lineations observed near the ocean bottom. *J. geophys. Res.* **74** (20), 4869-81.

——— 1970. Geological and geophysical observations in an abyssal hill area using a deeply towed instrument package. Thesis, Univ. Calif., San Diego, Marine Physical Lab. Scripps Instit. Oceanography, San Diego, California 92152 (SIO Reference 70-14, 1 June 1970).

——— 1970. Origin and history of abyssal hills in the north-east Pacific Ocean. *Bull. geol. Soc. Am.* **81,** 2237-60.

——— 1970. Dips of downgoing lithospheric plates beneath island arcs. *Bull. geol. Soc. Am.* **81,** 3411.

Luyendyk, B. P., Mudie, J. D. & Harrison, C. G. A. 1968. Lineations of magnetic anomalies in the northeast Pacific observed near the ocean floor. *J. geophys. Res.* **73** (18), 5951-7.

McBirney, A. R. 1969. Compositional variations in Cenozoic calc-alkaline suites of Central America. *Proc. Andesite Conference* (Ed. A. R. McBirney), *Bull. Ore. St. Dep. Geol. miner. Ind.* **65,** 185.

Macdonald, G. A. & Katsura, T. 1964. Chemical composition of Hawaiian lavas. *J. Petrology*, **5** (1), 83-133.

McDougall, I. 1963. K-Ar Ages of Some Rocks from Viti Levu, Fiji. *Nature*, **198,** 677.

McElhinny, M. W. 1968-72. Palaeomagnetic directions and pole positions VIII, X, XII. *Geophys. J. R. astr. Soc.* **15,** 409-30 (1968); **19,** 305-27 (1969). (In press, 1972.)

McKay, A. 1892. On the geology of Marlborough and South-East Nelson. *N.Z. Geol. Surv. Rep. geol. Explor. 1890-1*, 1-28.

Mackenzie, D. E. 1971. Intrusive rocks of New Britain. Rec. Bur. Miner. Resour. Aust. 1971/70 (unpubl.).

Mackenzie, D. E. & Chappell, B. W. (In press.) Shoshonitic and calc-alkaline lavas from the New Guinea Highlands. *Contr. Mineral. Petrol.*

McKenzie, D. P. & Morgan, W. J. 1969. Evolution of triple junctions. *Nature*, **224,** 125-33.

McMillan, N. J. & Malone, E. J. 1960. The geology of the eastern Central Highlands of New Guinea. *Rep. Bur. Min. Resour. Aust.* **48.**

MacNab, R. P. 1970. Geology of the Gazelle Peninsula, T.P.N.G. Rec. Bur. Miner. Resour. Aust. 1970/63 (unpubl.).

McTavish, R. A. 1966. Planktonic Foraminifera from the Malaita Group, British Solomon Islands. *Micropaleontology*, **12,** 1-36.

Malahoff, A. 1970. Gravity and magnetic studies of the New Hebrides Island Arc. *New Hebrides geol. Surv., Spec. Rept.* 64 pp.
——— 1971. The Murray Fracture Zone: history, structure, geology and comparison to other Pacific fracture zones. (Abstract). *Proc. Twelfth Pacif. Sci. Congr.* (Abstracts), Canberra 1971, p. 355
——— (In prep.) The Fiji plateau, an active spiralling tectonic system.

Mallick, D. I. J. 1971. Southern Banks Islands. *New Hebrides geol. Surv. Rept (1970)*, 12-16 (Ed. D. I. J. Mallick).
——— 1972. Some petrological and structural variations in the New Hebrides. This volume.

Mallick, D. I. J. & Ash, R. P. (In prep.) Geology of the Southern Banks Islands. *New Hebrides geol. Surv., Regional Rept.*

Mamayeva, R. B. 1968. Oceanographic investigations of the Pacific Ocean carried out by Soviet expeditions in 1967. *Int. Mar. Sci.* **6** (2), 11-13.

Manser, W. & Freeman, C. (In press.) Bibliography of the geology of eastern New Guinea (Papua New Guinea), *Rep. Bur. Miner. Resour. Aust.* **141.**

Markhinin, E. K. 1968. Volcanism as an agent of formation of the earth's crust. In *The Crust and Upper Mantle of the Pacific Area*, Am. Geophys. Un. Geophys. Monogr. **12,** 412-23. Washington, D.C.

Markov, M. S. 1970. Metamorphic complexes and their place in the evolution history of island arcs. *Geotektonika*, **2** (in Russian). (Eng. trans. *Geotectonics*, **2,** 1970).

Markov, M. S., Averianova, V. N., Kartanov, I. P., Solovieva, I. A. & Shuvaev, A. S. 1967. Meso-Cenozoic history and structure of the earth crust in the Okhotsk region. *Trudy Geol. Inst., Fasc.* **168,** Moscow (in Russian).

Markov, M. S., Seliverstov, V. A., Khotin, M. Yu. & Dolmatov, B. K. 1969. On the conjugation of structures of Eastern Kamchatka and Aleutian island arc. *Geotektonika*, **6** (in Russian).

Masaitis, V. L. (Ed.) 1964. *Geology of Korea.* Nedra Publ., Moscow (in Russian).

Matsuda, T., Nakamura, K. & Sugimura, A. 1967. Late Cenozoic orogeny in Japan. *Tectonophysics*, **4,** 349-66.

Matsuda, T. & Uyeda, S. 1971. On the Pacific-type orogeny and its model—extension of the paired belts concept and possible origin of marginal seas. *Tectonophysics*, **11** (1), 5-27.

Matsumoto, T. (Ed.) 1953. *The Cretaceous system in the Japanese Islands*. Japan Soc. Promotion Sci., Tokyo.

——— 1963. The Cretaceous. In *Geology of Japan* (Eds F. Takai, T. Matsumoto & R. Toriyama). Univ. Tokyo Press, Tokyo.

——— 1964. On the age of the geosynclinal volcanism. *Sci. Rep.Fac. Sci. Kyushu Univ., Geol.* **7,** 149-59 (in Japanese).

——— 1967. Fundamental problems in the circum-Pacific orogenesis. *Tectonophysics*, **4** (4-6), 595-613.

——— 1968. Bibliography of geochronological data in Japan. *Jap. J. Geol. Geogr.* **39,** 1-5.

Matsumoto, T. & Hirata, M. 1969. A new ammonite from the Shimantogawa group of Shikoku. *Trans. Proc. palaeont. Soc. Japan* (*n.s.*), **76,** 177-84.

Matsumoto, T., Yamaguchi, M., Yanagi, T., Matsushita, S., Hayase, I., Ishizaka, K., Kawano, Yo. & Ueda, Yo. 1968. The Precambrian problem in younger orogenic zones: an example from Japan. *Can. J. Earth Sci.* **5** (3), Pt. 2, 643-8.

Matsushita, S. 1963. Outline of geology. In *Geology of Japan* (Eds F. Takai, T. Matsumoto & R. Toriyama), 2-5. Univ. Tokyo Press, Tokyo.

——— 1971. *The Kinki district* (in Japanese). Asakura Shoten Co., Tokyo.

Maxwell, A. E. *et al.* 1970. Deep sea drilling in the South Atlantic. *Science*, **168** (3935), 1047-59. *Structure of the Earth's Crust in the Transition Region from the Asiatic Continent to the Pacific Ocean*. Nauka Publ., Moscow, 308 pp. (in Russian) 1964.

Melson, W. G., Jarosewich, E. & Lundquist, C. A. 1970. Volcanic eruption at Metis Shoal, Tonga, 1967-8: description and petrology. *Smithsonian Contributions to the Earth Sciences*, **4,** 18 pp.

Menard, H. W. 1964. *Marine geology of the Pacific*. McGraw Hill, New York. 271 pp.

——— 1967. Transitional types of crust under small ocean basins. *J. geophys. Res.* **72** (12), 3061-73.

——— 1969. Growth of drifting volcanoes. *J. geophys. Res.* **74,** 4827-37.

Menard, H. W. & Atwater, Tanya. 1968. Changes in direction of sea floor spreading. *Nature*, **219,** 463.

——— 1969. Origins of fracture zone topography. *Nature*, **222,** 1037.

Meng, C. Y. 1970. A conception of the revolution of the island of Taiwan and its bearing on the development of the Neogene sedimentary basins on its western side. *Econ. Comm. Asia & Far East* (*ECAFE*), *CCOP*, *Tech. Bull.* **3,** 109-26. Bangkok.

Merzlyakov, V. M. 1967. A new type of the Ordovician cross-section on the Kolymsky massif. *Kolyma*, **7,** 44-6. Magadan (in Russian).

——— 1971. *Stratigraphy and tectonics of the Omulev uplift, North-East Siberia*. Nauka Publ., Moscow (in Russian).

Mikunov, V. F. 1963. New works on the tectonics of China. *Izv. Akad. Nauk SSSR* (*geol.*), **2,** 50-9 (in Russian).

Milashin, A. P., Siplatov, V. A., Yunov, A. O. *et al.* 1970. Seismic data on the structure of the sedimentary layer in the southern part of the Tatarsky Strait. *Geotektonika*, **1** (in Russian).

Milashin, A. P., Snegovskoy, S. S. & Tuyezov, I. K. 1968. Structure of sedimentary strata of the Japan Sea from continuous reflection profiling data. *Dokl. Akad. Nauk SSSR.* **183** (5), 1060-3 (in Russian).

Milsom, J. S. 1970. Woodlark basin, a minor centre of sea-floor spreading in Melanesia. *J. geophys. Res.* **75,** 7335.

Minato, M., Gorai, M. & Hunahashi, M. (Eds). 1965. *The geologic development of the Japanese Islands.* Tsikiji Shokan, Tokyo.

Minato, M. & Hunahashi, M. 1970. Origin of the earth's crust and its evolution. *J. Fac. Sci. Hokkaido Univ.* **4** (Geol. & Miner) **24** (4), 515-61.

Mishin, V. P. 1968. Formation-tectonic division into districts of the Southern Primorie and the adjacent China and Korea territories for Late Palaeozoic. In *Geology of the Asia-to-Pacific Transition Zone* (Ed. N. P. Vassilkovsky). Nauka Publ., Moscow (in Russian).
——— 1970. On Middle Palaeozoic geosyncline structure of the Southern Sikhote-Alin. In *Problems of Geology, Geochemistry and Metallogeny of the North-Western sector of the Pacific Belt* (Ed. I. N. Govorov). Vladivostok (in Russian).

Mitchell, A. H. G. 1966. Geology of South Malekula. *New Hebrides geol. Surv., Rept.* **3,** 42 pp.
——— 1968. Sedimentological and geological evolution of Malekula Island, New Hebrides. Ph.D. thesis, Univ. Oxford.
——— 1970. Facies of an Early Miocene volcanic arc, Malekula Island, New Hebrides. *Sedimentology*, **14,** 201-44.
——— 1971. Geology of northern Malekula. *New Hebrides geol. Surv., Regional Rept.*

Mitchell, A. H. G. & Reading, H. G. 1971. Evolution of island arcs. *J. Geol.* **79,** 253-84.

Mitchell, A. H. G. & Warden, A. J. 1971. Geological evolution of the New Hebrides island arc. *J. geol. Soc. London.* **127,** 501-29.

Mitronovas, W. & Isacks, B. L. 1971. Seismic velocity anomalies in the upper mantle beneath the Tonga-Kermadec arc. *J. geophys. Res.* **76** (29), 7154-80.

Mitronovas, W., Isacks, B. & Seeber, L. 1969. Earthquake locations and seismic wave propagation in the upper 250 km of the Tonga Island arc. *Bull. seism. Soc. Am.* **59** (3), 1115-36.

Miyashiro, A. 1961. Evolution of metamorphic belts. *J. Petrology*, **2,** 277-311.
——— 1967. Orogeny, regional metamorphism, and magmatism in the Japanese Islands. *Meddr. dansk geol. Foren.* **17,** 390-446.

Miyashiro, A. & Haramura, H. 1962. Chemical composition of Palaeozoic slates. *J. geol. Soc. Japan*, **68,** 75-82 (in Japanese).

Moberly, R. 1971. Youthful oceanic lithosphere of marginal seas, western Pacific (Abstract). *Proc. Twelfth Pacif. Sci. Congr.* (*Abstracts*), Canberra, **1,** 393.

Mogi, A. & Sato, T. 1958. On the bottom configuration and sediments in the adjacent sea of Mogami Bank, Japan Sea. *Bull. hydrogr. Office Japan*, **55,** 37-53 (in Japanese).

Molnar, P. & Sykes, L. R. 1969. Tectonics of the Caribbean and Middle-American regions from focal mechanisms and seismicity. *Bull. geol. Soc. Am.* **80,** 1639.

Moores, E. M. & Vine, F. J. 1971. The Troodos massif, Cyprus and other ophiolites as oceanic crust: evaluation and implications. *Phil. Trans. R. Soc. London, Ser. A.* **268,** 443-66.

Morgan, W. J. 1968. Rises, trenches, great faults and crustal blocks. *J. geophys. Res.* **73** (6), 1959-82.

Morgan, W. R. 1966. A note on the petrology of some lava types from east New Guinea. *J. geol. Soc. Aust.* **13,** 583.

Morkovkina, V. F. 1967. *Metasomatic transformation of the ultrabasic rocks of Polar Ural.* Nauka Publ., Moscow (in Russian).

Mudie, J. D., Normark, W. R. & Cray, Jr., E. J. 1970. Direct mapping of the sea floor using side-scanning sonar and transponder navigation. *Bull. geol. Soc. Am.* **81,** 1547-54.

Murata, M. & Sugimoto, M. 1971. Late Triassic conodonts from the northern part of the Kitakami massif, North-east Japan. *J. geol. Soc. Japan*, **77,** 393-4 (in Japanese).

Murauchi, S. 1971. The renewal of island arcs and the tectonics of marginal seas. In *Island Arc and Marginal Sea.* Tokai Univ. Press, Tokyo (in Japanese).

Murauchi, S., Den, N., Asano, S., Hotta, H., Asanuma, T., Yosii, T., Hagiwara, K., Ichikawa, K., Iizuka, S., Sato, T. & Yasui, T. 1967. Crustal structure of the Japan Sea derived from the deep seismic observations. *J. Phys. Earth*, **72** (6).

Murauchi, S. *et al.* 1968. Crustal structure of the Philippine Sea. *J. geophys. Res.* **73,** 3143-72.

Murauchi, S. & Yasui, M. 1968. Geophysical studies of the ocean floors in the seas adjacent to Japan. *Kagaku* (*Science*), **34** (4), 192-200 (in Japanese).

Musper, K. A. F. R. 1930. Beknopt verslag over uitkomsten van nieuwe geologische onderzoekingen in de Padangse Bovenlanden. *Jaarb. Mijnw. Ned. Ind., Verh.* (1930), 261-331.

Nadai, A. 1963. *Theory of flow and fracture of solids.* Vol. 2. MacGraw Hill, New York.

Nagao, T. 1934. Cretaceous mollusca from the Miyako District, Honshu, Japan. *J. Fac. Sci. Hokkaido Univ.*, Ser. 4, **2,** 117-278.

Nakazawa, K. 1958. The Triassic system in the Maizuru zone, Southwest Japan. *Mem. Coll. Sci. Kyoto Univ.* Ser. B, **24,** 265-313.

Nicholls, J. & Carmichael, I. S. E. (In press.) The equilibration temperature and pressure (P_{total}) of various lava types with spinel- and garnet- peridotite. *Am. Miner.*

Niino, H. 1931. On the bottom deposits of Yamato Tai in the Sea of Japan. *J. geol. Soc. Japan*, **40** (472), 86-100.

——— 1948. Sediments of Oki Bank in the Japanese Sea. *J. sedim. Petrol.* **18** (2), 79-85.

——— 1952. The bottom character of the banks and submarine valleys on and around the continental shelf of Japanese Islands. *J. Tokyo Univ. Fish.* **38** (3), 391-410.

Normark, W. R. 1969. Growth patterns of deep-sea fans. Thesis, Univ. Calif., San Diego, Marine Physical Lab. Scripps Instit. Oceanography, San Diego, California 92152 (SIO Reference 69-29, 1 December 1969).

——— 1970. Growth pattern of deep-sea fans. *Bull. Am. Ass. Petrol. Geol.* **54** (11), 2170-95.

Obelliane, J. M. 1961. Contribution à la connaissance géologique de l'archipel des Nouvelles-Hébrides. *Sciences de la Terre*, **6** (*1958*), 139-68, Nancy.

Ojima, M., Kaneoka, I. & Aramaki, S. 1970. K-Ar ages of submarine basalts dredged from seamounts in the western Pacific area and discussion of oceanic crust. *Earth Planet. Sci. Letters*, **8,** 237-49.

Olgers, F. & Flood, P. G. 1970. An angular Permian/Carboniferous unconformity in south-eastern Queensland and northeastern New South Wales. *J. geol. Soc. Aust.* **17,** 81.

Oliver, J. 1970. Structure and evolution of the mobile seismic belts. *Phys. Earth Planet. Interiors*, **2,** 350-62.

Oliver, J. & Isacks, B. L. 1967. Deep earthquake zones, anomalous structures in the upper mantle and the lithosphere. *J. geophys. Res.* **72** (16), 4259-75.

Ongley, M. 1937. The Wairoa earthquake of 16th September, 1932. 1—Field observations. *N.Z. Jl Sci. Technol.* **18,** 845-51.

Ono, A. 1969. Geology of the Ryoke metamorphic belt in the Takato-Shiojiri area, Nagano Prefecture. *J. geol. Soc. Japan*, **75,** 491-8.

Ono, K. 1962. Chemical Composition of Volcanic Rocks in Japan. *Geol. Surv. Japan* (*Kawasaki*), 441 pp.

Onuki, Y. 1969. Geology of the Kitakami massif, Northeast Japan. *Contr. Inst. Geol. Paleont. Tohoku Univ.* **69,** 1-239 (in Japanese).

Ordoñez, E. & Reyes, M. V. 1970. Upper Cretaceous smaller foraminifera of the Philippines. *J. Geol. Soc. Philipp.* In press.

Orloff, O. 1968. Etude géologique et geomorphologique des massifs d'ultrabasites compris entre Houailou et Canala. (Thesis, University of Montpellier Library.)

Oxburgh, E. R. & Turcotte, D. L. 1970. The thermal structure of island arcs. *Bull. geol. Soc. Am.* **81,** 1665-88.

——— 1971. Origin of paired metamorphic belts and crustal dilation in island arc regions. *J. geophys. Res.* **76,** 1315-27.

Ozima, Minoru, Ozima, Mituko, & Kaneoka, I. 1968. Potassium-argon ages and magnetic properties of some dredged submarine basalts and their geophysical implications. *J. geophys. Res.* **73,** 711-23.

Packham, G. H. 1969. The geology of New South Wales. *J. geol. Soc. Aust.* **16,** 1.

Packham, G. H. & Falvey, D. A. 1971. An hypothesis for the formation of marginal seas in the western Pacific. *Tectonophysics*, **11** (2), 79-109.

Page, R. W. 1971. The geochronology of igneous rocks in the New Guinea region. Ph.D. thesis, Aust. Nat. Univ., Canberra.

Page, R. W. & McDougall, I. 1970. Potassium-argon dating of the Tertiary $f_{1\text{-}2}$ stage in New Guinea and its bearing on the geological time-scale. *Am. J. Sci.* **269,** 321-42.

Paine, A. G. L. 1969. Palaeovolcanology of central eastern Queensland. *Spec. Publs geol. Soc. Aust.* **2,** 183.

Pantazis, T. M. 1967. The geology and mineral resources of the Pharmakas-Kalavasos area. *Mem. geol. Surv. Cyprus*, **8,** 190 pp.

Papanastassiou, D. A. & Wasserburg, G. J. 1969. Initial strontium isotopic abundances and the resolution of small time differences in the formation of planetary objects. *Earth Planet. Sci. Letters*, **5,** 361-76.

Parfyonov, L. M. 1970. Precambrian structure of East Asia. In *Tectonic Problems of Precambrian of Continents* (Ed. Yu. A. Kosygin). *Trans. Inst. Geol. Grophys., Siberian Branch, Acad. Sci. USSR*, **129,** 131-54. Nauka Publ., Moscow (in Russian).

Parke, Jr., M. L., Emery, K. O., Szymankiewicz, R. & Reynolds, L. M. 1971. Structural framework of continental margin in South China Sea. *Bull. Am. Ass. Petrol. Geol.* **55,** 723-51.

Parkin, L. W. 1969. Handbook of South Australian geology. *Publ. geol. Surv. S. Aust.* Adelaide.

Pascal, G. 1970. Etude des O-C des ondes P de 30° à 100°, Relation avec l'hypothèse des plaques. *Rapp. ORSTOM*, Noumea.

Pavlov, Yu. A., Tuyezov, I. K., Yeryomina, G. F., Lyutaya, L. M., Pavlova, I. S. & Andreev, A. A. 1970. The gravity field of the Asia-to-Pacific transition zone, transformed into the upper semispace. In *Geophysical Investigations of Structure of Earth's Crust and Upper Mantle of the Asia-to-Pacific Transition Zone* (Ed. I. K. Tuyezov). *Trans. Sakhalin Complex Sci. Res. Inst., Yuzhno-Sakhalinsk*, **24,** 43-67 (in Russian).

Percherskiy, D. M. 1970. Paleomagnetic studies of Mesozoic deposits of the north-east of the

U.S.S.R. *Izv. Akad. Nauk. SSSR. Earth Phys. Ser.* 69-83.

Peive, A. V. 1967. Fracturing and tectonic motion. *Geotektonika*, **5,** 8-24 (in Russian).
——— 1969. Oceanic crust in past geological time. *Geotektonika*, **4** (in Russian). (Eng. trans. *Geotectonics*, 1969, **4,** 210-24.)

Peive, A. V., Schtreis, N. A., Knipper, A. L., Markov, M. S. Bogdanov, N. A., Perfil'yev, A. S. & Ruzhentsev, S. V. 1971. Oceans and the geosyncline process. *Dokl. Akad. Nauk SSSR*, **196** (3) (in Russian).

Petelin, V. P. 1964. Hard rocks in the deep-water trenches of the southwestern part of the Pacific ocean. *Int. Geol. Congr. 22nd Session, Doklady* (by the Soviet geologists), 78-86.

Peterman, Z. E. & Hedge, C. E. 1971. Related strontium isotopic and chemical variations in oceanic basalts. *Bull. geol. Soc. Am.* **82,** 493-500.

Peterman, Z. E., Lowder, G. G. & Carmichael, I. S. E. 1970. Sr87/Sr/86 ratios of the Talasea series, New Britain, Territory of New Guinea. *Bull. geol. Soc. Am.* **81,** 39-40.

Phillips, K. A. 1965. A provisional Geological Map of Fiji. *Ann. Rep. geol. Surv. Fiji* (*1964*), 4-6.

Philpotts, J. A. & Schnetzler, C. C. 1970. Phenocryst-matrix partition coefficients for K, Rb, Sr and Ba, with applications to anorthosite and basalt genesis. *Geochim. cosmochim. Acta.* **34,** 307-22.

Piroutet, M. 1917. Etude stratigraphique de la Nouvelle Calédonie. Thesis, Protat Frères, Mâcon, 313 pp.

Pitman, W. C., Herron, E. M. & Heirtzler, J. R. 1968. Magnetic anomalies in the Pacific and sea-floor spreading. *J. geophys. Res.* **73,** 2069.

Pitt, R. P. B. 1966. Tectonics in Central Papua and the adjoining part of New Guinea. Ph.D. thesis, Univ. of Tasmania, Hobart.

Pospelova, G. A., Larionova, G. Ya. & Anuchin, A. V. 1968. Paleomagnetic investigations of Jurassic and lower Cretaceous sedimentary rocks of Siberia. *Int. Geol. Rev.* **10,** 1108-18.

Powell, J. L. & DeLong, S. E. 1966. Isotopic composition of strontium in volcanic rocks from Oahu. *Science*, **153,** 1239-42.

Proshchenko, E. G. 1962. On the question about age of metamorphic rocks of the Selennyakhsky Mountain Ridge (Yakutskaya ASSR). *Geol. i Geofiz.* **3,** 41-8 (in Russian).

Pushcharovsky, Yu. M. 1965. Essential features in the formation of the Pacific Ocean tectonic belt. *Geotektonika*, **6,** 19-34 (in Russian).
——— 1967. The Pacific Ocean tectonic segment of the earth's crust. *Geotektonika*, **5,** 90-102 (in Russian).
——— 1968. The Pacific tectonic belt of the earth's crust. In *Tectonics of the Soviet Far East*

and the adjacent aquatic areas (Ed. Yu. A. Kosygin). Nauka Publ., Moscow (in Russian).
——— 1969. Resonance-tectonic structures. *Geotektonika*, **1** (in Russian).

Pushkar, P. 1968. Strontium isotope ratios in volcanic rocks of three island arc areas. *J. geophys. Res.* **73,** 2701-13.

Raitt, R. W. 1956. Seismic refraction studies of the Pacific Ocean Basin. Part 1: Crustal thickness of the central equatorial Pacific. *Bull. geol. Soc. Am.* **67,** 1623-40.
——— 1963. The crustal rocks. In *The Sea* (Ed. M. N. Hill). Interscience, New York.
——— 1967. Marine seismic studies of the Indonesian island arc. *Trans. Am. geophys. Un.* (abstract) **48,** 217.

Raitt, R. W., Fisher, R. L. & Mason, R. C. 1955. Tonga Trench. *Spec. Publ. geol. Soc. Am.* **62,** 237-54.

Raleigh, C. B. & Lee, W. H. K. 1969. Sea-floor spreading and island-arc tectonics. *Proc. Andesite Conference* (Ed. A. R. McBirney), *Bull. Ore. St. Dep. Geol. miner. Ind.* **65,** 99.

Reilly, W. I. 1969. Gravitational and magnetic effects of a right circular cylinder. *N.Z. Jl Geol. Geophys.* **12,** 497-506.

Reinhardt, B. M. 1969. On the genesis and emplacement of ophiolites in the Oman Mountains geosyncline. *Schweiz. miner. petrogr. Mitt.* **49,** 1-30.

Reynolds, M. A. 1958. Activity of Tuluman volcano, St Andrew Strait, Admiralty Islands, September 1955-March 1957. Rec. Bur. Miner. Resour. Aust. 1958/14 (unpubl.).

Reynolds, M. A. & Best, J. G. 1957. The Tuluman volcano, St Andrew Strait, Admiralty Islands. *Rep. Bur. Miner. Resour. Aust.* **33.**

Richard, J. J. 1962. Catalogue of the active volcanoes of the world. Part 13, Kermadec, Tonga and Samoa. *Int. volc. Assoc.* Naples.

Richards, M. L., Vacquier, V. & Van Voorhis, G. D. 1967. Calculation of the magnetization of uplifts from combining topographic and magnetic surveys. *Geophysics*, **32,** 678-707.

Rickard, M. J. 1963. The Geology of Mbalevuto area. *Bull. geol. Surv. Fiji*, **11,** 36 pp.
——— 1966. Reconnaissance Geology of Vanua Levu. *Mem. geol. Surv. Fiji*, **2,** 81 pp.
——— 1970. The geology of north-eastern Vanua Levu. *Bull. geol. Surv. Fiji*, **14,** 13 pp.

Rickwood, F. K. 1955. The geology of the Western Highlands of New Guinea. *J. geol. Soc. Aust.* **2,** 63-82.
——— 1968. The geology of Western Papua. *J. Aust. Petrol. Expl. Ass.* **8** (2), 51-61.

Rikitake, T., Miyamura, S., Tsubokawa, I., Murauchi, S., Uyeda, S., Kuno, H. & Gorai, M. 1968. Geophysical and geological data in and around the Japan Arc. *Can. J. Earth Sci.* **5** (4), Pt 2, 1101-18.

Ringis, J. 1970. Magnetic lineations in the Tasman Sea (abstr.). *Intern. Conf. Geophysics of the Earth and the Oceans*, Univ. N.S.W., Sydney.

Ringwood, A. E. & Green, D. H. 1968. Experimental investigation of gabbro passing into eclogite and some geophysical conclusions. In *The Upper Mantle Petrology* (Ed. Ryabchikov). Mir, Moscow (in Russian).

Ripper, I. D. 1970. Global tectonics and the New Guinea-Solomon Islands region. *Search.* **1,** 226.

Rivosh, L. A. 1963. On the tectonics of Kamchatka peninsula and the floor of adjacent sea regions (on the basis of geophysical data). *Geol. i Geofiz.* **6** (in Russian).

Robertson, E. I. & Kibblewhite, A. C. 1966. Bathymetry around isolated volcanic islands and atolls in the South Pacific Ocean. *N.Z. Jl Geol. Geophys.* **9,** 111-21.

Robinson, G. P. 1969. Geology of North Santo. *New Hebrides geol. Surv., Regional Rept.,* 80 pp.

Rodda, P. 1967. Outline of the geology of Viti Levu. *N.Z. Jl Geol. Geophys.* **10,** 1260-73.
——— 1969. Analyses of rocks from Fiji. *Geol. Surv. Dept,* Fiji.
——— (In prep.) The geology of northern and central Viti Levu. *Bull. geol. Surv. Fiji,* **13.**

Rodda, P. & Band, R. B. 1967. Part III—Geology of Viti Levu. *Ann. Rep. geol. Surv. Fiji (1966),* 8-16.

Rodda, P., Snelling, N. J. & Rex, D. C. 1967. Radiometric age data on rocks from Viti Levu, Fiji. *N.Z. Jl Geol. Geophys.* **10,** 1248-59.

Rodionova, R. I. & Fedortchenko, V. I. 1971. On some problems of abyssal geology and volcanism on Kurile Island arc. *Geol. i Geofiz.* **2** (in Russian).

Rodnikov, A. G. & Khain, V. E. 1971. Tendencies in the crust development in the north-western Pacific mobile belt (in the light of data on deep structure). *Geotektonika,* **3** (in Russian).

Rodolfo, K. S. 1969. Bathymetry and marine geology of the Andaman Basin, and tectonic implications for South-east Asia. *Bull. geol. Soc. Am.* **80,** 1203-30.

Roeder, P. L. & Emslie, R. F. 1970. Olivine-liquid equilibrium. *Contr. Mineral. Petrol.* **29,** 275.

Roever, W. P. de 1957. Sind die alpinotypen Peridotitmassen vielleicht tektonisch verfrachtete Bruchstücke der Peridotitschale? *Geol. Rundsch.* **46,** 137-46.

Rose, J. C. & Tracy, R. W. 1971. Gravity results in the Solomon Islands region, aboard H.M.S. *Dampier* in 1965. Data Report No. 17, Hawaii Inst. Geophys., Univ. Hawaii.

Rose, J. C., Woollard, G. P. & Malahoff, A. 1968. Marine gravity and magnetic studies of the Solomon Islands. In *The Crust and Upper Mantle of the Pacific area. Am. Geophys. Un., Geophys. Monogr.* **12,** 379-410.

Rotman, V. K. 1968. Andesitic arcs and their place in tectonic and magmatic history of the North-West Pacific. In *Volcanism and tectogenesis.* Nauka Publ., Moscow (in Russian).

Rotman, V. K. & Markovsky, B. A. 1968. Fundamental features in the geosynclinal development of the North-West Pacific. In *Volcanism and tectogenesis*. Nauka Publ., Moscow (in Russian).

Routhier. P. 1953. Etude géologique du versant occidental de la Nouvelle Calédonie entre le col de Boghen et la pointe d'Arama. *Mém. Soc. géol. Fr.* **67,** 1-271.

Rusakov, I. M. & Vinogradov, V. A. 1969. Eugeosynclinal and miogeosynclinal regions of the North-East of the USSR. In *Scientific Notes—Regional Geology. Trans. Sci. Res. Inst. Geol. Arctic, Leningrad,* **15,** 5-27 (in Russian).

Rutland, R. W. 1968. A tectonic study of part of the Philippine fault zone. *J. geol. Soc. London,* **123,** 293-325.

Ruxton, B. P. 1966. A late Pleistocene to Recent rhyodacite-trachybasalt-basaltic latite volcanic association in northeast Papua. *Bull. volcan.* **29,** 347.

Saito, M. & Takeuchi, H. 1966. Surface waves across the Pacific. *Bull. seism. Soc. Am.* **56** (5), 1067-91.

Samaniego, R. M. 1964. The occurrence of *Globorotalia velascoensis* in the Philippines. *Philipp. Geol.* **18,** 65-74.

Santiago, P. D. 1963. Planktonic Foraminifera species from west side of Tarlac Province, Luzon Central Valley. *Philipp. Geol.* **17,** 69-99.

Santo, T. 1970. Regional study of the characteristic seismicity of the world. Part III: New Hebrides region. *Bull. Earthq. Res. Inst. Tokyo Univ.* **48,** 1-18.

Santos, P. J. 1968. Geology and section measurements in Iloilo Basin Panay Island, Philippines. *Philipp. Geol.* **22,** 1-62.

Sawamura, K., Sumi, K. & Ono, K. 1970. Geology of the Shimoda district (in Japanese), with a sheet map 1:50,000. *Geological Survey, Japan.*

Schilling, J. G. 1971. Sea-floor evolution: rare-earth evidence. *Phil. Trans. R. Soc. London A.* **268,** 663.

Schimke, G. R. & Bufe, C. G. 1968. Geophysical description of a Pacific Ocean seamount. *J. geophys. Res.* **73,** 559-69.

Schnetzler, C. C. & Philpotts, J. A. 1970. Partition coefficients of rare-earth elements between igneous matrix material and rock-forming mineral phenocrysts—II. *Geochim. cosmochim. Acta,* **34,** 331.

Scholl, D. W., Buffington, E. C. & Hopkins, D. M. 1968. Geologic history of the continental margin of North America in the Bering Sea. *Marine Geology,* **6** (4), 297-330.

Scholl, D. W., Buffington, E. C., Hopkins, D. M. & Alpha, T. R. 1970. The structure and origin of the large submarine canyons of the Bering Sea. *Marine Geology*, **8** (3-4), 187-210.

Scholl, D. W., Christensen, M. N., von Huene, R. & Marlow, M. S. 1970. Peru-Chile Trench sediments and sea-floor spreading. *Bull. geol. Soc. Am.* **81,** 1339-60.

Scholl, D. W., Green, H. G. & Marlow, M. S. 1970. Eocene age of the Adak 'Paleozoic (?)' rocks, Aleutian Islands, Alaska. *Bull. geol. Soc. Am.* **81** (12), 3583-92.

Scholl, D. W. & Hopkins, D. M. 1969. Newly discovered Cenozoic basins, Bering Sea shelf, Alaska. *Bull. Am. Ass. Petrol. Geol.* **53** (10), 2067-78.

Sclater, J. G., Hawkins, J. W., Mammerickx, J. & Chase, C. G. 1972. Crustal extension between the Tonga and Lau ridges. Petrologic and geophysical evidence. *Bull. geol. Soc. Am.* **83,** 505-18.

Sclater, J. G. & Menard, H. W. 1967. Topography and heat flow of the Fiji Plateau. *Nature*, **216,** 991-3.

Scripps Institution of Oceanography, University of California 1970. *Deep sea drilling project.*

Segawa, J. 1970. Gravity measurement at sea by use of T.S.S.G. *J. Phys. Earth*, **18,** 19-49, 203-84.

Sereda, L. I. 1971. Alpides of Central and South-East Chukotka. *Summary of candidate's theses, MGU* (in Russian).

Seslavinsky, K. B. 1970. Structure and history of development of South-Aniuy suture trough (Western Chukotka). *Geotektonika*, **5** (in Russian).

Shashkin, K. S. 1967. On Early Paleozoic eugeosyncline system of the Mongolian-Okhotsky folded belt. In *Tectonics of Eastern Siberia and the Far East of the USSR. Theses of reports on Fifth Session of Scientific Council on tectonics of Siberia and the Far East* (Ed. Yu. A. Kosygin). Novosibirsk (in Russian).

——— 1968. On the metamorphic complex nature of the north-east framing of the Zeisko-Bureinsky massif. In *Problems of Geology, Petrology and Metallogeny of Metamorphic Complexes of East of the USSR* (Ed. A. M. Smirnov). Vladivostok (in Russian).

——— 1970. Structure-formational zones of the Mongolian-Okhotsky belt and some peculiarities of their development. In *Problems of Geology, Geochemistry and Metallogeny of northwestern sector of the Pacific Belt* (Ed. I. N. Govorov). Vladivostok (in Russian).

Shatsky, N. S. 1960. Geotectonic generalizations on the distribution of endogenic ore deposits. *Izv. vissh. ucheb. zaved. Geologiya i razvedka*, **11,** 9-18 (in Russian).

Shatsky, N. S. & Bogdanov, A. A. 1959. Explanatory notes on the tectonic map of the USSR and adjoining countries. *Int. Geol. Rev.* **1,** 1-59.

Shaw, D. M. 1970. Trace element fractionation during anatexis. *Geochim. cosmochim. Acta*, **34,** 237-42.

Shepard, F. P. & Curray, J. R. 1967. Carbon 14 determination of sea-level changes in stable areas. *Prog. Oceanogr.* **4,** 283-91.

Shepard, F. P., Dill, R. F. & Heezen, B. C. 1968. Diapiric intrusions in foreset slope sediments off Magdalena Delta, Columbia. *Bull. Am. Ass. Petrol. Geol.* **52** (11), 2197-207.

Shevchenko, V. V. 1969. Paleozoic deposits of the middle current basin of the Indigirka River. In *Transactions of Interdepartment Conference on the Development of the Unified Stratigraphic Scheme of the Yakutskaya ASSR, 1961. I—Precambrian and Paleozoic: Materials on Geology and Mineral Resources of the Yakutskaya ASSR* (Ed. I. S. Bredikhin). Rept 13, Yakutsk (in Russian).

Shibata, K., Adachi, M. & Mizutani, S. 1971. Precambrian rocks in the Permian conglomerate from central Japan. *J. geol. Soc. Japan*, **77,** 507-14.

Shilo, N. A. & Nikolayevsky, A. A. 1968. The structure of the earth's crust and upper mantle of northwestern part of the Pacific mobile Belt. In *Earth's Crust and Upper Mantle* (Ed. V. V. Beloussov). Nauka Publ., Moscow (in Russian).

Shishkin, V. A. 1969. On the crystalline basement exposures on the Shamanikho-Stolbovsky territory, Prikolymie. In *Mesozoic Tectogenesis. Theses of reports of Scientific Council 7th Session on tectonics of Siberia and the Far East* (Eds N. F. Sokolovskaya & T. V. Umnova). Magadan (in Russian).

——— Study of the Early Paleozoic gold-bearing metamorphic complex in the Shamanikha-Stolby region, Cis-Kolyma. *Summary of candidate's theses, Kaz. GU* (in Russian).

Shor, G. G., Jr. 1964. Structure of the Bering Sea and Aleutian Ridge. *Marine Geology,* **1.**

——— 1966. Continental margins and island arcs of Western North America. In *Continental margins and island arcs. Geol. Surv. Pap. Can.* 66-15, 216-21.

——— 1970. Island arcs and continental margins of the western part of North America. In *Continental Margins and Island Arcs* (Ed. U. H. Poole). Mir, Moscow (in Russian).

Shor, G. G., Kirk, H. K. & Menard, H. W. 1971. Crustal structure of the Melanesian area. *J. geophys. Res.* **76,** 2562-86.

Shpetny, A. P. 1969. The Omolonsky massif is the structure of Caledonian consolidation. In *Mesozoic Tectogenesis. Theses of reports of Scientific Council 7th Session on tectonics of Siberia and the Far East* (Eds N. F. Sokolovskaya & T. V. Umnova). Magadan (in Russian).

Shpetny, A. P. & Pepeliayev, B. V. 1969. The main tectonic features and the history of the Prikolymskoye Uplift development. In *Mesozoic Tectogenesis . . .* (in Russian).

Shuto, T. 1963. Geology of the Nichinan area. *Sci. Rep. Fac. Sci., Kyushu Univ.* **6,** 135-66 (in Japanese).

Simakov, K. V. 1967. Pre-Permian deposits of the Omolonsky Block. *Geol. i Geofiz.* **12,** 57-66 (in Russian).

Singleton, O. P. 1965. Geology and mineralization of Victoria. *8th Common. Min. Metall. Congr.* **1,** 440.

Skwarko, S. K. 1967. Mesozoic mollusca from Australia and New Guinea. *Bull. Bur. Miner. Resour. Aust.* **75.**

Sleep, N. & Toksoz, M. Nafi. 1971. Evolution of marginal basins. *Nature*, **233,** 548-50.

Smirnov, A. M. 1963. The conjugation of the Chinese platform with the Pacific folded belt. *Izdatelstvo Akad. Nauk SSSR.* Moscow-Leningrad (in Russian).

——— 1964. On the structural position and age of the metamorphic Kamchatka and Sakhalin strata. In *Materials on Tectonics and Petrology of the Pacific Ore Belt* (Eds N. P. Vassilkovsky & A. A. Marakushev). Nauka Publ., Moscow (in Russian).

——— 1968. Role of the Precambrian basement in structural evolution of the Pacific mobile belt (particularly its northwestern section). *Pacific Geol.* **1,** 145-65.

Smirnov, L. M. 1971. Tectonics of Western Kamchatka. *Geotektonika*, **3** (in Russian).

Smirnov, S. S. 1946. The Pacific Ocean mineral belt. *Izv. Akad. Nauk SSSR*, (*Geol.*) **2,** 13-38 (in Russian).

Smit, J. A. J. 1964. A review of the relationship between Cretaceous rock and the Kaindi Metamorphics at Snake River, New Guinea. Mines Dept., Territory of Papua & New Guinea, Geol. Invest. Note 64304 (unpubl.).

Smith, E. M. 1966. *Lexique stratigraphique International: Nouvelle Guinée*, **6,** *Océanie*, *fasc. 3a.* 136 pp. C.N.R.S., Paris.

Smith, I. E. 1969. Notes on the volcanoes Mount Bagana and Mount Victory, Territory of Papua New Guinea. Rec. Bur. Miner. Resour. Aust. 1969/12 (unpubl.).

Smith, J. G. 1965. Orogenesis in western Papua and New Guinea. *Tectonophysics*, **2,** 1-27.

Smith, J. W. & Green, D. H. 1961. The geology of the Musa River Area, Papua. *Rep. Bur. Miner. Resour. Geol. Geophys. Aust.* **52.**

Smith Sibinga, G. L. 1933. The Malay double (triple) orogen, I, II and III. *Proc. K. ned. Akad. Wet.* **36,** 202-10, 323-30, 447-53.

Smith, W. D. 1924. *Geology and Mineral Resources of the Philippine Islands.* Bureau of Printing, Manila, 1924.

Snegovskoy, S. S. 1971. On sedimentary deposits of the South-Okhotskaya abyssal basin. *Dokl. Akad. Nauk SSSR*, **196** (1), 87-90 (in Russian).

Snegovskoy, S. S. & Alexandrov, S. M. 1972. On tectonics of the western edge of the Kuril basin. *Geotektonika*, in press (in Russian).

Sokolov, B. S. 1961. Defectoscopy of materials. *Gostekhizdat* (in Russian).

Solomon, S. & Biehler, S. 1969. Crustal structure from gravity anomalies in the South-West Pacific. *J. geophys. Res.* **74,** 6696-701.

Solovieva, N. Z. 1970. The effect of volcanism on the formation of Upper Cretaceous volcano-sedimentary deposits on Lesser Kuril ridge. *Litilogia i poleznye iskopaemye*, **6** (in Russian).

Spiess, F. N. Luyendyk, B. P., Larson, R. L., Normark, W. R. & Mudie, J. D. 1969. Detailed geophysical studies on the northern Hawaiian Arch using a deeply-towed instrument package. *Marine Geology*, **7,** 501-27.

Sproll, W. P. & Dietz, R. S. 1969. The morphological fit of Australia and Antarctica. *Nature*, **222,** 345.

Spry, A. & Banks, M. R. (Eds). 1962. The geology of Tasmania. *J. geol. Soc. Aust.* **9** (2), 107.

Stanton, R. L. & Bell, J. D. 1969. Volcanic and associated rocks of the New Georgia Group, British Solomon Islands Protectorate. *Overseas Geol. Miner. Resour.* **10,** 113-45.

Stauder, W. 1968. Mechanism of the Rat Island earthquake sequence of February 4, 1965, with relation to island arcs and sea-floor spreading. *J. geophys. Res.* **73,** 3847.

Stearns, H. T. 1971. Geological setting of an Eocene fossil deposit on Eua Island, Tonga. *Bull. geol. Soc. Am.* **82,** 2541.

Steiner, A. 1958. Petrogenetic implications of the 1954 Ngauruhoe lava and its xenoliths. *N.Z. Jl Geol. Geophys.* **1,** 325.

Stephenson, P. J. 1971. Ambrym Island project. *New Hebrides geol. Surv., Rept (1970)* (Ed. D. I. J. Mallick).

Stille, G. 1964. *Circum-Pacific folding in space and time—Selective Publications.* Mir, Moscow (in Russian transl.).

Stille, H. 1945. Die zirkumpazifischen Faltungen in Raum und Zeit. *Geotekt. Forsch.* **7-8,** 261-323.

——— 1957. 'Atlantische' und 'pazifische' Tektonik. *Geol. Jb.* **74,** 677-86.

Stipp, J. J. 1968. The geochronology and petrogenesis of the Cenozoic volcanics of North Island, New Zealand. Ph.D. thesis, Aust. Nat. Univ., Canberra.

Stone, D. B. 1968. Geophysics in the Bering Sea and surrounding areas: A review. *Tectonophysics*, **6** (6), 433-60.

Stroev, P. A. 1971. Gravity anomalies in the Japan Sea. *Dokl. Akad. Nauk SSSR*, **198** (4), 818-21 (in Russian).

Suess, E. 1904. *The Face of the Earth*, **4.** Oxford, Clarendon Press.

Suggate, R. P., 1963. The Alpine Fault. *Trans. R. Soc. N.Z.* (*Geology*), **2,** 105-29.

Sugimura, A. 1958. Marianen-Japan-Kamtschatka Orogen Tatigkeit. *Earth Sci., Tokyo*, **37,** 34-9 (in Japanese with German abstract on p. 39).

——— 1960. Zonal arrangement of some geophysical and petrological features in Japan and its environs. *J. Fac. Sci. Tokyo Univ.* (Sec. 2), **12,** 133-53.

——— 1961. Regional variation of the K_2O/Na_2O ratios of volcanic rocks in Japan and environs. *J. geol. Soc. Japan*, **67,** 292-300 (in Japanese with English abstract on p. 292).

——— 1968. Spatial relations of basaltic magmas in island arcs. In *Basalts*, 2. (Eds H. H. Hess & A. Poldervaart). Interscience Publishers, New York-London, pp. 537-71.

Sugimura, A., Matsuda, T., Chinzei, K. & Nakamura, K. 1963. Quantitative distribution of late Cenozoic volcanic materials in Japan. *Bull. volcan.* **26,** 125-40.

Sugisaki, R., Mizutani, S., Adachi, M., Hattori, H. & Tanaka, T. 1971. Rifting in the Japanese late Palaeozoic geosyncline. *Nature* (*Phys. Sci.*), **233,** 30.

Summerhayes, C. P. 1967. Bathymetry and topographic lineation in the Cook Islands. *N.Z. Jl Geol. Geophys.* **10,** 1382-99.

——— 1967. New Zealand region volcanism and structure. *Nature*, **215,** 610-11.

——— 1967. Note on the Macquarie Ridge and the Tonga-Kermadec complex—are they parts of the mid-ocean ridge system? *N.Z. Jl Sci.* **10,** 808-12.

——— 1969. Marine geology of the New Zealand sub-Antarctic sea floor. *Bull. N.Z. Dep. scient. ind. Res.* **190,** 94 pp.

Sychev, P. M. 1969. Gravity anomalies and causes of crustal vertical motion in the Asia-to-Pacific transition zone. *Geotektonika*, **1,** 13-25 (in Russian).

Sykes, L. R. 1966. The seismicity and deep structure of island arcs. *J. geophys. Res.* **71,** 2981-3006.

——— 1967. Mechanism of earthquakes and nature of faulting on the mid-ocean ridges. *J. geophys. Res.* **72,** 2131.

——— 1968. Seismological evidence for transform faults, sea-floor spreading, and continental drift. In *History of the Earth's Crust* (Ed. R. A. Phinney). Princeton, New Jersey.

——— 1970. Seismicity of the Indian Ocean and a possible nascent island arc between Ceylon and Australia. *J. geophys. Res.* **75,** 5041-55.

Takeuchi, H. & Uyeda, S. 1965. A possibility of present-day regional metamorphism. *Tectonophysics*, **2** (2), 59-68.

Talwani, M. 1965. Computation with the help of a digital computer of magnetic anomalies caused by bodies of arbitrary shape. *Geophysics*, **30,** 797-817.

Talwani, M., LePichon, X. & Ewing, M. 1965. Crustal structure of the mid-oceanic ridges. 2: Computed model from gravity and seismic refraction data. *J. geophys. Res.* **70,** 341-52.

Talwani, M., Windisch, C. C. & Langseth, M. G. 1971. Reykjanes Ridge Crest: a detailed geophysical study. *J. geophys. Res.* **76,** 473-517.

Talwani, M., Worzel, J. L. & Ewing, M. 1961. Gravity anomalies and crustal section across the Tonga trench. *J. geophys. Res.* **66,** 1265.

Tamura, M. 1961. The Torinosu series and fossils therein. *Jap. J. Geol. Geogr.* **32,** 219-77.

Tamura, M. & Harada, S. 1971. Some molluscan fossils from the Shimanto terrain of Kyushu, Japan. *Mem. Fac. Educ. Kumamoto Univ.* **19,** 44-8 (in Japanese).

Tarakanov, R. Z. 1969. Velocity mosaic in the upper mantle and possibilities of area travel-time curve plotting. In *Geophysical Investigations of Structure of Earth's Crust and of Upper Mantle of the Asia-to-Pacific Transition Zone* (Ed. I. K. Tuyezov). *Trans. Sakhalin Complex Sci. Res. Inst. Yuzhno-Sakhalinsk*, **20,** 133-53 (in Russian).

Tarakanov, R. Z. & Leviy, N. V. 1968. A model for the upper mantle with several channels of low velocity and strength. In *The Crust and Upper Mantle of the Pacific Area* (Eds L. Knopoff, C. L. Drake, & J. Hart). *Am. Geophys. Un. Geophys. Monogr.* **12,** 43-50.

Tarling, D. H. 1965. The palaeomagnetism of some Hawaiian Islands. *Geophys. J. R. astr. Soc.* **10,** 93-104.

——— 1965. The palaeomagnetism of the Samoan and Tongan Islands. *Geophys. J. R. astr. Soc.* **10,** 497-513.

——— 1967. Some palaeomagnetic results from Rarotonga, Cook Islands. *N.Z. Jl Geol. Geophys.* **10,** 1400-6.

Tatsumoto, M. 1969. Lead isotopes in volcanic rocks and possible ocean-floor thrusting beneath island arcs. *Earth Planet. Sci. Letters*, **6,** 369-76.

Tatsumoto, M., Hedge, C. E. & Engel, A. E. J. 1965. Potassium, rubidium, strontium, thorium, uranium and the ratio of Sr-87 to Sr-86 in oceanic tholeiitic basalt. *Science*, **150,** 886-8.

Tayama, R. 1950. The submarine configuration off Shikoku, especially the continental slope. *Bull. hydrogr. Dep., Japan*, spec. publ. **7,** 54-82 (in Japanese).

——— 1952. On the depth curve chart of the adjacent seas of Japan (description of J.H.D. Chart 6901). *Bull. hydrogr. Dep., Japan*, **32,** 160-7 (in Japanese).

Taylor, G. A. M. 1958. The 1951 eruption of Mount Lamington, Papua. *Bull. Bur. Miner. Resour. Aust.* **38.**

Taylor, P. T. & Brennan, J. A. 1969. Airborne magnetic data across the Tasman Sea. *Nature*, **224,** 1100-2.

Taylor, S. R., Capp, A. C., Graham, A. L. & Blake, D. H. 1969. Trace element abundances in andesites. II. Saipan, Bougainville and Fiji. *Contr. Mineral. Petrol.* **23,** 1-26.

Taylor, S. R., Kaye, M., White, A. J. R. & Ewart, A. 1969. Genetic significance of Co, Cr, Ni, Sc and V content of andesites. *Geochim. cosmochim Acta*, **33,** 275-86.

Taylor, S. R. & White, A. J. R. 1966. Trace element abundances in andesites. *Bull. volcan.* **29,** 177.

Thompson, J. E. 1957. The Papuan ultrabasic belt. Rec. Bur. Miner. Resour. Aust. 1957/77 (unpubl.).

——— 1967. A geological history of eastern New Guinea. *J. Aust. Petrol. Expl. Ass.* **7,** 83.

Thompson, J. E. & Fisher, N. H. 1965. Mineral deposits of New Guinea and Papua, and their tectonic setting. *Proc. 8th Comm. Min. Metall. Congr., Aust.-N.Z.* **6,** 115-48.

Thompson, R. B. M. 1960. The geology of the ultrabasic rocks of the British Solomon Islands. Ph.D. thesis, Univ. of Sydney.

Tiedt, L. 1958. Die Nerineen der österreichischen Gosauschichten. *Sitzungsberichte, Osterreich. Akad. Wissensch.*, Abt. 1, **167,** 483-517.

Tjia, H. D. 1966. Structural analysis of the pre-Tertiary of the Lokulo area, Central-Java. *Bandung Inst. Techn., Contribs. Dept. Geol.* **63,** 110 pp.
——— 1967. Volcanic lineaments in the Indonesian island arcs. *Bull. volcan.* **31,** 85-96.

Tikhomirov, V. M. 1970. Thermodynamic conditions in the earth's crust and upper mantle of the Okhotsk Sea, Kuril Islands, and the Near Kuril Pacific. In *Geology and Geophysics of the Pacific Belt* (Ed. H. S. Gnibidenko). *Trans. Sakhalin Complex Sci. Res. Inst. Novo-alexandrovsk*, **25,** 23-33 (in Russian).

Tillman, S. M. 1962. Tectonics and history of development of the north-eastern Cis-Kolyma region. *Trudy SVKPIG* **1,** Magadan (in Russian).

Tissot, B. & Noesmoen, A. 1958. Les bassins de Nouméa et de Bourail (Nouvelle-Calédonie). *Revue Inst. Fr. Pétrole*, **13** (5), 739-60.

Todd, D. F. & Pulunggono. A. 1971. The Sunda basinal area, an important new oil province. *Oil-Gas J.*, June 14, 104-10.

Todd, R. 1970. Smaller foraminifera of late Eocene age from Eua, Tonga. *U.S. geol. Surv. Prof. Pap.* **640**-A, 23 pp.

Tokarev, P. I. & Zobin, V. M. 1970. Peculiarities of near earthquake seismic wave propagation in the earth's crust and upper mantle in the region of the Klyuchevskaya group of volcanoes of Kamchatka. *Bull. Volcanic Stations, SSSR*, **46,** Nauka Publ., Moscow (in Russian).

Tokuoka, T. 1967. The Shimanto terrain in the Kii peninsula, Southwest Japan—with special reference to its geological development viewed from coarser clastic sediments. *Mem. Fac. Sci. Kyoto Univ., ser. Geol. & Min.* **34** (1), 35-74.

Tokuyama, Z. 1962. Triassic and some other orogenic sediments of the Akiyoshi cycle in Japan. *J. Fac. Sci. Tokyo Univ.* Sec. 2, **8,** 379-469.

Tomita, T. 1935. On the chemical composition of the Cenozoic alkaline suite of the circum-Japan-Sea region. *J. Shanghai Sci. Inst.* **1,** 227-306.

Tomoda, Y. 1967. Continuous Measurement of Gravity and Magnetic Force in the 4th Southern Sea Expedition of the *Umitaka-maru. La Mer* (*Bull. Soc. franco-japonaise d'oceanographie*), **5,** 175-205.

——— 1968. Geophysical works of the *Umitaka-maru* in the southern sea 1964-1965. *J. Tokyo Univ. Fish.* **9,** 5-11.

——— 1969. West Pacific Ocean viewed from the magnetic anomalies. *J. seis. Soc. Japan* (2), **22,** 12-19 (in Japanese).

Tomoda, Y. *et al.* 1968. Preliminary Report of the *Hakuho-maru* Cruise KH-68-3 (July-August 1968), North Pacific Ocean. Publ. Ocean Res. Inst., Univ. Tokyo.

Tomoda, Y. & Kanamori, H. 1962. Tokyo Surface Ship Gravity Meter a-l. *J. geod. Soc. Japan*, **7,** 116-45.

Tomoda, Y., Ozawa, K. & Segawa, J. 1968. Measurement of gravity and magnetic field on board a cruising vessel. *Bull. Ocean Res. Inst., Univ. Tokyo*, **3,** 1-170.

Tomada, Y. & Segawa, J. 1966. Gravity measurement at sea in the regions; eastern part of the Indian Ocean . . . *J. Tokyo Univ.* Fish. **8,** 107-31.

——— 1967. Measurement of Gravity and Total Magnetic Force in the sea near and around Japan, 1966. *J. geol. Soc. Japan*, **12,** 157-64.

Tomoda, Y., Segawa, J. & Tokuhiro, A. 1970. Free air gravity anomalies at sea around Japan measured by the Tokyo Surface Ship Gravity Meter, 1961-69. *Proc. Japan Acad.* **46,** 9.

Tracey, J. I., Sutton, G. H., Nesteroff, W. D., Galehouse, J. S., von der Borch, C. C., Moore, T.C., Bilal ul Haq, U. Z. & Beckman, J. P. 1971. Leg 8 Summary. In Tracey, J. I. *et al.*, *Initial Reports of the Deep Sea Drilling Project*, **8,** 17-75. U.S. Govt. Printing Office, Washington, D.C.

Trescases, J. J. 1969. Premières observations sur l'altération des péridotites de Nouvelle Calédonie: Pédologie, Géochimie, Géomorphologie. *Cahiers ORSTOM*, (*Geol.*) **1** (1), 27-57.

Treskova, Yu. A., Kiselyova, L. G. & Gnibidenko, H. S. 1970. About the crustal structure of the Southern Sikhote-Alin (from deep seismic sounding reconnaissance survey profile of Spassk-Tadushi). In *Geology and Geophysics* . . . **25,** 66-70 (in Russian).

Tsuboi, C., Jitsukawa, A. & Tajima, H. 1956. Gravity survey along the lines of precise levels throughout Japan by means of a Worden gravimeter. *Bull. Earthq. Res. Inst. Tokyo Univ.*, Suppl. **4** (9); pts 1-9, 552 pp.

Tsuchi, R. 1966. Discovery of Nerineid Gastropoda from Seamount Sysoev (Erimo) at the Junction of Japan Trench and Kurile Trench. *11th Pacific Sci. Congr. Tokyo, Abst., Papers Oceanogr.* **2,** 90.

Tsuchi, R. & Kagami, H. 1967. Discovery of Nerineid Gastropoda from Seamount Sysoev (Erimo) at the Junction of Japan and Kuril-Kamchatka Trenches. *Rec. oceanogr. Wks. Japan*, **9,** 1-6.

Tupitsyn, N. V. (Ed.) 1962. *Principles of tectonics of China.* Gosgeoltekhizdat, Moscow (in Russian).

Turekian, K. K. & Wedepohl, K. H. 1961. Distribution of the elements in some major units of the Earth's crust. *Bull. geol. Soc. Am.* **72,** 175-92.

Turner, F. J. & Verhoogen, J. 1960. *Igneous and Metamorphic Petrology*. 2nd ed. McGraw-Hill, New York.

Tuyezov, I. K., Krasny, M. L., Pavlov, Yu, A. & Solov'iev, O. N. 1967. Magneto-active body distribution in earth's crust and upper mantle of the Far East sector of the Asia-to-Pacific transition zone. *Geotektonika,* **4,** 95-101 (in Russian).

Tuyezov, I. K., Sychev, P. M., Pavlov, Yu. A. & Gimpelson, M. S. 1967. Density substance inhomogeneities of the earth's upper mantle in the southern Soviet sector of the Asia-to-Pacific transition zone. In *Regional Geophysical Investigations in Siberia* (Eds V. N. Gaisky, G. I. Karataev, A. A. Kaufman, F. S. Moiseenko, N. N. Puzyryov & V. S. Surkov). Nauka Publ., Novosibirsk (in Russian).

Udintsev, G. B. (Ed.) 1964. Bathymetric map of the Pacific Ocean. Institute of Oceanology, Academy of Sciences of the U.S.S.R., Moscow.

Udintsev, G. B. & Dmitriyev, L. V. 1971. Evolution of the oceanic lithosphere and geological-geophysical investigation in the western part of the Pacific Ocean. *Vest. Akad. Nauk SSSR,* **11** (in Russian).

Ueno, N., Kaneoka, I., Ozima, M., Zashi, S., Sato, T. & Iwabuchi, Y. (unpubl. manuscript). K-Ar ages, ratio of Sr isotopes and ratio of K-Rb of igneous rock in the Japan Sea (in Japanese).

Umbgrove, J. H. F. 1949. *Structural history of the East Indies.* Cambridge Univ. Press, 64 pp.

Ustiev, Y. K. 1965. Problems of volcanism and plutonism and volcano-plutonic formations. *Int. Geol. Rev.* **7,** 1994-2016.

Utsu, T. 1966. Regional differences in absorption of seismic waves in the upper mantle as inferred from abnormal distributions of seismic intensities. *J. Fac. Sci. Hokkaido Univ.* (Ser. 7), **2,** 359-74.

——— 1971. Seismological evidence for anomalous structure of island arcs with special reference to the Japanese regions. *Rev. Geophys. Space Phys.* **9,** 839-90.

Uyeda, S. & Horai, K. 1964. Terrestrial heat flow in Japan. *J. geophys. Res.* **69** (10), 2121-41.

Uyeda, S. & Richards, M. L. 1966. Magnetization of four Pacific seamounts near the Japanese Islands, *Bull. Earthq. Res. Inst. Tokyo Univ.* **44,** 179-213.

Uyeda, S. & Sugimura, A. 1968. Island arcs. *Science, Tokyo,* **38,** 91-7, 138-45, 269-77, 322-31, 382-90, 443-7, 499-504 (in Japanese).

Vacquier, V. & Uyeda, S. 1967. Palaeomagnetism of nine seamounts in the Western Pacific and of three volcanoes in Japan. *Bull. Earthq. Res. Inst. Tokyo Univ.* **45,** 815-48.

Vallance, T. G. 1967. Palaeozoic low-pressure regional metamorphism in southeastern Australia. *Meddr dansk geol. Foren.* **17,** 494.

Van Bemmelen, R. W. 1949. *The geology of Indonesia.* Govt. Printing Office, The Hague, 732 pp.

Varne, R., Gee, R. D. & Quilty, P. G. J. 1969. Macquarie Island and the cause of oceanic linear magnetic anomalies. *Science*, **166,** 230-3.

Varne, R. & Rubenach, M. J. 1972. Geology of Macquarie Island and its relationship to oceanic crust. In *Antarctic Oceanology II: The Australian-New Zealand Sector*, *Antarctic Res. Ser.* (Ed. D. E. Hayes). *Am. Geophys. Un., Geophys. Monogr.* **19.**

Vashchilov, Yu. Ya., Gainanov, A. G. & Stroev, P. A. 1969. Layer-blocked structure of earth's crust and upper mantle in the Japan, Okhotsk, and Bering Seas from gravimetric data. In *Marine Gravimetric Investigations* (Ed. V. V. Fedynsky). Izdatelstov MGU, Moscow, **4,** 80-91 (in Russian).

Vassilkovsky, N. P. 1962. On the geologic process direction in the earth's history. *Geol. i Geofiz.* 1962-**11,** 41-51 (in Russian).

——— 1967. On the geological nature of the Pacific Mobile Belt. *Tectonophysics*, **4** (4-6), 583-93.

——— 1968. Structure peculiarities and geologic history of the north-Asiatic part of the Pacific Belt. In *Geology of the Asia-to-Pacific Transition Zone* (Ed. N. P. Vassilkovsky). Nauka Publ., Moscow (in Russian).

Vening Meinesz, F. A. 1951. A third arc in many island arc areas. *Proc. K. ned. Akad. Wet. B* **54** (*S*), 432-42.

——— 1954. Indonesian Ȧrchipelago; a geophysical study. *Bull. geol. Soc. Am.* **65,** 143-64.

Vereshchagin, V. I. (Ed.) 1970. Sakhalin Island. Geologic Description. In *Geology of the USSR*, **33,** Nedra Publ., Moscow (in Russian).

Verhoogen, J. 1951. Mechanics of ash formation. *Am. J. Sci.* **249,** 729-39.

Vernadsky, V. I. 1934. *Geochemical essays*, **4,** *Gorgeonefteizdat*. Moscow (in Russian).

Villavicencio, M. L. & Andal, P. P. 1964. *Distichoplax biserialis* (Dietrich) in the Philippines. *Philipp. Geol.* **18,** 103-14.

Vine, F. J. & Matthews, D. H. 1963. Magnetic anomalies over oceanic ridges. *Nature*, **199** (4897), 947-9.

Vinogradov, A. P. 1962. The earth mantle origin. *Izv. Akad. Nauk SSSR* (*geol.*). 1962-**11,** 3-17 (in Russian).

Visser, W. A. & Hermes, J. J. 1962. *Geological results of the exploration for oil in Netherlands New Guinea.* Govt. Printing Office, The Hague, 265 pp.

Vlasov, G. M. (Ed.) 1964. Kamchatka, the Kurile and Komandorskiye Islands. I—Geologic Description. In *Geology of the USSR*, **31,** Nedra Publ., Moscow (in Russian).
——— (Ed.). 1964. *The Geology of the USSR*, **31.** Nedra Publ., Moscow (in Russian).
——— 1969. Foredeeps and volcanism. In *Volcanic facies of Kamchatka.* Nauka Publ., Moscow (in Russian).

Vlassov, A. Ya & Popova, A. V. 1963. Position of the pole in the Permian, Triassic and Cretaceous periods according to the findings of palaeomagnetic studies of sedimentary rocks in the Soviet Far Eastern Maritime Province. In *Rock Magnetism and Palaeomagnetism* (Siberian Acad Sci., Krasnoyarsk), pp. 333-9 (Ed. A. Ya Vlassov). (Translated by E. R. Hope, Directorate of Scientific Information Services, DRB Canada T428R, 1965).

Wadati, K. & Takahashi, M. 1965. Seismic activity under the volcanic area. *Proc. Japan Acad.* **41,** 938-42.

Wageman, J. M., Hilde, T. W. C. & Emery, K. O. 1970. Structural framework of East China Sea and Yellow Sea *Bull. Am. Ass. Petrol. Geol.* **54** (9), 1611-43.

Walcott, R. J. 1970. Flexural rigidity, thickness and viscosity of the lithosphere. *J. geophys. Res.* **75** (20), 3941-54.

Walshe, H. E., 1937. The Wairoa earthquake of 16th September, 1932. 2—Earth movements in Hawke's Bay District disclosed by triangulation. *N.Z. Jl Sci. Technol.* **18,** 852-4.

Wang, Y. 1970. Variation of potash content in the Pleistocene andesites from Taiwan. *Proc. geol. Soc. China*, **13,** 41-50.

Warden, A. J. 1967. The geology of the Central Islands. *New Hebrides geol. Surv. Rept* **5.**
——— 1970. Development of Aoba caldera volcano, New Hebrides. *Bull. volcan.* **34,** 107-40.

Watkins, N. D. & Gunn, B. M. 1971. Petrology, geochemistry and magnetic properties of some rocks dredged from the Macquarie Ridge. *N.Z. Jl Geol. Geophys.* **14,** 153-68.

Webb, A. W. & McDougall, I. 1968. The geochronology of the igneous rocks of eastern Queensland. *J. geol. Soc. Aust.* **15,** 313.

Wegener, A. 1922. *Die Entstehung der Kontinente und Ozeane.* Viehweg, Braunschweig, 144 pp.

Weissel, J. K. & Hayes, D. E. 1971. Assymetric sea-floor spreading south of Australia. *Nature*, **231,** 518.
——— (In press.) Magnetic anomalies in the southeast Indian Ocean. *Antarct. Res. Ser.*

Weizman, P. S. 1966. On the deep structure in the Kuril-Kamchatka region. In *Continental margins and island arcs. Geol. Surv. Pap. Can.* 66-15, 244-51.

Wellman, H. W. 1956. Data for the study of Recent and Late Pleistocene faulting in the South Island of New Zealand. *N.Z. Jl Sci. Technol.* B**34,** 270-88.
——— 1970. In 'Tour Guide of North Island N.Z.' for Recent Crustal Movement Meeting. Feb. 1970. *Misc. Publs. R. Soc. N.Z.*

——— 1971. Reference lines, fault classification, transform systems, and ocean-floor spreading. *Tectonophysics*, **12.**

——— 1971. Age of Alpine Fault, New Zealand. *Proc. Sec. 4 22nd Intern. Geol. Congr.* India 1964.

——— (In press.) Rate of faulting in New Zealand. *Nature*.

Wells, F. G. 1949. Ensimatic and ensialic geosynclines. *Bull. geol. Soc. Am.* **60,** 1927.

Westerveld, J. 1933. Toelichting bij blad 3 (Bengkoenat), Geol. Kaart Sumatra 1:200,000. *Dienst Mijnb. Ned. Ind.*

——— 1941. Three geological sections across South Sumatra. *Proc. K. ned. Akad. Wet.* **44,** 1131-9.

——— 1949. Fasen van gebergtevorming en ertsprovincies in Nederlands Oost-Indie. *Ingenieur*, 1-25.

——— 1954. Phases of mountain building and mineral provinces in the East Indies. *Intern. Geol. Congr.* 1952, *Rept 8th Session*, pt 13, 245-55.

Westwood, J. V. B. 1970. Seismicity of the Solomon and Santa Cruz Islands, southwest Pacific. *J. geol. Soc. Aust.* **17** (1), 87-92.

Wickens, A. J. & Hodgson, J. H. 1967. Computer re-evaluation of earthquake mechanism solutions. *Publs Dom. Obs. Ottawa*, **33,** 1.

Wiebenga, W. A. 1972. Crustal structure of the New Britain-New Ireland Region. This volume.

Wilcox, R. E. 1954. Petrology of Paricutín volcano, Mexico. *Bull. U.S. geol. Surv.* **965**-C.

Wilkinson, P. 1969. Chemical comparison of New Hebrides with other Pacific volcanism. *Proc. geol. Soc. London*, **1662,** 51-5.

Williams, C. E. F. & Warden, A. J. 1964. *New Hebrides geol. Surv. Prog. Rept*, 1959-62.

Willmott, W. F. Palfreyman, W. D., Trail, D. S. & Whitaker, W. G. 1969. The igneous rocks of Torres Strait, Queensland and Papua. Rec. Bur. Miner, Resour. Aust. 1969/119 (unpubl.).

Wilson, C. J. L. 1968. Geology of the Narooma area, N.S.W. *J. Proc. R. Soc. N.S.W.* **101,** 147.

Wilson, J. T. 1959. Geophysics and Continental Growth. *Am. Scient.* **47,** 1-24.

——— 1965. A new class of faults and their bearing on continental drift. *Nature*, **207,** 343-7.

Wilson, R. A. M. 1962. Geology of the regior. (Borneo). *Brit. Borneo geol. Surv. Ann. Rept* (1962), 17-19.

Winterer, E. L. & Riedel, W. R. 1969. Deep sea drilling project: leg. 7. *Geotimes*, **14,** 12.

Wirthmann, A. 1965. Die Reliefentwicklung von Neukaledonien. In *Tagunsbericht und wissenschaftliche Abthandlungen*, 322-35. Deutsch. Geograph. Bochum. Juin.

Wood, B. L. 1962. Notes accompanying *Geological Map of New Zealand Sheet 22* Wakatipu. N.Z. Geol. Surv., Lower Hutt.

——— 1966. Notes accompanying *Geological Map of New Zealand Sheet 24* Invercargill. N.Z. Geol. Surv., Lower Hutt.

——— 1967. Geology of the Cook Islands. *N.Z. Jl Geol. Geophys.* **10,** 1429-45.

Wood, B. L. & Hay, R. F. 1970. Geology of the Cook Islands. *Bull. geol. Surv. N.Z.* (n.s. 82), 103 pp.

Woodward, D. J. & Hochstein, M. P. 1970. Magnetic measurements in the Cook Islands, South-west Pacific Ocean. *N.Z. Jl Geol. Geophys.* **13,** 207-24.

Woodward, D. J. & Hunt, T. M. 1971. Crustal structure across the Tasman Sea. *N.Z. Jl Geol. Geophys.* **14,** 39-45.

Woodward, D. J. & Reilly, W. I. 1970. Note on magnetic vertical force anomalies on Manihiki Atoll, Cook Islands. *N.Z. Jl Geol. Geophys.* **13,** 225-7.

Woollard, G. P. 1962. The relation of gravity anomalies to surface elevation, crustal structure, and geology. *Res. Rep. Series No. 62-9*, Univ. Wisc.

——— 1970. *Annual Progress Report*, Contract N00014-70-A-0016-0001, Jan. 1, 1970 to July 31, 1970. Hawaii Inst. Geophys. HIG-70-27.

Worzel, J. L. 1966. Structure of continental margins and development of ocean trenches. In *Continental margins and island arcs. Geol. Surv. Pap. Can.* 66-15, 357-75.

Wright, J. B. 1966. Convection and continental drift in the south-west Pacific. *Tectonophysics*, **3** (2), 69-81.

Wunderlich, H. G. 1966. *Wesen und Ursachen der Gebirgsbildung*. Mannheim.

Yabe, H. & Tayama, R. 1934. Bottom relief of the seas bordering the Japanese Islands and Korean Peninsula. *Bull. Earthq. Res. Inst. Tokyo Univ.* **12** (3), 562-5.

Yasui, M., Hashimoto, Y. & Uyeda, S. 1967. Geomagnetic studies of the Japanese Sea, (1)—anomaly pattern in the Japan Sea. *Oceanogrl Mag.* **19** (2), 221-31.

Yasui, M., Kishii, T., Watanabe, T. & Uyeda, S. 1968. Heat flow in the Sea of Japan. In *The Crust and Upper Mantle of the Pacific Area* (Eds L. Knopoff, C. L. Drake & P. J. Hart). *Am. Geophys. Un., Geophys. Monogr.* **12,** 3-16.

Yasui, M., Uyeda, S., Murauchi, S. & Den, N. 1969. Current aspects of geophysical studies in the Kuroshio and its adjacent seas. *Proc. CSK Symp.*, Apr. 29-May 4, East-West Center, Honolulu, Hawaii, 21 pp.

Yates, K. R. & De Ferranti, R. Z. 1967. The Astrolabe mineral field. *Rep. Bur. Miner. Resour. Aust.* **105.**

Yegiazarov, B. Kh. 1969. *Geologic structure of Alaska and Aleutian Islands*. Nedra Publ., Leningrad (in Russian).

Yen, T. P. 1967. Structural analysis of the Tananao Schist of Taiwan. *Bull. geol. Surv. Taiwan*, **18,** 110.

Yoshida, S. 1971. Significance of *Faltenspiegels* in analysing folds. *J. geol. Soc. Japan*, **77,** 295-300 (in Japanese).

Yunov, A. Yu. 1970. A new variant of the deep geologic structure of the Okhotsk Sea bottom. *Dokl. Akad. Nauk SSSR* (*geol.*), **191** (4), 893 (in Russian).

Zavaritsky, A. N. 1955. *Igneous Rocks*. Nauka Publ., Moscow (in Russian).

Zhuravlyov, A. V., Sevost'yanov, K. M. & Taboyakov, A. Ya. 1968. Some problems of the geologic development history of the Okhotsk Sea. *Geol. i Geofiz*. **8,** 27-35 (in Russian).

Zverev, S. M., Tulina, Yu. V., Livshits, M. K. & Treskov, Yu. A. 1969. New data on the crust structure in the Sakhalin-Hokkaido-Primorie zone. In *Structure and development of crust in the Soviet Far East*. Nauka Publ., Moscow (in Russian).

Subject Index*

* References thought to be especially noteworthy are indicated by page numbers in italics.